ECONOMICS

OF AGRICULTURAL PRODUCTION

AND RESOURCE USE

ECONOMICS
OF AGRICULTURAL PRODUCTION
AND RESOURCE USE

EARL O. HEADY

Professor of Economics
Iowa State College

PRENTICE-HALL, INC.
Englewood Cliffs, N. J.

Current printing (last digit):

16   15   14   13   12   11   10   9   8   **7**

PRINTED IN THE UNITED STATES OF AMERICA

22897—C

ERRATA

ECONOMICS OF AGRICULTURAL PRODUCTION AND RESOURCE USE
by
Earl O. Heady

Page

vi   Paragraph 2, line 12: For growth of important read an important.
Paragraph 3, line 6: For Stanifarth read Staniforth.

12   Paragraph 2, line 21: For aggregated read aggregate.

13   Footnote 2, line 1: For Reformulation read Reconstruction.

29   Figure 1: The bottom equality within the graph should read
$$\Delta Y/\Delta X = 36/1 \text{ or } 36$$

35   Paragraph 2, line 6: For Figure 2 read Figure 3.

41   Paragraph 2, lines 9 and 10: For Figure 2 read Figure 3.

43   Figure 6: The captions at the top of the graph refer to marginal products, i.e. increasing marginal products extend up to 12.5 inputs.

47   Figure 9: The point labeled 30 should be 40.

48   Paragraph 3, lines 13 and 14: Read Still the .6-bushel yield change per pound of fertilizer more nearly.

Paragraph 3, lines 16 and 17: For 15/1 read .6/1.

59   Footnote 7, line 1: Read $Y=m-ar^{X}$ or $Y=a(1-r^{X})$, in the special case where m=a, the Spillman production.

68   Footnote 13, line 1: For $X=aX^{b}_{1}X^{c}_{2}$ read $Y=aX^{b}_{1}X^{c}_{2}$.

Footnote 13, line 4: Read = . . . $\Delta_{n}y/\Delta_{n-1}y$
(See earlier footnote.)

- 2 -

Page

77 Line 9 from bottom of paragraph: **After the word variable add if both inputs have constant productivity coefficients.**

Last line of paragraph and first figure in column 3 in the example at the bottom of the page: For $8^4 5,000$ read $7^4 5,000$.

101 Paragraph 2, line 5: Read $P_x/P_y = \Delta Y/\Delta X.$

109 Figure 5: The word (cents) should not be on the left-hand axis.

11^4 Figure 8: Lower notation within graph should read $\Delta Y/\Delta X = 36/1 = 36.$

136 Paragraph 2, line ^{4}: For 22.5 read $2^4.5.$

137 Paragraph 2, lines 11 and 12 from bottom: Read 6.2 units of Z_1 and 1.3 units of $Z_2.$

$1^4 1$ Paragraph 3, line 5: Read X_3 for X_4 is -2.0.

157 Paragraph 1, line 2: For (i.e., FC read (i.e., FC.
Paragraph 1, line ^{4}: For FC and CN read FG and TN.

189 Paragraph 2, lines 8 and 9: Read if corn is priced at $1.68 per bushel, or 3 cents per lb., the particular protein should be priced at 12 cents per pound, or $30 per ton for a feed with 33.3 percent protein.

197 Equation IV: For the last term read $P_Y \dfrac{MP_{C_c}}{P_{C_c}}.$

223 Table 6, first line and last column: For figure (+79.8) read (+.25).

227 Paragraph 1, line 6: For table 7 read table 8.
Paragraph 1, line 7: For 10 units read 8 units.

232 Line 2 from bottom: Read less than zero and greater than negative infinity.

PREFACE

f any size, a point which has been overlooked too often in the past.
orker analyzing individual producing units has supposed that a
e" set of principles applies to his problems while the analyst con-
with more aggregative aspects of production has viewed his prin-
as a "mystic set" beyond the comprehension of others. Obviously,
aspects of production cannot be analyzed apart from each other.
hree is concerned largely with dynamics and resource management
imperfect knowledge. Part Four deals mainly with aggregative
ction relationships and problems. The book emphasizes throughout
conomic problems do not arise and economic analysis cannot be
when only 1 resource is concerned.

ay existed in our science when the fundamental scientist looked with
n upon the worker who busied himself with applied and "bread-and-
" research. Conversely, the applied scientist looked askance at the
of the fundamental scientist. As any true scientist knows, these
ts of analysis are not distinct poles of research and investigation,
present a continuum in scientific method. This book is devoted to a
r integration of these related steps in scientific analysis. It is partly
ted to those brave souls who continued their efforts to extend the
of science even when caught in the applied-fundamental cross-fire
those stalwart pioneers in agricultural production economics, Black,
an, Taylor, Warren, and others, whose early efforts helped the
h of important field of research, farmer education, and public policy
sis.

y errors and omissions in this study are entirely those of the author.
ver, much of the inspiration and many of the ideas grew out of dis-
n and debate with William Darcovich, Earl Kehrberg, E. J. Nesius,
Back, Carl Allen, Glenn Johnson, R. O. Olson, C. B. Haver, Gordon
Irving Fellows, Lee Day, John Hopkins, Earl Swanson, W. K.
erson, D. Gale Johnson, S. Stanifarth, Russell Shaw, Chester Baker,
Snare, C. E. Bishop, and the students of many seminars in agricul-
production economics. A debt of gratitude is owed particularly to the
l Science Research Council; through a Faculty Fellowship Research
d, the writer was able to develop and extend fundamental relationships
apply to agriculture. The efforts of Gordon Ball, Harald Jensen, and
Kehrberg have been important especially in evaluating the ideas pre-
d and in relieving the writer of other duties in order that this volume
t be completed. The suggestions of J. K. Galbraith, John Nordin, and
ks James have improved the presentation. The author is indebted to
Journal of Farm Economics, the *Journal of Land Economics,* the
hern Economic Journal, and the *Journal of Political Economy* for use
eas and data originally presented in these journals. Finally, the in-
t and encouragement of W. G. Murray and Sherman Johnson pro-
l the inspiration for completing the volume.

Preface

THE PRESENTATION in this book supposes that th
in appraisal, farm management, land economi
areas of agricultural production economics. The
of basic principles upon which problems in ag
resource use can be analyzed. While it may not
subject, it should serve as a skeleton around wh
tion economics can be centered. The method em
and setting forth fundamental principles and rel
these to agricultural data. Emphasis throughou
mentals in respect to production and resource re
under which efficiency is attained, and the beh
who serve as managers and administrators of ag
presented are suggestive of the application of ba
ciples to agriculture. Other hypotheses and da
Emphasis is also on principles, since these are
on and today's facts become out-of-date.

The first several chapters include an element
tion economics. Many of the concepts are those en
class of economic principles. This elementary an
for the benefit of readers who have had little pre
to progress to the more advanced analysis of lat
analysis is gradually stepped up as the reader pro
However, any person, if he begins with Chapter 2
through later chapters, can handle the more a
follows. All discussion which includes algebra or
gated to footnotes. Although analysis of the tex
simple geometry, a reader who has never studied
contents if he has knowledge of arithmetic.

This book treats agricultural production or res
the standpoint of both the individual farmer and s
cerned mainly with application of "static" or "p
ciples to the individual producing unit. Problem
inter-regional use or allocation of resources also ar
chapters. This procedure has been followed since
about the application of production or efficiency

unit
The
"uni
cern
cipl
the
Par
und
proc
that
mad

A
disc
butt
effo
2 fa
but
furt
dedi
caus
and
Spil
gro
ana

A
Hov
cuss
Bur
Bal
Mc
Joh
tura
Soc
Awa
whi
Ear
sen
mig
Bro
the
Sou
of i
tere
vid

Contents

Part One. Introduction

Part Two. Planning under Perfect Knowledge

Part Three. Planning under Imperfect Knowledge

Part Four. Aggregate Aspects of Production

PART ONE

Introduction

THE SINGLE chapter which follows summarizes the scope and method of agricultural production economics. The treatment does not do justice to this important field of applied economics, which is surpassed by no other in its accomplishment, its breadth, and its interesting history. In order to conserve space, however, we turn immediately to the purposes of this manuscript: the presentation and application of production economics or resource use principles to agriculture.

PART ONE

Introduction

1

Scope and Nature of Production Economics

AGRICULTURAL production economics is the oldest and most widespread specialization in the applied field of science known as agricultural economics; the science of agricultural economics originated as a study in farm production economics. The field has continued to grow until it now embraces more workers than any other specialization. In the field of agricultural economics the majority of outstanding names has been associated with some phase of production economics, both in farm and in national use of resources. The list in the United States has included such prominent persons as G. F. Warren, H. C. Taylor, T. N. Carver, W. J. Spillman, L. C. Grey, C. L. Holmes, J. D. Black, E. C. Young, H. Tolley, M. Ezekiel, A. Boss, O. V. Wells, H. C. M. Case, S. E. Johnson, T. W. Schultz, G. E. Forster, W. W. Wilcox, and W. G. Murray. The European list includes such well known names as J. Von Thunen, M. Kitchen, F. Aereboe, T. Brinkman, A. W. Ashby, G. Lauer, R. Cohen, and others. All of these scholars have been known for their findings or particular methods of analysis. In this list are not only persons who pioneered the field of agricultural economics but also those who contributed both to theory and to empirical knowledge. The central objective of their works has been to increase the efficiency with which farm resources are used.

Production economists who focus their attention on agriculture are concerned with choice and decision-making in the use of the capital, labor, land, and management resources in the farming industry. The goals of agricultural production economics are twofold: (1) to provide guidance to individual farmers in using their resources most efficiently, and (2) to facilitate the most efficient use of resources from the standpoint of the consuming economy. The implications of these objectives can be better understood if we pause briefly to review the scope and nature of economics.

Meaning of Economics

Economics deals with choice between alternatives. Problems of choice arise only when resources are limited and alternative uses can be made of them. The field of economics deals with means and ends. Ends or objectives

3

may deal with profits, consumer satisfactions, or even physical production during wartime. Means are concerned with the physical resources, funds, organizations, or institutions which can be used to attain the various possible ends or objectives of people.

The field of economics in relation to other branches of science and human activity can be illustrated by means of the illustration below. On the left-hand side we start out with pure resources, such as land, mineral deposits, and climate. These are the "ultimate or basic means" from which all products, services, enjoyment, or other ends of people must be fashioned. These resources, or "pure means," taken alone do not involve problems of economics. Description of these resources or their interrelationships involves physical or technical science; geology is concerned with the explanation of soil deposits; physics, chemistry, botany, and agronomy are the sciences which explain the interrelationships of soil and fertilizer in crop production. At the other extreme, the ultimate ends of the individual or group are represented at the right of the diagram. All objectives or ends of human activity except 1 are intermediate ends. These ends are

Fig. 1. Relationships between means and ends.

intermediate in the sense that attainment is sought only as a step to more ultimate ends. (The point U might be represented as an ultimate end toward which all means are directed.) This statement can be illustrated by starting with the "pure means," or resources, at the left. An "intermediate end" is that of organizing capital, human resources, and land into a firm or producing unit. The firm is not, however, an end in itself; it is only a means to a "higher end" of production. Production in turn is not an end or objective *per se*, but only a means of obtaining profit. While profit is partly an end to some people, it is ordinarily a means whereby consumption goods and services can be purchased in the market. While purchase of market products is an intermediate end, it is only a means to other more ultimate ends. If we follow this process, starting with physical resources as pure means, we move step by step up a scale where succeedingly higher ends are attained. Eventually we reach point U which is the highest end or value attainable. In the terms of economics, this point or ultimate objective refers to the maximization of satisfaction or welfare.

Ends are determined by the values of individuals and groups. They represent the decisions of people in respect to "what is right" or "what ought to be." Economics or the economist is not concerned with specifying which ends are "good" and which are "bad." These subjects fall in the category of ethics and religion. Economics can say only that given the means available, one end is in conflict with another; or that given the end, this choice of means or resources allows maximum attainment of the end. Choice is involved in either case. The economist can say that the alternatives of profit and leisure are in conflict; greater leisure can be had only with a sacrifice in profits. He cannot say that an increase in production for the market is "good" while the use of time for leisure is "bad." He can say that use of resources for tobacco production must reduce potato output by a stated amount; he cannot say that tobacco production or cigarette consumption is "bad." In a like vein, the economist can say that of 6 alternative combinations of resources, alternative 1 will allow attainment of a single end, such as maximum profits for a farmer or maximum welfare for the consumers of a nation.

Problems in economics exist at every point within the extremes of the means-end scale. Alternative means exist for attainment of all ends or objectives regardless of their position in the means-end scale. Selection of the most efficient means involves economics even if the end is an intermediate one such as profit maximization.

The position of production economics in the means-end scale is now apparent. Its role is that of facilitating choice in production patterns and resource use so that the ends or objectives of farmers and consumers can be attained. The consumers in question may be a farm family, and the means or resources at their command may include 160 acres of land, 15 months of labor, and $10,000 in capital. The consumers may also represent the nation's population while the means at their command include not only physical resources but also laws, governmental programs, market mechanisms, and other procedures which facilitate attainment of the ends deemed important by people.

Maximizing and minimizing. As a science of choice between alternatives, economics is also based on *maximizing* and *minimizing* conditions. It is concerned with the choice of goods and services which define the conditions of maximum utility or satisfaction of consumers. It is concerned with the conditions which must exist if business profits are to be maximized. As a corollary, economics is concerned with the conditions which are necessary if a given amount of product or profit is to be produced with a minimum of costs or resources. It also inquires as to the conditions under which the consumer can attain a given level of utility with a minimum outlay of money.

The concepts of maximizing and minimizing are best explained by the tools of mathematics. The farmer, as he makes estimates of how the farm can be organized to maximize profits, applies these tools of mathematics in the form of arithmetic or subjective estimates. The econometrician, as he sets forth the organization of production to maximize firm profits or national welfare, applies mathematical tools in the form of calculus and algebra.

Mathematics provides the logic of maximizing and minimizing. The individual who wishes to concern himself with the science of economics must be acquainted with the logic of mathematics. As a practitioner of economics, the businessman must be able to count, multiply, and apply others of the rudiments of mathematics. The professional economist should be able to go even further in the use of mathematical tools. The chapters which follow in this book resort to "advanced arithmetic" and "descriptive geometry" in explaining the principles of production economics.

The 2 over-all problems of economics. There are 2 major problems in economics. These must be solved by either the individual or the nation if the level of living is to be the highest possible from given resources. One problem concerns the organization of production. This problem of choice in production is given the term *resource allocation*. The question of the optimum allocation of resources is one which must be answered within a farm as an individual business firm, within a nation for a distinct society, or for producing units of any other magnitude. Problems in the organization of production involve questions of how resources should be allocated between different products or production methods at 1 point in time and how resources should be devoted to products in different periods of time.

The second over-all problem in economics is that of the organization of consumption. It is sometimes given the term of *income allocation* or *income distribution*. As in the case of production, problems of consumption are concerned with the allocation of income or product between different alternatives at one point in time or between different alternatives over a period of time. A single individual with $1,000 must decide how much of this to devote to present consumption and how much to allocate to future consumption. Of the portion set aside for the present, he must decide how much to allocate to bread, how much to shirts, and so forth. A family with an income of $4,000 and composed of 4 persons must not only decide these problems for each person but also must decide how the $4,000 is to be allocated between individuals. Similarly, these same choices must be made at the national level.

Economics involves very few basic principles, laws, or relationships. The individual who has knowledge of those applicable to production also has knowledge of those which apply to consumption, and vice versa; each relationship in one of these major problem areas has its counterpart in the other area. The beginning student often is amazed at the apparent complexity of economics and economic relationships. Economic analysis revolves around a few simple principles and relationships, however, and with only slight modification, some 3 or 4 basic relationships and principles apply to all of economics. While there are many other applied problems in economics, these are only special aspects of those 2 major areas, the organization of production and the organization of consumption.

We point out the "oneness" and "simplicity" of economics for 2 reasons: (1) students are prone to view economic principles in an overly-complex setting, and (2) applied economists often attempt to search out a "different" or "unique" set of principles to describe their subject matter or justify their field of specialization. Economic principle is simple and universal. Knowledge of a few basic concepts provides tools for handling a wide range of problems. There is no unique principle which defines how one resource should be used. Land problems, for example, if they are studied from an economic rather than an institutional standpoint, are only a part of the more general field of agricultural production economics. Finally, the principles of production economics or resource efficiency apply similarly to producing units of all magnitudes. The relationships and principles which apply to 2 pigs as a producing unit are the same as those which apply to the nation's agriculture as a producing unit. The individual who possesses the tools and subject matter knowledge for answering all the economic questions at the hog level also possesses the basic tools and information for providing answers at the level of the nation's agriculture.

The role of choice indicators. The "oneness" of economic principle in its application to all resources, all products, and all economic units grows out of the fact that the problems involved are always those of choice between alternatives and selection or decision between alternatives can be made only if a choice indicator is present. It is presence of a choice indicator which distinguishes between problems in technology and problems in economics. A choice indicator is the criterion, measuring stick, or index by which alternatives are selected. Choice indicators in economics are almost always given as ratios. A few simple examples will illustrate the nature of choice indicators and their role in decision-making. Suppose that a small boy is offered the alternative of 2 ice cream cones or 5 bars of candy. How can he make a choice? He must apply a choice indicator or choice function. His choice indicator is given by the ratio in which he weighs candy bars and ice cream cones. If his end is one of maximizing satisfaction and if 1 ice cream cone is equivalent to 4 candy bars in satisfying his wants, he will certainly select the 2 cones. He prefers cones to candy bars in the ratio of 4 to 1; he is offered bars for cones at the opportunity ratio of only 2.5 to 1. His choice ratio or indicator says that he will accept candy bars only if he can obtain them in at least the ratio of 4 to 1. As a second example, suppose that a farmer has 1 unit of resources which can be used to produce wheat or corn. His goal or end is one of profit maximization and the 1 unit of resource will yield 20 bushels of wheat or 50 bushels of corn. Should he select corn or wheat? His choice indicator is given by price ratios. If the price of wheat is $2 and the price of corn is $1, the "choice ratio" is $2/$1. Obviously, he should select corn at the expense of wheat. The unit of resource will return $50 if used for corn and $40 if used for wheat. If the price of wheat moves to $3, returns will be $60 for this crop but only $50 for corn. Since the yield ratio is 50 bushels of corn to 20 bushels of wheat or 2.5/1.0, the ratio of wheat price to corn price must be greater than 2.5/1.0 before resources should be used for wheat.

All problems in economics involve choice indicators or choice ratios. The choice indicator, as a yardstick by which selection between alternatives is made, indicates the relative value or weight which is attached to one as compared to another alternative. The individuals or group concerned simply must ask themselves "is this product or outcome worth twice as much or only one-half as much as an alternative or competing product." Choice indicators can be applied to problems in physical production as well as to those of profit maximization and consumer welfare. The principle always remains the same; only the choice indicator differs.

The Field of Agricultural Production Economics

Agricultural production economics is an applied field of science wherein the principles of choice are applied to the use of capital, labor, land, and management resources in the farming industry. As a study of resource efficiency, it is concerned with defining the conditions under which the ends or objectives of farm managers, farm families, and the nation's consumers can be attained to the greatest degree.

Problems in agricultural production economics relate to both intermediate and "higher level" objectives (ends) of farm families. On the one hand, the farmer with given resources may wish to know how resources should be organized to produce a maximum output of a single commodity. Choice is involved since there are many alternative ways of using resources to produce a given product. Technical science is involved, of course, in specifying the physical relationships between resources and product, but the problem of choice involved is one of economics, just as is the problem of how resources should be used to maximize profits of a farm. Although the maximizing of a physical product from given resources can be consistent with maximum profits, this end is only an intermediate objective of farmer activity. It is more nearly a means to profit maximization. Hence the production economist can relate his problem to ends or objectives at this level in the means-end scale; he will then outline the conditions under which profit is maximized. Since profit is only a means to increased levels of family living, the production economist may wish to relate his problem to the end of maximum family satisfaction. He may, in fact, find that profit competes with leisure, family vacations, education, and other activities which also contribute to family satisfaction and well-being. His task then is one of helping farm families choose the optimum distribution of their limited time and resources between producing profit and enjoying life.

A problem in economics exists then at the level of any end in the means-end scale. This statement applies similarly when the agricultural production economist's efforts are focused on resource use at the national level. During wartime he may concern himself with the physical conditions of production which must hold true if a given amount of agricultural product is to be produced with a minimum of resources or, conversely, if a maximum of product is to be forthcoming with a given amount of resources. Ten million tons of fertilizer can be distributed over farms and agricultural regions in many ways. His task is to select the one which is consistent with the end or objective at hand. Physical production is not itself an end, and he may therefore explore possibilities of how resources can be employed most efficiently in attaining wartime requirements of food nutrients. During peacetime he may, in attempting to specify conditions of efficient production, explore the physical alternatives in using resources. He may, however, relate his analysis to other ends and investigate resource use systems which allow a maximum value of output from the capital, labor, and land of agriculture; or he may direct his inquiry at the extent to which patterns of agricultural production conform with the maximum welfare of consumers.

Economic problems are almost always defined relative to ends or goals. On the one hand, the conditions of economics which define a maximum or a minimum can be used to specify problems. Given the end which is to be maximized (farm profit, family satisfaction, or national production efficiency), a problem exists if the optimum or maximum condition has not been attained. Or, if a new technique is developed, the previous use of resources no longer gives a maximum, and a problem has arisen. The production economist can himself define conceptual problems in this manner; the relationships and principles which follow are useful for this purpose. Farmers and consumers also define and express problems in relationship to ends or objectives. When they feel that the ends they deem important relative to agricultural production and resource use are not being fully attained, people seek the advice of research workers, educators, and legislators, or inquire how resources can be used to attain the ends they have in mind. The farmer, when he writes a letter to the college specialist asking which commodities to produce or which methods of production to employ, is indicating that he feels an optimum has not been attained on his farm. Sometimes these doubts, confusions, or felt difficulties are expressed in individual or public debate (or through letters to the editors of newspapers and magazines, community arguments, or otherwise); large groups of people may feel that labor resources in low-income areas are not being used efficiently, that too much or too little soil conservation is taking place or that a particular policy is inconsistent with farming efficiency. In their expressions of concern over these issues, they are defining the problem in terms of some end or set of ends; they feel that an optimum has not been attained in the sense of a full or maximum achievement of the relevant objective.

The agricultural production economist needs to employ both of these "normative" or "optimum" procedures in defining problems for solution. On the one hand, those reflected to him by farmers and consumers are suggestive of "current day" or "practical" problems; they indicate that people believe an optimum has not been attained in the use of resources. Similarly he can define problems in the conceptual manner whereby an optimum use of resources can be pictured mentally. The "optimum" or "ideal type" of resource use is defined by the stability or maximum conditions explained later; deviation of production away from this pattern is suggestive of a problem. This system of problem formulation is no less practical than that outlined previously; it allows the research work or extension specialist to "think ahead" of farmers and others in foreseeing problems and in putting into effect the machinery which will solve them. Physical scientists have used the "ideal type" of problem formulation with important success. Atomic energy was developed not because multitudes of people, worrying about splitting the atom, wrote letters to physicists, but because physicists took as an "optimum" or "ideal type" the splitting of matter into the smallest possible particles. The interest in any type of research is, of course, in its contribution to social welfare. The extent to which the 2 systems of defining problems are consistent depends on the research worker's ability to relate his analysis to ends or objectives which are relevant to the people who use his predictions and recommendations.

The subject matter. While the central concern of the agricultural production economist is with efficient choice of production patterns and resources uses, he necessarily devotes a large portion of his time to analysis of the relationships, the data and the principles which make choice and decision-making possible. These several types of information and logic are necessary before the two over-all objectives of agricultural production economics [(1) helping farmers and farm people to attain their stated objectives, and (2) facilitating the most efficient use of agricultural resources from the standpoint of the consuming economy] can be attained. Production economics is thus concerned with any subject matter which deals with how farm resources are used or should be used. It is concerned with the productivity, use, and income of labor; the productivity, use, and income of capital in its many forms; the productivity, use, and income of land; and the productivity, use, and income of management. It is concerned with soil conservation, a problem in production and resource use over a period of time. The time element also causes problems of risk, uncertainty, and decision-making to be those of production economics.

The field of study is concerned not with returns to a single factor of production but with returns to and income from all resources used in production; the process of product imputation or the existence and determination of rents, wages, interest, and entrepreneurial profits are important elements of the production economics field. The combination of time and income for particular resources therefore causes the valuation of resources to be important areas of study for decision-making and efficiency analysis.

Problems which have been the continued subject matter of agricultural production economics include questions of how crop and livestock enterprises should be combined, what method of production (which technique or resource combination) should be employed, and which size of farm is optimum. Questions of farm size or returns to scale also bring up questions of costs and cost structures, an important topic in agricultural production economics. The field of study also includes analysis of leasing and tenure systems as these affect farm cost structures, production possibilities and farming efficiency from the standpoint of the tenant, landlord, or consuming society. Farm ownership is a problem in choice which also is handled through the principles of production. Use of credit and capital are questions which are intertwined with those of farm size, risk or uncertainty, and decision-making, and cannot be handled apart from other aspects of production.

The terms *resource allocation* and *marginal productivity analysis* are the "by-words" of production economics. Any agricultural problem which falls in these fields is the concern of the agricultural production economist. He is therefore concerned with the location of production and interregional productivity comparisons. Subjects of this nature cannot be analyzed apart from supply curves or functions for products and resources. Resource mobility and low-income farms also are topics which will receive a great deal of attention from the agricultural production economist in the future. In summary, the production economist is concerned with any phenomena which have bearing on economic efficiency in the use of agricultural resources. Economic efficiency may be affected by governmental policies, customs and institutions, or any other developments which change production possibilities, cost structures, and resource management. Production economics policy can be studied from the standpoint of the individual farmer or from the standpoint of national resource administration. Policy is involved in either case; the farmer must decide on a production policy for each year and for his farming career; government agricultural programs always involve production economics or resource efficiency aspects. Other economic aspects of national policies include their market impacts and their effects on the distribution of income. Production economists have made important contributions to national programs and planning in both peace and war.

The laws of production explain the conditions under which quantities can be maximized (profit, physical output, national income) or minimized (cost, physical inputs) regardless of the criteria. Hence there is nothing unique about the principles of production as they define the most efficient resource use by individual farmers, the most efficient pattern of production in particular farming regions, or the most efficient use of resources in the agricultural industry. The objectives of the agricultural production economist can thus be restated as follows: (1) to determine and outline the conditions which give the optimum use of capital, labor, land, and management in the production of primary crops and livestock, (2) to determine the extent to which the existing use of resources deviates from the optimum use, (3) to analyze the forces which condition production patterns and resource use, and (4) to explain means and methods in getting from the existing to optimum use of resources.

Historically, the phase of agricultural production economics dealing with the intra-farm allocation or use of resources has been termed farm management. The aggregate or policy aspects of agricultural production sometimes have been looked upon as distinct from the individual farm aspects. This difference does not exist in any useful manner, however. The individual scientist who focuses his attention on the individual farm cannot be certain of accurate recommendations unless he also considers the aggregate or overall aspects of production; if he recommends one course of action (for example, a shift from hogs to cattle feeding) to individual farmers, the expected outcome may be reversed if large groups of farmers adopt his suggestions and, consequently, price ratios change to favor hogs. Contrariwise, recommendations based on mass observations and relationships may be entirely different from those which would be suggested if the analysis were based on the particular individuals and groups of individuals which make up the whole. Although the latter points have been emphasized by Arrow especially in their application to consumer choices, they apply similarly to production and individual farms.[1] Many agricultural policies would have been formulated differently had it been fully recognized that not all farms or groups of farms are affected similarly by governmental programs. The production economist must understand and be able to integrate both the individual and aggregated aspects of agricultural resource use.

Relationships to other fields of science. In terms of its relationship to other fields of science, agricultural production economics is one of the broadest fields of agricultural economics. The physical sciences, such as agronomy, geology, animal husbandry, engineering, and forestry, have great importance in production economics. They define the production possibilities from which choices must be made. Production economics

---

[1] An excellent illustration of this point is given in K. Arrow, *Social Choice and Individual Activity*. New York: Wiley, 1951. The points made in this book can be adapted to most problems of production and resource use.

would have little content if it were not able to base concepts of and draw data for input-output relations, production possibilities, substitution ratios, and scale or size relationships upon phenomena from these technical fields. Future research in land-grant colleges undoubtedly will involve close cooperation between production economists and physical scientists. The principles and models of production economics provide an important base for physical research and education in agriculture.

Production economics, more than any other phase of applied agricultural economics, must draw upon the subject matter of other social sciences. The process of decision-making under uncertainty involves psychology as much as it involves economics. The ends or objectives of agricultural production are to be explained as much by principles of consumption as by the principles of production. Sociology is necessarily involved in production and resource use. At the individual farm level, the extent to which profits or other alternatives become the family objectives depend partly on whether the operator makes decisions as a patriarch or whether choices are made by the family as a democratic group. Interfarm problems in production are partly those of community organization, and the acceptance of production policies or new techniques involves sociological as well as economic considerations. Political science, if it is considered from the standpoint of choice and decision, likewise becomes a field of science which must be integrated with the principles of production and consumption. Physical resources and physical science specify what can be produced. Economics specifies how resources should be used in production, while sociology, psychology, ethics, and political science specify the limitations which are placed on choice through laws, customs, and other expressions of individual and group values.

Future research and educational work in agricultural production economics must necessarily be integrated with that of other physical and social sciences. The need for integration has been pointed out by Boulding.[2] In attempting to reformulate the theory of production and consumption he has made some initial contribution to the process of integration. Agricultural production economists need to carry this process further. The tie between economics and other fields of science is evident.

---

[2] K. E. Boulding, *A Reformulation of Economics*. New York: Wiley, 1951, also emphasizes the need for developing a fundamental set of laws or principles which tie together the various phases of human behavior and choice. He also is correct in emphasizing that the descriptive efforts of institutional economists have made little if any contribution in this direction. His statement (pp. vii and 5) is this: "We are, I believe, on the threshold of a new attempt at integration of the social sciences, perhaps even in general science. Past failures in this respect—notably those of the Spencerians, the Marxists, and the institutionalists who integrated a number of specialized errors into erroneous generalities should not discourage us . . . 'Institutionalism' in economics may be regarded as a premature attempt at synthesis of the social sciences, an attempt to synthesize bad economics, bad sociology and bad anthropology in a medium of subconscious emotional bias."

The Role of Fundamental Principle

The chapters which follow in this book draw heavily upon basic laws or principles. The book does not dwell on the historic evolution of farm production, resource use, farm numbers and sizes, and government programs. This procedure is followed under the assumption that the reader already possesses knowledge of the descriptive side of agriculture. The reader who is not acquainted with the "figures" and "history" of farming can obtain this knowledge readily from elementary readings.

The purpose of this book is to review and develop fundamental relationships which are important for the analysis of agricultural production. In this sense the study provides tools of analysis which are important in the investigation of resource efficiency. Facts and figures exist in infinite and unlimited quantity. No single mind can comprehend and retain all of the possible facts which relate to a single object. The mind can, however, understand and encompass the basic laws and principles which relate to particular fields of science. These fundamental principles divide facts and figures into a few categories of common or like elements. By applying the principles of production to agriculture, we have attempted to isolate the few relationships which are relevant to decisions and choice in production. Some of these relationships are developed as models and hypotheses applicable to agriculture; alternative relationships are possible. The reader is encouraged to develop his own hypotheses and models where those of this text appear inadequate. Our prime purposes are the stimulation of thinking and the further development of a systematic logic which leads to a more efficient use of agricultural resources.

Role of fundamental principle in research. Agricultural production economics possesses no characteristics which cause it to stand apart from other fields of scientific research. Its procedures are simply those of the scientific method, which involves 2 major processes, deduction and induction. Deduction employs basic principle and logic in establishing hypotheses and formulating research procedures.[3] Induction employs statistical or empirical procedures in testing the hypotheses or models formulated in the deductive phase of research. The role of basic principle in these 2 phases of scientific investigation can be illustrated best if we look upon research as composed of the following 5 steps:

1. Formulating a problem. Problems can be formulated either (a) in terms of the doubt, confusion, or uncertainty which faces individuals, or

---

[3] Some research workers disclaim any association of their work with theory, hypotheses, and deduction. This condition is impossible, however, unless the individual simply repeats the same study and proves the same thing over and over. The research worker must have a theory or hypothesis (employ logic and deduction) if he even decides (has the hypothesis) that "appropriate" information can be obtained on a questionnaire or that it should be obtained from farms rather than filling stations.

(b) in terms of departure from the ideal or optimum conditions defined by economic principle. These points have been discussed previously.

2. Formulating hypotheses. Given a problem, the most important step in research is formulation of hypotheses or theoretical solutions. Herein lies the design of the entire empirical procedure. Again, it is the general or basic laws of any science which function as models, and hence provide hypotheses which guide the various empirical phases of investigation. Without a theoretical solution the probability is small that one will be found in reality. In a practical vein an analytical model can be looked upon as a mental picture of the relationships (qualitative and quantitive) involved. The model also suggests conditions which must hold for maximization of a given end, and thus indicates the kind and quantity of data necessary for its solution. Models are employed in all sciences and may be of either a physical or abstract type.

3. Designing empirical procedures. This step includes specification of (a) the evidence needed, (b) the statistical techniques to be employed, (c) the design of the sample or experimental method, and (d) tests of significance (or bases under which the hypotheses will be accepted or rejected). These aspects of empirical procedure should be decided upon before data are collected (in contrast to a common sequence whereby data are assembled and then questions of the appropriate statistical technique are examined) and are given automatically once the analytical model is specified in step 2. The appropriate statistical technique is given once the applicable model (hypothesis, theory) is formulated. In turn, the appropriate sample or experimental design and test of significance are given, once the appropriate statistical technique is determined.[4]

4. Assembling and processing data. This step is largely routine. It involves implementing the thinking which has taken place in steps 1, 2, and 3 through selecting the sample, devising a questionnaire, enumerating data, and so forth.

5. Interpreting findings. Interpretation of findings requires both statistical (mathematical) and economic analysis.

The important role of analytical models or basic principles in applied research is now apparent. They provide imagination at every turn and

---

[4] If the model involves functional relationships, as in economics, it specifies (1) use of regression analyses as the appropriate statistical techniques, which in turn specifies (2) a sample stratified by the independent variable, and (3) tests of significance of (or between) regression coefficients. If the model involves discrete populations and attributes it implies (1) use of means and frequency distributions as appropriate statistical techniques, and hence (2) a random sample and (3) analysis of variance or chi square as tests of significance. A model indicating a closed system and a simple relationship between a dependent and an independent variable would specify a single-equation, least-square regression analysis. A model indicating a system of interacting economic forces and jointly dependent variables would specify application of simultaneous equations.

function to systematize problems, express hypotheses, and outline empirical procedures. These elements of investigation are not distinct but flow simultaneously from single models. Deduction or logical analysis is involved as we move from top to bottom through the 5 steps above. Induction or statistical inference is involved as we turn around and move from bottom to top in testing our hypothesis and in solving our problem.

Economic principle provides a common logic whereby scientific objectivity and interpersonal validity of conclusions can be guaranteed even in the absence of empirical analysis. The laws or theorems of economics are a deductive set of propositions derived by the rules of logic from basic propositions called postulates. It is these laws which fashion patterns of uniformity into a coherent system. However, since alternative hypotheses or theorems are possible, depending on the underlying postulates and the end which serves as a frame of reference, mere application of economic logic is not a sufficient condition for attainment of mutually consistent solutions. It is also necessary that (1) the problem be defined relative to a given end and (2) that the underlying assumption and postulates be stated and reconciled. Accepted economic principle provides this framework for interpersonal validity of findings and recommendations.

The development of production principle and theory. No other field of agricultural economics is so well endowed with basic principle and theory as is production economics. Every scholar whose name has become known nationally and internationally in economics has contributed to the literature of production economics. The best developed principles of general economics include the theory of the firm and the principles of resource allocation, the basic concepts which are the core of agricultural production economics. From the standpoint of theory, production economics principles are either the core or an important part of the writings of such classicists as Smith, Ricardo, Malthus, and Sismondi, and also of Say, Senior, and Mills, who extended the classical tradition. Great contributions were made to production economics at the turn of the century by Marshall and Davenport. Literature in the theory of production has been enriched by the contribution to the theory of the firm and the production aspects of welfare economics by contemporaries such as Stigler, Hart, Boulding, Steindl, Samuelson, Douglas, Knight, Viner, Kalecki, Schackle, Reder, Arrow, Skitovsky, N. Kaldor, Pigou, Fischer, Chamberlin, Robinson, Carlson, Hicks, Allen, Little, Friedman, and others. Production economics has played a leading role in recent econometric developments by Lange, Frisch, Leontief, Tintner, Marshak, Mosak, Koopmans, Tinbergen, Chernoff, Hurwicz, and others. Similarly it was given a fundamental mathematical base in the earlier writings of Pareto, Cournot, Edgeworth, Bernoulli, and Walras. The important contributions of Haberler, Ohlin, Keynes, and Weber to location theory and mass producer adjustment stand high in the list. In no other field of pure economics have so many tenets been established as "laws." Production economics is "more exact" than other branches of economics because of this, and also because research can be developed in a controlled manner paralleling that of physical science.

The nature of agriculture. Although one of our objectives is to review and develop fundamental principles which relate to agricultural production, we also emphasize the application of these principles to farms and the farming industry. We explore the structure of agricultural production relationships, farmer decision-making, and the forces which condition farming efficiency. The data presented represent, in many instances, only a small portion of that available. Other quantitative data have not been presented because of space limitations. In other cases only the meager data presented are available, and although they suggest the nature of production relationships and the forces which play on efficiency, they do not provide sufficient data for firm statements and predictions. One of the important tasks of agricultural production economists and other scientists is to complete this inventory of knowledge so that more efficient choices and decisions can be made for those problems which are important to farmers and the nation's consumers.

The Plan of This Volume

As already stated, the chapters in this book review and develop the basic principles of production and apply these to farms and the agricultural industry. The procedure followed is first that of presenting the fundamentals and second that of applying the principles and concepts to agriculture. Variants of these routines are employed, however, as the need justifies. Some chapters involve only basic concepts and relationships; others involve mainly discussion of the data and structure of agriculture.

Space limitations have prevented a full development of principles in their application to agricultural production or resource use. Those presented should represent the minimum tools possessed by the research worker, the extension specialist, the teacher, or the administrator who plans to devote his life to pursuits relating to farm production and resource efficiency.

Agricultural economics has properties in common with other fields of applied science. Agronomy and animal husbandry are not unique sciences. Instead they represent applications to agriculture of the basic principles and theories from genetics, physics, chemistry, and physiology. This volume represents an attempt to integrate the fundamental and applied aspects of the science of agricultural production economics. Simple models or geometric illustrations have been employed for this purpose. Any reader who has a knowledge of advanced arithmetic can read and understand the complete volume if he starts from the beginning and progresses from chapter to chapter. Again we remind the reader that the materials in footnotes represent an advanced analysis. With few exceptions they provide additional refinements for the benefit of advanced students. *Knowledge of footnote materials is unnecessary for an understanding of the text. The beginning reader may disregard the equations and qualifying statements in the footnotes; his knowledge of production economics and resource use principles will be highly complete if he understands the arithmetic of the text.*

The levels of decision. In the economics of production (resource use) there are 2 basic decision-making units, the firm and the state, with various groups of individuals in between who enter into the decision-making process; the resource owner, the consumer and family, and the community or other economic units are included. Each economic unit must make certain decisions which, in turn, may influence the choices of other groups which make up our socio-economic structure. We are interested in decisions in production or resource use which relate to the various social aggregates. The goal of the agricultural production economist should be that of integrating the choice-making processes of individual firms, households, communities and other social aggregates; any analysis which deals only with individual economic units or single resources is incomplete.

Selected References

Cohen, M. R., and Nagel, E., *Introduction to Logic and Scientific Method*. New York: Harcourt, Brace, 1936, Chs. 10, 11, 20.

Haavelmo, S., "Quantitative Research," *Jour. Farm Econ.*, Vol. 29.

Heady, Earl O., "Elementary Models in Farm Production Economics," *Jour. Farm Econ.*, Vol. 30.

Heady, Earl O., "Implications of Particular Economics in Agricultural Economics," *Jour. Farm Econ.*, Vol. 31.

Keynes, J. N., *Scope and Method of Political Economy*. London: Macmillan, 4th Ed., 1930, Chs. 1, 2, 3, 4.

Lange, O., "Scope and Method of Economics," *Rev. Econ. Studies*, Vol. 13.

Myrdal, G., *An American Dilemma*. New York: Harper, 1944, pp. 1027-1032, 1059-1063.

Northrop, F. S. C., *Logic of Sciences and Humanities*. New York: Macmillan, 1948.

Robbins, L., *Nature and Significance of Economics*. London: Macmillan, 1946, Chs. 5, 6.

PART TWO

Planning Under Perfect Knowledge

THE CHAPTERS which follow analyze production and resource use with emphasis on the individual farm and the farm household. Principles also are developed and applied to the interfarm use of resources. The analysis is "static" in the sense that it assumes perfect knowledge except where otherwise indicated.

2

Relationships Between Resources and Products: the Production Function

THIS CHAPTER is devoted to analysis of certain fundamental relationships in production. The chapter which follows it relates these to agriculture. Production of farm commodities involves numerous relations between resources and commodities. Some of these relationships are simple, others are complex; knowledge of them is essential to any student of agricultural production economics. They provide the tools by means of which the problems of production or resource use can be analyzed. This statement applies equally whether interest is in the organization of resources in a manner to maximize the profits of an individual farm or to make available the most efficient product to society. Both are problems in production economics; both require knowledge of the same tools and relationships. In this chapter we initiate our examination of the relationships involved in production. We will not come to grips with questions of economic choice in the organization of resources and production until a later chapter. The tools for choice-making cannot be understood easily until we examine the fundamental relationships which underlie them. Accordingly, this chapter is devoted to the most elementary, but by no means the most unimportant, relationship in production. Here we examine the relationship between resources and products. The formal name under which it goes is the *factor-product* relationship; farm management specialists also call it the *input-output* relationship; an agronomist might call it the *fertilizer response curve*. It relates to the amount and nature of yield or product forthcoming as various quantities of labor, feed, fertilizer, or other factors of production are used on the farm.

Our procedure in the next several chapters is first to set forth the basic physical relationships that are involved in production and then to employ these along with the relevant choice indicators such as price relationships to indicate how maximum profits or other goals might be attained. In the first several chapters our analysis is focused on the individual farm and profit maximization. Even here we stop at convenient places to show how the same relationship or principle relates to national problems of production or resource efficiency. But before we begin with analysis of the simple input-output or factor-product relationship we need to view the nature of the factors and factor services employed in the production process. By *factor* or *resource* we mean any agent used in the production process. Even sunshine and carbon dioxide from the atmosphere are *resources* or *factors of production* and have to be considered in the production process. Interest of the farmer or society revolves mainly around labor, land and fertilizer, feed, machinery, or other forms of capital which are scarce and have a price attached to them.

The Nature of Production and Resources

Products such as wheat, corn, milk, or cotton are forthcoming only as a number of factors or resources are combined together. Notwithstanding the historical attempts of agricultural economists to specialize in single factors of production (land, labor, and so forth), production always requires at least 2 factors of production. (It is doubtful that any commodity is ever produced with so few resources.) This fact is easier to visualize if we consider that commodities are produced from the productive services embodied in resources as well as from the resources themselves. Production of corn involves the transformation of carbon dioxide from the atmosphere and moisture and nitrogen from the soil, along with services of labor, machinery, and tractor fuel, into a commodity. Services such as moisture or carbon dioxide and nitrogen are actually transformed into corn and the resources and the services of the resource are identical. While not transformed in a chemical or physiological sense, the services of labor, machinery, and other resources are equally important if a commodity is to be produced. Even though labor and tractor fuel never enter physically into the transformation process, we still consider the services of these resources to be transformed into products. The analysis which follows is concerned with the transformation of resource services into products. In order to economize on words we may sometimes speak of transforming resources into products. However, it should be remembered that we actually are interested in the services embodied in resources.

Flow and stock resources. Some resources embody *stock services*. This is the case with fertilizer and feed, which may be entirely "used up" in the production process. If the resource is not used up in one period of production, it can be stored for a later period. Other resources embody only *flow services*. If the services are not used when they are given off from the resource they will not be available in a later period; the services of a barn or even of labor are of this nature. If the energy of a laborer is not used today it cannot be stored until next year. On the other hand, if the flow services of one period are used, the flow of another period will still be forthcoming. A building is of this nature; if the farmer raises a barn full of cattle this year he can do the same next year.

Some factors of production embody both flow and stock services. This situation is true for machinery. Depreciation is a function of both use and time. Land also embodies both flow and stock resource services. From a purely spatial standpoint, its services are of a flow nature. Soil nitrogen, however, may represent a stock of services; if used up in one time period it will not be available in a later period. Sunshine is purely a flow service as are others derived from the atmosphere. Although buildings include both flow and stock services, the stock services are most important. Whether a service should be defined as *flow* or *stock* depends partly on the length of time under consideration. A building which lasts 50 years provides a flow of services in each of the individual years; still it provides a stock of services for a 50-year period. Similarly, the original phosphate deposits in a soil may provide a flow of crop services over 30 years. From the standpoint of the complete period, however, a stock of services is involved.

The production or transformation period. The production process involves services from resources which represent (1) a stock in a single year (seed, feed, tractor fuel), (2) a stock over a number of years but a flow in single years (machines, buildings, certain soil elements) and (3) a flow over all time (spatial characteristics of land, sunshine, and so forth). In other words, production involves use of several resources—some of which are transformed into product in a single year, others of which are transformed over a period of years, and still others of which are never completely transformed into product. We will refer to the time required for a resource to be completely transformed into product as the *production* or *transformation period*. The production period varies greatly between resources. This variation in the transformation period gives rise to complexities in decision-making. Economic analysis would be simple if production were carried on with resources which are completely transformed in a single year. In some few instances farmers or other producers may hire all resource services for a single year. Production then falls into this simple framework. Generally in agriculture, however, the farm as a business firm must own some of its resources such as machines. These resources represent investments and decisions which extend over several years. Time brings complexity into the period in several ways. First, the stock of services used in any year or production period becomes variable costs relating to the particular output, while the flow-service resources give rise to fixed costs. Cost calculations thus become complex. Second, time excludes the possibility of exact and perfect knowledge. Expectations and guesswork then must enter into the decision-making process. The really complex problems in resource use grow out of time and uncertainty. However, we are going to defer all considerations of time, lack of knowledge, and errors in estimation until later chapters. Here we largely disregard the time aspects of production.

Classification of factors. Historically, the factors of production have been classified as capital, labor, land, and management (entrepreneurship or coordination). This distinction is of limited use for a great number of problems in production and resource use. It has important shortcomings when adhered to with a "fervor" approaching religion. The classification would be meaningful if the various categories were distinct and homogeneous. Classically, *capital* has been used to refer to non-labor resources which have been produced by man, while *land* has been used to refer to the original and indestructible properties of the soil. Virgin fertility would thus classify as land while the stock of services from commercial fertilizer applied in a previous year would not. Only the spatial, texture, and similar properties of soil would be considered as land in the long run. However, we place little stock in these historic and arbitrary definitions. We do not go to the ridiculous extent of giving the name of land to rainfall, sunshine, and atmospheric nitrogen. In this day of sudden technological change, rainfall can be created as much by man as can any other form of capital. There is no physical basis for calling sunshine land. As is evident from the later chapter on resource classification, substitution and complementarity characteristics of rainfall, soil, sunshine, and space are not such that these factors can be aggregated meaningfully into a single resource called "land" any more than protein feed, corn, and hogs or tractors and labor can be aggregated into a single resource termed "unifactor." The principles of production economics or resource efficiency require that consideration be given to each particular resource if the ends of individuals or groups are to be attained. We are more interested in the particular and specific forms of resources which enter into the production process rather than in trying to divide them into historic or exclusive categories. Hence we will use the term land to have the same meaning as soil. Capital comes in many particular forms such as fertilizer, feed, tractors, barns, and even the most important aspects of land. Differences within the category of capital are likely to be more important than differences between this category of resources and other amalgamations or aggregations of resources. In addition, capital even can be invested in human beings, and it is because such possibilities have not been viewed in the light of "capital investment" that some important voids exist in the use of agricultural resources. Comparisons between horses and tractors (the factor-factor relationship to be mentioned later), even though both are "items of capital" may have ramifications as important as comparisons between machines and laborers. For purposes of clarity, however, we will use the term *labor* to refer to all human services except decision-making. We will call this process management. Capital is sometimes considered in terms of money or the total value of nonhuman resources including land. Accordingly, when we refer to capital in broad general terms (for example, the amount of a farmer's capital), we will consider it to encompass all resources but labor and to include land. It must be remembered for many problems in resource efficiency, however, that the particular form of physical capital may be more important than the quantity of capital.

In order to make distinctions between resources (or their services) which are transformed into product in a single discrete production period (for example, a single crop of cotton) as compared to those which are employed over several or an infinite number of periods, we refer to the first as mono-period resources and the latter as poly-period or durable resources. We will return later to the fundamental factor relationships and resource classification.

The Framework of Analysis

In order to simplify the analysis of production in the first several chapters we take three simplifying steps: first, we consider production as timeless, or from the standpoint of a single production period or year which does not involve uncertainty or imperfect knowledge. There is some basis for this step because farmers reckon their income on an annual basis. Of course, a calendar year seldom corresponds exactly to the period of production: corn may be grown in 90 days, while three years are required to produce a dairy heifer. The reader may imagine that the analysis through Chapter 9 either (a) refers to a production period corresponding to the time required to completely transform the relevant resource into product (for example, approximately 8 months are required to transform winter wheat seed into a crop) or (b) refers to a period of production long enough that the longest-lived resource is completely transformed into product and the output in the several cropping or breeding seasons are added together to represent the total time span. However, we do not consider a production period so distant in the future that the manager or other resource administrator must discount the returns from durable resources. This problem is considered in Chapter 12. Second, we suppose that the prices and production coefficients or yields (the input-output relationship) are known with certainty before production is commenced. Occasionally we will caution the reader as to the limitations of this supposition and refer him to later chapters. This "perfect knowledge" procedure is commonly employed by physical scientists in their recommendations to farmers, however. Third, we concern ourselves only with returns forthcoming from the physical production process and the sale of the commodities. We are not concerned with gains or losses growing out of changes in the market value of durable resources. Changes in the market values of assets will be analyzed in the chapters dealing with uncertainty.

In starting out within this simple framework, we are avoiding the real complex and difficult problems involved in choice and decision-making; the analysis is apart from the "real life blood" of production in this respect. However, the conditions outlined in the first several chapters are actually the ones any farm manager or resource administrator would like to attain. He can hope only that his guesses about the future will be accurate enough to allow attainment of the conditions to be outlined. This "static," or "timeless," and "perfect knowledge" analysis outlines the important relationships involved in resource use and should be "tools in the kit" of every production economist. As we take each step in the analysis of the next several chapters, we do not stick to the pure aspects of production relationships but relate them to situations in agriculture. This is the main objective of the study. In some cases it is necessary to outline the technical and theoretical considerations in detail before they are related to production in agriculture. In other cases the two are related as the analysis unfolds. We are now ready to turn to analysis of the first relationship in production.

Factor-Product or Input-Output Relationships

The remainder of this chapter deals with the most elementary aspects of the factor-product or input-output relationship. It is concerned with the transformation of a single variable factor into a single product. The factor-product relationship is only 1 of the 3 basic relationships in production economics. The other 2 basic relationships in production around which decision center are the factor-factor and the product-product relationships. There are, of course, numerous variations of these 3 basic relationships (such as time-time considerations in the use of a single factor or production of a single commodity) but these call for no additional knowledge on the part of the production economist (resource efficiency expert). The 3 basic relationships provide the framework within which economic efficiency is determined, whether the choices relate to an individual farm, the agricultural industry, or the national economy.

The method of this chapter is to consider one factor as variable and all others as constant. Many farm decisions fall within this framework. The problem is one of intensity of production. At the farm level the question relates to the number of units of a variable factor such as fertilizer which should be combined with (applied to) an acre of land. Similarly, the problem relates to the amount of feed to be fed per animal, the amount of labor or capital in aggregate to be applied per acre or to a farm of given size. The problem can also be framed in terms of output: "What level of production per acre, per animal, or for a farm is most profitable?" Problems of intensity also arise in respect to the total amount of resources which should be employed on the limited land of a particular farming area or in a single industry such as agriculture. Questions of an optimum population or the size of the population which can be supported on a given land area are largely ones of factor-product relationships.

While it is true that one factor usually cannot be varied alone (labor at least must always be varied as more fertilizer is applied per acre, as more feed is fed per animal, or as more capital is used for the farm as a unit), the logic and principle applies equally when more than one factor is varied in proportion to the fixed factor or factors. In some cases the "other" variable factors are represented by a fixed stock (a year's supply of operator or family labor) of resource services, or otherwise do not have costs attached to each unit of service. The relationship between the single variable factor and the product is then alone relevant for decision-making. In other instances, a second factor also must be varied in quantity but is held in a fixed ratio to the first. For example, each additional 100 pounds of fertilizer applied to an acre of land may require an hour of labor. In this situation labor and capital can be aggregated and considered as a composite labor-capital input and decisions can be made in the framework of a single variable factor. We consider one hour of labor and 100 pounds of fertilizer as the input; costs can be computed in a similar fashion.

Units of accounting. Application of inputs or measurement of output can relate to technical units, plants, or economic units. The term *technical unit* refers to a single, fixed unit in production for which output and returns may be calculated. Although the product or the costs may be analyzed or computed separately for each technical unit, profits or other economic objectives generally do not relate to the technical unit alone but more often to a plant. A *plant* generally refers to a fixed collection of technical units such as a complete dairy enterprise or a 160-acre farm (and, ordinarily, never 1 acre of the farm alone; an acre, in this instance being a technical unit). Likewise, profits or economic returns measured in other terms are not related to the plant alone unless it is identical with the economic unit or firm. Either a technical unit or a plant may serve as a fixed factor (or a collection of fixed factors). As pointed out later, the technical unit or plant usually gives rise to the fixed costs in production. The *economic unit* refers to the aggregation of resources for which economic return is related or computed. A farm may be the economic unit and include 2 plants (2 farming tracts or units in different locations), each of which is composed of distinct technical units in the form of acres of land and in the form of animals. As a complete economic unit (all plants under one management), a farm may be called a firm.

Production and resource relationships can be studied as they relate to either technical units, plants, or economic units. The application of principles is identical, regardless of the unit to be analyzed or its magnitude. Consequently, the particular implications of each relationship explained below are not outlined in detail for technical units, plants, and economic units or firms. The analysis begins with technical units, and then is related to economic units. The reader can apply the analysis of the technical unit to the economic unit (or vice versa) where the counterpart is not presented in detail.

Why a firm? In a later chapter we explain in detail the meaning of the term *firm* as it relates to decision-making. A further note on the term is worthwhile, however. Why should we call a farm a firm? Is this procedure followed simply to comply with the jargon of economics? It is not. An important reason is this: a farm includes more than 1 economic unit. On the one hand, production can be viewed as it relates to the business or profit side of farming alone (the firm aspect). On the other hand, the farm and production can be viewed from the standpoint of the family as a consuming unit (the household as the economic unit). The manner in which resources are or should be used depends on whether the criterion is one of the firm and profit maximization or of the household and the maximization of family satisfactions. The term farm includes both considerations but does not distinguish between them. Thus we use the term firm to indicate that profit maximization alone is being considered. We have additional reasons for speaking of a farm as a firm; these will unfold as we progress. Suffice it to say now that we use the term in early chapters to indicate that we are concerned with the use of resources which will maximize profits. Perhaps few if any farms are ever operated in view of profits alone. We recognize this aspect of resource use in a later chapter when we develop the relationship between the household or consuming unit and the farm as a business.

The Input-Output Relationship or Production Function

Our first interest is in the input of a resource and the resulting yield or output of product. This relationship between input and output is termed the *input-output relationship*. If a hog is fed a worm capsule which adds 10 pounds of pork without changing the quantity of feed or other resources, an input-output relationship is expressed; for an input of capsule the output of pork is ten pounds and the ratio of output to input is 10/1. The input-output ratio is always expressed in this form, rather than as 1/10, for reasons to be explained later. Similarly, an input-output relationship exists when corn yield per acre is 36, 48, 52, 52, and 44 for one, two, three, four, and five cultivations. Cultivations involve not a single resource but several complementary resources such as labor, tractor fuel, tractor services, and grease. However, we can simply aggregate these several services into one category and term it "cultivation services" or "inputs." If we make a chart of the figures cited we get the results shown in Figure 1. (The symbols may be disregarded for the present.) Here each of the 5 combinations between output and input has been indicated with a dotted line to show that the in-between points do not exist in any real sense; 2½ cultivations are impossible. However, as we will see later, each of the in-between segments such as *ab, bc,* and *cd* has the same implications as a linear (straight line) and continuous input-output relationship.

The production function. Both sets of input-output figures cited above were discontinuous. Because cultivations and capsules cannot be broken down into fractional units, outputs do not exist for anything but inputs indicated by whole integers. However, if our inputs refer to fertilizer measured in 100-pound units, the in-between outputs become meaningful since 100-pound units can be physically subdivided into 10 lb., 5 lb., or even .01 or .001 lb. units. In this case the input-output relationship becomes continuous and can be termed a *production*

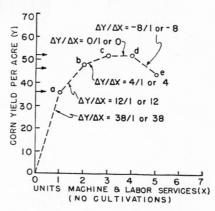

Fig. I. Relationship between corn yield per acre and application of cultivation services.

function. Even a discontinuous input-output relationship is a production function with certain unique properties. In the remainder of this book we will refer to both continuous and discontinuous relationships between input and output as production functions or input-output relationships. The two terms are synonymous. Discontinuous and linear production relationships are important in agriculture. However, since these are less difficult to understand and analyze, greater space will be devoted to continuous relationships. Finally, continuous relationships will be used as general conceptual tools which have similar application under conditions of discontinuity and linearity.

The term production function comes from mathematics and statistics. It is used less widely in agricultural economics than the term "input-output relationship" (the applied counterpart of "production function"). Although the notion of a function is abstract, the concept is very useful in economics and, indeed, should be a tool in the kit of every agricultural economist. Economics deals largely with functional relationships between variables. Any observed or assumed relationship between variables corresponds to a functional relationship between the variables. Examples of functional relationships are many: if gas is subjected to pressure at a given temperature, its volume "varies with" or "is a function of" the pressure. The amount of beef demanded in the market is "related to" the price of beef and hence is "a function of" price. In production, the output of a commodity such as wheat is "dependent on," "determined by," or "related to" the quantity of seed, fertilizer, labor, and other resource services. Accordingly, the product is again a "function of" the factor inputs. More specifically, the production function refers to the relationship between the input of factor services and the output of product; product output is a function of or is "dependent on" the input of resource services. A production function may be expressed in many forms. It can be shown in the form of an arithmetic table where one column (column 1 in Table 1) represents the input of the factor while another column (column 2 in Table 1) indicates the corresponding total output of the product. (These 2 columns constitute a production function, input-output relationship, or factor-product relationship.) The production function may also be illustrated geometrically by means of a graph where the horizontal or x axis represents the factor input and the vertical or y axis represents the resulting total output of product (see Figures 1, 2, and 3). Finally, a production function may be expressed as an algebraic equation of the form $Y = f(X)$, which means that Y is a function of X. The equation may be read simply as "Y is a function of X." The equation means that for each value of X there exists a corresponding value of Y. Generally, Y is considered the dependent variable (is a function of or is "dependent on" X) when it is included as the left side member of the equation. Our problem involving a single variable factor and a single product revolves around a simple production function such as $Y = f(X)$ because Y is a single product such as corn or wheat, while X is a single variable factor such as fertilizer or irrigation water.

As has been indicated already a product is never a function of (produced by) a single factor and most commonly does not result from a single variable factor, all other factors remaining fixed. Crop production involves the services of many specific factors such as seed, fertilizer, moisture, labor, machinery, land, and other resources. The same being true of livestock or any other commodity, a production function is more accurately expressed in the form of $Y = f(X_1, X_2, X_3)$, where Y refers to a single product such as cotton or wheat, and X_1, X_2, and X_3 refer to specific factors of production such as seed, fertilizer, and labor. Often a production function is expressed in the form $Y = f(X_1, X_2, X_3, X_4 \ldots X_n)$. Here again, Y refers to a single commodity which may be produced, while the X's refer to specific factors of production. For instance, X_1 may refer to labor, X_2 to capital in the form of machinery, X_3 to capital in the combined form of seed and fertilizer, and X_4 to land. The dots indicate that not all of the factors (variables) upon which Y (the product) is dependent have been specified. The symbol X_n signifies that it is the final specified resource. (While X_n is the final specified resource, all resources between X_4 and X_n are unspecified.) More explicitly, the dots and the term X_n indicate that production is a result not only of X_1, X_2, X_3, and X_4, but also of other non-specified factors or resources of which X_n is the last. The production function states that the product Y is a function of ("results from," is "dependent on," or is "determined by") the input of X_1, X_2, X_3, and X_4, as well as other resources up to and including X_n. The equation does not indicate, however, the number of units of the product Y which will result when the input of X_1, for example, is increased by 1 unit. The rate at which the product Y is changed as the input of any single factor or of all resources is varied can be specified only when the relationship between resource inputs is known. Analysis of this nature is included in the advanced section of this chapter.

Since their use is important in this and other modern texts on economics, some elaboration on the use of symbols is worthwhile. The last letters of the alphabet (Z, Y, X or z, y, and x) are generally used for the variables which change in magnitude throughout the phenomena or data being observed (although this is not a necessary or universal practice). We might, for example, denote labor by the term X, capital by the term Z, soil (land) by the term W, and a commodity such as tobacco by the term Y (because it corresponds to the vertical or y axis of a diagram). However, we might also denote capital, labor, and soil (land inputs) and tobacco output by the terms, C, L, S, and T. Both methods are used on following pages. When the discussion relates to relationships or principles generally applicable to all resources and all products, the first system of symbols will be employed. When the discussion centers around a specific factor of production such as labor, the symbol L may be used to indicate the quantity of labor. However, this system also leads to complications. Many of the factors (land or labor, fertilizer or feed) and products (pork, poultry, prunes) start with the same letter. Accordingly, a more general set of notations is used. The various factors are denoted by X_1, X_2, Z_1, Z_2 and Z_3, while the various products are expressed as Y_1, Y_2, Y_3, and so forth. The subscripts (figures below the letters) indicate that the X's, for example, refer to different factors. X_1 may be labor while X_2 is capital. One variation is made on the pages which follow. While factors may be indicated by X's and Z's, we sometimes refer to total physical product as Y_p in order to distinguish it from value product. Thus Y_{p_1} and Y_{p_2} refer to 2 distinct products. Pork production may be indicated as Y_{pl}, while milk production is referred to as Y_{pm}. The term Y or Y_p will refer to total product as distinguished from marginal product M_p, and average product A_p.

A production function written in the *general* form $Y = f(X,Z)$ simply represents an attempt to specify (in the parentheses) all the factors which contribute to the magnitude of the product Y. This symbolic representation does not explain the amount by which Y changes as X or Z is varied. In order to express quantitative relationships between variables, the production function must be expressed in algebraic form such as $Y = a + bX$ or $Y = aX^b Z^c$. A final word about the production function concept is useful in our discussion of a single factor and a single product, input-output relationship. The production function may also be expressed in general form as $Y_{p_1} = f(X_1, X_2 | X_3, X_4)$ or $Y_{p_2} = f(X_1, X_2 | X_3 \ldots X_n)$. The perpendicular bar is used here to indicate that all factors to the left of the bar are variable while all factors to the right of the bar are fixed in quantity. The first equation can be read to have this meaning: the commodity Y_{p_1} (wheat) is a function of X_1, X_2, X_3, and X_4 (labor, capital, land, and management) but factors X_3 and X_4 are held constant in quantity, while only X_1 and X_2 can be varied in amount.

The analysis of this chapter refers to a production function such as the second one in the preceding paragraph. Under study is the nature of the relationship between output of a single product Y_1 and a single variable factor X_1. Other factors such as X_2, X_3, and unspecified resources up to and including X_n are either held fixed or else are already available in quantities so great that their cost need not be considered. For purposes of analysis, the production function might also be considered as $Y_p = f(X_1)$ because the output of Y_p resulting as X_1 is varied in amount (while other factors are held constant in quantity or otherwise do not change cost considerations) is the central problem. Production functions can be derived when "fixed factors" are fixed in various combinations and at various levels. For example, the amount of feed fed per hog can be varied as hog numbers, farm buildings, and acres of land are held constant at any level, or both feed per hog and numbers of hogs can be varied while all other resources are held constant. Finally, all resources but land or all resources including land can be varied. Production functions which relate factor input and product output when some resources are fixed (regardless of the number of fixed resources and level at which each is held fixed) can be termed *short-run* production functions. Those input-output relations which involve variation in the input of all factors (none is fixed) can be termed *long-run* production functions. These long-run functions are discussed in a later chapter of this book as part of the problem of returns to scale and farm size.

Our concern is not only with highly refined continuous functions. We are interested equally in production relationships where only a single indivisible unit of a resource can be applied and several units of output result. Because the latter are more easily explained and analyzed, we employ notions of continuity for purposes of generalization and establishment of basic principle.

Technological considerations and homogeneity. Production and resource relationships are strictly meaningful only if they refer to factors and commodities which are homogeneous. A unique factor-product or input-output relationship is not given if the first inputs of labor refer to 5 months of labor from an able-bodied man, while additional inputs refer to labor of a child. Similarly, the true relationship between fertilizer input and corn output is not isolated if the first 5 increments of fertilizer were composed of ammonium nitrate while the next 5 included an 8-8-8 mixture. The product must be homogeneous. Even if the fertilizer is of 1 kind alone, the input-output relationship is not defined if the product represents 2 different qualities or kinds for different levels of input. (Also, as we point out later, a unique factor-factor relationship or substitution schedule for grain and hay cannot be established if the grade of beef varies for different combinations of the 2 feeds.) Finally, the input-output relationship or production function refers to a specific time period and a single technique. The relationship of the input of resource services and the output of product is meaningful only as it refers to a particular production period. The product attributable to 1,000 pounds of fertilizer applied to an acre of land will be different if the entire amount is applied in 1 year, rather than 100 pounds each year for 10 years. In the same manner, the production function relating input of fertilizer to output of corn is not the same for open pollinated and hybrid corn.

A product can be produced in a multitude of ways, depending on the particular combination of resources and techniques employed. A different production function exists for each single technique which is possible. The physical production function or physical input-output relationship is a phenomenon of engineering and physical sciences. Taken alone, it has no part in choice or decision-making, the core of all economics. Technical or physical considerations seldom if ever define which particular pattern of production or resource use is best. The most desirable combination of products or factors cannot be determined until a choice indicator of some sort is employed, which in effect moves production problems from the fields of physical sciences to the field of economics. A choice indicator can be defined as the criterion indicating which of 2 or more alternatives is optimum or will maximize a given end. When 2 products which can be produced with given resources are being compared, the choice indicator becomes an expression of the price relationship between (constant revenue curve for) the 2 commodities if the end is one of maximizing returns. If 2 factors can be used to produce a given output of product, the choice indicator or function for minimizing cost or outlay becomes an expression of cost relationship between (the constant outlay curve for) the 2 factors. The relative utility derived from alternative goods may serve as the choice indicator in family consumption. A choice indicator may also be in physical terms. During a war emergency, decisions may relate to how many acres should be planted to alternative crops. Choices may then be made in terms of the relative calories or other food nutrients (the isonutrient curve) to be derived from the various commodities. Given the end of maximum national welfare, other choice indicators or criteria of efficiency can be employed, such as relative value of product with or without the distribution of income given.

Laws of Return and the Nature of the Input-Output Relationship or Production Function

The relationship between input of a single variable factor (with the quantity of other resources held constant) and output of a single product can take on 1 of 3 general forms. These include (1) constant productivity, (2) decreasing productivity, and (3) increasing productivity of the variable factor. Constant or increasing productivity is seldom found when only 1 factor is varied in respect to all others in agriculture. We will discuss each one separately, however.

Constant returns. Constant productivity holds true if all units of the variable factor which are applied to the fixed factor result in equal additions to the total output of product. The relationship between factor input and product output is then termed linear. If only 1 capsule is effective in deworming a pig and a farmer has 100 pigs, worm capsules which each add 20 pounds of pork represent a linear production function when fed to 100 pigs; each input of capsule adds 20 pounds to pork production when fed to the first, second, third, and, finally, all of the pigs. Or if fertilizer applied at the rate of 0, 10, 20, and 30 lbs. per acre results in yields of 0, 20, 40, and 60 bushels of wheat respectively, constant productivity is realized for the fertilizer resource: Each 10 lb. unit of fertilizer adds 20 bushels to total production of wheat per acre. This production function or input-output relationship denoting constant or linear returns is shown in Figure 2. When the production function is graphed with total output on the vertical or y axis and factor input on the horizontal or x axis (and the line denoted by Y_p) the resulting curve is a straight line and the production function is said to be linear. Constant returns are apparent from the dotted triangles: the horizontal side of each triangle corresponds to an input of 5 units (pounds in this case) of the variable factor or in other words indicates an increase in the factor input by constant amounts. The vertical (or right) dotted side of all triangles is of equal length and indicates an addition to output of 10 units for equal inputs of the variable factor. The resultant linear production function (line or curve relating total output to factor input) represents constant returns to the variable factor.

While linear production functions are not commonly discussed in the literature of economics, their existence is widespread where technical units or plants (the so-called fixed factors) are readily divisible. As we shall see later, farmers with limited capital are often faced with a linear production function or constant returns to scale within the relevant range of credit or funds which they can obtain. If the operator has 100 acres, he may apply 10 lbs. of fertilizer on each of 50 acres and get the same gain in output for each 10 lb. input. This is possible because he does not have to apply the entire 500 pounds on 1 acre. Constant returns is possible in this case because the 100-acre unit is divisible. Although constant productivity of the nature mentioned in this paragraph is possible, a linear production function does not generally exist when inputs per acre or per animal are intensified. Physical scientists sometimes make recommendations as if the production function were linear. Agricultural economists have made recommendations implying that this is true; the statement that the farmer can increase profits by increasing yield per acre or milk production per cow, if not well qualified, implies a constant or increasing returns. Finally,

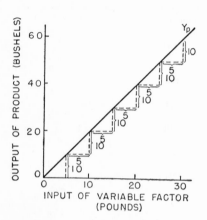

Fig. 2. Physical production function or input-output relationship indicating constant returns to a single factor.

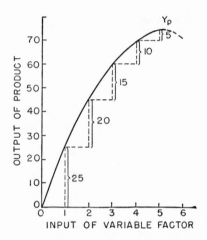

Fig. 3. Physical production function (input-output relationship) indicating diminishing returns to a single factor.

interregional comparisons, of the type frequently made, of average resource productivity in agriculture are meaningful only if the assumption of a linear production function is employed. (See Chapter 24.)

Diminishing returns. Diminishing productivity of the variable factor exists when each additional unit of input adds less to total output than the previous unit. Diminishing resource returns are realized, for example, if the first input adds 25 units to total output, while the second adds 20 units, the third adds 15 units, the fourth adds 10 units, and the fifth adds 5 units, as illustrated in Figure 2. Perhaps a sixth input might even cause output to fall to 71. The total product curve or input-output relationship (Y_p) is not a straight line, due to the fact that total product increases at a decreasing rate. This fact is illustrated by the triangles which show the quantity that each input adds to total output. While a production function representing constant returns (Figure 2) will always be a straight line, one representing diminishing returns can always be identified by its curvature towards the horizontal axis. The curve Y_p in Figure 3 is *concave* to the origin or "hollow" from the direction of the x axis. If total production were to fall to 71 with the addition of a sixth input of the variable factor, the production function curve would decline in the manner indicated by the dotted extension of Y_p.

Table I.

Inputs of 4-8-7 Fertilizer and Output of Potatoes (The Fertilizer Production Function) Aroostook Farm, Maine, 1927-41 *

Fertilizer input (500 lb. units)	Total yield attributable to fertilizer (bu. per acre) Y_p	Additional or marginal output for each added 500 lb. unit of fertilizer M_p (average method)[a] (bu. per acre)	Average output for each added 500 lb. unit of fertilizer A_p
(1)	(2)	(3)	(4)
0	0		0
		103	
1	103		103.0
		71	
2	174		87.0
		49	
3	223		74.3
		34	
4	257		64.2
		24	
5	281		56.2
		17	
6	298		49.7
		10	
7	308		44.0

* Source: Maine Agr. Exp. Sta. Bul. 414, *Potato fertilizer-rotation studies on Aroostook farm, 1927-41*. The total product includes only the increases in yield realized with fertilizer application.

[a] The term "average method" is mentioned in column 3 to indicate that the added output is actually the average for all fractional units of inputs between the two levels of inputs to which it corresponds. This consideration will be explained in detail at a later point. Here we simply wish to indicate that it is not the derivative or "exact marginal product" of any input.

A production function of the single variable factor nature and indicating diminishing returns throughout is outlined in Table 1. Fertilizer is the variable factor and an acre of land is the fixed factor. The data came from a physical experiment. Although the quantity of labor and harvesting services required varies with the amount of fertilizer applied and the total production of potatoes, these can, for many purposes, be considered in the vein of fixed factors (a) if labor and capital are available in fixed quantities for a farm as a whole and would not otherwise be employed (actually fixed for a farm but variable for the potato enterprise) or (b) have no cost attached (do not add any amount to total costs). If the data of Table 1 are graphed with input on the horizontal axis and output on the vertical axis, the functional relationship is similar to the input-output curve of Figure 3.

Diminishing returns throughout all input ranges of a variable factor occur only when the fixed factor is actually limited and not divisible (or when there is no interaction between factors the quantities of which are varied and combined in different ways). Using the experimental data from above, a linear production function (constant returns) can be obtained if 50,000 pounds of fertilizer (100 units of 500 lbs. each) are available and if the land factor or technical unit is fixed in quantity at 100 rather than 1 acre and is readily divisible. If the first 500 lbs. is applied to 1 of the 100 acres, the total product will be 103 bushels. If a second 500 lb. unit is applied to a second acre, the total product becomes 206. A third fertilizer input applied to a third acre results in a total product of 309. If this process is continued until 1 fertilizer unit of 500 pounds has been applied to each of the 100 acres, the total product will become 10,300, and each unit of fertilizer will have added 103 bushels to the total product. If these figures are graphed with fertilizer on the x axis and output on the y axis (from 1 fertilizer unit on 1 acre to 1 fertilizer unit on each of 100 acres) the curve will be a straight line as in Figure 2. The constant productivity of fertilizer arises in this case because land is not held fixed; although only 100 acres are available, the number of acres within this limit is variable. Hence, fertilizer and land are both variable resources. This changing of the quantity of fertilizer and land at the same time does not involve *variable proportioning* of the factors, because they are held in the fixed proportions of 1 acre of land and 500 lbs. of fertilizer up to the use of 50,000 lbs. of fertilizer and 100 acres of land. This takes us away from the problem of this chapter, variable proportions, and relates more nearly to the problem of *returns to scale* discussed in Chapter 7. If we attempt to use 3,500 pounds (7 units of 500 pounds each) on 1 acre of land or 350,000 pounds on 100 acres of land, we do vary the proportion of fertilizer to land and diminishing returns are expected.

Increasing returns. Increasing returns to a single factor exist when each successive input of the variable resource adds more to the total product than the previous input. Increasing factor returns are illustrated in Figure 4 by the curve Y_p. In contrast to the linear production function of Figure 2 and the concave curve of Figure 3, the production function denoting increasing returns is convex to the x axis. The dotted triangles illustrate increasing returns; while the return from the first input is 2, the return from the second is 4, the return from the third is 6, and so forth, until the seventh adds 14 to the total product: each additional input of the variable factor adds more to output than the previous unit.

Although it is true that a production function or set of input-output data may be derived showing increasing returns for 1 variable factor with all other factors fixed, it will ordinarily represent only 1 segment of a full production function. For example, a set of data from very small farms may show increasing returns to capital. Yet if capital were increased enough on a given land area, diminishing returns would certainly emerge finally. Thus the sample of small farms and little capital represents only a part of a production function. Because a range of increasing and decreasing returns to a single variable factor is most likely if the full possible range of inputs is examined, we examine this case below. Although it is logical that a production function may express diminishing productivity throughout all possible levels at which a single variable factor is applied to a fixed resource, it is not likely that increasing returns can be expressed throughout.

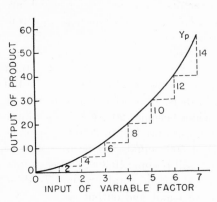

Fig. 4. Physical production function indicating increasing returns to a single factor.

Increasing-diminishing returns. Production functions are possible, if not the rule, which combine any 2 of the properties outlined above. Perhaps most production functions which appear to be of a constant or increasing returns nature are actually segments of curves such as those outlined here. Most common is one which combines the phase of increasing returns with one of decreasing returns. This is the classical production function of economic textbooks and while its existence is perhaps widespread, most literature tends to overemphasize the extent of the increasing returns phase. An everyday example of this input-output relationship can be found in seeding rates. If only 5 lbs. of oats are seeded per acre, the yield is low because weeds choke out the grain plants. Application of 10 pounds of seed may more than double oat yield, both because there are more oat plants and because they become effective in choking out some weeds. At some point, planting of more seed adds to total product but at a diminishing rate. For example, the third peck of seed may add 10 bushels to total yield, while the fourth and fifth may add only 8 and 6 respectively. In fact, so much seed can be planted that total yields per acre may be decreased. These possibilities are all included in the production function, illustrated in Figure 5. Returns are of increasing nature up to and including the third input, and hence the total product increases upward at an increasing rate (the total product curve is convex from below up to 3 inputs, as is also the case in Figure 4). From the third input through the seventh input, diminishing returns exist, and although the total product increases, it does so at a decreasing rate (as is illustrated by the concavity to the x axis of this portion of the curve Y_p). Application of more than 7 units of the variable resource to the fixed factor decreases the total product (a negative output results for the eighth and ninth inputs).[1]

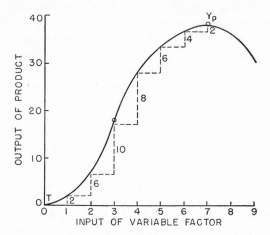

Fig. 5. Physical production function indicating both increasing and decreasing returns to a single factor.

When the relationship between a single variable factor and output of a single product is being compared, the total output often does not start from zero, because some output may have been forthcoming from the collection of fixed factors. When this is true, the product attributable to a single variable factor must be computed above that output which would be forthcoming in the absence of the particular variable service. If an acre of land yields 50 bushels of corn without the use of fertilizer, then as fertilizer is varied in amount, only any additional yield of corn above 50 bushels should be attributed to fertilizer. As the term implies, a variable factor refers to a resource different quantities of which are applied to a technical or economic unit of given or fixed magnitude. The factor (or combination of factors) which composes the technical or economic unit is thus termed "fixed," because it is held constant in amount (and its flow of services is held at a definite rate over the production period).

Average and Marginal Products

Discussion of the production function has been in terms of total output. We now see that the terms *total product curve* and *production function*

---

[1] A production function including phases of both increasing and decreasing returns, can be expressed by numerous equations of which (1) below is one.
$$Y_p = a + bX + cX^2 + dX^3 \qquad (1)$$
If this equation is used in deriving regression coefficients from experimental data or a farm sample it may take the empirical form of (2)
$$Y_p = 40 + 4.0X + .5X^2 - .15X^3 \qquad (2)$$

are closely associated. Knowledge of returns functions other than the total product is now necessary. The properties of these added productivity concepts help define the quantity of variable factor which should be employed with a given collection of fixed factors. They are important concepts for any problem in production economics, whether it involves profit of the farm or a national soil conservation or land use program. The 2 other important physical returns or productivity relationships can be termed (1) average curve and (2) marginal curve. Of course, it is not necessary that they be expressed as a curve. They can be shown as arithmetic quantities in a table such as Table 1. They can also be expressed as a function where A_p represents the average physical product of the variable factor while M_p represents the marginal physical product and X_1, X_2, and X_n represent production factors. (In later sections we use A_v to represent the average value product and M_v to represent the marginal value product. Where the subscript p is used it refers to a physical product. Where v is used it refers to a value of product.) Ordinarily, though, the average and marginal functions are derived from the total product function and are not expressed as functions of this nature. In this chapter we are interested in the average and marginal product of a single resource such as X_1 when X_2 and all other factors are constant (or have no costs even if they are varied in quantity). Both the average and marginal product curves or relationships can be derived once the total product relationship has been obtained. Therefore, most agronomic, animal husbandry, and economic studies attempt to establish the production function (since the average and marginal products can be determined from the same data). The average and marginal returns relationships define certain properties of the production function. Although the agronomist sometimes presents a marginal product curve under the heading of a fertilizer response curve, he necessarily derives it from total yields.

Average product. The term *average product* or *average productivity* refers to the average productivity of the variable resource. It can be expressed by the ratio Y/X, where Y refers to the total product and X refers to the total factor input. Thus the average product is the total output divided by the total input. The average product can be derived from the production function by dividing the total output at each level of input by the total number of inputs employed. In Table 1, for example, the average product in column 4 is obtained by dividing the total product of column 2 by the total inputs in column 1. When the production function or input-output curve is linear, the average product of input is constant. The average product continually decreases as more factor inputs are employed if the production function represents decreasing returns. This is evident in Table 1, where the average product in column 4 is obtained by dividing the total outputs of column 2 by the corresponding total inputs in column 1. Conversely, under an input-output relationship representing increasing returns throughout, the average product of the variable factor will increase continuously as more units are applied to the fixed factor. For a production function which includes both increasing and decreasing returns phases, the average product will first increase, then reach a maximum, and finally decline. The basis for this change in the average product of the variable resource will be discussed at a later point.

Marginal product. The term *marginal product* or *marginal productivity* refers to the quantity which each individual unit of factor input adds to the total product. Marginal products are illustrated in each of Figures 1, 2, 3, and 4 (the figures along the vertical side of the dotted triangle). In Figure 3, for example, the marginal product of the first input is 25, while the marginal products of the second, third, fourth, and fifth inputs are 20, 15, 10, and 5 respectively. The marginal product per unit of the variable input can be approximated by dividing the addition to total output by the addition to total input. Referring to Figure 2 again, when the total level of resource input is 1, the total output of product is 25. In other words, the addition to input is 1 and the addition to product is 25. If the addition (25) to total output is divided by the addition (1) to total input, the marginal product is 25. Similarly, when the total level of input is 2 the total level of output is 45. Since 20 units have been added to total product (45 minus 25) and 1 unit has been added to total input (2 minus 1), the marginal product is 20. When marginal product is calculated in this manner, it is an *average marginal productivity* figure. The number 20 actually refers to the average marginal product for all units of input between 1 and 2. It does not refer to the marginal productivity of exactly the second input but rather the average of all fractions of input between 1 and 2. Were it possible to add $\frac{1}{4}$, $\frac{1}{2}$, $\frac{3}{4}$ or any other fraction of an input (to the previous total input of 1), the marginal productivity figure would differ in each case. The number 20 (the marginal product when the second input is added) is actually the average for all possible fractions between inputs of 1 and 2 units of the variable factor. The "average marginal product" is easily illustrated with the data of Figure 2, where inputs are added in "lumps." Since the first 10 units of inputs add 20 units to total product, the "average marginal product" of each of the units of inputs is 2. Methods by which the exact marginal product can be obtained for each unit (or fractional unit) of input are explained in advanced sections of this chapter. Computation of marginal product in the manner outlined above is satisfactory for many or perhaps most purposes of analysis and decision-making (graphing marginal product curves where great precision is not required, approximating returns from use of additional resources, and so forth). On some of the pages which follow we have 2 marginal product columns. One is indicated as the *average* marginal product and is computed in the manner outlined above. The other is termed the *exact* marginal product and is computed in a manner to be outlined later. The reader may use the average marginal product which indicates the productivity value *between* the 2 relevant input levels. The *exact* figure indicates the marginal value product "*at exactly*" the input indicated.[2]

Marginality. The term *marginal* is synonymous with the term *additional* in economics and is the most powerful tool in the science. Strictly speaking, an optimum or maximum (maximum profits to a firm, maximum utility to a consumer or household, optimum resource efficiency for the nation) cannot be determined or defined except in terms of marginality. Although average productivity provides some guides to the manner in which resources should be allocated, it is marginal productivity which should serve as the final criterion in determining use of resources. Marginal quantities actually refer to ratios of change. The marginal product is the ratio of change in total output as related to the change in input. If we use the symbol Δ to mean "change in," ΔY to indicate "change in product output," and ΔX to mean "change in input," the marginal product is the ratio $\Delta Y/\Delta X$.

Product Relationships

Mention is made above that the marginal and average product relationships define certain of the properties of the production function or total product curve. Obviously, certain relationships between the different returns curves or functions must exist, since both the average and marginal products can be or are derived from the production function. The relationships between the total, average, and marginal productivity functions or curves are illustrated in Table 2 and Figure 6.[3] Both of these examples refer to a production function which includes both increasing and decreasing returns for the variable resource. If the production function displays

---

[2] By the *exact* method we refer, of course, to the marginal product as a derivative. Since we refrain from using anything but simple mathematics understandable to any reader who can do arithmetic, we do not present any calculus in the text of this volume. Readers who are not interested in refining the analysis beyond that presented in the text need not bother to absorb this or other footnotes which include more complex statements. A full understanding of later chapters requires only that the reader keep pace with the geometric illustrations presented in the text.

[3] The appearance of returns curves which are graphed on the basis of the method and data of Table 2 will depend on the procedure employed. Average and marginal productivity curves can be graphed by plotting columns 5 and 6 respectively against column 1. An alternative approach is to use the 5 lb. units in column 2 as the 1st, 2nd, 3rd, 4th, 5th, 6th, 7th, and 8th inputs (of 5 each). The corresponding marginal products then become 11, 13, 14, 11, 9, 3, —2, and —4 (column 4). The average outputs are 11, 12, 12.7, 12.2, 11.6, 10.2, 8.4, and 6.9, respectively. Regardless of the technique employed, a closer approximation of the marginal curve is often obtained by plotting the added output or marginal values in between the figures for inputs. This procedure should be employed when the marginal product is computed by the *average* method. If computed by the *exact* method (i.e., as derivatives) the marginal value should be plotted exactly above the input.

diminishing returns alone as in Figure 3, the relationship between the total, average, and marginal products is exactly the same as for the decreasing returns portion of the "combination" production functions in Table 2 or Figure 6. Similarly, the total, average, and marginal product relationships

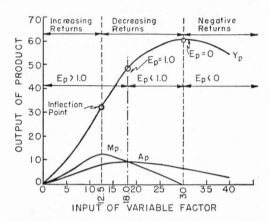

Fig. 6. Relationship of factor input to total, marginal, and average physical products.

for the increasing returns portion of a combination production function are the same as those for a production function which might involve only increasing returns.

Marginal and total products. In the terms of mathematics, the marginal product (curve M_p in Figure 6) indicates the change in total product (Y_p) for each unit change in resource input. Accordingly, as long as $\Delta Y/\Delta X$, or the marginal product of the variable factor, is increasing, the total product must increase at an increasing rate. This is indicated by the total product curve in Figure 6, which is convex to the x axis as long as the marginal product is increasing. The total product curve reaches an inflection point, a point where the curvature reverses (in this case, from convex to concave relative to the x axis), as the marginal product curve attains a maximum. Total product continues to increase, but at a decreasing rate as long as the marginal product decreases but is greater than zero. It reaches a maximum as the marginal product becomes zero (an input of 30 units in Figure 6), and then decreases as the marginal product becomes negative (for inputs greater than 30 in either Table 2 or Figure 6).

Laws of returns. The relationships discussed above fall under one of the most widely accepted laws in economics. It is the law of variable proportions, also called the law of diminishing returns, and can be stated as follows: *if the quantity of one productive service is increased by equal increments with the quantities of other resource services held constant, the increments to total product may increase at first but will decrease after a* "certain point." The point referred to is the maximum point on the mar-

Table 2.

Relationship of Resource Input to Total, Average, and Marginal Output (Hypothetical Data for a Single Product and a Single Variable Factor)

Total units of variable resource input (other resources fixed)	Addition to total input of resources [a]	Total output of product Y_p	Addition to total output [b] (marginal product of each single 5 lb. input)	Average product (output of product per unit of input) [c] A_p	Marginal product (addition to output by each additional input of resources) [d] M_p
(1)	(2)	(3)	(4)	(5)	(6)
0	0	0		0	
			11		2.20
5	5	11		2.20	
			13		2.60
10	5	24		2.40	
			14		2.80
15	5	38		2.53	
			11		2.20
20	5	49		2.45	
			9		1.80
25	5	58		2.32	
			3		.60
30	5	61		2.03	
			−2		−.40
35	5	59		1.69	
			−4		−.80
40	5	55		1.37	

[a] Computed by subtracting the previous total input from each successive total input in column 1.

[b] Computed by subtracting the previous total product from each successive total product in column 3.

[c] Computed by dividing each total product in column 3 by the corresponding total input in column 1.

[d] Computed by dividing the addition to total product in column 4 by the corresponding addition to total input in column 2. It is the "average" marginal product of 5 inputs rather than the marginal product of each fifth unit.

ginal productivity curve which also is identical with the inflection point on the total product curve. For greater increments of resource input, additions to total product become smaller and smaller. The law of diminishing returns refers particularly to the nature of the marginal productivity curve. The term "variable proportions" should be kept in mind also. The proportions of factor services change continuously when one factor is variable while other resources are fixed in quantity.

Marginal and average products. Important relationships also exist between the marginal and average productivity functions. As long as the marginal product is greater than the average product, the average productivity of the variable resource increases; if the marginal product is less than the average product, the average productivity of the resource decreases. These relationships between "addition" and "average" are common knowledge of students: if the student's "last test grade" is higher than his previous average, the average is increased. Farmers also know that if this year's oat yield is above the historic average, the average will be increased. A yield lower than the average will pull down the average. The application of these statements can also be seen in Figure 6 and Table 2. As long as the marginal product curve (M_p in Figure 6) is above the average productivity curve (A_p in Figure 6) the average product curve continues to rise (has a positive slope). The marginal curve intersects the average curve at the maximum of the latter. Finally, the average curve has a negative slope (the average product decreases) when the marginal curve falls below it.[4] As a basis for later analysis we emphasize that even though the marginal productivity of the variable resource is diminishing, its average productivity continues to increase as long as the marginal product is greater than the average product.

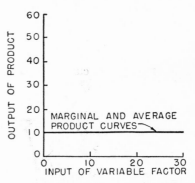

Fig. 7. Relationship of factor input to marginal and average physical products under constant returns to a single factor (based on the same data as the linear production function in Figure 1).

Figure 7 is of interest in this respect because it indicates the interrelationships of the marginal and average returns curves when the production function is linear. As we already know, a linear production function indicates constant returns to the variable factor. Hence, the marginal and average product curves are equal and identical. They can be graphed as a horizontal line indicative of constant productivity for the variable resource.

Derivation of average productivity from total product curves. Refinements in the relationships between marginal and average productivity curves can now be made. Knowledge of these is necessary for complete facility and competence in productivity analysis. Since the average product is the ratio of total output to total input (total output ÷ total input or Y_p/X), the average product is the slope or gradient (ratio) of any corresponding point on the total product curve. A number of straight lines can thus be drawn to indicate the average product of the variable factor. To

---

[4] In Table 2, the average product goes up when the marginal product is greater but decreases as soon as the marginal product becomes less than the previous average (between inputs of 15 and 20). Because inputs have not been broken down into infinitely small increments, the marginal product is not equal to the average product when the latter is at its maximum. This *exact* point could be determined, however, had we computed the marginal products as derivatives assuming fractional inputs of the resource.

define the average product, these straight lines must pass through the origin. Line T_1 in Figure 8 is such a line. It starts at the origin and intersects the total product curve at point a. At point a the total output is OR or 525 and the total input is ON or 5. The average product in numerical terms is then 525/5 (total output divided by total input) or 105. We can also express the average product as the ratio OR/ON. The ratio OR/ON is not only the average product (since it is equal to 525/5), but is also the slope or gradient of the line T_1; it increases in a vertical direction by OR for an increase in a horizontal direction by ON. In other words, at an input of ON (5) the line T_1 slopes upward at the ratio OR/ON or at the rate of 105 units of output for each unit of input.

A different straight line from the origin exists for each point on the total product curve. However, only 1 of the straight lines defining the average product can have a maximum slope. This is a line tangent to the total product curve and is indicated as OT_2 in Figure 8. Any straight

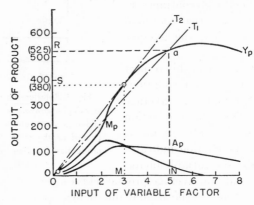

Fig. 8. Derivation of marginal and average productivity from total product curves.

line originating at O and with a slope greater than that of T_2 would fall entirely above the total product curve. Since the slope of this line is a maximum, the ratio of output to input is greatest at this point. Thus the point of tangency of line T_2 and the total product curve is directly above (at the same level of input) as the maximum point on A_p, the average product curve.

Marginal product. We have already indicated that the marginal product of a variable factor is the amount added to total product by 1 more unit of the resource. We can also refine our understanding of the term marginal. Referring back to Table 1, we see that addition of the second 500-lb. unit of fertilizer added 71 bushels to total yield. We are interested in change; the change concerning us is the change in output relative to the change in input. We can express this as a ratio in the manner indicated earlier of output change/input change or $\Delta Y/\Delta X$. In Table 1 this ratio is 71/1 for the second input, and, therefore, the marginal product of the second 500-lb. unit of fertilizer is 71 (71 divided by 1). If, however, we wish to compute the marginal product for a 1-lb. rather than a 500-lb. input of fertilizer, the ratio of change becomes 71/500 or .14. Each pound of fertilizer between the first and second total input levels adds .14 to total yield; the marginal product, on the average, of each pound of the second 500-lb. input of fertilizer is .14. We call this system of computing the marginal product the *average* method. The implications of computing marginal products by different methods are apparent if we continue to use the symbol Δ to mean *change* and refer to ΔY as "change in product" and ΔX as "change in resource input." We already know that the marginal product is the ratio of the change in total product to the change in total factor input or $\Delta Y/\Delta X$. Thus, in Table 1, $\Delta Y/\Delta X$ is 71/1 or 71, when fertilizer input is measured in 500-lb. units. It is 71/500 or .14 if output is related to a pound of fertilizer. In each case, $\Delta Y/\Delta X$ refers to the marginal product. This concept also can be applied to Figure 9 where Y is taken as the total product curve. If input of X is changed from 0 to 5, total output changes from 0 to 16. Therefore, $\Delta Y/\Delta X$ or the average

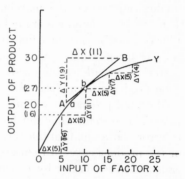

Fig. 9. Derivation of marginal product.

marginal product of input is 16/5 or 3.2. (If we take the 5 X as a single input, then $\Delta Y/\Delta X$ is 16/1 or 16). When input is increased to 10, the marginal product or $\Delta Y/\Delta X$ is 11/5 or 2.2. However, the figure 2.2 is not the marginal product of the 10th unit of input. Instead, it is the average for the 6th, 7th, 8th, 9th, and 10th units of input. If we take it to represent the marginal product of a single input, it best approximates that for the 8th unit. This is true because the changes in Y and X are not infinitely small. However, it is apparent that the slope or ratio of change in the total product curve is indicative of the marginal product. This is indicated by the fact that the little triangles underneath curve Y represent the change in output (ΔY) for each change in input (ΔX). As curve Y becomes flatter, or as its slope decreases, the ΔY side of the triangles become smaller. The quantity $\Delta Y/\Delta X$, the marginal product, also becomes smaller, since ΔX is of the same magnitude throughout.

Because the slope of the total product curve indicates the marginal product, changes can be made very small by drawing a straight line tangent to the total product curve. Line AB is thus tangent to the total product curve at point b. The slopes of tangent line AB and curve Y are equal at point b. Therefore, the slope of AB indicates the ratio $\Delta Y/\Delta X$

on curve Y, or the change in product for each unit change in input, and defines the marginal product for the 10th unit of input (point b). We now see that the slope or $\Delta Y/\Delta X$ of line AB is 19/11. The slope or $\Delta Y/\Delta X$ of the total product curve at point b is also 19/11. The marginal product of the 10th input is 1.7. This is the *exact* marginal product as compared to the *average* marginal product computed above. The *exact* method, when applied to the 10th input, refers to the marginal product of the 10th unit alone. The *average* method, in contrast to the *exact* method, referred to the average of the marginal products for inputs 6 to 10, and (if taken to suggest the marginal product for any one input) best describes $\Delta Y/\Delta X$ at point a (the 8th input).

A tangent line such as AB can be drawn for each point on the total product curve and the marginal product can be specified accordingly. Tangent lines defining marginal products need not pass through the origin. (There is only one such line that will define a marginal product.) The slope of tangent lines higher and higher on curve Y will have smaller and smaller slopes indicating smaller $\Delta Y/\Delta X$ ratios, and hence smaller marginal products for additional inputs.

Marginal productivity figures are seldom if ever computed by tangent lines. The system, while not less exact than the average method, is open to error; on a small graph the straight line is tangent over a wide area of the product curve. In empirical studies, exact marginal productivities can be derived easily by calculus. The tables which follow in the next several chapters employ mostly the *average* marginal product. When the *exact* marginal product is employed, it is so indicated. The marginal data presented in bulletins and other publications ordinarily are *averages*. They may show, for example, that a 25-lb. unit of ammonium nitrate adds 15 bushels to total yield. The addition to total output by one 25-lb. increment in fertilizer is 15 bushels and the economic question is one of whether the cost of the 25-lb. unit of fertilizer is more or less than the return from the 15 bushels of corn. Still, the 15-bushel change in yield more nearly (but not exactly) describes the rate of change in production for the 13th pound of fertilizer. Each pound from 1 through 12 probably has an output/input ratio greater than 15/1; each pound from 14 through 25 probably has a ratio less than 15/1. Profit calculations might be changed accordingly.

An important productivity relationship in economics is this: ANY 2 CURVES (OR LINES) WHICH ARE TANGENT HAVE THE SAME SLOPE OR RATE OF CHANGE AT THE POINT OF TANGENCY. THEREFORE, THE MARGINAL QUANTITIES OF 2 TANGENT CURVES ARE EQUAL. THIS CONDITION HOLDS TRUE WHETHER THE QUANTITIES REFERRED TO RELATE TO (1) TRANSFORMATION OF FACTOR INTO PRODUCT, (2) SUBSTITUTION OF FACTOR FOR FACTOR, (3) SUBSTITUTION OF PRODUCT FOR PRODUCT, OR (4) ANY OTHER QUANTITIES DISCUSSED IN LATER CHAPTERS.

Discontinuous inputs and marginal products. When inputs are discontinuous and output can be related only to whole units of factors, the derivation procedure then becomes that suggested in Figure 1 for corn cultivations. The only meaningful changes in output are those associated with one-unit changes in input. In Figure 1 the marginal product or ratio $\Delta Y/\Delta X$ is 38/1 or 38 for the first input. The slope of the dotted line oa between inputs of 0 and 1 thus indicates the marginal product. The slope of ab is 12/1, thus indicating that the $\Delta Y/\Delta X$, the marginal product, for the second input is 12. In the case of discontinuous inputs for a single indivisible technical unit or plant, an infinite number of tangent lines or marginal products does not exist. This statement has important implications for agriculture.

Marginal and average products. In the section above marginal product was defined relative to an input-output curve of diminishing marginal productivity throughout. Now turn back to Figure 8, where the marginal productivity of the variable resource first increases and then decreases. Any line drawn tangent to curve Y_p defines the marginal product for the corresponding input. Line T_2 is such a line; it defines the marginal product for an "input of 3." Previously, however, we indicated that line T_2 defines the average product when factor input is 3. This particular line defines both the average and marginal products and, as is evident in the graph, the marginal curve is equal to (intersects) the average curve at exactly this point. Both the marginal and average products are equal to 380/3 or 126.7. The line T_2 is the only line which expresses both average and marginal products. Tangent lines defining the marginal product for smaller outputs, none of which pass through the origin, will have a slope greater than the "intersecting" line, which always passes through the origin and defines the average product. For inputs smaller than 3, marginal product is always more than average product. The opposite is true for inputs greater than 3.

Elasticity of production. A final concept can be applied to the production function or input-output curve. It is the concept of *elasticity of production*. Many inferences in agricultural economics are based on assumption of production elasticity.[5] The elasticity of production refers to the percentage increase in output as compared to the percentage increase in input and can be denoted by the symbol E_p. It can be computed as $E_p =$ per cent change in output $\div$ per cent change in input. In a more formal manner it is represented in equation form as

$$E_p = \frac{\Delta Y/Y}{\Delta X/X} \text{ or } (\Delta Y/Y)(X/\Delta X) \text{ or } (X/Y)(\Delta Y/\Delta X)$$

[5] As an example, W. W. Wilcox, "Effects of Farm Price Change on Efficiency in Farming," *Jour. Farm Econ.*, Vol. 33, pp. 60-61, uses the results from a single fertilizer trial in North Carolina to infer that the agricultural production function is first highly elastic, and finally highly inelastic, and thus excludes adjustment to price by a large number of farmers.

Referring back to Table 1, we see that as input increased from 1 to 2, total output increases from 103 to 174. Output increases by 71.9 per cent and input increases by 100 per cent. Therefore E_p, the elasticity of production is $71.9/100 = .72$. If the data between the second and third inputs from Table 1 are substituted in the elasticity equation above, the elasticity is computed as .56.

$$E_p = \frac{49/174}{1/2} = (49/174)\,(2/1) = (2/174)\,(49/1) = \frac{.28}{.50} = .56$$

A production function with an elasticity of 1.0 $(E_p = 1.0)$ throughout indicates constant returns. A 1 per cent increase in input is always accompanied by a 1 per cent increase in output. The input-output curve of Figure 2 illustrates such a production function. The elasticity of the production function in Figure 8 is also 1.0 where line T_2 and the curve Y_p are tangent. This is true because the straight line tangent to the product curve passes through the origin.[6] The elasticity of T_2 and curve Y_p is the same here. Further relationships between the total product curve and the elasticity of production are indicated in Figure 6. The elasticity is more than 1.0 up to the maximum average product where it becomes 1.0 It is less than 1.0 between the maximum average product and the maximum total product. It becomes less than zero as total product declines.

Hence we have our final product relationship. *Marginal and average products* are equal when the elasticity of production is 1.0. This condition holds true at only 1 point on the increasing-decreasing production function of Figure 8. It is true for every point on the production function in Figure 2, as is indicated in Figure 7. A production function for which the elasticity is less than 1.0 throughout all ranges of input indicates diminishing returns of the nature in Figure 3.

Discontinuous Inputs

Some resources come in "continuous" or "completely divisible" units. Fertilizer, for example, can be applied to a fixed acre of land in continuous quantities ranging from a fraction of a pound up to several tons. Labor is also quite divisible because it can be used in minutes as well as man-year quantities. Capital in the form of tractors is not nearly so divisible. If tractors are to be used in production, no less than one can be effectively employed. However, tractor inputs can be varied by (a) using one tractor more or fewer hours per day, (b) employing tractors of various sizes, (c) substituting second-hand for new tractors, or (d) hiring tractor services. These service inputs, however. may also come in "lumps" rather than in continuous inputs such as indicated by the graphs of this chapter. Pro-

---

[6] The elasticity of a straight line or linear production function is 1.0 only if it passes through the origin.

ductivity figures for discontinuous inputs might be presented more realistically in the form of bar charts rather than graphs or continuous functions. Nevertheless, these "discontinuous" or "lumpy" inputs have either a constant, decreasing, or increasing productivity; the second tractor will either add more than, less than, or the same as the first tractor. The principles of later chapters are still applicable with slight modification. Actually these discontinuities facilitate rather than retard economic analysis and decision-making. Since the farmer can buy only a whole tractor he need only estimate the product and return from it for comparison with cost. He is saved the mental task of estimating the productivity and returns from ½ tractor, ¼ tractor, ⅛ tractor, and so forth.

While the problem under consideration in this chapter, factor-to-product transformation in its most elementary form, may involve only simple economic calculus, it also extends to problems and producing units of all levels. Factor-product relationships are identical regardless of the nature and magnitude of the fixed factor or factors. The fixed factor may be represented by a technical unit such as an acre of land or a hog. It may represent 160 acres as the producing plant of a farm. Finally, it may represent all of the land in a soils region or a state. We now turn to examination of these relationships as they relate to farm production.

Selected References

Allen, R. G. D., *Mathematics for Economists*. London: Macmillan, 1942, pp. 190-193.

Black, J. D., *et al.*, *Farm Management*. New York: Macmillan, 1948, Ch. 17.

Black, J. D., *Production Economics*. New York: Henry Holt, 1926, Ch. 11.

Boulding, K. E., *Economic Analysis*. New York: Harper, 1948, pp. 500-510.

Carlson, Sune A., *A Study on the Pure Theory of Production*. London: King and Son, 1939, pp. 10-23.

Heady, E. O., "Use and Estimation of Input-Output Relationships," *Jour. Farm Econ. Proceedings*, Nov. 1952.

Hopkins, J. A., *Farm Management*. New York: Prentice-Hall, 1939, Ch. 7.

Stigler, G., *Theory of Price*. New York: Macmillan, 1947, pp. 116-125.

Weintraub, S., *Price Theory*. New York: Pitman, 1949, pp. 77-86.

3

Simple Resource-Product Relationships
in Agriculture

SEVERAL FORCES determine how resources of a firm or an industry are used or should be used. Two of the most important of these are (1) the technical conditions of production and (2) the structure and relationships of market prices. Technical conditions of production refer to the nature of the relationships between resources and products. We have already examined one of these, the relationship between factors and products. Subsequent chapters will include analyses of relationships between one resource and another resource and between one product and another product. Finally, we will return and examine factor-product relationships. However, even now it is apparent that technical relationships between factors and products help determine the manner in which resources are used or should be used. The quantity of a single resource or of all resources to be used by a farm, by a producing region, or by the industry of agriculture depends as much on the nature of the production function as on the level and structure of prices. Forces other than market prices and the production function also condition the use of farm resources. Uncertainty, a subject discussed in later chapters, is one of these. Uncertainty itself results from particular characteristics of prices and production functions. Man-made institutions such as racial barriers and labor unions also condition the pattern of production. Similarly, special mechanisms of the market, such as leasing systems and direct relationships between producing and consuming units, alter resource use. The production economics or resource efficiency aspects of each of these forces will be analyzed in the following chapters.

We now extend our examination of simple factor-product relationships. The analysis of the previous chapter dealt with the fundamental relationships of a single factor being transformed into a single product; this chapter is concerned with the nature of simple production functions in agriculture. Does constant, increasing, or decreasing productivity prevail in this primary industry? What is the elasticity of production or the rate at which productivity of a resource declines as its use is extended? As in the previous chapter, we are concerned with production and resource use when one or more factors are fixed in quantity and another is variable. It should be emphasized that labor is the only homogeneous factor of production which can be varied without simultaneous variation in the quantity of other single resources. Even the agronomist who conducts a yield test through doubling and trebling the quantity of fertilizer applied on a plot of land must increase the input of labor and the services of capital in the form of fertilizer spreaders and other experimental equipment. Perhaps we should never speak in terms of a single variable factor of production. However, in cases where doubling the input of one resource also requires doubling the services of another factor, we can speak in terms of an aggregate or amalgam resource input. For example, if application of 500 pounds of fertilizer requires 1 hour of labor and machine services, while application of 1,000 pounds requires 2 hours of labor and machine services, an input-output curve such as those in the last chapter can be derived and graphed as if fertilizer inputs alone were concerned. Inputs on the horizontal axis might then be denoted in units of fertilizer or they could be denoted as units of F-L-P to indicate that they are made up of a bundle of resource services including fertilizer, labor and machinery. We might simply call this composite input of services, Z. This procedure of varying 2 factors of production at the same time and in the same proportions and giving them another name is not new. A common grain, corn, includes both protein and carbohydrate. In Figure 7, both protein and carbohydrate inputs from corn are varied but are called "grain" because they are combined in the grain by fixed proportions. Similarly the "composite" input of Figure 2 is called fertilizer even though it is composed of 3 elements (nitrogen, phosphorus, and potassium). This procedure is possible because the bundle of services is homogeneous; it is always made up of elements in constant proportions. The same logic applies to numerous of the productivity functions presented in this chapter; even though a graph or table relates crop yield to composite fertilizer inputs, it may also represent the nature of input-output relationships for all complementary factors had they been considered as a bundle of services.

The magnitude of fixed factors. Simple input-output relationships can be examined for factors fixed in any magnitude. First, we can view the nature of yield response as fertilizer is applied in varying quantities to a single acre of land, a technical unit. Here all resources but fertilizer, or its bundle of cooperating services, are fixed. In the same manner we can examine the nature of the feed input-pork output curve in hog production. Here the animal as a technical unit is fixed. However, the feed production function might also be considered in a different light. We can relate pork output to feed input when the number of hogs as well as the amount of feed is also varied while the size of the farm plant is held fixed. Finally, we can view feed-pork productivity when labor, housing, equipment, and all other resources of a farm, as well as feed and hog numbers, are increased. If the proper share of the product is imputed to each resource, feed productivity can be expected to vary under each one of these 3 situations. The same logic applies to any other variable resource, such as labor or land, or any form of capital such as fertilizer, cattle feed, cattle, irrigation water, or machinery. Obviously, then, a large number of production functions are possible for pork, cotton, wheat, or any other commodity, depending on the number of resources which are variable and the number which are fixed. We will look upon production functions as *short-run* input-output relationships when one or more factors are fixed, and as *long-run* when all resources can be varied. The nature of the long-run production function is a problem of returns to scale in farming and is discussed in a later chapter. In the sections which follow we examine the nature of the short-run production function in agriculture. First, the input-output relationship is examined with an acre of land as a technical unit. Farmers are concerned with fertilizer productivity in determining the level of yields which is most profitable. Society is concerned with this same relationship in determining such things as the size of the population which can be supported on a given land area or in deciding whether more or fewer resources should be used in agriculture while the product forthcoming is traded for non-industrial commodities of other nations. Next we examine productivity relationships for livestock as technical units. Here again, the farmer is interested in the most profitable yield per animal. National administrators may be equally interested in the marginal productivity of feed per animal. The productivity coefficients are important in determining which types of livestock should be produced in a food emergency or determining the yield which should be obtained from single types of livestock. After examining the input-output relationship for technical units in agriculture, we break away from our rigid adherence to a very simple production function and view the productivity of resources such as land or capital when they are varied but other resources are held fixed. A considerable amount of data is available to indicate the nature of production functions for technical units in agriculture. This is true because the efforts of physical scientists in the Land-Grant Colleges center around deriving production functions for feed, seed, fertilizer, and similar resources, applied to a single technical unit. Less is known about the nature of the production function for particular resources when parts of the farm plant, other than the technical unit, represent the fixed collection of factors.

Production Functions for Technical Units in Agriculture

Economists, more than any other scientists, have been concerned with the nature of production functions. Why should this be true if the production function is a physical phenomenon? The answer is obvious. While the input-output relationship *per se* is a technological consideration, its specific nature has many economic implications, as outlined on the pages which follow. Besides, it is doubtful whether a fine line can or should be drawn either within or between the various physical and social sciences. Every practical problem has roots in numerous sciences. Finally, the basic phenomena which underly the important structural relationships in economics stem either from psychology or from the physical sciences. Although economics deals quite largely with the maximization (profit, national product) or minimization (cost, resource outlay) of quantities important in the value framework of individuals, communities, and nations, there is no manner in which these principles and logic can be put into application unless knowledge of production possibilities is available on the one hand, while knowledge of prices or the psychology of the individual as a consumer is available on the other hand.

Historically, scientists in agriculture have followed a somewhat rigid specialization in deriving production functions. Physical scientists have concerned themselves with physical production functions when the technical unit is the fixed factor. Experimental procedures have been employed to predict the relationship of product output to resource input when fertilizer, seed, or irrigation water is applied to a single acre of land in varying quantities or when different quantities of feed are fed to a milk cow or other animal. Agricultural economists have concerned themselves quite largely with the nature of the production function when factors are fixed in magnitudes greater than the technical unit. Also, the input-output relationships of the economist are ordinarily derived from farm samples rather than from experimental observations. Agricultural production economists have derived input-output or productivity relationships for situations such as these: (1) when the size of the farm is held fixed and the number of cows and the amount of feed, labor, and cooperating services are varied; (2) when machinery is held fixed and the number of acres is varied along with labor, tractor fuel, and cooperating services; and (3) when the land area of a region is fixed and the labor and capital inputs are subject to variation. These and the many other studies which revolve around physical input-output relationships ordinarily are not published in the formal vein of production functions. Some simply relate profit to numbers of dairy cows for farms of different acreages. Others show the nature of returns for farms of different sizes. Finally, those dealing with regions or the agricultural industry may simply show rough average productivity figures for labor or capital when these resources are applied in varying levels of intensity to the fixed soil resources of different producing areas. The latter may be labeled as "studies in resource efficiency." But, regardless of their nature, all of these studies have a common element; they involve the nature of the production function or the output of product as related to the input of resource. Economists have, however, concerned themselves with the nature of production functions for technical units. Those classical studies which attempted to relate profits to the yield index of crops or dairy cows were of this nature. Obviously, the level of output and, consequently, the level of input per animal or acre which results in maximum profits depends on whether physical returns are increasing, decreasing, or constant, as well as on the rate at which they decrease when diminishing productivity holds true. Many studies of this nature have been derived from farm data. Farm production economists also have employed experimental procedures in deriving production functions for technical units. The most elaborate input-output study ever made was inspired by production economists and carried out cooperatively by economists and dairy scientists.[1] The illustrations of productivity relationships on the following pages do not exhaust the examples available. They are simply employed to suggest the nature of resource productivity in agriculture and to provide data for later illustration of basic production economics or resource allocation principles.

Soil Production Functions

The nature of the fertilizer-crop production function has been a subject for debate for generations. Early production economists (Von Thunen, Aereboe, Ricardo) put forth the hypothesis of diminishing productivity. Agronomists and agricultural chemists were less well-agreed on the nature of the input-output relationship with an acre of soil as the technical unit or fixed factor.[2] This debate centered around the so-called "law of the soil" or "law of the minimum."

Limitational factors and fixed coefficients. Early soil scientists put forth this notion: if all other factors are present in quantities sufficient to allow a physical maximum yield per acre while one single element is a limiting factor, increases in output will be directly proportional to the increase in input of this *minimum* or *limitational* factor; the production function for the limitational factor is linear and each 1 per cent increase in input is accompanied by a 1 per cent increase in output. Constant productivity prevails until input of the minimum or limitational factor is great enough

---

[1] See E. Jensen, *et al., Input-output Relationships in Milk Production.* U.S.D.A. Tech. Bul. 815, Washington, 1942.

[2] Refer to Justus von Liebig, *Die Grundsätze der Agriculturchemie.* Braunschweig: 1855; Adolph Mayer, *Das Düngerkapital und der Raubbau.* Heidelberg, 1869; E. Woolny, *Untersuchungen über den Einfluss der Wachstumsfaktoren auf das Produktionsvermögen der Kulturpflanzen. In Forschungen auf dem Gebiete der Agrikulturphysik.* Heidelberg: 1897-98; Paul Wagner, *Beiträge zur Ausbildung der Dungungslehre.* Berlin: Theils Landw. Jahrb, 1883; and E. A. Mitscherlich, *Das Gesetz des Minimums und Das Gesetz des Abnehmenden Bodenertrages.* Berlin: Landw. Jahrb, 1909.

to allow a maximum yield per acre. The 2 examples below illustrate the hypothesis. Both suppose that 30 pounds of phosphorus (P), 60 pounds of nitrogen (N), and 15 pounds of potash (K) are necessary for production of a maximum (an optimum in the terms of Woolny, Mayer, and Von Liebig) physical output per acre. In Example A, yield would be proportional to the availability of nitrogen. No amount of P or K would result

Example A				Example B			
Pounds available			Yield	Pounds available			Yield
N	P	K		N	P	K	
20	15	30	20	60	5	30	20
40	15	30	40	60	10	30	40
60	15	30	60	60	15	30	60

in a total yield above 40 bushels if N were constant at 40 pounds. In Example B, yield would relate in a linear manner to input of P. All resources would then serve as limitational factors. The term *limitational* means that production can be no greater than allowed by input of a single factor; some minimum quantity of the limitational factor must be present for each level of output, and there can be no substitution between factors. In the example above, a yield of 20 bushels would be possible with inputs of 20, 5, and 10 pounds of N, P, and K respectively, while a yield of 40 bushels would be possible with inputs of 40, 10, and 20 pounds.

This "law of the soil" or "law of the minimum" has long been abandoned. The works of Mitscherlich [3] particularly lead to acceptance of diminishing rather than constant productivity of single factors applied to a fixed area of land. A vast amount of soil fertility research has established that increased inputs of homogeneous fertilizer (ammonium nitrate, 8-8-8, super-phosphate, or other fertilizers when the different levels of input are always represented by the same combination of elements) results in diminishing returns.[4] It has also been shown that even if soil amendments are applied to an acre of land in unlimited quantities and in constant proportions, diminishing returns still prevail. Sunlight and perhaps

---

[3] See also A. E. Mitscherlich, *Bodenkunde für Land und Forstwirte*. Berlin: Pfeiffer und Seine, 1913.

[4] Ware and Johnson, Alabama Agr. Exp. Sta. Bul. 269, Auburn, 1949, p. 24, provide data which show the manner in which each element varied alone on a particular soil type (Hartsell) gives rise to an increase in total product but at different rates. Inputs are given in pounds and output is in bushels.

Input N	Marginal output beans	Input P₂O₅	Marginal output beans	Input K₂O	Marginal output beans
30	69	20	11	22.5	−2
60	24	40	21	45.0	10
90	13	60	8	67.5	10
120	7	80	1		

even carbon dioxide then become limiting factors in production. The debate now centers less around the notion of a linear production function and more around the elasticity of production and the particular type of function which best describes the input-output relationship. One widely held notion is that the production function for a single factor such as nitrogen fertilizer, phosphate, seed, or irrigation water can be described as a decreasing geometric series wherein each marginal product represents a constant percentage of the previous one.[5] Under this supposition, if the first 20 pounds of fertilizer or the first inch of irrigation water adds 10 bushels to total yield, the second will add 9 bushels, and the third will add 8.1 bushels, with each increment equal to 90 per cent of the previous one. W. J. Spillman, an agronomist turned production economist, illustrated how an equation of this sort could be fitted not only to soil input-output relationships but even to the feed production function for livestock. Many agricultural scientists still employ the Spillman production function, which is of the nature $Y = m - ar^x$, where Y is total production, X is the quantity of the variable factor, m is the maximum output which can be attained from the fixed technical unit, r is the ratio by which increments are added to total production, and a is the maximum output which can be added by the particular variable factor.[6] Not all agronomists would agree that the marginal products of fertilizer, irrigation water, or other soil capital can be represented by a decreasing geometric series. The Maine potato data

---

[5] W. J. Spillman, *Exponential Yield Curves in Fertilizer Experiments*. U.S.D.A. Tech. Bul. 348, Washington, 1933; and W. J. Spillman and E. Lang, *The Law of Diminishing Returns*. New York: World Book Company, 1924.

[6] The Spillman production function, $Y = m - ar^x$, can be explained by means of the illustration below. The value of m indicates the maximum output which can be attained from the technical unit (an acre of land, a dairy cow). The term r indicates the ratio in which increments are added to total production. Since each increment represents a given percentage of the previous marginal quantity, then

$$r = \frac{\Delta_2 y}{\Delta_1 y} = \frac{\Delta_3 y}{\Delta_2 y} = \frac{\Delta_4 y}{\Delta_3 y} \cdots = \frac{\Delta_n y}{\Delta_{n-1} y}$$

where $\Delta_1 y$ represents the marginal product of the first input, $\Delta_2 y$ represents the marginal product of the second input, and so on. The quantity y_0 indicates the amount of

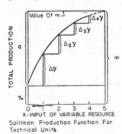

the product forthcoming even if none of the particular resources were used, while a indicates the maximum amount which can be added to the total product by the variable factor. The total production approaches m as the input of the variable factor becomes infinitely large.

The value of r must be less than 1.0 if diminishing returns are to hold true. Thus, with an r of less than unity (less than 1.0), and as the input of X grows larger, the term r^x becomes smaller. For example, with an r of .6 the term r^x is .60, .36, and .22 for 1, 2, and 3 units of X respectively (.6¹, .6², .6³). With an infinitely large X, the term

TOTAL PRODUCTION

Value Of m
$\Delta_4 y$
$\Delta_3 y$
$\Delta_2 y$
$\Delta_1 y$
m
y_0
0 1 2 3 4 5
X - INPUT OF VARIABLE RESOURCE
Spillman Production Function For Technical Units

r^x is (approaches) zero. The term ar^x also approaches zero, and hence $m - ar = m$, the maximum yield.

Table I.

Fertilizer Input as Related to Corn Yields in North Carolina*

Lbs. nitrogen fertilizer per acre	Yield per acre		Marginal product		Ratio of successive marginal products	
	Normal weather	Dry weather	Normal weather	Dry weather	Normal weather	Dry weather
0	29	27				
			26	18		
40	55	45			.81	1.00
			21	18		
80	76	53			.57	.16
			12	3		
120	88	56				

* Source: North Car. Agr. Exp. Sta. Bul. 366, Raleigh, 1949.

of Table 1 in Chapter 2 suggest this relationship, since the ratio between marginal products is approximately .7. Table 1, while based on scanty data, does not necessarily support this hypothesis. The production function shown in Figure 1 for irrigation not only shows diminishing productivity of this form of agricultural capital but also conforms closely to the Spillman production function in the sense that each increment in yield is a constant percentage of the previous increment.[7] On the other hand, the fertilizer-cotton production function in Figure 2 is more nearly described as one with a production elasticity which falls rapidly as inputs of fertilizer increase. This full input-output curve, including the range of decreasing total returns, could not,

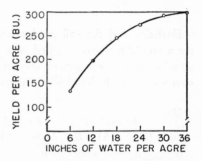

Fig. I. Input-output curve or production function for irrigation water applied on potatoes in Idaho (Source: U.S.D.A. Tech. Bul. 339).

of course, be described by the Spillman production function; the latter allows only for a maximum and not a decline in total production.

---

[7] We term the function $Y = m - ar^x$ or $Y = a(1 - r^x)$ the *Spillman production function* in the same manner that the equation $Y = aX^{b}{}_1 X^{c}{}_2 X^{d}{}_3$, employed for single or multiple factor situations, is termed the *Cobb-Douglas production function*. Spillman's production function is similar to a formula provided by Mitscherlich, which can be stated $Y = a(1 - e^{-kx})$. Since the Spillman function assumes a constant ratio of one marginal product to the succeeding marginal product while the Cobb-Douglas function assumes constant elasticity of production, both are somewhat less acceptable than even a simple polynomial of the form $Y = a + bX - cX^2$, since it does allow a negative marginal product. Even then, the other 2 functions may serve satisfactorily over observations on the production function which do not extend to negative productivity.

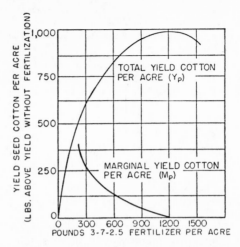

Fig. 2. Production function or input-output relationship showing diminishing total returns and a negative marginal product (Source: North Carolina Agr. Exp. Sta. Bul. 313).

Elasticity and the soil production function. The elasticity of production for a single resource applied to a limited soil area is important from the standpoint of both farmer decision-making and the administration of resources at the national level. A production function may display constant,

Units of input *	Example A[a]			Example B[b]			Example C[c]			Example D[d]		
	Yield	ΔY	E_p	*Yield*	ΔY	E_p	*Yield*	ΔY	E_p	*Yield*	ΔY	E_i
0	0	—		0	—		0	—		0	—	
1	10	10		10	10		10	10		10	10	
			.9			.9			.80			.4
2	19	9		19	9		18	8		14	4	
			.9			.85			.65			.4
3	27.6	8.6		27.1	8.1		23.5	5.5		16.8	2.8	
			.9			.82			.50			.4
4	35.8	8.2		34.4	7.3		27.4	3.9		19.0	2.2	
			.9			.77			.35			.4
5	43.9	8.1		41.0	6.6		29.8	2.4		20.9	1.9	
			.9			.72			.20			.4
6	51.8	7.9		46.9	5.9		31.0	1.2		22.6	1.7	

[a] Consant elasticity.
[b] Increment of a decreasing geometric progression nature with each increment equal to .9 of the preceding increment.
[c] Declining elasticity.
[d] Constant elasticity.

* The term ΔY refers to the increment in yield (the marginal product) due to each additional input, while E_p as the elasticity of production refers to the per cent change in total output divided by the per cent change in total input.

increasing, or decreasing elasticity throughout all ranges of input. Diminishing physical productivity always holds true for an elasticity coefficient less than 1.0. If the elasticity is constant and only slightly less than 1.0, the marginal productivity of the variable resource will decline at a slow rate. A constant elasticity approaching zero signifies a rapid decline in the marginal productivity of the resource. Examples of these 2 situations are presented under A and D below. The example under C is one of declining elasticity; in this particular case, the elasticity is high at the outset but declines rapidly. Example B illustrates the Spillman input-output relationship where the ratio of marginal products is constant $(9/10 = 8.1/9 = 7.3/81 \cdots = .9)$ but the elasticity declines at a medium rate. (In a graph such as Figure 3, the elasticity E_p is 1.0 for any line tangent to the product curve and passing through the origin; it is greater than 1.0 for any tangent line intersecting the horizontal axis, and less than 1.0 for a tangent line intersecting the vertical axis.) If we turn to Figure 3, we see the nature of the input-output curve corresponding to each of these elasticity situations. An elasticity figure which is constant but very low (D) corresponds to a total product curve with a relatively small slope, as does an elasticity coefficient (over most of its range such as C) which is initially high but declines very rapidly. Production functions with a constant and high elasticity (A) have a great slope, as do those with an elasticity coefficient which is initially high and which declines slowly (B). The ability of a fixed soil area to absorb capital and labor inputs will depend to a large extent on the elasticity coefficient. If the elasticity coefficient is initially high but sharply turns to a low level (column 7 in Table 1 for dry weather or C in Figure 3) the structure of costs will be one which causes use of a small amount of the resource to be highly profitable. However, neither large increases in the price of the product or large decreases in the price of the resource can cause use of the resource to be extended by important amounts; also the quantity used may be quite stable as price relationships change. Resource-product relationships which are associated with high elasticity throughout (the fertilizer-potato data in Table 1 of Chapter 2 or Example A in Figure 3 above) can result in large adjustments in use of factors as the fertilizer/product price ratio changes.

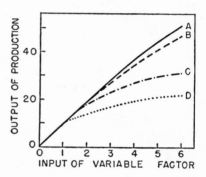

Fig. 3. Elasticity of production and input-output relationships.

Agronomists suggest that no single elasticity situation characterizes all soils and climatic conditions. Some soils have high elasticities over wide ranges of inputs.[8] Others have an elasticity coefficient which is high for 1 or 2 units of input but drops near 0 for greater inputs. The elasticity of the product curve depends on the quantity of limiting factors (fixed service stocks) which are present in or attached to the soil. The elasticity of production tends to be higher over wide ranges of fertilizer inputs in a humid region with ample rainfall than for one with limited rainfall. Resources such as seed, soil amendments, and the cooperating services of labor have a high initial elasticity in the Great Plains semi-arid region, but the elasticity quickly declines for more intensive applications. This same situation exists in other areas where the soil itself contains limited stocks of elements which cannot be added easily or economically.

Average elasticity. The figures presented in the examples above represent *arc* or *average* elasticities since they refer to the average elasticity over a segment of the production function or between 2 discrete levels of input. Elasticity can also be computed for each point on the input-output curve (at each individual level of input). It is then termed *point* elasticity. The difference between *arc* and *point* elasticity is substantially the same as the difference outlined in the previous chapter between *average* and *exact* marginal products.

Increasing soil productivity and negative returns. For all practical purposes, the soil production function is of a diminishing-returns nature throughout. This situation holds true for any specific form of capital, such as seed, irrigation water, fertilizer, and conservation installations. Indications are, however, that a short range of increasing returns does exist for some factors of production. This is especially true for seeding rates of broadcast or drilled crops (small grain, grasses, and legumes) because of competition between the cultivated and non-cultivated (weed) crops. A range of increasing returns exists also for fertilizer or lime applied to

---

[8] The existence of widely different production elasticities for the same crops on different soils is indicated by the production functions or input-output curves in the graph below. These are based on Alabama experiments (*Phosphorous Studies With Vegetables on Different Crops.* Alabama Agr. Exp. Sta. Bul. 268, Auburn, 1949) and employ a production function or regression equation with a squared term.

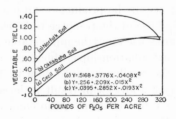

some crops and soils.[9] A small amount of fertilizer may increase per-acre yield very little or not at all, because the amount of N, P, or K added may not be sufficient for chemical reaction with other elements and compounds already in the soil; a doubling or other fractional increase of the application rate more than doubles yield or does give some increase, an infinite marginal product. Small amounts of irrigation water also may give little or no increments in crop yield while a doubling of the application may increase output by more than 100 per cent. Some farmers apply lime at a rate so light that no yield response is realized even though yields would increase greatly from a slightly heavier application. It appears universally true that the stage of increasing returns, where it does prevail, extends over a more limited range of the soil production function than that of decreasing returns. In fact the increasing returns range is so limited that most fertilizer experimental results show only a decreasing marginal productivity; the mathematical functions fitted to yield response data seldom if ever give an S curve such as Y_p in Figure 6 of Chapter 2 because increasing returns are absent or extend over a too narrow range of the observations.

That resources may be applied to land so intensively as to cause marginal productivity to become negative is well-known to farmers and agricultural scientists. Nearly all farmers have experienced rates of water application, even in the form of rainfall, which were heavy enough to cause diminished yields. Excessive applications of nitrogen, with moisture or other elements limited, are also known to cause total yields to decline. An example of this is given in Figure 2. Another experience in the inventory of operating farmers is that of excessive seeding rates.

The level of fixed factors. The phenomena around which Mayer, Woolny, Von Liebig, Wagner, and Mitscherlich centered their debate does have some application to the soil production function, although not in the rigid framework originally supposed. The early concept of a single production element as a limitational factor and of fixed production coefficients does not hold true except under special cases and circumstances. However, with nitrogen as the variable factor, the productivity of this resource will depend partly on the levels at which phosphorus and other production

---

[9] Georgia Agricultural Experiment Station Bulletin 196 shows the following marginal products for inputs of 4-8-4 fertilizer in 100 pound units:

Units of fertilizer	Incremental yield of cotton
1	—
2	70
3	72
4	72
5	70
6	63
7	53
8	43
9	35

elements are fixed. This same phenomenon is illustrated in Figure 4, which shows differences in phosphorus input-corn output ratios, depending on the level at which corn is seeded. A similar difference is displayed in Table 1, where the marginal product of nitrogen varied with the input of moisture.

While we have been discussing an acre of land as a fixed technical unit (the dependence of the productivity of one resource on the level of input of other resources which may be fixed but which can also be varied), the same logic applies to producing units of other sizes. The productivity of 1,500 bushels of corn will depend upon whether it is fed to 80, 100, or 120 hogs; the productivity of 12, 24, or 36 months of labor applied to a farm on any soil area will depend on whether the producing unit includes 160, 240, or 480 acres and whether the capital which cooperates with labor

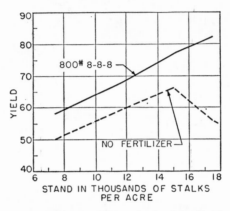

Fig. 4. Seed input and corn output with different levels of fertilization, Webster Silt Loam (Source: *Iowa Farm Science*, Vol. I, No. 10).

amounts to $10,000 or $20,000. While important as applied to soil productivity, this point has perhaps even greater relevance as we move into the analyses of later chapters; the productivity of labor in several major farming regions of the United States is low because the farm plant of the area includes a fixed land area and a small collection of capital. Increases in the working force through births quickly drive the marginal product of labor to low levels in the same manner that the seed of Figure 4 has a rapidly-declining productivity when the input of capital in the form of fertilizer is low.

We draw this parallel between fertilizer and labor productivity to illustrate the universality of the relationships and principles which are being unfolded in this study. The study of low labor productivity in the Mississippi Delta or the Alabama Piedmont does not involve a set of high, mighty, and mystic principles apart from those necessary for the investigation of fertilizer productivity in the Marcus soil area of Iowa. A production economist tooled to analyze the one set of phenomena is similarly tooled to analyze the other as far as economic problems and principles are concerned. Both problems involve similar pitfalls. A study of labor productivity in the Mississippi Delta necessitates that the proper share of the total product be imputed to capital. As we will see later, not all economic studies have recognized the necessity of this procedure. If the data behind Figure 4 are to be used as the basis for recommendations to farmers, what portion of the greater total product should be imputed to capital in the form of fertilizer and capital in the form of seed? The two types of problem simply represent different facets of the same complex.

Our discussion here has taken us into the realm of 2 variables. It there-- fore touches upon the subject matter of later chapters. Yet a discussion of the productivity of single resources would be incomplete if it did not explain that the productivity of any single variable factor depends on the level at which other resources are fixed, except for constant productivity of all factors.

Feed-Livestock Production Functions

Continuing our analysis of the productivity relationships for resources which enter physically into products and are forthcoming from fixed technical units, we now turn to livestock. Again it should be mentioned that, while the quantity of labor applied to a single unit of livestock does not entail the use of more capital, the reverse is not true; as an animal is fed more grain, cooperating labor or other capital services in the form of equipment are necessary to get the feed to the livestock. Also, the marginal productivity of 200, 400, or 600 bushels of grain will depend on whether it is fed to 5, 10, or 15 cows. These problems have already been discussed and are to be treated in greater detail later.

Diminishing productivity. The feed production function for livestock includes mainly a short range of increasing marginal productivity and a wider range of decreasing marginal productivity. Increasing marginal productivity of feeds exists particularly when the ration is below the level required for maintenance. An increase in the feed input by 10, 20, or 30 per cent which carries the ration out of the maintenance range will normally increase the product by more than 10, 20, or 30 per cent. While the factor-product relationship in livestock feeding is mainly one of decreasing marginal feed productivity, decreasing total and negative marginal returns also prevail. On the one hand the daily input of concentrates can be so great that the animal is thrown off feed and the total livestock output declines. On the other hand, the animal can be fed to such great weights and for such long periods that it finally dies of old age. The total and average products then fall to zero.

The phenomenon of decreasing marginal productivity of variable resources applied to single units of livestock is easily explained. It arises mainly from physiological processes. For meat-producing animals such as hogs, sheep, beef, and poultry, the output per animal can be increased only by carrying the animal to heavier and heavier weights. A greater marketing weight requires that the animal be fed over a longer period of time and part of the feed intake goes into maintenance of body weight as well as into production of added body tissue. Too, while the daily rate of gain increases in the first phrases of the growing and fattening processes, the rate of gain eventually diminishes. Therefore, previous gains must be maintained over a longer period of time as an added gain of 50 pounds is made late rather than early in the growing period. Also, the digestive process becomes less efficient; cattle digest smaller proportions of the grain in a high concentrate ration.

Milk and egg production differs from meat production in the sense that, for the former products, an increased output per animal does not entail a longer time period. Thus maintenance of body weight is less important in providing a hypothesis of diminishing feed productivity. There is a physiological basis for diminishing productivity in milk, however. The heavier rates of feeding necessary for greater production cause cows to put on more weight and hence again require increased energy for body maintenance; [10] heavier grain rations also put a heavier burden on the animal's digestive system and are less conducive to maintenance of health; small inputs of grain have a stimulating effect on milk secretion while larger rates of grain feeding do not.[11] Finally, maximum feed intake and maximum milk output is possible only as grain is substituted for forage, and rates of substitution are probably at a diminishing rate. Aside from maintenance of body weight, diminishing marginal returns in egg production are less easily explained. One notion, as in milk production, is that a liberal ration is not as readily and completely digested as a scanty ration.

Simple feed input-output relationships are outlined below. The data and graphs of this chapter are not presented as inferences for all farms in the United States. Instead they, like other data presented above, are used as suggestions of the general nature of agricultural production functions.

The milk production function. A milk production function (Y_p) and a marginal productivity curve (M_p) derived from experimental data by means of the Spillman production function are shown in Figure 5. The solid portion of each curve refers to values estimated within the output ranges actually

---

[10] Morrison (*Feeds and Feeding*. Ithaca: Morrison Publishing Co., 1937, p. 382) states: "For this reason ... a cow in milk which is fed with the liberality necessary to produce a greater yield of milk undoubtedly needs more grain for mere body maintenance than she would if fed a scanty ration."

[11] See V. P. Saarinen, *et al.*, "The Adequacy of an All-Alfalfa Hay Ration for Milk Secretion," *Jour. Dairy Sci.*, Vol. 34; and C. F. Huffman and L. D. Duncan, "The Nutritive Value of Alfalfa Hay," *Jour. Dairy Sci.*, Vol. 27.

observed in the experiments.[12] Above a maintenance ration, the feed input-milk output relationship is one of diminishing returns. Marginal and average physical productivity of feed decline from the outset. Since any level of feeding below the maintenance level falls in the range of increasing returns, only feed inputs above this level are relevant in defining the milk production level which is economic. Feed through the maintenance

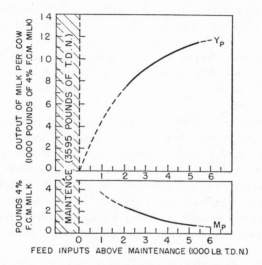

Fig. 5. Total production and marginal productivity curves for different levels of feeding dairy cows (Source: U.S.D.A. Tech. Bul. 815).

level might thus be considered in the vein of a fixed resource or fixed cost. If milk is to be produced at all, no less than maintenance requirements should ever be fed. For this production function, the marginal product ranges from about 2.5 pounds of milk per pound of feed to about .75 pounds over the input range actually observed.

The production function presented is one in which hay and concentrate feeds have been aggregated into a single input in the form of T.D.N.'s (total digestible nutrients). The T.D.N. measure does not retain our condition of a homogeneous resource since, as the level of feeding is increased, T.D.N. is made up of a smaller proportion of forage and a greater proportion of concentrates. This hybrid relationship arises, since in the experiment grain was hand-fed while the cows were allowed free choice of hay

---

[12] Figure 5 has been broken into 2 parts to facilitate presentation. The upper section is in units of 1,000 pounds and the lower section is in pounds of milk. The marginal curve would appear much flatter were it expressed on the upper portion where the scale is in 1,000-lb. units. These data may be somewhat unrealistic since they are in terms of T.D.N. and assume, in the conversion process, that T.D.N.s from different feeds substitute at constant rates, an unlikely relationship for all feeds. Also, the factor-product and factor-factor relationships are confounded in the procedure used.

and pasture; with heavier grain rations they consumed less forage. The result, unless grain and forage substitute at a constant rate, is a hybrid between the factor-product relationship being discussed in this chapter and the factor-factor relationship discussed in a later chapter. How-ever, the practical farm method for increasing milk output per cow is to follow this same procedure; free choice rather than hand-feeding of forage saves labor inputs. Table 2 presents data on the grain input-milk output relationship when hay input is considered constant and grain input is varied over several levels. These have been computed by means of a production function (input-output relationship) of the Cobb-Douglas type, which, in contrast to the Spillman production function, assumes con-stant elasticities of production.[13] While the data are not ideally adapted to the fitting of true input-output curves, they are statistically acceptable and provide further evidence of diminishing feed productivity in milk production. Grain productivity would be greater if hay were "fixed" at a level lower than 6,500 pounds and less if hay were at a level greater than 6,500 pounds, providing the hay were fed prior to the grain.

While agreement was not complete among dairy scientists, historical recommendations suggested that dairy cows be fed grain at some constant rate for each pound of milk produced. Implicit in these recommendations is the assumption that the milk input-output relationship is linear as in

---

[13] The Cobb-Douglas production function of the form $X = aX^b_1X^c_2$ allows dimin-ishing productivity but holds elasticity constant. The Spillman production function assumes declining elasticity and diminishing marginal productivity but constant ratios of change in the sense that $\Delta_2y/\Delta_1y = \Delta_3y/\Delta_2y = \Delta_4y/\Delta_3y = \cdot \cdot \cdot \Delta_ny/$ (See $\Delta_{n-1}y$. earlier footnote.) These figures above were derived by the writer from individual cow observations included in the data upon which U.S.D.A. Tech. Bul. 815 is based. The production function, of the Cobb-Douglas type, is for 74 heavy breed cows in which X_1 is hay in pounds, X_2 is grain in pounds and Y_m is milk production per cow. The derived total production function is

$$Y = 3.6X_1^{.44}X_2^{.50}$$

The equation for the marginal product is given by differentiation as

$$\frac{dY}{dX_2} = 85.5X_2^{-.5}$$

where X_1, hay input, has been "fixed" at 6,500 pounds. Here dY/dX_2 has the same meaning as the term $\Delta Y/\Delta X_2$ (change in Y or milk output relative to change in X_2, grain input) used in the text except that the notation d rather than Δ is used to indicate that it is the derivative whereby the change in X_2 is infinitely small (ap-proaches the limit zero). This function does not place an upper limit on total output in the manner of the Spillman production function and it should not be used outside of the range of observations included in the original data. The values of t for the X_1 and X_2 regression coefficients were 2.39 and 2.74, both significant at an acceptable probability level.

A production function which has some advantage for substitution purposes over the Cobb-Douglas function is the one shown below where Y refers to milk output, X_1 is the estimated milk capacity of the cow on a standard ration, X_2 is grain input, X_3 is hay input and X_4 is predicted milk output from a production function equation. The equation below has been estimated for 171 cows in the U.S.D.A. study.

$$Y = 749.3 + .37X_1 + 6.08X_2 + 11.28X_3 + .051X_2X_3 - .476X_2X_4 - .483X_3X_4.$$

Table 2.

Total Milk Output Per Cow and Marginal Productivity of Feed with Forage Input Fixed at 6,500 lbs. of Hay Equivalent *

Grain input lbs.	Computed total milk output	Exact marginal product $\Delta Y / \Delta X_2$[a]
1200	5,917	2.5
1800	7,250	2.0
2400	8,379	1.8
3000	9,371	1.6
3600	10,260	1.4

* Source: See footnote accompanying text.

a Change in total output in milk for each one unit change in grain input (with units of X approaching the limit zero). The marginal product figures, derived from the original production function, refer to the increments in milk production, "at exactly" the grain levels specified in Column 1. They are not averages between levels of feeding.

Figure 6. Here the total product increases at a constant rate to a maximum (OB) where added feed inputs result in no more milk but only in additional body weight. Marginal milk product remains constant at OA until total product reaches a maximum after which marginal product falls to zero; average milk product remains constant and identical with the mar-

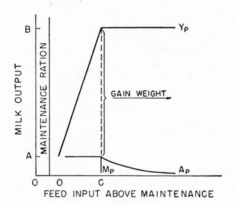

Fig. 6. Nature of feed productivity assumed under "standard" feeding recommendations (above maintenance level).

ginal product until the total product becomes a maximum; then the average product declines gradually. Under these assumptions there would be only 2 alternative courses of action in milk production: (1) produce no milk at all, or (2) produce a maximum amount of milk per cow. Farmers recognize the fallacy of this logic and do vary rates of grain feeding and milk production (between the two extremes) in line with the feed/milk price ratio.

Input-output relationships in pork production. Diminishing marginal productivity of feed starts from weaning when an individual pig is considered as the fixed technical unit and output is measured in live weight. Accordingly the average product also declines from weaning. If the grain fed to the sow previous to farrowing is included in calculations, however, the average amount of pork produced per pound of feed increases for a period after birth of the pig. Feed production functions of the diminishing marginal productivity nature are shown in Figure 7.[14] Marked differences in the nature of feed productivity relationships exist, however, depending on whether output is measured in live weight, dressed weight, or edible pork. Even when output is related to a single pig starting from weaning, average feed productivity may increase when output is measured in some form of dressed pork.

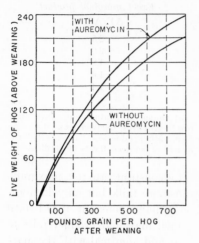

Fig. 7. Relationship between feed input and pork output. (Source: Derived from Iowa experimental data with a Cobb-Douglas production function of $Y = 1.34X_1^{.696}X_2^{.139}$ with aureomycin and $Y = 1.56X_1^{.652}X_2^{.139}$ without aureomycin. Protein (X_2) was held constant to obtain the corn-pork, input-output relationships of $Y = 2.41X_1^{.696}$ with aureomycin. Protein has been "fixed" at 70 pounds for both curves above; i.e., "fed" as a constant amount spread over "feeding periods" of different length and including various amounts of grain.) The quadratic production function mentioned in footnote 14 gives similar differences with and without aureomycin inputs.

Numerous production functions can be derived for a hog as a fixed technical unit. In addition to the feed-pork output relationship, the live weight of the hog can be taken as the input and dressed pork, edible pork, edible fat, or edible lean cuts can be taken as the output.[15] In Figure 8, we present the average and marginal productivity of feed in terms of the live weight of the hogs. Feed for the breeding herd has been included in computing the average figures. This is a practical measure since decisions of farmers or national administrators are made in terms of hog weight rather than in terms of feed

---

[14] The marginal product equation for the aureomycin curve in Figure 7 is $\frac{dY}{dX_1} = \frac{1.67}{X_1^{.304}}$ A production function of a somewhat different algebraic nature for the curve without aureomycin is $Y = 6.8 + .34X_1 - .002X_1^2 + .32X_2 - .0001X_2^2 + .0003X_1X_2$. A production function should be based upon the logic relating to the situation to which it applies. For extreme ranges of data, it is sometimes desirable to use a function which does not cause the iso-product or factor-product curves to serve as asymptotes. This statement applies particularly to extreme ranges of data where diminishing total productivity or complete rivalry between factors is encountered.

[15] Using dressed pork as the output and live pork as the input the production function and marginal product equations below can be derived from the data of J. Atkinson and L. Klein, *Feed Consumption and the Production of Pork and Lard*. U.S.D.A.

input (although indirectly feed input is the important criterion). As Figure 8 indicates, the average productivity of feed in terms of live weight increases up to nearly 180 lbs. when the feed of the breeding herd is included. The marginal productivity of feed in terms of live weight diminishes throughout the range of weights shown. When output is measured in dressed weight, marginal productivity of feed also declines, starting with lighter weights. However, average productivity increases over a much wider range of feed inputs for dressed pork than for live pork. The greater range of increasing average productivity for dressed pork as compared to live weight exists because marginal productivity does not drop so rapidly under the former measure. When measurements are in terms of edible pork, both the average and marginal productivity of feeds increase throughout the weight ranges shown. Increasing productivity of feed in terms of edible pork exists because (1) the dressing percentage of the hog increases with heavier weights, and (2) a decreasing percentage of the hog carcass is made up of bones, hide, body organs, and other inedible cuts. The weight of skin and bones becomes nearly constant at 200 lbs. live

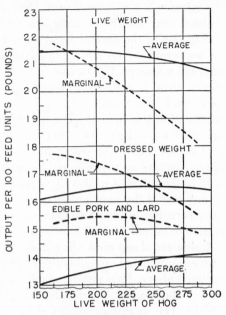

Fig. 8. Average and marginal productivity of feed for hogs fed to different weights, in terms of live weight, dressed weight, and edible pork. (Corn Belt conditions includes breeding herd.) The average output of live weight per 100 feed units reaches a peak of 21.5 pounds at 175 pounds marketing weight. The decline in average output is very gradual. The average output of dressed weight per 100 feed units reaches a peak of 16.5 pounds at 250 pounds marketing weight but is only 1 per cent less at 200 and again at 300 pounds marketing weight. The average edible product per 100 feed units rises throughout the range of marketing weights shown. (Source: U.S.D.A. Tech. Bul. 917.)

Tech. Bul. 917, Washington, 1946. D refers to output in dressed weight and L refers to input in live weight per hog.

(production function) $D = 65.2L + 7.0L^2 - 0.8L^3$

(marginal product) $\dfrac{dD}{dL} = 65.2 + 14.0L - 2.4L^2$

Using E to denote output of edible pork (all cuts) and L to denote input in live weight per hog, the following equations can be derived:

(production function) $E = 43.8L + 8.49L^2 - 0.1316L^3 - 0.0464L^4$

(marginal product) $\dfrac{dE}{dL} = 43.8 + 16.98L - 0.3948L^2 - 0.1856L^3$

weight. Although the marginal productivity of feeds in terms of edible pork eventually declines, it is greater than average productivity even for the extreme hog weights shown. Declining average productivity would be realized were feed input and market weight per hog extended far enough.

Any one of the several input-output relationships outlined above may be important to resource administrators, whether they are farmers or national planners. The farmer as an administrator of resources on a particular farm is concerned especially with the relationship between feed input and live weight output; prices which he receives relate to pork measured in this manner. The hog is really a composite commodity made up of joint products including inedible parts as well as edible fat and protein. During a war emergency or in a planned economy, government administrators, as managers of agricultural resources, are more concerned with feed input as it relates to output of edible pork (protein, food calories, or any one of the joint products included as lean cuts and lard). We will have occasion to return to decision-making and resource allocation as it relates to output of both live hogs and edible pork.

Cattle and sheep production functions. Production functions for all types of meat-producing animals display physical relationships similar to those outlined above. In general a single meat animal starting from birth provides a short range of increasing marginal returns for feed in terms of live weight. The marginal product shifts from an increasing to a decreasing nature before weaning, however. The average product in terms of live weight may increase even after weaning if feed for breeding animals is included in the calculus. Average productivity for a single animal increases for a short extent beyond weaning when output is measured in dressed weight. Both marginal and average products in terms of edible meat increase at first as growth continues but finally decrease as growth ceases and fattening is continued. There are, of course, as many feed-meat production functions as there are classes and capacities of livestock. Figure 9 illustrates differences in production functions between types of choice feeder cattle in the grain fattening process.[16] Calves are more efficient in

---

[16] These total output curves were derived by Nelson (*Relationship of Feed Consumed to Food Products Produced by Fattening Cattle.* U.S.D.A. Tech. Bul. 900, Washington, 1945), and are based on a production function defining output per animal after the feeding process has begun:

$$Y = m - ae^{-rX}$$

Here Y refers to total output in live weight per animal; m is the maximum live weight attainable in the total growth process, but not as a result of fattening alone; a is the total gain in live weight in reaching the maximum; e is the base of the natural system of logarithms; r is the constant ratio indicating the decline in rate at which feed adds to product; and X is feed input per animal. The corresponding empirical production functions are

$$\text{Calves} \quad Y = 1446 - 1049e^{-.000257X}$$
$$\text{Yearlings} \quad Y = 1446 - 805e^{-.000281X}$$
$$\text{2-year-olds} \quad Y = 1446 - 610e^{-.000372X}$$

terms of gain per pound of feed than yearlings; yearlings in turn are more efficient than 2-year-olds in transforming feed into live weight. Again, both farmers and national planners are concerned with feed/meat transformation rates. Given limited feed resources and different price expectations for the various types of feeders, the farmer makes profit decisions in terms of live weight relationships. In every case he is faced with a production function having an elasticity coefficient less than 1.0 or a declining marginal productivity of feed. This statement applies, of course, only to feeding operations. When growing and fattening are considered jointly and the feed to the breeding herd is included, increasing average productivity

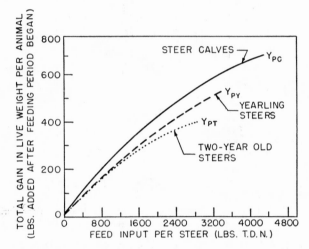

Fig. 9. Production function indicating relationship between feed input and beef gain for 3 classes of choice feeder steers (Source: U.S.D.A. Tech. Bul. 900).

holds true for light weights of calves. A national manager of farm resources, faced with maximizing output of calories or food measured in any other manner, would be more interested in the feed input-calory output relationships expressed in Figure 10. As is suggested by the nature of the marginal and average curves, a stage of increasing returns (in calories) exists for each class of feeder steer and the relative marginal productivities differ considerably from those suggested in the production functions relating feed to live weight. The calves compare less favorably with older cattle on a calory than on a live weight basis because, although the rate of transforming feed into live weight is greater, the growth is made up of a greater proportion of bone and other non-edible parts. Mature animals convert feed mainly into edible protein and fat rather than into body organs. Again increasing returns are realized under the calory measure because the proportion of water in the animal's body declines and dressing percentage increases with greater weights. The marginal and average calory productivity of feed is initially greater for a 2-year-old than for a yearling and greater for a yearling than for a calf. However, as feed input is extended, its productivity drops off sooner and at a much faster rate for older than for younger cattle.

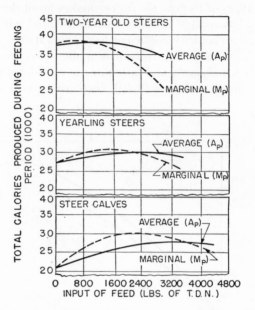

Fig. 10. Relationship between feed input and total calorie output per steer during feeding period (Source: U.S.D.A. Tech. Bul. 900).

Poultry products. Available knowledge indicates that poultry meat production obeys the physical relationships outlined above. Two sets of estimates over a period of time in Figure 11 display a meat/feed transformation rate which declines with output per bird. The capon curve is of historic interest because it was derived by Spillman while the fryer curve

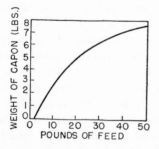
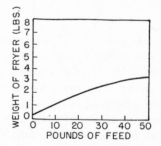

Fig. 11. Relation of feed input to live weight in capon and fryer production (Source: Spillman, W. J., *Law of Diminishing Returns.* New York: World Book Co., 1924, p. 26 for capons, and Baum, E. L., "Fryer Production," *Jour. Farm Econ.*, Vol. 33, p. 95, for fryers).

is of interest because it is derived from a similar function.[17] Poultry scientists have generally supposed a linear production function for eggs. The review of literature by Hansen generally supports this notion of constant marginal efficiency of feed until a maximum egg output per hen is attained.[18] A constant feed/egg transformation rate has a logical and physiological basis for support. With a straight-line relationship between feed input and egg output, the limit of a hen's capacity to produce eggs economically, if egg production is profitable at all, lies in her ability to assimilate feed. More eggs can be obtained by stepping up the hen's physiological capacity and a chief technical problem may be that of getting each bird to consume feed at a level consistent with her egg-laying capacity. Since egg production is more nearly of an instantaneous nature than meat production, added feed need not go into maintenance of body weight over a longer period. The input requirements are mainly for the elements which are transformed directly into the egg. Some physical scientists do claim that the extra strain on and energy required in the physiological process cause a slightly diminishing rate of transformation. Even were this

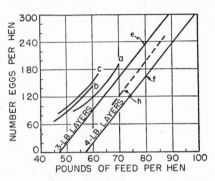

Fig. 12. Marginal efficiency of feed in egg production. The curves a, b, and c refer to physical experiments, while e and f are estimates by the national research council, and h is based on the Maryland egg laying contest (Source: Hansen, P. L., "Input-Output Relationships in Egg Production," *Jour. Farm Econ.*, Vol. 31).

so the curve of egg output perhaps would allow decisions as if it were linear, especially when price uncertainty is considered. Only scanty data are available on the egg production function. The more acceptable of these are presented in Figure 12, where 3 of the production functions indicate constant transformation rates and an additional 3 suggest a slightly increasing marginal efficiency of feed. The slope of the curves is roughly the same in all cases suggesting approximately the addition of 65 eggs for each additional 10 pounds of feed.

Other resources applied to animal units. When resources other than feed are applied to a technical unit of livestock, the transformation ratio is

[17] Both product curves in Figure 11 have been derived from the Spillman production function. In empirical form they are given below where output (Y) is measured in grams for fryers and pounds for capons and feed (X) is measured similarly.

$$\text{(fryers)} \quad Y = 1060 - (1020)(.8^X)$$
$$\text{(capons)} \quad Y = 8.63 - (9.78)(.6^{-X})$$

[18] P. L. Hansen, *Input-Output Relationships in Egg Production. Jour. Farm Econ.,* Vol. 31, pp. 687-697.

mainly one of a diminishing nature. If cows are milked 3 times rather than 2 times per day, output is increased for high-capacity animals, but it is not increased by 50 per cent. Also, the non-feed services which cooperate with feed in taking animals to heavier weights display transformation ratios paralleling those for feed. If an additional 100 bushels of corn fed to 50 hogs results in a decline in the pork/feed transformation ratio by one-third, the productivity of the labor which complements the feed will also decline by one-third, if added feed and labor are employed in fixed proportions. The productivity of any category of resource applied to a technical unit of land or livestock will always depend on the capacity (grade, quality, inherent productivity) of the soil or animal as well as the

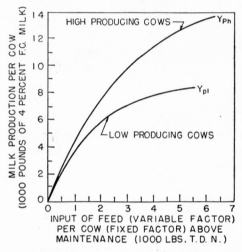

Fig. 13. Feed input-milk output curves for cows of different inherent productivities (Source: U.S.D.A. Tech. Bul. 815).

technique of production. This point is illustrated in Figure 13. In later chapters we need to examine the value productivity rather than the physical productivity of resources. We will use value productivity measures to examine the cause of variable resource returns in different farming regions. Figure 13, while referring to a cow as a fixed technical unit, has the same implications in value productivity as any other differential in physical productivity.

Reversibility of Proportions

The analysis of agricultural technical units has been in terms of these resources (land and animals) as fixed. It should be remembered, however, that the procedure can be reversed. Technical units can become variable while resources otherwise considered variable can become fixed. These notions of reversibility of fixed and variable resources are important from the standpoint of farmer or national allocation of resources. Within a cropping year, a farmer may consider hog numbers as fixed and corn as variable; he can either sell the year's corn crop or feed it in varying amounts to a given number of spring-farrowed pigs. Or, he can consider the corn crop as fixed and vary the number of hogs in proportion to it; the corn can be stored into the next year and opportunities will be open for farrowing more pigs. At the national level, food emergencies may arise which call for either feeding more or less grain to a given number of hogs within a year or storing the corn and increasing the number of hogs to which it might be fed. Which system will give greatest profits to the farmer or food to the nation? The same question arises in respect to fertilizer during war. The stock of fertilizer may be fixed and the relevant question is this: On how many acres of land should the fertilizer be used? Land now becomes the variable factor and fertilizer is the fixed resource. (This relationship can be visualized easily if we imagine a graph in which crop output is measured on the vertical axis and fertilizer input, as applied in varying quantities on a given land area, is measured on the horizontal axis. As we move to the right of the graph, the ratio F/L—total quantity of fertilizer divided by the total quantity of land—increases; as we move to the left, the ratio L/F increases. This phenomenon also gives rise to the diminishing rate of substitution discussed in a later chapter.) Reversing the position of the resources does not change the physical relationships of production, however. A production function which is linear when factor X_1 is fixed and X_2 is variable will also be linear when X_2 is fixed and X_1 is variable. This application of this general statement can also be seen if we turn back to the Maine potato data of Table 1 in Chapter 2. The example below, based on this experimental data, suposes that 1.5 million lbs. (15,000 units of 500 lbs. each) are available for potato production; fertilizer is fixed at 1.5 million lbs., and land can be varied in proportion to this fixed stock by applying fertilizer at different rates. If 2,500 acres of land are used with the 1.5 million lbs. of fertilizer (600 lbs. of fertilizer per acre), total potato production attributable to fertilizer will be 745,000 bushels. The first 2,500 acres of land adds 845,000 bushels to production,

Example of Diminishing Land Productivity with the Stock of Fertilizer Fixed at 1,500,000 lbs.

Acres of potatoes on which total stock of fertilizer is applied	Pounds fertilizer per acre	Total production of potatoes from fertilizer	Additional production
(1)	(2)	(3)	(4)
0	0	0	
			745,000
2500	600	845,000	
			370,000
5000	300	1,115,000	
			280,000
7500	200	1,395,000	

while the second 2,500 acres adds only 370,000. A third 2,500 acres of land adds only 280,000 bushels. While diminishing marginal productivity of land exists when it is added to a given stock of fertilizer, it is important to note that the stock of fertilizer still results in a greater total production when it is spread over more acres. This is a salient point from the standpoint of a farmer who can afford only limited quantities of fertilizer or a national economy which can furnish agriculture with only a fraction of the fertilizer which might otherwise be used profitably. Similarly, a given stock of 45 million tons of grain will result in a greater output of live pork if it is fed to 100 million hogs than if fed to 80 million head. Live pork output will increase as the stock of feed is spread over more hogs but the increase will be at a diminishing rate.

We wish to say more later about livestock capital in variable form. However, it is of interest to note that when animals are variable and other resources are fixed, capital in the form of animals can be extended so far relative to fixed resources that total product declines. Some farmers feed too many animals on a given stock of grain. Since the livestock is fed below maintenance levels, more total meat or milk could be produced if fewer animals were kept and fed to higher levels. This situation holds true particularly for many over-grazed pastures. Frequently so many hens are kept in one house that egg production is less than maximum; reduction in hen numbers to conform with the building space available would increase total egg production.

Variable Proportions and Resource Productivity for Economic Units

We have employed a great deal of detail in describing the marginal efficiency of a single variable resource when a technical unit (an animal or an acre) serves as the fixed unit in agriculture. There were important reasons for doing so: first, the laws of production can nowhere be better illustrated than from the data of physical experiments. Second, the productivity relationships displayed for a single technical unit also apply to an entire enterprise or the complete producing plant of a farm. Aside from questions of scale to be discussed later, the marginal efficiency of fertilizer applied to 100 acres of corn should display the same relationships as that indicated in Table 1. Addition of 4,000 lbs. of fertilizer can be expected to add 2,600 bushels to output on 100 acres; addition of 8,000 lbs. should add 4,700 bushels if weather is similar. Or, if an increase in feed input from 600 to 700 lbs. increases live weight per hog by 30 lbs. (Figure 7) then another 5,000 pounds of feed should add 1,500 lbs. of live weight from 50 hogs. Scale relationships are involved in adjustments of this type. They will be discussed later, however.

The production functions examined so far in this chapter have been of the nature $Y = f(X_1 | X_2, X_3, X_4, X_5 \ldots X_n)$ where X_1 refers to feed or fertilizer and X_2 refers to technical units such as acres or animals. By this production function we indicate that while output will vary depending on the magnitude of resources X_1 through X_n, changes in Y depend entirely on changes in X_1 for the situation considered. As a second step we can view the production function in the form $Y = f(X_1, X_2|X_3, X_4, X_5 \ldots X_n)$ where X_2 or the number of acres or animals also becomes variable while X_3 (labor), X_4 (machinery and equipment) are fixed; variations in output now result from variations in both X_1 and X_2. We might also consider X_1 (feed) and X_2 (hogs) as a composite resource denoted by Z (in the same manner that spark plugs, tires, and steel are called a tractor). Thus as long as feed (X_1) and hogs (X_2) are in constant proportions, variation in Z entails the same relationship which we have been examining above; services X_3 through X_n, denoting labor, equipment, land, and all other resources of the farm are held constant. What is the nature of the input-output relationship in agriculture when the number of technical units can be varied along with the physical resources such as feed or fertilizer which are transformed directly into product? Our concern is with a composite resource such as Z where the feed and animal components are held in constant proportion. A later chapter will consider nonproportional changes in variable factors as well as proportional or scale adjustments in all resources.

Farm input-output relationship. Up to the point where the services of fixed resources are quite fully utilized, the short-run farm production function is evidently highly elastic when technical units as well as resources which enter physiologically into the production process are varied. From the standpoint of crops a Cornbelt farm with fixed resources in the form of (1) 12 months of operator labor, (2) a general purpose tractor with auxiliary 2-row equipment and (3) the customary farm buildings can operate a considerable range of acreages without encountering any sharp decline in the marginal efficiency of the variable resources in the form of seed, fertilizer, tractor fuel, and land. Preliminary estimates indicate that from the standpoint of crop production alone (for example, all of the land in a single crop such as corn or a fixed combination of crops in rotation) the production function is linear for acreages ranging from zero to 160 when the farmer's managerial ability is average. In other words, the marginal product of a composite variable resource (including the services of land, seed, fuel, and so forth, held in constant proportions as land is varied) is constant over the range indicated. Similar calculations would indicate that a fixed collection of resources in the Great Plains of (1) a general purpose tractor, (2) the labor of the operator with perhaps 3 months of family labor, and (3) the conventional buildings provide a linear crop production function over an average range of zero to 640 acres. A fixed combination of resources including the services of (1) two general purpose tractors and complementary equipment, (2) an ordinary set of farm buildings, and

(3) 18 months of labor appear to provide a linear short-run crop production function up to 240 acres in the Cornbelt. A linear production function even exists within the bounds of a single farm for a particular resource such as fertilizer as long as it can be used on various acreages within the farm. Thus a farmer on 160 acres may apply 10 lbs. of ammonium nitrate to 1 acre of corn and obtain a yield increase of 12 bushels; 800 lbs. applied to 80 acres may give 960 bushels while 1,600 lbs. on 160 acres can give 1,920 bushels. Within the bounds of the average farm there is no reason to suppose that the production function is other than constant for resources applied in this manner. The same situation holds true for productivity relationships in other types of crop production. Once even the smallest power and machine units have been purchased the fixed stock of services which they embody along with that of the operator's labor allow a constant marginal product from land when acreage is extended proportionately along with those services which enter directly into crops. Even where production is by near-hand methods, a constant marginal efficiency of land and its cooperating resource services can be realized from the fixed stock of labor represented by the labor of a single farm operator and a very small amount of capital. The fixed services in the form of a share-cropper's labor, a hoe, and a plow, plus a team of mules and feed for their keep can allow operation of up to 40-50 acres of cotton and other crops without any decline in yield per acre. The linear crop production function exists within an acreage range which does not strain the physical capacities of either the mules or the share-cropper. Linear crop production functions are evidently widespread in agriculture for farm plants represented by fixed factors in various combinations of labor, machinery, and buildings. The production function is linear largely because the fixed factors themselves are divisible. A tractor or a machine shed provides a stock of services only part of which are used for 20, 40, 80, or 100 acres of corn. It is this divisibility of "fixed factors" which allows other resources to be varied without a decline in marginal efficiency.

As soon as the stock of services represented by fixed factors becomes quite fully engaged in the production process, further increases in the composite input of variable factors immediately lead to a decline in the product added by the latter. Timeliness and the limits of weather eventually serve as the forces which cause the productivity of land and complementary capital to decline as it is increased in proportion to an aggregation of fixed resources such as that outlined above. While the services of the operator and machines can be more fully utilized over a longer season, experimental and farm data show rapid declines in per acre yields as planting and tillage dates extend further into the season.

The problem of timeliness and seasonality might be met, of course, not only by varying land, but also by varying labor or equipment. This point brings out further aspects of the agricultural production function.

We started out by considering a production function of the nature $Y = f(X_1|X_2, X_3, X_4, X_5 \ldots X_n)$ where X_1 was fertilizer (and the directly complementary resources) as a variable factor while X_2 (land and directly complementary resources) was fixed along with resources X_3 through X_n. Then we considered a production function of a nature $Y = f(X_1, X_2|X_3, X_4, X_5 \ldots X_n)$ where X_2 (land) as well as X_1 (fertilizer) were variable while X_3 (labor) was fixed along with resources X_4 through X_n. Now we can consider one of the nature $Y = f(X_1, X_2, X_3|X_4, X_5 \ldots X_n)$ where labor (X_3) also becomes variable while X_4 (machinery) and other resource services are fixed in quantity. Variation of labor inputs will allow an increase in the productivity of fertilizer and land resources which were previously variable. If we go far enough in switching resources from the fixed to the variable category, we come to

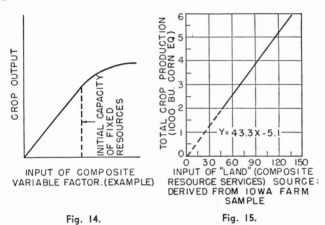

Fig. 14.   Fig. 15.

Short run crop production function with machine combination fixed.

the scale relationships in later chapters. We will not pursue the procedure further at this time. It is now evident, however, that the elasticity of the production function depends on the number of resources which can be varied in quantity. If fertilizer alone is variable on an 80 acre farm, its productivity diminishes quite rapidly. If fertilizer can be varied along with land, the productivity of added fertilizer is quite constant. For the most part the typical farm plant is faced with a crop production function of the nature indicated in Figure 14. Here the elasticity of variable resources tends to be constant at 1.0 until the readily available services of fixed resources become engaged in production.[19] It then tapers off due to

---

[19] More exactly the production function for each process of a complete farm may take on the appearance of the linear-segment curve of the first figure in Chapter 2. Here fertilizer, labor, plowing, or cultivating services may bear a linear relationship as they are extended in first application over all technical units of the farm (for example, section Oa). A second application of fertilizer or a second operation over all technical units of the farm may give rise to a segment such as ab.

weather, timeliness, and similar considerations. The long-run production function discussed in a later chapter may still display great elasticity, however. Figure 15, while perhaps preliminary and in the form of an "empirical hypothesis," shows a linear production function for corn on a sample of Iowa farms all with approximately the same fixed machine combination. The equation employed cannot be extended to inputs greater than those observed. (Diminishing productivity could be expected at some greater input.) The services of land, labor, seed, fertilizer, and fuel, and machine repairs attributable to the corn enterprise have been aggregated into a single composite input which is the measure along the horizontal axis. Since each unit of this composite input includes approximately 1 acre of land, the production function thus suggests the nature of the short-run production function when land and a set of directly complementary services are varied in respect to a fixed machine combination. While these data do not serve as inferences for all other farm types and situations, they are suggestive of the short-run crop production function which faces farmers with a fixed machine combination.

We can also turn in other directions in considering the crop production function. All resources including land might be held constant while labor is varied. Labor is the only single resource which can be varied without a simultaneous variation in some other resource. While increasing returns holds for labor when it is spread too thinly over a given number of acres or animals, the marginal productivity of labor in agriculture is ordinarily low when it is increased in the absence of cooperating capital. This point is emphasized in a later chapter when low income and low productivity farms are discussed.

The farm and the livestock production function. The types of adjustment outlined above can also be made in livestock production with a farm fixed in acreage and with a stock of services on hand in the form of labor and buildings; the input-output relationship is again linear over a range as both feed and livestock numbers are varied from zero up to the "first capacity" of the limiting fixed factor. For example, a farm which has building and equipment space for 200 hens and can consider labor as fixed or as attaching no costs can probably realize a constant marginal productivity of feed and hens until housing has been utilized to a point where egg production per hen begins to decline. The same situation holds true for hogs, milk, or other types of livestock products where the existence of a given set of buildings is simply a historic fact. At the limits of pasture carrying capacity, added animals will cause sharply decreasing and even negative returns in a grazing-type operation. Expansion of livestock to a point where building facilities are overtaxed also eventually leads to a short-run production function of the nature shown in Figure 14. Between years, however, high elasticity of livestock production can be retained through the addition of buildings and equipment and up to the limits imposed by the fixed land area of the farm and the individual's ability to manage more livestock and keep it free from disease. The many farm management studies made over time suggest that for a farm of a given acreage (land alone as the fixed factor) an important range of constant returns (or even increasing returns if the proportions of variable services are allowed to vary) exist for most types of livestock where feed resources can be purchased off the farm.

Linear programming and budgeting. Many processes in farming do involve linear relationships when the farm plant as a divisible producing unit is concerned. This statement does not, of course, apply to single animals as technical units which are indivisible. Yet, if we consider all animals and acres which make up a farm of fixed size or with fixed facilities and equipment, they commonly do represent a series of straight-line or linear steps or relationships. Preparation of a seedbed for corn is of this nature; each added acre plowed, unless the size of the farm is very large, requires an equal input and can be considered to add an equal increment to output. Corn planting, corn cultivation, and corn harvesting involve linear relationships between input and output over all technical units if the farm is small enough that decreasing returns to scale are not encountered.

The existence of linear steps or relationships facilitates research studies of the budgeting type which attempt to predict the cost-returns effect of certain readjustments in farm resources. This budgeting procedure has been given the more formal name "linear programming" by econometricians where it is supposed that the production process can be broken down into a series of "straight-line" relationships.[20] The task is then one of comparing the single input-output ratio for one method of completing the step with the single input-output ratio for a different technique. The 2 ratios can then be compared with the factor/commodity price ratio and the most advantageous procedure can be applied to all technical units. Each linear process of a firm can be studied in this manner and the several steps can then be fitted together. Farms are admirably adapted to this "process analysis" but the investigator must not confuse the linear steps with those non-linear relationships which relate to technical units or large scale operation. (A curvilinear relationship can be approximated by isolating many linear segments on a curve.) The assumptions underlying farm budgeting are definitely those of linear relationship or discontinuous segments, assumptions with similar implications.

---

[20] See Koopman, T., *Activity Analysis of Production and Allocation.* New York: Wiley, 1951.

Capital Addition

We may now relax our assumptions of fixed proportions and homogeneity of variable inputs and examine the nature of the farm production function when capital in aggregate is added to units of given size. This is the practical form in which farmers must view the addition of resources in total. We now simply consider dollar capital as the homogeneous input. It will, of course, take on varying forms as it is added to the farm as physical capital in the nature of machines, livestock, buildings, feeds, and supplies.

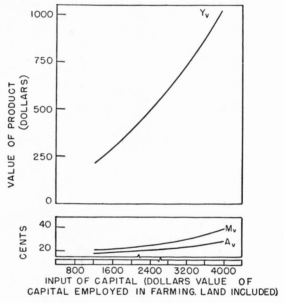

Fig. 16. Value productivity of non-labor resource on small farms (Source: Derived for year 1939 from Iowa Agr. Exp. Sta. sample census data).

Small farms. There are some important areas of increasing returns in agriculture. One of these is the small-capital, part-time, subsistence or low-income farm with a given stock of labor, ordinarily that of the operator plus some provided by the housewife and/or other family members. Here labor can be considered as fixed if outside employment opportunities are unimportant. Farms of this nature are scattered throughout the United States but are concentrated in such areas as the southern Cornbelt, the Appalachian mountain highlands, the Ozarks, the Ouachita mountains, the eastern part of the Cottonbelt and the cut-over areas of the lake states. Figure 16 illustrates a production function derived for a sample of small farms in Iowa, all of which employed limited quantities of capital and used no more than 12 months of labor per year. Labor is considered as fixed in the sense that no farms using more than 12 months were included.[21] Input refers to capital employed in farming for the year (not the service of capital for 1 year) while output is measured in a value sense. These data illustrate marginal productivity of the capital throughout the range studied. The total value of product curve in Figure 16, however, is simply a portion of a production function. Were capital inputs extended even further with labor fixed, diminishing marginal productivity un-

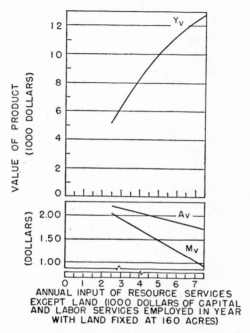

Fig. 17. Value productivity of non-land resources on 160 acres of Marshall silt loam, southwestern Iowa, 1945. (Source: Derived from homogeneous sample of farms employed in project study 1085, Iowa Agr. Exp. Sta. Includes 38 owner-operated farms producing same aggregate combination of crops and roughly the same proportion of beef and hogs.)

doubtedly would be expressed. Increasing returns to dollar capital on small farms with a fixed supply of labor arises mainly for this reason: some capital (but not all) is discontinuous or indivisible in the sense that in its particular forms it must come as whole machines or animals. One tractor or horse is the smallest unit, aside from manpower, possible for operating 5 acres but the same tractor may also service 10 acres, 20 acres, or a larger area. However, in many cases, not enough funds are available

[21] Capital has been considered as a single physical resource (measured in dollars) in deriving the simple production function of Figure 16. In this sense the factor input is not homogeneous as the quantity of capital is increased. The proportions of specific farms (land, seed, power units, machines, and so forth) change with the level of input of total capital.

to allow investment in those techniques or practices which cause still other forms of capital to be highly productive. An investment of $100 in livestock or seed may return less than half as much as $200 invested in the same stock along with efficient feeds, insecticides, lime, and supplies in general.

Intensity of the farm. It is obviously true that when the size of the farm is limited in acreage, added capital and labor must eventually result in diminishing productivity. The rate of decline will depend upon the type of production and the capacity of the land. In arid grazing regions, the decline will be rapid once pastures are highly stocked. In more humid areas where fertilizer can be added to crops and where feeds can be purchased for livestock, more intensive applications of labor and capital to a given land area may bring about only a gradual decline in resource productivity. Figure 17 provides an agricultural example of the latter nature. The data are for a sample of farms in which land is homogeneous and constant at 160 acres. (All farms are homogeneous in respect to soil. Agronomists made soil maps of the farms and only those with near-identical land were retained. Here all non-land resources have been converted to a common service input basis. The value of all non-land services used in a year and measured in dollars serves as the variable input. The quantity of these "variable" resource services was great enough on all farms included that no stage of increasing returns is indicated even if present. The general form of the production function, while not necessarily representative of other farm situations (the farms upon which the observations are based were owner-operated and include only units producing the same product), parallels existing hypotheses about the nature of value returns to be expected under operation of given acreages at varying levels of intensity.[22]

Universal Application

Examples of productivity functions in agriculture with the technical unit or farm plant fixed have been discussed in this chapter. Those examined ranged from physical input-output relationship for small technical units such as an acre of land or a dairy cow to the nature of returns for farms with fixed producing plants. The general relationships outlined also apply to technical and economic units of other magnitudes. We might examine, for example, the marginal productivity of capital or labor applied in varying quantities to an agricultural region such as the Piedmont or the Great Plains. Similarly, we might examine the marginal and average returns in an entire industry such as agriculture, labor being used in varying quantities while other resources are constant. In production economic

---

[22] For a description of the farms see Heady and Allen, *Returns From Capital Invested in Soil Conservation.* Iowa Agr. Exp. Sta. Bul. 381, Ames, 1951.

analyses, we are interested in production functions of the nature of those in Figure 3. Rather than view fertilizer or feed on the x axis while an acre or cow is fixed, we then view labor on the horizontal axis while the land area of an entire region is fixed. Analyses involving relationships of this nature are presented in later chapters.

Discontinuous Inputs and Fixed Coefficients

The discussion of this chapter so far has centered on resources where the unit of input is divisible and continuous.[23] Fertilizer, for example, can be applied to an acre of land in quantities ranging from a gram to several tons and in any quantity between these extremes. The production function or input-output curve is also highly continuous. This same situation does not exist for all resources, however. Some come in "lumpy" or discontinuous units. As was pointed out in the last chapter, the farmer generally must buy a whole tractor if he is to own it singly. There are many "lumpy" and "discontinuous" resources of this nature to be found on farms. The "degree of lumpiness" depends, however, on the manner in which the services of the resource are varied. It is true that, if a tractor is purchased, the farmer must buy the complete stock of productive services involved in it. Yet the input of services need not be in this same lumpy manner. From the stock of services embodied in the tractor, any amount ranging from 1 hour to 1,000 hours can be used as an input in a single year. Further, the services of machines are highly continuous if they are acquired on a custom basis rather than through ownership. Physically, it is possible to hire a machine for 1 hour, 10 hours, or 100 hours. Economically, the farmer may not do so because of costs or uncertainties, but discontinuity is not the limiting factor. While lumpy factors are important in agriculture, this notion can be overdone.

Discontinuity in the input-output relationship exists for production processes which involve fixed coefficients of production. By *fixed coefficients* is meant production processes which require a given and exact ratio between input and output. Examples are found mainly in chemistry and variable proportions between 2 factors are not possible. One atom of oxygen must always be combined with 2 atoms of hydrogen to produce H_2O. With O held constant, H can be increased infinitely without any increase in the product. Oxygen is thus a *limitational* factor, since some minimum and fixed quantity is always necessary for each output of H_2O.

---

[23] The existence of discontinuous and discrete relationships does not negate the need for use of refined economic principle; the logic is exactly the same as for continuous relationships and choice. Discussion of continuous relationships does not, in the words of Poe, involve "boring, probing and scrutinizing with a microscope or the dividing of a building into registered square inches." It is simply an attempt to define a set of logic and principles which apply to both continuous and discontinuous situations; any logic applying to the former applies readily to the latter.

Numerous farm practices are of this nature. A cow must be bred once before any calf is forthcoming. Additional inputs of bull service for a cow as a fixed technical unit have a zero productivity, once ovum and sperm have been combined in a 1:1 ratio. The bull/calf input-output ratio can be varied by quality of bull services, there are many cases of discontinuous inputs and linear production relationships in agriculture. While bull services are "discontinuous" for 1 cow, the bull may be used for cow numbers ranging from 1 to 20 with a constant or linear input-output ratio. Practices such as castration of pigs represent a discontinuous input for 1 pig as a technical unit but a continuous one for a drove of pigs. Any input-output relationship for castration services or similar discrete techniques is linear for the entire drove.

Refinements in input-output ratios. This chapter and the previous one have made distinctions between *average* and *exact* marginal products for resources of a "continuous" nature. The question thus arises as to the use which can be made of the *average* marginal productivity figures which are

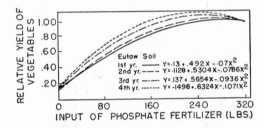

Fig. 18. Inter-year variations in the fertilizer-vegetable production function (Source: Ala. Agr. Exp. Sta. Bul. 268, Auburn, 1949).

ordinarily provided in the publications of colleges and the United States Department of Agriculture. The amount of fertilizer used on a given acreage and for a given price ratio can differ depending on whether the *exact* or *average* marginal ratio is employed. The former gives the correct answer. However, it is perhaps true that refinement for purposes of decision-making need not extend beyond that inherent in average marginal product figures and the assumption of linear segments of the production function. The reason is this: Both the production function and prices fluctuate in an unpredictable manner between years. The nature of variability in the fertilizer-vegetable production function over a 4-year period of relatively stable rainfall in Alabama is illustrated in Figure 18. The degree of variability is much greater for crops produced in other regions. Too, production relationships predicted from farm samples and experimental data provide *the* input-output ratio only within probability limits; even if the weather and other technical conditions of production are the same from year to year, there is not a "100 per cent chance" of getting the same results twice. Because of variability and inability to make perfect predictions, average marginal products (the assumption of linear segments of constant productivity) perhaps provide as much refinement as is necessary in decision-making by farmers or other resource administrators. The same can be said for input-output curves in any form. Knowledge of labor "requirements" in the sense of average or approximate marginal products may be sufficient for decision-making where uncertainty of price is great. We delay further consideration of this problem, however, until later chapters, and now turn to the first principles of choice and resource allocation.

Selected References

Atkinson, L. G., and Klein, J. W., *Feed Consumption and Production of Pork and Lard.* U.S.D.A. Tech. Bul. 917, Washington, 1946.

Black, J. D., *Production Economics.* New York: Macmillan, 1924.

Black, J. D., *et al., Farm Management.* New York: Macmillan, 1947, Chs. 7, 9, 17, 37.

Carlson, S., *A Study in the Pure Theory of Production.* London: King & Sons, 1939, pp. 21-23.

Heady, Earl O., "Use and Estimation of Input-Ouput Ratios," *Jour. Farm Econ. Proceedings,* Vol. 34.

Heady, Earl O., "Data Needed for Economic Analysis of Grazing Experiments," *Proceedings,* Sixth International Grassland Conference.

Holmes, C. L., *Economics of Farm Organization.* New York: Heath, 1928, Chs. 8, 12, 13.

Jensen, E., *et al., Input-Output Relationships in Milk Production.* U.S.D.A. Tech. Bul. 815, Washington, 1942.

Lerner, A., *Economics of Control.* New York: Macmillan, 1924, pp. 106-173.

Mitscherlich, E. A., *Zum Gesetz Vom Minimum Eine Antwort* an Th. Pfeiffer und Seine Mitarbeiter. Landw. Vers. Sta. 77, 1912.

Nelson, A. G., *Relation of Feed Consumed to Food Products in Cattle Fattening.* U.S.D.A. Tech. Bul. 900, Washington, 1945.

Samuelson, P. A., *Foundations of Economic Analysis.* Cambridge: Cambridge Univ. Press, 1948, pp. 69-75.

Spillman, W. J., *Use of the Exponential Yield Curve in Experiments.* U.S.D.A. Tech. Bul. 348, Washington, 1933.

Spillman, W. J., and Lang, E., *The Law of Diminishing Returns.* New York: World Book Co., 1924.

Stigler, G. J., *Theory of Price.* New York: Macmillan, 1947, pp. 125, 168-171.

Tolley, H. R., Black, J. D., and Ezekiel, M. J. B., *Input as Related to Output in Farm Organization Studies.* U.S.D.A. Bul. 1277, Washington, 1924.

4

First Principles of Choice and Resource Allocation

Wᴇ ʜᴀᴠᴇ examined the basic relationships involved in the transformation of single resources into a single product. These same relationships have also been examined as they relate to the agricultural production process. While only the more elementary relationships in resources and products have been examined to this point, we now have sufficient knowledge of production relationships to outline the first principles of choice and resource allocation in agriculture. The procedure of the current chapter is this: first, resource use principles are outlined within a physical framework and in terms of rational resource use; next, the role of decision-making and choice indicators in production is reviewed. The principles of choice are outlined first as they apply to the maximization of farm profits and second as they apply to certain national production or resource use problems. While we do not attempt to adhere unrealistically to the framework, the setting of this chapter is choice as it relates to the transformation of a single variable factor into a single product; other principles of choice will be unfolded in later chapters. Finally, this chapter discusses value productivity and its determination as well as other concepts useful in subsequent sections.

Physical Relationships and Choice

While the physical relationships discussed in previous chapters do have economic implications, they alone do not specify the exact quantity of variable resources which should be applied to the fixed factors representing a technical unit, a plant, or a farm as an economic unit. Yet as indicated below, knowledge of the physical laws of production are useful in explaining the basic fundamentals of resource allocation. These physical relationships define the stages of *rational production*.

Stages of production. Production functions of the classical type which include ranges of increasing marginal returns, decreasing marginal returns, and negative marginal returns can be divided into 3 segments. With reference to the total product curve, these are denoted as the 3 *stages of production,* and are illustrated in Figure 1 of this chapter and also in Table 2 in Chapter 2. In Figure 1, stage 1 ranges from a zero input to a 17.5 input of the variable factor. In other words, stage 1 extends to the input which results in a maximum average productivity of the variable factor; the maximum point on the average curve defines the end of stage 1. Stage 2 extends from the input denoting a maximum average product, 17.5 units of input in Figure 1, to the one defining the maximum total product, 30 units of input in Figure 1. In other words, all resource inputs between (a) the one consistent with a maximum product per unit of variable factor

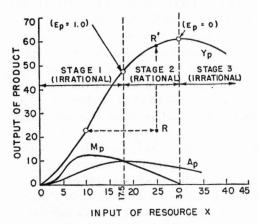

Fig. I. Stages of production and rational resource use.

and (b) the one consistent with a maximum product from the fixed factor, fall in stage 2. Stage 3 includes all inputs which have a negative marginal product and extends over the entire range of declining total output (all inputs greater than 30 in Figure 1). A production function characterized by increasing marginal returns alone would have only a stage 1. One characterized by decreasing marginal returns from the outset would not have a stage 1 but might include both stages 2 and 3.

Irrational production in stage I. Any level of resource use falling in stage 1 is uneconomic. Returns, measured in profits to the individual or in social product to a nation, can always be increased by applying a greater quantity of variable resource services to the factors which are otherwise considered fixed. The average productivity of all previous inputs of the variable resource increases continuously as additional amounts of variable resource services are added within stage 1. As production per unit of fixed factor is pushed to the limits of stage 1, a greater product is forthcoming from the fixed factors as well as from each unit of the variable factor. Rather than cease application of variable resources to fixed factors before the limit of stage 1 has been reached, the farmer or other manager of resources can always obtain more product from the same resources by rearranging the combination of "fixed" and "variable" factors within stage 1. This possibility exists even where there is an upper limit on the amount of "variable factor" which is available. A greater product from given resources can be attained by discarding or leaving idle part of the factor which was otherwise considered fixed. With reference to Table 2, Chapter 2, for example, suppose the figures in columns 1 and 3 refer to the application of fertilizer to a single acre of land and that fertilizer up to 1,500 lbs. is available to a farmer who operates 300 acres (the 300 acres constitute the so-called fixed factor). If 5 lbs. are applied to each acre, total production from fertilizer is 3,300 bushels (300×11). However, if 200 acres are left idle and the 1,500 lbs. of fertilizer are applied to the remaining 100 acres, total production is 3,800 bushels; a greater product can be obtained with an equal outlay of fertilizer and a smaller outlay of land. Returns must increase if the product has any value whatsoever attached to it. This statement is true also regardless of whether the fixed factor (land) has a price attached to it or is a free agent of production.

Stage 3 and irrational production. Stage 3 is also an area of irrational production, and, as in stage 1, resources can be cast aside or left idle with the effect of increasing total product. The only difference is that now it is the variable factor rather than the fixed resource which is withdrawn from use. (The variable factors simply are not applied to the fixed factor.) The logic also can be illustrated with data of Table 2, Chapter 2, by supposing that the input-output data shown for a single acre apply to a farm. If 12,000 lbs. of fertilizer are applied to the farm, the total product from fertilizer is only 16,500 (55×300). If fertilizer application is cut back to 9,000 lbs. (30 lbs. on each acre) total output will be 18,300 units (61×300). Again, any resource manager can obtain a greater product from a smaller resource outlay by recombining fixed and variable resources in this manner. If the product has any price or value whatsoever, economic return always must increase as resources are rearranged within stage 3. Even if the variable factor is a free agent of production, a greater economic return can always be had by using less of it.

Rational production and resource allocation. Even without attaching prices to the resource services or products concerned, it is evident that stage 2 alone is an economic area of production. The rate at which variable factors are applied to fixed factors can never fall outside of this stage if economic return is to be maximized. However, the exact *intensity of production* which is economic cannot be specified within stage 2 until prices and costs or other choice indicators can be specified.

Irrational production can now be defined as it relates to profit maximization. Irrational production exists if resources can be rearranged in any manner whatsoever to either (a) give a greater product from the same collection of resources or (b) give the same product with a smaller aggregate outlay of fixed and variable resources. Thus irrational production exists, aside from uncertainty considerations mentioned later, in any instance in which farmers combine fixed and variable resources in a manner which falls in stage 1 or stage 3. An important characteristic of irrational production is this: in cases of irrational production, knowledge of price relationships is not necessary as an indicator of the direction resources, and products should be recombined. Even without knowledge of prices we can say that resources are used inefficiently when they can be recombined to give more product from the same resources or the same product with fewer resources. In the case being analyzed, we need only know that (a) from the standpoint of farmer profit, the product has a price greater than zero; and hence (b) from the standpoint of society, the product adds something to utility or welfare. We need not know the exact level of price for the product, only that it is greater than zero. We need know nothing about the prices of the factors. As long as they can be rearranged to give a greater product from the same resources or the same product from fewer resources, farmer profit and national welfare can always be increased. The existence of irrational (technically inefficient) production indicates that a greater value of product can always be produced with the same or a smaller outlay of resources.

Irrational or technically inefficient production may exist not only because resources are combined in a manner falling within stage 1 or stage 3 on the production function, but also because an inefficient technique is employed. An irrational technique also is defined when resources are arranged in a manner which (a) does not allow a maximum physical product from given resources, or (b) otherwise would allow the same product from fewer resources. Point R in Figure 1 denotes an inefficient technique if the production function denoted by Y_p is known to exist. (R can be looked upon as a single point on a production function differing from Y_p.) A production technique which results in the input-output ratio indicated by R is obviously inefficient even if we know nothing about prices but know only that the input is the same as for point R' on curve Y_p. For the technique denoted by R, an input of 25 units of variable factor gives a total output of only 23. The technique represented by production function Y_p results in an output of 61 from an input of 25, or conversely, allows 23 units of output with an input of 10 units of variable service. Again, no knowledge of factor prices is needed to indicate that R represents an economically as well as technically inefficient use of resources. Irrational techniques can be defined, however, only if both methods of production involve the same kinds and forms of resources. If R' in Figure 1 requires use of large intricate machines while R does not, then the latter technique cannot necessarily be defined as uneconomic or irrational; the cost of the large machine may not merit an increase in the productivity of the variable factor X in this manner. An illustration of an irrational technique is provided in experimental data from Maine. Table 1 shows yields of potatoes for 2 different techniques in applying nitrogen fertilizer. (The 459 and 461 bushel yields represent 2 points on a production function

Table I.

Input-Output Relationships and Irrational Techniques *

	Total yield per acre with	
Pounds nitrogen applied per acre	*Fertilizer all applied in row side-band at planting: technique A*	*30 lbs. applied row side-band at cultivation with rest at planting: technique B*
(1)	(2)	(3)
90	459	409
120	461	415

* Source: Maine Agr. Exp. Sta. Bul. 490, Orono, 1951, p. 34.

defining one technique. The 409 and 415 yields represent 2 points on a production function defining a second technique.) Both of these techniques involve the same amount of fertilizer, labor, land, and machine services. Technique B is thus irrational. Even without knowing the prices of factors, we can always say that farmer profits will be greater and consumer welfare will be increased if A is selected rather than B, because this technique allows a greater product from given resources.

Irrational production in agriculture. Because stages 1 and 3 represent irrational ranges of production, discussions of resource allocation are usually in terms of production functions with elasticities throughout of less than 1.0 but greater than zero (such as those in Figures 2, 5, 7, and 9 of Chapter 3). This procedure is employed in graphic presentation in order to facilitate discussion and conserve space. Since most problems of economics fall in stage 2, it is taken as self-evident that economic units will not or should not employ resources in either stage 1 or stage 3. With certain exceptions, later chapters of this study follow a parallel procedure, and graphs do not show stages of increasing average and decreasing total returns even if they are assumed to exist. This procedure is not to be taken to suggest, however, that farms or other firms do not sometimes employ resources in an irrational manner. There are numerous examples where agricultural production is carried on in stage 3. Included here are cases in which too many hens are housed in one shelter, crops are planted too thickly, an excess number of cows or sheep is grazed on a single pasture, or the number of cows serviced by one bull is too great. While less prevalent, a small amount of production is carried on in stage 1: situations in which cows (or brood sows) are fed a winter ration too far below maintenance levels, or lime and fertilizer are not applied at a rate great enough to allow sufficient chemical action of soil elements. When the "fixed" factor or technical unit is divisible so that resources can be combined in any proportion, lack of knowledge mainly explains why most managers employ resources in an irrational fashion. The pioneer farmers of America recognized the rational stages of production: even though land was free for all practical purposes and could be considered as a variable factor, they did not, as a rule, apply so much of it with their limited or fixed supply of labor and capital as to cause the total product to diminish. Their objective was mainly one of maximizing the product per unit of limited capital and labor. In the current day when the supply of "free land" is exhausted, production in many countries is at the other extreme; soil has become the fixed resource in many countries and capital or labor is employed in quantities which are in the direction of a maximum product per unit of land.

The small farmer who is limited in funds because of uncertainty, and operates in a range of increasing returns to capital, is not an "irrational producer," however. The central problem here is one of capital limitations rather than ignorance. This problem is analyzed later. The small-scale farmer often can only maintain production in stage 1 if he is to produce at all since he does not have enough resources to extend production into stage 2. Furthermore, his resources are not always divisible in the sense that part of the technical unit can be discarded to allow production in stage 2 for the remainder. He would often aggravate his problem were he to discard part of his fixed soil area in an attempt to combine more capital with each acre of land. This is true because tractors, machines, and numerous other non-land resources come in partially discontinuous units.

Irrational techniques mainly are employed because of either lack of knowledge or pure inertia. The labor or work routine on many farms is often so complex and cumbersome that the same product could be processed with less effort. In addition to uncertainty and capital rationing there are some other important exceptions to the statement that operation in the area of stage 1 or stage 3 is the result of lack of knowledge. This is particularly true when time is taken into consideration. An individual, cognizant of his less-than-optimum operation at one point in time and knowing for certain that the causative forces are temporary, may be wise to maintain production in such an irrational area. Catastrophic conditions such as floods and drought, anticipated price changes, and unavailability or irreplaceability of resources of the desired kind and quality, are a few examples supporting such action.

Necessary and sufficient conditions for economic efficiency. Distinction can now be made between the *necessary* and the *sufficient* conditions which define economic efficiency in production. The *necessary* condition has been outlined above. Given resources must be combined in such a manner that they cannot be rearranged to give (a) a greater physical product with the same collection of resources or (b) the same physical product with less of one or more resources. This condition is *not sufficient* in the sense of defining the proportions in which variable and fixed resources should be combined within stage 2, the rational area of production, when rational techniques are employed. The *sufficient* condition can be defined only when price relationships are employed to denote maximum profits for the firm, or when other choice indicators are employed to denote the maximization of other economic objectives. The *sufficient* condition is outlined in the sections which follow.

Relevance for Economic Research

The measure or criterion of efficiency used in the previous analysis has been the maximum output of product for a given amount of factors. This criterion of efficiency is adequate for the analysis of several problems that relate to the organization of resources within a given farm as a firm and to several problems involving allocation of resources among farms. A few such problems can be indicated here: Many studies of the single farm assume that, as a firm, it is employing the best technology, but in agriculture, with its many small firms, this assumption is not too realistic. Consequently, farm management studies that are designed to (a) describe the technology actually used and (b) indicate the nature of an improved technology, can contribute to achieving greater resource efficiency from the standpoints both of the farm operator and of society. If carefully conceived, work simplification research contributes to this end. Such research should indicate how farmers can produce the same output with fewer resources (or more output with the same resources). Studies of location of fields and buildings, methods of applying fertilizer, and selection of livestock breeds or quality contribute to finding the best technology.

However, knowing the best technology is a necessary but not a sufficient condition for achieving a maximum of Y for a given input of X. As will be demonstrated later, it is also necessary that certain relations hold between the rate at which factors are transformed into products and the ratio of product and factor prices. The budget method of research and farm planning, if carefully used, is capable of answering questions of this sort, if there are sufficient data to estimate the marginal productivities of the factors. Analysis of the ratios of the marginal productivities of factors cannot indicate whether a particular product should be produced on a given farm, but it can indicate whether the output of one or more products can be increased without the addition of more resources.

A somewhat broader area of farm management problems is introduced when consideration is given to the organization of production by different farms. An extension of the above propositions is that the ratios of the marginal productivities of identical factors must be the same for all firms using these factors and producing the same products. If these ratios are not identical, the output of some or all firms can be increased by transfers among farms. Even questions of whether agriculture has the appropriate relative quantities of labor and capital can be answered within this framework. If the ratio of the marginal productivity of capital and labor is higher in agriculture than in the rest of the economy, this implies, aside from work preference, that there is too little capital and too much labor in agriculture (too much capital and too little labor in the rest of the economy). If such a result were obtained, research could then be directed to an understanding of the circumstances associated with the divergence from the most efficient allocation. These questions will be reserved, however, for the discussion of product-product relationships.

Technical efficiency and physical research. Most physical scientists concern themselves with technical efficiency. Technical efficiency may or may not be identical with economic efficiency (as will be pointed out in later chapters). Technical efficiency is measured by the magnitude of the physical ratio of product output to factor input; the greater the ratio, the greater the degree of technical efficiency. Technical efficiency is denoted by a "movement" from R to R' in Figure 1. A "movement" of this nature involves a change in techniques. Technical efficiency may also be denoted, where the technique is given, by the manner in which fixed and variable resources are combined. For single techniques or input-output relationships such as those examined in this chapter, physical efficiency can be studied from the standpoint of either of 2 ratios: one is the ratio of product output to variable factor input; the other is the ratio of product output to input of fixed factor. In Figure 1, for example, average output per unit of variable factor (average productivity of the variable factor) is greatest when input is 17.5. Animal husbandrymen concerned with hogs, beef cattle, and market poultry center their research around maximum average productivity of the variable factor, feed. Their criterion of efficiency is largely one of a maximum average meat product per unit of feed (the variable factor), rather than the greatest output per animal (the fixed factor). Output of the fixed factor is greatest in Figure 1 with an input of 30 units of variable factor. Agronomists and other plant scientists often use maximum total product as their measure of physical efficiency: fertilizer, seed, or other single elements of production (the variable factor) applied to a given plot of land (the fixed factor) to analyze the magnitude of yields per acre (and almost never to analyze the average yield per unit of fertilizer). Dairy and poultry husbandrymen are also interested in maximum product per unit of fixed factor (milk per cow or eggs per hen). Physical scientists might well compromise on these 2 efficiency goals. Obviously, both combinations of resources cannot be economically efficient at the same time. The great need, of course, is for physical scientists to incorporate the concepts of marginality into their research. Their findings would then better lend themselves to economic analysis and decision-making. Use of the production function concept would itself allow better estimates of marginal products. Use of production function models as a basis for experimental designs would require variations in experimental designs and statistical techniques applied to technical research. Most physical research supposes discrete phenomena which can be best analyzed by means of replication of individual treatments and analysis of variance of mean differences. Under the production function model, emphasis would be on regression analyses and estimation of functional relationships. Not all physical research fits into this frame of analysis, but an important portion does.

Economic Efficiency

The *sufficient* conditions for economic efficiency can now be defined. As has been indicated previously, economic efficiency is denoted when resources are used in a manner to maximize the particular objective or end quantity which is relevant to the economic unit under consideration. If the unit is a farm as a pure firm, the relevant quantity to be maximized is profit; efficiency in production is attained when resources are organized to give a maximum profit. If the economic unit includes the farm business and the family household in combination, the relevant quantity to be maximized is family welfare or utility and resource efficiency is so measured. If national welfare is the relevant quantity to be maximized, then economic efficiency in production is attained when agricultural resources are used to conform with maximization of this end.

Choice indicators and price ratios. The problem in production is one of making a *choice* or *decision* on which one of many uses of resources and patterns of production will maximize the relevant end. The most efficient use of resources can be defined only in terms of a *choice indicator*. A choice indicator defines the condition of a maximum (for example, maximum farm profits), and, as is illustrated in this and subsequent chapters, is always given as a ratio. Choice between the production of hogs or beef depends on the ratio of prices of beef and pork. The price ratio thus becomes an index or criterion by which choice or decision can be or is made (a choice indicator). Problems of production move out of the realm of technology or physical science and into the domain of economics when choice indicators are present and can be used for the purpose of defining efficiency.

We now turn to questions of choice or decisions in the transformation of a single factor into a single product. We wish to know the intensity with which variable resources should be combined with fixed factors if profits are to be at a maximum. The ratio which serves as an indicator of choice for this problem is the factor-product price ratio. This ratio can be expressed P_x/P_y, where P_x refers to the price of the factor X and P_y refers to the price of the product Y. To specify the rate at which variable resources should be applied to fixed resources, the factor/product price ratio (P_x/P_y) must be related to the marginal product $(\Delta Y/\Delta X)$ of factor X.

This point was long ago recognized by agricultural economists when they coined the term "corn/hog ratio." The corn/hog ratio is used to indicate the amount of corn which can be purchased by 100 pounds of pork; a corn/hog ratio of 10:1 indicates that 100 lbs. of pork has a value equal to 10 bushels of corn and suggests the price comparison in which we are interested. When corn is $1 per bushel and pork is $10 per cwt., the corn/ hog price ratio, expressed in the manner of interest to us, is 1:10. This form of ratio has the same meaning as the common usage of the term hog/corn ratio; both indicate that a bushel of corn is worth only one-tenth as much as 100 lbs. of pork.

Given the problem of choosing the level at which variable factors should be applied to fixed factors for profit maximization, the following law or *necessary* condition can be set down: The factor/product price ratio must equal the marginal productivity of the resource. (As will be pointed out later, the amount of profit for the combination where the price ratio is equal to the transformation ratio is the same as the amount of profit when one less unit of resource is used. We state equation I to illustrate the importance of the two equations.) This *necessary* condition for profit maximization can be stated in the form of either equation I or equation II below:

$$\frac{\text{price of factor}}{\text{price of product}} = \text{marginal product of resource} \qquad \text{I}$$

$$P_x/P_y = \Delta Y/\Delta X \qquad \text{II}$$

These 2 equations state the same thing; since P_x denotes the price of factor X; while P_y denotes the price of product Y; and $\Delta Y/\Delta X$, the change in output of Y for each 1-unit change in input of X, denotes the marginal product of each unit of the resource. Since $\Delta Y/\Delta X$, the marginal product of the resource, is indicative of the rate of change in product Y for each unit change in factor X, profits are at a maximum when the ratio of prices is inversely equal to the ratio at which resource is transformed into product; as equations I and II indicate, the price of the factor is always "over" the price of the product while the change in product is always "over" the change in factor. We can also employ equation II above to derive III below. Equation III indicates that profits can be at a maximum only when the value of the change in input of factor is equal to the value of the change in output of the product. If 1 unit of

$$(P_x)(\Delta X) = (P_y)(\Delta Y) \qquad \text{III}$$

factor with a price of $10 is added to input while 10 units of product with a price of $1 are added to output (the marginal product of one unit of factor is 10) equation III becomes ($10)(1) = ($1)(10) or $10 = $10 and profits are at a maximum. If the price of the factor multiplied by its input is less than the price of the product multiplied by its output ($P_x\Delta X < P_y\Delta Y$), then use of additional resources will add more to revenue than to costs, and profits can be increased. At a later point we will call $P_x\Delta X$

the marginal cost of the resource (when ΔX represents a change in input by 1 unit) and $P_y\Delta Y$ the value product of the resource.

Table 2.

Optimum Level of Applying Variable Resources to Fixed Resources *

Number of 500-lb. units of fertilizer applied per acre	Total output (bu. per acre)	Marginal product ($\Delta Y/\Delta X$) for each 500-lb. unit of fertilizer	Value of added fertilizer at $9.60 per 500-lb. unit	Value of added potatoes at 40¢ per bu.
(1)	(2)	(3)	(4)	(5)
0	0			
		103	$9.60	$41.20
1	103			
		71	9.60	28.40
2	174			
		49	9.60	19.60
3	223			
		34	9.60	13.60
4	257			
		24	9.60	9.60
5	281			
		17	9.60	6.80
6	298			
		10	9.60	4.00
7	308			

* Source: Based on Table 1, Chapter 2.

Maximization of profits in terms of the conditions outlined above can now be illustrated. Table 2 provides a beginning example. Let us inquire whether the second unit of fertilizer is profitable when the price of a 500-lb. unit of fertilizer is $9.60 and the price of potatoes is 40 cents per bushel. If we put these figures in equation I above, the price ratio becomes 24:1.0 ($9.60/.40) while the ratio of change in product or factor or the marginal product is 71:1. Therefore, profits are not at a maximum, because the 2 ratios are not equal. The reason is obvious. The 1 unit of fertilizer has a value of $9.60 ($9.60 × 1), while the 71 units of potatoes have a value of $28.40 (.40 × 71). Thus by adding $9.60 to cost, $28.40 can be added to revenue and net profits can be increased by $18.80. The factor/product price ratio is less than (<) the marginal product, as indicated in IV below.

$$\$9.60/.40 < 71/1 \text{ (or } 24 < 71) \qquad \text{IV}$$

Because the sign in IV above reads "less than" (<) rather than "equal to," profits can be increased by greater use of the variable resource. Any time the factor/product price ratio can be stated in the manner of V below, profits are not at a maximum.

$$P_x/P_y < \Delta Y/\Delta X \qquad \text{V}$$

With prices for fertilizer and potatoes remaining as previously, use of the sixth unit of fertilizer can be appraised. If the physical quantities from Table 2 are substituted in the formula it then becomes

$$\$9.60/.40 > 17/1 \text{ or } 24 > 17 \qquad \text{VI}$$

which states that the factor/product price ratio is greater than ($>$) rather than equal to the marginal product of the resource. Profits are not increased by use of the sixth input. It adds $9.60 ($9.60 $\times$ 1) to costs but only $6.80 (.40 $\times$ 17) to revenue. Accordingly, net income decreases by $2.80. Whenever the factor/product price ratio is greater than ($>$) the marginal product, profits can be increased by using less of the factor.

Maximum profits are attained with the addition of the fifth unit of fertilizer, since here the 2 ratios are equal as indicated in VII;

$$\$9.60/.40 = 24/1 \text{ or } 24 = 24 \qquad\qquad \text{VII}$$

the fifth unit of fertilizer adds $9.60 ($9.60 $\times$ 1) to cost and $9.60 (.40 $\times$ 24) to revenue.

We are, of course, speaking in terms of the *exact* marginal product rather than the *average* marginal product when we say that the price ratio *must equal* the transformation ratio. For farmer decision and with the marginal product measured in average terms, profits are more nearly at a maximum when 1 factor unit less than that defining $P_x/P_y = \Delta Y/\Delta Y$ is used. Comparisons can be made quite simply with marginal product measured in the average sense. Suppose, for example, that the price of each 500-lb. unit of fertilizer is $9.60 while potatoes are priced at 50 cents. The relevant price ratio is then $9.60/.50, or 19.2. If we look in column 3 of Table 2, it shows a transformation ratio $\Delta Y/\Delta X$, the marginal product, greater than 19.2 between the fourth and fifth 500-lb. inputs but less than 19.2 between the fifth and sixth inputs. Thus the fifth input can be applied profitably if these prices and yields are realized and 500-lb. inputs are considered.

Graphical presentation of economic efficiency. The conditions outlined above defining the economic rate at which variable resources should be applied to fixed factors can be presented graphically. The graphical presentation not only adds precision to the principle already outlined but also provides a tool useful in later analysis. As a first step in the geometric illustration, Figure 2 is presented to show the nature of factor/product price ratios. It is based on the examples below which indicate 2 factor/product price ratios. The figures from example A are graphed to indicate

Example A				Example B			
Price of factor at $1;				Price of factor at $4;			
Price of product at $2				Price of product at $2			
$P_x/P_y = .5{:}1.0$				$P_x/P_y = 2.0{:}1.0$			
Product		Factor		Product		Factor	
Units	Value	Units	Value	Units	Value	Units	Value
(1)	(2)	(3)	(4)	(5)	(6)	(7)	(8)
1	$ 2	1	$1	1	$ 2	1	$ 4
2	4	2	2	2	4	2	8
3	6	3	3	3	6	3	12
4	8	4	4	4	8	4	16
5	10	5	5	5	10	5	20
6	12	6	6	6	12	6	24

the number of units of product which are equal in value to various units of factor; 2 units of factor have a value of $2 and therefore are equivalent to only 1 unit of product. Accordingly, the slope of line A is .5:1.0; each horizontal increase of 1.0 is accompanied by a .5 unit increase vertically. When example B is graphed, line B results. Here the slope is 2.0:1.0 indicating that 2 units of product are required to give a value equal to that of 1 unit of factor. Line C, which has a 1.0:1.0 or 45° slope, has been graphed to indicate equal prices of product and factor. It is now evident that as the price of the product rises relative to the price of the factor (P_x/P_y becomes smaller) the price ratio line has less slope (becomes flatter); as the price of the factor increases relative to the price of the product, the price ratio line becomes steeper (P_x/P_y becomes larger). This is exactly the meaning of the corn/hog ratio or the feed/milk price ratio.

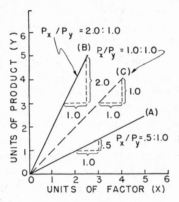

Fig. 2. Factor/product price ratios.   Fig. 3. Equation of price ratio and marginal product to maximize profits.

A corn price of 4¢ per lb. and a milk price of 4¢ per lb. would give a price ratio (P_x/P_y) line such as C in Figure 2. A corn price of one cent and a milk price of 1¢ per lb. would give the same line, because the ratio is 1.0:1.0 in either case.

Knowledge of the relationship between price ratios and the slopes of price lines now makes possible graphic specification of maximum profits. In Figure 3, curve Y represents a production function or input-output curve of the nature discussed previously. Maximum profits can be denoted for any given factor/product price ratio by tangency of the physical product curve and the price ratio line. Lines with the slopes of A (a low P_x/P_y ratio) and B (a high P_x/P_y ratio) have been transposed from Figure 2 to Figure 3. Since (a) the slope of the input-output curve at any one point denotes the marginal product of the factor, and (b) the slope of the price line indicates the factor/product price ratio, and (c) the slopes or ratios are equal for 2 tangent lines, tangency of any one of the price lines with the total product curve denotes the input which gives maximum profits; the slope of the product curve indicates $\Delta Y/\Delta X$ or the marginal product, while the slope of the price line indicates P_x/P_y or the factor/product price ratio. Hence the factor/product price ratio is equal to the marginal physical product of the factor ($P_x/P_y = \Delta Y/\Delta X$ or $P_x\Delta X = P_y\Delta Y$) at the points of tangency. The addition to cost of the factor unit indicated is *exactly* equal to the value of the resulting addition to output. In Figure 3, tangency of the price ratio line A, indicating a price of \$1 for factor and \$2 for product, gives a maximum profit when the marginal product ($\Delta Y/\Delta X$) is equal to .5 with 30 units of input. Prices of \$15 and \$30 for the factor and product respectively would specify the same input and same output because this factor/product price ratio also is .5:1.0. When the price ratio line B from Figure 2 is applied to the production function curve, maximum profits are denoted by an input of 7, since here the marginal product of 2.0 is equal to the price ratio of 2.0:1.0.

Universal application of choice indicators and production economics principles. The factor/product price ratio lines have now fulfilled their role as choice indicators. They specify the choice of factor input and product output which will give maximum profits, the immediate end in view. Aside from denoting rational areas of production, physical or input-output relationships specify nothing about economic efficiency in level of resource use for a producing unit. Economic efficiency can be denoted only when the relevant end or quantity (profit in this case) is at a maximum as denoted by the relevant choice indicator. The analysis which follows will make use of choice indicators throughout. These will take numerous forms. In many instances they will, as in the example above, be price ratios. In other cases physical yield ratios may serve as choice indicators in specifying how resources should be allocated between 2 land areas to attain an end of a maximum physical product, or calorie ratios may be used to indicate the optimum allocation of feed resources between different types of livestock in a food emergency. While economic ends and choice indicators may differ, the principles which serve as the foundation of agricultural production economics (resource efficiency) are always the same. This characteristic distinguishes agricultural production economics from specializations such as land tenure economics, where the objective is more nearly one of analyzing the historic evolution and the legality of land use patterns, tenure systems, or similar institutions, which may change with time. The objective of agricultural production economics is, again, that of (a) aiding farmers in the best use of their resources in a manner to maximize profits or other ends and (b) bringing about the most efficient use of agricultural capital, labor, land, and management resources in a manner to increase welfare of the national economy. Thus the *sufficient* and *necessary* conditions of optima (maximum profits, maximum family satisfactions, maximum national welfare, or other ends of individuals and groups) become the goals towards which analyses in agricultural production economics are directed. The data and relationships employed in denoting the maximization of ends indicate the type of information and the principles which must be provided by research. The analysis above indicates, for example, that maximum profit per acre can be specified only if appropriate information is available in the form of production ratios and price relationships. Similarly, the principles of production specify the type of information necessary for solution of any other problems in resource efficiency such as use of resources during war, the optimum level of conservation or the quantity of resources to be employed in agriculture.

Changes in factor/product price ratios. Factor/product price ratios, while subject to less variation than those of many non-farm industries, are continually changing in agriculture as is indicated in Table 4. These changes are important from several standpoints. First, they indicate that the optimum proportioning of variable to fixed resources should undergo constant change if profits are to be maximized: milk production per cow, marketing weights of hogs, and the amount of fertilizer or other resource applied per

Table 4.

Changes in Selected Factor/Product Price Ratios, United States, 1919-50 *

Year	Index of prices paid by farmers	Index of prices received by farmers	Ratio of prices received to prices paid in percent	Corn/hog price ratio	Labor/milk price ratio
1919	202	215	109	.11	.92
1920	201	211	104	.07	1.13
1921	152	124	75	.06	.73
1922	149	132	80	.10	.78
1928	155	151	90	.10	.95
1929	154	149	89	.09	.88
1930	146	128	80	.07	.94
1931	126	90	64	.05	.96
1932	108	68	55	.09	.94
1933	108	72	60	.13	.85
1934	122	90	70	.10	.81
1935	125	109	84	.08	.76
1940	122	100	80	.12	.87
1941	131	124	94	.08	.89
1942	152	159	106	.07	.97
1945	180	202	117	.09	1.36
1946	202	233	121	.09	1.20
1947	246	278	120	.09	1.20
1948	264	287	116	.06	1.09
1949	240	249	100	.07	1.39

* Source: *Agricultural Statistics.*

acre should all be changed to conform with changes in price ratios. Similarly, the number of hogs produced and the number of cows milked should be varied in line with price ratios if profits of the farm are to be maximized. Second, price changes serve as a mechanism whereby the consuming society indicates preference in the pattern of production and resource use: changes in factor/product price ratios specify that resources should be added to or withdrawn from agriculture. Third, constant change in factor/product price ratios gives rise to uncertainty and complicate the process of management and decision-making. Farmers can only anticipate prices. Their ability to produce the products selected by society and to maximize profits depends on the accuracy with which they can guess or formulate expectations of prices. These problems of production dynamics are analyzed in later chapters.

Linear production functions and recommendations to farmers. Economic efficiency seldom is consistent with a maximum yield per acre or animal or with a maximum physical product from a single farm. Perhaps there is only one case in which a maximum physical product from a technical unit is consistent with maximum profits: It is the case of a straight line, input-output relationship (a linear production function) which becomes horizontal or declines. Under this situation either 1 of 2 extreme uses of resources denotes economic efficiency: (1) use of no resource with the technical unit or (2) use of enough resource to give a maximum output per technical unit. Output per technical unit should be pushed to a physical maximum when the factor/product price ratio is less than the marginal product of the factor, because, under a linear production function, the marginal product ($\Delta Y/\Delta X$) is a constant for all resource units. No product should be produced and no variable resource should be employed when the factor/product price ratio is greater than the marginal product. The feed-egg relationship from Figure 12 in Chapter 3 provides an example here. If proven that the marginal productivity (change in eggs/change in feed or $\Delta Y/\Delta X$) of feed is constant at 6.5 eggs per pound of feed, hens should be fed to produce a maximum of eggs if the price of a pound of feed is not 6.5 greater than the price of an egg. No eggs should be produced if the price of feed is 6.5 times greater than the price of an egg. Similarly, if the feed-milk production function were of the nature assumed by historic recommendations of dairy husbandrymen (illustrated in Figure 6 of Chapter 3), a maximum milk output per cow would denote maximum profits. Because a diminishing, rather than constant productivity of feed holds true for milk, however, this use of resources is not often or always economically efficient. Many farm techniques are represented by resource units discontinuous for 1 technical unit but more or less continuous for all technical units of a farm plant and profit maximization ordinarily results if the technique or special form of resource is applied to all technical units. A single medicinal capsule which adds 20 lbs. to pork production per pig should not only be applied to 1 pig if its price is less than 20 times greater than the price of pork per pound (so that P_x/P_y is less than $\Delta Y/\Delta P$ or 20/1), but also should be applied to all pigs on the farm.

Many recommendations of agricultural scientists assume a linear production function and that the factor/product price ratio is less than the constant marginal product of the factor. These assumptions are implicit in recommendations which exhort farmers to push to physical maximum yields per acre or animal. Agricultural economists also have employed recommendations which suppose constant marginal products. The historic finding that farm profits could be increased by continuous increases in the yield per acre or the output per animal were generally of this sort; limits were seldom if ever placed on the level to which physical production might be increased without decreases in profits. This type of finding may have resulted because (1) farmers do not push resource input to a level consistent with maximum profits because of reasons outlined elsewhere in this chapter; (2) the agricultural production function is linear; or (3) the design of research procedures did not allow estimation of the appropriate production, cost, or revenue relationships. The linear production function must be rejected as a basis for these findings except for special situations; it may serve as a sufficient reason for explaining greater profits as output is increased along a linear short-run production function for the farm but it seldom applies to a technical unit. The design of research procedures which give these "apparent linear relationships" undoubtedly resulted in many findings of this nature; conditions of homogeneity of inputs were not attained in sampling procedures, with the effect that the relationships estimated were hybrids rather than true relationships to be found on individual farms.[1] Problems of homogeneity and research design are discussed further in the chapter on resource classification.

An additional note on linear or straight-line relationships is of interest. Most farmers have limited funds with which to purchase labor, feed, fertilizer, or other resources. If the production function were linear, they could allocate all of their fertilizer, feed, and labor to a single animal or acre and profits would be maximized. Similarly, the entire food product of the nation could be produced on a single acre. These possibilities do not exist, of course, because the production function is not linear for an acre or animal as a fixed technical unit.

Value Productivity and Maximum Returns

The conditions of production and resource use which define maximum profits also can be explained in other terms: *net returns from a single technical unit are at a maximum when the marginal cost of the resource is*

---

[1] See E. O. Heady, "Elementary models in farm production economics research," *Jour. Farm Econ.*, Vol. 30.

equal to the marginal value productivity of the resource. Similarly, it can be said that profits are at a maximum under perfect competition when the marginal cost of a unit of output is equal to the marginal revenue of a unit of output. These 2 statements simply represent different ways of saying that maximum profits for the farm as a firm exist if the factor/ product price ratio is equal to the marginal physical product of resources. However, since many problems must be analyzed in terms of these 2 additional statements, they will be discussed further. The concept of value productivity is also useful for the analysis of later chapters. We will consider the problem of equating the value productivity and the marginal cost of a resource in this chapter. Consideration of marginal cost and marginal revenue will be reserved mainly for the chapter on costs.

Value productivity. Value productivity relationships or value production functions exactly parallel their physical counterparts, the difference being only one of unit of measurement (dollars instead of bushels or tons). The total value product is derived by multiplying total output by the commodity price. The marginal value product is derived either (a) by multiplying the marginal physical product by the price of the product or (b) computing it as the change in the total value product.[2] It was encountered, perhaps unwittingly, by the reader on previous pages in the form $P_y \Delta Y$, where P_y refers to the price of the product and ΔY refers to the change in output of product Y (the marginal product of the factor when the ΔX of the $\Delta Y/\Delta X$ is equal to 1). The average value product represents the total value product divided by the units of input or can be derived by multiplying the average physical product by the price of the product. All concepts including the stages of (a) increasing and decreasing returns, (b) elasticity, and (c) rational areas of production are identical (fall at the same input) for physical and value production functions or input-output curves. This is illustrated in Figure 4, where the value curves have been derived by application of prices to the physical curves or data of Figure 5 in Chapter 2. The maximum total, average, and marginal products come at identical levels of resource input for the value and the physical curves. Some economists claim that physical production functions deal with technical phenomena while value production functions deal with economic phenomena. There is actually no difference (both are physical concepts) except that the product is expressed in different units of measurement.[3]

---

[2] For monopoly or non-competitive firms, the marginal value product must be computed as the change in total value product associated with the derivative of each input of resource. This is true since demand is not infinitely elastic and a greater output can be sold only at a lower price. The terms marginal value product and value of the marginal product are not then synonymous. This situation describes a few monopolistic firms in agriculture such as milk retailing farms, "giant" vegetable farms, and so forth.

[3] Units of measurement would differ in a similar way were physical product expressed in bushels as compared to hundred-weights of wheat.

Study of production functions has historically followed a division of labor wherein agronomists, animal husbandrymen, and other physical scientists have estimated physical production functions for technical units such as an acre of land, a dairy cow, or a hog, while agricultural production

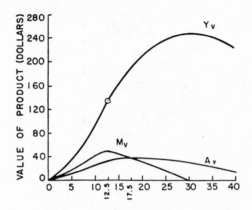

Fig. 4. Value production function including marginal and average product curves (based on same data as curves in Fig. I with price of $4 per unit).

economists have estimated (1) physical and value production functions for technical units involving an entire herd of animals or several or many acres of land, economic units such as farms, and for regions of agriculture or the entire agricultural industry; and (2) value production functions for technical units. This division of labor is not particularly useful in analysis of production problems.

Basis for variation in value productivity. Physical production functions for particular resources vary between technical and economic units, depending on techniques employed, the capacity of the technical unit or producing plant, and the "level at which other resources are fixed." Each specific technical unit, plant, firm, or producing region does have a single or unique *physical* production function at a given point in time. However, there are as many *value* productivity functions for a technical unit, farm, producing region, or industry as there are levels of price. The single production function for dairy cows shown in Figure 5 of Chapter 3 may be taken as an illustration. With milk at (1) $4.00, (2) $3.00, and (3) $2.00, 3 different value production functions (relationship between physical input and value of product) exist and are indicated as Y_{v_1}, Y_{v_2} and Y_{v_3} respectively, in Figure 5 below. Differences such as these might exist for several reasons, even for a given physical production function: Y_{v_1} and Y_{v_3} might be the value production functions for milk producers in 2 different markets, or Y_{v_1} might be the feed input-value of product relationship for a single producer in 2 different price periods (Y_{v_1} in prosperity and Y_{v_2} in depression). The value productivity of labor or capital in any specific region or on any farm in agriculture will vary similarly as price levels differ. If we hold prices constant and apply them to production functions representing fixed resources (a cow, a farm, or a producing region) of different inherent capacities, we have the second reason for differences in value productivities. For example, if we apply a constant milk price of $4 to the 2 input-output relationships of Figure 13 in Chapter 3, we will get 2 value production functions such as Y_{v1} and Y_{v2} in Figure 5 (shown) and 2 marginal value product curves such as M_{v1} and M_{v2}, not because prices differ but because feed productivity differs when applied to the 2 cows of different capacity. While a cow as a technical unit has served as the example, the same logic applies to capital applied on a farm of Drummer silt loam in Illinois as compared to a farm on Knox loam in Kansas or Guin-Atwood-Savannah soils of Alabama.

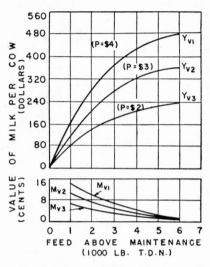

Fig. 5. Value production functions and marginal value productivity of feed at $4, $3, and $2 per cwt. for various levels of feeding dairy cows (Source: Prices applied to data from U.S.D.A. Tech. Bul. 815).

The term marginal productivity, whether in physical or value terms, applies best to a particular unit of resource. Except for linear production functions the average or marginal productivity of each unit of resource is different. The term "productivity" is often used loosely in such statements as this, "The marginal value product of capital in agriculture is high" or "The marginal value productivity of labor in the Mississippi delta is low." The concept of productivity is mainly useful when qualified in terms of the level of input to which it applies. The marginal value product of a single unit of resource depends not only on the 2 considerations outlined above, the level of prices, and the capacity or inherent productivity of the fixed resource, but also on the number of units of variable resource employed. In Figure 5, for example, the marginal value product of a unit of feed, with milk at $4, is $14 when only 1,000 pounds of feed are applied per cow, but $2 when 6,000 pounds of feed are used. Thus the marginal value productivity of a unit of feed can be changed by variations in the amount used. Use of a large amount will drive value productivity low in the same manner as low product prices or low levels of physical productivity for the fixed or inflexible resources. Value productivities for different units of feed can be made equal by varying the number of units used with different cows. Although the example cited was applied to feed and dairy cows, the same basic relationships apply where value productivity of any physical resources (fertilizer applied to land, labor applied to farms, and so forth) differs between technical or economic units. The concepts of value productivity will have important use in later chapters where production efficiency is to be analyzed in terms of different farms and regions. Comparisons between farms or areas of efficiency in the use of labor or another resource are possible only if a common index of output such as value of product is employed. Other indices of output or productivity commonly used include man-work units, all products converted to a basis of a single product, and so forth. These have the same general implication as a value product measure. However, at this point we return to the problems of farm profit maximization and use the concepts of value productivity to illustrate the optimum proportioning of variable and fixed resources.

Value productivity and profit maximization. A production function relating value of output to physical input of resource does not immediately indicate the optimum proportioning of fixed and variable factors; the rate of applying variable resources to fixed resources to maximize profits is given only as the marginal cost of the factor, as well as its marginal value product, is known. The term *marginal cost of a resource* (not to be confused with *marginal cost of output* discussed later) refers to the cost of the last unit of resource. For business firms such as farms, which operate under competitive conditions, the marginal cost of each unit of resource is the same: if a farmer can buy 1 day's labor services for $5, he can buy 2, 6, or 200 days of service at the same price per day. Similarly, if he can buy 1 bushel of corn for $1.40, he can generally buy 10,000 bushels at the same price per unit; the marginal cost of each unit of factor is identical, since equal amounts are added to total costs by each unit of factor purchased. The term *marginal resource cost* is identical with the term *resource supply curve* or *factor supply function* for a farm; a graph of marginal costs (or a schedule if presented in tabular form, or an equation if presented in algebraic form) also represents the factor supply curve facing the individual business. A curve of this nature is illustrated in Figure 6. The curve MC_r (marginal cost of resources) indicates that a single farm might buy any of the quantities of fertilizer included at a price of $30 per ton. The nature of marginal resource costs is also indicated in columns 7, 8, and 9 of Table 5. The marginal cost of resources (the factor supply function facing a farm) will differ, depending only on the level of factor prices.

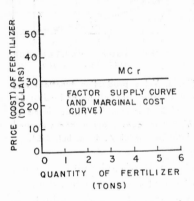

Fig. 6. Nature of (a) supply curve and (b) marginal cost curves for resources.

Table 5 now can be used as an arithmetic illustration of profit maximization. Columns 4, 5, and 6 indicate the marginal value productivity of fertilizer when the seed cotton price is $10, $15, and $20 per cwt. respectively. (These columns are the counterpart of the marginal value productivity curves M_{v1}, M_{v2} and M_{v3} for dairy cows in Figure 5.) With the marginal cost of fertilizer at $2.00 (column 7), application of all physical inputs up to the 12th is profitable when the marginal value productivity of fertilizer is based on a cotton price of $10 per cwt. With the fertilizer price

Table 5.

Marginal Value Productivity and Marginal Factor Cost for 8-8-8 Fertilizer Applied to Seed Cotton *

Fertilizer input (cwt.)	Total production (lbs. over production without fertilizer)	Marginal physical product (average)	Marginal value product when price of seed cotton is [a]			Marginal cost of fertilizer when price is		
			$10 cwt.	$15 cwt.	$20 cwt.	$2.00 cwt.	$4.25 cwt.	$6.25 cwt.
(1)	(2)	(3)	(4)	(5)	(6)	(7)	(8)	(9)
0	0	0	0	0	0	0	0	0
1	107	107	$10.70	$16.05	$21.40	$2.00	$4.25	$6.25
2	206	99	9.90	14.82	19.80	2.00	4.25	6.25
3	297	91	9.10	13.65	18.20	2.00	4.25	6.25
4	381	84	8.40	12.60	16.80	2.00	4.25	6.25
5	456	75	7.50	11.25	15.00	2.00	4.25	6.25
6	523	67	6.70	9.05	13.40	2.00	4.25	6.25
7	583	60	6.00	9.00	12.00	2.00	4.25	6.25
8	635	52	5.20	7.80	10.40	2.00	4.25	6.25
9	678	43	4.30	6.45	8.60	2.00	4.25	6.25
10	714	36	3.60	5.40	7.20	2.00	4.25	6.25
11	742	28	2.80	4.20	5.60	2.00	4.25	6.25
12	762	20	2.00	3.00	4.00	2.00	4.25	6.25
13	775	13	1.30	1.95	2.60	2.00	4.25	6.25
14	779	4	.40	.60	.80	2.00	4.25	6.25
15	775	−4	−.40	−.60	−.80	2.00	4.25	6.25
16	764	−11	−1.10	−1.65	−2.20	2.00	4.25	6.25
17	744	−20	−2.00	−3.00	−4.00	2.00	4.25	6.25

* Source: Adapted from South Carolina Exp. Sta. Bul. 219.

[a] Can be computed either (a) by multiplying the marginal physical product (column 3) by the price per unit or (b) by subtracting from each successive total value of output the previous total value of output.

at $2 (column 7) and cotton price at $15 (column 5), application of the 12th unit of fertilizer is profitable because the marginal value product of $3.00 is greater than the marginal factor cost of $2.00. With fertilizer priced at $6.25 and cotton priced at $10, application of the 7th unit of fertilizer is not profitable, because the marginal value product is less than the marginal cost of the resource.

Because costs of fixed factors are not included in the examples cited above, no statement can be made about the profitability or economy of the complete production process. It is entirely possible that application of fertilizer may be profitable to an individual farmer even though he is losing money for his farm as a complete production unit. However, where other factors are fixed or have no particular costs attached to them, decisions can be made in the vein of a single variable factor as indicated above. If the labor used to apply the fertilizer is not available as a "fixed stock of services" (for example, family labor), it also must be included in cost calculations. To the extent that labor and fertilizer (or irrigation water, seed, feed, or any other form of capital) are complementary factors (for example, if 1 hour of labor is needed for each 100 lbs. of fertilizer applied), the 2 can be "aggregated" into a single labor-fertilizer input with marginal factor costs and marginal value productivities so computed.

The principle of profit maximization also is illustrated graphically in Figure 7. The marginal value productivity of feed, with a milk price of $4.00 per cwt., is indicated as M_v. (The curve M_v is the same as curve M_{v1} in Figure 5. It appears to have a greater curvature only because the scale differs.) The line (curve) MC_1 represents the marginal cost of feed when the price is 4¢ per lb. while MC_2 represents the marginal factor cost with feed at 2¢. Equation of marginal value productivity and the marginal cost of feed is indicated by intersection of M_v with MC_1 and MC_2. With feed priced at 4¢ per lb., profits per cow (with factors other than feed costless or fixed in quantity) are maximized with a feed input of ON

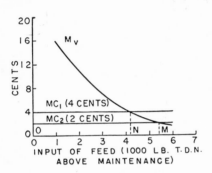

Fig. 7. Maximization of returns in feeding a dairy cow with marginal value productivity based on milk at $4 per cwt. and with feed at 2¢ and 4¢ per T.D.N. (Source: Based on physical production functions from U.S.D.A. Tech. Bul. 815).

(roughly 4,200 lbs.). Maximum profits are denoted by a feed input of OM (5,400 pounds) when feed price is 2¢ per lb. This principle is exactly the same as that indicated in the previous section, where maximum profits were defined by equating the factor/product price ratio with the marginal physical product of the factor. Here we simply assume that factor input always changes by 1 unit.[4] While technical units in the form of

---

[4] The marginal value product of a unit of factor (X) is the price of the product times the change in output of the product.

The reason why the 2 methods of specifying maximum profits are identical is apparent. Previously, we indicated that profits are maximized when the factor/product price ratio is equal to the marginal physical product of a unit of resource. With Y denoting product, X denoting factor, Δ denoting change, and P_y and P_x denoting prices of product and factor, then profit maximization is given when $P_x/P_y = \Delta Y/\Delta X$. However, the marginal value product of a unit of resource is the price of the product multiplied by the marginal output of the resource or $(P_y)(\Delta Y)$. But the equation from above can also be written $(P_y)(\Delta Y) = (P_x)(\Delta X)$ to indicate that profits are at a maximum when the marginal value product of an input is equal to the input

cows and acres have been used to illustrate profit maximization for the fixed factor, the same principles apply to a farm as an economic unit under conditions of unlimited capital.

Alternative criteria and derived demand. The production economist will note another feature of the marginal value productivity curve. Where derived or estimated for a farm or business firm (including all technical units), it becomes the basis for the demand curve for the resource in question. Further use of the marginal value productivity curve as a firm demand function for resources will be made later. Because of uncertainty and imperfect knowledge, some "discounted" concept of value productivity may more nearly serve as the final foundation of resource demand.

In comparing the analysis which has just been completed with that of the later chapter on costs, the reader will also note that maximum profits can be denoted either through (1) equation of the marginal value product of a resource with the marginal cost of the resource (the analysis above) or (2) equation of the marginal cost of product output with the marginal revenue from the product (the method employed in the cost chapter). In the first case the emphasis is on the optimum quantity of the resource to be demanded. In the second case emphasis is on the optimum quantity of product to be supplied. The two are simply different facets of the same thing; both define an identical level of resource use and output for a single producing unit.

Discontinuity Considerations

Discontinuity in resource units does not negate the marginal analysis. The application of production principles and logic is the same as in the case of continuous resource units: if lime must be applied at the rate of 400 lbs. per acre before any crop yield response is realized, and if greater rates of application do not increase the total product, only 1 of 2 extreme rates of application is profitable. Either (a) no lime, or (b) 400 pounds of lime should be applied per acre, depending on the lime/product price ratio and the marginal physical productivity of the 400-lb. unit of lime. Similarly, the marginal value product (the addition to total income possible by "jumping" tractor numbers from 1 to 2) of a second tractor on a wheat farm may be $300. If the tractor adds $350 to annual costs, the marginal value product is less than the marginal cost of tractor services, and addition of the "second" tractor input is uneconomic. The fact that the farmer cannot add one-half a tractor simplifies calculations. He does not have to

---

multiplied by the unit price of the factor. If ΔX is taken as 1 unit of factor, then $(P_x)(\Delta X) = (P_x)(1) = P_x$ which is the marginal cost per unit of resource. Thus the two equations $P_x/P_y = \Delta Y/\Delta X$ and $(P_y)(\Delta Y) = (P_x)(\Delta X)$ are the same, and with X equal to 1 they become $P_x/P_y = \Delta Y$ (the factor/product price ratio equal to the marginal product of 1 unit of X), and $(P_y)(\Delta Y) = P_x$ (the marginal value product equal to the price or marginal cost of a unit of resource).

compare an infinite number of alternatives, as in the case of continuous inputs or production functions such as characterize livestock rations. In the case of continuous factor units, each change in product price causes the strain of recomputing optimum levels of variable factor input. Not so in the case of discontinuous inputs such as bull services; if a cow has been bred once an infinite increase in product prices will not cause her to be bred again; hence the simplicity of economics and decision-making under discontinuous resource services such as characterize many so-called farm practices. The case of discontinuous inputs, a common production situation for farms, and profit maximization can also be illustrated graphically as in the case of Figure 8 below. This is the input-output relationship assumed for corn cultivations in Chapter 2. While the first cultivation adds 36 bushels to yield, the second and third add only 12 and 4, respectively. Cultivation services must be applied in units of 1; application of

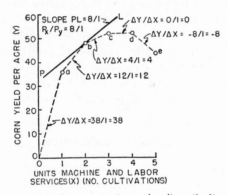

Fig. 8. Profit maximization under discontinuity.

1½ cultivations is impossible. Hence the input-output combinations indicated by the broken segments Oa, ab, bc, and cd do not exist in any attainable or meaningful sense. If the price or cost for cultivation services bears an 8/1 ratio to corn price, the second cultivation is most profitable, and it will remain so unless the cultivation/corn price ratio falls to 4/1 or less, or climbs as high as 12/1 or greater. The second cultivation is most profitable over a wide range of ratios defining corn prices and cultivation costs. With the price of corn at $2.00 per bushel, the price of cultivation services (the cost of each cultivation) would have to be higher than $24 or lower than $8 to cause any but 2 cultivations to be most profitable. While the cost ratios are not applicable, the example itself is applicable to the western Cornbelt where corn is commonly cultivated twice, to areas where cultivations are made 3 and 4 times, or to any other cropping practice which is discontinuous.

We can now see why input-output relationships of a discontinuous nature may provide behavior characteristics similar to those of a linear production function. Each segment *Oa, ab,* and *bc,* although it does not exist in a real sense, is the same as a linear production function where inputs actually are divisible. Thus, if under a discontinuous production function the slope of the price line in Figure 8 falls from 8/1 to 4/1, cultivation inputs will jump from 2 to 3; an increase in the slope of the price ratio line to 12/1 will cause input to fall back to 1. Similarly, if *ab* were a continuous-linear production function with all points between *a* and *b* indicative of an attainable output, input would be jumped from 2 to 3 any time the factor/product price ratio fell from 8/1 to less than 4/1; the entrepreneur would never stop at in-between points if he were to maximize profits.

Farmer Economists

Farmers do not always extend resource use to a point where the factor/ product price ratio and the marginal physical product of a resource unit are equal. This action cannot be taken as a clear indication, as some individuals suggest, that (a) marginality has no application in farming, (b) economic principle is not understood in rough fashion by any of the mass of farmers, (c) farmers are not rational in their use of resources, or (d) all resource inputs in agriculture are discontinuous. The reasons behind farmers' inability to equate marginal value products with the marginal cost of resources, either for technical units or for the farm as a firm, extend beyond the current factor-product relationship and include, in addition to lack of knowledge of principle, these considerations: (1) lack of knowledge of the relevant input-output relationships and cost structures (even after nearly a century of research in land-grant institutions over the nation, only a meager inventory of production functions is available); (2) the uncertainty of future prices and yields (uncertainty gives rise to discounting of future returns and, as explained in later chapters, the *ex ante* ["from before"] view and decisions of the farmer thus may be entirely rational even though the *ex poste* [historic or "from behind"] view may indicate that resource application was short of the level necessary to equate marginal costs and marginal revenue); and (3) the existence of severe capital limitations. (Often the operator simply cannot borrow or refuses to borrow, because of imperfect knowledge about the future, to an extent allowing use of resources to equate marginal quantities. It is obviously true, however, that farmers in aggregate recognize the principle of marginality in rough fashion if not by name. For convincing evidence of this, one need only examine the amount of fertilizer used, the weights at which meat animals are marketed, or the rate of feeding dairy cows as commodity price-factor cost relationship vary.)

Limited Resources and Maximization of a Physical Product

The relationships presented above can also be used to illustrate the first principles of resource allocation. By *resource allocation* we refer to the distribution of a given amount of factor between alternatives in production in a manner to maximize the relevant end of the economic unit in question. The end may be a maximum physical product from given resources during wartime or it may be maximum profits for a farm firm. The problems of allocating resources between alternative products are brought into focus in later chapters. Here we will concern ourselves with the allocation of a given stock of a resource between technical units in a manner to maximize the physical output of a single product. While it is a technical concept of efficiency, the principle illustrated also is consistent with economic efficiency in the sense that it brings about greater profit to the individual farmer and a greater product to society from given resources. The manner in which a limited quantity of a single factor should be allocated between technical units to maximize a physical product is of concern to the individual farmer at all times. Usually, farmers are faced with limited funds, and hence are able to buy or hire only a limited quantity of a specific resource or resource service such as fertilizer, land, or labor. While the process is left to the market mechanism in an enterprise economy, nations are also concerned directly with the manner in which a given stock of machinery, fertilizer, feed, or other resources should be allocated between technical units, farms, and producing regions in a period of national emergency. The problem was at the fore in the United States during World War II. Similarly, it is a continuing problem under planned agricultural economies such as that which came into existence in the United Kingdom after World War II.

An individual farmer. In illustrating the first principles of resource allocation, fertilizer and land are considered limited in the sense that a maximum quantity of either is available. It is assumed that the total stocks of each are divisible; a stock of land totaling 100 acres can be broken down into 100 units of 1 acre each, or 10,000 lbs. of fertilizer can be subdivided into 200 units of 50 lbs. each. Prices are not attached to the product, but it is simply assumed that (a) the commodity has value, and (b) all units are equal in value. In this case, any reorganization of the resources which results in a greater physical product from a given quantity of resources will result in a *greater* economic product (profit to the farmer or social product to a nation) although it need not result in the *maximum* economic product. Under the competitive conditions of a farm, an increase in the physical product from given resources will always increase gross revenue, and hence net income, because the outlay for resources is constant. This is in contrast to the situations analyzed in previous sections, where the quantity of resources was variable and net income increased along with physical product and gross revenue only if the value of the marginal product was greater than the marginal cost of the resource.

Suppose a farmer with 3 acres of potatoes has funds or can obtain credit for the purchase of 3,000 lbs. of 4-8-7 fertilizer to be applied on potatoes. Further, suppose that the production function or response curve is that shown in Table 1 of Chapter 2. If fertilizer costs $2 per cwt., while potatoes sell for $1.50 per bushel, application of at least 3,000 lbs. of fertilizer per acre would be profitable with capital unlimited. However, the farmer in question does not have the 9,000 lbs. of fertilizer for application at the rate of 3,000 lbs. per acre. Should he apply 3,000 pounds on 1 acre and none on the remaining 2 acres? Or should some other pattern be employed in allocating the 3,000 lbs. of fertilizer between acres?

A fundamental rule in resource allocation is this: irrespective of the end in question, its maximization can be attained with marginal products defined relevant to the end only if resources are allocated between alternatives in a manner corresponding to the magnitude of their marginal products. Since the end under discussion here is one of maximizing the physical product from 3 acres of land and 3,000 lbs. of fertilizer, the relevant criterion is the marginal physical productivity of fertilizer. The most efficient use of the resource has been attained when use of 1 fertilizer unit in any different manner will reduce the quantity of product (result in lower attainment of the end). The marginal figures of Table 1, Chapter 2, can be used to illustrate the application of this principle. Rather than use 3,000 lbs. on 1 acre, while 2 acres receive no fertilizer, a greater output of potatoes can be produced if each of the 3 acres is given an application of 1,000 lbs. The arithmetic is simple. The first, second, third, fourth, fifth, and sixth increments of fertilizer (in 500 lb. units) add 103, 71, 49, 34, 24, and 17 bushels to the total product when applied to a single acre. However, the marginal product of each of the first 3 (500-lb.) units of fertilizer is 103 when they are applied to 3 different acres, and the marginal product of each of the second 3 increments of fertilizer is 71 bushels when they are allocated to all rather than 1 acre. The second 100 lbs. of fertilizer adds only 71 bushels (the marginal product) to total product when used as the second increment on 1 acre but adds 103 bushels when used as the first increment on a second acre. Under the first allocative system, 3,000 lbs. of fertilizer on 1 acre and none on 2 acres, the total product from 3 acres attributable to fertilizer is 298 bushels (298 + 0 + 0). Under the second system the total product from 3 acres attributable to fertilizer amounts to 522 bushels (174 + 174 + 174). Potato output can be maximized only if each increment of resource is used where its marginal productivity is greatest.

Farmers often violate the marginal productivity system of allocating a limited variable resource between technical units. Some feed all cows the same amount of feed irrespective of differences in the marginal physical productivity of feed when fed to cows of varying capacities. Contrariwise, some farmers apply all of a given stock of fertilizer to a portion of their corn acreage while other acres go unfertilized. While some sort hogs carefully, other operators sell their hogs in mixed droves and at widely varying weights, even though feed input and productivity is not the same per hog. The farm operator could be indifferent in allocating "variable resources" between technical units only under 1 condition: if the production function or input-output curves are linear and of identical slopes, then he need not bother about calculating marginal products. The marginal product will be the same, irrespective of the number of units of resource applied to any 1 technical unit.

Where a range of the production function has an elasticity greater than 1.0, variable resources such as fertilizer or feed should be allocated between technical units in this manner: fertilizer or feed should be applied to a single acre of land or animal until the maximum average productivity of fertilizer or feed has been attained; then the second, third, and other acres or animals should be treated similarly until the limited stock of "variable" resources is exhausted. The principle outlined above parallels the discussion of rational production in a previous section. We need not know the price of the product to state the principle: a given stock of a resource should be allocated between technical units in a manner to maximize the physical product. As long as the commodity has any price whatsoever, total revenue and net profit will be increased as resources are rearranged between technical units to bring about a greater physical product; if the resource or technical units have prices attached to them, a rearrangement of the resource between technical units to allow the same product with fewer resources will allow the same revenue with a smaller cost, hence greater profits to an individual competitive farm must result.

The general concept. The arithmetic example fully illustrates the marginal productivity method of allocating resources to maximize a given end. The principle has been applied to the allocation of a single resource between alternative technical units in producing a single product but it applies equally to other cases of economic choice. General content can be given to the principle through the details which follow. The physical production functions in Figures 9 and 10 represent the output of a single product as it relates to resource input for identical technical units. The inputs may represent fertilizer applied to an acre of land or feed and labor applied to 1 head of livestock. The marginal productivity curves are identical; any 1 particular unit of the "variable" resource results in an equal addition to output when applied as the first or second input for the first or second technical unit. Since the 2 production functions are identical, their slopes are also the same for any single resource input. This fact is illustrated by the T lines which are tangent with both Y_{p_1} and Y_{p_2} at 4 units of input. From previous discussion of tangency points, it is known that 2 tangent lines with the same slope have equal rates of change and, therefore, indicate equal marginal quantities. In Figures 9 and 10, the slope of both tangent lines is at the rate of 51 units of output for 1 unit of input. Accordingly, the marginal productivity of the fourth input is the same

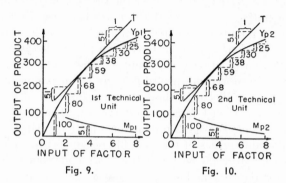

Fig. 9.   Fig. 10.

Relation between resource output and input for identical technical units.

for both technical units. (The tangent lines have a slope of $51Y/1X$ at an input of exactly 4.) Thus the marginal product of 1 unit of resource is *exactly* 51 for the fourth input. (As the small triangle below the product curve indicates, the *average* marginal product between the third and fourth input is 59 $[59Y/1X]$.)[5] We will use the *exact* measure of marginal product for the analysis which follows. If a total of 8 units of the resource is available for use on the 2 technical units, 4 inputs should be allocated to each. The product is at a maximum of 614 under this pattern of allocation, since marginal productivities of the last 2 inputs of variable resource are equal (the slopes of the total product curves are equal). Obviously, the product would be less were 7 units of the variable resource applied to the first and 1 unit of resource applied to the second technical unit. As the triangles indicate, the marginal product of the seventh unit of resource applied to 1 technical unit is only 25, while the marginal product of the first unit of resource applied to the second technical unit is 100. The total product from 8 units of resource applied to the 2 technical units would be only 497 (397 + 100) under this pattern of allocation.

The basis of product maximization from given resources can be illustrated also by means of Figure 11. Here the production function for the second technical unit is turned counter-clockwise and superimposed over the production function for the first technical unit. Inputs of resources and

---

[5] The small triangles below the product curve indicate *average* marginal products *between* units of input while the small triangle on the tangent line represents the *exact* marginal product *at* a single input. Thus the average product of 100 for the first "whole" input better defines the marginal product of the .5 unit of input than the 1.0 unit of input if the "variable" resource is divisible.

outputs of product are read from the input-output curve in the conventional manner. However, the inputs for the second production function read from right to left across the top axis, while output is read from top to bottom on the right-hand axis. In superimposing the second graph, its zero axis has been placed directly over the first graph at 8 units of input, the given amount which is available for use between the two technical units. (Had only 6 units of resource been available, the zero input for the second production function would have been placed directly over "6" on the first production function.) The graph for the second production function has then been moved downward in a perpendicular fashion (keeping the y and x axes parallel with the latter at a distance of 8 input units) until the curve Y_{p_2} is just tangent to curve Y_{p_1}. The point of tangency indicates equal slopes for the 2 production functions and, therefore, that the marginal productivities of the variable resources are equal at 4 units (reading from left to right on the bottom axis and from right to left on the top axis for the first and second technical units respectively) of resource for each technical unit. With 4 inputs allocated to each technical unit, the total product is 614 (307 + 307). The marginal physical product (as indicated in Figures 9 and 10) is 59 at the fourth input for each technical unit. The total product from 2 technical units and 8 inputs of resource is thus a maximum.

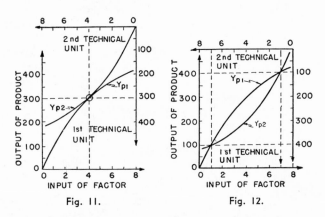

Fig. 11.   Fig. 12.

Allocation of resource inputs between producing units.

Figure 12 provides graphic illustration of inefficient use of resources for 2 producing units when marginal productivities are not equated. As was shown previously by arithmetic, when 7 units of variable resource are applied to the first technical unit and 1 is applied to the second technical unit, the total product forthcoming is only 497 (100 as read from top to bottom on the right axis for the second technical unit, and 397 as read from bottom to top on the left axis for the first technical unit). Comparisons of the marginal curves for the same 2 production functions (see Figures 9 and 10) indicate marginal productivities of 25 for the seventh input on the first technical unit and 100 for the first input on the second technical unit. Therefore, the total product cannot be at a maximum for the pattern of resource allocation indicated in Figure 12.

Allocation between technical units with different production functions. Commonly, the production function differs between technical units on a given farm. A single field may include several types of soil and yield responses will differ greatly for resources applied on the different soils: A few acres may lay in a bottom where the level of nitrogen and organic matter is maintained by erosion from hilly acres in the same field. Variability also is to be found in single herds of livestock. Rarely do all animals in a herd respond equally to inputs of labor, feed, or other forms of capital. Even greater variability exists between farms and between geographic regions for input of capital in crop production. Thus both a farmer and nation are faced with the same question, "How should a limited quantity of a variable resource be allocated between technical units when their production functions differ?" We shall first discuss the problem from the standpoint of an individual farmer.

The principle of allocation is the same for production functions which differ between technical units, plants, or regions as for identical ones. This point can be illustrated with production functions for two producing units

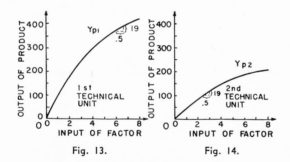

Fig. 13.   Fig. 14.

Production functions which differ between producing units.

such as those shown in Figures 13 and 14. The marginal physical productivity of a resource unit applied to the second technical unit is much lower than would be the case if the parallel unit of resource were applied to the first technical unit. Evidence is given in the greater slope of Y_{p_1} as compared to Y_{p_2}. If the total product is to be maximized, not all units of the variable resource should be allocated to the first technical unit, however. The marginal productivity of the eighth unit of resource applied to the first technical unit is less than the first unit of resource allocated to the second technical unit. Figure 15, which represents Figure 14 superimposed over Figure 13 indicates, since Y_{p1} and Y_{p2} are tangent at this point, that marginal products of mobile or variable resource inputs are equal when ON (5.6) units are applied to the first technical unit while O'M (2.4) units are applied to the second technical unit. No other pattern of resource allocation will result in a physical output of the single product as great as that indicated. The total output of O'R plus OQ (or 90 + 368) represents a greater value from given resources than would be possible under any other pattern of resource allocation.

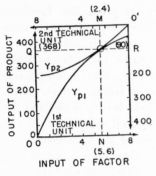

Fig. 15. Equating productivity between producing units.

Maximizing value productivity. The conditions under which the total value of product is maximized from a given stock of resource and limited technical units are the same as those for a physical product. In fact, a pattern of allocation which maximizes the physical product from given resources will also result in a maximum value of product from given resources when a single product is being produced on an individual farm and where all units of product sell at the same price. The pattern of allocation which maximizes the physical product does not always maximize the value product between 2 distant regions where prices differ, however. This point is discussed in more detail in the chapter on location.

Equal marginal products are always denoted by tangency of 2 total product curves whether these are in physical or value terms. The transition can be illustrated by returning to Figures 9 and 10, where we now might suppose that physical inputs are measured on the horizontal axis while the value of product (each unit of output priced at $1) is measured on the vertical axis. The value production function thus has the same slope as its physical counterpart. (This statement applies to a competitive firm or to technical units within a monopolistic firm where the total volume of product concerned is not great enough to alter the market price for the commodity.) Accordingly, Figure 11 indicates how resources can be allocated between technical units to maximize the total value of product from given resources; Figure 12 illustrates a pattern of resource allocation when this end is not attained.

Interfarm allocation and agricultural productivity. The general production economics principle of allocating limited resources has been applied to a single product forthcoming from technical units. The principle has universal application when related to economic problems of any magnitude whether these be at the farm or national level; with slight modifications it can be applied between enterprises within a farm, between farms, between farming regions, and between industries.[6] Its use is the same whether the quantity to be maximized is a physical product, farm profit, national value of agricultural products, or any measure of product or income. Use of this production-economics' principle in a quantitative manner is easiest when applied to problems of the nature discussed above. Although the logic is equally applicable and useful when applied to industry and national problems, empirical application is extremely difficult and impossible in some cases because of a lack of quantitative data.

When the allocative principle illustrated above is applied between farms, it is obviously true that the total product from agricultural resources now in use is not being maximized. This statement applies not only between regions, as will be pointed out later, but also between neighboring farms at a given location: farmers with ample funds apply fertilizer at rates which cause marginal returns to approximate marginal costs, while their neighbors across the road apply none. Some farms apply large amounts of labor and capital in the form of livestock per 100 acres of land, while others in the same locality have very little of either to apply to the same land acreage. Another great difference is in the management input applied to a fixed collection of other resources. The reasons for these differences will be discussed later. The implications of this pattern of resource allocation are obvious. Two farmers acting independently of all other farmers, with such wide differences in resource use as are illustrated in Figure 12, could always combine their limited stocks of labor, capital, land, and management to produce a greater physical and value product as well as a greater dollar profit. After a rearrangement of this sort, both could be made "better off" dollarwise than previously, although the freedom of either in choice and decision-making might be restricted.

In the same vein, a readjustment of resources between all farms in the industry would give the consuming society more product with the same resources or the same product with fewer resources. In the latter case, resources could be freed for other lines of production where alternatives exist. An adjustment of this nature between all farms would not, however, leave all farmers "better off" as compared to before the inter-farm rearrangement of resources. (These points will be discussed in detail in later chapters). The low price elasticity of demand for farm products precludes aggregative adjustments of the industry which make all farmers better off through an extension of total output. Even if the majority of farmers did readjust their resources in the optimum interfarm manner with the

---

[6] While the first principle of allocating units of a given stock of resource has been illustrated geometrically for 2 producing units, the same graphic illustration could be applied to all pairs of producing units and the principle is equally applicable and is not violated. It can, of course, be applied simultaneously in an algebraic manner to any number of producing units.

effect of increasing output and lessening total revenue, any single pair of operators could still have greater profit by an interfarm organization of resources such as that indicated by Figure 11 than by that indicated in Figure 12.

National Production Policies

Application of this principle of production, explaining how a given stock of a resource should be allocated between different technical units in producing a single product, is especially pertinent at a national level during wartime. Under conditions of food emergency, emphasis is on the maximization of physical product from a given number of technical units with limited variable resources. The problem exists and the principle tends, albeit roughly, to work out automatically on a value basis through the pricing mechanism of a peacetime economy. The latter aspect is brought into focus in a later chapter. Here we concern ourselves with emergency management of farm resources. A nation faced with an emergency finds itself in a position where resources such as fertilizer, feed, machinery, or labor, otherwise freely available to the agricultural industry except for limits established by market institutions, are severely restricted because materials must be channeled to defense or similar needs. Two important problems then exist: (1) What quantity of a variable resource should be used for a single product? (2) Once established, how should the limited quantity of resource be allocated between technical units? The technical units now are scattered over different farms and different producing regions. The first problem is one of allocating resources between alternative commodities and is discussed in a later chapter. The principle of production economics applied in defining the optimum allocation of resources between different technical units within a farm also applies to specifying the optimum pattern of allocation between technical units of different farms and different regions. There are not, as some production economists suppose, different sets of principles which apply in the 2 cases. The agricultural production economist is equally an expert in national and farm management of agricultural resources. Both areas of resource administration require knowledge and use of identical principles and the same subject matter and technical data.

Technical units limited. At the outset of an emergency or other national planning period, the number of technical units is given (a) for a short time into the future for livestock products and (b) for all time in the case of all crop products (if land is fully in cultivation). Although quantities are given at the outset of the planning period, the number of hogs, dairy cows, feeder cattle, or range sheep can be increased as new breeding or production periods come into being. The number of acres of crop land is essentially fixed (either in the existing or potential supply) and has to be considered in this context over the complete planning period. Thus the problem of how feed should be allocated between an existing number of hogs, feeder cattle, or other class of livestock at the outset of the planning period is the same as the problem of how fertilizer should be allocated between the given acres of land in each period.

During 1942, the first full crop year of World War II for the United States, 9,949 thousand tons of fertilizer were used. Under what conditions would this quantity of fertilizer have allowed a maximum total food output? The answer to this question was given in the principle illustrating fertilizer allocation between different acres. (See the analysis of Figures 9 and 15.) Certainly the quantities of fertilizer actually used during the war period on any single crop were not allocated in a manner to maximize the total output of the crop from the number of acres and quantity of fertilizer devoted to it. Farmers were free to use fertilizer in the manner which they deemed most efficient, providing they could obtain it. The greatest number of farmers using fertilizer probably allocated it within their farm in a manner to roughly maximize the product from the limited quantity available. While the intra-farm allocation of fertilizer perhaps approximated an optimum where the resource was available, not all farmers who wished to use fertilizer were able to obtain it; it was not available for many farms where yield response, because of previous conditions of leasing arrangements, capital limitations and lack of knowledge, would have been very great. The interfarm and interregion allocation of fertilizer was not consistent with a maximum product from a given resource stock. (The system of resource allocation followed would have been consistent with a maximum physical product from given resources only under linear and identical production functions for all farms. Obviously this is not and was not the case.) In essence, the system of allocation, arbitrary use, and rates of application depending on the availability of materials and knowledge of fertilizer potentialities resulted in a pattern of resource use which can be illustrated by Figures 13 and 14. Farmers on heavily-cropped land or operating under similar situations who did not use fertilizer actually had high response curves such as Y_{p_1} while other who did use fertilizer were faced with a lower fertilizer productivity such as denoted by Y_{p_2}. Given 6 farms, 3 of which had production functions Y_{p_1} and 3 of which had Y_{p2} and a total of 24 units of fertilizer, the product would not have been at a maximum with (a) 3 separate farms with production function Y_{p1} using 6, 2, and zero units of fertilizer, and (b) 3 separate farms with production functions Y_{p_2} using 7, 1, and zero units. The 24 units of fertilizer would allow a maximum output of the product in question only if each of the farms with curve Y_{p_1} used 5.6 units of fertilizer, while each of the 3 with Y_{p2} used 2.4 units (Figure 15).

Allocative controls, such as those applied in Great Britain, were not employed in the United States but represent a mechanism whereby limited resources can be distributed to maximize the relevant product. Perhaps the

United States was not in a burdened state of emergency such that it was willing to implement production or resource efficiency (in the sense being discussed) in preference to other intermediate ends such as freedom of action and decision. Reconciliation of competing ends such as these is the warp and woof of economic choice and resource use, irrespective of the time and social environment. Perhaps a proper balance was struck between these wartime conflicting goals. In order to bring about resource allocation consistent with production efficiency during emergency, some scheme of resource rationing other than that provided in free factor and product markets must be used. While physical rationing, if it recognizes differences in resource productivity can be used as one means to this end, it is not the sole mechanism. Administered prices for factors and products can also be used. If the national managers of farm resources decided that fertilizer could be used for corn up to the point where 1 unit of fertilizer adds 10 bushels to total corn production, the economics of the firm or the principle of profit maximization outlined previously (product/factor price ratio equals marginal physical product of factor) could be used as the basis of pricing. Since the necessary condition for maximum profit is given by the formula $P_x/P_y = \Delta Y/\Delta X$ and the "permissible" marginal product $(\Delta Y/\Delta X)$ has been set at 10/1 by the national farm managers, the equation becomes $P_x/P_y = 10/1$. The price to be established for fertilizer (P_x) is then $10 and the price (P_y) to be established for corn is $1 in order that the ratio is $10/1. If corn is already priced at $2, the relevant price for fertilizer is $20. This system supposes that farmers have the capital for and do follow maximizing principles. Since neither is universally true, the pricing method must always be accompanied by effective education. Even then physical rationing schemes may be necessary if production problems are extremely urgent.

Livestock problems. Problems of feed allocation, with animal numbers given, parallel those for fertilizer or other crop supplies. Yet more alternatives exist, and the problem is more complex because meat animals represent not a single product such as pork or beef but joint products such as fat cuts, protein cuts, and hide. Increasing feed productivity exists when dressed products are under consideration; a war economy is interested mainly in the food components of animals rather than in live weight. Still, the basic problem is the same: "What level of feed should be applied per animal where the amount of feed and the number of each type of animal is limited?" We are still concerned with feed allocation between technical units producing 1 product. Problems of allocation between products will be discussed in a later chapter. Since increasing feed productivity does not exist beyond maintenance rations for dairy cows, the limited feed supplies earmarked for milk production should be allocated between cows of the same and different farms in accordance with marginal response of milk output to feed input. It is not a sufficient condition, as was assumed the case in Great Britain and some European wartime economies, that each cow be allotted an equal amount of feed where cow capacities differ between farms; milk output per cow is a better criterion than numbers of cows alone in establishing the quantity of feed which should be made available to each milk-producing farm.

Feed allocation in meat production must relate to particular products. In the early months of World War I, fats were in particularly short supply, while the aggregate supply of food seemed ample at the time. Later, the total food shortage was more pressing. With reference to hogs in the early period, a production function relating lard to feed input was a relevant basis for allocating grain between hogs and farms. Output of edible pork and lard was important in the later period. Since some form of edible pork rather than live weight of animals is in such instances the relevant measure of product, allocative schemes must recognize production functions with elasticities greater than 1.0: with edible products as the criterion, hogs should not be fed less feed than the amount which results in a maximum average output of edible pork per pound of feed. In terms of the input-output relationships of Chapter 3, this would require a total feed input of 1,546 lbs. and a marketing or live weight of 320.3 lbs. An extreme possibility is that drought or other forces might cause the number of hogs to be so great relative to the amount of feed available that feed input per head would not allow maximum average productivity of feed. Rather than feed the given number of hogs a quantity falling within the range of increasing feed efficiency, a greater pork output could be attained from the limited feed supply, however, by slaughtering some of the hogs for immediate use with the remainder fed to a weight denoting a maximum pork product per unit of feed. If the supply of feed for hogs within the particular year is great enough, the problem is one of feeding beyond maximum average feed returns and of allocating concentrates between hogs and between farms in a manner to equate their marginal physical productivity in pork production. A maximum pork product cannot be attained from given feed stocks if farmers who have ample feed and capital market 300-lb. hogs, while operators with limited resources market 190-lb. hogs. Similar considerations apply to cattle, sheep, or poultry. As Figure 10 of Chapter 3 suggests, the minimum feed inputs for 2-year-olds, yearlings, and calves, if they are to be fed, should approximate 967, 2,144, and 3,666 lbs. per animal respectively if a maximum output of calories is to be forthcoming from an established quantity of feed. If feed is available for each class of livestock in quantities great enough to extend output per animal beyond the maximum average product, it should be allocated between classes of feeders in a manner consistent with the marginal productivity of feed. Generally, a greater amount of grain per head should go to calves because the marginal product does not decline so rapidly.

When the planning period extends beyond one production year, the number of animal units can be changed. Animal units then become the "variable" factor while feed stocks represent the fixed factor if labor and other resources which go into animal production are not the limiting resources. The number of animal units then should always be extended to a point where feeding rates allow a maximum average product for feed (but never a maximum marginal feed product where elasticities greater than 1.0 exist). If food stocks allow flexibility between production periods, animals should not be fed beyond the level of maximum average productivity even in the first period of the emergency. Stocks of grain beyond this level should be carried into a second production period with animal numbers fitted to the supply of feeds to maximize the average product of a unit of feed. The total output of livestock product from given feed stocks can then be at a maximum in the 2 periods.

Other allocative problems in planned agricultural economies. Feed and fertilizer have been used to indicate the application, during a national emergency, of the simple allocative principle which relates a single product to a single resource. This production principle applies similarly to other categories of resources. The important calculus always revolves, of course, around the resource the stock of which is most severely limited. During the early stages of World War II some production economists suggested that credit and capital in its various forms should be extended to small farms where labor was "underemployed." Others argued that small farms with a low level of output were not necessarily the farms which should be extended additional resources. While these viewpoints can be in conflict, they need not conflict when the basic principles of production or resource allocation are applied. While questions of whether small farms should be consolidated and part of the labor force transferred to defense or other critical industries can be posed, the logic is otherwise the same as that applied above to animals and acres. Where resources are so short on small farms that a stage of increasing productivity reigns, these farms should certainly be given greater resources if the product is to be maximized from given resources and if small farms are to remain in production. Decreasing returns may exist on small farms as well as large farms. For all farms with similar production functions, the effect of management on productivity of other resources considered, those farms with few resources should receive additional inputs prior to farms which already employ large amounts of resources. The logic can be illustrated by letting Figure 9 represent the situation for the small farm using only 2 units of the resource and Figure 10 represent a large farm using 6 units. An additional unit of resource, if it is to make the greatest contribution to total production, should be allocated to the small farm. The marginal product of a third unit here is 68; the marginal product of an additional unit, the seventh, is only 25 on the large farm.

However, if production functions differ between farms because of inherent limitations of management, soil, or any other factor, use of additional resources on small farms is not a necessary condition for product maximization. Suppose that Figure 13 represents the production function for a farm using 5 units of resource, while Figure 14 represents a farm using 2.5 units of resource. If an additional ½ unit of resource is rationed to the latter producing unit, the marginal product is only 19. The same ½ unit used on the farm already employing 5 units of resource would add a product of 38 to total output. Even though labor is fixed (family labor) and "underemployed" on small farms, added resources in the form of fertilizer, feed, livestock, or machines need not be directed to these units. If marginal productivity is to serve as the criterion, part of labor resources on small farms might well be transferred to large farms where labor and capital productivity differ in the manner suggested in Figures 13 and 14. Where resource productivity is low on small farms because of the small fixed input of management, the production function might be "raised" by aiding management through educational activities. Management or advisory boards, established in Great Britain during the war and still in existence, aided individual farmers in managing their resources. In fact, the inefficient manager was evicted from his farm if he did not avail himself of the added management resources in a manner to "raise the production function." Even in the postwar period, the system was still employed, although the regulations were not severely applied.

Use of Allocative Principles

The concept of a single factor production function or input-output relationship has been used, both in strict and relaxed form, to set forth the first principles of resource allocation. These are basically the same principles involved in later chapters dealing with value productivity and the interfarm, interarea and interindustry allocation of resources. The highly technical conditions outlined above must hold true if the conditions of economic efficiency outlined in later chapters are to exist. Not all agricultural economists recognize this point and, consequently, some search for a uniquely mystic set of production principles to explain the later phenomena. Contrariwise, others try to outline the technical conditions of efficiency in an equally incomplete and partial analysis. The result is this: some economists cannot see the forest because of the trees and others cannot see the trees because of the forest.

We now turn to the subject of the next chapter which involves not only the transformation of resources into products but also the substitution of one resource for another. The discussion to this point has involved the relationship known in production economics as the factor-product relationship. The discussion which follows revolves around the factor-factor relationship, as it is termed in production economics.

Selected References

Allen, R. G. D., *Mathematics for Economists*. London: Macmillan, 1942, pp. 152-153, 190-191.

Atkinson, J. W., and Klein, R., *Feed Consumption and Market Weight of Hogs*. U.S.D.A. Tech. Bul. 200.

Black, J. D., *et al.*, *Farm Management*. New York: Macmillan, 1947, Chs. 17, 18.

Black, J. D., *Production Economics*. New York: Henry Holt, 1926, Ch. 12.

Boulding, K. E., *Economic Analysis*. New York: Harper, 1948, Ch. 22.

Forster, G. W., *Farm Organization and Management*. New York: Prentice-Hall, 1946, Ch. 5.

Hicks, J. R., *Value and Capital*. Oxford: Clarendon Press, 1939, Ch. 7.

Holmes, C. M., *Farm Organization*. New York: Heath, 1928, Chs. 8, 12, 13.

Hopkins, J. A., *Elements of Farm Management*. New York: Prentice-Hall, 1939, Ch. 8.

Jensen, E., *et al.*, *Input as Related to Output in Milk Production*. U.S.D.A. Tech. Bul. 815, Washington, 1942.

Myint, Hla, *Theories of Welfare Economics*. Cambridge: Harvard University Press, 1948, Ch. 7.

Reder, M. W., *Studies in the Theory of Welfare Economics*. New York: Columbia University Press, 1947, pp. 25-30.

Samuelson, P. A., *Foundations of Economic Analysis*. Cambridge: Harvard University Press, Ch. 4.

Stigler, G., *Theory of Price*. New York: Macmillan, 1947, Ch. 8.

Tolley, H. R., Black, J. D., and Ezekiel, M. K., *Input as Related to Output in Farm Organization Studies*. U.S.D.A. Bul. 1277, Washington, 1924.

Weintraub, S., *Price Theory*. New York: Pitman, 1949, pp. 86-102.

5

Resource Substitution and Factor Relationships

Discussion in the 3 previous chapters centered around the factor-product relationship. Initial concern was with an input of a single resource and output of a single product or, in the case of continuous relationships between factors and products, a production function of the nature $Y = f(X_1|X_2, X_3, X_4, X_5 \ldots X_n)$ where the input of all resources except X_1 was fixed. This rigid input-output relationship was relaxed to allow resources which serve as direct complements with X_1 to vary in proportion to this particular factor in the same sense that water is composed of hydrogen and oxygen but is considered as a single production element. The effect of the number of variable resources on the elasticity of production was also examined. Finally, a production function of the nature $Y = f(X_1, X_2|X_3, X_4, X_5 \ldots X_n)$ was examined, wherein an upper limit existed for the stock of X_1 and X_2, but both were variable and divisible. This production situation was of great use in explaining how a maximum product might be attained from a given stock of 2 resources. Still, the central concern of foregoing chapters was the transformation of a single factor into a single product, and, for all practical purposes, the relevant short-run production function was of the nature $Y = f(X_1)$, where Y refers to the output of product, X_1 refers to the input of variable resources, and all other resources are fixed. We now turn to a production function in the manner of $Y = f(X_1, X_2|X_3, X_4, X_5 \ldots X_n)$, where never less than 2 factors are variable. For estimational purposes this production function can be considered as $Y = f(X_1, X_2)$. In contrast to previous chapters, we are not especially concerned with holding X_1 and X_2 in constant proportions as output is varied. We are equally interested in non-proportional changes in X_1 and X_2. Changes in product Y are examined as either or both factors are varied. Our particular concern now is with the possibilities of substituting X_1 for X_2 as Y is held constant at some particular level.

Factor-factor problems. Factor-factor or resource substitution relationships can be analyzed for producing units of any magnitude; fixed factors (the resources on the right-hand as compared to the left-hand side of the bar in the equations above) can vary in magnitude as well as number. An animal can be taken as a technical unit, while building services and other resources also are fixed and only two feeds, protein and carbohydrates or forage and grain, are variable. Or an acre of land as a technical unit can be fixed, while fertilizer and seed can serve as substitutes for each other. Or substitution of labor and machine capital can be extended across all animals or acres of a farm which is fixed in terms of acres and other resources. Finally, factor-factor relationships similarly apply to the agriculture of a region or the whole of the agricultural industry. In this chapter we are not concerned with production situations where all resources on a farm are variable and aggregate input is related to output as a problem of returns to scale. This chapter is directed mainly at determining the combination of 2 resources which is economic for production of a given output. The question is not distinct and separable, of course, from that of previous chapters, since (1) the economic level of output from a combination of fixed factors depends on the manner in which variable resources are combined, and (2) the optimum combination of resources may well depend on the level of output. Profit maximization actually involves determination of the least-cost combination of variable resources for each possible output, the subject of this and the next chapter, and then of extending output for the fixed producing unit, as long as the value of the marginal product is greater than the combined costs of the variable resources. In the first case the direct objective is one of minimizing costs, while in the second case minimum costs are of no particular concern; profit can increase as marginal cost increases but is not greater than the value of the marginal product. Farmers look upon problems in factor-factor relationships as those of farm practices; machine production is looked upon as a "practice" different from hand production; production of beef from hay is considered a different method than production of beef from grain.

The problem under consideration embraces a wide and varied range of questions in resource use, such as the installation of a hook in the dairy barn to substitute for labor, the use of capital in the specific form of more efficient buildings as a substitute for feed in producing a given amount of livestock, and the substitution of capital in the form of a hay baler or cotton picker for labor. It also includes aspects of animal nutrition which involve feed substitution and such broad substitution problems as the cultivation of more acres (extensive cultivation) with a given amount of labor and capital or the production of the same output on a smaller acreage (intensive cultivation) with more labor and capital. Finally, it concerns the substitution of capital in aggregate for labor in the agricultural industry. These many and varied problems can be analyzed in the framework of the factor-factor relationship. They belong to a "common family" of economic problems.

Obviously, few production processes involve only 2 specific variable factors. Substitution of a tractor for labor requires addition of tractor fuel and grease. Except where one of the resources serves as a limitation factor with a fixed coefficient (bears a direct and constant relationship to the product and is not affected by the combination of other resources) the fuel or grease often can be looked upon, along with the tractor, as individual components of a single aggregate set of machine services, however. While production ordinarily involves more than 2 variable resources, simple geometry or 2-dimensional presentation cannot be used to illustrate the substitution relationships for 3 or more factors of production. This limitation is not as great as it might appear, however. The relationships outlined on the following pages apply equally and in the same manner regardless of the number of variables. Furthermore, while substitutions between 2 factors often require 1 or more additional factors, the substitution of hay for grain or horse equipment for tractor equipment may also involve the use of more or less labor; the third factor does not always relate to decision-making since it may be (a) available in large (but divisible) stocks and would otherwise go unused, (b) is free, or (c) otherwise has no direct costs attached.

That resources can be and are substituted for each other in the agricultural production process is a well-known fact. Some farmers produce choice beef on a little corn and much pasture while others use more grain and a small amount of forage. Milk is produced entirely by hand methods, or with milking machines and other capital along with less labor. Some pork producers use large amounts of protein and small amounts of corn while others use mainly corn or even garbage. Cotton is produced by mule and man power along with a few primitive tools, or with a small amount of labor and costly equipment in the form of cotton pickers and other machinery. With this recognition of the many ways in which a given farm commodity can be produced we turn to fundamental relationships and will return later to the problems of agriculture.

The Production Function

A production function involving 2 variable factors cannot be illustrated by means of a 1-way table such as Table 1 in Chapter 2 or a single graph such as Figure 1 in Chapter 3. If it is to be presented in table form, it must be in the vein of a 2-way table such as the one below. Daily input of corn is indicated in the left-hand column while daily hay intake is indicated in the top row. The figure corresponding to each individual input of grain or hay is the daily gain or output per steer. These figures show that when the steer is taken as a fixed factor along with other resources, the 2 variable factors, grain and hay, can be juggled in numerous ways to increase output. Three distinct types of adjustments in factors can now be pointed out: (1) both resources can be increased in the same propor-

Table I.

Daily Gains Per Head from Feeding Various Combinations of Corn and Alfalfa Hay to Steers of 847 lbs. Initial Weight for 138 Days *

Corn input per head per day (lbs.)	Hay input per head (lbs. per day)			
	8	12	16	20
(1)	(2)	(3)	(4)	(5)
10	1.61	1.81	1.98	2.13
15	1.96	2.16	2.33	2.48
20	2.27	2.47	2.64	2.79
25	2.41	2.61	2.78	

* Source: Adapted from H. R. Tolley, J. D. Black, and M. K. Ezekiel, *Input as Related to Output in Farm Management Studies.* U.S.D.A. Tech. Bul. 1277, p. 25.

tion, an increase from a daily ration of 10 lbs. of grain and 8 of hay to 20 of grain and 16 of hay changes daily gain from 1.61 to 2.64; (2) one feed can be held constant while the other is increased, with daily hay intake held constant at 8 lbs. as a fixed resource, the marginal product of grain declines; and (3) output can be held constant while 1 feed resource is increased and the other is decreased in quantity, a daily gain of approximately 2.3 lbs. of beef is possible when hay and grain are fed in either the proportion 16 lbs. of hay and 15 lbs. of grain, or the proportion 8 lbs. of hay and 20 lbs. of grain. Thus the full implications of a multi-variable production function are illustrated in the data of Table 1. A point from preceding chapters should be emphasized: a different grain-beef input-output relationship exists for each level at which hay is held constant. Or contrariwise, a different hay-beef production function exists for each level at which grain is held constant. Any one of the rows or columns in Table 1 represents a single-factor production function of the nature discussed in Chapters 2 and 3. The productivity of the feeds taken together or alone also would differ if any other resource going into beef production were varied. The production function illustrated in Table 1 is of the form $B = f(G, H | W, T, X_1 \ldots X_n)$ where B, the output of beef, is a function of or changes with input of grain and hay, while W, the original weight of the steer, is held fixed, as is T or time. Although the original weight of the steers is the same in the table, the weight of a steer at the start of the feeding period also can be varied as can time or the length of the feeding period.

Although our concern in this chapter is in all 3 of the types of adjustment mentioned above, we are interested mainly in the third or the factor-factor relationship. The question in farm efficiency which springs from it is this: What is the optimum or low-cost manner of combining 2 or more resources in producing a given or fixed amount of output? Minimum costs in this sense, aside from time and uncertainty considerations, also contribute to maximum profits; because a given number of units of output has a constant value, any reshuffling of resources to reduce costs will increase profits. The interest of society is similar except that the index of measurement is not always profit.

Other examples. Similarly, Figures 1 and 2 contain data indicating the nature of 2-factor production functions. For these purely illustrative data the inputs read from the lower left-hand corner: In Figure 1, increases in input of resource X_1 are measured from bottom to top along the y axis, while inputs for resource X_2 are read from left to right of the x axis. Each box of the table includes the output which corresponds to the X_1 and X_2 inputs indicated on the axes. If we start from a zero output and add 1 unit of each factor, 12 units of product are forthcoming. If the resources are held in constant proportions and input is increased to 2 each, total output becomes 20; diminishing marginal productivity is indicated for both resources taken together. Three units of each factor result in an output of 24 and 4 units of each factor pull total output down to 23; diminish-

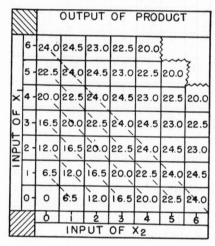

Fig. 1. Input-output relationship with two variables.

ing total returns and a negative marginal product also exist. Any diagonal movement in a northeast direction (towards the upper right-hand corner) similarly results in diminishing productivity of the 2 factors. Output is 6.5 for an original combination of a zero input of X_1 and a 1-unit input of X_2. Output becomes 16.5 when inputs are increased to 1 of X_1 and 2 of X_2. Addition of still 1 more unit of each factor pushes output to 22.5. Adjustments of this nature fairly well characterize the cattle-feeding process illustrated in Table 1. Cattle ordinarily are produced on forage up to some initial grain-feeding weight (just as the initial input included 1 unit of X_2 and 6.5 units of output in Figure 1), after which both grain and forage are fed in some combination ration. The data of Chapter 3 indicated different feed productivities, depending on the previous intake of feed and hence on the initial live weight of the cattle. Figure 1 illustrates a similar phenomenon. If the original X_2 input is 2 rather than 1 and the X_1 input is zero, the output is 12; addition of 1 unit of each factor adds 8 to total output, as compared to 10 in the previous case. These adjustments are of the factor-product type, since the relationship is one of output as compared to input when more than 1 factor is varied.

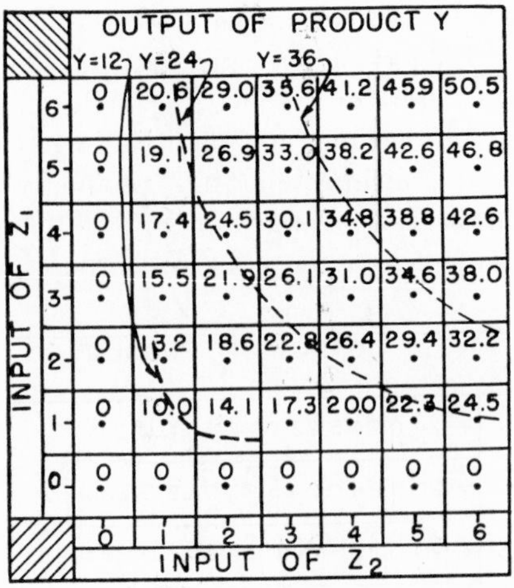

		OUTPUT OF PRODUCT Y						
		Y=12	Y=24		Y=36			
INPUT OF Z₁	6	0	20.6	29.0	35.6	41.2	45.9	50.5
	5	0	19.1	26.9	33.0	38.2	42.6	46.8
	4	0	17.4	24.5	30.1	34.8	38.8	42.6
	3	0	15.5	21.9	26.1	31.0	34.6	38.0
	2	0	13.2	18.6	22.8	26.4	29.4	32.2
	1	0	10.0	14.1	17.3	20.0	22.3	24.5
	0	0	0	0	0	0	0	0
		0	1	2	3	4	5	6
				INPUT OF Z₂				

Fig. 2. Input-output and resource substitution.

The single-factor production function is illustrated in Figure 1, when either X_1 or X_2 is held constant and the other is varied. With input of X_2 held fixed at 3, additional inputs of X_1 increase total product at a diminishing rate until a maximum output of 22.5 has been attained. A diagonal movement in the northwest or southeast direction of the table in Figure 2 illustrates the factor-factor relationship. Output can be held constant while input of X_1 is decreased and X_2 is increased or vice versa; 20 units of product can be produced even when resource combinations are changed from 4 of X_1 and none of X_2 to 3 of X_1 and 1 of X_2.

The data of Figure 2 represent a production function entirely different from that illustrated in Figure 1. The axes indicate the input of 2 variable factors Z_1 and Z_2, while the boxes show the corresponding outputs of a product Y. An increase in input with resources Z_1 and Z_2 held in constant proportion results in a diminishing marginal product. Diminishing marginal productivity also holds true as 1 factor is held constant and the other is increased. Figure 2 differs from Figure 1, however, in 2 ways: (1) No amount of Z_1 will result in a product unless a minimum of 1 unit of Z_2 is present. This is the case of crop production, where Z_1 represents fertilizer and Z_2 represents seeds. Factor Z_2 serves in a *limitational* capacity, since some minimum quantity must be present if production is to take place.

(2) Factors Z_1 and Z_2 do not replace each other at a constant rate but at a diminishing rate. The 3 dotted lines now indicate a constant product. Reading from bottom to top, they show outputs of 12, 24, and 36. Accordingly, the factor-factor or resource substitution relationship forms a curve rather than a straight line through the boxes. This point will be explained further in a later section.

Production surfaces and forms of relationship. Production functions such as the one presented in Figure 2 or Table 1 can no longer be presented geometrically as a single input-output curve when both factors are variable. Instead, if they are to be presented in geometric form, they must appear as a production surface such as the one illustrated in Figure 3.[1] If the surface of Figure 3 is taken to represent a production function such as the one presented in Figure 2 or Table 1, it is apparent that output can be increased

(a movement "up and over" the surface) by increasing both Z_1 and Z_2. We can also "move up" the surface (increase output) by holding Z_2 constant at 1 level and increasing Z_1, or by holding Z_1 constant while input of Z_2 is increased. Finally, we can retain output at a constant level or height on the surface and move "around" from Z_1 to Z_2 or from Z_2 to Z_1. By moving around the contour at a level indicating 24 units of Y the

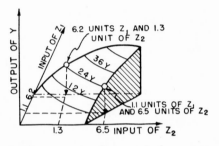

Fig. 3. Production surface relating output of product to input of factors Z_1 and Z_2.

extreme combinations of Figure 2 can be attained. Movement around the contour to the left results in the combination of 6.2 units of X_1 and 1.3 units of X_2. Movement towards the right on the contour leads to 1.1 units of Z_1 and 6.5 units of Z_2. Similarly, output can be held constant at a contour level of 36 units of Y, while the direction of movement is from one toward the other factor axis. The movement around a contour of given height (a constant output) represents the factor-factor relationship. Movement up one ridge of the surface (one of the factors held constant) represent the factor-product relationship. Any number of horizontal slices (the factor-factor relationship) can be made through the surface (slices parallel to the Z_1Z_2 plane) thus representing an output held constant at different levels. Similarly, any number of vertical slices (the factor-product relationship) can be made across the top of the surface indicating one

---

[1] A surface of the nature indicated might be pictured mentally or visually as follows: First, cut a solid rubber ball into 2 halves. Second, place 1 of the halves on its flat surface and cut it (over the top) into 4 quarters. As each one of these quarters sets upright, it symbolizes a physical production surface. The height of the surface represents the output of product while the input of each factor is represented by the horizontal axes. It is not necessary to present the production as a wedge. We do so only to ease presentation.

factor constant while input of the other factor and output of product are varied (as moving down a column or across a row in Table 1).

Many types of production surfaces are possible depending on the underlying production function. Figure 3 represents the case in which diminishing marginal productivity holds for both factors. Figure 4 illustrates a

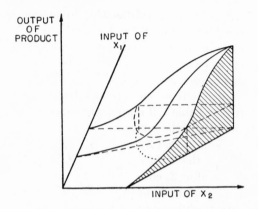

Fig. 4. Production surface with increasing and decreasing returns to both factors.

production surface where the elasticity of production first is greater and finally less than 1.0 for both resources. It also illustrates how either horizontal (output held constant) or vertical (input of 1 or both resources held constant) slices can be made through the surface. In a case of constant productivity and divisibility of both factors, the surface is linear in all directions. Under increasing returns to both factors, the surface is convex to the $Z_1 Z_2$ plane rather than concave as in the case of Figure 3.

Iso-product contours and maps. Since each point on a diagonal line such as those in Figure 1 or on a contour such as those indicated in Figures 2 and 3 represent an equal product, they are termed iso-product (equal product) contours. Iso-lines (curves) are used widely in economics. Later reference will be made to iso-revenue, iso-cost, and iso-resource curves. As in the case of iso-product contours or curves, the iso-line always refers to an *equal quantity*.

A 2-factor production function can also be presented as a contour map. In this form it has the same meaning as a production surface but is more useful for analytical purposes. Just as civil engineers, geologists, agronomists, and conservation planners can draw a hill or mountain as contours on a flat surface, so the production function or production surface can be graphed as a contour map. For example, if we draw a map of the 12, 24, and 36 output levels from Figures 2 or 3 as contours, Figure 6 is the result. Each contour line represents all of the possible combinations of Z_1 and Z_2 which will produce the constant quantity of Y indicated. The series of

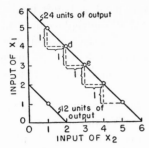

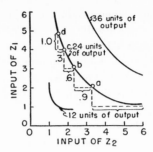

Fig. 5. Iso-product contours with constant substitution rates.

Fig. 6. Iso-product curve and diminishing rates of substitution.

curves from 1 production function or surface constitutes a *"family of contours."* The contours representing greater outputs are "higher and higher" on the production surface just as a contour map pictures a mountain or hill rising upward from a plain.

Resource Substitution Relationships

We can now return to the factor-factor relationship for examination of detail. In Figure 1 an output of 12 can be attained with numerous combinations of resources including (a) 2 of X_1 and none of X_2, (b) 1 of X_1 and 1 of X_2, and (c) 2 of X_2 and none of X_1. Similarly, other levels of output can be attained with several combinations of resources. The diagonal lines from northwest to southeast illustrate all of the possible resource combinations which can be employed in producing a single output. If the units of resources are infinitely divisible, any factor combination falling on an individual line can be employed. Factors X_1 and X_2 might refer to white and yellow corn, respectively, measured in bushels. These units could be subdivided into pounds, grams, or any other fraction of a bushel. If factors are indivisible, only the circles on the contour line in Figure 5 represent attainable resource combinations.

Factors X_1 and X_2 are clearly *substitute* or *competitive* resources, since one can be used to replace the other. While the transformation of either or both factors into product is at a diminishing rate, the substitution of one factor for another is always at a constant rate; 1 unit of X_1 always replaces 1 unit of X_2 when output is held constant. In order that the factor-factor relationship might be better visualized, the lines indicating the possible combinations of X_1 and X_2 for producing 12 and 24 units of output have been transferred to Figure 5. These continuous and linear iso-product lines characterize resources which substitute at constant rates such as is often true for 2 different machines, 2 different grades of grain, or even 2 different grains fed to livestock. The factor substitution rates are constant because, when product is held constant at one level, a 1-unit increase in X_1 always results in a 1-unit decrease in X_2. While replacement in this case is at a 1:1 ratio, it is not a necessary condition for constant substitution rates. Substitution at a constant rate is one of the extremes in factor-factor relationships. The other extreme is represented by resources which must be combined in fixed proportions.

Constant substitution rates are further illustrated in the example of Table 2. Six possible combinations of resources X_3 and X_4 can be used in producing the given quantity of product, or any other of the combinations

Table 2.

Iso-Product Relationship Indicating Constant Rate of Substitution with Output Fixed at 100 (Hypothetical)

Quantity of factor X_3	Quantity of factor X_4	Marginal rate of substitution of X_3 for X_4
(1)	(2)	(3)
(1) 0	50	2
(2) 5	40	2
(3) 10	30	2
(4) 15	20	2
(5) 20	10	2
(6) 25	0	2

indicated. As X_3 input is increased from zero to 5, 10 units of X_4 are replaced. Similarly, addition of another 5 units of X_3 replaces another 10 units of X_4. One unit of X_3 substitutes for 2 units of X_4. Conversely, 1 unit of X_4 substitutes for .5 unit of X_3. The substitution ratio is constant throughout all combinations of the 2 factors. The product contour figures of Table 2 give the line or curve I_1S_1 when graphed in Figure 7. In contrast to those of Figure 5, the dotted triangles show that the slope of I_1S_1 is not 45°, because 1 unit of X_3 always substitutes for 2 of X_4. The iso-line I_2S_2 also indicates a constant rate of substitution but in this case the ratio is always 2 of X_3 to 1.0 of X_4 (or .5 of X_4 for 1.0 of X_3). The 2 resources represented by the curves I_1S_1 and I_2S_2, while substituting at a constant rate, are not perfect substitutes since in the one case 2 units of X_3 are necessary to replace 1 unit of X_4, while the situation is reversed in the other case.

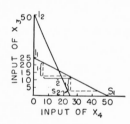

Fig. 7. Substitution at constant rates.

Marginal rate of substitution. The term *marginal rate of substitution* applied to the factor-factor relationship has a meaning similar to the term *marginal product* or *marginal rate of transformation* applied under the factor-product relationship. The marginal rate of transformation (the marginal product) denoted the amount (rate) of change in the total product for each 1-unit change in factor input. The marginal rate of substitution refers to the amount by which 1 resource is decreased as input of another resource is increased by 1 unit. In Table 2 the marginal rate of substitution of X_3 for X_4 is constant at 2. Similarly, the slopes of the iso-lines in Figures 5 and 7 define the marginal rates of substitution between factors. The "contours" in Figure 5 have a slope of 45° or a 1:1 ratio indicating that the marginal rate of substitution of X_2 for X_1, and conversely, X_1 for X_2, is 1; the slope of curve I_1S_1 in Figure 7 indicates that the marginal rate of substitution of X_3 for X_4 is constant at 2 (or the rate of substitution of X_4 for X_3 is .5).

The marginal rate of substitution of X_2 for X_1 in Figure 5 can be denoted as the ratio $\Delta X_1/\Delta X_2$ where Δ again refers to "change in," ΔX_1 refers to "change in X_1" and ΔX_2 refers to "change in X_2." The quantity will always be negative when the slope of the constant product contour is also negative. In Figures 1 or 5 the marginal rate of substitution of X_2 for X_1 is -1.0 ($\Delta X_1/\Delta X_2 = -1.0/1.0 = -1.0$). Since the rate of factor substitution is negative in all rational areas of production, we do not always bother to include the minus sign.

The marginal rate of substitution can be calculated in the form of an *average between 2 distinct combinations* of resources or as an *exact figure at a single level* of combination. In Table 2, the change in X_3 is 5 and the change in X_4 is 10 between the first and second combinations. The marginal rate of substitution of X_1 for X_2 is -2.0 ($-10/5$), indicating that, "as an average," each one of the 5 units of X_3 substitutes for 2 units of X_4. The "average" marginal rate of substitution is also the *exact* rate of substitution in this case because the product contour is linear. As indicated at a later point, the *average* and *exact* marginal rates of substitution are not the same under other types of factor-factor or substitution relationships. As in the case of input-output relationships the *average* marginal rate of substitution refers to an *arc* or *range* of the product contour and the rate of substitution for the median unit of the range (depending, of course, on the particular function under consideration). The *exact* refers to the marginal rate of substitution at a single point on the equal product curve. It can be estimated only if the magnitude of change in factors is small enough (approaches zero).[2]

---

[2] If the *exact* rather than *average* rate of substitution is desired, it must be derived by calculus. It can then be computed as a derivative with $\Delta X_1/\Delta X_2$ or $\Delta X_2/\Delta X_1$ expressed as $\dfrac{dX_1}{dX_2}$ or $\dfrac{dX_2}{dX_1}$ where the change in X_2 or X_1 becomes infinitely small (approaches the limit zero). For the contour of Figure 8, the original contour equation was $G = 327.5 - .5111H + .00423H^2$ where G refers to grain in pounds and H refers to hay in pounds. Marginal rates of substitution are thus given as

$$\frac{dG}{dH} = -.5111 + .00846H$$

With hay input at 35 as indicated in Figure 8, the marginal rate of substitution of hay for grain is $-.215$. At this level of hay input, 1 lb. of hay replaces .215 lbs. of grain. For hay quantities of 5, 15, 25, and 45, the marginal rates of substitution are respectively $-.469$, $-.384$, $-.300$, and $-.131$.

Diminishing rate of substitution. A very great number of resource decisions revolve around factors which substitute for each other at diminishing rates. This is the case illustrated by the iso-product contours in Figures 2 and 6. The dotted triangles on the curve indicating 24 units of output in Figure 6 indicate the nature of diminishing rates of substitution. If we start with the combination indicated by a, use of 1 additional unit of Z_1 replaces .9 of a unit of Z_2 as the factor combination is moved to point b. One unit of factor Z_1 substitutes for .6 of a unit of Z_2 between points b and c and for .3 of a unit between c and d. In these instances the *average* marginal rate of substitution of Z_2 for Z_1 ($\Delta Z_1 / \Delta Z_2$) is .9/1.0, .6/1.0, and .3/1.0, or .9, .6, and .3 respectively. Table 3 provides tabular material indicating diminishing marginal rates of substitution between 2 feeds. The marginal rate of substitution of hay for grain becomes smaller and smaller as hay continuously replaces grain with milk output constant. In other words, increasingly greater quantities of hay are required to offset or re-

Table 3.

Grain-Forage Iso-Product Contour (Feed Combinations and Marginal Rates of Grain-Forage Substitution) for Milk Output Level of 8,500 lbs.*

Lbs. hay (1)	Lbs. grain (2)	Average rate of grain/hay substitution (3)	Exact rate of grain/hay substitution (4)
5000	6154		−1.55
		1.40	
5500	5454		−1.25
		1.32	
6000	4892		−1.02
		.94	
6500	4423		−.86
		.79	
7000	4029		−.72
		.65	
7500	3694		−.62
		.58	
8000	3406		−.54
		.50	
8500	3156		−.47
		.46	
9000	2937		−.41
		.40	
9500	2744		−.36
		.32	
10000	2572		−.32
		.31	
10500	2419		−.29
		.27	
11000	2281		−.26
		.25	
11500	2157		−.24

* Source: Derived from experimental data. (Figures show pounds of grain replaced by 1 lb. of hay.)

place each successive decrement in grain input (with milk output held constant at 8,500 lbs.). Column 3 shows the average marginal rate of substitution of hay for grain. As hay input is increased from 5,000 to 5,500 lbs., each 1 of the added 500 lbs. of hay substitutes, on the average, for 1.4 lbs. of grain (Δgrain/Δhay $= 700/500 = 1.4$).[3] Column 4 shows the exact marginal rate of substitution. It indicates that if feed is being combined in the ration at the rate of 5,500 lbs. of hay and 5,454 lbs. of grain, an infinitely small adjustment away from this combination will cause hay to substitute for grain at the rate of 1.25 pounds (1.25 lbs. of grain are replaced by each pound of hay added).

Product contours of the nature indicated in Table 3 (columns 1 and 2) are again illustrated in Figures 8a and 8b. In Figure 8a, the contour lines represent a pork output of 100 lbs. Curve A represents the product contour when the protein from soybean meal was fortified with vitamin B-12 while B represents the same feeds with aureomycin added. Both curves show the combinations of corn and protein (with supplemental feed elements) which would produce the equivalent of 100 lbs. of pork when hogs approximate the weight of 150 lbs. Curves C and D illustrate the same relationship with pigs approximating the weight of 100 lbs. Figure 8b represents a small enlarged portion of curve B in Figure 8a; the scale and unit of measurement has also been changed for grain. A glance at either figure tells one that if the marginal rates of substitution are computed, they will be of the diminishing nature in the manner of Table 3. The small dotted triangle indicated as n can be used to compute the average marginal rate of substitution between protein and corn; at point e, 314 lbs. of corn and 35 lbs. of protein feed are required per 100 lbs. of pork; at point f, the combination includes 306 lbs. of corn and 40 lbs. of protein. The corn input decreases by 8 lbs. while the protein input increases by 5 lbs. between points e and f. Accordingly, each 1 of these 5 lbs. of protein substitutes, as an average, for 1.3 lbs. of corn. Average figures such as these are approximations but probably are of sufficient accuracy for most farmer decisions.

---

[3] These estimates were derived from individual cow data as a preliminary step in feed substitution research and for illustrative purposes alone. They are based on heavy-breed cows included in the Jensen-Woodward study *Input-Output Relationships in Milk Production.* U.S.D.A. Tech. Bul. 815. With milk indicated by Y, hay by X_1, and grain by X_2, the production function, product contour (with milk constant at 8,500 lbs. per cow), and marginal rate of substitution of hay for grain are given by equations (1), (2), and (3) below:

$$Y = 3.56X_1^{.5053}X_2^{.4} \tag{1}$$

$$X_2 = \left(\frac{8500}{3.56X_1^{.5053}}\right)^{2.5} \tag{2}$$

$$\frac{dX_2}{dX_1} = \left(\frac{.5053X_2}{.4X_1}\right) \tag{3}$$

As indicated at a later point in the text, an entirely different function may better describe the substitution ratios in dairy feeding.

The exact rate of substitution at 1 point on the contour can be denoted by
a tangent line. The straight line TN is tangent to the product contour at
an input of 30 lbs. of protein and 324 lbs. of corn; the slopes and rates of
change in the 2 lines are equal at this point of tangency. The triangle

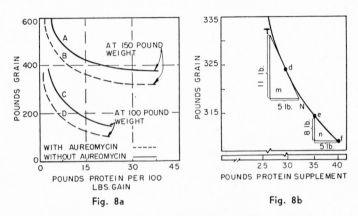

Fig. 8a   Fig. 8b

Corn-protein substitution relationships in pork production (Source: Derived from experimental data of Iowa Agr. Exp. Sta. project 506).

formed by line TN indicates that the tangent line "drops vertically" by
11 lbs. of corn for the "horizontal movement" by 5 lbs. of protein. The
slope of line TN is 11/5 or 2.2 at the tangent point d. Since the slopes of
2 tangent curves are equal, the product contour line also has a slope of 2.2
at point d and $\Delta C/\Delta P$, the marginal rate of substitution of protein feed
for corn is 2.2 at this feed combination.[4]

Elasticity of substitution. The concept of relative change under the factor-
factor relationship has a meaning similar to the notion of relative change
under the factor-product relationship. When applied to the input-output
relationship, the elasticity of production (E_p) referred to the percentage
change in output accompanying a given percentage change in input. The
percentage or relative change by which factors combine in producing a
constant output on a production contour can be defined similarly as the
percentage change in one factor divided by the percentage change in the
other factor or by $\Delta X_1/X_1 \div \Delta X_2/X_2$, where Δ again refers to "change
in." ΔX_1 refers to change in X_1, ΔX_2 refers to change in X_2, and X_1 and X_2
refer to the original quantities of the 2 factors. Other concepts of substitu-

---

[4] The production function upon which the curve of Figure 8a is based has been
mentioned earlier. The product contour equation derived from the production function is

$$C = \left(\frac{115}{1.34P^{.139}}\right)^{\frac{1}{.696}}$$

where C refers to corn input, P refers to protein and the weight added after weaning
at 35 lbs. is 115.

tion elasticity are employed in economic literature.[5] However, the simple one employed here has a parallel meaning and is sufficient for the analyses of later chapters. If we use the figure computed in this manner as an indication of the elasticity of substitution (E_s), the elasticity of substitution (E_s) is always negative for substitute resources and indicates how fast the slope of a product contour changes (how rapidly the marginal rate of substitution declines).[6] If we substitute the first two feed combinations from Table 3 into the formula the average or arc elasticity becomes $700/6154 \div 500/5000$ or $.11/.10 = 1.1$ as forage is substituted for grain. E_s (as in the case of E_p) can be computed either as *arc elasticity* or *point elasticity*.[7] Arc elasticity refers, as in the example above, to substitution over an entire portion of a product contour (between hay inputs of 5,000 and 5,500 lbs. in Table 3). The value of E_s computed by the "arc" method has a meaning similar to that of the *average* marginal rate of substitution. "*Point elasticity*" refers to the elasticity at one particular factor combination and therefore corresponds to the *exact* marginal rate of substitution.

Other Substitution Relationships

The several factor-factor relationships already outlined cover an important portion of the situations found in agriculture. However, there are numerous variations of these which are also relevant in resource coordination. These are discussed below.

Fixed coefficients. While rates of substitution constant at a 1:1 ratio represent one extreme in the relationship of one resource to another, fixed coefficients represent the opposite extreme. Although the situation has been mentioned previously, the details now can be made apparent. Chemistry provides the main examples of resources which combine only in fixed proportions; production of 1 molecule of water is possible only with 1 atom of oxygen and 2 atoms of hydrogen and an increase in 1 element alone

---

[5] Elasticity of substitution can be defined more rigorously as the relative change in ratios of the factors as compared to the relative change in the marginal rate of substitution of the factors. (See Allen, R. G. D., *Mathematics for Economists*, London: Macmillan, 1942, p. 341; and Weintraub, S., *Price Analysis*, New York: Pitman, 1949, p. 67, for discussions of alternative methods.) The elasticity equation, independent of unit of measurement, then becomes $E_s = \Delta(X_1/X_2)/(X_1/X_2) \div \Delta(\Delta X_1/\Delta X_2)/(\Delta X_1/\Delta X_2)$ where $\Delta(X_1/X_2)$ refers to the change in the ratio at which factors combine (X_1/X_2) refers to the original ratio or combination of factors, $\Delta(\Delta X_1/\Delta X_2)$ refers to the change in the marginal rate of substitution, and $(\Delta X_1/\Delta X_2)$ refers, as already indicated in the text, to the original marginal rate of substitution between the factors. This equation defines the elasticity of the ratio at which the marginal rate of substitution changes as one factor is substituted for another.

[6] E_s, as used in the text, can also be computed as $(\Delta X_1/X_1)(X_2/\Delta X_2)$ or $(\Delta X_1/\Delta X_2)(X_2/X_1)$.

[7] If the formula presented above is employed, it gives arc elasticity when E_s is computed by arithmetic over a range of inputs. It results in point elasticity when computed by calculus and in reference to an infinitely small change in resource input.

cannot increase output. The product contour under fixed coefficients reduces to the form of contour map illustrated in Figure 9. There is only 1
combination of resources for producing the quantity of product represented
by the "contour" I_1S_1. A product output of 100 units requires an input ok
of resource X_1 and om of resource X_2. If input of X_1 is increased to ol
while X_2 is held at om, the output remains at 100. An increase in X_2 to on
while X_1 is constant does not add to the total product. However, a simultaneous increase in X_1 to ol and X_2 to on results in a doubling of the
product as the factors are held in constant proportions. Both X_1 and X_2
are limitational factors since output is limited by input of either. A factor
which is limitational in the sense of Fig-
ure 9 has a marginal productivity of zero
when it alone is increased in quantity.

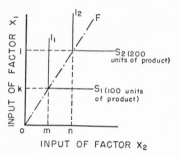

Fig. 9. Fixed coefficients.

There are many examples of farm
resources which combine in fixed proportions although these are not so widespread as might be imagined, and difficult
decisions do not revolve around them.
The example of breeding services and the
combination of 1 sperm and 1 ovum is
an illustration. Chemical and biological
processes underly all crop and livestock
production. Output of 1 lb. of animal fat or plant carbohydrate requires an
exact combination of the elements which constitute it. Yet this fixed-pro-
portion phenomenon does not so often present itself at the decision-making
level of farm resource use. While a minimum of various chemical elements
are required for production of a given output of lean pork, the farmer can
obtain these required elements in a number of different feeds. Animal and
plant proteins obtained from various sources serve as substitutes for each
other. Manure, ammonium nitrate, mixed fertilizers, and legume residues
also serve as substitutes in producing the minimum nitrogen required for
a bushel of grain of specific chemical makeup. There are also other obvious
cases of limitational factors and fixed coefficients: a minimum of 1 spark
plug is necessary for a 1-cylinder gasoline engine and 1 nut is necessary for
1 machine bolt. Yet the limitational factors to be explained below provide
a greater problem area in decision-making.

Technical complements and substitutes. Resources can be either *technical
complements* or *technical substitutes*. They are, of course, technical complements when they must be combined in fixed proportions. There are also
other cases of technical complements where a reduction in input of one
factor cannot be replaced by an increase in another factor. Factors are
technical substitutes, as already indicated, when output can be maintained
as resources are reshuffled; when 1 factor is reduced in quantity, a second
factor must always be increased. Substitution is sometimes visualized

more accurately if the services of resources rather than the resources themselves are considered. It is true that protein feed substitutes for carbohydrate feeds in the manner prescribed at 1 point in time by the livestock production process. However, substitution rates cannot be defined within a crop season for tractors and labor. The complete quantity of labor for which a tractor substitutes must be defined over the complete life of the latter resource. Within a single production period or year, substitution is between so many units of tractor services and labor. Other units of tractor services will be forthcoming in a second year as potential displacers of labor. This problem of longevity in the stock of resource services gives rise to the problems of discounting and uncertainty discussed in later chapters.

Limitational factors. Most production processes in agriculture involve complementary or limitational resources of some nature although they are not limitational in the strict manner of Figure 9. Raw materials which are chemically and physiologically transformed into products assume limitational characteristics. The amount of pork which can be produced from a single hog, the amount of milk from a cow, or the amount of corn from an acre of land depends at some point on the amount of feed or fertilizer elements present. Other resources can be substituted for feed through better care and housing of animals. Eventually, however, no additional pork is forthcoming or indeed pork output must be decreased if feed is reduced further in amount. Similarly, a corn yield of 60 bushels per acre may be obtained as labor and capital in the form of more timely and effective seed-bed preparation or cultivation are substituted for seed and fertilizer. Even in the presence of effective seeding and cultivations, however, the yield eventually will be reduced below 60 bushels if seed or fertilizer are reduced far enough.

Many other resources employed in agriculture also serve both as substitutes and technical complements over different ranges of combination. Machinery and labor are substitutes over a wide range of combinations; still, at some point, capital in the form of machinery no longer substitutes for labor: various sizes of tractors (different amounts of capital) can be used with, and as a substitute for, labor, but one man is required to operate a tractor regardless of its size. Tractor fuel can be displaced to some extent by other machine gadgets, but below some minimum fuel input, machines cannot be powered without fuel.

Iso-product contours for complementary or limitational factors of this nature are shown in Figures 10 and 11. In Figure 10 resource X_1 serves in a limitational or complementary capacity to X_2; X_1 can be substituted for X_2 until the X_2 input falls to om and the X_1 input reaches ol. No amount of X_1 will substitute for further quantities of X_2; as is indicated by the fact that, as IS becomes vertical, (a) the product remains constant and (b) the minimum quantity of X_2 cannot be replaced even if X_1 is increased by infinite amounts beyond ol. Both factors eventually serve in limitational and complementary capacity for the family of contours indicated in Figure 11. If output is to be held at 100, X_1 can be substituted for X_2 only until contour line I_1S_1 becomes vertical. Conversely, X_2 can be substituted for X_1 only up to the point where curve I_1S_1 becomes horizontal. The 2 resources are substitutes inside of the ranges traced out by the border or ridge lines OA and OB. They are complements for combinations falling outside of the borderlines. For the vertical portions of the product contours above OA, X_2 is complementary with X_1: (a) no increase in product is forthcoming unless X_2 is increased along with X_1, while (b) no amount of X_1 will substitute for X_2 if the product is not to be decreased. For the horizontal portions of the contours below OB the same conditions hold in respect to the relationship of X_1 with X_2. In the case of the fixed coefficients illustrated in Figure 9, the 2 strictly limitational factors are technical complements throughout and the border lines merge until they coincide at OF. In the case of resources which substitute at constant rates through all possible combinations, the borderlines diverge until they become identical with the x and y axes in Figures 5 or 7.

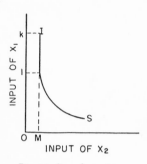

Fig. 10. Complementary resources.

There are even more extreme examples of resource complementarity than those presented in Figure 11. The quantity of one factor can be extended so far that output can be maintained at a constant level only if the quantity of another factor is also increased. This situation is found where hogs on pasture are produced with a level of grain feeding so low that growth and gain are retarded to a point where later dry-lot feeding results in greater grain requirements per 100 lbs. of pork than would have been the case had no forage been fed. Experimental data also show that the level of protein feeding can be so high that animals are "thrown off feed"; the slow-down in rate of gain and eventual recovery then causes

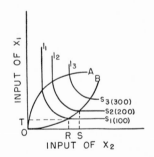

Fig. 11. Border or ridge lines.

more of both grain and protein to be required for a given output (even though protein substituted for grain in the early feeding combinations). A product contour characterizing this situation is illustrated in Figure 12. If output is to be maintained at the 100 units indicated by contour IS, X_1 and X_2 serve as substitutes only between the ranges including OL of the former and OR of the latter. Beyond an input OR of X_2, increases in this resource require that inputs of X_1 also be increased. If inputs of X_2 are extended to OV, inputs of X_1 must be increased to OM for the given output. The irrationality of this combination is obvious: Fewer of both resources can be employed and the same product attained, or less of one or both resources can be used while a greater product is attained.

Resources which are technical complements or technical substitutes now can be defined more rigorously. Resources are *technical substitutes* when the marginal rate of substitution is less than zero. In other words, the sign of $\Delta X_2/\Delta X_1$ or $\Delta X_1/\Delta X_2$, the marginal rate at which one factor substitutes for another, must be negative. The ratio of change between OL of X_1 and OR of X_2 is negative in Figure 12, since a positive change in one factor is always associated with a negative change in the other. If the combination of factors is changed from a to b, $\Delta X_1/\Delta X_2$ or the rate of substitution for this wide change is $-LH/SR$. If $-LH$ is equal to 8 and SR is equal to 10, the numerical value of the substitution ratio is $-8/10$ or $-.8$. Resources are *technical complements* when the ratio of substitution is zero or greater.

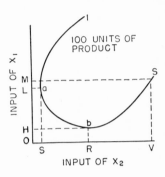

Fig. 12. Areas of irrational resource combination.

In Figure 11, the ratio of change, $\Delta X_1/\Delta X_2$, is zero when output is constant at 100 and input of X_1 is at the minimum of OT: If X_2 is increased beyond OR, none of X_1 is replaced. Between X_2 inputs of OR and OS, the substitution ratio is O/RS or zero. In Figure 12 the ratio of change is positive for addition of factors outside of the border points a and b; a wide change in input of X_2 from OR to OV, with output constant at 100, also causes input of X_1 to increase from OH to OM. Hence $\Delta X_1/\Delta X_2$, the ratio of change, is HM/RV, a positive quantity. If RV is equal to 20 while HM is equal to 2, then $\Delta X_1/\Delta X_2$, the ratio of change becomes $2/20$ or $+.1$.

Single factor fallacies. While all major categories of resources serve as rivals or substitutes at some level of combination, they are also technical complements at other levels of production. No product can be produced with land alone or even with land and capital alone. Some minimum quantity of labor is always necessary. Similarly, labor has a production coefficient of zero unless some capital or land is available to be combined with it. Or, it might be said that capital, labor, or land taken together have zero production coefficients unless some management is present to decide on a plan of some minimum nature. Since all factors are technical complements at some level of combination, no aspect of production is involved when a single factor is considered. The economics of resource use can be analyzed only as factors are considered together when they serve as complements. Even when they serve as rivals or substitutes, economic considerations and problems are involved only as 2 or more resources are related in the production process. It is these aspects of production which cause economic analysis of single factors to be somewhat fruitless.

Independent pairs of factors. Where the production function is of the form $Y = f(X_1, X_2, X_3, X_4 | X_5 \ldots X_n)$, individual pairs of factors may be substitutes while other pairs are technical complements. For example, in the production function above, suppose that X_1 and X_2 are 2 kinds of carbohydrate feeds such as yellow corn and white corn (or wheat and corn) while X_3 is labor and X_4 is capital in the form of machinery and equipment for handling grain. Now X_1 (yellow corn) may be substituted for X_2 (white corn) without changing either the total input of labor and equipment or the combination of these two resources. Conversely, grain-handling equipment may be substituted for labor without affecting the quantity of either type of feed or the rate at which they substitute. The rates of substitution between each pair are independent of the manner in which the other 2 are combined. In cases such as this, the rates of substitution between one pair of the factors can be derived without concern for the other pair. Similarly, decisions in respect to combinations of 2 factors such as X_1 and X_2 need not change the combination or decision in respect to the other 2 factors. A situation of this type exists mainly when one set of factors is of a limitational nature and enters the production process in a chemical or biological manner while the other pair provides mechanical services which are not materially transformed into product.

Discontinuous or indivisible factors. The case of indivisible or discontinuous resource units is a variant of the factor-factor relationships already described. They cause decisions on resource combination to be less complex than when substitution is at a continuous rate. A hog's ration can be made up of infinite numbers and kinds of feeds but a tractor always needs 1 man to go along with it, or it will always substitute for (say) 6 horses, and never 1,000 different fractions of horses. Indivisible factors are fairly prevalent in agriculture but the general principles to be outlined later still apply; variations in the analysis can be made in line with the "lumpiness" of the factors. As indicated in an earlier chapter, many resources which appear "discrete" can be broken down into continuous inputs if the services of the resource rather than the resource are considered. Machines and tools manufactured in given and discrete sizes represent the main category of "indivisible" factors. Although a farmer cannot substitute 4½ horses for a ¾ tractor unit, he can use fewer horses and hire tractor services in any magnitude. Also, he has the opportunity of acquiring machines and tools which embody different amounts of services by buying those of different ages or those different in brand. Only the pure flow services embodied in a machine actually should be considered as indivisible. While the entire stock of services embodied in a machine must be purchased with the machine, stock services can be made divisible over time by using the machine different amounts in different periods. Similarly, while he cannot hire the services of half a man for 2 weeks, he can hire 1 man for a single week. Even with these possibilities, though, certain services of tractors or other machines of a given size, type, or age can be looked upon as indivisible while the labor, fuel, and other resource services used with them are divisible. A tractor requires at least 1 man to operate it, but labor can be used in varying quantities with the single tractor to attain a greater product. However, aside from custom hire, tractors can be added only in units of 1. If labor is held constant, addition of a second tractor ordinarily will not add to the product: one tractor and 1 man may be used to farm 320 acres of wheat. The same tractor may be used with 2 men for a farm of 480 acres if 1 man operates it during daylight and the other operates it at night. If tractor numbers are increased to 2, 1 man can still operate only 320 acres; he can drive only 1 tractor at a time. Still, 2 men may be able to operate 540 acres. While output is not increased nor labor replaced as 2 tractors are combined with 1 man, the combination of (a) 2 men and 1 tractor or (b) 2 tractors and 2 men can allow an increase in output. The contour map and iso-product curves indicating a production function and factor-factor relationship for situations of this sort are illustrated in

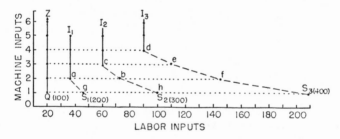

Fig. 13. Product contours and resource substitution with one indivisible factor.

Figure 13. The vertical scale indicates the number of machines. Machines are indivisible and can be added in units of 1 only; a fraction of a machine is impossible. The horizontal scale indicates labor inputs. Although measured in units of 20, they can be broken down into any fraction of this amount. The amount of labor required to operate 1 machine, the smallest possible machine input, is 20 units. An output of 100 units can be produced with 1 machine and 20 units of labor. If the machine is held constant at 1, product can be increased to 200 by adding 26 units of labor as indicated by the line QS_1. Addition of 54 more units of labor to the single machine increases output to 300 as indicated by S_1S_2. This movement along QS_3 is of the factor-product nature, since tractors are fixed and labor is variable. Output is constant, however, if machines are increased along QZ while labor is fixed at 20 units. At the minimum, machines and labor must be combined in the fixed proportions of 1 machine and 20 units of labor for an output of 100 units. There are, however, possibilities of substitution. Suppose that the initial output is 100 (Q) and the inputs include one machine and 20 units of labor. Output is then increased to 200 (product contour I_1S_1) by using approximately 46 units of labor with the single machine (the factor combination indicated at the point S_1). The 200 units of output can also be produced with 2 machines and 37 units of labor, the factor combination indicated at point a. Thus the product contour for 200 units of output becomes I_1S_1 and includes the 2 points a and g as well as the vertical portion of the curve, indicating a zero rate of substitution of machines for labor. In other words, a machine substitutes for approximately 9 units of labor as machine input is increased from 1 to 2 and labor inputs are decreased from 46 to 37. The marginal rate at which a machine substitutes for labor is −9 between g and a yet beyond a the marginal rate of substitution is zero; machines and labor are complements. Alternatively, the farmer may start with one machine, 20 units of labor and the product of 100 indicated at point Q. Output can be increased to 300 by combining one machine and 100 units of labor at point h. There are, however, 3 tractor-labor combinations which will produce the 300-unit output. A second machine can be added and labor input can be reduced from 100 to 73 as indicated by b. Finally, a third tractor can be added and labor inputs can be decreased from 73 to 60 as noted by c. These 3 labor-machinery combinations produce the same output and product contour I_2S_2 arises. Substitution is possible in "discrete jumps." The marginal rates of substitution of the second, third, and fourth tractor for labor, as indicated on the 300 or I_2S_2 contour, are 27, 13, and zero respectively.[8] The fourth tractor is not a substitute for labor and has a marginal product greater than zero only if labor is added as a complementary factor. Addition of labor as a complementary factor carries the output to higher levels, and additional contours such as I_3S_3 are then possible.

The presence of "corners" such as a, b, c, d, e, and f on a product contour gives rise to important implications. As can be explained in the analysis of the next chapter, any one of the corner combinations causes factor combinations at these points to be highly stable. Price ratios have to change outside of wide ranges before substitution is profitable.[9] This is the reason why farmers often cling to given techniques or even new techniques as factor prices and farm costs vary.

---

[8] These substitution rates are negative. Henceforth we do not include the positive or negative sign unless distinction must be made between rational and irrational resource combinations.

[9] As is apparent from the analysis of the next chapter, the ratio of machine price (P_m) to labor price (P_1) must vary by more than the difference in the slopes of cb and bh if an original machine-labor combination at b is to be discarded as unprofitable.

Farm practices and factors replaced as products. Farmers would be quick
to say that capital resources in the form of new techniques do not always
substitute in the formal fashion of the iso-product curves in Figures 5 and
6; not only does capital representing new technologies substitute for capital representing old forms, but it often boosts output, rather than retaining
it constant in the vein of an iso-product line. Hybrid seed corn, for example, substitutes for open-pollinated seed and also increases output per
acre. The same is true for capital represented in improved insecticides,
fertilizers, strains and varieties of crops, or even new machines and feeds.
In this case, however, the entire production-function and factor-factor
line has changed because of the new technique; a new set of relationships
can be drawn up. This type of change is akin to that represented in Figure
13 of Chapter 3. Here we may not only substitute a good cow for a poor
cow but, with input of feed and other resources held constant, also increase
milk output. The situation is still one of substitution, however, since we
can now compare cow replacement rates. It is probably true that high-
producing cows substitute at a constant rate for low-producing cows, since
a total milk output of 72,000 pounds may be obtained with 6 good cows
or 9 poor cows. In any case, the value of the product from capital representing the new technique may be considered to include the value of the
added product as well as the value of the resource which it replaces.

If factors replaced are considered as products, the marginal physical
product or marginal value product of a variable resource can be computed
in either 1 of 2 ways (or both in the new
technique case above): If input of factor
Z_3 is held constant in Figure 14 at 120
units, input of Z_4 can be increased from
10 to 25 with an increase in output of
product Y from 100 to 200, as indicated
by the iso-product curves. The average
marginal product ($\Delta Y / \Delta Z_4$) is then 100/15
or 6.67. With output held constant at 100
of Y, an increase in Z_4 from 10 to 25 can

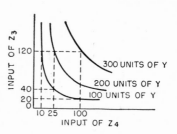

Fig. 14. Factor productivity.

also be considered as "producing 80 units of factor Z_3," since this is the
quantity for which it substitutes. The ratio $\Delta Z_3 / \Delta Z_4$ is 80/15 or 5.33.
The entrepreneur thus must consider whether either the addition of 6.67
units of Y or the saving of 5.33 units of Z_3 merits the use of another
unit of Z_4. Both types of adjustment will be considered together at a
later point.

Basis of Resource Substitution in Agriculture

Agriculture displays a wide and varied set of relationships in resource
substitution. Many factors substitute at constant rates. Equally or more
widespread are diminishing marginal rates of substitution. Also, particular

resources used in agriculture are characterized by continuous and discrete or lumpy units which cause substitution rates to be affected accordingly. The following paragraphs provide notes on agricultural resource substitution in addition to the examples already cited.

Intra-technical unit substitution. The technical unit in agriculture can be held constant or fixed while the resources which go into the production process are varied in quantity relative to each other. For the livestock technical unit, feeds represent a major category of substitutable resources. Problems in animal nutrition are quite largely those of factor substitution. Some feeds substitute at constant rates within the livestock technical unit. This statement applies to different grades of one grain or carbohydrate feed. Constant or near-constant rates of substitution likely hold true within most categories of feeds such as carbohydrates, proteins, and forages. Even then, many pairs within these groups substitute at diminishing rates. Animal and plant proteins, because of differences in content of amino acids and other constituents, substitute at diminishing rates in pork production. A combined feed including plant protein and APF may allow constant or near-constant rates of substitution with animal proteins, however. Grains and high-protein feeds normally substitute at diminishing rates for this reason: Without supplementary proteins the growing animal must obtain its full protein requirements from grain or hay. The animal's ability to assimilate carbohydrates and other feed constituents is thus limited by the digestible proteins which it can obtain from the same feeds. Within the animal's physiological processes, feed elements do combine in fixed proportions. However, this fixed-proportions feature causes feed elements from different sources to substitute at diminishing rates. A hog fed only corn has its growth rate retarded and the production period extended to such an extent that the greater quantity and proportion of the grain which it does consume must go into maintenance of body weight over a longer period of time. Hence diminishing rates of substitution exist between carbohydrate and protein feeds. The rate of substitution changes, however, as the animal matures and the growing process slows down and the fattening process is accelerated. Constant rates of substitution may more nearly hold true between certain feeds in egg production where time is not so greatly involved and the product represents an aggregate of elements in fixed proportion.

Forage and carbohydrate feeds substitute at diminishing rates over a wide area of livestock production. However, for animals fed a ration so light that the digestive organs can handle the entire bulk with facility, substitution is often at a constant rate. Heavier rations, especially in the fattening process, cause diminishing rates of substitution because the total feed intake under roughage feeding is limited by the animal's stomach capacity, and the period of growth required for a given gain is longer. Again, a greater proportion of the energy derived from feed must go into body maintenance rather than addition of weight. Too, the greater bulk of a high forage ration may itself require a greater amount of energy for the digestive process. The rate of grain/hay substitution is greater for high-quality than for low-quality hay. These conditions apply particularly in cattle and sheep fattening in the manner illustrated by Table 4.[10] Diminishing marginal rates of substitution may also exist in milk production, because a small amount of grain has a stimulating effect on milk production. Increasing amounts of energy are required for digestion of the greater bulk in high forage rations. Some dairy scientists claim that the milk contour is sharply curved on each end (because of the stimulant

Table 4.

Forage-Grain Combinations and Substitution Relationships in Producing a 25-lb. Gain on Lambs *

Feed combinations in producing 25 lbs. of gain		Marginal rates of substitution of hay for grain (exact)
Lbs. of hay X_1	Lbs. of grain X_2	$\dfrac{\Delta X_2 / \Delta X_1}{\Delta X_1}$
40	130.9	.65
50	125.1	.53
60	120.1	.46
70	115.7	.41
80	111.8	.37
90	108.3	.33
100	108.1	.30
110	102.3	.27
120	99.7	.24
130	97.4	.21
140	95.4	.18
150	93.8	.15
160	92.5	.11

* Source: Iowa Agr. Exp. Project. Econ. 1085. (Lbs. grain replaced by lbs. hay.)

---

[10] The feed contours and substitution rates in Table 4 have been derived by the writer from an experiment in the Animal Husbandry Department of Iowa State College. For details of this experiment see C. C. Culbertson, *et al., Different Proportions of Corn and Hay in Fattening Lambs.* Ia. Agr. Exp. Sta. A.H. Leaflet No. 178, 1951 (mimeographed). Two approaches were tried in deriving substitution contours. One included the derivation of the production function and the other involved the direct derivation of the product contour (feed combination curve). Examination of the coefficients suggested that the first system gave better estimates of the production relationships. The resulting production function (selected out of 5 models examined) included the following regression coefficients (with Y designating gain per lamb, X_1 designating hay input, and X_2 denoting grain consumption per lamb):

$$X_2 = \frac{2.3118 - .0037X_1 \pm \sqrt{(2.3118 - .0037X_1)^2 + .021175X_1 - .000031X_1{}^2 - 5.4267}}{.014792}$$

The equation defining marginal rates of substitution of hay for grain ($\Delta X_2 / \Delta X_1$) is given below:

$$\frac{dX_2}{dX_1} = -.250676 - \frac{9.210359 - .078568X_1}{\sqrt{18.42072X_1 - .078568X_1{}^2 - 375.5419}}$$

effect of either hay or grain when the ration is altered from one including only hay or only grain), but may be nearly linear in the middle.

The intra-animal feed-production surface is not always symmetrical in the manner of Figure 3. The upper capacity of a milk cow's stomach, for example, limits her daily intake of bulk. Thus while she may be able to produce as much milk from hay alone as from grain alone for rations only slightly over the maintenance level, the maximum milk output must be lower for a hay ration than for one including more grain. In other words,

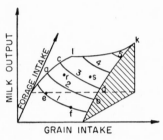

the production surface takes on the appearance of Figure 15. Here the level of milk output indicated as 3 might be attained with many combinations of the 2 feeds. That indicated by 5, however, could be obtained only with rations containing large amounts of grain and less hay.[11] The portion of the production surface lk indicates the maximum milk output per cow for different hay rations.

Fig. 15. Milk production surface for a cow as a fixed technical unit.

Actually the product contour map for a dairy cow may be pictured in the manner of Figure 16. (It is still to be established how much curvature exists for the contour lines or whether they are almost linear in the middle with "hooks" on the ends.) The line FG is the line of stomach capacity for the cow; it suggests the maximum forage input and the minimum grain input possible for any level of production. Since stomach capacity is limited, the movement over product contours A, B, C and D to higher levels of output is possible only as the maximum input of forage decreases. Line TN is the line of physiological well-being of the cow; as a ruminant, her digestive organs may not function effectively without some minimum of forage and therefore forage intake cannot be reduced below the level of this horizontal line. Supposedly lines FG and TN meet at a point defining the physical maximum in milk output of the cow and consequently the combination of feeds which will allow it. Lines FG and TN thus define the limits within which substitution of feed resources can take place. Under this contour situation, we can find price ratios for forages or grains which

---

[11] While most animal nutrition experiments do not provide data entirely appropriate for estimating feed substitution relationships, they could be easily redesigned to do so. An experiment in milk production aimed at establishing substitution rates alone would hold milk per cow constant while feed combinations are varied around contours such as ab and cd in Figure 15; or several contours between ab and cd or an entire portion of the production surface such as $abcd$ could be estimated if enough cows were available. Similarly, an experiment with hogs, cattle, or sheep might start all animals at a weight such as that suggested by contour ab. With different rations such as a, e, f, and b, the animals should be carried to the same weight as indicated by contour cd.

will cause the expansion in milk output to follow along the extremes of FG or TN as the milk price increases. (i.e., FC is an expansion path for all iso-cost curves with a slope greater than the product contours at their intersection with FC while CN is an expansion path for all iso-cost curves with a slope less than the product contours where they intersect TN.)

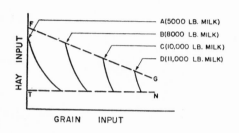

Fig. 16. Boundary of substitution opportunities and expansion path limits for milk per cow (also for daily gain on hogs or production of given grade of meat on steers).

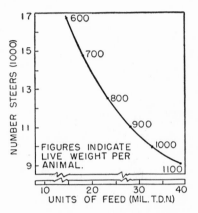

Fig. 17. Beef iso-quant. showing substitution between livestock numbers and feed in beef calf production (Source: Based on U.S.D.A. Tech. Bul. 900).

Animal units can also be made variable and serve as a substitute for feed in producing a given level of output. Rather than hold an animal fixed as a technical unit while varying amounts of feed are applied to it, both livestock numbers and feed per head can be rearranged in time. Whenever a first factor of production as a variable resource has a diminishing marginal productivity when applied to a second factor as a fixed resource, the 2 resources will substitute for each other at a diminishing rate, when both can be freely reapportioned relative to each other and the product is held constant. Thus feed productivity data of the nature indicated in previous chapters can be employed in deriving a beef iso-quant such as that indicated in Figure 17. It shows the combinations of feed and calf numbers which can be used to produce 10 million lbs. of live beef. Substitution rates are also of a diminishing nature on an individual farm where smaller numbers are concerned. Other meat animals show a similar feed-animal unit substitution relationship when the feed-meat transformation is at a diminishing rate. Other types of estimates show that historically livestock in the United States has been produced under diminishing rates of substitution between feed and livestock numbers.

When an acre of land is taken as the technical unit, substitution rates are also constant and diminishing in nature. Two fertilizers or varieties of seed may substitute for each other at constant rates as is often true for 2 types of capital representing different techniques in crop or livestock production. When substitution is between resources of distinct character such as seed and fertilizer or nitrogen and phosphate fertilizer, however, which enter biologically into the production process, substitution is most often at a diminishing rate (as is evident from the data of Figure 2 in Chapter 3). Substitution can be made in crop production between such distinct resources as land and fertilizer, or more accurately between elements stored in the soil and those obtained from fertilizer. Figure 18, which is based on Table 1, Chapter 4, explains why land and capital in the form of fertilizer may substitute at diminishing rates. Cotton output is at the rate of 1,292 lbs. for 1 acre of land and 1,400 lbs. of fertilizer. The same output of 1,292 lbs. (646 lbs. from each of 2 acres) can be produced with 2 acres of land and 420 lbs. of fertilizer (210 lbs. applied per acre). Three

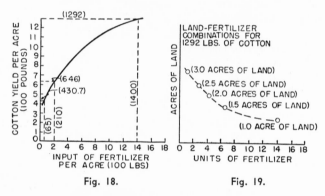

Fig. 18.   Fig. 19.

Substitution between land and fertilizer capital (Source: Experimental data of Table I, Chapter 4).

acres of land will also produce this output if 495 lbs. of fertilizer (165 lbs. on each of 3 acres) are used. Because the factor-product curve in Figure 18 is non-linear, the product contour derived from these substitution figures denotes diminishing rates of substitution between land and fertilizer. If the input-output curve in Figure 18 were linear, the substitution curve in Figure 19 would also be linear. Imperfect substitution between land and chemical elements, organic matter, or irrigation water arises especially because of the limited store of production elements in the soil and because the fertilizer services available from soil stocks are more severely limited in short time periods than those derived from other sources.

Farm recommendations and substitution rates. Many recommendations are made in agriculture which rest on assumptions of constant rates of substitution. While constant rates of substitution do exist and are important in the sense of both continuous and lumpy factor units, assumptions of linear substitution rates are often carried beyond the confines of their applicability. A few such assumptions can be reviewed: conservation planners often compute alternative cropping plans for individual farms and aggregate the small grains, corn, and forage produced in each into a total T.D.N. figure. This procedure assumes that a digestible nutrient of one feed replaces a digestible nutrient of another feed, regardless of the proportions in which they are combined. Some animal husbandrymen also use this procedure of evaluating a feed stock or an animal ration in terms of T.D.N.'s. Finally, many farm management surveys have assumed that machinery and labor substitute at constant rates. This assumption was implicit in the historic finding that profits increased directly with labor efficiency. Labor efficiency is ordinarily measured in these studies in terms of the amount of product produced or the work accomplished per man. Output or ac-complishment per man can be increased in many ways, and some of these always increase farm profits. However, even in the case of discontinuous factors such as machines, dimin-ishing rates of substitution can eventually hold true. Also, the substitution rates between 2 factors need not hold true for all levels of output for a technical unit or for a farm. This point was implicit in the discussion of Figure 15 relative to dairy cows. Also, it is obvious that, while a corn picker or cotton picker

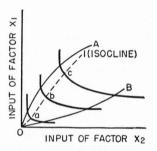

Fig. 20. Isocline indicating equal marginal rates of sub-stitution for different outputs.

may substitute for labor at a ratio of 1 machine to 60 days' labor on a large farm, the substitution rate is much lower for a small farm. Different rates of substitution between 2 resources may well hold true for farms of different size. It is true, of course, that marginal rates of substitution can be equal for different levels of output. This possibility is illustrated by the isocline OI in Figure 20. Here OA and OB are the borderlines which separate complementarity from substitution. The isocline OI falls within this range and defines points which denote equal marginal rates of substi-tution on the family of constant product curves. Thus the ratio $\Delta X_1/\Delta X_2$, the marginal rate of substitution, is equal at points $a, b,$ and c for all 3 product contours; since the slope or incline is equal, the isocline OI is traced out. There is a continuous isocline for each $\Delta X_1/\Delta X_2$ ratio which is common to all constant product contours. However, substitution rates need be equal only over a portion of the separate constant product curves (for example, rates of substitution may be found on the upper contour which do not exist on the lower contour). In the case of farms of different sizes, as well as for animals of different qualities, or even a cow of a given capacity fed to different levels, the product contours may change slopes and the marginal rates of factor substitution may well differ and recommendations to farmers should be so conditioned. Some will need to use factors in one proportion while others will want to use factors in another proportion if profits are to be maximized.

Intra-farm substitution. The greatest range of factors which substitute at a constant rate is to be found in mechanical processes, and hence in those resources, such as machines and labor, the services of which are not assimilated biologically by crops and animals. An important range of substitution at constant rates exists both between machines and between machines and labor. A 2-unit milking machine may save 300 hours of labor on a farm producing a given milk output while a 4-unit milking machine may save 600 hours. In many cases the substitution is between resources with discontinuous units such as 2 machines which are used for a given number of technical units and a given output on the farm. This often is the case for 2 different brands of tractor or for 2 different machines such as a lister and a corn planter, even when no differences in labor inputs or crop yield results. In this case the product iso-quant is not a smooth continuous line, but only 2 points such as d and e in Figure 5. Or, it may also take the "bent form" of points c, b, and h in Figure 13, where the "in-between" combinations of factors cannot be attained because of discontinuous units. In numerous cases several techniques exist on the farm and each is represented by a distinct combination of machine capital and labor. Corn, for example, may be (a) bound, husked at the barn, and shelled; (b) picked by hand and shelled; or (c) picked by machine and shelled. Within the limits of the corn acreage and output on a single farm, machine capital and labor can be substituted largely in discrete jumps and the production function or input-output relationship is linear over the range of technical units which make up the farm. The possible resource combinations are then represented by a 3-corner contour such as cbh in Figure 13.[12]

---

[12] The "production surface" under this situation can better be represented by the figure below rather than by Figures 3 or 4. In the figure below, we suppose that 3 discrete techniques exist and are applicable for outputs ranging from zero to nm from the fixed number of technical units composing the farm plant. A minimum quantity of labor is necessary for the high-machine technique represented by a while a minimum quantity of capital is required for the high-labor technique of c. Technique c may be used on all technical units with a

resulting linear input-output relationship sm. Technique a or b may be used alone and the linear production function tm or om results. More exactly, the technical units of the firm may limit or specify output at the level indicated as 3. The problem, then, is whether technique or resource combination, represented by a, b, or c should be used. In the case of this "surface," factor combinations represent jumps between the 3 circles at level 3; adjustments do not allow an "inch-by-inch movement around" the contour as in the case of Figures 3 and 4. (We might actually look upon nm as a stake driven vertically into the ground. Lines tm, om, and sm then represent poles resting at an angle on nm. A worm can attain the height nm only by crawling up the poles. It cannot otherwise attain nm because there is no surface between the poles on which to climb.)

Many mechanical processes do involve diminishing rates of substitution, however, particularly where machine or labor timeliness affects crop or livestock output per technical unit. If machine capital is viewed broadly, a wide range of diminishing substitution rates exist between labor and equipment. A farmer may first invest in a tractor which, when compared to other types of power, has the greatest effect in substituting for labor.

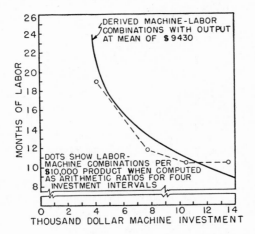

Fig. 21. Machine-labor investment (iso-product) line for sample of 160-acre Iowa farms (Source: Iowa Agr. Exp. Sta. project 1135).

Next, he may use a combine rather than a binder, and a baler rather than a hay loader. Each additional $1,000 invested may thus displace less and less labor. Figure 21, which has been derived from a homogeneous sample of Iowa farms, illustrates the possibilities here. Machine capital investment in dollars substitutes at a diminishing rate for labor, especially since the form of the capital changes as the total dollar quantity increases.[13]

---

[13] These data were derived from a sample of 40 southwest Iowa farms, all of 160 acres and producing mainly livestock products. The farms were owner-operated and all located on Marshall silt loam. (See Iowa Agr. Exp. Sta. Bul. 381 for a description of the sample.) In deriving the production function upon which the figure is based, labor and machines are taken as mechanical resource services which are not transformed into product, with the assumption that other factors are freely available for the chemical and biological aspects of production, and therefore that these categories of factors can be treated independently (see discussion in text). This assumption cannot be held to in a strict fashion because even machinery has biological effects. The production function derived is $Y = .611M^{.41}L^{.52}$, where Y is the value of crop and livestock produced in the year, M is machine and equipment investment in dollars, and L is labor in months. The marginal productivities of labor and machinery computed (approximately) at the means of $9,430 in product, $8,530 machine investment, and 14.9 months of labor were $454 for machine capital (per $1,000) and $395 for labor. The factor substitution relationship represented by the curve in Figure 21 is not exactly the same as that suggested by the dots. The derived curve suggests factor combinations at 1 level of output, or a single contour. The dots more nearly suggest a curve which is an average of all contours over the $6,500-$16,000 range of output studied.

Perhaps much of the substitution on farms is of the discontinuous nature indicated by the dotted lines for major pieces of equipment, but is of that indicated by the smooth curve when electrical equipment, small labor-saving devices, and adjustments in age, make, and quality of equipment are included in the analysis.

Substitutions of other techniques across technical units within the farm are also often at a constant rate. Several different practices and types of resource are possible in attainment of a given level of conservation on a farm, for example. These can be looked upon as substitute means to a given end and evaluated in the vein of any other factor-factor relationship in production. Many possibilities exist in combining conservation resources; 1 acre can be terraced, while 99 acres are contoured and strip cropped, or the proportions reversed. Except for topography differences, one method is or should be generally used, since substitution of practices and resources acre by acre is at a constant rate.

Intra-industry substitution. Adjustments in resource combinations which can be made by entire regions parallel those of the farm and the technical unit. One difference does exist, however. Resources represented by discontinuous units for a farm may take on continuity characteristics for an entire region. Because of the magnitude of the area and its output, tractors, in relation to production of the Cornbelt, are more "continuous" than hogs and chickens on a single farm. The greater divisibility in the total stock of any one resource also allows an entire region or the agricultural industry greater facility in withdrawing units of labor with small capital additions (or no additions at all if interfarm adjustments in production organization are to be made, while output is held at a constant level). Even then, capital in the form of machinery substitutes at a diminishing rate for labor and becomes a technical complement if decrements in labor are carried far enough. One estimate for United States agriculture as a whole illustrates this eventual complementarity between labor and capital. Johnson derived estimates based on 1939 data, showing that a reduction of the farm labor force by 20 per cent would reduce the marginal productivity of capital in agriculture by 2 per cent.[14] A 10 per cent reduction in labor would not likely reduce capital productivity but would more likely increase it. A similar estimate for Southern Iowa in 1951 indicated that a reduction in labor by 20 per cent would require a 6 per cent addition of machinery, while the marginal productivity of labor would be increased by 70 per cent.[15]

This labor-capital complementarity, along with the low price elasticity of demand for farm products, causes labor to have a very low or even a

---

[14] Reported in T. W. Schultz, *Production and Welfare of Agriculture.* New York: Macmillan, 1949, pp. 61-62.
[15] See Earl O. Heady and Earl R. Swanson, *Resource Productivity in Iowa Farming.* Iowa Agr. Exp. Sta. Bul. 388, Ames, 1952.

zero value productivity when it becomes backed up on farms during depression—or in low-income areas where labor is in surplus quantities and funds are not available for acquisition of capital. Machine capital and labor are complements, not only in the sense that enough labor can be withdrawn to cause ineffective operation of machines, but also in the sense that labor can be added to a point at which both more of capital and labor are required for a given output of product. The creation of more small farms results in duplication of power, machine, and building equipment on farms. (Many of these forms of capital are not used across farm boundaries; consequently, the upward-sloping portion of curve IS in Figure 12 is attained when X_2 refers to labor and X_1 refers to capital.) Or conversely, over some range both labor and capital could be withdrawn from agriculture without a reduction in the aggregate output; the stock of power and machine services is great enough in many farming regions that liquidation of small farms and consolidation of these with other farms would allow output on the former to be maintained with the machinery already on the latter. Finally, when substitution is viewed over producing areas, diminishing substitution rates grow partly out of non-homogeneity in land. National agricultural production could be increased by 5, 10, or 15 per cent through use of more labor and capital on the existing cultivated area. It could also be increased by these amounts through addition of acres not now cultivated and use of the labor and capital now employed. (Some of the labor and capital could be transferred from currently cultivated land to newly cultivated acres.) However, if the increments of land added to cultivation are lower and lower in productivity, diminishing substitution rates are realized as one rather than the other increase in resources is brought about.

Multiple Resources and Factor Productivity

While examining production functions with two variable resources, we should recognize that the productivity of any single factor, or any pair of factors, depends on the magnitude of input of still other resources. Substitution rates between pairs of factors also depend on the input of other resources which go to make up the production function. Aside from situations where the production and substitution coefficients are constant, this statement applies to technical units such as an animal, to economic units such as a farm firm or to economic aggregates such as a farming region. The facts can be illustrated with data drawn from a production function which includes more than two variable resources. First, we use a feed production function for choice yearling steers in Table 5 to illustrate how substitution rates between two feed resources depend on input of a third. Here we see that with protein held constant at 150 lbs., the first 500-lb. increment of hay substitutes for 223 lbs. of grain, the second substitutes.

Table 5.

Three-variable production function from experimental data. Feed quantities in producing 300 pound gain on choice yearling steers

Lb. of hay	Lb. of grain with 150 lbs. protein		Lb. of grain with 300 lbs. protein		Lb. of grain with 450 lbs. protein
500	2061	352	1709	277	1532
	(223)	—	(185)	—	(156)
1000	1838	314	1524	158	1366
	(120)	—	(99)	—	(89)
1500	1718	293	1425	148	1277
	(79)	—	(66)	—	(59)
2000	1639	280	1359	_141_	1218
	(60)	—	(50)	—	(44)
2500	1579	270	1309	135	1174

* Source: Derived from experimental data of Iowa State College from the production function $Y = 2.20\ G^{.490}\ H^{.081}\ P^{.133}$ where Y is beef production in pounds while G, H and P refer respectively to grain, hay and protein per steer. Substitution rates are averages between feed combinations.

for 120 lbs., the third substitutes for 79 lbs. and so on in line with our earlier notes on diminishing rates of substitution. (The pounds of grain replaced by each increment of hay are in parentheses in the grain columns.) However, with protein fixed at 300 lbs., the first three increments of hay substitute for only 185, 99 and 66 lbs. of grain respectively; the animal depended less on protein from legume hay as protein supplement is increased. Now if we follow across the lines of the table we see that if hay is held constant at 500 lbs., the first 150-lb. increment of protein substitutes for 352 lbs. of grain while the second substitutes for only 277 lbs., a diminishing rate of substitution of protein supplement for grain. (The pounds of grain replaced by 150 lbs. of protein are underlined between the columns.) However, with hay input fixed at 1000 lbs., the two increments of protein substitute for only 314 and 158 lbs. of grain.

If we hold hay and protein constant at 1000 and 450 lbs. respectively while we increase grain input, we obtain a lower marginal productivity of the latter feed than if we held hay and protein constant at 2000 and 300 lbs. respectively; this fact is obvious in the production function of footnote Table 5. However, we will illustrate this relationship between the productivity of one variable factor and the "fixed" level of input of other factors with the 1951 data in Table 6 for a sample of Montana farms. When all resources but labor are held constant at the mean quantity found on the farms, the marginal value productivity of labor varies from $246 with an input of 4 months per farm to $88 with an input of 12 months. (Inputs are those used in crop production and not those available on farms.) With input of cropland and crop services twice that found on the average farm, the marginal productivity of 4 months of labor jumps to

Table 6.

Marginal value productivity of labor with inputs of other resources fixed at different levels. Montana dryland wheat farms

Months labor input	All other inputs constant at mean quantity	Cropland and crop services doubled; other inputs constant at mean	Machine services doubled; other inputs constant at mean	Cropland, crop and machine services doubled
4	$246	$398	$311	$503
6	168	272	213	344
8	129	208	163	263
10	104	169	132	214
12	88	142	111	180

. * Source: Derived from a Montana farm sample with the production function $Y = 8.51 \ X_1 \cdot {}^{22} \ X_2 \cdot {}^{00} \ X_3 \cdot {}^{07} \ X_4 \cdot {}^{34} \ X_5 \cdot {}^{47}$ where Y refers to output measured in value while the inputs refer in order named to cropland, pasture land, labor, machine services and crop services.

$398 while that of 6 months is $272. A doubling of machinery inputs, with other resources held constant, causes labor productivity to increase but by a smaller amount than when land and crop services were increased; productivity of the 4th month of labor increases by only $65 while the productivity of the 12th month increases by only $23. When the several categories of resources are doubled in this production function for crops, the productivity of the 4th labor input becomes $503 while that of the 6th becomes $344, quantities considerably greater than when either category was held fixed at the larger input.

As we will see in a later chapter one of the important needs in American agriculture is that of adjustments such as those illustrated here. Labor productivity in areas of low average output such as the Southeast can be increased by (1) adding more capital for workers now on farms or by (2) decreasing the number of farm workers in the region. This same principle is illustrated in Figure 14 where the productivity of Z_4 jumps from 100 to 300 as input of Z_3 is increased from 20 to 120, i.e., is "held fixed" at different levels.

Selected References

Allen, R. G. D., *Mathematical Analysis For Economists*. London: Macmillan, 1942, pp. 284-289, 340-343, 369-374.

Black, J. D., *et al.*, *Farm Management*. New York: Macmillan, 1947, Ch. 26.

Boulding, K. E., *Economic Analysis*. New York: Harper, 1948, Ch. 31.

Carlson, S., *The Pure Theory of Production*. London: King and Son, 1939, Ch. 3.

Darfman, R., *Application of Linear Programming to Theory of the Firm*. Berkeley: Univ. of Cal. Press, 1951, Ch. 2.

Georgescu-Roegen, G., "Fixed Coefficients of Production and Marginal Productivity," *Rev. of Econ. Studies*, Vols. 3-4.

Heady, Earl O., "Marginal Rates of Substitution in the Utilization of Feed Resources," *Jour. Farm Econ.*, Vol. 33.

———, "Use and Estimation of Input-Output Coefficients," *Jour Farm. Econ.*, Proc. Vol. 34.

Heady, Earl O., and Olson, Russel V., *The Economics of Forage Crop Utilization*. Iowa Agr. Exp. Sta. Bul. 390, Ames, 1951.

Hopkins, J. A., *Elements of Farm Management*. New York: Prentice-Hall, 1941, p. 263.

Johnson, D. Gale, "Price Policy for Agriculture," *Jour. Farm Econ.*, Vol. 26, pp. 639-645.

Kaldor, N., "Limitational Factors and Elasticity of Substitution," *Rev. of Econ. Studies*, Vols. 3-4.

Koopmans, T. J., *Activity Analysis of Production and Allocation*. New York: Wiley, 1951, Chs. 1, 2, 3.

Lerner, A., *Economics of Control*. New York: Macmillan, 1942, Chs. 12, 13.

Samuelson, P. A., *Foundations of Economic Analysis*. Cambridge: Harvard University Press, 1948, pp. 69-76.

Schultz, T. W., *Production and Welfare of Agriculture*. New York: Macmillan, 1949, pp. 61-63.

Tolley, H. R., Black, J. D., and Ezekiel, M. K., "Input as Related to Output," in *Farm Organization Studies*, U. S. Dept. of Agr. Bul. 1277, Washington, 1924.

Weintraub, S., *Price Theory*. New York: Pitman, 1949.

6

Resource Combination and Cost Minimization

THE PROBLEM in resource substitution is one of combining factors in a manner to minimize the cost of producing a given amount of product. It is one which faces the individual entrepreneur in maximizing his profit. It also is one which concerns a nation or an economic unit of any other magnitude. The economic product from given resources, measured in profit at the farm or in other terms at the national level, can be at a maximum only if each unit of commodity is produced with a minimum cost or resource outlay. Cost or resource minimization is a goal in the factor-factor sense, but not in the factor-product sense. The analysis which follows first defines efficiency in producing a given output. Emphasis is first on the individual farm as a firm and second on national production and resource use. Other substitution problems are also analyzed. Finally, the economic problems which arise under both the factor-product and factor-factor relationships are studied together.

An important portion of this chapter is devoted to problems of decision-making and resource administration when factors substitute in a continuous manner. Questions of discontinuity and linear substitution rates are given less space since they are less difficult to comprehend. At the outset we consider the optimum manner of producing a given output such as illustrated by the 24-unit contour in Figure 6 of Chapter 5. We are not concerned with adjustments between the 24 and 36 product curves. The farmer, because he has limited resources, often looks at production in this vein; he has 20 acres of cotton or 75 market hogs and searches for the lowest cost method for the probable output. Similarly, during a food emergency national planners may specify the quantity of food and question the optimum manner of producing it. However, the optimum level of output also depends, in either case, on the economy with which resources can be combined.

As in all other areas of economics, the factor-factor relationship implies a choice. Which combination of factors should be selected for greatest attainment of the end in question? As in other situations requiring choice, decision can be made only if a choice indicator (criterion for indicating which of many alternatives is most desirable) is present. The relevant choice indicator for an end of maximum profits is that of price ratios or, as indicated later, an iso-cost line. In sections which follow, a maximum physical product becomes an intermediate end in production. The choice indicator then becomes the substitution ratio or product contour for 1 technical or economic unit as compared to the product contour for a second unit. The basic principles of choice remain the same, regardless of whether the choice indicator is a price ratio (iso-cost curve), a substitution ratio (product contour or iso-product line), or a consumer preference function (indifference curve). Similarly, the principles of production or resource allocation are the same regardless of the end to be attained.

In Chapter 4, the combinations of resources was held constant and only 1 factor and output were varied. In early parts of this chapter, output is held constant and 2 or more factors are varied; again, concern is with the most efficient combination of resources to produce a given amount of product.

Technical Efficiency and Irrational Resource Use

Even in the absence of choice indicators, minimum conditions of economic efficiency again can be specified in the context of technical ratios. A necessary condition (but not a sufficient condition) for economic efficiency is always that a maximum product be attained from given resources, or, conversely, that a minimum of resources be used for a given product. Ranges of irrational resource use also can be outlined under the factor-factor relationship. Irrational ranges of production again are those in which increased technical efficiency, a greater physical output/input ratio, is always consistent with increased economic efficiency; prices of factors or product need not be known. Irrational resource combinations are those segments of the product contour denoting technical complementarity. Rational and irrational resource combinations are segregated in Figures 11 and 20 of Chapter 5 by the borderlines OA and OB. Just as the 3 stages existed under the factor-product relationship, 3 ranges also exist in the factor-factor case. First, using Figure 12 of Chapter 5 for discussion purposes, any resource combination outside of the substitution range (above OM or beyond OR) is irrational, since factors can always be rearranged to give the same product with less of both resources: (1) The combination OV of X_2 and OM of X_1 could always be used to produce a greater product by shifting to a contour indicative of a greater product than IS.[1] (2) The product output indicated by curve IS can be attained by dropping input

---

[1] One condition for a family of constant product curves indicating a single technique is that they do not cross. Hence, a curve indicating a greater product always could be attained by using somewhat less than OV of X_2 and OM of X_1.

of X_1 back to OH and input of X_2 back to OR. Knowledge of exact price relationships is unnecessary for either type of adjustment. In the first case, the output and its value will increase while the cost outlay for resources will remain constant. In the second case, output and gross revenue are constant while the cost outlay for factors is reduced. Net profit must increase in either case. In reference to Figure 11 of Chapter 5, a reduction of X_2 input from OS to OR, with output remaining constant at 100, will always increase profits as long as any costs attach to this factor. Even if X_2 is free or has no variable cost attached to it, as is the case of certain family labor or resource services hired for a specified period irrespective of their use, there is no economic advantage in using more than OR units for an output of 100 if farm profit is the relevant end.

Irrational factor combinations and technical inefficiency also can be defined in other terms. Technical efficiency also denotes economic efficiency in this context: A different product contour (production surface or production function) denotes each technique involving the same kind and quantity of resources. Alternative product contours are pictured in Figure 1 and Figure 2 by the isoquants I_oS_o, I_nS_n and I_mS_m. Each contour represents the same output, say 100 lbs. of milk. (The several contours should

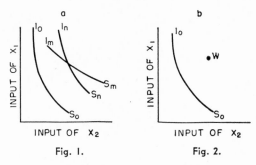

Fig. I.   Fig. 2.

Technical and economic efficiency.

not be confused with those used elsewhere to denote different outputs). Both I_nS_n and I_mS_m require more of factors X_1 and X_2 (for the 100 units of output) than I_oS_o. The product contour I_oS_o might be looked upon as a boundary line; it defines the product contour which falls lowest in the plane (or it might actually be composed of the lower segments of 2 contours which cross each other). With the input of one factor given, it defines the minimum quantity of the other factor which will result in the specified output (100 lbs. of milk). The boundary line or product contour I_oS_o is also pictured in Figure 2. Any resource combination lying above or to the right of I_oS_o and representing an output of 100 pounds is an irrational combination. It is uneconomic as long as the price for the product or either one or both of the factors is greater than zero. The point W represents such an inefficient point or irrational combination of X_1 and X_2.[2] The same product could always be produced (a) by using less of one factor (by a vertical or horizontal movement until I_oS_o is reached) or (b) by using less of both factors (a diagonal movement toward the origin). If the product has a price and the factors do not, a greater value of product can be produced with the same physical outlay of factors. If both factors and product have prices, the same value of product can be attained with a smaller cost outlay. Our definition refers only to the same kinds of resources. It does not include new techniques which require machines or other resources not included in previous techniques.

Irrational production in agriculture. Numerous examples of "apparent" irrational resource combinations can be found in agriculture. Irrational factor combination by the individual farmer must be explained largely in terms of lack of knowledge, where profit maximization is the goal. Farmers often can reorganize labor or capital inputs and obtain the same output with less of 1 or more resources. The time and motion or labor efficiency studies emphasized during World War II uncovered many possibilities here. Where labor routines are not carefully planned, use of a hook for hanging milk pails in a convenient place or of an inexpensive wheel barrow for hauling feed often require no additional capital. These minute outlays simply replace capital in the form of the extra scoops and pails required to handle the feed and milk under the irrational chore routine. Yet remarkable savings in labor can be made where the farmer does not make a trip to each cow with a scoop of feed or from each cow to the house with a pail of milk. Some farmers need only reorganize their travel paths to do the same job with less labor and less capital. This efficiency step-up has mainly the effect of reducing labor (X_1) from ok to ol in Figure 10 of Chapter 5, while capital (X_2) remains constant at om, milk output being given by IS. Similarly, capital investment in the form of machinery and equipment is so great on many farms that it no longer reduces labor below a limitational minimum nor does it, therefore, represent a rational use of the resource if profit is the individual farmer's goal. If the goal is one of maximum utility and greater enjoyment is derived from having more machines and tools around, the resource combination is not then irrational. (See the chapter on firm-household interrelationships.)

If a maximum of agricultural products from given resources can be taken as an end at the national level, additional areas of irrational resource combination can be pointed out. A previous chapter indicated that creation of large numbers of small farms can result in use of both more labor and capital for the same output. Very small farms thus stand to

---

[2] If we use the terms of Koopman's, *et al.*, *Activity Analysis of Production and Allocation*. New York: Wiley, 1951, only line I_oS_o defines the "set of efficient points" for the particular product and level of output.

obviate resource savings which go with larger units. Any production policy designed to create a large number of small, owner-operated farms must add both labor and capital to agriculture, since power and equipment units must be duplicated. If society places such high values on the virtues of farming, however, that it is willing to invest more resources to get the same product, combinations of capital and labor falling in the complementary range could not be termed irrational. A problem of American agriculture is in the opposite direction, however. In such low-income areas as the Appalachian highlands, the Ozark Mountains, and the Lake states cut-over region, labor should be withdrawn, not only to remove production from labor-capital complementary ranges, but also to provide the farm people concerned with greater income opportunities.

Importance of Price Relationships

Rational resource combinations have been defined as those falling on the portion of the product contour with a negative slope; the marginal rates of substitution between factors must be negative indicating that an increase in one factor allows a decrease in another. Rational resource use is never represented by points on constant product contour indicating a zero, infinite, or positive slope, since one or more resources are then redundant or excess factors. While irrational resource combinations can be specified in the absence of price information, selection of the one factor combination within the rational range (the negatively slope portion of a constant product contour) is possible only by means of a choice indicator. The relevant choice indicator for profit maximization is the factor price ratio. While our first discussion refers to profit maximization we will discuss factor combinations from the standpoint of national production and resource use policies in a later section.

Fixed coefficients. An extreme in factor-factor relationships is that of fixed coefficients (Figure 9 in Chapter 5). Only 1 resource combination is possible in production processes which require combination of 2 resources in fixed proportions; factors must be combined in the manner dictated by this extreme technique of production. Either it does or it does not pay to combine resources in the fixed proportions and produce the product. The only economic question is this: Is the marginal value of the product greater than the marginal cost of the 2 factors combined?

Constant rates of substitution. When 2 factors, X and Z, substitute continuously at constant marginal rates, only 1 of 2 unique combinations will minimize the cost of producing a given output. The given output should be produced entirely with X and none of Z, or entirely with Z and none of X. The illustrative data of Table 1 can be used to explain this statement. The 2 resources X and Z substitute for each other at the constant and continuous rates $\Delta Z / \Delta X = 4.0$ or $\Delta X / \Delta Z = .25$. Our problem, then, is to compare these marginal rates of substitution with the price ratios for the factors. (In Chapter 4 we compared the factor/product price ratio with the marginal product of the factor.) Using P_x to denote the price of X and P_z to denote the price of Z, comparison is between the price ratio P_x/P_z and the substitution ratio $\Delta Z/\Delta X$, when X is being substituted for Z. It is between P_z/P_x and $\Delta X/\Delta Z$, when Z is being substituted for X. If Table 1 is examined, we see that the cost of producing 100 units of product is at a minimum when the price of X is \$2 and the price of Z is \$1, with use of 25 units of X and none of Z. The constant product is forthcoming at minimum cost with use of Z alone when prices are \$5 for X and \$1 for Z. With prices at \$8 and \$2, any one of the many factor combinations results in the same cost outlay.

Table 1.

Product Contour (Combinations of X and Z in Producing 100 Units of Product Y), Rates of Substitution, and Cost Outlays Illustrating Cost Minimization (Hypothetical Data)

Quantity of resources for producing 100 units of output		Marginal rates of substitution		Cost of producing 100 units of Y with factor prices of		
X	Z	$\Delta Z/\Delta X$	$\Delta X/\Delta Z$	$X = \$2$ $Z = \$1$	$X = \$5$ $Z = \$1$	$X = \$8$ $Z = \$2$
(1)	(2)	(3)	(4)	(5)	(6)	(7)
0	100	−4	−.25	\$100	\$100	\$200
5	80	−4	−.25	90	105	200
10	60	−4	−.25	80	110	200
15	40	−4	−.25	70	115	200
20	20	−4	−.25	60	120	200
25	0	−4	−.25	50	125	200

The reasons for these differences is to be found in price and substitution ratios. The P_x/P_z price ratio of 2/1 or 2.0 in column 5 is less than the $\Delta Z/\Delta X$ substitution ratio of 20/5 or 4; by using 5 units of X with a total value of \$10, 20 units of Z with a total value of \$20 can be replaced. In column 6, 5 units of X have a value of \$25, while 20 units of Z have a value of \$20, and the latter should always be used at the expense of the former. The price ratio is just equal to the substitution ratio in the last column and no cost reduction results; \$40 of X substitutes for \$40 of Z. The phenomenon of constant substitution rates explains why farmers should always use either grade number 1 or grade number 2 of corn or why they should obtain all of their credit from one lender rather than another when price ratios differ from substitution ratios. Different brands or makes of the same machine also substitute at constant rates and one brand should be used to the exclusion of another if costs are to be minimized and the price ratio diverges from the substitution ratio.

Diminishing rates of substitution. A principle of cost minimization can now be stated: *If two or more factors are employed in production of a single*

*product, cost is at a minimum when the ratio of factor prices is inversely
equal to the marginal rate of substitution of the factors.* The condition
can be expressed in equation form as $\Delta Z/\Delta X = P_x/P_z$ where the term
$\Delta Z/\Delta X$ refers to the marginal rate of substitution of factor X for factor
Z and P_x refers to the price per unit of X and P_z refers to the price per
unit of Z. A corollary of the principle, and the one actually used in the
preceding section, is this: If the price ratio P_x/P_z is less than the substitution ratio $\Delta Z/\Delta X$, costs can be lessened by using more of X and less of
Z; if P_z/P_x is less than $\Delta X/\Delta Z$, costs can be lessened by using more of
Z and less of X. For column 5 in Table 1, the price ratio P_x/P_z was less
than the substitution ratio $\Delta Z/\Delta X$ for all combinations of the 2 factors.
Therefore, costs could be minimized by using all of X. In column 7 the
price ratio equals the substitution ratios and one factor combination therefore does not cost less than another.

The principle of cost minimization can be illustrated better when substitution is at a diminishing rather than at a constant rate. Using the
exact substitution rates in Table 2, and with X_1 priced at 84¢ and X_2 at
$1.00, 100 units of commodity Y can be produced with a minimum cost
outlay when 20 units of the former and 26.6 units of the latter resource
are used. Here the price ratio P_{x_1}/P_{x_2} of .84 (.84/1.00) is equal to the exact
substitution ratio of .84. That the combination 20 units of X_1 and 26.6
units of X_2 should be used is also specified by the *average* ratio of substitution. It indicates that the price ratio of .84 is equal to a substitution
ratio falling between .80 and .88 in column 4; the corresponding factor
combination is that indicated. With factor prices of $1.36 and $2.00, and
hence a P_{x_1}/P_{x_2} price ratio of .68 (1.36/2.00), minimum costs are denoted

Table 2.

Minimizing Costs for a Specified Product Contour and Varying Prices for Factors (Hypothetical Data)

Product contour: combination of factors X_1 and X_2 which will produce a given output (100 units) of product Y		Marginal rate of substitution of X_1 for X_2 $(\Delta X_2/\Delta X_1)$		Cost of producing 100 units of Y with factor prices of:	
Units of factor X_1	Units of factor X_2	Exact	Average	$X_1 = \$ .84$ $X_2 = \$1.00$	$X_1 = \$1.36$ $X_2 = \$2.00$
(1)	(2)	(3)	(4)	(5)	(6)
10	35.4	−.92		$43.80	$84.40
			−.88		
20	26.6	−.84		43.40	80.40
			−.80		
30	18.6	−.76		43.80	78.00
			−.72		
40	11.4	−.68		45.00	77.20
			−.64		
50	5.0	−.60		47.00	78.00

by a factor combination which includes 40 units of X_1 and 11.4 of X_2, since here the marginal rate of substitution (X_1 for X_2) is also .68. Obviously, the optimum resource combination varies as price ratios vary.

Graphic Indication of Minimum Costs

Just as an iso-product curve can be constructed to indicate all possible combinations of factors which will produce an equal or constant amount of commodity, an iso-cost (equal cost or iso-outlay) line can be drawn to indicate all possible combinations of 2 factors which can be purchased with a given outlay of funds. Let us apply prices of 50¢ and $1 to 2 factors, X_1 and X_2, respectively. If we have $10 to spend on these 2 factors, an iso-cost line such as L_1A_1 indicated in Figure 3 can be constructed: 20 units of X_1 can be purchased if nothing is spent on X_2; 10 units of X_2 can be purchased if nothing is spent on X_1. If one-half the funds are spent on each factor, 10 units of X_1 and 5 units of X_2 can be purchased. Hence, the iso-cost line indicates all combinations of X_1 and X_2 which can be purchased with $10, a constant cost outlay. Constant outlay lines are always linear for a farm or other competitive firms which do not purchase enough of the factor to affect the market price. The slope of the iso-cost line is an indication of the factor/factor price ratio. The slope of L_1A_1 (or P_{x_2}/P_{x_1}) is 2/1 or 2.0, indicating that if the cost outlay is to remain constant, 1 unit of X_2 can be exchanged for 2 units of X_1 without changing the amount spent.

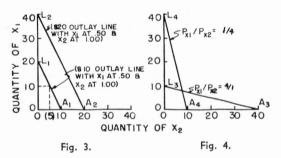

Fig. 3.   Fig. 4.

Iso-cost (equal cost) lines.

The curve L_2A_2 in Figure 3 represents the iso-cost line when $20 can be spent on X_1 and X_2, with prices remaining at 50¢ and $1 respectively. It again shows all the possible combinations of X_1 and X_2 which can be purchased with the given outlay of $20. It has the same slope as the $10 iso-outlay line ($L_1A_1$), since the price ratio is identical. The height of L_2A_2 ($20 outlay) is, of course, twice that of L_1A_1 ($10 outlay), since the outlay is doubled. In Figure 4, the iso-cost line L_4A_4 indicates a price ratio P_{x_2}/P_{x_1} of 4/1, when the price of X_1 is $1, the price of X_2 is $4, and the total cost outlay is \$40. Iso-cost line L_3A_3 reverses the ratio, because here the price of X_1 is \$4, and the price of X_2 is \$1 (a P_{x_2}/P_{x_1} price ratio of 1/4). Again the constant outlay is \$40. From these illustrations it is apparent that the slope of the iso-cost line is indicative of the factor price ratio.

Knowledge of the meaning and implications of iso-cost lines allows geometric illustration of cost minimization. Since (a) the slope of the *iso-cost curve* indicates the ratio of factor prices and (b) the slope of the *iso-product curve* represents the marginal rate of substitution, minimum costs for a given output can be indicated by tangency of 2 such iso-lines. Figure 5, which employs the product contour data of Table 2, can be used to illustrate this condition of cost minimization and profit maximization. When the price of X_1 was 84¢ and the price of X_2 was \$1, costs were at a minimum with 20 units of X_1 and 26.6 units of X_2. The cost outlay was then \$43.40. Line LA in Figure 5 represents an iso-cost curve of \$43.40, when prices are 84¢ and \$1, respectively, for factors X_1 and X_2. Its slope indicates that 52.1 units of X_1 or 43.8 units of X_2 can be purchased with \$43.80. The slope of 43.8/52.1 indicates the P_{x_1}/P_{x_2} price ratio of .84/1.0 or .84. The marginal rate of substitution, $\Delta X_2/\Delta X_1$, is .84 when 20 units of X_1 and 26.6 units of X_2 are employed. Hence, tangency of the iso-cost

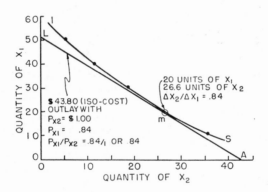

Fig. 5. The use of iso-cost and iso-product curves to indicate minimum costs (adapted from Table 2).

line LA and the iso-product line IS at point m indicates minimum costs for 100 units of output, since here the 2 ratios $\Delta X_2/\Delta X_1$ and P_{x_1}/P_{x_2} are both equal to .84. (Or conversely $\Delta X_1/\Delta X_2$ and P_{x_2}/P_{x_1} are both 1.19.)

Further details on the geometry of minimizing costs are indicated in Figure 6. If the output indicated by product contour I_1S_1 is to be produced with minimum costs, OK of X_1 and ON of X_2 (as indicated by tangency of the iso-product and iso-cost lines at point n) must be used. Tangency of the 2 lines again indicates that their slope or ratio of change is equal, and, therefore, that the marginal rate of substitution is equal to the price ratio at this point. While smaller outlays such as that indicated by iso-cost

line L_1A_1 are possible, they will not allow production of 100 units of prod·
uct. (Iso-cost line L_1A_1 is too low in the plane to be tangent with I_1S_1.)
Many other combinations of X_1 and X_2 also are possible but each costs
more than the quantities OK and ON. For example, if OL units of X_1 and
OM units of X_2 are employed, the cost outlay indicated by L_3A_3 will result.
However, since L_3A_3 is higher than L_2A_2, the OL-OM factor combination
represents a greater cost outlay than the OK-ON combination. Only tangent iso-cost lines denote minimum costs. Those which intersect product
contours never denote minimum costs. While we have illustrated the principle of *minimizing* costs for a given output, we also have indicated the
principle of maximizing output from given costs. The output of 100 (I_1S_1)
is the greatest amount which can be produced with the cost outlay represented by L_2A_2. Most farmers operate in this framework. Because of
uncertainty the quantity of resources which they can obtain is limited.

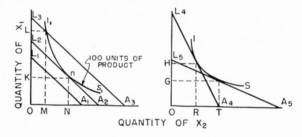

Fig. 6. Factor combina-
tions associated with minimum costs as indicated by
iso-product and iso-cost
curves when factor price
ratios are constant.

Fig. 7. Factor combina-
tions associated with minimum costs as indicated by
iso-product and iso-cost
curves when factor price
ratios vary.

Hence their problem is quite largely one of getting the greatest possible
product from the resources which can be purchased with given funds. A
maximum product from given funds is consistent with profit maximization,
since it always results, under competitive conditions, in a greater gross
revenue and hence a greater net profit.

Figure 7 illustrates how the optimum resource combination changes with
variations in the ratio of factor prices. Under the price ratio of iso-cost
line L_5A_5, costs are at a minimum with OG and OT units of X_1 and X_2
respectively. A change in the price ratio, as suggested by L_4A_4, either
through an increase in the price of X_2 or a decline in the price of X_1, shifts
the minimum cost combination to OH of X_1 and OR of X_2. As an aid in
geometric analysis, the reader may wish to remember this point: As long
as the absolute slope towards the horizontal axis of the iso-cost line is
greater than the absolute slope of the iso-product line, costs are lessened

(profits are increased) as the resource measured on the vertical axis is substituted for the resource measured on the horizontal axis. If the slope of the cost line is less than the slope of the product line, the horizontal-axis factor should be substituted for the vertical-axis factor. Tangency of the 2 iso-curves indicates that a dollar spent on one factor returns exactly the same amount as a dollar spent on the other factor.

Farmer combination of resources. Important changes in factor price ratios do take place in agriculture and farmers substitute resources accordingly. The cost ratio for new machinery and farm labor varies greatly throughout the various stages of depression and prosperity. Similarly, the price ratio for 2 feeds such as corn and protein varies depending on the annual supply of each. However, when price ratios are compared for second-hand machinery and labor, protein and carbohydrate feeds or other pairs of farm-originated resources, a high degree of constancy is denoted throughout the business cycle. This tendency towards constant factor price ratios also leads to a tendency for factors to be combined similarly irrespective of the general level of farm prices. These supply characteristics of agriculture are discussed further in a later chapter.

Farmer combination of resources is not always in a manner to minimize costs for a given output and hence to maximize profits. This behavior pattern can be explained partly by the fact that profit maximization is not the ultimate end of farming. Utility maximization is more nearly the goal. Accordingly, farmers sometimes use labor-saving equipment, though it cannot be justified in terms of resource prices and substitution ratios, in order to lessen the drudgery of farm work and increase the satisfactions of living. Part of the behavior pattern can also be explained in terms of lack of knowledge. One need not go far to find hog-producing farms where 1 lb. of high-protein feed will substitute for 20 lbs. of grain. Seldom in history has the protein/grain price ratio been as great as 20. On the other hand, many of the apparent less-than-optimum combinations of resources represent rational farmer decision even where profit maximization is the relevant end. Comparison of price and substitution ratios alone is a sufficient step in specifying resource combinations which will maximize profits only if the product is homogeneous with respect to time.

A special substitution problem in agriculture is that of complementarity between time and a factor of production.[3] Protein or forage can be substituted for grain in the ration of a meat animal, but the period of production is lengthened. Hogs fed low protein rations require extra time before reaching 225 lb. or other marketing weights; protein is a substitute for both time and grain; time and grain are complementary factors of

---

[3] Comparisons thus far have included only 2 substitute factors. Many production decisions involve the rearrangement of more than 2 resources. While analyses of these problems cannot be made conveniently with geometric illustrations, the principles and conditions of cost minimization are the same.

production. Thus the pork producer attempting to maximize profits is concerned not only with minimum costs for pork but also with prices for pork sold at different points in time. Longer periods of production introduce greater uncertainty, because the opportunity for price changes is increased and the ability of the producer to formulate accurate price expectations is lessened. In decision-making the farmer can make several adjustments under this situation. First, he can use more time and less protein by farrowing his pigs earlier, and can thus market them at the same date as if they had been given more protein. He also would need to consider equipment costs, which are complementary with time for earlier farrowings, but are necessary for a homogeneous product with respect to time. Second, he can use price differentials to place a value on the pork sold at different times and estimate an iso-value instead of an iso-pork curve. The iso-cost line might then be related to the iso-value line in determining which combination of grain and protein gives minimum costs for an equal value of product. Third, he can consider pork marketed at different points in time as different products. The relevant analysis then falls under the product-product relationship of Chapter 7.

The fact that many decisions in production revolve around more than 2 variable factors does not negate the conditions under which cost or resource outlays are minimized. The principles can be extended to any number of factors. If a production process can employ 3 substitute resources X_1, X_2, and X_3, minimum costs for a given output are realized when $\Delta X_1/\Delta X_2 = P_{x_2}/P_{x_1}$, $\Delta X_3/\Delta X_2 = P_{x_2}/P_{x3}$, and $\Delta X_3/\Delta X_1 = P_{x_1}/P_{x_3}$.

Questions of time and product homogeneity are also important in substitution of other livestock feeds. Forage can be substituted for grain as cattle are fed on pasture, as they are pastured and then fed out, or through rations in dry-lot containing different proportions of hay and grain. Product contours or substitution rates derived from data of this nature define a homogeneous product only if the animals are taken to the same grade. Feeding to the same grade again requires more time when forage is substituted for grain and the uncertainty complex mentioned above may arise to cause use of the method which does not result in minimum costs for each 100 lbs. of beef. Time problems in substitution also arise where the life of one or more factors extends beyond a single production period. This again is the question of a machine when the farmer buys the complete stock of services embodied in it rather than hiring machine services on a custom basis. Since part of the services embodied in the machine are not used until a later year, their costs or prices must be compounded from the year of purchase until the year of use. The same procedure need not be followed for a substitute resource such as labor the price of which is paid, or the investment made, only in the year of use. Hence, in any period looking ahead, the farmer may equate the expected prices of machine services and labor, but in a contemporary or current production period, substitution and price ratios need not be equal to define rational planning. This problem is discussed further in later chapters dealing with time, uncertainty and discounting.

Discontinuous factors and linear programming. The foregoing discussion involves substitution decisions when resource units are continuous and divisible. We recognize that most factors are continuous and divisible if resource services, rather than the resource itself, are considered. However, since important problems in agriculture do revolve around discontinuous resource units we must turn our attention in this direction. A "lumpy" factor such as a cotton picker, along with purely complementary resource services, may replace the labor of 10 men for each year. Still the principles of cost minimization outlined above hold true: Aside from the discounting problem mentioned above, the machine/labor price ratio must be greater than 10/1, the discontinuous substitution ratio. The presence of discontinuity again eases the problem of decision-making, since there are not an infinite number of price and substitution ratios which are relevant. Instead, only the 10/1 ratio is relevant, and machine services should not be substituted for labor unless the machine/labor price ratio (for services) is less than 10/1 (except when time and timeliness must be considered).

Different machines and techniques do, however, give product contours with corners in them, such as those illustrated in Figure 13 of Chapter 5 or the footnote figure of the same chapter. These discontinuous or broken constant-product contours arise in the following practical sense: (1) A machine, a discontinuous and indivisible unit, may be substituted for labor on a farm with a limited output. By hand methods, the output may require 30 days of labor, while each machine may substitute for 20 days. Hence the first machine will substitute for 20 days, but the second machine can substitute for only 10 days because there are only 30 days of labor to be performed. The contour then becomes that of the linear-discontinuous nature indicated in Figure 8. (2) Several different techniques may exist and substitute for each other in a linear fashion. As an example we may suppose that 3 techniques for putting up hay include (a) conventional hand methods, (b) a hay loader and mow fork, or (c) a baler and complete mechanization. If b replaces 20 days of labor as compared to a, and if c replaces 10 days when compared to b, the contour again appears of the nature indicated in Figure 8 if we measure labor on the x axis and each discrete method as dollar capital along the y axis. (The constant product contour in Figure 8 below may be considered as a reproduction of contour 3 in the footnote of Chapter 5).

The "contour" in Figure 8 supposes that only the factor combinations circled are relevant, since discontinuity prevents attainment of the in-between combinations. For all practical purposes, the 2 segments ds and st of constant product contour dst can be considered the same as linear substitution lines denoting that either 1 of 2 extreme resource combinations should be employed for the given output. Since the second machine displaces 20 days of labor, substitution of the machine will lower costs if the ratio of prices for machine services as compared to labor is less than 20/1 or 20. Since the marginal rate of substitution ($\Delta L/\Delta M$) of the third machine for labor is 10/1, it should not be added unless the machine service costs less than 10 times the price of a day's labor. Corners such as s on a contour, or linear-discontinuous factor substitution relationships, result in great stability in resource combinations. Price ratios may swing

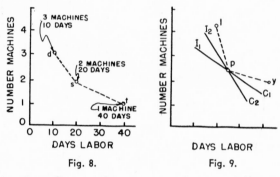

Fig. 8.   Fig. 9.

Discontinuous-linear product contours and resource substitution.

widely without causing an existing combination of resources (technique or method of production) to become uneconomic. For the example of Figure 8, the machine-service/labor price ratio can fluctuate anywhere in the range 20/1 to 10/1 (not greater than 20/1 or not less than 10/1) without causing either combination d or combination t to become less costly than s. The same logic is illustrated by the discontinuous contour lpy in Figure 9. Although iso-cost lines I_1C_1 and I_2C_2 specify quite different factor price ratios, the combination of machine services and labor indicated at point p is optimum for both. A swing to technique or combination l is economic only if the iso-cost line has a slope equal to or greater than that of lp. A swing to y is economic only if the slope of the iso-cost line becomes equal to or less than the slope of py.

Many agricultural specialists have wondered why farmers stick persistently to old techniques rather than shifting immediately to new technologies. The corner-type factor relationship is one explanation, along with the transformation consideration to be mentioned later. This phenomenon also helps explain why farmers retain given techniques and resource combinations as price ratios swing in various directions throughout the several stages of the business cycle. When a person adds to this phenomenon still another, namely, the tendency for price ratios of farm-originated resources to remain constant over the business cycle, further basis is laid for fixity of techniques over time.

Relevance in research and education. The several cost-minimizing conditions set out above have numerous implications in research. One problem is that of isolating irrational areas of factor combination. While the problem is relevant for the farm particularly in labor efficiency studies, it is also relevant for the nation's agriculture. Welfare of a nation always can be increased as these are removed, as long as resources have alternative employment opportunities. Studies are currently needed which estimate the loss in product growing out of small, low-income farms and, hence, resource combinations which are in the complementary range. The costs of this resource combination need to be compared with the product which might be added were society to invest in the persons and capital involved and transfer them to other economic pursuits. In a similar vein, the costs of complementary-range production need to be estimated before the extreme family-farm reforms sometimes suggested by the land devout are brought about.

The optimum selection of resource combinations in the competitive range can be made only if farmers have available information on substitution ratios and price ratios. Substitution ratios for resources characterized by continuous units such as feeds and fertilizer will continue to be furnished by animal, plant, and soil scientists. Greater use of this factor-factor data could be made were it provided in a manner cognizant of marginal quantities. A high degree of refinement in substitution ratios is merited for feeds, since here the combination can be varied today and the output and its price are often known on the same day. Uncertainty does not overshadow the technical substitution relationships so greatly as in the case of machines and other polyperiod resources. It is probably true that the burden of providing technical factor ratios such as those of machine/labor or labor/land substitution will continue to fall on the agricultural production economists. Here approximations may be sufficient for planning purposes; often the substitution ratios can be provided in the vein of linear relationships, because time and uncertainty associated with machine ownership bears more heavily on the decision-making process than do small differences in substitution ratios. The second important task of the production economist, in his effort to guide resource administration by the individual farmer, is that of providing price outlook or expectations in a manner to allow proper investment in alternative resources and methods of production. This type of inference involves costs-and-returns studies designed to show whether one or another method of production is better. Differences between continuous, discontinuous, and linear and diminishing factor substitution ratios are then important; they should be recognized where farm record surveys and budget studies are used to predict the least-cost technique or resource combination. When substitution is at a continuous rate, the findings under one set of prices may be entirely misleading as even small changes come about in price ratios. Where substitution is of a discontinuous nature, however, the inferences based on budget or record studies may have application under a wide range of price ratios for the reasons suggested in Figures 8 and 9. Again it can be said that the linear programming assumptions outlined in Chapter 3 cause the budget method and similar research procedure to have great application under linear-discontinuous substitution rates.

In his role as a formulator of and adviser to national production and resource-use policies, the agricultural production economist needs to provide information and attempt to specify optimum choice in a manner paralleling that for individual farms. The problems and principles are the same; only the end and choice indicator have changed. Use of the principles is illustrated further in the section which follows.

Factor-Factor Relationships and Resource Allocation

The elementary factor-product relationship presented in early chapters served to explain the optimum yield and resource intensity level for a single farm. It also served as a powerful production economics tool in specifying the optimum allocation of limited stocks of 2 resources, at both the farm and the national levels. The factor-factor relationship can be applied similarly. We employ it below in some 3-resource examples, although it is applicable for any number of resources. First, consider a farmer who, as is typical of farmers operating under uncertainty, has a limited quantity of all resources. His farm is made up of a given number of technical units (fixed resources) in the form of acres and animals to which he can apply 2 resources, such as labor and machinery or protein and grain, which are also limited in amount. How should the limited amount of the 2 resources be allocated between the "fixed" resources represented by technical units? If the labor and machinery (or grain and protein) can be rearranged between technical units to give a greater physical product, the individual farmer's income, given the level of prices, can be increased. Since the limited stock of the several resources represents a constant cost outlay, any increase in the physical product must result in a greater gross revenue, and net profits must increase. Or conversely, if the same physical output and value of product can be obtained from fewer resources and a saving in costs, net returns must also increase. The principle to be explained provides a condition necessary for the most efficient use of resources from the standpoint of aggregate efficiency as well as from the standpoint of the individual farm. We explain this necessary condition first as it applies to the individual farm and profit maximization.[4]

---

[4] A *sufficient* condition which accompanies this *necessary* condition for resource allocation deals with the distribution of resources between alternative products either at the farm or national level and is presented in Chapters 7, 8, and 9.

Inter-technical unit and intra-farm allocation. Given a physical stock of resources in the manner outlined above, the allocation of this stock between *technical units* to maximize the physical product and the value of output within the farm can be specified in a simple manner: Suppose that in Figure 10 a stock of resources including 20 units of X_1 and 20 units of X_2 is available to be allocated between 2 technical units (2 acres or 2 animals) which make up the farm plant or firm. Figure 10 shows the production surface or contour map for either 1 of the 2 technical units taken separately; the 2 technical units are of equal productivity. Three factors of production are then involved, since the technical units can be

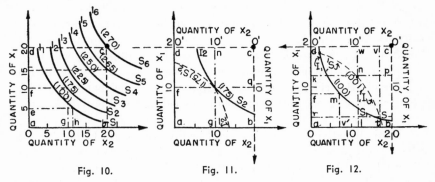

Fig. 10.   Fig. 11.   Fig. 12.

Optimum allocation of resources between technical or economic units to maximize production in physical or economic terms.

classed as factor X_3; the total stock of resources from which a maximum product is to be obtained includes 2 units of X_3 and 20 each of X_1 and X_2. How should resources X_1 and X_2 be allocated between the 2 units of X_3 if product is to be maximized from the limited stocks of 3 resources? Factors X_1 and X_2 may be grain and protein feeds, while X_3 represents 2 hogs. Alternatively, X_3 may represent 2 units or acres of land, while X_1 represents labor and X_2 represents capital in the form of machine services. Should the farmer allocate all of the protein to one hog and all the grain to another? Should he use most of the labor on one field and most of the machine services on another? The answer is given in the principle of resource allocation defining the optimum use of 2 or more resources between 2 or more producing units (cows, acres, farms, producing regions). *Given maximization of product (in either physical or value terms) from given resources as an intermediate end, resources are allocated optimally only when the marginal rate of substitution of one factor for another factor is equal between producing units.* Farmers are becoming aware of this principle, which can be illustrated with arithmetic and hogs: If the level of protein feeding is (a) so high for hog A that 1 lb. of protein substitutes for 2 lbs. of corn and (b) so low for hog B that 1 lb. of protein substitutes for 20 lbs. of corn, a transfer of protein from hog B to hog A and corn from A to B must lessen total pork production from given grain and protein stocks. One lb. of protein transferred from B to A will replace 2 lbs. of corn for the latter animal. Yet 20 lbs. of corn are required to replace 1 lb. of protein taken from the former animal. Pork production must thus decline if the transfer is to take place.

The principle is illustrated in Figures 10, 11, and 12. First, suppose that in Figure 10, 20 units (ad or bc) of X_1 and 20 units (ab or dc) of X_2 are used for 1 (A) of the 2 technical units. None of X_1 or X_2 is then available for the second (B) technical unit. Production from the 2 technical units with the 20 units of X_1 and the 20 units of X_2 is then 270 (contour I_6S_6 or point c); since all of the X_1 and X_2 resources are allocated to unit A, its output is 270 while the output of unit B is zero. However, if only one-half the stock of X_1 and X_2 (af of X_1 and ag of X_2) is used for the first (A) technical unit, the smaller output indicated by contour I_2S_2 will be attained for it. If the other one-half (10 units) of X_1 and X_2 are used for the second (B) technical unit, the output will also be that indicated by I_2S_2. Accordingly, the output of each technical unit will be 175, and total output will be 350.

A third allocative pattern also might be investigated in Figure 10: Five units (ae quantity) of X_1 and 11.5 units (ah quantity) of X_2 can be allocated to technical unit A while the remainder or ed (ad minus ae) of X_1 and hb (ab minus ah) can be allocated to technical unit B. All of the opportunities for dividing the stock of X_1 and X_2 between the 2 technical units are therefore given by the limits of the rectangle $abcd$ in Figure 10. Each point within this "box" represents an allocative possibility. If all of the 2 factors (ab of X_2 and ad of X_1) are allocated to the first technical unit, none of either factor is available for the second technical unit. If 10 units (af) of X_1 and 10 units (ag) of X_2 are used with the first technical unit, then 10 units (fd) of X_1 and 10 units (gb) of X_2 are available for the second technical unit. Use of ah of X_2 and ae of X_1 on 1 technical unit allows hb and ed for the other technical unit.

More output from the same resources. By setting up the "opportunity box" $abcd$ in Figure 11, the bottom and left axes can be used to graph the factor inputs and the iso-product contours for the first technical unit. The upper and right axes can be used to graph the contour map for the second technical unit. The contour map for the second technical unit has been superimposed over that for the first technical unit in much the same manner as one input-output curve was placed over another in Chapter 4. The contour I_2S_2 in Figure 11 is the same as I_2S_2 (175) of Figure 10, when reference is to the solid or left hand axes. The curve $I'_2S'_2$ of Figure 11 is in reference to the dotted (upper and right) axes and also is identical to I_2S_2 (175) in Figure 10. (The reader need only turn Figure 11 upside down to determine that the dotted axes and the relevant contour are identical with those viewed in Figure 10 or viewed from below for Figure 11 in reference to the solid axes.) When all (*ab*) of X_2 is used for the first (rightside-up) technical unit, none is available for the second (upside-down) technical unit. The problem is to find a pair of product contours which are exactly tangent. Tangency of the iso-product curves denotes equal slopes, and, hence, that the marginal rates of substitution of X_1 for X_2 are the same between technical units. Under this condition, *ag* or *dn* of X_2 should be allocated to the first technical unit, and *gb* or *nc* of X_2 should be allocated to the second technical unit. Similarly, *af* or *bq* of X_1 should be allocated to the first technical unit, and *fd* or *qc* should be allocated to the second technical unit. Under these conditions the stock of the factors is exhausted and the output of the product from the 2 technical units is maximized. The product is 350 (175 × 2).

The opportunity box of Figure 12 illustrates a pattern of resource allocation wherein the stock of X_1 and X_2 is exhausted but the product is not maximized. Contour I_1S_1 (100 units of output) is transposed from Figure 10 to Figure 12 for the first technical unit and is in reference to the bottom and left axes. The same product curve, indicated as $I'_1S'_1$ in reference to the top and right hand or dotted axes, for the second technical unit has been transposed in an "upside-down" fashion (with a one-half turn in a counter-clockwise direction) over the graph for the first technical unit. If 100 units of commodity are produced from each technical unit, *at* or *dv* of X_2 can be allocated to the first technical unit, while *tb* or *vc* units of X_2 are allocated to the second (or upside-down) technical unit. Similarly, *ar* or *bs* of X_1 can be used for the first (or rightside-up) technical unit, and *rd* or *sc* can be used for the second. The total product of 200 (100 from each technical unit) is not, however, the maximum possible from the stocks *ab* (equals *dc*) of X_2 and *ad* (equals *bc*) of X_1. Geometrically, this fact is denoted by the fact that the contour curves, I_1S_1 and $I'_1S'_1$ for the 2 technical units are not tangent but intersect each other. The marginal rate of substitution of X_1 for X_2 is not then equal between technical units. Given the fixed stocks of X_1 and X_2, a maximum product of 350 (175 from each) can be produced from the 2 technical units. An output from each of two technical units in the magnitude indicated by contour I_5S_5 in Figure 10 is not possible from the quantity of resources which defines the opportunity box in Figure 12.

Fewer resources for the same output. The procedure above of maximizing the product from given resources also involves diminishing marginal productivity in the manner outlined in Chapters 2 and 3.[5] It is not a sufficient

---

[5] If the input-output or factor-product relationship is linear and the production coefficient is the same, while substitution is at a diminishing rate, a maximum product from given resource stocks can be attained when X_1 and X_2 are allocated entirely to technical unit A or to technical unit B. The same product would also be forthcoming under a linear factor-product transformation if one-half the X_1 and X_2 stock were allocated to technical units A or B. However, substitution ratios would still have to be equal.

condition that we locate iso-product lines which are tangent; an infinite number of pairs of these exist. We must find the pair which defines an equal product/factor transformation ratio.

We also can illustrate a condition of resource allocation which involves the substitution relationships alone. Suppose that output indicated in Figure 12 is to be retained at 200 (100 from each technical unit as indicated by I_1S_1 and $I'_1S'_1$). This same quantity can always be produced with less than the total stocks ab (at plus tb) of X_2 and bc (bs plus sc) of X_1. For example, suppose the combination for producing 100 units of A is changed from at of X_2 and ar of X_1 to av of X_2 and af of X_1 (for example, to combination m). Also suppose that the combination of resources for producing 100 units of product from unit B (the upside-down figure) is changed from cv of X_2 and sc of X_1 to cw of X_2 and cp of X_1. The marginal rates of factor substitution are equal at points m and n. The total output remains at 200 (100 from each unit) but resources have now been saved. The saving in X_2 amounts to $v'l$, while the saving in X_1 amounts to fk. Under the combinations indicated by m and n (1) the total stock ab of X_2 is allocated av' to A and lb to B, with a saving equal to $v'l$, and (2) the total stock ad of X_1 is allocated af to A and kd to B with a saving equal to fk when compared to the alternative combination. As long as either factor has a value, the output of 200 can be produced at a lower cost by the m and n combination than by the original combination.

Farmer allocation. There are many known examples in which farmers do not allocate limited resources between technical units in a manner to maximize the product. An outstanding illustration is that of a dairy herd wherein cows are fed free choice and some animals consume mostly grain while others must content themselves with a high-forage ration. This illustration can also be extended to other feeds and other classes of livestock. However, the cost of the additional labor and capital necessary to segregate and feed animals separately often makes the practice prohibitive. A further malallocation example is found in the tendency of farmers to spread manure, a substitute for commercial fertilizer, on acres near the barn and commercial fertilizer on distant parts of the farm. The practice may or may not be rational when labor costs are considered. A very great misallocation of resources, in the sense outlined above, exists between farms.

Interfarm allocation. The principles illustrated above for allocation of limited resource stocks between technical units within a farm also apply to the allocation of resources between farms. If we consider that Figure 12 now refers to 2 farms while X_1 and X_2 refer to labor and capital, the maximum product possible from 20 (ad or bc and ab or cd) units each of capital (X_1) and labor (X_2) is not attained when (1) at or dv units of labor are allocated to the first farm, and tb or cv units are allocated to the second (upside-down) farm; or (2) ar or bs units of capital are allocated to the first (right-side-up) farm, and rd or sc units are allocated to the second farm. In the case of farms, as in the case of technical units, labor and capital resources must be allocated in a manner to equate their marginal rates of substitution between farms. A maximum product from given resources is thus illustrated in the opportunity box of Figure 11 by tangency of the 2 iso-product curves for the 2 farms. Here the first (or right-side-up) farm would receive ag or dn units of labor (X_2), while the second farm would use cn or gb units. Capital (X_1) would be allocated af or bq units to the first and cq or df units to the second (upside-down) farm. Or, if Figure 12 is examined again, it is evident that for the pattern of allocation which gives at of X_2 and ar of X_1 to the first farm and cv of X_2 and cs of X_1 to the second (upside-down) farm, a surplus of resources are employed for the 200 units of output. The same output can be attained by resource combinations indicated by m and n, where marginal rates of substitution are equal. The saving (see intrafarm discussion) in $v'l$ of labor (X_2) and fk of capital in producing 200 units of product could then be diverted to other products (a) on the same two farms, (b) on different farms, or (c) in non-farm industries.

That resources are not allocated between farms in a manner to maximize the product forthcoming from limited factor stocks is common knowledge. Two neighboring farms can be found in any producing region where resource combinations are in opposite directions. Some farmers use a high-protein or high-forage ration, while their neighbors use high-grain rations. One operator may use labor while his neighbor uses machinery, or one may use only manure as fertilizer while his neighbor uses only commercial sources. Allocative inefficiency arises not because different combinations are used but because resources are not arranged between producing units in a manner to equate substitution ratios. Two such farmers could always pool their resources and produce a greater combined product and revenue from the given stock of resources or produce the same output and revenue with a smaller outlay of resources. Acting independently from other farmers they would also have a greater net profit to divide between themselves. Both could be made better off in terms of dollar profit and neither need be made worse off. From the standpoint of aggregate or interfarm factor productivity and returns, the conventional distribution of resources would be consistent with a maximum product from a given collection of resources, or, conversely, a minimum input for a given output, only if input-output relationships and the marginal rates of resource substitution were linear and identical for all farms.

If all farmers collectively pooled their resources and allocated them optimally between units, the value of product and income resulting would not necessarily increase. Because of the low price elasticity of demand for farm products, this procedure would actually tend to decrease the value product of given resources in agriculture. However, if the majority of farmers took this action, individual pairs always could be made better off profit-wise if they did than if they did not follow suit. In the absence of this action by the majority, individual pairs can make the adjustment a means to increasing rather than maintaining their income position. From a societal standpoint, and where resources have alternative employments with greater priorities attached to them, this allocation of factors between farms represents a misuse of resources. A rearrangement of resources between farms would generally result in the same product from fewer resources and cause certain resources, through the medium of lower returns, to be driven out of agriculture. Although individual remaining farmers might have greater incomes, a lower income per farm would result were the previous quantity of resources and numbers of farms to be retained in agriculture.

The interest of agricultural production economics is obviously rooted in national welfare. Were this not true, effort would never be directed toward organizing resources more efficiently. Instead, it would be directed at helping farmers to organize monopolies and otherwise restrict output in a manner to increase total revenue and net returns of agriculture. The complex mentioned above will be discussed in greater detail in later chapters.

Emergency production policies. The principles of production outlined here are of concern to a nation faced with a war or other emergency when physical aspects of production become particularly important. The principles are equally relevant and in practice during peacetime and under a market economy. Then, however, attainment of the conditions specifying an optimal distribution of resources is more nearly left to the multitude of individual producers. Hence we turn our attention to allocative problems in food emergencies. It is not possible for either (a) a maximum product output from given resources, or (b) a minimum resource input for a given output, to be attained when some producers are able to obtain large quantities while other producers must go without or with very little of a particular resource. In World War II, many United States farmers were able to obtain supplies of animal proteins while others were forced to use imperfect vegetable protein substitutes or high-grain rations. Some farmers could obtain only nitrogen fertilizers; others could obtain only phosphates, even though they are imperfect substitutes. Similar problems arise during emergency in respect to the quantity of machinery and labor available to different farms. In periods of short labor supplies and relatively high wage rates, farmers with ample funds can acquire machines, while operators with limited funds go less well equipped. This use of resources is inconsistent with the conditions of a maximum product from given resources or a minimum of resources for a given product and can be improved upon only when scarce and competing resources are allocated between farms to give approximately equal rates of substitution (for example, in the vein of Figure 11). Attainment of this optimum condition requires that, after the optimum level of output per technical unit has been decided, the desired proportion of substitute resources (corn vs. protein, machinery vs. labor, and so forth) be allocated to each technical unit and farm.

Again there were 2 mechanisms for bringing about the desired resource combinations: (1) The pricing mechanism can be employed. Here prices might be established in line with production models wherein prices are proportional to substitution rates. If, for example, national resource managers decided that protein feed should be used as long as each pound replaces 4 lbs. of grain, the grain/protein substitution ratio of $\Delta G/\Delta P$ or 4/1 provides the basis for establishing price relationships. The protein/ grain price ratio should also be 4/1; and, if corn is priced at \$1.68, the particular protein should be priced at \$80 per ton. The same considerations would apply to substitute proteins as well as machine and labor or other competing pairs of resources. This mechanism can be successful only if enough farmers have knowledge of substitution relationships and possess capital in quantities such that equal productivity of resources between farms is brought about. While complex and perhaps impossible to design perfectly, the price procedure would not, as in the case of the rationing alternative, require knowledge of substitution relationships on each farm by the national resource administrators. (2) Direct rationing, including the physical allocation of each resource to each farm, can be employed. Here resource planners must make estimates of rates of substitution for each individual farm and allocate protein, machinery, and other factors accordingly. This knowledge of substitution ratios by national planners is not required under the price alternative. The task of administration is difficult in either instance: Lack of knowledge on the part of farmers and the emergence of black markets which divert resources between farms are important obstacles under the price alternative. The very great variation in substitution rates between livestock of the same and different species, between soil types, and between farms of various sizes increases the complexity in the rationing alternative. However, the important point is this: The basic principles of production must be recognized in the emergency production and pricing policies formulated if use of resources is to conform with necessary and sufficient conditions of efficiency.

Other substitution problems in agriculture. Many substitution problems are important in agriculture, both at the farm and at the national level. Feed substitution rates such as those outlined previously are not only important to the individual farmer in maximizing his returns, but are also important in determining the combination of grasses and legumes which should be produced throughout the nation if the soil is to be conserved at economic levels. The rate at which the resources involved in mechanical soil conservation practice substitute for grasses and legumes in erosion control is similarly important. A major factor substitution problem is to be found in cotton-producing areas. Development of mechanization poses important adjustment problems, not only as capital in the form of modern machinery is substituted for labor and other forms of capital, but also as adjustments in population or industrialization become widespread throughout.

Level of Output and Combination of Resource

In the immediately preceding sections we considered factor substitution principles when resources for the producing unit were limited. We are now ready to examine the same problem in a situation where the farm firm has unlimited capital. We can then combine the 2 economic considerations of the last several chapters. Since an input-output relationship or production function gives rise to both the factor-product and factor-factor relationships, the 2 questions of (a) the optimum yield or output level and (b) the optimum combination of variable resources for a fixed technical unit, farm, or producing region must also be decided. The analysis which follows is from the standpoint of (a) the farm as firm and (b) profit maximization as the relevant end. The problem is one of how resources should be combined for the fixed technical unit or farm plant if output is to be expanded from zero to the most profitable level (the factor-product relationship) with variable resources combined in a least-cost manner (the factor-factor relationship) for each level of output. The student of production economics is now aware that minimum costs are consistent with maximum profits in the factor-factor sense but not in the factor-product sense.

Expansion path and maximum profits. For an initial example of the combined problem we can return to Figure 2 of Chapter 5. Suppose the firm is to expand output for the technical unit or plant represented by the series of boxes relating output to 2 variable resources. If the principles of profit maximization are to be followed, should Z_1 and Z_2 be expanded in fixed proportions, with output following a linear path from southwest to northeast? Or should the expansion path veer towards the Z_1 or Z_2 axis, indicating that, as output is expanded, greater proportions of one factor are used at the expense of the other? The answer is given in the price and substitution ratios. If the price of Z_2 is high relative to the price of Z_1, the expansion path will veer towards the Z_1 axis. A high price for Z_1 will cause it to veer towards the Z_2 axis, depending on how substitution rates change as output is expanded (as higher and higher constant product curves on the contour map are attained). This point is illustrated in Figure 13, where net returns, excluding fixed costs attached to the technical unit or producing plant, have been computed for each output and factor combination of Figure 2 in Chapter 5. We may suppose that factor units are discontinuous in this case. The firm thus does not decide on an exact output and, hence, on the fractional amount of each input necessary to attain it. Instead, it must decide on applying whole units of input and evaluate the economy of the product forthcoming.

The expansion path for increasing output is indicated by the figures in parentheses: The first input-output combination will include 1 unit each of Z_1 and Z_2 and 10 units of output. As production is adjusted from this cell, it can move to any of the 3 bordering cells. Profit is greatest if movement is to the adjoining diagonal cell of $34.40 net return and 2 units each of Z_1 and Z_2. Factor Z_1 is not used to replace Z_2 at this point because its marginal rate of substitution is too low. (See the 12-unit contour line in Figure 2 of Chapter 5.) The next step in expansion calls, however, for 3 units of Z_1 and 2 of Z_2. The higher rates of substitution of Z_1 for Z_2 in this direction of output cause the veering in the expansion path to be economically desirable. (See the 24-unit contour in Figure 2 of Chapter 5.) The path traced out suggests the direction of least-cost outputs, and production is expanded as long as the marginal cost of additional resources is less than the value of the marginal product. The limits to expansion are not indicated in Figure 13.

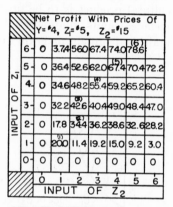

	Net Profit With Prices Of $Y=\$4$, $Z_1=\$5$, $Z_2=\$15$						
6–	0	3.74	560	67.4	74.0	78.6 (6)	
5–	0	36.4	52.6	62.0	67.4 (5)	70.4	72.2
4–	0	34.6	48.2	55.4 (4)	59.2	65.2	60.4
3–	0	32.2	42.6	40.4	49.0	48.4	47.0
2–	0	17.8	34.4 (3)	36.2	38.6	32.6	28.2
1–	0	20.0 (1)	11.4	19.2	15.0	9.2	3.0
0–	0	0	0	0	0	0	0
	0	1	2	3	4	5	6

INPUT OF Z_1 (vertical), INPUT OF Z_2 (horizontal)

Fig. 13. Net returns for output and inputs indicated in Figure 2 of Chapter 5.

Expansion path and isoclines. The expansion path principle can be illustrated geometrically in Figure 14 where we can also suppose divisible inputs. The lines indicated as *IP* are iso-product contours, each representing a different level of output. Given the price relationship for factors indicated by the slope of the several equal cost lines indicated as *EC*, the minimum cost for each output is represented by tangency of the product contours and the cost lines. The expansion line *E* has been drawn through these minimum cost lines and indicates how the relative proportions of the factors changes as output is increased, and if costs are minimized for each particular output. The expansion line *E* has an "upward curvature," and indicates that, as output is extended, relatively greater proportions of capital should be employed. Output should be expanded along the expansion line as long as the marginal value of the product is greater than the marginal cost of the resources added. The marginal physical product is the difference in output represented by the series of contours, while the added resources are indicated on the x and y axes. The expansion line is thus an isocline of the nature indicated in Chapter 5, since, with the factor/price ratio constant for each level of output, the marginal rate of substitution between factors is the same for each level of output. This fact is denoted by tangency of the iso-cost lines, all of the same slope, with the product contours.

Agricultural isoclines and resource combination. Isoclines for fixed agricultural producing units perhaps are typically curved rather than linear, and optimum resource combinations for different outputs must be varied accordingly, if farm profits are to be maximized, or if the national agricultural product is to be produced most efficiently. For meat animals as technical units, the marginal rate of substitution between such feeds as grain and protein or grain and forage change as the animal is taken to

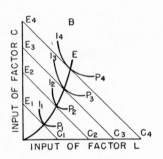

Fig. 14. Profit maximization and the expansion path.

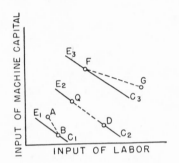

Fig. 15. Linear-discontinuous substitution and nonlinear isoclines.

heavier weights. The grain/protein substitution ratio $(\Delta G/\Delta P)$ declines as the growing process slackens and the fattening process comes to the fore. Hence different rations are economically optimum at different weights. The isocline is obviously non-linear for dairy cows as is suggested by the analysis of Figure 15 in Chapter 5. If level of milk output is to be raised above the point indicated as l, substitutions between grain and forage are necessary. In crop production the rate of substitution, except in instances of pure limitational conditions, changes with yield per acre and the addition of fertilizer elements. One element may be of a limitational character at low yield levels but the addition of this element may shift the relative position of nutrients and cause other elements to become more nearly limitational.

Curved isoclines also exist for farms as fixed producing units. Although it is true that one farmer seldom if ever adjusts output along a long-run expansion line (he may select 1 point on it and adjust later to this fixed plant), the concept of the expansion path is of value in interpreting the resource combinations which do or should exist on farms of different sizes. If the marginal rate of factor substitution changes with output level, either because of changes in the form or divisibility of factors or because of other reasons, then it is obvious that farms of different size should use resources in different proportions. The production economist should not survey a group of large farms, isolate the factor combination which is most efficient for these, and infer that these same resource combinations should be superimposed on small farms. Resource combinations on large farms can be taken as the most efficient pattern for small farms only when the expansion line is linear.

An important instance of non-linear isoclines is to be found in resources with discontinuous units and discrete or linear substitution relationships such as are pictured in Figure 15. While touching near the scale relationships to be discussed later, we may suppose that AB, QD, and FG are the discontinuous-linear constant product contours for farms of 3 different sizes. For the unit indicated by AB, the B combination of labor and capital may include 30 days of labor and 1 machine unit. Use of a second machinery unit will shift the combination to A (the in-between points are not attainable because machine inputs are indivisible) and will substitute for 10 days of labor, while the remaining 20 days of labor are of a complementary or limitational nature. Line FG represents a large farm where there are more days of work to be accomplished; consequently, the addition of a machine unit, which shifts the combination to F, substitutes for 40, not 10, days of labor. The constant product line QD represents a farm falling in between these extremes. If the machine service/labor price ratio is of a magnitude suggested by the iso-cost curves E_1C_1, E_2C_2, and E_3C_3 (all with the same slope and hence indicative of the same price ratio), the farm with the low output will realize minimum costs and maximum profit from the output indicated if it uses the B combination of labor and machine capital. The farm with the large output will minimize costs with the opposite extreme indicated as F. The farm with the medium output can be indifferent to the Q or D combination; they both represent the same cost outlay as is evidenced by coincidence of the iso-cost line E_2C_2 and the iso-product line QD. These differences exist for farms of different sizes and should be recognized by farmers and in the research procedures and recommendations of scientists who provide guidance for farmers. Again they simply infer that while a cotton picker, hay baler, or combine may be profitable for the large farm, a hoe, pitchfork, or binder may be economically efficient for a small farm. Also, the expansion path suggested (one passing through B, any point on QD and finally through F) is the type which would define profit maximization for farmers were they to start at zero and make continuous adjustments in resources used and in output.

Substitution and expansion effects. Changes in the price of factors can give rise to two types of adjustments worthy of note: These include (1) *the substitution effect* and (2) *the expansion effect* and apply equally to (a) business units which have unlimited capital and (b) firms which have limited capital and can produce only the quantity attainable with given resources. Both types are illustrated in Figure 16.[6] *Substitution effect:* This adjustment has been encountered previously and can be illustrated again with iso-product curve I_1P_1 (output fixed at 100 units) in Figure 16. With factor-price ratios as indicated by the slope of iso-cost line 1, the least-cost combination of factors X and Z includes ox_3 of the former and oz_1 of the latter. If the price of factor Z falls relative to price of X, as is indicated by the new iso-cost line 2, an input of ox_1 of X and oz_2 of Z will minimize costs for 100 units of product. A *substitution effect* has now taken place: input of Z has increased by z_1z_2 while input of X has decreased by x_3x_1. The substitution effect, use of more Z and less X for the same output of product, results from changes in the relative prices of the factors. (2) *Expansion effect:* After a fall in the price of factor Z, output of the product can be increased because of either or both of the following: (a) the same cost outlay will allow the firm with limited funds to hire more factors and (b) the lower cost ratio (due to a decrease in price of Z and substitution of this factor for X), allows output to be extended further before the marginal cost of resources exceeds the value of their marginal product for a farm with unlimited capital. The expansion effect is illustrated in Figure 16 where output is increased to I_2P_2 (150 units of inputs) after the price change and ox_2 units of X and oz_3 units of Z are used. In respect to factor Z, the *substitution effect* resulted in an increase in its use by z_1z_2 units; the *expansion effect* resulted in use of another z_2z_3 units. In respect to factor X, the expansion effect partially offset the substitution effect; while the substitution effect reduced use of X by x_1x_3 units, the expansion effect restores x_1x_2 units to use.

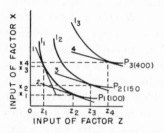

Fig. 16. Substitution and scale effects in factor use.

Economic complements. It is not impossible for the expansion effect to result in increased use of both factors. If in Figure 16 the expansion effect is so great that it carries output to I_3P_3 (400 units), use of X will increase to ox_4 while input of Z will increase to oz_4. This combination includes more of both factors than the original quantities ox_3 and oz_1. Factors X and Z have now become *economic complements.* When 2 factors X and Z can be used in producing a single commodity Y, and a fall in the price of factor Z leads to an increase in output of Y and an increase in use of both factor X and Z, the factors are *economic complements.* If more of factor Z is used while less of factor X is

---

[6] Conventionally the 2 types of adjustment are termed the *substitution* and *scale* effects. We use the term *expansion* effect to describe the one type of adjustment in order to avoid confusion with later discussion of scale. Adjustment to changes in factor-price relationships may well be along an expansion rather than a scale line.

used, with output of Y increasing or remaining the same, the 2 factors are *economic substitutes* or rivals.[7] Previously, we defined factors as *technical complements* when an increase in input of one factor alone did not result in a greater output or did not substitute for another factor. Technical complementarity always leads to economic complementarity. However, 2 factors can be economic complements even though they are technical substitutes.

Factor-Product and Factor-Factor Equilibrium

Farm firms typically operate under conditions of uncertainty and capital limitations. Historic or *ex post* profits therefore are seldom maximized because of the circumstances to be outlined in later chapters. The task of the farmer with limited capital then is one of (a) allocating given stocks of resources between technical units devoted to a single commodity in a manner to maximize the physical product and its value, and (b) allocating given resources between alternative commodities or enterprises in a manner to maximize the value of product. Even when these conditions are attained the factor/product price ratio (Pf/Pp) may still be less than the product/factor transformation ratio $(\Delta P/\Delta F)$, indicating that profits are not as great as they could be were funds unlimited and foresight perfect. However, since some farm firms do have access to capital in quantities which allow maximum returns from their existing farm plant and would like to predict the future in a manner allowing attainment of this position, the conditions of short-run equilibrium or profit maximization are outlined

---

[7] This concept does not include the regressive adjustment of Hicks, *Value and Capital*. London: Clarendon Press, 1939, p. 93, where a reduction in the price of factor Z results in a greater employment of it but a decline in (a) output of Y and (b) use of X. The economic complement case mentioned above can be extended to include that of Hicks, which he describes as:

Suppose that the firm still has to produce a fixed output, but now employs three factors A, B, C. Suppose the price of A falls. Then, since the ratio of the prices of B and C remains unchanged, they can (as in utility theory) be treated as a single factor. Consequently the demand for A must still necessarily expand; and the demand for B and C (taken together) must contract. There must be a substitution in favour of A at the expense of the other factors taken together.... As before, however, the substitution need not be at the expense of each of the other factors. B may be complementary with A, in which case the demand for B will expand. There will be a substitution in favour of A and B against C.... First of all, let us take a limiting case, in which it is possible to prove that the two factors must be complementary. The two factors will be complementary, we must remember, if an increase in the employment of A (with B constant), and consequent increase in the output of product X, moves the marginal rate of transformation of B into product Y in favour of B; that is to say, raises the marginal product of B. (The criterion for the two factors being complementary is therefore nothing else but the well-established and familiar criterion for the two factors being "co-operant"; an increase in one must raise the marginal product of the other. In this case we do not need to disturb currently accepted definitions.)

below. These also provide a later framework for evaluating the aggregate producing efficiency of agriculture. The conditions outlined below will be extended in the chapter on scale relationships.

Equilibrium in hiring of resources. The analysis of Figure 14 indicates that profits for a firm producing a single commodity with capital and labor can be maximized if the least-cost combination for each level of output is attained by (a) equating the price ratio P_C/P_L with the substitution ratio $\Delta L/\Delta C$, and (b) extending output as long as the marginal cost of the resources is less than the marginal value product (or until the factor/ product price ratio is equal to the marginal productivity of the factors). When this condition has been attained, resources cannot be rearranged to add more to net profit and the marginal value productivities of all resources are equal. Attainment of this condition defines equilibrium in hire of factors by the firm. Consequently at each output level, maximum profits can be expressed in the manner below where C, L, and M refer to different factors used for a single product. P refers to the price of the factor indicated by the attached subscript and MP refers to the marginal physical physical product of each factor. (The marginal physical product MP_C of factor C is the same as $\Delta Y/\Delta C$ indicated in previous chapters, where ΔY refers to change in output of product and ΔC refers to change in input of resource C. The same statement applies to other factors.) The positions of tangency shown in Figure 14 indicate that at each output level the ratio of marginal physical products is equal to the ratio of prices for each pair of factors in the manner of I below:

$$\frac{MP_C}{MP_L} = \frac{P_C}{P_L}, \quad \frac{MP_C}{MP_M} = \frac{P_C}{P_M} \text{ and } \frac{MP_L}{MP_M} = \frac{P_L}{P_M} \tag{I}$$

This condition of equilibrium or profit maximization also can be expressed in the form of II below. It states that, for each output level, the ratio of the marginal products as compared to price of the resource must be equal for all factors. In other words, if a unit of C adds 1 unit to output, while 1 unit each of L and M add 10 and 30 units respectively, the prices of C, L, and M must be of the manner \$1, \$10, and \$30 respectively. Or the prices might be \$3, \$30, and \$90 respectively; the important condition is that the marginal products and prices bear the same ratio as is indicated in I above. If C costs \$1 and L costs \$10 and M is priced at \$25 per unit, profits can be extended by using more of M until its marginal physical productivity is driven down to 25 and the condition of II below is attained. If the farm has limited capital, maximum profit is still denoted by equation II (except that the constant in III is no longer 1.0; it may be 2, 9, 10, or any other number, but it must be the same for all resources).

$$\frac{MP_C}{P_C} = \frac{MP_L}{P_L} = \frac{MP_M}{P_M} \tag{II}$$

By multiplying each physical marginal product by its price we have the condition indicated below where P_Y refers to the price of the product. This equation states

$$P_Y \frac{MP_C}{P_C} = P_Y \frac{MP_L}{P_L} = P_Y \frac{MP_M}{P_M} = \text{constant of } 1.0 \qquad \text{(III)}$$

that with profits maximized, \$1 invested in factor C will return as much as \$1 invested in L or M. With a product price (P) of \$2, and with the physical productivities and factor prices (\$1, \$10, and \$30) mentioned above, these quantities become $(\$2)(1/\$1) = (\$2)(10/\$10) = (2)(30/\$30)$, and \$1 invested in each factor returns \$2 in product. Profits are not at a maximum for a farm with unlimited capital, however, unless the quantity of each resource employed results in a marginal cost for each factor (the denominators in equation III) equal to its marginal product (the numerators in equation III) multiplied by the price of the product. The ratios must be equal but need not equal 1.0 for profit maximization by a farm with limited capital.

Interfarm equilibrium. The conditions outlined above not only are necessary for profit maximization by the individual farm unit when it can acquire ample capital and predict the future with sufficient accuracy, but also define the optimum allocation of resources between farms when certain specified conditions hold true for production functions and market prices. Each individual resource then must be allocated between farms and producing regions in the manner of equation III above. If we refer to factor C (capital) used by three farms a, b, and c as Ca, Cb, and Cc respectively, we then obtain equation IV, which also applies to other resources. This statement says, where P_Y refers to the product price while P_C refers to the factor price,

$$P_Y \frac{MP_{Ca}}{P_{Ca}} = P_Y \frac{MP_{Cb}}{P_{Cb}} = \frac{MP_{Cc}}{P_{Cc}} \qquad \text{(IV)}$$

that a dollar invested in resource C and used on farm a must give a return equal to a dollar invested in C and used on b or c. In this instance, if the equation IV (or its intra-farm counterpart in equation III) can be stated as

$$P_Y \frac{MP_{Ca}}{P_{Ca}} > P_Y \frac{MP_{Cb}}{P_{Cb}} > P_Y \frac{MP_{Cc}}{P_{Cc}} > 1.0 \qquad \text{(V)}$$

then resources are neither (a) allocated between farms to give a maximum value product from a given outlay for resources, nor (b) used on any one farm in quantities which cause the marginal value product of the resource to be equal to the marginal cost of the resource.[8] If the ratios in equation

---

[8] Since the ratio for farm a is greater than ($>$) the ratio for b and c, resources should be switched from c to b and from b to a. Since the ratio is greater than 1.0 for all farms, no single farm has attained conditions where marginal costs of resources

IV are not equal, a greater value of product can be attained by moving resources to farms where the ratios are greatest. This movement can, in the absence of production elasticities equal to 1.0 or greater, cause the marginal physical products (the numerators in equations III and IV) to fall on farms receiving resources and to increase on farms losing resources until the ratios are made equal for all farms. The adjustment applies similarly to any one of the many diverse resources used in agriculture such as protein feed, hay, labor, land, fertilizer, or machinery. This principle states the same conditions which were outlined earlier under physical factor-product and factor-factor allocations for 2 neighboring farms: A rearrangement of limited resources between farms to give the greatest value of product for each $1 invested in resources would allow 2 farmers a maximum net return to divide. However, the principle now applies to farms in different regions which produce a similar product; we now consider resources in terms of value or cost rather than in terms of physical inputs alone; differences in product and factor prices brought about by distance, transportation costs, or other forces are included in the analysis. While there are gaps in resource returns between farms in one locality, the gaps are, on the average, even greater between farms of different regions. Johnson estimated that the 1940 pattern of resource allocation gave average differences in value products for capital as great as 20 per cent in Georgia and 10 per cent in Iowa.[9] Studies in Iowa indicate average capital productivities which differ by as much as 100 per cent between areas in both 1939 and 1951.[10] Farm management surveys and records from the state colleges also show these differences over time. The farm manager could often add more to his profits by shifting capital from his own farm to one in another region than by resorting to refined intertechnical unit allocations within his own farm. The principle of (a) allocating resources between farms in different regions and (b) allocating resources between technical units within a farm involve exactly the same principles. These are stated in equations I, II, III, and IV above. Identical technical information also is involved, and both are resource or farm management problems of the same degree. The only difference is that land, an immobile and

---

are equal to the marginal value product. Since any one of the ratios such as (P_Y) $(MP_{Ca})/P_{Ca}$ is greater than 1.0, the value of the marginal product is greater than the marginal cost of the factor (for example, the price of the product, P_Y, multiplied by the marginal physical product, MP_{Ca}, of 1 unit of resource is greater than the price, P_{Ca}, of 1 unit of factor.)

[9] Reported in T. W. Schultz, *Production and Welfare of Agriculture*. New York: Macmillan, 1949, p. 61.

[10] See E. O. Heady, *"Production Functions From a Random Sample of Farms,"* *Jour. Farm Econ.*, Vol. 28, for one indication of the 1939 figures. Differences of the same magnitude were also indicated for livestock when computations involved arithmetic averages only. The statement referring to 1951 is based on data not yet published.

passive factor, can be shifted back and forth between enterprises and farms of one locality, but cannot take part in the interfarm and inter-region movement of resources. This fact has been too often overlooked by production economists who have tied themselves to the land and devoted large efforts to small intra-farm shifts in resources, while individual farmers themselves could profit more by interfarm movements of manage-ment, capital, and labor resources. Interfarm adjustments require less refined technical and price information than the many infinitely small adjustments which can be made within the farm to increase returns by another $25 or $50. Detailed information on substitution ratios and re-source-product transformation rates is needed where single farms are near equilibrium and small final adjustments are needed to squeeze out the last net dollar. The very great gaps between farms and regions point, however, to needed and profitable adjustments, even if substitution and transforma-tion ratios must be estimated with errors as high as 50 per cent. Farm management specialists need to devote more effort to the interfarm and interregional allocation problems. Failure to do so has undoubtedly arisen because of the difficulties mentioned in later chapters. Important among these are the uncertainties which grow out of inability to transfer manage-ment between farms because of the close tie between the business firm and the consuming household in agriculture. The interfarm and interregional movement of labor and capital resources is extremely low except in those cases mentioned subsequently. An important farm management research problem is the investigation of the causes of this immobility and the for-mulation of means whereby it can be overcome to the benefit of individual farmers and society.

Later chapters are devoted to other problems of aggregate efficiency. However, we should pause here to recognize that the intra-farm and inter-farm principles of resource management defined above (equations I through IV) also give a maximum consumer or social product when prices accurately reflect the values of households and the market mechanism works with some degree of perfection in a competitive market. Thus criteria are provided which point in the direction toward which efforts of agricultural production economists can be made in facilitating aggregate efficiency in the use of farm resources.

Selected References

Black, J. D., *et al.*, *Farm Management.* New York: Macmillan, 1947, Chs. 21, 22, 23.

Boulding, K. E., *Economic Analysis.* New York: Harper, 1948, pp. 682-688.

Carlson, Sune, *Pure Theory of Production.* London: King, 1939.

Darfman, R., *Application of Linear Programming to Theory of the Firm.* Berkeley: Univ. of Cal. Press, 1951, Ch. 2.

Heady, E. O., and Olson, R. V., *Economics of Feed Utilization*. Iowa Agr. Exp. Sta. Bul. 390, Ames, 1952.

Heady, E. O., "Use and Estimation of Productivity Coefficients," *Jour. Farm Econ.*, Vol. 34.

Hicks, J. R., *Value and Capital*. Oxford: Clarendon Press, 1939, Cns. 3, 7.

Hopkins, J. A., *Farm Management*. New York: Prentice-Hall, 1941, p. 263.

Lerner, A., *Economics of Control*. New York: Macmillan, 1944, Chs. 5, 6.

Little, I. M. D., *A Critique of Welfare Economics*. Oxford: Clarendon Press, 1939, Ch. 8.

Myint, Hla., *Theories of Welfare Economics*. Cambridge: Harvard University Press, 1948, Ch. 7.

Rebman, J., "Feeding for Milk Production," *Jour. Farm Econ.*, Vol. 34.

Reder, M. W., *Studies in the Theory of Welfare Economics*. New York: Columbia University Press, 1947, p. 29.

Samuelson, P. A., *Foundations of Economic Analysis*. Cambridge: Harvard University Press, 1949, pp. 71-80.

Tolley, H. R., Black, J. D., and Ezekiel, M. K., *Input as Related to Output in Farm Organization*. U.S.D.A. Bul. 1277, Washington, 1924.

Weintraub, S., *Price Analysis*. New York: Pitman, 1949, pp. 56-62, 66-88.

7

Resource Allocation and Enterprise Combination

THE THIRD basic relationship in production economics involves the allocation of given resources between competing commodities or enterprises. It is termed the *product-product relationship*. It again refers to the choice between 2 or more alternatives. Choice is now between competing products in a manner paralleling selection between factors: under the factor-factor relationship, output of product could be held constant while resource combinations were varied; under the product-product relationship, resources can be held constant in quantity and variety while products are varied.

Diversification or specialization. Product-product problems are important from the standpoint of either the individual farmer or the nation. To the farm operator, the problem presents itself as a question of the combination of crops to be grown on the limited farm or land area and from given quantities of labor, capital, and management resources. It is also a question of what kinds and amounts of livestock products should be produced with the limited stock of resources available to the farmer. In practical terminology, it concerns the extent to which the farm should be diversified or specialized. At the national level, the question becomes one of the cropping and livestock patterns to be encouraged through governmental programs.

Economic aspects of crop production or "land use" have always been important considerations in the maximization of individual farm profits or in the most efficient utilization of the nation's resources. However, the question of which pattern of crop production is economic took on increasing importance during the 1940's, because of the large number of programs, popular movements, and economic forces that impinged on crop production. Prior to the outbreak of World War II, farmers were being encouraged, through monetary and technical assistance of governmental action agencies and educational institutions, to increase the acreage of grasses and legumes (the so-called soil-saving crops) and to decrease the acreage of grain and similar crops (the so-called soil-depleting crops). Emphasis was shifted in the opposite direction during the war period as consumer demand and national defense needs called for greater acreages of grain and fiber crops. Current uncertainties on the world political horizon suggest that cropping patterns may need to be geared in either 1 of 2 directions in the future, depending on (1) the probability of world conflict, wherein rotations must be rapidly adapted in the direction of high-calorie crops, with a heavy drain on soil nutrients stored in an earlier period, or (2) the probability of peace (or the absence of armed conflict), wherein relative consumer values represent the dominant factor in determining the optimum pattern of crop production. Monetary incentives and technical assistance were again used, in postwar years, to effect a shift of acreage from grain to forage crops.

The fluctuations in farm prices and costs during the 1940's provided a complex decision-making environment for farmers. The various programs and economic influences mentioned above emphasize the need for development of basic principles that apply to crop rotations and livestock production. Not only do certain market influences (inflation, market uncertainty, acquisition of farms, and so forth on the one hand, and action programs on the other) conflict in the emphasis placed on the relative need for various products, but other long-standing problems are still unsolved. Problems of this nature can be solved only if relevant information of the nature suggested in the production economics models of this and the next chapter is made available.

Resource use. While the problem of product-product relationships is no more one of resource use than those already outlined, it is sometimes given the specific term of *resource use*. It refers to the allocation of all resources including labor, management, land, and capital in its many forms, between competing alternatives. As stated previously, an economic problem never arises in use of a single factor such as labor or land taken alone, since, within some range of combination, all factors are complementary. Study relating only to "labor use" or "land use" has physical content alone. Consequently, factor specialists such as labor economists or land economists devote major efforts to collective bargaining studies or economic geography (the description of cropping patterns in various parts of the country at a given point in time). The need from the standpoint of both farmer and national welfare is analysis in the broader production economics or resource efficiency setting, wherein use of all resources is considered. Questions of crop or livestock combinations can be answered only in the general framework of production economics or resource allocation. Our task, then, includes economic analysis of capital, labor, land, and management use in agriculture. Our problem is one of economic balance in production of crop and livestock products.

The procedure of this and the following chapter parallels that of earlier chapters: first, the fundamental physical or technological relationships between enterprises are outlined; second, the economic implications of these production possibilities or technical relationships are indicated; third, principles of economic choice are applied in selecting between alternatives. Adaptations of general relationships are made for problems unique to agriculture throughout the chapter. The technical nature of product-product relationships in agriculture is complex. However, these must be understood if production opportunities are to be determined and the most efficient use of agricultural resources is to be specified. This chapter deals with short-run production functions and production possibilities, and applies to farms with a fixed plant in terms of the amount and nature of buildings, machinery, labor, land, breeding stock, and materials or expense funds which can be transferred between competing products. The analysis applies similarly to producing regions with fixed quantities of resources. To facilitate exposition, differences between short-run and long-run production possibilities have been delayed until a later chapter.

As in the case of factors, products bear several physical relationships to one another. Enterprises may be (1) joint products in (a) fixed proportions or (b) variable proportions; (2) competitive independent products with (a) constant or (b) increasing rates of substitution; (3) complementary products; (4) supplementary products; or (5) antagonistic products (a special form of competitive enterprises).

Joint Products

One of the extreme product-product situations in agriculture is that of joint products in fixed proportions. Since this case is easily understood, it will be discussed before the details of other product-product relationships are examined. *Joint products* are produced through a single production process; one of the commodities cannot be produced alone but must be accompanied by one or more others. All agricultural production includes joint products in some form. Wheat and straw, mutton and wool, corn and stocks, hogs and manure are common examples. There are many others. In some of these cases, the farmer looks upon a product such as hogs as a single commodity. However, even a hog includes a multitude of joint products such as bone, fat, lean, bacon, and ham.

Joint products in fixed proportions. Joint products in fixed proportions refer to commodities which, if they are to be produced at all, are forthcoming only in inflexible proportions. Examples are found mainly in chemistry; if 1 molecule (a given quantity of resource) of sodium chloride is decomposed, it results always in 1 atom of sodium and 1 of chlorine. It is unlikely that any important products in agriculture are produced in fixed proportions. Where they do exist they are of the nature illustrated diagrammatically in Figure 1. The vertical axis measures the quantity of the first product, Y_1, while the horizontal axis measures the quantity of the second product, Y_2. Given a fixed amount of resources or a limited fund of $1,000 to be invested in these, 4 units of Y_1 and 2 units of Y_2 might be produced. Opportunities of combination reduce to the single point a. If the given resources or cost outlay are to be transformed into product, the only choice is one of producing Y_1 and Y_2 in the ratio of 4:2 or 2:1. If the second quantity of resources is used, the greater combined output, b, of the 2 products is forthcoming. The ratio again is 8:4 or 2:1.

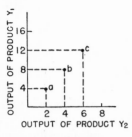

Fig. I. Joint products in fixed proportion.

Joint products with a latitude of substitution are a more important case in agriculture. In the long run, adjustments can be made in the combination of mutton and wool produced from given resources by selecting alternative breeds of sheep. Even after one breed has been selected, minor adjustments in wool and mutton output can be made through marketing of lambs at different weights. While cows cannot be diverted between producing (a) partly milk or partly cream to (b) all cream, adjustments can be made in product combination through the ration fed and through breed selection. Adjustments in the ratio of beef to milk also can be brought about within a given breed by allowing calves to run with the cows part or all of the time or by varying the weight at which calves are marketed (for example, by feeding a given stock of grain and forage to fewer milk cows, while their calves are fed to heavier weights). We defer study of joint products which have a range of substitution until our discussion of purely competitive relationships. The analysis is less complex if this procedure is followed.

Competitive Enterprise and Constant Rates of Substitution

Two enterprises are competitive in the use of given resources if output of one can be increased only through a sacrifice in production of the other. Wheat and oats are competitive crops in most regions, since, with resource inputs constant, a greater acreage of one crop requires fewer acres and a smaller output of the other. The concepts of enterprise competition and substitution can be developed best through the examination first of 2 independent enterprises which compete at constant rates. The nature of the enterprise relationship (transformation or iso-resource curve) is dependent upon the nature of the production function for each independent enterprise. Table 1 includes illustrative data indicating linear production functions for 2 products, Y_1 and Y_2. The factor (or factors) indicated can be used in production of either commodity. If 10 units of resources are available and are used entirely for Y_1, output will be 40. Use of the same resources for Y_2 alone will result in an output of 20. Now suppose that exactly 10 units of resources are available for production of the 2 independent and competing products. If all 10 units of resource are used for Y_1, output of Y_2 must be zero. Use of 9 units of resource for Y_1 and 1 for Y_2 will allow an output combination including 36 units (column 2) of Y_1 and 2 units (column 4) of Y_2. Allocation of 8 units of resources to Y_1 and 2 units to Y_2 allows output of 32 and 4 respectively. Use of all 10 units of resource for Y_2 necessitates a zero output of Y_1. If all possible patterns

Table I.

Linear Production Functions for 2 Competing Enterprises Y_1 and Y_2 (Hypothetical Data)

Production function for Y_1		Production function for Y_2	
Input of variable factor	Output of product Y_1	Input of variable factor	Output of product Y_2
(1)	(2)	(3)	(4)
0	0	0	0
1	4	1	2
2	8	2	4
3	12	3	6
4	16	4	8
5	20	5	10
6	24	6	12
7	28	7	14
8	32	8	16
9	36	9	18
10	40	10	20

of resource allocation and combinations of Y_1 and Y_2 are included, the data can be used to set up a production possibility schedule such as Table 2. The production possibility or opportunity schedule will vary, depend-

Table 2.

Linear Production Possibility Table with 10 and 7 Units of Resource to Allocate Between Enterprises Y_1 and Y_2 (Hypothetical Data)

10 *units of resources*					7 *units of resources*				
Units of resources to		Output of		Marginal rate of substitution of Y_2 for Y_1	Units of resources to		Output of		Marginal rate of substitution of Y_2 for Y_1
Y_1	Y_2	Y_1	Y_2		Y_1	Y_2	Y_1	Y_2	
(1)	(2)	(3)	(4)	(5)	(6)	(7)	(8)	(9)	(10)
10	0	40	0		7	0	28	0	
9	1	36	2	−2.0	6	1	24	2	−2.0
8	2	32	4	−2.0	5	2	20	4	−2.0
7	3	28	6	−2.0	4	3	16	6	−2.0
6	4	24	8	−2.0	3	4	12	8	−2.0
5	5	20	10	−2.0	2	5	8	10	−2.0
4	6	16	12	−2.0	1	6	4	12	−2.0
3	7	12	14	−2.0	0	7	0	14	−2.0
2	8	8	16	−2.0					
1	9	4	18	−2.0					
0	10	0	20	−2.0					

ing, of course, on the amount of resources to be allocated between the 2 competing products. If only 7 units of resources are available, use of all these for Y_1 will allow output of 28 of Y_1 and none of Y_2. Use of all 7 resource units for Y_2 causes its output to be 14, while output of Y_1 is zero. Use of 4 of the 7 resource units for Y_1 and 3 for Y_2 will allow an output of 16 of the former and 6 of the latter product. A pattern of resource allocation with 2 resource units to Y_1 and 5 to Y_2 will result in outputs of 8 and 10 for the 2 products respectively. If the data from columns 3 and 4 of Table 2 are placed on a graph with Y_1 on the vertical and Y_2 on the horizontal axis, a line or curve of the nature indicated by I_1P_1 in Figure 3 results. (Figure 2 includes the 2 production functions from Table 2.) If columns 8 and 9 are graphed they give the line indicated as I_2P_2. The line

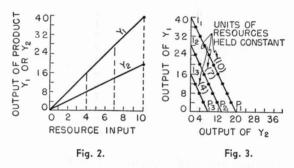

Fig. 2.   Fig. 3.

Linear production functions and opportunity curves (transformation functions).

I_3P_3 is also derived from Table 2 (or Figure 2) and indicates alternative combinations of Y_1 and Y_2, when a total of 4 units of resources can be allocated between the 2 products. Thus a different line or curve, showing the alternative product combinations which can be produced from a given stock of resources, is possible for each given level or stock of resources.

Equal Resources or Costs and the Production Possibility Curve

The lines in Figure 3 can be given the formal term *transformation functions*. When resources are fixed in quantity, the output of one of a pair of competing commodities "is a function of" the output of the other commodity. In effect, one product "is transformed" into the other product as resources are shifted back and forth. The production function for each of the 2 commodities taken singly is of the general form $Y_1 = f(X_1, X_2 \ldots X_n)$ and $Y_2 = f(X_1, X_2 \ldots X_n)$. Yet, since the quantity or form of resources is constant while products are variable, the transformation functions can be considered as $Y_1 = f(X_1, X_2 \ldots X_n, Y_2)$ or simply $Y_1 = f(Y_2)$ and $Y_2 = f(X_1, X_2 \ldots X_n, Y_1)$ or simply $Y_2 = f(Y_1)$. If we wanted to be highly technical we could say that output of Y_2 sacrificed represents an input or cost in production of Y_1 and, conversely, negative outputs of Y_1 (product sacrificed) serve as inputs for Y_2. This concept has the same meaning as the term *opportunity cost* long in use by farm management workers; historic use of the term opportunity cost has referred to the quantity of beef sacrificed as the farmer diverts his resources to hogs or the loss in cotton output as land is shifted to peanuts. Transformation curves are also called iso-resource curves, iso-factor curves, iso-cost curves, or iso-outlay curves. The term *iso* again means equal; curve I_1P_1 in Figure 3 is an *equal resource* curve or line since it indicates the possible combinations of products Y_1 and Y_2 when an equal (the same or a given) total quantity of resources is available for the 2 products. Finally, these isolines can be called *opportunity curves* or *production possibility curves*, since they indicate the opportunities or possibilities in production of 2 competing enterprises when resources are constant. In order to avoid confusion in the forthcoming chapters of this book, the following classification of terms will be employed: the terms *transformation curve, iso-resource curve,* and *iso-factor curve* are synonymous and refer to the production opportunities when the *given quantity* to be allocated is a physical stock of a resource or combination of resources (for example, 100 acres of land, 12 months of labor, or 1 tractor, which can be allocated between products); the terms *iso-cost* and *iso-outlay* refer to a *given quantity* in the form of money or value (for example, $20,000 which can be used for 2 or more products); the terms *opportunity curve* or *production possibilities* will refer to alternatives in production when the given allocative stock can be in the form of either physical resources or monetary value.

Linear production possibilities. Whenever the production functions for 2 or more commodities are linear (Figure 2) the opportunity curves (Figure 3) are also linear. A linear iso-resource curve indicates that the marginal rate of substitution of one product for the other is at a constant rate: for each 1-unit gain in one commodity, a constant amount of another must be sacrificed. This condition is obvious from line I_2P_2 in Figure 3. It is also apparent in Table 2, columns 6-9 inclusive. Starting from a point where all 7 units of resources are employed in production of Y_1, a shift of 1 unit of resource from Y_1 to Y_2 causes output of the former to drop by 4 units and output of the latter to increase by 2 units. Shift of a second unit of resource from Y_1 to Y_2 again causes a sacrifice of 4 units of Y_1 and a gain of 2 units of Y_2. Therefore, 1 unit of Y_2 substitutes for 2 units of Y_1 in both steps.

Marginal rate of substitution. The term *marginal rate of substitution* has the same meaning under the product-product relationship as under the factor-factor relationship. It refers to the absolute change in one product associated with a change of 1 unit in a competing product. It is again measured as a ratio of the form $\Delta Y_1/\Delta Y_2$, where ΔY_1 refers to the change in output of commodity Y_1 and ΔY_2 refers to the change in commodity Y_2. The ratio $\Delta Y_1/\Delta Y_2$ indicates the number of units of Y_1 sacrificed for each unit of Y_2 gained as resources are shifted to Y_2. For the data of Table 2, the marginal rate of substitution of Y_2 for Y_1 at each combination is $-4/2$ or -2.0. Conversely, the marginal rate of substitution of Y_1 for Y_2 is a constant of $-2/4$ or $-.5$. Since the production functions for the 2 products are linear and the production possibility or iso-resource curve is also linear, the marginal rate of substitution $(\Delta Y_1/\Delta Y_2$ or $\Delta Y_2/\Delta Y_1)$ is constant for all combinations of the 2 products. (As in the case of factor-product relationships, the marginal product, and factor-factor relationships, the rate of factor substitution, the marginal rate of product substitution can be defined as a derivative.) Constant rates of substitution exist in the presence of linear production functions only if units of resources shifted back and forth are homogeneous. Heterogeneity in resource units gives rise to increasing substitution rates in the manner to be outlined later.

While 2 independent commodities with linear production functions always give rise to linear opportunity curves, linear production functions are not necessary for constant rates of product substitution. Opportunity curves may be linear and indicate constant rates of substitution when (a) one of the production functions has an elasticity greater than 1.0 the other has an elasticity of less than 1.0 or (b) both production functions have stages of both increasing and decreasing returns. The production possibility or opportunity curve will be linear under these conditions only if the increasing productivity of resources for one commodity just offsets the decreasing productivity of resources for the other commodity. The concept of marginal substitution ratios can be explained more effectively in later sections dealing with non-linear opportunity curves.

Constant Rates of Substitution in Agriculture

There are many examples of constant substitution rates in agriculture. First, we may take distinct products with linear production functions. In Chapter 3 we indicated that, on many farms of limited size, the input-output relationship for single enterprises is of a linear or straight-line nature as output is varied between zero and the upper limit possible in terms of the quantity of available resources. Where 2 such enterprises are compared they appear as competitive products which substitute at constant rates if the enterprises (a) require the same physical resources and at the same time of the year, (b) are produced at identical times of the year, and (c) do not produce by-product services which aid in the production of each other. Where these 3 conditions do not hold true, the products more often are complementary or supplementary or substitute at increasing rates. Constant substitution rates always exist for products which fit into these 3 conditions if output of 1 product does not extend into ranges of diminishing returns. Field corn and sweet corn, clover and alfalfa, oats and barley, and, in some cases, oats and flax or corn and soybeans are examples of crops which substitute at constant or near-constant rates on farms of typical size in the Cornbelt. Wheat and barley, barley and oats, and, in some instances, wheat and corn, wheat or cattle and sheep are examples in the Great Plains. Peanuts and soybeans, and, even within a range, cotton and tobacco may substitute at constant rates on small farms in the Southeast. Whole milk and the joint products of butterfat and skimmilk or certain pairs of vegetables substitute at constant rates on typical New England farms. Products with constant substitution rates tend to be those which perform the same role in the crop rotation or livestock system.

A second category of constant substitution rates is involved in choice between 2 competing varieties or strains of crops and livestock. If 2 varieties of the same crop are treated as different products, they almost always substitute at constant rates. When Pawnee wheat yields 20 bushels per acre while Turkey Red yields 15 bushels, 20 bushels of the former are gained for each 15-bushel sacrifice in the latter as each acre of 1,000 acres (and complementary capital and labor) is shifted between the 2 varieties. The same statement also holds true for 2 competing varieties or strains of corn, oats, cotton, apples, oranges, hogs, chickens, cattle, and sheep. Rare indeed is the case where 2 competing varieties deviate from constant rates of substitution. Hence the opportunity curve or transformation function for competing varieties is almost always linear and the unique element of choice outlined later becomes effective.

Competitive Products Under Increasing Rates of Substitution

An equally common relationship between competing products is that of substitution at an increasing rate. This substitution relationship exists between independent products when, if resources are held constant, successive increases in output of one product entail increasing sacrifices in the other product. Increasing rates of substitution always hold true when the production function for each independent commodity is one of decreasing resource productivity (an elasticity of production less than 1.0). This case is easily illustrated in tabular or graphic form. Table 3 includes production functions (columns 1, 2, and 3) for 2 commodities, Y_1 and Y_2, where both are produced under conditions of decreasing returns. The production opportunity schedules in columns 4 and 5 have been computed from the separate input-output data in columns 2 and 3. If resource inputs, held constant at 10, are allocated entirely to Y_1 and none to Y_2, output of Y_1

is 55 and output of Y_2 is zero. Diversion of 1 resource input to Y_2 while 9 are used for Y_1 causes production to become 54 of Y_1 and 10 of Y_2. As additional resources are diverted from Y_1 to Y_2, output of the former eventually falls to a minimum of zero and output of the latter climbs to a maximum of 40.4. Column 6 indicates increasing marginal rates of

Table 3.

Production Function, Opportunity Schedule and Marginal Rates of Substitution for Two Independent Commodities Competing at Increasing Rates (Hypothetical Data)

Production function			*Production opportunity schedule (possible combinations of 2 products) with resources constant at 10 units*		*Marginal rate of substitution of Y_2 for Y_1 $(\Delta Y_1/\Delta Y_2)$ average*
Input of factor	Output of Y_1	Output of Y_2	Output of Y_1	Output of Y_2	
(1)	(2)	(3)	(4)	(5)	(6)
0	0	0	55.0	0	
1	10.0	10.0	54.0	10.0	−.1
2	19.0	16.7	52.0	16.7	−.3
3	27.0	21.7	49.0	21.7	−.6
4	34.0	25.7	45.0	25.7	−1.0
5	40.0	29.0	40.0	29.0	−1.5
6	45.0	31.9	34.0	31.9	−2.1
7	49.0	34.4	27.0	34.4	−2.8
8	52.0	36.6	19.0	36.6	−3.6
9	54.0	38.6	10.0	38.6	−4.5
10	55.0	40.4	0	40.4	−5.6

substitution between Y_2 and Y_1. An increase in Y_2 from zero to 10 through a shift of 1 unit of resource, causes production of Y_1 to drop from 55 to 54. The sacrifice in Y_1 is .1 unit for each unit of Y_2 gained. Hence the marginal rate of substitution, $\Delta Y_1/\Delta Y_2$, is −.1. Transfer of 1 more unit of resource from Y_1 to Y_2 causes output of Y_1 to be reduced by 2 units and output of Y_2 to be increased by 6.7 units. Hence the increasing rate of sacrifice is now indicated by the fact that the marginal rate of substitution of Y_2 for Y_1 $(\Delta Y_1/\Delta Y_2)$ climbs to 2.0/6.7 or −.3. Diversion of a third unit of resources causes the marginal rate of substitution to climb to .6. Transfer of the last resource unit drives the ratio of sacrifice to 10/1.8 or −5.6.

Since substitution between products Y_2 and Y_1 is at increasing marginal rates (increasing amounts of one must be sacrificed for each successive gain of 1 unit in the other) the transformation or opportunity curve is concave to the origin (an increasing rate of curvature towards either axis) as indicated for I_1P_1 in Figure 5. Curves Y_1 and Y_2 in Figure 4 represent the production functions for each product, while I_1P_1 in Figure 5 illustrates an opportunity curve from Table 3. This production possibility curve indicates the opportunities in production of Y_1 and Y_2 when the total quantity of resources is constant at 10 units. While I_1P_1, Figure 5, can be derived from the production possibility schedule of Table 3, it can also be derived from Figure 4 in the sense of "moving up" curve Y_2 (starting from the origin) and down curve Y_1 (starting from 55 units of output) when the quantity of resources is fixed at 10. Lines I_2P_2 and I_3P_3 represent the iso-resource or opportunity curves when resources are constant at levels of 7 and 4 units respectively. Given the production function for both products, the slope of the transformation or opportunity curves varies depending on the quantity of resources to be allocated between the 2 competing commodities. The curvature of line I_3P_3 in Figure 5 is small because only 4 units of resources are shifted between Y_1 and Y_2; the change in slopes

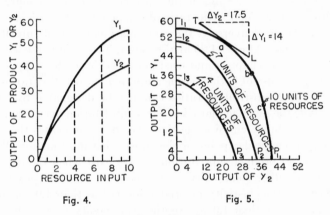

Fig. 4.   Fig. 5.

Production and transformation functions.

or production elasticities of the curves in Figure 4 are only slight up to 4 units of input for each product. However, the slopes change quite rapidly in Figure 4 as inputs are increased to 10, because of declining marginal productivity of resources used for either product. Hence, it is true that production possibility curve I_1P_1 in Figure 5, representing 10 units of resources, also has a sharp curvature towards the axes. If we start with 10 units of resources devoted entirely to Y_1, a shift in 1 unit to Y_2 will allow a large gain in the latter product for a small loss in the former; consequently, the top portion of I_1P_1 is nearly horizontal. Additional shifts in resources, however, cause greater sacrifices in Y_1 and smaller gains in Y_2 until I_1P_1 curves rapidly towards the horizontal axis.

Average and exact substitution rates. The marginal rates of product substitution shown in column 6 of Table 3 also explain the degree of curvature in I_1P_1 in Figure 5. Production possibility curve I_1P_1 is nearly flat at the outset since, as is illustrated in column 6 of Table 3, the marginal rate of substitution of Y_2 for Y_1 is low at the outset. Curve I_1P_1 finally becomes nearly vertical, however, as the marginal rates of substitution increase.

The marginal substitution ratios in Table 3 can be termed *average* rates. They show the ratio of substitution over a range of several units of Y_2. As the last unit of resource is shifted from Y_1 to Y_2 (columns 4 and 5 of Table 3) the substitution ratio becomes $-10/1.8$ or -5.6. However, we cannot say that the marginal rate of substitution of exactly the 38th, 39th, or 40th unit of Y_2 is -5.6; instead, the substitution ratio of all units of Y_2 between 38.6 and 40.4 averages -5.6. We can, however, specify the *exact* marginal rate of product substitution of units of one product in the same manner that the *exact* marginal rate of factor substitution or the *exact* marginal product was specified in earlier chapters. The tangent curve in Figure 5 shows the *exact* ratio of change $\Delta Y_1/\Delta Y_2$ when Y_2 output is 20. Since the slopes of 2 tangent lines are equal, the *exact* marginal rate of substitution of Y_2 for Y_1 (the ratio of change) is $-14/17.5$ or $-.8$ when output of Y_2 is 20. Conversely, the *exact* marginal rate of substitution of Y_1 for Y_2 is $-17.5/14$ or -1.25 at this point. The logic is the same as indicated in previous chapters and need not be reviewed here. We will have occasion to make use of both *average* and *exact* substitution ratios in later sections. These 2 substitution ratios can also be designated by the terms *arc* and *point;* the average figure indicates substitution over a range of the production possibility curve while the exact figure indicates the substitution ratio at a particular point of the transformation function. While increasing rates of product substitution always exist when the elasticity of production for either commodity is less than 1.0, the same situation may hold true if (1) the elasticity of production is less than 1.0 for one commodity but greater than 1.0 for another commodity or (2) the resource units being transferred are not homogeneous in respect to either quality or time. These points will be illustrated later with agricultural examples.

Elasticity of substitution. The *elasticity of product substitution* (E_{ps}) measures the percentage decrease in output of one commodity Y_1 associated with a given percentage increase in a second commodity, Y_2. It can be computed simply from the formula $E_{ps} = \Delta Y_1/Y_1 \div \Delta Y_2/Y_2$ or $\Delta Y_1/\Delta Y_2 \cdot Y_2/Y_1$ (or per cent change in Y_1 divided by per cent change in Y_2, where Y_1 and Y_2 refer to the "original output" of the 2 commodities while ΔY_1 and ΔY_2 refer to the change in output). The elasticity of product substitution is useful mainly in suggesting the change in curvature of an opportunity curve. As the elasticity of substitution of Y_2 for Y_1 increases, the opportunity line has a greater curvature towards the axis (or, an opportunity line with a high elasticity will have a much sharper curvature than one with a low elasticity of substitution).

Iso-cost curve. While the lines of Figure 5 are iso-factor curves, a parallel set of production possibilities can be charted when a given amount of costs rather than a fixed amount of physical resources are available for allocation between competing commodities. (This section is presented before an analysis of costs. The knowledge of costs required is very elementary and will be possessed by most readers. However, those completely unacquainted with cost analysis may wish to defer this particular section until after the chapters on costs.) Production possibility or iso-cost curves of this nature can be illustrated in Figures 6 and 7. Figure 6 shows the total cost curves (short-run) for 2 commodities and Figure 7 shows the corresponding iso-cost or production opportunity curve. The fixed costs attached to products Y_3 and Y_4 are $500; plant and equipment are already on hand for producing either commodity. If the fixed costs associated with each product refer to equipment which cannot be used for the other product, then $500 is "tied up" in fixed charges even if none of either commodity is produced. If $3,000, including $1,000 in fixed costs for the 2 products,

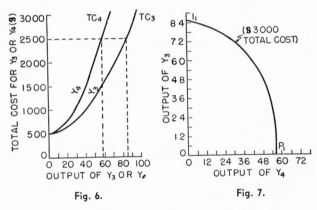

Fig. 6.   Fig. 7.

Increasing productivity and concave opportunity curves.

are available for use in production, only $2,000 is free to be allocated between the 2 products.[1] Hence the production possibility or iso-cost line $I_1 P_1$ in Figure 7 can be derived from the short-run cost curves TC_3 and TC_4 in Figure 6. With a constant cost outlay of $3,000, 85 units of Y_3 and none of Y_4 can be produced if all the variable costs ($2,000) are used for Y_3 and none are used for Y_4. Use of $500 in variable costs for Y_4 (a total of $1,000 in costs for Y_4, since its fixed costs are $500) and $1,500 for Y_3 (a total of $2,000 in costs for Y_3, since its fixed costs are $500) allows output of 28 units of Y_4 and 73 units of Y_3. Transfer of another $500 to Y_4 from Y_3 ($1,500 in total costs allocated to Y_4 and $1,500 allocated to Y_3) causes production of the former to move to 40 and output of the latter to

---

[1] If the equipment for one product can also be used for the other product then the total outlay which can be devoted to either product is $3,000. The problems of adaptability and flexibility in this vein are discussed in Chapter 9.

drop to 58.[2] A graph of these points gives curve I_1P_1 in Figure 7 which indicates all possible combinations of products Y_3 and Y_4 when total costs are fixed at $3,000.

Since the total cost function for both independent products curves upward (increasing marginal and average costs), the marginal rate of substitution between the 2 commodities is at an increasing rate when total costs are constant at $3,000; as successive cost units are diverted from Y_3 to Y_4, increasing amounts of Y_3 are sacrificed for each unit of Y_4 gained. Accordingly, the iso-outlay or production possibility curve is again concave to the origin (curved toward the axes). Whether they are expressed as iso-factor (Figure 5) or iso-cost (Figure 7) lines, production possibility curves always indicate increasing rates of sacrifice (are concave to the origin) if they are based on physical production functions with decreasing marginal returns and hence cost functions which indicate increasing marginal costs.

Opportunity costs and the "oneness" of economics. The iso-factor or iso-cost relationship can now be viewed as the "opportunity cost" curve. In contrast to the direct cost of producing a commodity (the factor-product relationship) it shows costs in terms of an alternative product given up. As indicated earlier, the product sacrificed can be looked upon as the input while the product gained is the output. In Table 3, Y_1 becomes the "input" and Y_2 the "output." Starting from the top of the table in columns 4 and 5, one unit of "input" of Y_1 is required to obtain the first 10 units of Y_2, while approximately 5 "inputs" of Y_1 are required for the second 10 units of Y_2. Figure 5 can be given a quarter-turn to the right so that Y_1 falls on the horizontal axis and Y_2 falls on the vertical axis. The resulting line rises at a diminishing rate from left to right and can be viewed in the vein of an input-output curve; each unit of Y_1 sacrificed is an input for Y_2. This is the counterpart of the early concepts of opportunity costs expressed by production economists.

Basis of increasing rates of substitution in agriculture. Increasing rates of enterprise substitution in agriculture grow out of 3 somewhat distinct phenomena. One of these, illustrated above, is the factor-product condition of diminishing marginal productivity. Under diminishing productivity for each commodity the opportunity curve or iso-line for any resource or combination of resources will be concave to the origin regardless of whether the constant quantity refers to labor, fertilizer, feed, capital in some other

---

[2] With a total outlay, $3,000, the movement down I_1P_1 (substitution of Y_4 for Y_3) in Figure 7 represents a "movement up" TC_4 starting from $500 (the amount of fixed costs) and down TC_3 starting from $2,500 (since $500 of the $3,000 are fixed costs for Y_4). A "movement" up, I_1P_1 (substitution of Y_3 for Y_4) represents a "movement up" TC_3 (starting from $500) and a "movement down" TC_4 starting from $2,500. Where the total outlay is $2,500, the "movement up" starts at $500 (fixed cost) and the "movement down" starts at $2,000 (since the other $500 of the total cost of $2,500 is "tied up" in the form of fixed costs for the other product.)

specific form, or an aggregate of these resources. With the supply of other resources held constant or available in unlimited quantities (for example, a family labor supply beyond that needed for seasonal requirements of crops or livestock possible from the more limited stock of capital and land) the question may be one of whether 2 tons of fertilizer should be allocated to corn, oats, or wheat. If other resources do not limit choice or decision-making, the relevant opportunity curve then becomes an iso-fertilizer curve referring to a 2-ton quantity, or if a given stock of feed can be used for hogs, cattle, or chickens already in existence on the farm and the supply of labor and equipment is great enough, feed becomes the truly scarce resource around which decisions must rest. The opportunity curve relevant to decision-making then becomes an iso-feed curve. (It is a short-run iso-feed curve since animal numbers are already given. The nature of long-run opportunity curves is explained in the next chapter.) With numbers of each type of livestock given, the iso-line defining the choices in feeding livestock to different levels is concave because of diminishing feed productivity when animals as technical units are fixed. Similarly, a different iso-curve representing the relevant decision-making opportunities exists when animal numbers as well as the output per animal can be varied while labor or land is fixed. This iso-line will be concave where increasing costs exist as the scale of each livestock enterprise is increased. On many farms of typical size, it will be linear between years for the reasons explained in earlier chapters. Hence a different production possibility curve exists as additional resources can be shifted between enterprises: The opportunity curve within a year may refer to a single resource such as feed or fertilizer after crop acres and livestock numbers have already been decided for a single year. Between years, production possibilities allow variation in acres and animal numbers as well as in fertilizer and feed. Over longer periods, labor, buildings, and machinery services may also be shifted from one to another enterprise even though they are specialized for single products in the short run. The intra-year and single-factor production possibility curve (technical units fixed) may be concave to the origin, indicating increasing rates of substitution, while the interyear (technical units variable) production possibility curve is linear, indicating constant rates of substitution within the limits of a farm with modest resources. When all resources are variable between enterprises and the quantity of resources is sufficient to give diminishing returns for each enterprise, the opportunity curve will also be concave indicative of increasing rates of product substitution. This point will be illustrated further and related to farm size in a later section.

A second force which can give rise to increasing marginal rates of product substitution on a farm with limited resources is non-homogeneity in quality of resources. The land area of the farm (or producing region as indicated at a later point) may be made up of several soil types each adapted differently to corn and wheat. A shift of one soil type from wheat to corn, if it is better adapted for corn than wheat, will cause a smaller sacrifice in wheat output for each gain in corn production than will shifts of additional land increasingly well adapted to wheat.[3] The same logic applies to non-homogeneity in labor: operator, hired, and family labor may be better adapted for one enterprise than for another.

Quasi-supplementary conditions provide a third reason why products may substitute at increasing rates. Here resources are non-homogeneous in respect to time and concave opportunity curves relate to the seasonality of production. The tendency is towards the supplementary relationships discussed in a later section of this chapter. Even where the production functions for homogeneous resources are linear, an element of increasing substitution rates exists for certain farm enterprises which can be produced at different times of the year. Feeder cattle and corn are examples in which the quantity of labor, land, machinery, and other resources is fixed for a farm of given size. Production of a small amount of corn-fed beef during the winter months may curtail corn output very little. Labor, machinery, money, and other resources which give off flow services throughout the year can be used on crops only during the summer months. An expansion in the cattle feeding enterprise conflicts with corn for labor and machinery, particularly during the planting season. The added beef, however, may reduce total corn production little if it only slightly retards timeliness of corn planting. Greater expansions in beef may cause further losses in corn output, if diversion of labor at critical cultivating and harvesting dates causes severe reduction in per acre yields from a given land area. Finally, the 2 enterprises come into full competition if cattle are fed year around in quantities which require use of all land for feed lots and none for corn. The amount of corn sacrificed as beef output is expanded increases due to different degrees of competition for factors throughout the year.

Joint Products with Competitive Range

The enterprise relationship between joint products with a latitude of substitution (mutton and wool, cotton and oilseed through selection of

---

[3] If the production function for each crop is linear within the limits of the farm, existence of land of 2 different qualities will cause the production possibility curve to have a corner such as that indicated below. Here 20 bushels of wheat may be sacrificed for each 1-ton gain in hay between points a and b. This section of the possibility curve represents changes in product combinations as land best adapted to wheat is shifted to hay. Between points b and c substitution rates may also be linear but 1 ton of hay now substitutes for only 12 bushels of wheat, as land best adapted to hay is shifted away to wheat. The same logic applies to other non-homogeneous labor applied to livestock and has the stability implications outlined later. Non-homogeneity of resource services also gives rise to the short-run transformation functions outlined in Chapter 9.

different strains, harvesting methods, and so forth) are hybrids of the general product-product situations discussed to this point. The opportunity curve for a single level of factor or cost outlay is of the nature of J_1P_1 in Figure 8. Here "mutton" can be increased at the expense of "wool" up to a maximum output of OY_2 of the former and a minimum of OY_1 of the latter. However, if "wool" output with resources held constant is decreased further, output of mutton must also decline. Wool output can be less only if mutton output is less. At this point the 2 products bear the same relationship as joint products in fixed proportions. Substitution of "wool" for "mutton" would lead to the same situation at the other extreme of J_1P_1.

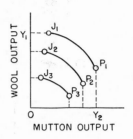

Variation in the proportions of joint products from given resources can generally be made in agriculture only through changes in breeds and strains (different techniques). The choice is not

Fig. 8. Joint products and range of substitution.

open for extracting 300 lbs. of butterfat and 10,000 lbs. of skim milk or 400 lbs. of butterfat and 8,000 lbs. of skim milk from a single cow. Yet these types of adjustments can be made through shifts in the breeds and number of cows handled on a farm of a given size and with a given outlay for feed, labor, and related resources. Linear segments of the production possibility curve then exist between breeds.

Competitive Products Under Decreasing Rates of Sacrifice

Production possibility curves for products produced under conditions of increasing returns give rise to diminishing rates of substitution: as one product, Y_6, is substituted for another, Y_5, smaller and smaller sacrifices are made in the latter for each unit gain in the former. This situation can be illustrated in the production possibility schedule in Table 4 and from the transformation curve in Figure 10. Since each commodity is produced under increasing returns (columns 1, 2, and 3 of the table and the corresponding production functions Y_5 and Y_6 in Figure 9), smaller and smaller sacrifices are required in one product for each unit increase in output of the other. Starting in Table 4 with resources devoted entirely to Y_5, transfer of 1 unit of resource from Y_5 to Y_6 causes output of the former to decrease by 10 and output of the latter to increase by .5. The average marginal rate of substitution $\Delta Y_5/\Delta Y_6$ is —10/.5 or —20. Transfer of a second resource unit causes a sacrifice of 9 units of Y_5 and allows gain of 1 unit of Y_6. Hence the marginal rate of substitution drops to —9/1 or —9. Transfer of the third resource unit lowers the marginal ratio of substitution to —5.3, and the decline continues as additional resources are diverted to Y_6.

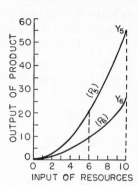

Fig. 9.

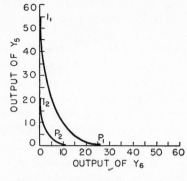

Fig. 10.

Increasing productivity and convex opportunity curves.

Since the elasticity of both the Y_5 and Y_6 production functions is greater than 1.0 throughout (Figure 9), the elasticity of substitution necessarily declines as one commodity is substituted for another and the transformation curve becomes convex to the origin as is illustrated by I_1P_1 in Figure

Table 4.

Production Functions, Production Possibilities and Marginal Rate of Product Substitution Under Increasing Returns (Hypothetical Data)

| Input of factor | Output of product | | Production possibilities with 10 units of resources | | Marginal rate of substitution of Y_6 for Y_5 average |
	Y_5	Y_6	Y_5	Y_6	
(1)	(2)	(3)	(4)	(5)	(6)
0	0	0	55	0	
					−20.0
1	1.0	.5	45	.5	
					−9.0
2	3.0	1.5	36	1.5	
					−5.3
3	6.0	3.0	28	3.0	
					−3.5
4	10.0	5.0	21	5.0	
					−2.4
5	15.0	7.5	15	7.5	
					−1.7
6	21.0	10.5	10	10.5	
					−1.1
7	28.0	14.0	6	14.0	
					−.8
8	36.0	18.0	3	18.0	
					−.4
9	45.0	22.5	1	22.5	
					−.2
10	55.0	27.5	0	27.5	

10.[4] Curve I_1P_1 represents the production opportunities when a total of 10 resource units are available for production of Y_5 and Y_6. Graphically, it can be derived as a "movement up" Y_6 and a "movement down" Y_5 in Figure 9 (or vice versa). Iso-line I_2P_2 represents the possibilities when resources are held constant at 6 units. It is also convex to the origin indicating decreasing marginal rates of substitution between the products since both are produced under conditions of increasing returns.

While not as common as those with linear and increasing substitution rates, production possibilities with decreasing substitution rates can be found in agriculture. (The opportunity curves are convex to the origin.) These production situations are found particularly on small farms where capital is extremely limited and production of any one commodity cannot be extended to a point where ranges of increasing returns have been exhausted. They also exist where production must take place on a mass-scale basis and the commodities are competitive.

Other combinations of independent products and farm recommendations. While pairs of production functions representing distinct situations (linear, increasing, and decreasing returns) have been compared, the alternative of combining enterprises with entirely different production situations exists. Although many opportunity curves are then possible, most of these fall in the categories already outlined. Combination of an increasing returns product and a constant returns product gives a convex (decreasing sacrifice) opportunity curve.[5] The iso-factor curve is concave (increasing sacrifice) when a constant return product is compared with a decreasing return product. Combination of a decreasing return product with an increasing return product may give linear, convex, or concave opportunity curves, depending on the production coefficient for the 2 products. Aside from the complementary enterprises discussed later, other combinations of competing and independent products may give "kinky" opportunity curves; combination of a constant return enterprise with one of both increasing and decreasing returns gives an opportunity curve with both convex and concave portions.

Two products, both with production elasticities greater and less than 1.0 (increasing and decreasing marginal productivity), may result in (a) linear, (b) convex, (c) concave or (d) "wavy" opportunity curves, depending on the span and degree of increasing or decreasing returns and the

---

[4] Were opportunity curves to be derived as iso-cost lines from total cost functions under increasing returns to scale, they would also represent decreasing marginal rates of substitution. While the total cost functions would increase at a diminishing rate (the obverse of those in Figures 6 and 7) the corresponding iso-outlay or iso-cost curves would be convex to the origin.

[5] The curvature of the opportunity line becomes much greater toward the axis of the increasing returns product than for the constant returns product. For a constant return-decreasing return combination, the opportunity line also has a greater curvature near the axis of the decreasing returns product.

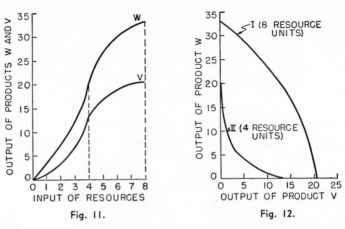

Fig. 11.   Fig. 12.

Opportunity curves for firms of different size.

quantity of resources to be allocated between the 2 products.[6] This statement can be illustrated by means of Table 5 and Figures 11 and 12. The first 3 columns of the table indicate that both products W and V are produced under increasing returns for resource units 1 to 4 inclusive. Resource

Table 5.

Production Functions and Production Possibilities Under Increasing and Decreasing
Resource Productivity (Hypothetical Example)

	Production Functions		Production possibilities with 8 resource units		Production possibilities with 4 resource units	
Resource input	Output of W	Output of V	Output of W	Output of V	Output of W	Output of V
(1)	(2)	(3)	(4)	(5)	(6)	(7)
1	2	1	33	0	20	0
2	6	3	32	1	12	1
3	12	7	30	3	6	3
4	20	13	26	7	2	7
5	26	17	20	13	0	13
6	30	19	12	17		
7	32	20	6	19		
8	33	20.5	2	20		
			0	20.5		

units 5 to 8 give decreasing returns for each product. Columns 4 and 5 provide a production possibility schedule when 8 units of resources can be allocated between commodities W and V. The corresponding iso-resource

---

[6] If the output of product A is 2, 5, 9, 14, 18, 21, and 23, while output of product B is 4, 10, 18, 28, 36, 42, and 46 for factor inputs 1, 2, 3, 4, 5, 6, and 7, respectively, the corresponding opportunity curve will be linear although increasing and decreasing returns exist for both products when 7 homogeneous units of resource are available for the 2 enterprises.

curve is indicated as *I* in Figure 12. The curve II is based on columns 6 and 7 in Table 5 and indicates the allocative opportunities when resources are limited to 4 units. The contrast is apparent; availability of 8 resource units causes substitution to be at increasing rates (curve I is concave), while 4 resource units cause substitution to be at decreasing rates (curve II is convex). This difference has important implications for research and recommendations in agriculture. Even though the enterprise and techniques of production are the same for a farm with few resources and a farm with large resources, their production possibilities may be extremely different. Hence the optimum resource use pattern for one need not be the same as for the other. This point is illustrated further in later discussions of product-product choices.

Antagonistic Competitive Enterprises

While all competitive products are rivals in the use of resources, certain agricultural enterprises are antagonistic. *Antagonism* is expressed when the production function for 2 independent products changes as the 2 enterprises are produced in the presence of each other. Diseases may creep into turkeys when they are produced in conjunction with chickens and vice versa. The "degree of antagonism" is expressed in the slope of the opportunity curve. If turkeys and chickens are produced as competitive enterprises from a given outlay of resources, the production possibility curve may have a negative slope even if the 2 enterprises are produced several miles from each other. Production of more turkeys at one location requires diversion of feed, labor, and investment from chickens at another location. However, if the 2 enterprises are produced at the same location, the sacrifice in chicken output accompanying each shift in resources to turkeys may be greater than if the enterprise were to be produced at different locations; the disease factor causes this difference to arise. In a sense, antagonism is the opposite of the complementarity relationship discussed in a later section.

Complementary Enterprises

Product-product relationships also parallel factor-factor relationships in the sense that 2 or more commodities can be technical complements as well as technical substitutes. Two products are technical complements when an increase in output of one, with resources held constant in amount, also results in an increase in output of the other. In other words, a shift of resources from a first crop to a second crop will increase rather than decrease output of the first. This production situation prevails widely in agriculture. However, many of the so-called complementary enterprises in agriculture do not fall strictly in this category in the sense that resources are held constant in quantity. While corn may contribute feed to hog production, the 2 enterprises may compete for labor; an increase in the corn may require a sacrifice in pork if the quantity of labor is not increased. Technical complementarity may arise because of any 1 of 3 reasons: (1) One enterprise may contribute an element of production, a joint product of the first, required by a second enterprise. (2) One enterprise may divert surplus resources from a second product. (3) The products may interact with each other as the proportions of non-usable joint products change with varying levels of output from a fixed technical unit. These 3 situations are explained below. Perhaps the first is the most important in agriculture. In production economics it is the problem of crop rotations economics or land use.

Joint products, rotation relationships and land use. Legume and grass crops may contribute elements required in production of grain, fiber, or other crops by (a) increasing fertility through addition of nitrogen, (b) improving soil structure through addition of organic matter, (c) preventing soil erosion, and (d) controlling insects. As long as these effects are great enough land can be shifted from grains to forages while the total output from a given acreage of both is increased. Table 6, drawn from Cornbelt experimental data, illustrates simple complementary relationships between forage and grain crops. When 2 crops are complementary, use of resources for the 2 makes possible a greater output of one or both than if each category were grown independently.

As the substitution column indicates for Ohio soils, a shift of 20 acres from grain to alfalfa causes grain production to increase by 10.9 pounds for each pound of hay gained. A shift in 13 more acres to alfalfa causes the ratio $\Delta G/\Delta H$ (change in grain/change in hay) to become negative indicating competition between crops. A shift from the second to the third rotation causes a sacrifice of .19 lbs. of grain for each 1-lb. gain in hay. With land fixed at 100 acres, a shift between the third and fourth rotations causes the marginal rate of substitution to climb to $-.22$. A further shift causes it to climb to $-.53$. Complementarity is "one way" in the sense that a shift of land from grain to hay increases output of the former. Were the crops mutually complementary, output of hay also would be increased as land was shifted to grain at the lower end of the table. The experiments examined do not include the extremes in cropping combinations wherein grain becomes complementary with hay. However, this relationship is a distinct possibility in agriculture and exists in the western periphery of the Cornbelt on such soils as Ida, Monona, and Pawnee, where hay, down too long, exhausts moisture supplies or yields lightly because of winter killing or other cropping hazards.

Nitrogen, organic matter, and soil structure serve as the joint products from one enterprise which can increase output from a second product in Cornbelt, New England, and southern agricultural areas. In areas of tobacco production, a crop such as small grain, hay, or even weeds in

Table 6.

Enterprise Relationships, Marginal Rates of Substitution and Related Items for Specified Rotation and Corn Belt Soils. Total Production Figures Based on 100 Acres of Land *

Cropping system [a]	Acres of land out of 100 in		Total Production (lbs.) [b]		Rate of substitution of hay for grain (lbs. of grain sacrificed for each lb. of hay gained)
	Hay	Grain	Grain	Hay	
Drummer silt loam, Urbana, Illinois, 1904-1949:					
C	0	100	136,248		
C-O-Cl	33	67	149,891	54,200	Complementary (+79.8)
Wooster and Canfield silt loams, Wooster, Ohio, 1937-1943					
C	0	100	217,840		
C-C-C-W-A	20	80	229,776	128,800	Complementary (+10.9)
C-W-A	33	67	215,480	203,200	— .19
C-C-W-A-A	40	60	190,672	316,000	— .22
C-W-A-A	50	50	165,928	363,000	— .53
Clarion-Webster silt loam, Ames, Iowa, 1915-1948					
C	0	100	224,000		
C-C-O-Cl	25	75	212,920	89,600	— .13
C-O-Cl	33	67	166,194	96,400	—5.0
Clarion-Webster silt loam, Ames, Iowa, 1945-1948					
C	0	100	180,320		
C-C-O-Cl	25	75	217,360	85,000	Complementary (+ 2.3)
C-O-Cl	33	67	182,333	132,660	— .71
Marshall silt loam, Clarinda, Iowa, 1933-1949					
C	0	100	156,912		
C-O-Cl	33	67	149,122	110,880	— .07
Marshall silt loam, Clarinda, Iowa, 1941-1949					
C	0	100	118,720		
C-O-Cl	33	67	183,019	148,500	Complementary (+ 2.3)

* Source: Heady and Jensen, Iowa Agr. Exp. Sta. Bul. 383.
[a] C = corn; O = oats; Cl = clover; A = alfalfa.
[b] Corn, 56 lbs. per bushel; oats, 32; wheat, 60.

rotation with tobacco can prove to be complementary; these crops provide an "input" (they remove a "negative" input) for tobacco to the extent that they are effective in controlling such diseases as root knot and root rot nematodes. Moisture may serve as the element which leads to complementarity in the Great Plains and semi-arid farming regions. Wheat and fallow sequences parallel the grain-legume rotations in the Cornbelt. Fallow land can be treated simply as a "crop," one of the by-products of which is moisture. Up to the rotation or cropping system including 1 year of fallow out of 3 at Fort Hayes, Kansas (Table 7, column 4), fallow is complementary with wheat. Added fallow competes, however, with wheat production from a given area of land. It is also likely that cattle and wheat are complementary over a slight range in winter wheat areas; production of wheat allows fall grazing of cattle and an increased output

Table 7.

Yield of Wheat Per 100 Acres Under Various Wheat-Fallow Rotations at Fort Hayes, Kansas, 1918-1949.*

Rotation [a]	Per cent of land in wheat	Yield per acre [b]	Production of wheat per 100 acres (bushels)
(1)	(2)	(3)	(4)
Continuous wheat	100	14.6	1460
F-W-W-W	75	20.5	1538
F-W-W	67	21.1	1414
F-W	50	23.8	1190

* Source: Agronomy Department, Kansas State College. [a] W refers to wheat and F refers to fallow. [b] Yield for year land is in wheat.

of beef; pasturing of wheat by cattle may cause the grain to stool better and to produce a higher yield. Experiments in North Carolina over the period 1940-48 show a winter cover crop of vetch to be complementary with corn for the land resources alone; corn yields per acre averaged 21.5 bushels without vetch and 74.9 bushels with a vetch cover crop.

When enterprises are complementary, the opportunity curves are of the general nature indicated in Figures 13 and 14. The product-product relationships from Table 6 give the production possibility curve I_1P_1 in Figure

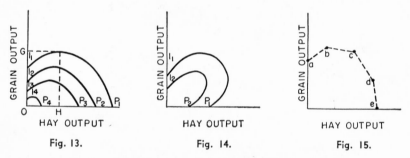

Fig. 13.   Fig. 14.   Fig. 15.

Complementary-competitive production possibilities.

13. Hay is complementary with grain until production of the latter reaches a maximum of OG and output of the former reaches OH. The products then become competitive, and hay substitutes for grain at an increasing rate (increasing amounts of grain must be sacrificed for each 1-lb. gain in hay). Again, an entire family of opportunity curves is possible, depending on the quantity of resources used; a different opportunity curve exists for each level at which resources are held constant. Curve I_4P_4 can be taken as a 20-acre plot upon which the agronomist conducts experiments, while I_3P_3, I_2P_2, and I_1P_1 represent crop combinations on farms with 60, 80, and 100 acres of land respectively.

Where mutual complementarity exists (for example, hay with grain and grain with hay), the iso-factor line becomes as indicated in Figure 14, where each iso-resource curve, representing different quantities of resource, has 2 segments with a positive slope and 1 segment with a negative slope; for extreme enterprise combinations, a fixed quantity of resources can always be rearranged to increase the output of both products.

Discontinuity. Generally the product-product relationship is of a non-linear nature when enterprises are complementary. A high degree of continuity exists in product substitution. Discontinuity is not so much a problem as under factor-product and factor-factor relationships, since the services of discontinuous inputs such as tractors can be allocated between enterprises in fractional amounts. Similarly, the land area of a farm can be divided in a continuous manner between crops by using different combinations of rotations. However, when the alternative rotations are compared for the entire farm, each rotation presents a discrete possibility. Agronomists and farmers often consider cropping systems in the vein of sequences such as continuous corn, corn-corn-oats-meadow, corn-corn-oats-meadow-meadow, or corn-oats-meadow (see Table 6). When each crop combination is considered as a discrete possibility the iso-resource curve is of the nature indicated in Figure 15. Only the combinations denoted as *a, b, c, d,* and *e* are relevant, since it is supposed that the in-between combinations are not attainable or are not practicable. This is the vein in which data such as those of Table 6 are presented by agronomists or soil conservation planners; flexibility is not assumed. In Figure 15, point *a* might refer to continuous grain, point *e* might refer to continuous hay, while other points refer to rotations, such as grain-grain-hay or grain-grain-hay-hay. These points or corners on the production possibility curve have stability and research implications to be discussed later.

Complementarity based on a joint product furnished by one enterprise as an input for another is often expressed only over time. Increased grain output from a given land area comes about only as these crops follow hay and benefit from nitrogen, organic matter, or other production elements furnished by forages. Hay and corn are almost always competitive within the time span of a single year; the more hay produced on a given land area, the smaller the grain output must be within the same year. Time and complementarity thus provide important production economics problems under farm leasing situations. It is possible, however, for 2 crops to bear a complementarity relationship even within a single year. New seedings and small grains as nurse crops fall partly in this category.

The data provided by agronomic experiments are the basis for iso-land possibility curves since other resources are not included in experimental data. Even after several decades of agronomic research, comparatively little is known about the nature of rotation possibility curves. Although data such as those from Table 6 prove that complementarity between grain and forage exists, on some soils, little is known about the extent of complementarity. The Ohio data show that the C-C-C-W-A rotation results in complementarity when compared to continuous corn, but it does not indicate whether this cropping combination is the counterpart of the grain-maximum (point b) in Figure 15. It is possible either (a) that the C-C-C-W-A rotation is a point such as c and extends beyond a maximum grain output from a given land area, or (b) that this rotation does not reach the point of maximum grain output. One of the more important tasks facing agronomists is isolation of the cropping system which divides complementarity from competition. With data of this nature, agronomists and production economists then could team up better to help farmers in their economic choices and to formulate the details of national conservation and land-use policies. Conservation and land-use policies, except for their legal and institutional aspects, are problems in production economics and make little sense except as they consider the several phases of the production possibility curve and all resources including capital, labor, land, and management. More often, it is limitations in capital and management or prices and uncertainty, rather than land phenomena, which prevents farmers from following rotations and cropping practices which society or public administrators deem efficient.

Complementarity and removal of "surplus" resources. The second type of complementary relationship grows out of "surplus" factors or the fact that diminishing total returns may exist where too many resources are applied in producing either one of 2 products. There are numerous examples of this type of complementarity in agriculture. When a farmer runs too many beef cows on a given pasture acreage, output of beef and another product such as hogs can be increased simultaneously by transferring some of the limited capital and labor from the beef to the pork enterprise. In other words, the farmer could sell some beef cows and use the same capital to buy brood sows and feed without changing the total outlay. Likewise, when total egg production is beyond the maximum because too many hens are housed in the shelter available, production of eggs can be increased by diverting capital investment, labor, and feed to another enterprise, such as dairy cows, where maximum total returns have not been attained within the framework of buildings and other fixed resources available. Here dairy cows do not compete with poultry for resource services, but allow transfer of surplus resources from the latter enterprise. The nature of this complementary situation can be illustrated by means of the experimental data from Table 5, Chapter 4. Using 2 acres, A and B for illustrative purposes, a production schedule such as that indicated in the first 2 columns of Table 8 exists, where the total stock of fertilizer is fixed at 1,700 lbs. (or a value of $51 with a price per cwt. of $3) between acres A and B. We will simply consider output from acre A as if it were a different product than output from acre B. If the entire amount of fertilizer is allocated to

Table 8.

Production Possibilities for Cotton with Varying Amount of Fertilizer to Allocate Between Units A and B *

Production possibilities with 17 units (cwt.) of fertilizer resources to allocate		Production possibilities with 15 units (cwt.) of resource		Production possibilities with 8 units (cwt.) of resource	
A	B	A	B	A	B
(1)	(2)	(3)	(4)	(5)	(6)
744	0	775	0	635	0
764	107	779	107	583	107
775	206	775	206	523	206
779	297	764	297	456	297
775	381	742	381	381	381
762	456	714	456	297	456
742	523	678	523	206	523
714	583	635	583	107	583
678	635	583	635	0	635
635	678	523	678		
583	714	456	714		
523	742	381	742		
456	762	297	762		
381	775	206	775		
297	779	107	779		
206	775	0	775		
107	764				
0	744				

* Source: Derived from experimental data Table 5, Chapter 4.

A, total production is 744 lbs., while output from B is zero. Use of 2 fertilizer units on B and 15 on A allows outputs of 775 and 206 lbs. respectively. These production possibilities with 17 fertilizer units are graphed as iso-resource curve I_1P_1 in Figure 16. When the total amount of fertilizer is fixed at 1,500 rather than 1,700 pounds, complementarity still exists (see columns 3 and 4 in Table 7) and the corresponding opportunity curve, I_2P_2, crosses I_1P_1 in Figure 16. However, when only 10 units of fertilizer are to be allocated between A and B (see columns 5 and 6), the iso-factor or iso-cost curve has only a negative slope denoting competition alone: the amount of fertilizer is not great enough to extend production into the range of decreasing total returns for either A or B, and hence a complementary phase does not exist.

The opportunity curve I_2P_2 crosses I_1P_1, because the 15 resource units of the former do not push inputs so far into the range of decreasing returns as the 17 units of the latter. The combined product can be greater under I_1P_1 than under I_2P_2 (I_1P_1 is "above" I_2P_2 over a wide range), however, since a greater number of resource units is available where production does fall outside of the competitive range for both A and B. (An iso-factor curve based on 14 units of resources would originate "outside" of I_2P_2 but would also intersect it). Transformation curves, indicative of a single technique, which intersect are to be found only under the surplus resource-type of complementarity just outlined, and never under the joint-product interaction discussed previously. The relationships outlined here are identical with those which would exist were A and B entirely different products and if the resources in question represented labor, capital, or land as an aggregate of resources which might be applied where diminishing total returns prevail. It should be emphasized that under no condition does the complementary relationship extend indefinitely. It always merges into a competitive relationship.

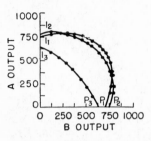

Fig. 16. Production possibilities for different quantities of resources.

Complementary effects through changing proportions of joint products. Complementary relationships may also arise when an enterprise includes several joint products which change in proportions as output is increased or rearranged. Complementarity arising for this reason is to be found mainly in livestock production. These complementary relationships do not express themselves in direct physical form to the farmer, although they are reflected in the prices which he receives for animals of different grades and weights. They are important from the standpoint of consumers who must express their preferences through the market or to a nation in

Table 9.

Output of Pork and Pork Products from 88 Billion Feed Units (Million Units of Production) *

	Barrows and gilts weighing			
Item	125 lbs.	175 lbs.	225 lbs.	275 lbs.
No. hogs produced	129.0	96.8	76.5	62.5
Lbs. live pork produced	16,125	16,940	17,212	17,188
Per cent edible portion	65.7	66.8	68.6	70.8
Total lbs. edible pork	10,594	11,316	11,807	12,169
Per cent separable fat	31.9	34.3	37.8	41.8
Total lbs. separable fat	5,144	5,810	6,506	7,185
Per cent separable lean	33.8	32.5	30.8	29.0
Total lbs. separable lean	5,450	5,506	5,301	4,985
Dressed wt. per hog	104.5	148.2	190.1	232.5
Total lbs. dressed pork	13,480	14,346	14,543	14,531

* Source: Computed from data in U.S.D.A. Tech. Bul. No. 917 and Iowa Experimental Data.

periods of national emergency or planned economies. The complementary relationships in meat production actually grow out of a complex of forces including (1) diminishing returns under the feed-pork transformation relationship, (2) increases in dressing percentage as animals are fed to greater weights, and (3) changes in the composition of the total animal carcass at various weights. The relationship is expressed in the iso-feed schedule of Table 9, which provides estimates of the amounts of 2 pork products possible from a constant outlay of 88 billion feed units. The estimates are not strictly of iso-resource possibilities because hog numbers, labor, and related inputs are variable. However, a corresponding iso-resource schedule could be constructed. Although more hogs can be pro-

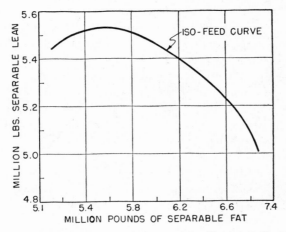

Fig. 17. Iso-feed combinations for separable lean and fat (Source: Table 8). Input of hog resources and hog weights variable.

duced at the lighter marketing weight, a maximum amount of live pork is obtained when 68.9 million hogs are fed to 250 lbs. each. Up to this point the diminishing productivity of grain fed to live hogs is more than offset by (a) the spreading of grain over fewer litters and (b) the increase in dressing percentage. More pounds of both fat and lean cuts are possible from the given feed stock as hog marketing weights are increased and hog numbers are decreased up to a combination including 85.6 million hogs fed to 200 lbs. Beyond this combination, an increase in separable fat is made at a sacrifice in separable lean as is illustrated in Figure 17. Similar relationships exist between total lean cuts and total fat cuts.

Boundary Lines and Isoclines

As in the case of factor-factor relationships, borderlines can be used to separate ranges of product competition from ranges of product complementarity. These are illustrated in Figure 18 by lines A and B which intersect each of the production possibility curves where complementarity gives way to competition between products. More specifically, A and B are

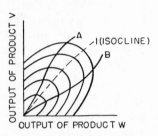

Fig. 18. Boundary (ridge) lines and isoclines.

isoclines (ridgelines), since the slope of the iso-resource curves are identical at the points of intersection. Line A intersects each possibility curve where the possibility curve is horizontal; line B intersects each curve where the possibility curve is vertical. The path traced out by A indicates all points where the marginal rate of substitution of product W for product V is infinite. The path traced out by B indicates combinations where the ratio of substitution $\Delta V/\Delta W$ is zero. Consequently, the portion of each possibility curve falling between A and B has a negative slope indicating competition. Portions outside of A and B have a positive slope indicating product complementarity.[7]

Isoclines and farm size. Other isoclines can also be constructed. Line I in Figure 18 is such a line. It connects all points on the possibility curves where the slope is $1.8\,V/1.0\,W$, indicating a marginal substitution rate (of W for V) of 1.8. Although the ratio of change is always negative when the products are substitutes, the minus sign will be omitted in subsequent chapters except where distinction between supplementary, complementary, and competitive relationships must be made.

The concept of a product isocline has important implications in recommendations made to operators on farms of different sizes. Should the 40-acre farm produce a different combination of products than a 160- or 320-acre farm? Many recommendations suggest that small-scale operators should produce labor-intensive products such as milk or poultry, while large-scale units might move in a different direction. The correct answer depends, of course, not only on the resources available to the farmer, but also on the nature of his production possibilities and the rate at which one enterprise substitutes for another. Even though the operator is not fully occupied, it is entirely possible that his production opportunities do not differ from those of a large-scale operator who must hire labor. This point is discussed further in the chapter on scale relationships.

---

[7] Another parallel between factor-factor relationships and product-product relationships can also be made: if the enterprise provides joint products in fixed proportions, the boundary lines coincide in the manner of a line which might be drawn from southwest to northeast through points a, b, and c in Figure 1. When the products are competitive throughout all possible combinations, boundary line A becomes identical with the vertical axis while boundary line B becomes identical with the horizontal axis.

Supplementary Products

The *supplementary relationship* is the last major category of enterprise relationships. Two enterprises bear a supplementary relationship when, with resources constant, output of one product can be increased with neither a gain nor a sacrifice in another product. Supplementary conditions arise mainly out of time and are to be found especially where (a) enterprises can be produced only during a distinct and limited period of the year and (b) the resources employed give off a flow of services over all time periods. Where resource services are of the pure stock variety, enterprises concerned are only competitive. When resources employed for one product are in the form of fixed equipment which gives off services irrespective of use in production, these services may be captured in production through a second commodity forthcoming in the off-season of the first. The second product does not, therefore, require a diminution in output of the first product during its "active season," since flow factor services are generated irrespective of their use in production. In addition to the foregoing case of non-homogeneity of resource services in respect to time, supplementary enterprises may be produced simultaneously whenever the flow services of resources are concerned, and one product does not completely exhaust these.

Non-homogeneous resource services. The resource services which provide the basis for supplementarity between enterprises are not interchangeable in the sense that all units can be withdrawn from one enterprise and used for another enterprise. The distinction here can be illustrated with a series

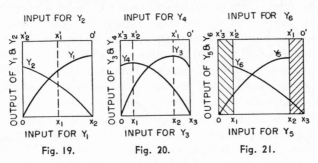

Supplementary enterprises.

of diagrams such as Figures 19, 20, and 21, which illustrate the allocative possibilities for competitive, complementary, and supplementary enterprises. Figure 19 illustrates production functions which serve as the basis for competitive product opportunity curves: the input-output curve for product Y_1 is graphed in the customary manner, while the curve for Y_2 is reversed, with inputs reading from right to left above the top of the graph and, with output reading from bottom to top in the usual manner. When the constant or total quantity of resource services forthcoming from the stock of resources on hand is allocated to Y_1, then none is available for Y_2 and output of the latter must be zero. Use of ox_1 resource services for Y_1 leaves x_1x_2 (equals $o'x'_1$,) for Y_2 in the manner outlined on previous pages. Figure 20 illustrates production functions which may give rise to complementary relationships. In Figure 20, use of more than ox_2 (equals $x'_3x'_1$) resource services for Y_3 or more than $o'x'_2$ (equals x_1x_3) resource services for Y_4 causes the 2 products to be complementary. For example, if ox_3 units of resources are in use for Y_3, a transfer of x_2x_3 units to Y_4 will cause output of both products to increase, because it withdraws resource services from the range of decreasing total returns for Y_3. They are competitive only for resource inputs falling in the x_1x_2 (equals $x'_2x'_1$) range; units of the same resource, perhaps because of time, lack homogeneity.

All units of resource services are homogeneous and interchangeable for the competitive and complementary products illustrated above. In the case of supplementary products, however, some resource inputs are not interchangeable and homogeneous in the sense that they can be stored and shifted over time or otherwise substituted in the production process. While a bushel of feed can be used in either summer or winter, and thus give rise to competition for its use at all times, services flowing from building, machine, or labor resources during the winter cannot be stored for or used in corn production during the summer. Figure 21 illustrates this situation: only x_1x_2 (equals $x'_2x'_1$) units of services are homogeneous in the sense that they are completely interchangeable between products and production periods. While units of services up to x_2 can be used in production of Y_5, resource service units in the range x_2x_3 do not add to output of Y_5. Similarly, services falling in the range x_1x_3 can be used for Y_6, those falling in the range ox_1 do not add to output of Y_6 for reasons of seasonality or technical conditions. When the total flow of resource services is composed of x_1x_2 interchangeable units plus ox_1 (equals $x'_3x'_2$) and x_2x_3 (equals $o'x'_1$) units, which are neither storable nor interchangeable, the range of output for either falling in the shaded area does not compete with the output of the other product. The output of Y_5 corresponding to the ox_1 range of inputs is supplementary to Y_6 while the output of Y_6 corresponding to the x_2x_3 range of inputs is supplementary to Y_5.

The transformation or production possibility curve which parallels the production functions of Figure 21 is shown in Figure 22. The supplementary range is denoted by the linear portions of curve SP and indicates that approximately 21 units of Y_6 can be produced without a sacrifice in Y_5, while roughly 16 units of Y_5 can be produced without a decrease in Y_6. Beyond the linear portions, the transformation function takes on a slope greater than zero and less than infinity, and the 2 commodities are competitive. Many other forms of supplementary-competitive relationships are possible. An entire family of iso-factor curves again exists for each level at which resources might be stocked to give off a constant flow of services over a specified time span.

Many examples of supplementary relationships, or "tendencies" in this direction, can be cited for agriculture. Wherever a stock or flow of resource services is available and cannot be absorbed entirely by one enterprise, the possibilities of supplementarity exist. The enterprise may include a small flock of geese or ewes which glean waste grain and use labor and equipment which is on hand but cannot be applied to other enterprises. The existence of family labor provides a basis for supplementary products when it can be used for gardening, poultry enterprises and dairying but not for other farm enterprises. It should be remembered, however, that while enterprises may be supplementary in respect to one factor of production, they may be entirely competitive for others. Asparagus is supplementary with winter wheat for the use of labor but competitive for the use of land. The wide range of supplementary relationships on farms is important, as is indicated later, in explaining (a) why certain products are produced at very low prices or (b) why resources remain in use when their value product "appears" low when compared to other alternatives. The "degree" to which enterprises are supplementary depends on the number of common resources used and the extent to which these resources give off non-homogeneous services with respect to time. If all units of service are homogeneous (or are stock service entirely), 2 products are competitive only. If both enterprises involve exactly the same resources and each resource gives off supplementary (non-homogeneous or flow) services, the 2 enterprises will have a pure range of supplementary relationship. If the enterprises compete for 2 sets of limitational services but supplement each other for a third set of services, the enterprises will be competitive. The rate of competition will be "more severe" than if they compete for 1 and are supplementary for 2 services. These varying degrees of supplementarity are prevalent throughout agriculture. Most farm poultry flocks are of this semi-supplementary nature. They use grain which would otherwise go to hogs, cattle, or sheep, and tie up capital for investment in birds, building, and equipment which otherwise could go into other enterprises on the farm. On the other hand, they use the time of the housewife which cannot or would not be employed in other livestock enterprises. Dairying is also a semi-supplementary enterprise in many farming regions, and

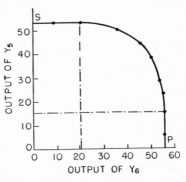

Fig. 22. Production possibilities and range of supplementarity.

within the supplementary range it has a high comparative advantage although it cannot always compete with corn, hog, wheat, or cotton production for use of those directly-competitive factor services.

Restatement of Enterprise Relationships

The distinctions outlined above can now be used for a more sophisticated formulation of enterprise relationships. These are summarized below for 2 products Y_1 and Y_2.

Marginal rate of substitution	Enterprise relationship
$\Delta Y_1/\Delta Y_2$ or $\Delta Y_2/\Delta Y_1 <$ zero	Competitive
$\Delta Y_1/\Delta Y_2$ or $\Delta Y_2/\Delta Y_1 =$ zero	Supplementary
$\Delta Y_1/\Delta Y_2$ or $\Delta Y_2/\Delta Y_1 >$ zero	Complementary

If the marginal rate of substitution is less than zero, output of one product must be sacrificed as output of the other is increased and the two products are competitive. A marginal rate of substitution equal to zero indicates that one product can be increased in quantity without a sacrifice in the other and the two are supplementary. Finally, a substitution ratio greater than zero indicates that an increase or decrease in one product is accompanied by an increase or decrease in the other product and the 2 are complementary.

Other Product-Product Relationships

The product-product relationships outlined above have many other adaptations in agriculture. They can be applied to secondary products as well as to primary products and to product competition over time.

Secondary products and livestock farming systems. The analysis of previous pages made no distinction between primary and secondary farm products. The question arises, however, as to the nature of the production possibility curve when the commodities produced for the market are from livestock, while primary farm crops serve as inputs.

The substitution ratios between primary crops as (a) product from resources, (b) feed inputs for livestock products, and (c) feed-livestock transformation ratios together determine the adaptation of different livestock systems to the crops of a farm or an area. This statement can be illustrated by means of Figures 23, 24, and 25. The soil or climate may be of a nature to cause a low forage/grain substitution rate as is illustrated in Figure 23. All the crops grown on the farm or in the area are to be fed to 2 alternative classes of livestock such as hogs and sheep; the livestock opportunity curve will depend on the feed-livestock transformation ratio and the grain-forage substitution ratios for each type of animal. If grain substitutes for forage at a sufficiently high rate for pork as compared to sheep, the livestock production possibilities, based on the crop possibilities

(Figure 23), will be of the nature indicated in Figure 24. With sufficiently high feed-mutton transformation ratios and with forage substituting at a high rate for grain in the sheep ratios, the livestock production possibilities

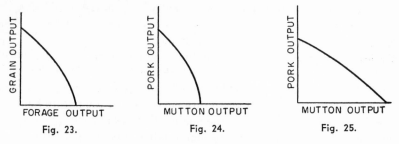

Fig. 23.   Fig. 24.   Fig. 25.

Transformation functions and farming systems.

will be of the nature indicated in Figure 25; mutton substitutes for pork at high rates even though crop production possibilities (Figure 23) include high forage/grain substitution ratios.

Time-time relationships and seasonality of production. When they do not involve aspects of expectations and uncertainty, questions of timing of production can be analyzed in the vein of a product-product relationship. The problem is simply one of allocating a limited quantity of resources between 2 time periods for the same product. Should milk be produced in summer or winter? Should sows be farrowed in February, May, or August? Should a storable commodity such as wheat be marketed at the time of harvest or another time of the year? Answers to these questions depend partly on the nature of production possibilities over time.

Competition between outputs of the same commodity in 2 different time periods involves opportunity or iso-resource curves of the nature outlined on previous pages. The opportunity curve now indicates the rate of substitution between outputs of the same product in the 2 different time periods. Although there may be some unimportant exceptions, the time opportunity curves are generally either concave to the origin or linear, indicating increasing or constant rates of substitution, respectively. Increasing rates of substitution hold true where temperature and biological considerations become important as animal or crop production is shifted between seasons or points of time within the year. The opportunity

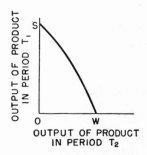

Fig. 26. Production possibilities in two time periods.

curve then appears in the nature of SW in Figure 26. The period t_1 may refer to pigs farrowed in late spring, while t_2 refers to pigs farrowed in the winter. The time opportunity curve is linear if the production function is identical in the 2 periods. This situation exists in some warm climates. However, productivity of resources is often less for winter as compared to summer months. Attempts to shift more and more of the product from warm to cold months encounter increasing diminutions in the output to be expected from given stocks of resources. Consequently, the output (OW) possible from given resources during the winter is less than that (OS) possible from the same resources allocated to summer production.

Quality substitution. Analysis of quality or grade problems in agriculture also fall in the category of product-product relationships. Different grades or qualities of the same commodity can simply be considered as different products, and the production possibility curves are of the nature indicated in previous sections. Ordinarily, the quality opportunity curve has a slope of less than 45°, indicating that a high-quality product substitutes for a low-quality product at a ratio of less than 1:1. If this were not true, farm profits would always be maximized with production of the high-quality product when its price was equal to or greater than the price of the low-quality product. Often, but not universally, the quality transformation function is linear.

Selected References

Allen, R. G. D., *Mathematics for Economists*. London: Macmillan, 1942, pp. 121-124.

Benedict, M. R., "Opportunity Costs and Principle of Substitution," *Jour. Farm Econ.*, Vol. 14.

Black, J. D., *Production Economics*. New York: Henry Holt, 1924, Ch. 8.

Black, J. D., *et al.*, *Farm Management*. New York: Macmillan, 1947, Part 2.

Boulding, K. E., *Economic Analysis*. New York: Harper, 1948, pp. 707, 708.

Cady, G. J., *Economics of Business Enterprise*. New York: Ronald Press, 1950, Chs. 10, 11.

Carlson, Sune, *A Study on the Pure Theory of Production*. London: King & Son, 1939, Ch. 5.

Heady, Earl O., "Economics of Rotations With Farm and Production Policy Applications," *Jour. Farm Econ.*, Vol. 30.

Heady, Earl O., and Jensen, Harold R., *The Economics of Rotations and Land Use*. Iowa Agr. Exp. Sta. Bul. 383.

Heady, Earl O., "Economics of Forage Production." In Hughes, H. D. (Editor), *Forages*. Ames: Iowa State College Press, 1951.

Holmes, C. E., *Farm Organization*. New York: Heath, 1928, Ch. 14.

Hopkins, J. E., *Elements of Farm Management*. New York: Prentice Hall, 1941.

Johnson, S. E., "Theory of Combination of Farm Enterprises," *Jour. Farm Econ.*, Vol. 15.

Lerner, A. P., *Economics of Control*. New York: Macmillan, 1944, Chs. 5, 11.

Pareto, Vilfredo, *Manuel d'Economie Politique*. Paris: Marcel Giard, 1927, p. 607.

Stigler, George, *The Theory of Price*. New York: Macmillan, 1947, Ch. 16.

8

Choice Between Products and Resource Uses

CHOICE in the use of resources for alternative products parallels the decision-making procedures outlined for factors in Chapter 6. Emphasis is in a slightly different direction, however. The firm or nation is now interested in a maximum return from given resources. Previous interest was in a minimum of resources for a given return. This chapter deals with the combination of enterprises or products which conflict in the use of limited resources. We will not inquire why resources are limited to the individual farm as a business firm. The answer lies in the analysis of later chapters dealing with uncertainty. Some of the more interesting aspects of enterprise or product combinations are those which relate to imperfect knowledge and price or production variability. Here we explain the combination of enterprises which maximize revenue and profits from given resources. The conditions specified always apply in a historic sense; they indicate what "would have been" most probable had yields and prices been known. However, they also suggest the conditions toward which the farmer must "shoot in the dark" if he is to maximize profit in an environment of imperfect knowledge and forward planning. While the choice indicator differs, the principles of production or resource allocation outlined in subsequent sections are the same, whether the economic unit is an individual farm, a producing area, or the agricultural industry. In the early part of this chapter application of principles is made to profit maximization by an individual farm. The optimum combination of products or enterprises, the most efficient allocation of given resources, is then extended to include public problems in resource use. The basic problems and principles of choice are again identical. Only the ends and choice indicators differ. The agricultural production economist possessing the tools and technical data to provide solutions at the farm level is equipped to provide solutions at the national level and vice versa.

Efficiency in a Technical Framework

The greatest number of problems in resource allocation require knowledge of price relationships or choice indicators as well as technical product relationships. Economic efficiency can be denoted, within limited ranges, by technological data, as in the case of factor-product transformation and factor-factor substitution. Irrational areas of resource use also exist under product-product relationships. Irrational resource allocation relates, in one of its aspects, to complementary relationships. The irrational area of the production possibility curve is that portion with a positive slope, the complementary range: under these technical conditions, given resources can always be rearranged to allow a greater output of both products and, as explained in detail later, the total value of product always increases. Knowledge of price relationships is not necessary for a competitive firm in denoting that a reorganization of resources will result in a greater economic return. The technical knowledge that an increase in one product is accompanied by an increase in another indicates that returns can be increased as long as the price of either product is greater than zero; greater returns can be attained from given resources, or the same return is attainable with fewer resources. In Figure 18 of Chapter 7, the areas of rational and irrational resource allocation are divided by the boundary lines A and B. The rational area is located between the line A and the line B. As will be pointed out subsequently, irrationality is not the basis of tenant action when crops are produced within the range which is complementary in the long-run but competitive in the short-run decision-making period. Irrationality which grows out of a complementary relationship arises particularly when the crops or livestock are produced in the same period. There are many examples of production within the complementary range. Some of these are explained by lack of knowledge. The farmer who runs too many cows on a given pasture acreage and can increase returns by selling part of the beef herd and diverting investment to poultry, falls in this category. Agronomists suggest that the forage acreage on many farms is so small that crop combinations fall in the complementary range. Often these cropping patterns have been adopted because of lack of knowledge and are truly irrational. In other cases the choice is rational since it includes considerations of time. Legumes are complementary with grain mainly over time and as crops are grown in sequence. The tenant who has a 1-year lease has little interest in the product of the future. Similarly, the price expectations of the owner may cause him to produce more grain in the immediate future and less over the long run.

Irrational resource use also can arise under competitive or supplementary enterprise relationships. Selection of techniques which do not denote product combinations on the boundary of production opportunity curve, where the choice is not based on the uncertainty considerations discussed later, is irrational. A farmer producing tobacco and cotton can select any number of techniques for either. Thus, in Figure 1 below, T_1Q_1, T_2Q_2, T_3Q_3, and T_4Q_4 may represent the opportunity curves when a given stock of resources can be used to produce 2 products under 4 different techniques. This series of opportunity curves representing different techniques is in contrast to earlier and later analyses which assume each curve to represent a different cost or factor outlay. Since all of the opportunity curves involve the same quantity of resources or funds, adoption of any technique other than that indicated by T_4Q_4 is

inefficient. With resource input constant, more of product Y_1 can be produced without a sacrifice in Y_2 (and vice versa) as techniques are adopted to allow a movement towards the T_4Q_4 boundary. Any single point such as E within the boundary line T_4Q_4, represents economic as well as technical inefficiency.[1] A movement from E to K allows an increase in Y_1 without a diminution in Y_2; a movement from E to L allows an increase in Y_2 without a diminution

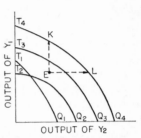

Fig. 1. Efficiency specified by technical conditions.

in Y_1. Any movement from E in a northeast direction (within the quadrant EKL) to the T_4Q_4 boundary allows a simultaneous increase in both products from the given resources. Therefore, T_4Q_4 represents all of the possible sets of efficient points; any set within T_4Q_4 is inefficient. Knowledge of prices is not necessary to specify that techniques should be adopted which allow movement to the boundary. As long as either product has a price greater than zero, (a) output of one commodity and the income from it can be increased with given resources, or (b) the same product and income can be attained with fewer resources. A physical scientist as an agronomist can suggest adjustments alone which fall in the quadrant KEL; without an economic criterion, he cannot specify choices along the boundary T_4Q_4.

Choice in Competitive Products

When products are competitive, the optimum allocation of given resources between enterprises can be made only if the choice criterion is known. For farm profit maximization, product price ratios provide the choice indicator. *Maximum profits are attained, with costs or resources fixed in quantity, when the marginal rate of product substitution is in-*

---

[1] While opportunity curves representing a given technique and constant resources never cross each other in the competitive range, opportunity curves representing the same outlay under different techniques may cross. An entire family of non-crossing opportunity curves representing the same technique as T_4Q_4 would fall entirely within T_4Q_4. The curve T_4Q_4 also can be composed of segments of different curves (techniques) and thus define the boundary of all curves representing different techniques.

versely equal to the product price ratio. For products Y_1 and Y_2, the condition of maximum profits is given in equation I below, where $\Delta Y_1 / \Delta Y_2$ refers to the marginal rate of substitution of Y_2 for Y_1, and P_{Y_1} and P_{Y_2} refer to the prices of Y_1 and Y_2 respectively.

$$\Delta Y_1 / \Delta Y_2 = P_{Y_2} / P_{Y_1} \qquad \qquad \text{I}$$
$$(\Delta Y_1)(P_{Y_1}) = (P_{Y_2})(\Delta Y_2) \qquad \qquad \text{II}$$

Once the substitution and price ratios have been equated, the following conditions of equal productivities are attained: equation II, derived from equation I, states that with resources allocated to maximize profits, the marginal value product of a unit of resource allocated to Y_1 is equal to the marginal value product of a unit of resource allocated to Y_2. A corollary of equation I is this: as long as the marginal rate of product substitution, $\Delta Y_1 / \Delta Y_2$, is less than the price ratio, P_{Y_2} / P_{Y_1}, profits can be increased by substituting Y_2 for Y_1. If $\Delta Y_1 / \Delta Y_2$ is greater than P_{Y_2} / P_{Y_1}, profits can be increased by substituting Y_1 for Y_2. These conditions are explained further in the sections which follow.

Joint products in fixed proportions. Since only 1 combination of products is possible for commodities produced in fixed proportions, only 1 combination of commodities is profitable. Economic questions of joint products in fixed proportions are twofold: (1) Which scale of output for the two products, as one composite commodity, is profitable? (2) What combination of factors should be employed in producing any amount of the composite product? Joint products in fixed proportions do not give rise to the product-product choices outlined below.

Competitive products at constant rates of substitution. Only 1 of 2 unique patterns of resource use define maximum profits when the production possibility curve is linear and substitution of products is at a constant rate. Using the production possibility schedule for 10 units of resources in Table 1 and except for the qualification to be made later, a firm should produce either all of Y_1 or all of Y_2. Under price situation I, the marginal rate of substitution of 4/2 or 2.0 is less than the P_{Y_2} / P_{Y_1} price ratio of 11/5 or 2.2, and profits can be increased continuously as Y_2 is substituted for Y_1. A gain in 1 unit of Y_2 causes a sacrifice of 2 units of Y_1, but the unit of Y_2 has a value 2.2 times that of 1 unit of Y_1. Under situation II, the $\Delta Y_1 / \Delta Y_2$ substitution ratio of 2.0 is greater than the price ratio of 10/8 or 1.25, and profits can never be increased by substituting Y_2 for Y_1. (Conversely, the $\Delta Y_2 / \Delta Y_1$ substitution ratio of .5 is less than the P_{Y_1} / P_{Y_2} price ratio of .8 and indicates the same adjustment.) The producer should specialize in one or the other of the 2 products under linear transformation functions, if price and substitution ratios are not equal. When these ratios are equal, as under situation III, the producer can be indifferent; any one of the several combinations will bring in the same revenue. The income figures of Table 1 represent total or gross revenue. However, they also define a maximum net income or profit. Since an opportunity schedule or

Table I.

Profit Maximization Under Constant Rates of Product Substitution (Hypothetical Data)

Production possibilities		Marginal rate of substitution of Y_2 for Y_1 $(\Delta Y_1/\Delta Y_2)$	Revenue under three price situations		
Y_1	Y_2		I: $P_{Y_1} = \$ 5$ $P_{Y_2} = \$11$	II: $P_{Y_1} = \$ 8$ $P_{Y_2} = \$10$	III: $P_{Y_1} = \$10$ $P_{Y_2} = \$20$
(1)	(2)	(3)	(4)	(5)	(6)
40	0	2.0	$200	$320	$400
36	2	2.0	202	308	400
32	4	2.0	204	296	400
28	6	2.0	206	284	400
24	8	2.0	208	272	400
20	10	2.0	210	260	400
16	12	2.0	212	248	400
12	14	2.0	214	236	400
8	16	2.0	216	224	400
4	18	2.0	218	212	400
0	20	2.0	220	200	400

curve represents all product combinations forthcoming from a given or constant outlay of factors or costs, the use of resources denoting maximum total revenue also denotes profit maximization.

Since only infrequently and by chance are price and substitution ratios equal, it is easily understood why farms tend to produce only 1 of 2 competing strains of crops or livestock. (Different strains of crops and livestock are common examples of alternatives which substitute at constant rates.) For the same reasons, barley or oats, clover or alfalfa, and other enterprises which fill a competitive role in crop rotations and have similar costs are ordinarily produced alone rather than in combination. In areas such as the Great Plains, small grains and pasture often substitute at near-constant rates. Although a very small supplementary or even complementary range may exist, sheep and cattle also are often constant-rate competitors.

Increasing rates of competition and optimum allocation of given resources. Specialization in a single commodity is less frequent when products substitute at increasing rates. In Table 2, enterprises Y_1 and Y_2 compete at increasing rates in the sense that increasing amounts of Y_1 are sacrificed for each successive increase in Y_2 and vice versa. With a P_{Y_2}/P_{Y_1} price ratio of 2/1 or 2.0, profits are at a maximum when output includes 44 units of Y_1 and 70 of Y_2, since the exact substitution ratio is equal to the price ratio. If each of the product combinations is considered as discrete and discontinuous, the average substitution ratio also specifies this selection. The average substitution ratio is 1.9 just after it. Hence the combination including 44 of Y_1 and 70 of Y_2 again conforms with the price ratio of situation I. Under price relationship II, .80/1.00, or .8, returns are maximized by the second combination, since the marginal rate of substitution of Y_2 for Y_1 also is .8. While any P_{Y_2}/P_{Y_1} price ratio falling in the range .6 to 2.4 will lead to some output of both enterprises, if profits are to be maximized, a price ratio falling outside of this range must lead to specialization in a single product.

Table 2.

Production Possibilities, Rates of Substitution and Income Under Increasing Rates of Substitution (Hypothetical Data)

Production possibilities with 9 units of resources (costs)		Marginal rate of substitution of Y_2 for Y_1 $(\Delta Y_1/\Delta Y_2)$		Income under 2 price relationships:	
Y_1	Y_2	Average [a]	Exact [b]	I: $P_{Y_1} = \$1.00$ $P_{Y_2} = \$2.00$	II: $P_{Y_1} = \$1.00$ $P_{Y_2} = \$ .80$
(1)	(2)	(3)	(4)	(5)	(6)
135	0		.6	\$135	\$135
		.7			
128	10		.8	148	136
		.9			
119	20		1.0	159	135
		1.1			
108	30		1.2	168	132
		1.3			
95	40		1.4	175	127
		1.5			
80	50		1.6	180	120
		1.7			
63	60		1.8	183	111
		1.9			
44	70		2.0	184	100
		2.1			
23	80		2.2	183	87
		2.3			
0	90		2.4	180	72

[a] Computed as an arithmetic average between pairs of combinations.
[b] Computed in the "exact" manner (tangency and derivatives) outlined previously.

Iso-revenue curves as choice indicators. Whether the objective is one of maximizing farm profits, food calories, or national income, the conditions of resource allocation which define maximization of the particular end can be illustrated graphically. The 2 relationships used in illustrating this equilibrium are the production possibility curve and the choice function. For a farm as a business firm with maximum profits as its goal, the choice function is an iso-revenue curve which indicates the ratio of prices for the competing products. The iso-revenue curve is a line which defines all of the possible combinations of 2 products which will bring in an equal revenue. If the price of corn is \$1, while wheat is \$2 per bushel, a \$2,000 revenue can be attained by any number of combinations such as 1,000 bushels of wheat and no corn, 2,000 bushels of corn and no wheat, or 500 bushels of wheat and 1,000 bushels of corn. If all combinations returning the same revenue are graphed, they give an iso-revenue curve such as E_2R_1 or E_1R_1 in Figure 2. The slope of the iso-revenue curve denotes the ratio of prices between the 2 products. For example, the line E_1R_1 has a slope denoting that 2 bushels of corn are necessary to offset 1 bushel of wheat when the wheat/corn price ratio is 2/1 and total revenue is constant at $2,000. With corn and wheat both priced at $2, a 1/1 ratio, the slope of the iso-revenue curve E_2R_1 which denotes a $2,000 income is 1/1 or 45°. Although the slope of the iso-revenue curve changes with each change in the price ratio, each iso-revenue line for a given price ratio has the same slope, as is illustrated by the family of iso-revenue lines in Figure 3.

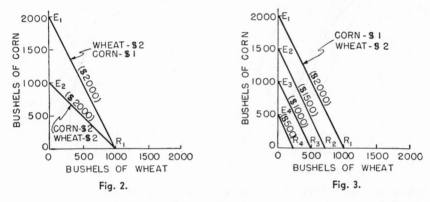

Fig. 2.   Fig. 3.

Iso-revenue curves.

With wheat priced at $2 and corn at $1, a total revenue of $2,000 can be attained with sale of 2,000 bushels of corn and no wheat, 1,000 bushels of wheat and no corn, or any other combination (point) indicated on E_1R_1. A $1,000 revenue can be attained under the same price ratio with 1,000 bushels of corn and no wheat, 500 bushels of wheat and no corn, or any other combination represented on iso-revenue line E_3R_3. While the goal under the factor-factor relationship was to attain the lowest possible iso-cost curve for a given output of product, the goal under the product-product relationship is to attain the greatest possible revenue from a given quantity of resources.

The conditions outlined in Table 2 can now be illustrated in Figure 4. The curve IP represents the production possibilities illustrated in the first 2 columns of the table. With a P_{Y_2}/P_{Y_1} price ratio of 2/1 or 2.0, the iso-revenue curves E_3R_3, E_2R_2, and E_1R_1 illustrate the many combinations of products which will bring in the equal revenues of $148, $175, and $184 respectively. Production of 128 units of Y_1 and 10 units of Y_2 represents 1 possibility on the opportunity curve. However, this combination does not represent maximum returns from a given resource or cost outlay. Not only is this apparent in Table 2, but a higher revenue curve can be attained in

Figure 4 as more of Y_2 and less of Y_1 is produced. This combination allows a revenue of only 148, as is indicated by intersection of the iso-resource curve IP and the iso-revenue curve E_3R_3. The combination 95 of Y_1 and 40 of Y_2 allows attainment of iso-revenue curve E_2R_2, denoting an income of \$175. Without changing the slope of the revenue curve, E_1R_1 can finally be attained and profits are at a maximum of \$184. Iso-revenue line E_1R_1

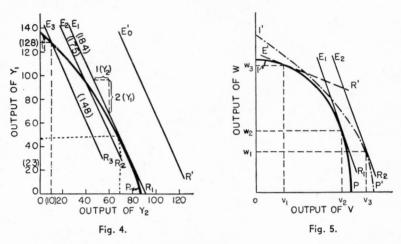

Fig. 4.

Fig. 5.

Profit maximization under increasing substitution rates and changes in price and substitution ratios.

is just tangent to the opportunity curve. As we already know, tangency of 2 lines denotes equal slopes and ratios. The slope of iso-revenue line E_1R_1 is $2Y_1/1Y_2$. The slope of the opportunity curve is also $2Y_1/1Y_2$ at the point of tangency, and the marginal rate of substitution, as denoted by the slope of IP, is 2/1 or 2. Thus the marginal rate of substitution, $\Delta Y_1/\Delta Y_2$, is equal to the price ratio, P_{Y_2}/P_{Y_1}, and maximum profits are denoted by tangency of IP and E_1R_1.

The goal in Figure 4 is to attain the highest possible revenue line. Since IP is a boundary line, any point on it can be attained with the given amount of resources or costs involved. However, no point or revenue curve (such as $E_0'R'$) above it can be attained with the specified stock of resources. Therefore, the tangent iso-revenue line, E_1R_1, defines the maximum revenue attainable under the production opportunities expressed by IP and with a P_{Y_2}/P_{Y_1} price ratio of 2.0.

A restatement. With a price ratio of 2.0 (the prices of \$1 and \$2 in Table 2) the iso-resource curve has a slope, at the point of intersection, less than that of the revenue curve E_3R_3 in Figure 4. Hence, revenue can be increased with a smaller output of Y_1 and a greater output of Y_2. Maximum revenue is denoted only by tangency of the iso-revenue and opportunity curves and never by their intersection. Only at the point of tangency is the marginal value product of resources equal between products. A small amount of reiteration at this point may help to clinch the resource use conditions which define maximum efficiency. When 2 products, Y_1 and Y_2, are being compared, substitution of Y_2 for Y_1 is profitable as long as the marginal rate of substitution, $\Delta Y_1/\Delta Y_2$, is less than the price ratio, P_{Y_2}/P_{Y_1}. Graphically, this statement means that substitution of Y_2 for Y_1 (where Y_2 is on the horizontal and Y_1 is on the vertical axis) is always profitable as long as the slope of the opportunity curve is less (in absolute terms) than the slope of the iso-revenue line. Substitution of Y_1 for Y_2 is always profitable when the slope of the opportunity line is greater than the slope of the iso-revenue line. Thus in Figure 4, substitution of Y_2 for Y_1 should take place "above" the point where E_1R_1 and IP are tangent. Substitution in the opposite direction should take place "below" the point where the 2 are tangent.

At the point of tangency the ratio of marginal costs of the 2 products is equal to the ratio of their marginal value products. In other words, the value productivity of the last unit of resource allocated to either product is equal. This is obviously true, because (a) the single unit of resource service which can be shifted to either product costs the same, and (b) the price multiplied by the number of units of either product is identical for both commodities. While Figure 4 has been discussed in the vein of a maximum condition, it also illustrates a minimum condition. Although revenue line E_1R_1 denotes the *maximum* revenue which can be attained with a given factor or cost outlay, IP represents the *minimum* factor or cost outlay which will allow attainment of a given revenue equal to $184. The combination of 44 units of Y_1 and 70 units of Y_2 thus represents the least cost method of producing a $184 revenue.

Two changes cause the optimum pattern of resource use to vary. One is a change in the rate at which products substitute; a change in the slope of the transformation function brought about by changes in techniques for either commodity. In Figure 5, for example, the initial transformation function is IP and the constant revenue line is E_1R_1. Use of resources to produce ow_2 of commodity W and ov_2 of commodity V results in maximum profit. If a change in techniques results in a new opportunity curve $I'P'$ with the price ratio remaining unchanged (the slope of E_2R_2 the same as the slope of E_1R_1), the optimum combination of products shifts to ow_1 and ov_3 of products W and V respectively.[2]

---

[2] We suppose that the opportunity curve $I'P'$ represents the same outlay under the new technique as IP does under the former technique. This statement also applies to situations where one product is produced under conditions of constant returns and the other is produced under increasing returns.

Joint products in variable proportions. Joint products which can be produced in variable proportions require no unique adaptations of profit maximizing conditions. Through the range of competition, the maximum-profit allocation of resources is denoted by tangency of the iso-outlay and iso-revenue curves and depends on the slope of the two. As in the case of any opportunity curve, a new equilibrium in combination of products will be defined for (a) each change in the slope of the outlay curve (change in techniques for one commodity at a faster rate than for the other), and (b) each change in the slope of the revenue line.

Decreasing rates of substitution. In the absence of price change and uncertainty, profits are maximized by specialization in a single product when the production opportunity curve is convex, indicating decreasing marginal rates of substitution. Diversification is never profitable when both of 2 products are produced under conditions of increasing returns. This fact is illustrated in Table 3. Under the second price ratio of 10/10 or 1.0, the substitution ratio $\Delta Y_1/\Delta Y_2$ can be made less than the price ratio as more

Table 3.

Decreasing Rates of Substitution and Maximization of Returns (Hypothetical Data)

Production possibilities with 10 units of resources (costs)		*Marginal rate of substitution of Y_2 for Y_1 $(\Delta Y_1/\Delta Y_2)$*		*Income under 2 price relationships*	
Y_1	Y_2	Average	Exact	I: $P_{Y_1} = \$10$ $P_{Y_2} = \$3$	II: $P_{Y_1} = \$10$ $P_{Y_2} = \$10$
(1)	(2)	(3)	(4)	(5)	(6)
80.0	0		−1.3	$800	$ 800
		−1.25			
67.5	10.0		−1.2	705	775
		−1.15			
56.0	20.0		−1.1	620	760
		−1.05			
45.5	30.0		−1.0	545	755
		− .95			
36.0	40.0		− .9	480	760
		− .85			
27.5	50.0		− .8	425	775
		− .75			
20.0	60.0		− .7	380	800
		− .65			
13.5	70.0		− .6	445	835
		− .55			
8.0	80.0		− .5	320	880
		− .45			
3.5	90.0		− .4	305	935
		− .35			
0	100.0		− .3	300	1000

of Y_2 and less of Y_1 is produced. Returns are at a maximum with specialization in Y_2 alone. With a P_{Y_2}/P_{Y_1} price ratio of 3/10 or .3, returns are at a maximum with production of Y_1 alone.

As is illustrated graphically in Figure 6, an iso-revenue line representing a price ratio of 1.0 intersects the opportunity curve IP. Curve E_2R_2 shows all combinations of Y_1 and Y_2 which will sell in the market for \$835 with a price of \$10 for either product. As is indicated by intersection of IP and E_2R_2, an income of \$835 is attained with outputs of 13.5 and 70 units of Y_1 and Y_2 respectively. However, any iso-revenue curve with a slope equal to that of E_2R_2 has a slope greater than IP. Profits can be increased (higher iso-revenue curves can be attained) by substitution of Y_2 for Y_1. E_1R_1, denoting specialization in Y_2 alone, is the highest revenue attainable. While E_1R_1 intersects IP on the horizontal axis (a zero output of Y_1), a larger revenue such as E_oR_o cannot be attained with the resources represented by opportunity curve IP in Figure 6. Similarly, with prices of \$10

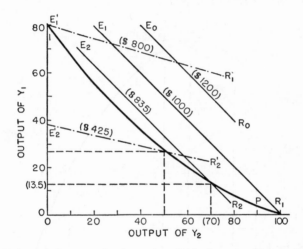

Fig. 6. Profit maximization under decreasing substitution rates (Source: Table 3).

and \$3 for Y_1 and Y_2, the opportunity line $E'_2R'_2$ representing an income of \$425 does not indicate maximum returns. As long as the slope of the iso-revenue line is less than the slope of the opportunity curve, Y_1 should be substituted for Y_2 until specialization in the former product is denoted. Higher and higher revenues can be attained up to $E'_1R'_1$ or \$800.

Farm recommendations. Many agriculturists argue that all farms should be diversified. There often is important logic behind the action of the farmer who specializes in one crop, however. Even under situations of increasing substitution rates for crops, specialization may well be consistent with substitution and price ratios. Conditions favoring specialization are strongest in highly mechanized areas such as wheat, and in other cash crop areas. This specialization stems partly from the high productivity of labor and capital devoted to grain as a result of the high rates of product substitution. The small-scale farmer who does not have enough capital to exhaust the "lumpy-input" stage of increasing returns also has a sound economic basis for specialization in single products.

Complementary products. When 2 commodities bear a relationship of technical complementarity to each other, profits can be maximized only if some of both commodities are produced. As indicated in a previous section, this statement applies even if the price for one of the commodities is zero. It is illustrated in Table 4, where, with a zero price for Y_2, 106.1 units of Y_1 and 27.5 units of Y_2 should be produced if revenue is to be maximized. While units of Y_2 add nothing to revenue, a greater output of this product is accompanied by greater outputs of Y_1, which do add to revenue. If its price is zero, however, resources should never be arranged so that Y_2 is produced beyond the point defining its final complementary effects (the apex of IP in Figure 7).

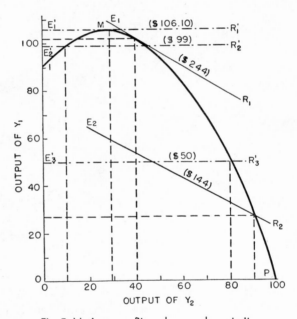

Fig. 7. Maximum profits under complementarity.

The condition under which returns from complementary products are maximized is illustrated in Figure 7. These illustrations are drawn from Table 4. With a price ratio of 1/2 or .5, profits are at a maximum where the iso-revenue curve, E_1R_1, denoting a \$244 return is tangent with the iso-product curve. The corresponding outputs include 102 of Y_1 and 40 of Y_2. With this same price ratio, another output such as 27 of Y_1 and 90 of Y_2 will result in a lower revenue. Here the iso-revenue curve, E_2R_2, intersects the opportunity curve, and revenue is only \$144. With a zero price for Y_2, the iso-revenue line becomes horizontal. A given revenue line

Table 4.

Complementary Enterprises and Income Under 3 Price Situations (Hypothetical Data)

Production possibilities with resources (costs) constant		Marginal rate of substitution of Y_2 for Y_1 $(\Delta Y_1/\Delta Y_2)$		Income under two price situations		
Y_1	Y_2	Average	Exact	I: $P_{Y_1}=\$1$ $P_{Y_2}=\$0$	II: $P_{Y_1}=\$2$ $P_{Y_2}=\$1$	III: $P_{Y_1}=\$1$ $P_{Y_2}=\$3$
(1)	(2)	(3)	(4)	(5)	(6)	(7)
90	0		+1.1	$ 90	$180	$ 90
		+ .9				
99	10		+ .7	99	208	129
		+ .5				
104	20		+ .3	104	228	164
		+ .2				
(106.1)	(27.5)		(0)	(106.1)	(239.7)	(188.5)
		(− .5)				
105	30		− .1	105	240	195
		− .3				
102	40		− .5	102	244	222
		− .7				
95	50		− .9	95	240	245
		−1.1				
84	60		−1.3	84	228	264
		−1.5				
69	70		−1.7	69	208	279
		−1.9				
50	80		−2.1	50	180	290
		−2.3				
27	90		−2.5	27	144	297
		−2.7				
0	100		−2.9	0	100	300

can be attained only through Y_1, and cannot be increased irrespective of increases in Y_2. The maximum revenue which can be attained under the $1 and zero prices is $106.10 and is denoted by tangency of $E'_1R'_1$ and IP for a product combination including 106.1 and 27.5 units of Y_1 and Y_2 respectively. While a combination such as 99 units of Y_1 and 10 units of Y_2 can be produced within the complementary range, the return of $99 (denoted by intersection of the iso-revenue curve $E'_2R'_2$ and the iso-outlay curve) is not a maximum.[3] Similarly, an allocation of resources which pushes output of Y_2 into the competitive range as denoted by intersection of $E'_3R'_3$ does not define maximum returns from a constant cost or resource outlay.

---

[3] Under the iso-revenue line $E'_2R'_2$, the opportunity and iso-revenue curves are equal (intersect) at 2 points, thus denoting that 2 patterns of resource allocation will give an income of $99 (99 of Y_1 and 10 of Y_2 or 99 of Y_1 and 45 of Y_2). Similarly, in Figures 5 or 6 the iso-revenue line may cut the opportunity curve in 2 places (such as the $775 income for 2 output combinations in column 6 of Table 3).

Rotation, land use and feed economics. It is now apparent that on many farms where forages are complementary with other crops, some hay or pasture should be grown even if no direct return is realized from it. The same logic applies to wheat and fallow in the Great Plains. For an operator who will be on his farm during the period in which a forage-grain complementary relationship is expressed (and in the absence of the major fluctuations in grain-forage price relationships which are discussed in a later section) returns can never be maximized by a forage acreage short of that necessary to exhaust the complementary effect and maximize total grain production. (As examples, a forage acreage will never maximize profits short of that necessary to attain the grain production represented either by (a) point M in Figure 7 or by (b) the 5-year Ohio rotation of Chapter 7, if the latter represents the greatest possible grain production.) Irrespective of prices for the crops, returns can always be increased by extending forage acreage as long as legumes or grasses are complementary to grain. Even if the price of forage is zero, its production is still profitable. The hay or pasture represents only one of the products of forages. Other important products are in the form of nitrogen, better soil tilth, erosion, pest and disease control, or other direct and indirect contributions of grasses and legumes to yield of subsequent grain crops.

When forage crops are complementary with grain in the rotation, a greater total production of both hay (or pasture) and grain can be attained through extending the acreage of grasses or legumes. The hay harvesting methods being used on some farms result in per-acre costs of production for hay which are about equal to those for corn. (In Table 5, for example, the total costs per acre for clover are only slightly higher than those for

Table 5.*

Per Acre Costs of Growing and Harvesting Specified Grain and Hay Crops, 1940-49 [a]

Crop	Yield per acre	Growing cost per acre	Harvesting cost per acre	Total cost of growing and harvesting per acre [b]
Oats	42	$5.84	$ 4.09	$ 9.93
Corn	67	9.27	3.80	13.07
Soybeans	20	9.93	3.28	13.21
Wheat	20	7.50	6.72	14.22
Red clover hay	1.6	6.69	10.03	16.72
Alfalfa hay	2.7	6.71	12.62	19.33

* Source: Heady and Jensen, *Economics of Rotation.* Iowa Agr. Exp. Sta. Bul. 383.

[a] The cost figures do not include a charge for land or similar items which are the same regardless of the crop being grown. Since costs such as these are constant, their inclusion or exclusion does not affect the relative profitability of the different crops. These costs are based on survey, record, and other data which indicate the physical input-output requirements for various crops. Costs for the period specified have been applied to these physical inputs. Cost allowances include labor, machinery power, and all other operating costs as well as seed, and fertilizer applied at the recommended rates on Clarion-Webster soil.

[b] The harvesting figures are based on costs under baling. Under the conventional hay loader system, acre costs would be increased about $1.63 for clover and $2.75 for alfalfa.

corn.) Thus, as an acre of land is shifted from corn to hay, costs remain constant while grain production increases along with hay production. With hay costs equal to those of corn on the Marshall silt loam soils (see Table 6) over the period 1941-49, an annual average of only 2,122 bushels of corn (from 100 acres of land) would be produced under the continuous corn rotation. However, with the same total costs under the C-O-M rotation, total grain production would amount to the equivalent of 3,201

Table 6.

Production, Gross Return, Net Value of Grain and Production Costs for Specified Rotations on Basis of 100 Acres of Land *

Rotation	Total production (lbs.) Grain (corn equiv.) lbs.	Hay lbs.	Gross value of grain with zero value for hay [a]	Total costs of production [b]	Net value of production with zero value on hay
Canfield-Wooster soils, Columbus, Ohio, 1937-43					
C	217,840	0	$3,579	$1,307	$2,272
C-C-C-W-A	230,496	128,800	3,762	1,203	2,559
Marshall silt loam, Clarinda, Iowa, 1941-49					
C	118,720	0	$1,611	$1,307	$ 304
C-O-M	179,368	148,000	2,434	993	1,441

* Source: Heady and Jensen, *Economics of Rotation.* Iowa Agr. Exp. Sta. Bul. 383.
a Prices used include the average for Ohio and Iowa for the period of 1940-44. Only the value of corn and small grain has been included. Hay has been given a zero price for illustrative examples.
b Costs included are total growing and harvesting costs for grain and growing costs for forage.

bushels of corn. An annual average of 74 tons of hay would also be produced. Thus, net return must necessarily be greater for the meadow rotation as compared to continuous corn. Even if the hay brings only $1 (or less) per ton, gross income is greater, while costs do not increase.

The haying methods employed on a very great number of farms result in greater per-acre costs for hay than for the common grain crops. Yet, even on these farms, returns can be increased by increasing the acreage of forages if the grasses or legumes are complementary with grain. As is indicated in Table 5, the total per-acre costs of growing and harvesting hay are greater than those for the common grains of the Cornbelt. Yet the costs of growing hay are generally less than the total costs of growing and harvesting grains. Thus gross and net income can still be increased as forage acreage is increased within the complementary range, irrespective of the market price for forage or the return which can be realized on it through utilization by livestock. As is indicated in Table 5, since the growing costs of alfalfa are less than the total of growing and harvesting costs of all grains listed, costs can always be reduced by shifting an acre from grain to alfalfa, if the hay is not harvested. For example, a shift of 1 acre from oats to alfalfa would lower costs by $3.22, while a shift from corn would save $6.36. Thus as long as forage is complementary to grain and costs of growing forage are less than the costs of growing and harvesting grain, income must always increase as more forage is grown. The shift of land from grain to hay, which is not harvested, must increase the total production and gross return from grain, while total costs are lessened. These relationships are expressed in Table 6, where the cost figures of Table 5 are applied to the grain production figures for the range of complementarity on Canfield-Wooster soils over the period 1937-43 and Marshall silt over the period 1941-49.

Complementarity and forage utilization. Since gross income from grain always increases and total costs can always be decreased, net income necessarily increases as land is shifted from grain to forage within the complementary range. Again, the price of hay or the returns to be realized from hay through livestock are unimportant. Production of more hay is always profitable whether the return per ton from hay is zero, $100, or another quantity. The hay can simply be turned under as a green manure crop and the growing costs alone are realized. Its profitability comes indirectly through increases in total grain production from a given land area.

Thus forage utilization is not a problem when grasses and legumes are complementary with grain, and has no place in determining which crop should be grown. A large number of individuals mistakenly pose forage utilization as a major obstacle to a greater acreage of grasses and legumes. Grass and legume production is not a utilization problem as long as forages are complementary. No direct return need be realized on these crops to make their production profitable. They need not be utilized and can simply be plowed under, and the farm operator need not have capital invested in livestock to make complementary forage production profitable. It is true, of course, that any price or return that can be realized from forage represents an addition to net profit.

Time span. Thus far no mention has been made of the time span or economic horizon which is relevant. The discussion relating to Figure 7 referred to a time period in which the full effects of a rotation could be reflected in yields through either an increase in soil fertility or a decrease in soil erosion or structural deterioration. This is the situation which faces the owner-operator with a near-full equity in his business. Not all operators are able to formulate income expectations over a time span of this extent. The operator with a small equity in his resources and highly concerned with the possibility of loss from a given price decline, or the tenant with assurance of only a brief stay on the farm is likely to attempt maximization of returns over a shorter time period. Accordingly, the range of complementarity between forage and grain enterprises tends to be contracted for a shorter time period. Within a given year there is often no complementary range, and forage is competitive throughout with grain—the more hay produced, the smaller the output of grain possible within a given year, since the effects of the hay in the rotation can be reflected in grain yields only over a period of years. The tenant (or bankrupt owner) who must move at the end of the year is faced only with the competitive relationship between hay and grain and acts accordingly in curtailing hay and pasture acreage. The iso-cost (iso-factor) curve then appears to the operator in the form of Figure 4 only, and grain/hay price relationships are important immediately. These points will be discussed further in the chapter on leasing.

Rotations and fertilizer substitution. When complementarity between 2 crops arises because a joint product of one serves as an input of the other, the "interaction effect" may be eliminated by combining resources in a manner such that a still different factor substitutes for the joint product or interaction factor. Nitrogen can be provided for the grain crop through commercial fertilizer or manure, as well as through a legume in the rotation. The relationship then changes in the manner suggested in Figure 8. Curve I_3P_3 may represent the form of the rotation relationship when the

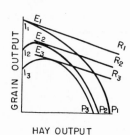

Fig. 8. Substitution for complementary factors.

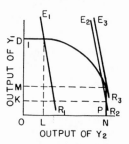

Fig. 9. Supplementary products and profit maximization.

given stock of resources includes no fertilizer, terraces, and other practices which substitute for the nitrogen, organic matter, and fibrous growth of grasses and legumes. Hay is complementary to grain throughout a wide range of outputs. Curve I_2P_2 may be the opportunity curve when the same kinds and amount of resources are used except that a small amount of nitrogen fertilizer is employed. Finally I_1P_1 may represent the situation in which the collection of resources is the same as for I_3P_3, except that terraces and ammonium nitrate are used. The complementary range narrows under I_2P_2 and disappears under I_1P_1. Resources in the form of terraces and nitrogen fertilizer become a substitute for the elements (nitrogen, erosion control, and so forth) furnished by legumes in the rotation.[4]

Supplementary Enterprises

Price relationships again play no role in determining the combination of 2 supplementary enterprises which should be produced. In the supplementary relationship illustrated by Figure 9, the price of Y_2 is high relative to the price of Y_1, as indicated by the slope of the iso-revenue curves. Yet a combination within either of the supplementary segments of the opportunity curve cannot result in maximum returns. In the case of the upper segment, higher and higher revenue lines can be attained by a horizontal movement through the supplementary range. In the lower supplementary range, higher revenue lines can be attained by a vertical movement. Under the price relationship indicated by the slope of E_1R_1, E_2R_2 and E_3R_3, profit equilibrium is attained with an output of OM and ON of Y_1 and Y_2 respectively. Thus no less than the supplementary quantity (OM) of Y_1 will be produced even though its price is low relative to that of Y_2.

The conditions outlined above explain the strong persistence of certain agricultural regions in maintaining a large production of supplementary enterprises. Poultry flocks are found in most sections of the nation, even though the resources concerned often are more productive when used for other products during competitive production periods. In the Cornbelt, for example, the value productivity of labor and capital used for certain types of competitive poultry and dairy enterprises is lower than for other major enterprises. Yet within the supplementary range, the former enterprises are profitable even under relatively low price levels, and there is little possibility that they will be eliminated through the competition from other crops within the region or the same products from other regions. While these enterprises are not purely supplementary because some of the resources employed have opportunities of employment in other enterprises,

---

[4] The relationship then involves factor-factor substitution as well as product-product substitution. Since I_3P_3, I_2P_2, and I_1P_1 represent different resource outlays, the farmer can view the problem as one of using additional resources on a given farm area. (The scale of the farm is limited in the sense of land area, while the amount of capital and labor is not.) Under the price relationship suggested by iso-revenue lines E_1R_1, E_2R_2, and E_3R_3, the question simply becomes one of whether the marginal cost of the additional fertilizer resources is greater than the income added as higher revenue curves are attained (E_2R_2 minus E_3R_3 and E_1R_1 minus E_2R_2). Hay will not be produced under I_1P_1 if profits are maximized and the return from the fertilizer is greater than its cost. The 3 opportunity curves in Figure 8 may also represent different soil types. I_1P_1 may represent a bottomland which is furnished nitrogen and organic matter through annual floods, I_2P_2 may represent a level upland soil requiring nitrogen alone, and I_3P_3 may represent hill land where forage crops provide both nitrogen for plant growth, organic matter for moisture retention, and fibrous covering to retain soil.

the "supplementary tendency" is great enough to cause the resultant output to be highly stable as prices vary; the "corner" separating competition and supplementarity causes the corresponding outputs to be most profitable over a wide range of price relationships.

When the farmer has a limited quantity of one resource such as land or buildings but the quantity of other resources is not fixed in the iso-quant sense (the farmer has or can borrow funds to acquire labor and material to use with the land and is restricted by only one factor), supplementary products can be analyzed in a somewhat different manner. (The production possibility curve is now an iso-land curve but is not an iso-cost curve including all resources.) Here 2 products such as those illustrated in Figure 9 can be treated as independent products and starting at the point D, product Y_1 should be produced as long as the added return is greater than the added cost; profit comparisons need not be made with product Y_2 and price or substitution ratios are unimportant. However, once the competitive sets of combinations have been reached, product Y_1 should be produced, not only unless the added return is greater than the added cost for this particular commodity, but also only if a dollar in labor or capital inputs returns more than if used for product Y_2; profit comparisons must now be made between products and relative yields and prices are again important.

Multiple Products and Discontinuous Opportunities

Principles of resource allocation have been outlined for 2 enterprises. However, the conditions of profit maximization are the same regardless of the number of commodities which compete for use of the same resources. Given 3 products, Y_1, Y_2, and Y_3, which can be produced from given resources, profits are at a maximum when the conditions outlined under III below are attained; this equation states that substitution and price ratios

$$\Delta Y_1/\Delta Y_2 = P_{Y_2}/P_{Y_1},\, \Delta Y_3/\Delta Y_2 = P_{Y_2}/P_{Y_1},\, \Delta Y_3/\Delta Y_1 = P_{Y_1}/P_{Y_3} \quad \text{III}$$
$$(\Delta Y_1)(P_{Y_1}) = (\Delta Y_2)(P_{Y_2}) = (\Delta Y_3)(P_{Y_3}) = \ldots (\Delta Y_n)(P_{Y_n}) \quad \text{IV}$$

must be equal for each pair of products. As equation IV (which can be derived from III) indicates, the marginal value product (the change in output of any one product multiplied by its price) for a unit of resource must be equal between all products. Problems of crop rotations ordinarily involve 3 or more crops, while many farmers have the alternative of producing 20 different products.

Discontinuous opportunities and stability. Not only can rotations include more than 2 crop possibilities but the product combinations are sometimes considered as discontinuous alternatives. This situation, representing an adaptation of those already outlined, involves no new principles; price ratios must be equated in the manner illustrated by II and IV above. The simple 2-crop example is employed below to illustrate the case.

Opportunity curve *abcde* represents rotation possibilities when only the crop combinations indicated as *a*, *b*, *c*, *d*, and *e* can be attained. The in-between or dotted portions cannot be attained and the production possibility curve has corners indicating high stability in the crop combinations grown. When the forage/grain price ratio is of the magnitude represented by the slope of iso-revenue curve *ER*, rotation or crop combination *c* results in maximum profits for the fixed quantity of resources. This rotation is most profitable over a wide range of price relationships. A shift to rotation *d* is not profitable unless the relative price of hay increases sufficiently to cause the slope of the revenue line to become greater than the slope of the *cd* portion of the opportunity curve. Conversely, rotation *b* will not be profitable until grain prices increase sufficiently to cause the revenue line to have a slope of less than *bc*. For all practical purposes, each of the discontinuous segments on the opportunity curve in Figure 10 can be considered the same as a continuous, linear production possibility line. Since the ratio of substitution of hay for grain is 1/4 or .25 between *b* and *c* and 5/5 or 1.0 between *c* and *d*, the hay/grain price ratio can also vary over the range from .25 to 1.0 before crop combination *c* becomes unprofitable. For example, with a hay price of 50¢ combination *c* is most profitable for any grain price between 50¢ and $2.

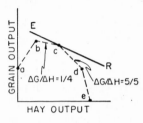

Fig. 10. Stability under discontinuous opportunities.

This stability situation is found on a great number of farms, and is the antithesis of constant and close rates of substitution between competitive crops, where profit maximization may require that resource use "flop" from specialization in one crop to specialization in another crop as prices change between years. The situation of Figure 10, except for the complementary range, also is approximated somewhat in livestock production. Although some variations can be made within a breed, changes in the proportion of milk and butterfat, eggs and meat, or mutton and wool require shifts from one breed to another. The jumps between combinations then become discontinuous and the stability situation outlined above arises.

Research implications and linear programming. Production possibility with corner positions or discontinuous opportunities provide conditions which simplify research procedures and recommendations to farmers and national administrators. This statement has particular applicability for production economics or farm management problems falling under the heading of rotation relationships and land use. Either survey records or the budgeting procedures, recently termed linear programming, have greater applicability under product-product relationships of this nature than where substitution ratios are continuous and change only gradually. Once a maximum condition such as that outlined in Figure 10 has been determined, the extension specialist or production economist can recommend the specific combination to farmers or national administrators with some degree of confidence; the combination or "efficient point" recommended will not be obsolete with each small change in price ratios or national needs.[5] Finally, all costs associated with different resource use patterns can be integrated into the farming system considerations. If the production possibility data (such as those suggested in Figure 10 or those presented in Tables 6 and 7 of Chapter 7) are in the vein of an iso-land curve, while labor and capital costs vary as a given quantity of land is shifted between crops, evaluation of enterprise or product combinations also can be made with ease when crop substitution relationships are discontinuous and linear. It is attained when the ratio of net price (the market price less the marginal per-unit variable cost of production, excluding land) is equated with the discrete substitution ratio. In other words, if the farmer has limited land or building resources and can produce crops or livestock with these fixed resources while he is able to add labor and other capital as he changes enterprise combinations, the problem of choice refers only to use of the fixed or given quantity of land or buildings. In this case where two products W and Y can be produced, as competitive enterprises from the given land or building resources, maximum profit is denoted when the condition $\Delta W/\Delta Y = P_y - C_y/P_w - C_w$ where ΔW and ΔY refer to the substitution increments, P_y and P_w refer to the prices of the two products, and C_y and C_w refer to the "direct" costs of the 2 products. When the 2 products substitute in a discontinuous manner, both the market prices and the labor and capital costs for the alternative products can vary over a range before changes in net price ratios merit a shift between the combinations suggested.

Regardless of whether substitution rates are constant and discontinuous or changing and continuous, the conditions of V and VI state resource adjustment patterns necessary for profit maximization. These conditions apply to the common situation where given inputs of buildings, land, or labor define the iso-quant but other inputs and cash costs differ as the "fixed" resources are shifted between products. If the price of W is greater

$$P_w > \frac{\Delta Y}{\Delta W}(P_y - C_y) + C_w \qquad\qquad \text{V}$$

$$P_w < \frac{\Delta Y}{\Delta W}(P_y - C_y) + C_w \qquad\qquad \text{VI}$$

[5] The budgeting process can also be carried out by means of simultaneous equations when linear segments (discrete opportunities) exist on the production possibility curve. See T. Koopman, *Activity Analysis of Production and Allocation*. New York: Wiley, 1951, Ch. 11.

than the sum of a, the substitution ratio multiplied by the net ratio for Y (i.e., the price of Y less the marginal unit cost of Y) plus b, the marginal unit cost of W (or the average unit cost if marginal cost is constant), product W should be substituted for Y; the reverse holds true in VI.

Seasonal selection of products. Product-product relationships which involve time in a simple fashion, have many applications. One of these problems is that of the seasonal selection of products. It is discussed below, where aspects of discounting do not arise between seasons. The fact that product prices are highest in low-volume marketing months has caused many agriculturists to imply that pigs should be farrowed, cows freshened, and hens put to laying in the off-season. Whether production should be shifted depends, however, on the substitution of products between seasons as well as the relationship between prices at 2 points in time. In Chapter 7 we suggested that products from summer and winter months often do not substitute at a constant and 1:1 ratio. As an example (Figure 11), the pattern of production over time which maximizes returns is not one speci-

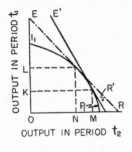

Fig. 11. Seasonal produc-
tion.

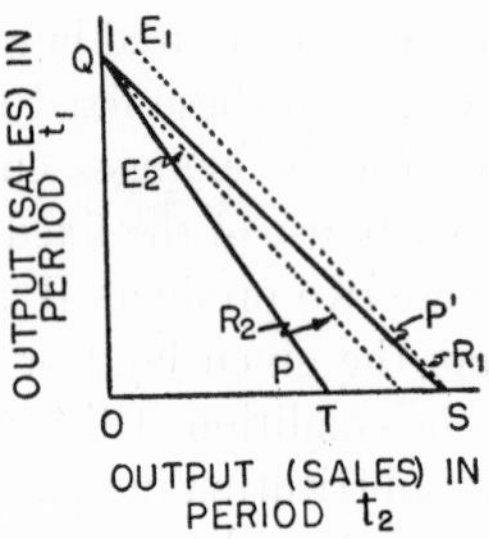

Fig. 12. Storage.

fying a single marketing date. For iso-revenue curve $E'R'$, the price is higher in period t_2 than t_1 ($E'R'$ has a slope greater than 45°). Since maximum returns are denoted by tangency of the revenue and production curves, the most efficient pattern of resource allocation over time is one which gives OK output of the product marketed in period t_1, the period of seasonally low prices, and OM in period t_2, the period of seasonally high prices. The agricultural expert must specify the time-time substitution ratio as well as the price ratio before he makes "either or" recommendations.

Seasonal storage presents a similar problem and is illustrated in Figure 12. The opportunity curve is of the nature of IP' [6] when the product does

---

[6] The quantity of wheat, corn, or grain can be looked upon as the given or constant resource to be allocated between the 2 time periods if the labor and other inputs are either available in non-limiting quantity or are required in equal quantities for products marketed in either period. The allocation problem is then one of determining what portion of the given grain stock should be used in "producing" a t_1 or a t_2 product.

not deteriorate and when direct costs do not attach to storage. A farm which has storage facilities on hand can view costs in this manner if the facilities depreciate equally, irrespective of use. (Where buildings do depreciate with use, the tenant need not consider this cost when it is borne by the landlord.) With a higher seasonal price in period t_2, profits will be maximized by storing the entire product until t_2. Where the product deteriorates in storage (from weevil and rodent damage, shrinkage, and so forth) or requires additional outlays for storage, the opportunity curve has a slope of less than 45°, such as IP. Under this opportunity curve and the same price relationship as previously (E_2R_2 has the same slope as E_1R_1), the entire product should be sold in the early period, t_1, if profits are to be maximized.[7]

Quality competition. One aspect of choice which has particularly drawn the attention of market specialists is the allocation of resources between competing grades of the same commodity. Trade people and agriculturists have focused great effort on getting farmers to produce eggs, milk, vegetables, or pork of the highest quality. Some imply that (a) farmers and the consuming society would be better off if only the "higher" grades were produced when consumers reflect their preferences through price differentials, (b) farmers do not maximize returns unless they produce the "high grade" alone, or (c) consumers do not know the virtue of quality when they refuse to reflect price differentials great enough to cause farmers to divert resources to higher grades. The problem posed is one in resource allocation and differs not at all from other problems in production economics. The fallacy of the logic in the arguments presented becomes evident when analysis is in terms of the conventional relationships in production. In Figure 13 the opportunity curve IP_1 is linear with a 1:1 or 45° slope (1 unit of grade B is sacrificed for each unit of grade A gained) indicating equal per-unit costs for either grade. If consumers express no choice through price differentials, the iso-revenue curve for the 2 grades

---

[7] Given the opportunity curve IP, no product should be stored until t_2 unless the price in t_2 increases relative to that of t_1 until the slope of the iso-revenue curve becomes greater than IP. Then the entire amount of resources (stock of grain) would be diverted until the later or t_2 period, since the slope of the revenue line is greater than the slope of the opportunity line. If prices of the future are discounted, then the price in period t_2 must be sufficiently great to offset the discount and the product deterioration (storage cost) if the commodity is to be held until the later period.

The possibility curve IP conforms quite well to the nature of storage relationships for non-perishable products. While the deterioration is a function of time (the opportunity lines would "curve" toward the horizontal axis if time were plotted on the y and quantity plotted on the x axis), the amount of deterioration is generally at a constant rate between 2 discrete points in time, although there are exceptions. The presentation here has opened up some elementary problems of decision-making which relate to time. The more complex aspects of time can be introduced through the discounting of future prices and costs. In Figures 11 and 12, for example, the price relationship expressed might include a discount of the price in period t_2. However, we postpone these considerations for a later chapter.

also has a 45° slope and producers can be indifferent as to the proportions of A or B produced. However, if the costs of production are constant and sufficiently greater for grade A, as indicated by opportunity curve IP_2 in Figure 13, the producer and consumer both will be "better off" with production of grade B alone (since the slope of the revenue line or the price ratio is less than the slope of the opportunity line or the substitution

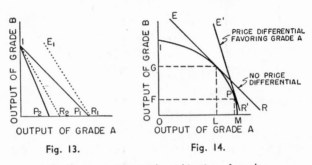

Fig. 13.   Fig. 14.

Quality competition and combination of grades.

ratio). Given the situation suggested by IP_2, grade A alone should be produced only if the values of the consumer provide sufficiently great price differentials (the iso-revenue line must have a slope greater than IP_2). Where the 2 grades substitute at an increasing rate, as in Figure 14, the likelihood that either grade should be produced alone is remote if farmer return and consumer utility are to be maximized with resources given.

Other Maximizing Problems

While the opportunity curves and the choice functions explained above define maximum farm profits from given resources, they also provide tools for analyzing other problems in production. Resource use problems often revolve around intermediate ends of a physical character. Some of these are outlined below.

Interrelations between product and resources and crop rotations. Many primary products such as coarse grains and hay are not consumed directly as food. While they are final products on some farms, they become resource inputs on other farms. Two problems are important in respect to commodities with primary product-resource input characteristics: (1) What pattern of primary production will allow a maximum output of the secondary product when resources for the former are limited? (2) What quantity of primary product should be sold or purchased if returns through the secondary product are to be maximized?

For reasons based on risk and uncertainty many farmers neither buy nor sell feeds but keep a type and quantity of livestock which will utilize the crops grown on their farms. The question then arises, with the land area fixed and labor and capital variable, of which rotation or cropping system is optimum when crops as primary products do not enter the market but serve as feed inputs for livestock output. The farmer may wish to produce crops which will allow a maximum output of livestock from the limited land and other resources available. The conditions under which output of one type of livestock is maximized from a given land area can be illustrated by means of the iso-resource relationships discussed in this chapter and the iso-product relationships discussed in earlier chapters. In order to simplify the analysis, discussion first will relate to land as the limited resource for which livestock output is to be maximized. (Capital and labor will be neglected momentarily or it can be assumed that the limited land area of the farm causes decisions or choice-making to center around this resource.) This environment typifies many farms where the

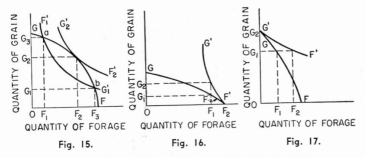

Fig. 15.   Fig. 16.   Fig. 17.

Maximum livestock production from a given quantity of land or other resources.

management task is one of maximizing returns from a given land area. The conditions which define a maximum livestock product from the feeds grown on a given land area are illustrated in Figures 15, 16 and 17. On soils where competitive crops include forage and grain, the rotation relationship can be represented in the form of the opportunity curve GF in Figure 15. The curves $G'_1F'_1$ and $G'_2F'_2$ represent iso-livestock product curves, and indicate the general manner in which feeds combine in the livestock ration.[8] Feeds can be produced and fed in many different combinations. For example, livestock output may be held constant at the level indicated by the iso-product curve $F'_1G'_1$. The rotation which allows the livestock output indicated by $F'_1G'_1$ includes crop outputs OG_3 of grain

---

[8] While the iso-resource relationship is presented as a continuous function with increasing rates of substitution, and while the iso-product curve is presented as a continuous function with decreasing rates of substitution, the former may, for certain products and certain resources, involve discrete production opportunities, while the latter may involve continuous and constant substitution rates. These modifications are not discussed because they represent adaptations from the fundamental conditions illustrated.

and OF_1 of forage, as indicated on the crop production possibility curve GF. The crop combination OF_3 of forage and OG_1 of grain will also allow this same output of livestock product (that indicated by iso-product curve $F'_1G'_1$). However, neither the combination on the livestock ration curve nor that on the crop rotation curve defines the maximum livestock output which can be produced from a given land area, since GF (the iso-land curve) and $G'_1F'_1$ (the iso-livestock curve) intersect. The slope of $G'_1F'_1$ is greater than the slope of GF at the point of the upper intersection. Accordingly, $\Delta G/\Delta F$, the marginal rate of substitution of forage for grain in the crop rotation, is less than $\Delta G'/\Delta F'$, the marginal rate of substitution of forage for grain in the livestock ration. In numerical example, this may mean that 1 lb. of forage substitutes for 1 lb. of grain in the rotation, while 1 lb. of forage substitutes for 2 lbs. of grain in the livestock ration. The slope of GF is greater than that of $G'F'$ at the lower intersection point. Hence $\Delta G/\Delta F$, the marginal rate of substitution of forage for grain in the rotation, is greater than $\Delta G'/\Delta F'$, the marginal rate of substitution of forage for grain in the livestock ration. In numerical example, this may mean that in the rotation 1 lb. of forage substitutes for 1 lb. of grain, while in the ration 1 lb. of forage substitutes for .5 lbs. of grain; 2 lbs. of grain are required to offset 1 of hay in the ration.

Either of 2 types of adjustment is possible, starting from the intersection points: (1) The same amount of livestock, that indicated by $G'F'$, can be produced under a different rotation and a different ration, and some grain can be left over to sell as a cash crop. For example, starting at point a, production of 1 more pound of hay causes a sacrifice of 1 of grain in the rotation, while use of 1 more pound of hay saves 2 lbs. of grain in the ration, and 1 lb. of grain is saved for the market. (2) A greater amount of livestock can be produced if hay is substituted for grain in the rotation and all of the forthcoming feeds are fed to livestock. In other words, it is possible to move to higher and higher iso-product curves, indicating greater livestock outputs, until one is reached which defines a maximum of livestock product from the given land area. The iso-product or ration line $G'_2F'_2$ which is tangent to GF, the rotation opportunity curve, defines the maximum livestock product. At the point of tangency the slopes of the 2 curves are equal and $\Delta G/\Delta F$, the marginal rate of feed substitution in the crop rotation, is exactly equal to $\Delta G'/\Delta F'$, the marginal rate of feed substitution in the livestock ration. The crop rotation which will maximize livestock output from a given area is represented by an output OG_2 of grain and OF_2 of forage, as is evidenced by the fact that the slope of the rotation curve is greater than the slope of the ration curve for outputs of forage greater than OF_2. In numerical example, beyond the tangency point 1 lb. of hay may substitute for $1\frac{1}{2}$ lbs. of the grain in the rotation, while 3 lbs. of hay may be required to replace $1\frac{1}{2}$ lbs. of grain in the ration. Hence the level of livestock output represented by $G'_2F'_2$ cannot be maintained by a forage output greater than OF_2 on the production opportunity curve.

The same general conditions specify the crop rotation-livestock ration combination which will maximize livestock output when primary crops are complementary over some range. In Figure 18, the livestock output designated by iso-product curve $G'_1F'_1$ is not the maximum attainable from the land area represented by iso-factor curve GF. Greater livestock outputs can be attained through movement to higher and higher iso-product curves until $G'_3F'_3$ is attained.[9] Contrary to the historic specializations in research of the Land Grant Colleges, the optimum crop rotations and the optimum livestock rations are not entirely independent, but often are mutually determined in the manner of the production economics relations outlined above.

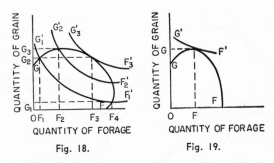

Fig. 18.   Fig. 19.

Interrelationships between crop rotations and livestock rations.

The conditions outlined above can be summarized conveniently. The first condition states that when the substitution rate for primary crops is greater than the substitution rate for the secondary product, and hence the ratio of the first divided by the second is less than 1.0, output of the secondary product is not at a maximum and can be increased by the adjustment mentioned. The second condition states that when the corresponding ratio is equal to 1.0, a maximum secondary product is attained; for condition 3, the ratio is greater than 1.0 and primary products must be substituted for each other.[10]

---

[9] With outputs of OG_2 and OF_3 of grain and forage respectively, the marginal rate of substitution of forage for grain in the rotation is equal to the rate of substitution of the 2 crops in the livestock ration. The exact point of the ration-rotation optimum will vary, of course, with the slope of the 2 curves, depending on the soil type and the class of livestock. In cases such as that illustrated in Figure 19, where the rate of substitution between crops as feed resources is low relative to the rate of substitution of crops as primary products, maximum livestock output is defined approximately at and never before the peak of the complementary range.

[10] If the ratios are less than zero (negative) the primary products are complementary and output of the secondary product can be increased as primary products are adjusted until the ratio becomes positive and equal to 1.0.

Reorganization of resources needed to give a maximum
Condition   *secondary product from given resources*

1. $\dfrac{\Delta G/\Delta F}{\Delta G'/\Delta F'} < 1.0$ substitute forage for grain (primary product) in both the crop rotation and the livestock ration (secondary products)

2. $\dfrac{\Delta G/\Delta F}{\Delta G'/\Delta F'} = 1.0$ no adjustment: output of secondary product is at a maximum from given resources devoted to primary products

3. $\dfrac{\Delta G/\Delta F}{\Delta G'/\Delta F'} > 1.0$ substitute grain for forage in the crop rotation and livestock ration

Agricultural example. The curves CR and LF of Figure 20 have been derived from rotation experiments on Marshall soils in Iowa and the estimates of dairy feed substitution mentioned earlier. While the data are not

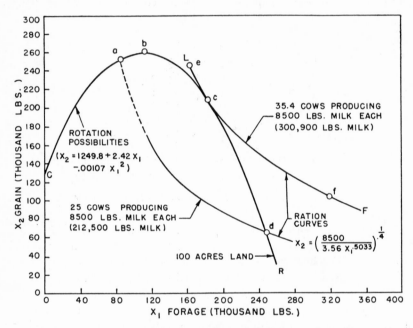

Fig. 20. Maximum milk product from 100 acres of Marshall silt loam in Iowa. (Source: Heady, E. O., and Olson, R. O., Iowa Agr. Exp. Sta. Bul. 390.)

perfect, they provide empirical examples for illustrative purposes. The point of tangency c indicates that a rotation of corn-corn-oats-meadow would allow a maximum milk product from a given land area.[11] Approximately 35.4 cows, each producing 8,500 lbs. of milk, could be maintained on 100 acres under this rotation.[12] Rations and crop rotations indicated as

---

[11] Although many tangency points are possible, only the one which denotes feed fed in the same proportions as it is grown denotes a maximum livestock product.

[12] If rotations are considered as discrete production opportunities, a 4-year rotation of corn-corn-oats-meadow still allows a greater milk output from 100 acres than the next closest rotation.

a and d would allow only 25 cows to be supported on 100 acres. Tangency of the 100-acre iso-land curve and the ration curve can be attained either by (1) varying the number of cows with production per cow held constant at some level such as 8,500 lbs., and/or (2) varying both the numbers and output per cow. Maximum milk output from 100 acres is forthcoming, of course, when rotations, rations, and cow numbers are adjusted to conform with diminishing marginal rates of feed-milk transformation as well as diminishing rates of feed substitution. Although the resource curve presented above is for land alone, other factors such as labor and capital can also be employed in deriving the production possibilities and the iso-livestock curves, or the costs of labor and other capital can be compared with the added return when the number of animals and output is arranged as a maximum for a given land area. In the study upon which the data of Figure 20 are based, the net return, after including labor and other costs, was estimated at $5,535 for the 35.4 cows and $4,195 for the 25 cows. If the ration curve were representative of beef, mutton, or pork, time would also be involved.

Systems of farming. The comparison of the 2 curves aids in explaining the determination of farming systems. Where the grain/forage substitution rate of the rotation is high enough relative to the rate at which the 2 feeds substitute in the livestock ration, the market product from a given land area may be maximized if a forage-consuming type of animal (high marginal rates of substitution of forage for grain) is adopted and the entire land area is planted to forage. The situation is illustrated in Figure 16, where the slope of $G'F'$ is greater than the slope of GF up to the point F_2, where the latter intersects the forage axis. The combination suggests a grazing type of livestock where grass alone is produced and where forage constitutes the entire ration. The counterpart of this situation is found in the beef- and sheep-ranching areas of the nation where the yield of grain is ordinarily low relative to grass. Complementarity of grain and forage crops always leads to a mixed system of grain- and forage-consuming livestock. Figure 17 illustrates the opposite situation where $\Delta F/\Delta G$, the marginal rate of substitution of grain for forage in the rotation, is high relative to $\Delta F'/\Delta G'$, the substitution rate in the livestock ration. Since the slope of $G'F'$ is less than the slope of GF ($\Delta G'/\Delta F' < \Delta G/\Delta F$) even at the grain axis, a maximum livestock product is forthcoming when grain alone is produced and the entire ration is composed of this feed. The situation is approached on the level or bottomland soils of the Cornbelt.

Trading products in the market. Although the sizes of their farms are limited, farmers can also consider the rotation and ration relationships as distinct through the purchase and sale of feeds. Equation of the marginal rates of grain-forage substitution between the ration and rotation curves need not specify the maximum amount of animal product attainable from a given land area when primary products can be exchanged in the market.

Suppose, for example, that the land area of a farm presents the production possibilities for grain and forage illustrated by curve GF in Figure 21. Grain and forage price relationships are of the nature indicated by the iso-revenue curve ER. The crop combination which maximizes total revenue from the given land area is OG_2 of grain and OF_1 of forage. Now the revenue obtained from the sale of the crops from the given land area can be considered as a constant cost outlay in the purchase of feeds (an iso-cost curve). The equal revenue and equal cost lines (ER and IS) are identical if selling and buying prices are the same. Hence, as an iso-cost curve, IS represents all the quantities of grain and forage which can be purchased with the funds derived from the sale of OG_2 of grain and OF_1 of forage. Curve $G'F'$ is the iso-product contour indicating the manner in which grain and forage substitute in producing a given amount of livestock. It represents the highest livestock output attainable from the given

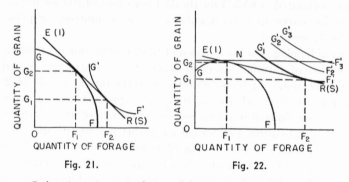

Fig. 21.   Fig. 22.

Exchanging primary products and feed resources in the market.

cost outlay represented by IS. Thus the livestock output and the value of livestock from the given land acreage is at a maximum if the farmer (1) produces OG_2 of grain and OF_1 of forage, (2) sells G_1G_2 of grain and purchases F_1F_2 of forage, and (3) feeds OG_1 of grain and OF_2 of forage. If (a) the price of hay is low enough relative to the price of grain (a revenue line with less slope than ER) or (b) the rate at which forage substitutes for grain in the ration is low enough (an iso-product or ration curve with less slope than $G'F'$), these maximum quantities define a farming system which includes sale of hay and purchase of grain.

Similar conditions hold true with 2 primary crops possessing a range of complementarity. In Figure 22, the allocation of resources which will maximize the value of crops from a given land area includes OG_2 of grain and OF_1 of forage.[13] A maximum livestock product again is forthcoming if F_1F_2 of forage is purchased and G_1G_2 of grain is sold.

---

[13] Given the nature of the substitution between grain and forage, the maximum amount of livestock attainable from the value of crops produced (ER as an iso-revenue curve again becomes IS, an iso-outlay curve) is represented by $G'_1F'_1$. Again

Factor interrelations and production policy. The production relationships outlined above are the ones of importance in devising national conservation or land-use programs. Again they illustrate the inadequacy of analyses which revolve around a single relationship or single resource. Optimum resource use and product combinations can be specified only as the several factors and products and their interrelationships are considered.

The analysis here has explained the farming system which allows a maximum value and quantity of livestock products from a given land area. The same conditions are applicable when the opportunity curve is an iso-resource or cost line including capital and labor as well as land, while the product contour defines grain and complementary labor and capital on the one hand and forage and complementary factors on the other. The conditions specified above are also relevant when national policy places emphasis on physical choices. In Figure 15 for example, the production possibility curve may represent corn and soybeans, which, as alternative primary crops, can be used as competitive protein and carbohydrate feeds in livestock production. The basic decisions to be made may be either of these: (1) With a given land area available for corn and soybeans, what cropping pattern and, hence, livestock ration will allow a *maximum* output of pork from a limited land area? (2) Given the output of pork, what cropping system and ration will require a *minimum* land input for the specified amount of pork? While other resources again must be included in the final analysis, the basic conditions are illustrated by tangency of GF and $G'_2F'_2$, defining equal rates of substitution between crops as primary products and as feed resources.

Production Policy and Physical Choice Problems

During emergencies, a nation is concerned with allocating resources between alternative products in a manner to maximize physical quantities of food. The choice indicator then becomes one expressing the relative quantity of calories, protein, or other food nutrients which can be derived from different agricultural products. Decisions must relate to all factors of production, but must particularly revolve around those which are severely limited and have alternative uses outside of agriculture. Capital, in its many forms, and labor ordinarily are the crucial factors which can be

---

G_1G_2 of grain should be sold and F_1F_2 of forage should be purchased if the physical output and the value of livestock products is to be maximized for a given land area. If forage has no sale value and is free in the market, as indicated by the horizontal iso-revenue curve N, no less than the complementary quantity of forage should ever be produced (the iso-revenue curve N and the iso-factor curve GF are tangent at the apex of the latter). The farmer should substitute forage for grain, as denoted by movement to higher and higher iso-product curves such as $G'_2F'_2$ and $G'_3F'_3$, until the marginal rate of substitution of forage for grain is driven to zero and the 2 feeds become technical complements.

moved between agriculture, defense industries, and civilian industries. Land is the passive agent of production in the sense that it is immobile and the percentage which can be used for defense or non-agricultural uses makes up an unimportant part of the total. Thus aggregate or interindustry considerations of land use, even in peace time, are only secondary.

That there are wide differences in the physical quantity of food nutrients obtainable from various livestock and crop products is evident in Table 7. Generally, a unit of resource produces more food nutrients when primary crops are used for human consumption rather than as resource inputs for livestock products. Variations do exist within the crop or livestock groups, however, and many animal products provide more nutrients per unit of resource than do individual crops. Pork and lard produce, on the average, many more units of the food nutrients per resource-unit than does asparagus.

Table 7.

Average Yield of Food Nutrients Per Unit of Specified Resource, United States *

Crop or livestock product	100 *calories energy value per*			Pounds of protein per	
	100 hrs. labor	acre of land	unit of all resources [a]	100 hrs. labor	acre of land
Wheat, whole flour	12,582	1,132	1,120	1,002	90
Corn, yellow meal	4,109	1,122	987	211	57
Irish potatoes	3,358	2,283	258	174	118
Dry beans	4,159	1,081	407	576	150
Peanuts	1,301	755	312	0	0
Soybeans	5,103	612	392	0	0
Cucumbers	160	190	22	18	21
Asparagus	93	178	20	16	31
Strawberries	56	273	17	3	12
Whole milk	791	352	139	89	39
Butter	425	189	145	[b]	[b]
Eggs	313	144	43	56	26
Broilers	279	117	23	64	27
Pork and lard	1,618	500	196	58	18
Fattening steers	289	57	50	42	8
All beef cattle	310	47	77	45	7
Fattening lambs	521	115	68	58	13
All sheep	310	47	77	34	5

* Source: U.S.D.A. Tech. Bul. 963.

[a] A unit of aggregate resource refers to the quantity and combination of various forms of capital, labor, and land to produce a common amount of each product in the base period. Other data refer to average yields.

[b] Less than 1.

The data of Table 7 are not sufficient for determining exactly how the nation's agricultural resources should be allocated during a war or food-emergency period, when the quantity to be maximized is calories or food nutrients. Use of data in this average productivity form for all units of resource would suppose linear opportunity curves. Therefore, under these assumptions, certain crop or livestock products would be produced at the complete exclusion of others. There are scattered instances where this situation holds true. It cannot be followed as a general rule for all resources, however. The wide geographical range upon which agriculture is based gives rise, not to constant marginal rates of product substitution over all resource units of all farming areas, but to increasing sacrifices as resources are shifted between products. Shift of an acre of land from sheep to soybeans on the level soils of the Cornbelt causes a relatively small sacrifice in mutton for each bushel gain in grain output. Yet if land and other resources are next withdrawn from sheep and devoted to soybeans on the hilly lands of the Cornbelt and eventually on the range areas of New Mexico, increasing amounts of mutton must be sacrificed for each bushel gain in soybeans. The physical productivity of resources in arid regions is not great when used in grass and sheep production, but these regions are even less productive when used for soybeans. When production possibilities are computed as averages between areas and each figure so computed is considered as a point on the "national production possibility curve," the opportunities then take on the appearance of "curve" *bcde* in Figure 10.

When the maximizing problem is one of the greatest food product from given resources, it again must be solved in the conceptual framework provided by Figure 23. The choice indicator may now be an equal calorie (iso-food) curve such as *EC,* which indicates the many combinations of 2 products which provide an equal number of calories or other food nutrients. The slope of *EC* depends on the number of calories which can be derived from a unit of sheep as compared to a bushel of soybeans and the slope of the opportunity curve, *MS,* indicates the sacrifice in sheep necessary for each unit gain in soybeans. A maximum quantity of food nutrients is forthcoming from given resources, or a minimum of resources is required for a given food output, when *OL* of sheep and *OB* of soybeans are

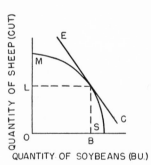

Fig. 23. Maximizing food production and iso-food lines.

produced. For this combination, the marginal rate of substitution of beans for sheep, $\Delta S/\Delta B$, is equal to the soybean/sheep calorie ratio (the number of calories which can be obtained from 1 bushel of soybeans as compared to a hundred weight of sheep). The calorie (or other food nutrient) ratio now becomes the choice indicator and defines the most efficient allocation of resources for the end specified. While they are suggestive of directions, the average productivity figures of Table 7 do not provide the detail needed (because of insufficient indication of increasing substitution rates) in determining the exact allocation of resources for efficiency in food production during emergency periods. At the very minimum, substitution rates need to be estimated for each major farming area in order that some notion of production possibilities is available even in the manner of the discontinuous opportunities shown in Figure 10.

Production and price policy. If resources were allocated optimally during wartime or other emergencies, administrative details might be carried to a point where each farmer is instructed on how to allocate each unit of resource between products. This degree of detail would suppose that national administrators of production know the production possibility schedule or curve for each farm. Since this inventory of knowledge is not available, the burden of estimating the nature of production possibilities can be thrown on each farmer. The only necessary step is that product price ratios be established in line with the ratio of food nutrients forthcoming from each product. For example, if product V results in 100 food nutrients (calories, protein, or some other common denominator) per bushel, while product W results in 200 food units per bushel, the "choice ratio" is 200/100 or 2.0. The need is to get farmers to allocate resources between the products in a manner such that the substitution ratio $\Delta V/\Delta W$ becomes 2.0. This would be encouraged by a W/V price ratio of 2.0. In other words, if a price of \$1 is established for product V, the price for W should be \$2. If farmers maximized their profits under this price structure, they would also maximize output of food nutrients from given resources.

The Optimum Combination of Resources for Two Products

We have been discussing the optimum allocation of given resources between different products when factors are fixed for the producing unit. This is a central problem in agriculture, since most farmers have limited capital and cannot extend production of any one commodity to an optimum scale. Supposing a farm which produces 2 commodities, we may now inquire how different resources should be combined for different products when resources can be shifted between technical or producing units. The farmer with limited funds must determine the optimum combination of grain and forage in producing milk and beef, or the optimum combination of capital and labor in producing cotton and tobacco, when both are grown on the same farm.

In an oversimplification of the problem setting, we illustrate the logic of factor combination with 2 products and limited resources. The procedure is an extension of the analysis made in Figures 11 and 12 of Chapter 6 for a single product. In Figure 24 we return to the opportunity box shown previously. The axes (or the box itself) measure the given stock of 2 factors. On the left axis the total stock of X is OM. This is the same quantity of X, as indicated by $O'Q$ on the right axis. On the bottom axis the limited quantity of factor Z amounts to OQ and is equal to that indicated as $O'M$ on the top axis. The solid or left and bottom axes represent alternatives in using X and Z in producing product Y; the contour or iso-product map for product Y is in reference to the OM and OQ axes. Possibilities also exist for using the entire stock of X and Z in producing product W. The dotted or right and upper axes represent alternatives in using factors X and Z in producing W; the iso-product curves now are in reference to $O'M$ and $O'Q$. The "upside-down" graph provides the situation for W, while the "right-side-up" graph provides the situation for Y. (The W contour map has simply been inverted over that for Y in the manner outlined in Chapter 6.) Obviously, many combinations of factors can be used in producing the 2 products; also, many combinations of the 2 products can be produced. Any point selected within the opportunity box indi-

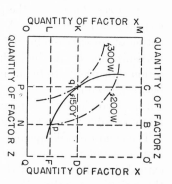

Fig. 24. Optimum combination of resources for two products.

cates an alternative method of allocating the given stock of factors X and Z between the products Y and W. One such point is p. It denotes intersection of an iso-product contour for W (200 units) with an iso-product contour for Y (150 units). Thus if 200 of W and 150 of Y are to be produced, the manner in which the total stock of resources can be divided between the 2 products is indicated at point p. The 150 units of Y are produced with ON inputs of factor Z. The 200 units of product W are produced with NQ (equals $O'B$) inputs of Z and the complete stock (OQ) of Z is used. Similarly, point p indicates that 150 units of Y are produced with OL inputs of factor X while 200 units of W are produced with LM (equals $O'F$) of X and the total stock (OM) of X is exhausted.

This pattern of allocating the given stock of the 2 factors between the 2 products does not allow maximum profits if the price for either or both commodities is greater than zero. The optimum pattern of resource combination is attained only under certain conditions, one of which is that *the final combination of products and factors must be such that the marginal rate of substitution of factor* X *for factor* Z *is the same between the 2 products.* Several such conditions can be attained in an opportunity box such as that indicated. One such point is illustrated at point q, where the iso-product line for W is tangent to that of Y, thus denoting equal rates of factor substitution for both products. Under this particular combination of factors and products, OK units of X are used for Y, and KM (equals $O'D$) units are used for W. The total stock OQ of Z is used, OP units for product Y and PQ (equals $O'C$) units for product W. The firm can now produce 300 units of W and 150 units of Y. At point p the output included 150 of Y and only 200 of W. Without knowledge of price ratios, we can always say that revenue and profits can be increased by shifting from a combination such as p, where the rates of factor substitution are not equal, to a point such as q where substitution ratios are equal. The output of W can be increased without decreasing the output of Y by this rearrangement of resources. Therefore, the point p cannot possibly denote the most efficient allocation of factors X and Z between products Y and W. The allocation of resources indicated at point q is a necessary condition for profit maximization by the individual firm. It is not, however, a sufficient condition. For profits to be at a maximum, resources must also be organized between products to equate price and substitution ratios in the manner outlined previously. (This qualification must be made because there are many possible sets of tangent curves in the box.)

The conditions illustrated above also could be stated algebraically in a manner similar to equations IV and V in Chapter 6. If equation IV is extended to all products within the farm and the ratios are all equal to 1.0, the optimum quantity of resources, the optimum combination of resources, and the optimum combination of products have been attained for a farm with unlimited capital. If the ratios are all equal between products at a constant greater than 1.0 for a farm with limited capital, it has attained optimum factor and product combinations. Aside from cost aspects to be mentioned later, these same conditions define an optimum interfarm and interregional allocation of resources where multiple products are concerned.

Agricultural examples and the inter-farm allocation of resources. There are many agricultural examples where resources are not allocated between products in the manner outlined. Often farmers use high-capacity equipment for grain crops, while hay on the same farm is harvested by methods requiring large amounts of labor. Similar discrepancies exist in rations for different classes of livestock. Still greater discrepancies exist between farms. Some operators use a large amount of labor while others use large amounts of capital. Resource combinations differ greatly, for example, in corn or wheat production as compared to cotton. The nation's consuming society could have a greater agricultural product from the same resources or the same product from fewer resources if resources were allocated between the products of different regions in the manner suggested by Figure 24. While the outcomes for mass and individual adjustment mentioned in early chapters also apply here, the possibility also exists for neighboring farms of the same community. Two farmers, as well as society, could have a greater product to divide between themselves if they were to pool resources and organize factors and products in an optimum fashion. Again, it is probably true that farmers do not make these interfarm adjustments because (a) of the uncertainty with which one views another's management, (b) market institutions have not developed which facilitate inter-farm resource organizations (c) farmers place a high value on independence in the management function, and (d) farmers lack knowledge of interfarm possibilities.

The combination of products between technical units or farms producing the same product. Principles similar to those outlined above also apply to the interunit allocation of resources for a single product. Within the farm firm and from the standpoint of profits, the question is one of the manner in which products should be combined for given technical units producing the same commodities. Should different rotations be followed on 2 fields of the same or different soil types? Should different proportions of mutton and wool be obtained from each ewe? The problem is again one of obtaining a maximum of products from given resources or using a minimum of resources for a given output of products. Readjustments in resource use which result in the first allow the individual farmer a greater product to market from given resources, while those resulting in the second allow the same value of output with a smaller input of resources.

Similarly, these adjustments can allow society a greater product from the same resources or the same agricultural product with fewer resources. If all farm resources were to be reorganized in this manner, the total revenue of the industry would not necessarily increase because of the low price-elasticity of demand for farm products. Given this adjustment in the industry, individual farmers or pairs of farmers would still be better off to make the adjustment, however. We outline the principle below as it applies between farms. Its application between technical units within the farm is identical. In contrast to the analysis of the previous section, the discussion assumes that, while product combinations can be changed, resources cannot be transferred between producing units. The logic is illustrated in Figures 25, 26, and 27, where concave opportunity curves are employed. Suppose that we have 2 farms each producing the same product with given resources and the production possibility curves indicated in Figure 25 and Figure 26. How should the 2 commodities Y_1 and Y_2 be combined on each farm if a maximum product is to be forthcoming from the total stock of resources on the 2 farms? The necessary condition is this: the marginal rates of product substitution must be equal between farms. It can be illustrated by rotating Figure 26 counterclockwise through 180° and transposing it over Figure 25 in the manner illustrated in previous chapters. The comparisons indicated in Figure 27 result. First, let Figure 26 be placed over Figure 25 in the manner indicated by the dotted axes $c'o'd'$ and the broken opportunity curve $c'd'$. (Disregard all lines and figures above and to the right of $c'o'd'$ for the time being.) Here the opportunity curve for B intersects that for A at 2 points. (Many points of intersection can be obtained simply by "moving" the B figure up and down or to the right and left.) Let us start with the combination of products on each farm indicated by intersection of opportunity curves ab and $c'd'$ at point f. With this organization of production, farm A produces os of Y_1 and on of Y_2, while B produces $o'p$ of Y_2 and $o'w$ of Y_1. The total output is os plus $o'w$ of Y_1 and on plus $o'p$ of Y_2. However, more of one or both products can always be produced by a rearrangement of products on the 2 farms, since the 2 opportunity curves intersect, indicating that marginal rates of product substitution are not equal between producing units. By

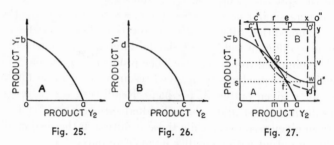

Fig. 25.   Fig. 26.   Fig. 27.

Optimum combination of products between producing units.

moving the B figure upwards and to the right we finally reach the position indicated by the solid axes $c''o''d''$ and the solid opportunity curve $c''d''$. The curve of B then becomes tangent to the curve of A, denoting that marginal rates of substitution are equal between producing units.[14] Here farm A would produce ot of Y_1 and om of Y_2, while B would produce $o''r$ of Y_2 and $o''v$ of Y_1. Total output of both products is then increased to ot plus $o''v$ of Y_1 and om plus $o''r$ of Y_2. In other words, the output of Y_1 increases by $o''y$ and the output of Y_2 increases by $o''x$.[15] Even if one of the products were to remain constant, the output of the other could always be increased from a given stock of resources by changing the degree of specialization in a manner allowing equal substitution rates.

Many individual farmers do not combine enterprises between technical units within the farm in a manner which results in a maximum product. The disparity is even greater between farms. Within the Cornbelt, one farmer often produces grain alone while his neighbor produces a crop combination and follows a systematic rotation. While product substitution rates do differ between farms, it is clearly evident that the pattern of

[14] This point of tangency may or may not be on a straight line through the origin on a 45° angle with the x axis.

[15] This is evident from the fact that in moving the B (obverted) production possibility curve from the "dotted" to the "solid" position, output of Y_2 falls back by mn on the lower horizontal axis at the same time it increases by re on the upper horizontal axis. Since mn and re are equal, the gain in Y_2 is $o''x$ because the solid (obverted) figure lies to the right of the dotted (obverted) figure by $o''x$. Similarly, while moving from point f to point g causes Y_1 output to increase by st on the "left hand" vertical axis and at the same time to slide up the "right hand" vertical axis by an equal amount vd, the net gain in Y_1 output becomes $o''y$.

specialization between farms is not one which allows 2 farmers or society the greatest return from a given stock of resources. Attainment of this optimum degree of specialization between farms is prohibited not only because of the reasons already cited but also because of uncertainty, short-term lease contracts, and other considerations outlined in subsequent chapters.

Selected References

Black, J. D., *et al., Farm Management*. New York: Macmillan, 1947, Ch. 10.

Carlson, S., *Study on the Pure Theory of Production*. London: King & Sons, 1939, pp. 88-102.

Darfman, R., *Application of Linear Programming to Theory of the Firm*. Berkeley: Univ. of Cal. Press, 1951, Ch. 4.

Heady, Earl O., "The Economics of Rotations," *Jour. Farm Econ.*, Vol. 30.

Heady, Earl O., and Jensen, Harold L., *The Economics of Rotations and Land Use*. Iowa Agr. Exp. Sta. Bul. 383.

Heady, Earl O., and Olson, Russell O., *Economics of Forage Utilization*. Iowa Agr. Exp. Sta. Bul. 390.

Koopmans, T., *Activity Analysis of Production and Allocation*. New York: Wiley, 1951, Chs. 3, 11.

Lerner, A., *Economics of Control*. New York: Macmillan, 1944, Ch. 7.

Little, I. M. D., *Welfare Economics*. Oxford: Oxford University Press, 1951, pp. 127-130.

Myint, Hla., *Theory of Welfare Economics*. Cambridge: Harvard University Press, 1948, pp. 108-114.

Stigler, G. J., *Theory of Price*. New York: Macmillan, 1947, pp. 314-320.

Weintraub, S., *Price Theory*. New York: Pitman, 1949, pp. 289-296.

9

Resource Allocation and Enterprise Combination to Meet Price Variability

In the analysis of the previous chapters, the principles of resource allocation were outlined for situations in which prices might be the same over time, and in which, therefore, an enterprise combination, once selected, could be maintained indefinitely.[1] Most production takes place, however, in an environment where prices do change over time, and the entrepreneur may wish to select a plant which allows adjustment to changing price ratios. This problem is particularly important for durable capital such as the buildings and machinery which provide services over a period of 20, 40, or even 100 years. A young farmer makes commitments which extend several decades into the future. If he uses funds to construct a dairy barn, the investment may prove inefficient if he later shifts production to an emphasis on poultry or hogs. The problem is accentuated on a rented farm where successive tenants have different quantities of resources and specialize in different enterprises. What is the nature of the opportunity curve once resources have been committed to a specific form such as dairy barns, hog houses, and chick brooders? What alternatives are open to the entrepreneur in minimizing sacrifices in products as price changes dictate reorganizations of resources? These questions properly fall under the heading of risk and uncertainty and are discussed in detail in later chapters where other dynamic aspects of enterprise combinations are also analyzed. Accordingly, this chapter is concerned with outlining the technical conditions of product flexibility, and is mainly in the vein of "change which is known." It also treats miscellaneous aspects of product-product relationships. Production control policy is one such problem.

Short-Run and Long-Run Planning Curves

Two types of transformation or opportunity curve face the entrepreneur as he first engages in decision-making. One is the long-run opportunity

---

[1] Additional details on production situations such as those outlined here can be obtained in E. O. Heady, "Resource Allocation in the Short-Run," *Jour. Farm Econ.*, Vol. 32.

relationship; the other is the short-run production situation. (Only the portion of the opportunity curve which defines competition or rivalry between the products is considered in this chapter.) The long-run opportunity or planning curve alone is relevant before capital is committed in any specialized form. A farmer with $30,000 can weigh the possibilities of dairy production against poultry production. If he decides on dairy products alone, all buildings and equipment can be specialized to the dairy enterprise. Similarly, the $30,000 can be invested in specialized poultry equipment. The fixed but uncommitted outlay of $30,000 also can be allocated to any number of combinations of specialized equipment for the 2 products. While the entire range of long-run opportunities is open before funds have been committed, once a specific level of diversification has been decided upon and specialized resources have been acquired, only short-run production opportunities face the manager: If cost and resource outlays remain constant, poultry now can be produced at the expense of dairy products only if some of the specialized dairy equipment is used for chickens and contrariwise. Labor, feed, and similar factor services are still adaptable to either enterprise, but buildings designed for poultry are not likely to be efficient, in either a technical or an economic sense, for milk production.

This situation can be illustrated by the data of Table 1, which indicates the production functions for 2 competing commodities produced with resources specialized for one commodity or the other. The production possibilities which exist for a constant outlay of 10 resource units before any resources are committed in a specialized form can be derived from columns 2 and 3 in Table 1, and are arrayed in columns 1 and 2 of Table 2. These

Table I.

Production Functions for Y_1 and Y_2 with Adapted and Unadapted Resources
(Hypothetical Data)

Factor input	Output with resources adapted to the specific product		Output with resources adapted to the opposite product	
	Y_1	Y_2	Y_1	Y_2
(1)	(2)	(3)	(4)	(5)
0	0	0	0	0
1	20	20	4.0	4.0
2	38	38	7.5	7.5
3	54	54	10.5	10.5
4	68	68	13.0	13.0
5	80	80	15.0	15.0
6	90	90	16.5	16.5
7	98	98	17.5	17.5
8	104	104	18.0	18.0
9	108	108	18.25	18.25
10	110	110	18.38	18.38

Table 2.

Long-run and Short-run Production Possibilities After Specialization of Resources (Based on Hypothetical Data of Table I)

Long-run production possibilities (before resources committed)		Short-run production possibilities after long-run decision to produce					
		110 of Y_1 0 of Y_2		80 of Y_2 80 of Y_1		68 of Y_1 90 of Y_2	
Y_1	Y_2	Y_1	Y_2	Y_1	Y_2	Y_1	Y_2
(1)	(2)	(3)	(4)	(5)	(6)	(7)	(8)
110	0	110	0	95.5	0	84.5	0
108	20	108	4.0	93.0	20	83.0	20
104	38	104	7.5	90.5	38	81.0	38
98	54	98	10.5	87.5	54	78.5	54
90	68	90	13.0	84	68	75.5	68
80	80	80	15.0	80	80	72	80
68	90	68	16.5	68	84	68	90
54	98	54	17.5	54	87.5	54	94
38	104	38	18.0	38	90.5	38	97.5
20	108	20	18.25	20	93.0	20	100.5
0	110	0	18.38	0	95.5	0	103

are the long-run possibilities. Suppose that the manager selects the single long-run opportunity including 110 units of Y_1 and zero units of Y_2, and funds are invested in resources specialized for the Y_1 enterprise. If the specialized resources are used for production of Y_2, the production opportunities assume the form indicated in the schedule of columns 3 and 4 of Table 2. These are short-run production possibilities. If 1 resource unit is diverted from Y_1 to Y_2, output of the former drops by 2, while output of the latter increases by only 4 units. In contrast, the long-run opportunities (columns 1 and 2) allow a gain of 20 units of Y_2 for the 2-unit sacrifice in Y_1. While the long-run possibility schedule of Table 2 is derived by "moving up" column 2 and "down" column 3 of Table 1, the short-run opportunities are derived by "moving up" column 2 and "down" column 5 in Table 1. In other words, once equipment has been purchased for production of Y_1, commodity Y_2 must be produced with equipment adapted to Y_1 and is represented by a "mongrel" production function.

When the long-run opportunity curve is graphed, it appears as TF in Figure 1. If the short-run opportunity curve is graphed, it appears as s_1r_1. The long-run curve TF is relevant for decision making before resources have been committed, while the short-run curve s_1r_1 is relevant for decisions once the long-run opportunity which includes 110 of Y_1 and zero of Y_2 has been selected. Production opportunities open after selection of the specialized plant are represented by movement along s_1r_1 rather than along TF. The long-run opportunity curve is of historic interest only once funds or materials have been converted to particular forms of resources such as dairy barns or milking machines are adapted to one enterprise but not to another.[2] Selection of the long-run opportunity which includes 110 of Y_2 and zero of Y_1 gives another extreme short-run possibility curve indicated as s_2r_2 in Figure 1. Again, after this short-run possibility has been accepted, s_2r_2 rather than TF is relevant for decision relative to shifting resources between Y_1 and Y_2. The iso-outlay or production possibility

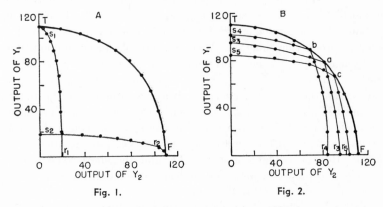

Fig. 1.   Fig. 2.

Long-run and short-run production possibilities.

curves s_1r_1 and s_2r_2 are 2 extremes of an entire family of short-run opportunity lines. One exists for each possible combination of products in the long-run possibility schedule. For example, suppose that the manager selects, from the long-run possibilities in columns 1 and 2 of Table 2, 80 units of each commodity. The short-run curve relevant for decision-making is now illustrated in columns 5 and 6 of Table 2. If resources are shifted from Y_1 to Y_2 (away from the 80-80 combination), the effect is one of "moving down" column 5 of Table 1, starting from zero, and "moving up" column 2, starting from 80. A similar pattern of change holds for shifts of resources from Y_2 to Y_1. The corresponding opportunity curve appears as s_3r_3 in Figure 2. Starting from point a on the long-run planning curve, "movement" is along s_3r_3, rather than along TF, as resources are shifted between Y_1 and Y_2. Similarly, if a long-run opportunity such as 68 of Y_1 and 90 of Y_2 (columns 7 and 8 in Table 2) is selected, it gives rise to

---

[2] The curve s_1r_1 (and subsequent short-run opportunity curves) is based on the supposition that while some resources such as labor and feed are not specialized to either enterprise and that, while certain semi-durable resources for one enterprise can be sold and thus converted to resources adapted to the other enterprise, other resources are either (a) permanent and must be used or (b) cause a loss in market exchange and thus allow a smaller amount of resources as production is shifted to an alternative product.

short-run opportunity curve s_5r_5 in Figure 2.[3] Selection of an original output which includes 90 of Y_1 and 68 of Y_2 gives the short-run opportunity curve s_4r_4 in Figure 2.

Equal resource outlays. The long-run planning curve TF is the envelope of an entire family of short-run opportunity lines including the extremes of s_1r_1 and s_2r_2 in Figure 1, as well as s_3r_3, s_4r_4, and s_5r_5 in Figure 2, and other possibilities which are not indicated. For each point on the long-run curve, a short-run curve exists and is just tangent to the planning curve. The short-run, iso-outlay curves can be termed "mongrel" opportunity lines, since the segment on either side of the tangency point is derived from a different production function.[4] When all possible long-run opportunities have been considered, the short-run transformation curves always fall inside the long-run planning curve. The marginal rate of substitution of Y_2 for Y_1 on the short-run curve is always greater below the tangency point and less above the point of tangency on the short-run opportunity line than it is for the long-run planning curve. Even though they are of different shapes, all of the opportunity curves represent the same resource or cost outlay. The planning curve TF and the short-run curves s_1r_1 through s_5r_5 in Figures 1 and 2 all indicate production possibilities when resource input is constant at 10 units.

Agricultural situations. Many products in agriculture are produced with resources originally designed for other products. Horse barns are used to house hens, hogs, cattle, or sheep, and farrowing houses are used as chicken brooders. Many "degrees" of planning curves exist in agriculture. "Long-run" plans may first relate to the construction of new buildings for feeder cattle or milk cows. Later, short-run decisions can be made in respect to whether milk or beef should be produced with the existing building facilities. Once the decision has been made to feed 20 steers and milk 12 cows, an even "shorter-run" decision can be made as to the quantity of fluid resources such as labor and feed which should go to the 12 cows or the 20 steers. The sacrifice in milk output per unit of beef gained will always be

---

[3] A shift of resources from Y_2 to Y_1 is now equivalent to "moving down" column 4 of Table 1, starting from zero, and a "movement up" column 3, starting from 90. A shift of resources from Y_1 to Y_2 is equivalent to "moving down" column 5 of Table 2 starting from zero and up column 2 starting from 68.

[4] In the data presented it has been supposed that the "mongrel" production function (production of Y_1 in resources specialized to Y_2 and vice versa) is the same for the situations presented regardless of the original long-run opportunity selected. This supposition was employed in order to minimize the complexity of the presentation. Actually the mongrel production function (except where it is linear) will differ with each starting point on the long-run curve. Use of a single "mongrel" production function regardless of the long-run combination selected would result in short-run curves (at the extreme) which would fall outside the planning curve. This would represent an irrational long-run planning situation, however, since it would indicate that the optimum or most efficient (the boundary of opportunities) possibilities have not even been selected for planning purposes.

greater if feed alone is varied between enterprises than if both feed and animal numbers are varied for each enterprise. The short-run opportunity curve is always flatter, on either side of the tangency point, than the planning curve. The slope of each of the short-run curves is a function of (a) proportionality and (b) lack of adaptability of resources specialized for particular commodities. (The slope of the long-run curve is more closely related to returns of scale.) A shift of resources from pork to poultry can be made in the short-run as given numbers of hogs are fed to heavier weights or as more hogs are raised in existing hog houses. In light of the diminishing returns relations outlined earlier, smaller and smaller increments of pork can be expected as successive increments of grain, labor, and other unspecialized resources are transferred to hogs from the poultry enterprise. Conversely, as each unit of unspecialized resource is withdrawn from poultry, increasing sacrifices of the latter product will be entailed because of intensity considerations. Pork also can be increased in the short-run at the expense of poultry by farrowing pigs in hen houses. However, if houses best adapted for poultry are not technically as efficient for hogs as buildings adapted to pork production, output of the latter enterprise will not increase in proportion to the resources diverted to it. Similarly, greatest flexibility in planning of crops comes before they are planted. Some flexibility in allocation of resources exists up through harvesting, however, since the farmer can give priority in harvesting services, for example, to wheat rather than oats. Many machines are equally adaptable to the alternative crops. A tractor may serve equally well for oats and wheat or corn and soybeans. The most important differences between short-run and long-run opportunities exist in livestock and fruit output. Buildings or growing stock represent investments which are transformed into product only over extremely long periods.

Price Relationships

One optimum short-run plant exists for each possible price relationship. This point is illustrated in Figure 3 for 2 short-run opportunity curves indicated as sr and s_1r_1. For a price relationship represented by the iso-revenue line E_1R_1, short-run plant sr allows a maximum total revenue from the given outlay. A different firm employing another short-run plant also could be in equilibrium under this same price relationship. For example, tangency of iso-revenue line $E'_1R'_1$ with plant curve s_1r_1 represents short-run equilibrium for the same price relationship (the slope of $E'_1R'_1$ is equal to that of E_1R_1). Under the same price relationship, short-run plant s_1r_1 is less efficient than sr, since it does not allow as great a total revenue from an equal resource outlay ($E'_1R'_1$ is lower than E_1R_1). Short-run plant s_1r_1 is most efficient under the price relationship represented by E_2R_2, however, since it allows a greater total revenue than does sr.

Research implications. Our model suggests why two farms with similar investments might produce different combinations of products even under the same price ratio. Once each of 2 farms has adopted a short-run plant, both can maximize profits by producing different proportions of products. With the realized ratio of prices indicated by the slope of iso-revenue curves E_1R_1 and $E'_1R'_1$ in Figure 3, firm sr should produce a "large" amount of poultry and a "small" amount of pork, while firm s_1r_1 should reverse the proportions. Both firms will be maximizing their revenue, given the established short-run plant layout. This is a consideration which is especially important in recommendations to farmers where buildings and equipment found on farms have been constructed by previous operators with entirely different expectations of price relationships and the most profitable combination of enterprises. Once a farm has long-lived, specialized resources on hand, it must make decisions in light of the production opportunities which are then present.

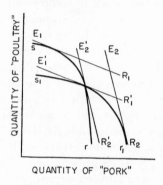

QUANTITY OF "PORK"

Fig. 3. Profit maximization in relation to price ratios and short-run opportunity curves.

This situation should be recognized by production economists and resource administrators whether they are farm operators or national planners. Recommendations that the pattern of production and resource use which maximizes profits (or conforms with other choice indicators) on one farm should be employed on a second farm may be erroneous if the structure of short-run production opportunities is not recognized by the research worker or educational expert in his suggestions to farmers.

If the firm is certain that one combination of enterprises will be maintained once funds are committed to the form of specialized equipment, it should build a single "inflexible" short-run plant. However, expectations may exist that price ratios will not be constant over time but will vary between the 2 extremes suggested by the slopes of E_1R_1 and E_2R_2 in Figure 3. Since the firm cannot have 2 short-run plants, given the limited total outlay suggested by either sr or s_1r_1, what short-run plant is most efficient?

Flexibility

Techniques exist for constructing many different physical short-run plant layouts. The equipment of the short-run plant can be highly specialized and give a low marginal rate of product substitution. It can also be constructed in a manner which allows flexibility and greater substitution rates in shifting from one product to another; the farmer can construct a pen-type rather than a stanchion barn, and if he chooses to shift resources from dairy cows to beef cattle he can do so more readily. Conversely, the pen-type barn is even more flexible than an open cattle shed for expanding dairy production. Dual-purpose cows provide greater flexibility than highly specialized milk or beef cows. Similarly, the construction of poultry houses and brooders can be compromised to allow mobility and space adaptations if possibilities exist to increase pork output at the expense of chickens. Because of biological and engineering characteristics, however, hog houses used for poultry production are not as efficient technically as poultry houses designed specifically for poultry.

Even though the factor-product transformation coefficient for either product is less under a flexible than under an inflexible plant arrangement, the farm may prefer flexibility to the extent that substitution rates are sufficiently greater. The difference between flexible and inflexible production functions and opportunity curves is illustrated in Figures 4 and 5. Curve A in Figure 4 represents the production of either commodity Y_1 or Y_2 when each is produced with resources adapted to the specific commodity. Curve C represents the production function for Y_1 when it is produced with resources adapted to Y_2 and vice versa. (It is a "mongrel" production function of the nature illustrated in Table 1.) Curve B represents the production function for Y_1 or Y_2 when either is produced with resources adaptable to the other product but not most efficient for either. Curve A may represent the production of milk from dairy cows and beef from beef cows, while C represents production of milk from beef cows and beef from milk cows, and B represents production of milk from dual-purpose cows. Alternately, A may represent chickens (pork) produced in poultry (hog) houses, while C represents chickens (pork) produced in hog (poultry) houses, and B represents chickens (hogs) produced in flexible or "dual-purpose" buildings.[5] In addition to a large number of short-run opportunity curves, 9 distinct transformation functions are immediately possible from the 3 pairs of production functions in Figure 4, assuming that ox_2 quantity of resources is available. Of the 4 important for our analysis, 1 is the long-run planning curve already discussed and indicated

---

[5] Our analysis might be given greater refinement by basing the allocative opportunities on 2 production functions of the nature $Y_1 = f_1(X_1, X_2, X_3 \ldots X_n; Z_1, Z_2, Z_3)$ and $Y_2 = f_2(X_1, X_2, X_3 \ldots X_n; Z_1, Z_2, Z_3)$ where resources represented by X are those which do not become specialized in the production of either Y_1 or Y_2 (such as feed and labor which might be used in producing either hogs or poultry). The resources indicated by Z are those which become specialized to a single enterprise upon the commitment of production plans. Z_1 may be buildings and equipment rigidly adapted to poultry production, Z_2 representing those rigidly adapted to hog production and Z_3 representing those adaptable to both enterprise although not technically most efficient for either enterprise. Thus curve A represents production of $Y_1(Y_2)$ with Z in the specialized form of $Z_1(Z_2)$ while the input of $Z_2(Z_1)$ and Z_3 is zero. Curve C would represent output of $Y_1(Y_2)$ with Z in the specialized form of $Z_2(Z_1)$ and zero input of $Z_1(Z_2)$ and Z_3. B would represent Y_1 or Y_2 produced with Z_3, the adaptable form of specialized resources (and a zero input of Z_1 and Z_2).

as TF in Figure 5. Two represent the extreme short-run opportunity lines outlined above, indicated as s_1r_1 and s_2r_2 in Figure 5, and the third is the flexible curve indicated as fl in Figure 5. It is derived from production function B in Figure 4 as a "movement up" B starting at the origin for Y_1, and a "movement down" B starting at ox_2 resources, if the opportunity curve fl is viewed from top to bottom. Opportunity line fl has a greater curvature than the planning curve TF because of the reasons mentioned earlier; a greater amount of Y_1 must be sacrificed for a unit-gain in Y_2

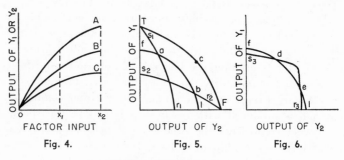

FACTOR INPUT   OUTPUT OF Y_2 OUTPUT OF Y_2

Fig. 4.   Fig. 5.   Fig. 6.

Flexible and inflexible plants.

and vice versa. In the same vein, fl has less slope and lower substitution rates than s_1r_1 or s_2r_2. For any output of Y_1 above that indicated by the intersection of fl and s_1r_1, the latter opportunity curve is more efficient than fl; for a specified output of Y_2, it allows a greater output of Y_1. Below the intersection of fl and s_2r_2, the latter curve again indicates greater efficiency than fl, since for a specified output of Y_1, output of Y_2 is greater. However, for the ab portion of the flexible plant, fl, it is more efficient than either of the inflexible plants, s_1r_1 or s_2r_2. The curve fl is both a long-run planning curve and a short-run opportunity curve. Once resources have been specialized, its slope does not change from *ex ante* appearances.

The flexible opportunity curve also can be compared to an inflexible short-run curve in the manner indicated by Figure 6. Curve s_3r_3 represents the iso-outlay curve when ox_1 resources in Figure 4 are originally committed to specialized equipment in both Y_1 and Y_2 (a point such as c in Figure 5). The upper segment of s_3r_3 represents a "movement up" C for Y_1 in Figure 4, starting at zero, and "down" A for Y_2, starting at ox_1. The lower segment represents parallel "movements" in respect to Y_2. Thus the flexible opportunity curve intersects the inflexible possibility line at points d and e.[6] For product combinations falling above and below the intersection of fl

---

[6] Whether or not the flexible curve intersects the inflexible curve depends on the exact one of the short-run curves under examination. The flexible curve may, for example, intersect one "leg" of the inflexible curve and fall entirely within the other "leg." This is particularly true for short-run curves originating at or tangent to the upper and lower extremes of the long-run planning curve.

and s_3r_3, the flexible plant is now more efficient than the inflexible plant. For combinations falling within the de portion of s_3r_3, the specialized short-run plant is more efficient than the adaptable plant, since more of Y_1 can be obtained for any single output of Y_2 and vice versa.

Maximum Revenue Under Instability

The firm may prefer plant fl to s_3r_3 if it expects prices to vary widely from one period to the next, as is suggested by the slopes of the iso-revenue curves illustrated in Figures 7 and 8. Figure 7 represents a case in which the correlation coefficient between changes in prices of the 2 commodities is $+1.0$; prices change by the same ratio and in the same direction. Figure 8 represents a case in which the correlation coefficient for price changes is -1.0; prices change by equal proportions but in the opposite direction. Under the expectation of price variations of the first nature, the firm

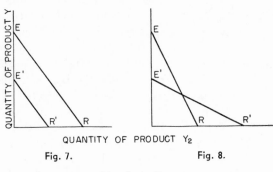

Fig. 7.   Fig. 8.

Price fluctuations.

should select the best adapted inflexible plant such as s_3r_3 in Figure 6. If prices fall, the ratio remains the same and the firm will produce commodities in the previous proportions. Although income will be less than previously, it will still be at a maximum. If the expectation is for a sufficiently low correlation coefficient (with $+1.0$ as the maximum and -1.0 as the minimum) between price movements for the 2 commodities, the firm should select a flexible plant such as fl in Figure 6 in order to gear enterprise combinations to fluctuations in price relationships.

The limits within which the flexible or inflexible plant is to be preferred can be illustrated geometrically in Figure 9. The plants are equally efficient under one set of price relationships: Iso-revenue curves E_1R_1 and E_2R_2 are tangent to both the flexible and inflexible short-run plants. Identical revenues and outlays are thus represented for both plants. At the points where E_1R_1 and E_2R_2 are tangent to s_3r_3 and fl the slopes of the two transformation curves are equal indicating identical marginal rates of product substitution. Accordingly, the return on resources allocated to either product is equal at the points of tangency both (a) between enterprises on a single opportunity curve and (b) between curves s_3r_3 and fl. The firm with given resources could be indifferent in constructing plant s_3r_3 or fl if it were certain that the price ratio would always vary exactly between E_1R_1 and E_2R_2. The flexible plant is most efficient (profitable) for variations in

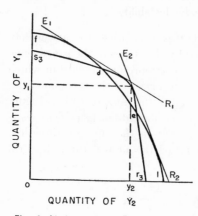

price ratios falling outside the limits indicated by E_1R_1 and E_2R_2. While revenue lines with slopes less than that of E_1R_1 can be tangent to both transformation curves, a single revenue line cannot be tangent simultaneously to both. An iso-revenue curve with a slope of less than that of E_1R_1 and tangent to s_3r_3 must lie lower in the plane and denote less return than one of the same slope but tangent to fl. Similarly, price relationships represented by iso-revenue curves with slopes greater than that of E_2R_2 result in higher total revenue for the flexible than for the inflexible plant.

Fig. 9. Limits in price fluctuations for flexible and inflexible plants.

The same reasoning applies to price variations denoted by iso-revenue curves with slopes falling between those of E_1R_1 and E_2R_2. While all revenue curves with slopes less than E_2R_2 and greater than E_1R_1 can be tangent to both fl and s_3r_3, those tangent to the inflexible opportunity curves are higher and denote a greater total revenue than those tangent to the flexible curve. A firm which expects its output combination to average oy_1 of Y_1 and oy_2 of Y_2 over a period of years, but to vary from the combinations (a) a large Y_1 and a small Y_2 output to (b) a large Y_2 and a small Y_1 output, would still employ the flexible plant. The inflexible plant should be employed for combinations which also average oy_1 and oy_2, but vary within the range de.[7]

Adaptations to agriculture. The concept of enterprise flexibility should be used particularly by engineers in the design of farm buildings. Perhaps there is little economic justification for farm buildings which last through several generations of farm operators in regions where products have close substitution rates and where farms are operated over short periods by

---

[7] An added technical possibility is that the flexible plant is more efficient than the inflexible plant for every possible combination of products. Here the transformation curve for the inflexible plant will always lie within the area outlined by the flexible transformation curve. Regardless of the exact price ratio or the nature of variations in price ratios, the flexible plant will always bring in the greatest revenue from a given or equal outlay. The flexible plant curve will never be entirely above the short-run curve, however, if the boundary line of long-run planning opportunities was originally selected.

tenants. Given a future in which the relative demand for products and the techniques of production are uncertain, farm buildings might best be designed to give maximum flexibility and to last fewer years. Even a system of forward prices which would reduce short-run uncertainty can hardly serve to eliminate resource inefficiency which stems from these long-range unpredictable forces.

Commodity cycles would be accentuated indeed were the majority of farms to operate with perfectly flexible plants (constant marginal rates of substitution); cycles would be short but production of pork, for example, would vary between a zero output in one year and an enormous output in another were all firms to formulate similar price expectations. The higher interyear variation in output for some agricultural products (potatoes, pork, poultry) as compared to others (dairy and fruit) undoubtedly stems from the degree of short-run flexibility and adaptability of resources employed for the particular commodities as well as from reasons ordinarily cited, such as magnitude of price variations and the length of the production period.

Short-Run Opportunities Under Linear and Convex Opportunity Curves

While there are many cases in which the transformation curves for farm products approach linearity, the flexibility considerations outlined above plus the uncertainty elements outlined later provide logic for diversification rather than specialization. Once the "mongrel" opportunity curves and flexible plants are considered, the possibility that commodities produced under increasing returns may be produced in combination also arises. These situations represent modifications of those already outlined and are summarized on the following pages. The relationships are treated in brief fashion since they parallel those already discussed. The graphs and discussion for increasing and constant returns products are discussed side by side to save space. The "corners" on the opportunity lines help explain why price responsiveness is not always accompanied by change.

Production functions. The transformation function for increasing and constant returns products are derived from production functions such as those presented in Figures 10 and 11 respectively. Production function D represents the relation between input and output of products Y_1 or Y_2 when resources are adapted to each individual commodity. (To facilitate the discussion, we assume that the production functions for the competing commodities are identical.) Production function F represents the relationship between resource input and output of Y_1 when it is produced in a plant specialized specifically to commodity Y_2 and vice versa. Curve E represents a compromise and indicates the relationship of input to output of Y_1 or Y_2 when neither plant nor equipment is highly specialized for either enterprise but adaptable to both.

Transformation functions. Long-run opportunity curves C_2N_2 and L_2N_2 in Figures 12 and 13 are derived from production functions indicated as D in Figures 10 and 11. They represent long-run allocative opportunities. The transformation functions C_2N_1 and L_2N_1 are derived from production function D for product Y_1 and F for product Y_2.[8] Again they are extreme

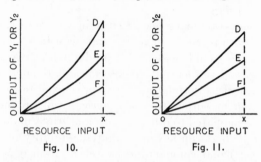

Fig. 10.   Fig. 11.

Flexible and inflexible short-run production functions.

"mongrel" possibility curves, since they represent the allocative opportunities when Y_1 is produced with resources adapted specifically to it while Y_2 is produced with resources adapted to Y_1. Although the output of Y_1 can be as great under C_2N_1 or L_2N_1 as under C_2N_2 or L_2N_2, the output of

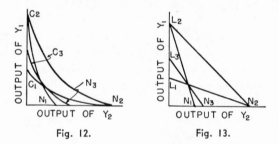

Fig. 12.   Fig. 13.

Planning curves and short-run production possibilities.

Y_2 is necessarily less for any given resource outlay. Another "mongrel" curve is also possible, as is illustrated by C_1N_2 and L_1N_2, derived from production function F for product Y_1 and production function D for Y_2. Its properties are similar to that of C_2N_1 and L_2N_1, except that the state-

---

[8] Substitution of Y_1 and Y_2 for each other actually can be made through 2 general methods in the short-run plant: (1) Non-specialized resources can be shifted to $Y_1(Y_2)$ from $Y_2(Y_1)$ while the added $Y_1(Y_2)$ output is produced in specialized resources adapted to $Y_2(Y_1)$ (without a more intense use of specialized resources adapted to Y_1). (2) Non-specialized resources can be shifted to $Y_1(Y_2)$ while the additional output is produced in specialized resources adapted to $Y_1(Y_2)$ (a more intense use of $Y_1(Y_2)$ specialized resources while $Y_2(Y_1)$ specialized resources are left unemployed). Although both types of adjustments are implied in later discussions, the applications are related in detail only to the first.

ments must be reversed in application to Y_1 and Y_2. The fourth transformation function C_3N_3 or L_3N_3 is derived from the adaptable production function E for both commodities.

Long-run planning curves and short-run possibilities. Curves C_2N_2 and L_2N_2 are long-run planning curves and are of historic importance only once a particular plant has been built. Curves C_2N_1 and L_2N_1 or C_1N_2 and L_1N_2 in Figures 12 and 13 are the extremes of the family of short-run opportunity curves. Aside from these, each short-run curve is composed of 2 segments such as those illustrated in Figures 14 and 15. The segments are "parallel" in the sense that (a) the upper portion results from a "movement up" production function F for Y_1 in Figures 10 and 11 and a "movement down" production function D for Y_2, while (b) the lower segment represents a "movement up" F for Y_2 and a "movement down" D for Y_1. The long-run planning curve again is an "envelope" of the short-run iso-resource curves in the manner suggested by Figure 2. If the firm were

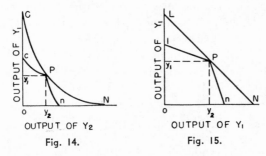

Fig. 14.   Fig. 15.

Relationship of planning curves and short-run production possibilities.

to decide on point P for the long-run planning curves CN or LN, the actual opportunities facing it after construction of the relevant plant are those represented by the short-run curves cn and ln. While the long-run planning curve in Figure 14 for 2 commodities produced under conditions of increasing returns to scale is convex to the origin, the short-run curves include 2 distinct segments and are of concave "general form," although the segments on either side of the tangency point are convex. The short-run "mongrel" curves have corners with the implications discussed earlier.[9] The relationship between the short-run transformation functions and th long-run opportunity curve for products with linear production function

---

[9] If the firm builds a plant (point P in Figure 14) which includes an output oy_1 of Y_1 and oy_2 of Y_2, and then decides to shift output in favor of the former product, it "moves up" production function F (for Y_1 in Figure 10), starting at the origin, and "moves down" production function D for Y_2 (in Figure 10), starting at a point of resource input consistent with the output oy_2 of Y_2 (Figure 14). Again it is true that a different mongrel production function (F in Figure 10) exists for each "starting point" on the long-run curve. However, because of space limitations these possibilities are not presented; the general relationships are the same as those presented.

is shown in Figure 15. While the short-run curves are of concave "general form," the segments on either side of the tangency point are linear. All short-run opportunity curves consistent with a long-run planning curve represent the same cost or resource outlay.

Stability and flexible plants. Given perfect knowledge and lack of price change, the firm with a linear or convex opportunity curve should specialize in a single product. (Select a point on the long-run planning curve C_2N_2 or L_2N_2 in Figures 12 and 13 indicating all of Y_1 or all of Y_2.) The point selected depends on the price relationship or the slope of the iso-revenue curve: (1) If its slope is less than the slope of the long-run planning curve at its intersection with the Y_1 axis, the firm should build a plant to specialize in Y_1. (2) If its slope is greater than the slope of the long-run curve at its intersection of the Y_2 axis, specialization should be in the latter product. If the firm views only the long-run curve C_2N_2 or L_2N_2 in Figure 14 and 15, the slope of the iso-revenue curve must vary between these ratios (1 and 2 above) before it is profitable to shift from one to the other product. This condition does not hold true after the short-run specialized plant has been built, however; price variations must be even greater if shifts are to be made between products. Suppose the firm has originally decided to produce only Y_1 (points L_2 or C_2 in Figures 12 and 13). It is then faced with the short-run opportunity curve C_2N_1 or L_2N_1. (3) Now, before a shift entirely to Y_2 is profitable, the iso-revenue curve must have a slope greater than the slope of L_2N_1 or C_2N_1 at their points of intersection with the Y_2 axis. The variation in price ratios necessary to cause a reversal in product specialization is greater for the short-run opportunity curve than for the long-run planning curve. Stable production in the use of resources is now given if the variation in slope of the iso-revenue curve (changes in price relationships for Y_1 and Y_2) ranges within the extremes of (1) and (3) above. With variations in the slope of the iso-revenue curve always outside of this range, the firm which maximizes profits must adopt a "Balaam's ass" policy and rush from production of Y_1 alone in one period to production of Y_2 alone in another period. After short-run plant C_2N_1 in Figure 12 has been constructed, the "Balaam's ass" action gives greater profits than were the firm to continue producing only Y_1 when price ratios vary sufficiently. However, profits may be less under C_2N_1 and instability than they would be were the firm to adopt a point such as P in Figure 14 and operate a plant with short-run production possibilities such as cn. Thus conditions can exist under which a firm faced with decreasing costs for 2 commodities can maximize profits by diversifying rather than by specializing in a single commodity. If the firm selects a diversified plant such as cn in Figure 14, production will be highly stable. Since the short-run opportunity curve cn has a "corner" or "apex," one combination of 2 commodities, rather than specialization, will be most profitable over a

wide range of price ratios or slopes of the iso-revenue curve.[10] The logic
outlined for products of decreasing costs also applies to products produced
under constant costs.

While a firm might rationally diversify in the sense of adopting a short-
run plant such as *cn* or *ln* in Figures 14 and 15, rather than a highly
specialized plant such as C_2N_1 or L_2N_1 in Figures 12 and 13, it also has
the opportunity to select a flexible plant such as those indicated by C_3N_3
and L_3N_3 in Figures 12 and 13.

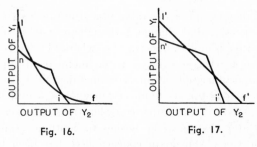

OUTPUT OF Y₂   OUTPUT OF Y₂

Fig. 16.   Fig. 17.

Flexible and inflexible plants.

Flexible plant curves (derived from production functions of the nature
of E for both Y_1 and Y_2 in Figures 10 and 11) are shown as *lf* and *l'f'* in
Figures 16 and 17 for increasing and constant returns commodities respectively. The parallel inflexible curves are indicated as *ni* and *n'i'*. The flexible plant is more efficient than the inflexible plant for some outputs, while
the inflexible plant is more efficient for others.[11] Under changing price
ratios, and if the 2 plants represent equal cost outlays, the flexible plant
is more profitable than the inflexible plant, when price relationships range
outside the limits represented by iso-revenue curves (a) tangent to the
"apex" of the inflexible transformation function and intersecting the Y_1
axis at a point identical with the inflexible opportunity curve and (b)

---

[10] In the example shown in Figure 14 for curve *cn* the firm should produce the same
proportions of Y_1 and Y_2 for all iso-revenue curves having a slope (1) greater than
the slope of *cn* at its point of intersection with the Y_1 axis or (2) less than the slope
of *cn* at its point of intersection with the Y_2 axis.

[11] These are indicated by the points of intersection of the flexible and inflexible
possibility curves. For outputs of Y_1 greater than that indicated by the intersection
of *lf* and the upper segment of *ni* and for outputs of Y_2 greater than that indicated
by the intersection of *lf* and the lower segment of *ni*, the flexible plant is more efficient. The inflexible plant is more efficient for outputs of either commodity falling
within these limits (since it always allows a greater output of the other commodity).
Numerous other relationships are also possible. It is technically possible for the curve
for the flexible plant to fall entirely below or entirely above (not intersect) the curve
for the inflexible plant. The flexible curve may also intersect the inflexible curve at
only 1 point (one extreme of the flexible curve which intersects the Y_1 or Y_2 axis
"inside" and another "outside" the inflexible curve).

tangent with the inflexible curve's apex and intersecting the Y_2 axis at a point identical with the inflexible opportunity curve. The inflexible plant is more efficient if variations in slopes of transformation curves always fall *within* this range. Again, smaller changes in price relationships are necessary to cause complete shifts between products if the flexible rather than the inflexible plant is to be built.

Application in Uncertainty

Product flexibility would be desirable in a situation in which knowledge of the future is perfect and change, although present, is foreseeable. Its greatest application is under uncertainty, where change is expected but cannot be foreseen with certainty at the moment of initial planning. Therefore the important application of product flexibility has been delayed for the chapter on adjustments to uncertainty. Here they become one element in a larger body of flexibility considerations. The reader may turn directly to the later chapter if he wishes to continue immediately with flexibility applications. Our main concern here has been to outline the "technological base" and the "static logic" of product flexibility. This statement has relevance here, however. While investment in flexibility *per se* represents an economic loss to the individual firm and society when uncertainty can be eliminated, it can represent a gain to either when uncertainty is present. Government resource-use programs, like farm organizations, should entail flexibility when the future cannot be foreseen with certainty and is subject to change.

Note on imperfect markets. In the last 3 chapters, a competitive market alone has been considered. Under this condition, which predominates in agriculture, no single farm sells enough of any product to alter the market price. Hence the iso-revenue line is linear. However, some few farms do operate on a large enough scale in a restricted market such that their volume of sales does affect market prices. This situation characterizes dairy farms selling milk or cream in small-town markets. Here the iso-revenue line is no longer straight but is convex in the manner of curve $G'_1F'_1$ or $G'_2F'_2$ in Figure 18. The conditions of profit maximization remain unchanged, however. Maximum returns is still denoted by tangency of the iso-revenue curve (now identified as $G'_2F'_2$) and the production possibility curve GF, where the substitution ratio is inversely equal to the product price ratio.

Product Relationships in Control Programs

We conclude our study of product-product relationships with investigation of alternative outcomes in agricultural control programs. This problem is representative of the broad category of policies which the production economist is called upon to analyze and which he is equipped, both in basic principle and technical information, to answer. While other resource-use policies might also be analyzed at this point, we reserve them for later chapters.

Objectives. Production control programs have been tried in many countries. They were in effect in the United States from 1933 to 1941, and again in 1950. The prime objective of production control programs in agriculture is one of transferring income from non-farm to farm segments of the economy. Obviously, monopoly policy is an inefficient means of redistributing income if total welfare is to be maximized, since (a) it does not give proper recognition to the distribution of income within agriculture, and (b) it conflicts especially with other economic goals, such as resource efficiency.[12] We thus dismiss the above (perhaps paramount) problems of investigation and turn to the immediate purposes of this chapter which include analysis of the conditions under which production control programs of the nature applied to United States agriculture might (1) curtail output and (2) increase revenue of the industry. We employ some simple production economics models to illustrate the basic logic involved in the analysis. These are provided as hypotheses suggestive of needed empirical research and as additions to the existing literature relating to the basic logic of control programs.

Resource withdrawal. Production control programs can have nothing but a minor (and probably a negative) effect in curtailing the quantity of resources employed in agriculture. Control programs of the nature of those applied in the United States are not designed to withdraw resources *en masse*, but rather to withdraw or shift the use of a small portion of resources on millions of farms. Farm operators still have the individual incentive to expand production with the hope that others will not do so. An additional effect is that increased incomes resulting from monopoly control or the direct subsidies allied with it retard the movement of resources out of agriculture, due to the increased certainty of income directly or indirectly attributable to control programs.

Conditions of control. Two general methods of production control have been tried in agriculture. One method is *acreage control,* whereby land is withdrawn from production of basic crops but can be employed for non-controlled crops. Total output from the "allotted acreage" of basic crops is not controlled. The second method is *marketing quotas* wherein total sales are controlled; the farmer is not allowed to sell a quantity of product beyond that representing the "average" or "base" yield on the allotted (controlled) acreage. Resources withdrawn from basic crops under marketing quotas can, however, be used for production of "non-control" crops

---

[12] Neither does it give proper recognition to problems of poverty which exist in non-farm segments of the economy. A large number of commercial farmers have in-comes above those of the low income strata of the non-farm population.

Whether or not production can be reduced (and hence income can actually be increased) through production control *per se* depends on several factors. In order to isolate the relevant elements, we delineate some "pure" cases and discuss the problem from the standpoint of distinct groups of firms (a) producing 2 (or more) primary products (corn and hay) both of which are used in production of a secondary product (livestock products) but only one of which is controlled and (b) producing a single product (wheat or cotton) which moves directly into consumption as food or fiber.

Primary products used in secondary production. One "pure" situation in agriculture is that of primary commodities which are not used directly as food or do not move directly into the market, but instead serve as inputs for production of secondary food commodities.[13] An important example is feed crops; only a small fraction of the total production of corn, oats and barley and other coarse grains is used as human food. The major part of the feed grain output is used as a further input in livestock production. However, hay and pasture crops also serve as substitute feeds for livestock production. Control programs have attempted to reduce output of feed grains but allow the land and other resources so released to be planted to hay and pasture, and hence to be used in livestock production. Since livestock is largely the end product in farming systems of this nature (which includes use of the major portion of the resources in the Cornbelt), control programs can increase farm income only if the reduction from the shift among individual crops results in a reduction in output of livestock products. Whether or not livestock production is decreased from a shift of resources between grain and forage crops depends largely on (1) the initial combination and use of alternative feed crops, (2) the relationships between feed crops as product outputs, and (3) the relationship between feed crops as factor inputs. These conditions have already been discussed in Chapter 8, but are shown again in Figure 18. The curve GF illustrates the production opportunities when grain and forage crops serve in both complementary and competitive capacities. (A relationship of competition alone would suggest modifications which are obvious.) The curves $G'_1F'_1$ and $G'_2F'_2$ indicate the iso-product or substitution relationships for grain and forages as feed crops in livestock output. Curve $G'_2F'_2$ because of its higher location in the plane, represents a greater output than $G'_1F'_1$.

If the acreage control program requires a shift of land from grain to forage, it specifies a movement from left to right along the crop production line GF. If the original crop combination (a single farm or the total of agriculture) included *on* production of grain and *ok* production of hay,

---

[13] The most exhaustive treatment of control aspects of this general nature are to be found in T. W. Schultz, *Agriculture in an Unstable Economy.* New York: McGraw-Hill, 1946, Ch. 8, and E. O. Heady, "Resource and Revenue Relationships in Agricultural Production Control," *Rev. Econ. and Stat.*, Aug., 1951.

the control program will actually bring about an increase in grain production as it moves up and over curve GF. Grain output can be reduced below the original level of on only if forage output is extended beyond ol. However, an extension of forage beyond ol need not reduce livestock output. The logic can be explained thus: With the original outputs on of grain and ok of forage, the total livestock can be that indicated by $G'_1F'_1$. However, the quantity so represented is not a maximum from the land area available, since it is not tangent but intersects GF; substitution rates for feeds in production are not equal to those in livestock consumption. Accordingly, every movement of grain output up GF allows higher and higher outputs of livestock products until the maximum indicated by $G'_2F'_2$ is attained. Livestock output will be less than the maximum attainable if grain production is reduced below on with forage increased beyond ol. However,

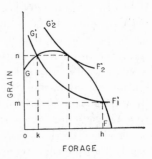

Fig. 18. Crop and livestock control.

livestock output can remain above the pre-control level (as indicated by the livestock iso-product curve $G'_1F'_1$) until grain production is reduced below om and forage production is extended beyond oh. If the original crop production and aggregate livestock ration includes on of grain and ol of forage, the control program becomes effective immediately. In the absence of new techniques and the addition of resources, both grain output and livestock production must decrease as forage output is extended beyond ol through a shift of land from grain to hay.

We have made no attempt to describe what farmers do under control programs. We have simply outlined the possibilities which are open. It is obvious, however, that a control program (which allows or requires shift of resources from forage to grain) may actually increase total livestock output if crops are not already being grown in the optimum proportions or if feeds are not already combined optimally in the livestock ration. The several possibilities here can be summarized as follows where G and F refer to grain and forage crops respectively as product outputs (GF in Figure 18) and G' and F' refer to these same crops as feed inputs ($G'F'$ in Figure 18): a control program which allows (requires) a substitution of forage for grain (as product outputs which in turn are used as feed inputs) (1) will *decrease* livestock output if the ratio $\dfrac{\Delta G}{\Delta F} \Big/ \dfrac{\Delta G'}{\Delta F'}$ is initially equal to $+1.0$ or greater than $+1.0$, (2) will *increase* livestock output if $\dfrac{\Delta G}{\Delta F} \Big/ \dfrac{\Delta G'}{\Delta F'}$ is initially less than 1.0 (or if it is negative). Under the latter conditions, livestock output will continue to increase until the ratio becomes both positive and greater than 1.0.

Thus as long as crop production is in the complementary range livestock output can be increased especially by shifting land from grain to forage production; although fewer acres are planted to grain, both more of grain and forage can be produced because of the complementary relationship between the 2 crops. Agronomists extend the hypothesis that farmers of the Cornbelt generally are producing combinations which fall in the competitive range. There is important reason to believe that this might especially be true on tenant-operated farms. The complementary effect of forage crops on grain crops ordinarily comes throughout a rotation of 3 to 5 years, since grain yields are increased (in the short-run aside from erosion considerations) by the nitrogen and improved soil tilth provided by legumes and grasses. Forages and grains are almost entirely competitive within a single year (the more one is produced, the less the other can be produced). Short-run and year-to-year planning therefore is more nearly the rule than the exception on tenant-operated farms. In contrast to its direct goals, a control program which forces a shift of land from grain to forage crops is indeed likely to increase rather than decrease grain production in the long-run on tenant-operated farms. Our surveys have indicated that in the Iowa farming area in which nearly one-half the farms are tenant-operated, 79 per cent of the land in grain has been planted continuously to grain for 5 or more years. Many agronomists would suggest that fewer acres of grain and more of forage would increase total grain production, particularly on land which has been in grain continuously for 5 or more years. The logic presented is that which should be examined and tested empirically before control is initiated.

Single product firms. The farm firms which produce a single product are few in number. However, the adjustment possibilities which face a farm producing a single crop are also open to a firm which produces several crops of which only one is subject to control regulation. Figures 19 and 20, which employ the factor-factor relationship alone, illustrate both the logic implicit in this type of acreage control and the possible types of adjustments which the farmer can make to control. Figure 19 illustrates the case in which production control would be effectively achieved through acreage control. It is the case in which land and other resources are limitational and must be combined in fixed proportions. This situation is illustrated by the nature of the iso-product contours I_1P_1 and I_2P_2. If, as applied to Figure 19, the original output of the product is indicated by I_1P_1 and includes use of ol_2 and on of non-land resources, a reduction from ol_2 to ol_1 in land planted to the crop will reduce output to the level indicated by contour I_2P_2. Even if non-land inputs remain at on the reduction is still effected because of the fixed coefficients. The extent to which a 10 per cent reduction in acreage will decrease output depends, under this situation, on the nature of returns to scale. With constant returns to scale or a production elasticity of 1.0, output would also be decreased by 10 per cent; with decreasing returns, output would be decreased by less than 10 per cent.

More accurately, though, labor and capital resources serve as substitutes for land in agricultural production. This is the situation illustrated in Figure 20. For example, as line IP illustrates, $3N$ units of product might be produced with (a) ok_2 units of land and oc_2 units of labor and capital, (b) ok_1 units of land and oc_3 units of labor and capital, or (c) any other combination consistent with the equal-product curve IP. Production control (for a single-product firm) might suppose that given the initial factor inputs of ok_2 land and oc_2 capital and labor, withdrawal of k_1k_2 units of land from production would result in withdrawal of c_1c_2 units of non-land resources from production. Output would then decrease (a) in the same proportions (as the decrease in factor inputs) if the production function were linear, (b) by greater proportions if the elasticity of production were greater than 1.0, and (c) by smaller proportions if the elasticity were less than 1.0. Empirical evidence suggests that decreasing returns hold true in agriculture. However, even if the production function were linear, the possibility that input of labor and capital would be reduced by the same proportions as land is very remote.

The difference in outcome under the several possibilities open is illustrated in Figure 20. If the reduction in crop acreage by k_1k_2 were to result in a proportional reduction of labor and capital equal to c_1c_2, output would

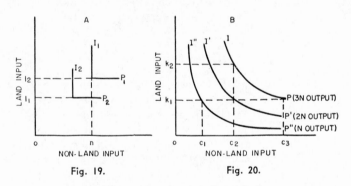

Fig. 19.   Fig. 20.

Production control and single products.

drop from $3N$ (iso-product curve IP) to N (curve $I''P''$). However, if capital and labor inputs remain at the original level of oc_2, output will drop to only $2N$ (curve $I'P'$). If farm firms were to extend input of non-land resources to oc_3, output would remain at the level of $3N$. Agriculture is notable as an industry of limited capital. The amount of capital used by individual farmers is almost universally at a level short of that necessary to equate the marginal value productivity of borrowed funds with market interest rates. The most probable adjustment for a single-product farm firm (with no alternative crops) is that while the input of land is reduced, the total input of labor and capital may remain near previous levels (a more intensive cultivation of land remaining in production).

If all production control were to take place within the framework of single-product firms and without technical advance and above-normal weather, it appears a reasonable hypothesis that acreage restrictions would result in a reduced output of crops. The situation of single-product firms is perhaps best illustrated by highly specialized wheat farms where returns from grazing are low relatively and a shift from continuous wheat to a summer fallow wheat-cropping system is more remunerative than a shift to other grain crops for which acreage is not controlled. Even here it is possible for new techniques to be adopted and for any decrease in output to be offset by improved farming practices. Another possibility is that production control may cause farmers to discard irrational resource combinations (see earlier discussions). For example, when wheat acreage control was first initiated, many great-plains farmers shifted their idle acres to summer fallow. The result, as would have been the case under a fallow farming system even in the absence of acreage control, was the same or more wheat from fewer acres.

Other situations. One other "pure" case of control could also be analyzed. This is the case of 2 market commodities produced in combination where only 1 is controlled. The outcome here is implicit, however, in the analysis of control in Chapter 22. Problems of market quotas and income effects are treated in detail elsewhere.[14]

Selected References

Cady, G. J., "An Approach to the Theory of Multiple Products," *Southern Econ. Jour.*, Jan., 1950.

Heady, Earl O., "Resource and Revenue Relationships in Control Programs," *Rev. Econ. Stud.*, Aug., 1951.

———, "Uncertainty in Price Relationships and Resource Allocation in the Short-run," *Jour. of Farm Econ.*, May, 1950.

Samuelson, P. A., *Foundations of Economic Analysis.* Cambridge: Harvard University Press, 1947, pp. 230-236.

Schultz, T. W., *Agriculture in an Unstable Economy.* New York: McGraw-Hill, 1946, Ch. 8.

---

[14] See E. O. Heady, *ibid.*

10

Resource Classification and Other Problems in Aggregation

Although science has many other characteristics, one universal aspect is the classification of phenomena. Physical science in agriculture can even be looked upon as an activity relating to the isolation and classification of production functions. Classification in a purely statistical context involves drawing samples from different populations (a species of animals, a complete population of farms, and so forth) and testing homogeneity in a probability sense. Not all effort in classification is research in the sense of experimentation and inferences based on samples of a population, however. The process of classification outlined in this chapter involves a procedure somewhat similar in the sense that an attempt is made to place factors or products in homogeneous classes.

Purpose of Resource and Product Classification

Classification of resources and products (or producing units) in agriculture evidently has great importance; if it did not, fewer persons would engage in the activity. The mere counting and cataloguing of phenomena, however, is not in itself useful. Classification is important only insofar as it is directed toward some useful objective. From a production economics standpoint, classification is important if it (1) aids resource administrators, whether farm operators or national planners, in making decisions; (2) aids consumers in reflecting choices to producers; (3) as a corollary of (1) and (2), provides information on the supply of resources and products; and (4) increases the accuracy with which farm-directed recommendations can be made. Given these objectives, the principles which are important in classification are discussed on the following pages. Previous chapters have already touched upon problems of factor classification. These have involved distinction between (1) resources which embody flow and stock services; (2) resources embodying services which are transferred into product in one or several periods; (3) fixed resources and variable resources; (4) complementary, competitive, or supplementary products and

299

factors; and others. These distinctions are part of the general problem of classification in agriculture, but will not be treated again in greater detail; we emphasize other problems of factor and product classification in this chapter and attempt to set forth the fundamentals from the standpoint of production economics.

Basis for Classification

Classification activity *per se* can include either 1 of 2 somewhat distinct processes. One process is *stratification*. Here an attempt is made to break an aggregate population into homogeneous components: the farms of a state may be classified into groups by type of commodities produced; soils may be stratified on the basis of physical properties; grains may be classified or graded in terms of the rate at which they can be transformed into livestock. The criterion by which homogeneity is determined differs, depending on the purposes of classification. The other process is *aggregation*. Here an attempt is made to transform the units from each stratum or segment of the composite population into a single stock or inventory of factors, products, or producing units. The process includes weighting each distinct component in a manner that will result in a single composite stock or population.

Common attempts at stratification by agriculturists include land classification, grades and standards for grains and hays, livestock judging (the entire population at hand, even if it consists of only 4 steers, is classified), and classification of farms by size and systems of farming. The annual feed budget and supply prepared by the Bureau of Agricultural Economics represents an attempt to classify and aggregate the various feed crops as a basis for outlook information to individual farmers and national planners. Classification, aside from scientific inference, is perhaps a problem in technology more than a problem in economics. Yet, since it does have production economic implication, criteria of classification are outlined below. The 2 areas of stratification claiming the attention of the greatest numbers of agriculturists are livestock judging and land classification. Here an animal or an acre of land is classified as a technical or producing unit through which other resources are to be processed.

Livestock classification. Livestock classification generally is termed "judging." While fat stock may be judged from the product standpoint (from a class of Angus steers, prediction may be made as to which will grade "good," "choice," or "prime," or will "fall highest" in the grade), the economic problem is actually one of classifying a live steer as a resource and estimating the rate and manner in which it will transform into a dressed product. The important aspect of judging for breeding and growing stock, as is the case for classification of other resources as technical units, is the prediction of the physical production function. Faced with 4 animals, the classifier or judge of animals should view them in the light of Figure 1 if the results are to be of value to the farm entrepreneur. Animals with production functions I and IV should be placed at the top and bottom of the class respectively. In other words, the judge should attempt to picture or predict the product forthcoming from each animal as feed, labor, or other resource inputs are varied (predict the elasticity of production or marginal productivity of the variable resource). The production function concept for classifying animals and other resources as technical or producing units is useful where the product is homogeneous. The problem here is not very difficult for land, or for dairy cows where the product can be converted to some common basis, such as 4 per cent fat-corrected milk. It is more difficult for cattle, where the quality of the product as well as the input-output relationship can vary between animals. With a product homogeneous in respect to location as well as grade, classification can be entirely in physical terms: since both the resource inputs and the output are homogeneous, the technical unit with the more elastic production function will also result in the greatest return. Where the products are not homogeneous, classification, if it is to be useful in decision-making, must be more nearly in terms of value of product rather than in physical product.

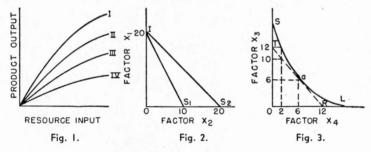

Fig. 1. Fig. 2. Fig. 3.

Basis for factor classification.

Animal classification which focuses on national livestock shows is of value to the majority of the nation's farmers only if the product which is related to input for the show ring is the same as the product which farmers sell in the market, or if the 2 are positively and highly correlated. There is indication that show-ring classification or judging is not in terms of the input-output relationship which is of greatest economic concern to farmers. The product viewed is often the "ribbon-winning" ability rather than the commercial farm product. Were one factor alone to serve as the criterion for classification of livestock, it should be feed. Not only are other factors highly complementary with feed, but also, for the major meat-producing animals, feed costs constitute on the "average" 70-85 per cent of total costs. Use of feed productivity as an index of classification is somewhat less satisfactory for hens and dairy cows, where labor is relatively more important as an input.

Capacity and efficiency of technical units. Early agricultural production economists emphasized capacity and efficiency characteristics of factors as technical units. These concepts are important particularly for livestock classification or judging. Capacity refers to the quantity of variable resources which a fixed factor (technical unit) might absorb without causing the marginal product to become zero or negative. An acre of land in the Cornbelt thus has a greater capacity than an acre of soil in the Great Plains; a farm manager who can operate up to 1,000 acres and continue to increase the product has greater capacity than one who can operate only 500 acres. When capacity refers to physical ability of a technical unit to absorb variable factors without causing the marginal product to drop to zero, efficiency is taken to mean the net return per technical unit. The 2 terms are not necessarily identical. A large dairy cow may be able to consume greater quantities of feed, while a small dairy cow may return larger profit. Under such circumstances, the elasticity of the production function must be higher for small feed inputs with the small dairy cow, but lower for large feed inputs with the large cow. The small cow may then have greater efficiency but a smaller capacity. These indices again depend on the nature of the production function. A unit of factor with high efficiency (curve *E* in Figure 4) and low capacity has an input-output curve with a steep slope in the beginning input ranges but a small or negative slope in large ranges. One with low efficiency and high capacity (curve *C* in Figure 4) is represented by a smaller elasticity in the beginning ranges but continues at a greater positive slope in later ranges of input. Under a narrow product/factor price ratio, the factor unit with the greatest capacity need not have the greatest efficiency. Under a wide product/factor price ratio, the greatest capacity and greatest efficiency may be found in the same unit. Again the production function itself, rather than the capacity and efficiency concepts *per se*, becomes the basis for classifying resources. Aside from the elasticity and transformation ratio characteristics outlined above, the capacity and efficiency concepts have no particular implications in production. They should be employed, however, by the classifier or judge of livestock; one animal may be economically more efficient than another at one price level, while the position may be reversed for a high price level.

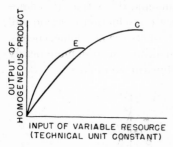

Fig. 4. Capacity and efficiency.

Land classification. As is true for other factors, many characteristics of land may be used as the basis for classification. Soils are classified by agronomists in terms of origin, topography, mineral content or other physical characteristics. Land also is classified on the basis of historic (the types and sizes of farms that have existed over time), geographic (amounts and locations of various crops at a given point in time), and institutional (tenure form of ownership, tax delinquency, mortgage foreclosure) criteria. From the standpoint of production economics and decision-making, however, the important basis of classification is the production functions for individual products and the production possibilities for alternative crops. The relative advantage of one crop or use as compared to another always depends on the production function for the individual uses. (See the explanation of transformation functions in Chapter 7.) The production function is also of great importance in explaining other, though not all, phenomena (such as type of farming, mortgage foreclosure, and so forth) which sometimes serve as the basis for classification. For purposes of resource administration or management, all soils which have or will maintain the same production function over the relevant time period, whether they are of glacial or loessal origin, can be placed in a single class. Although highly related, knowledge that 2 soils have identical production functions is of greater value to decision-making than knowledge of the fact that they differ in respect to time or manner of origin. Classification by institutional and geographic characteristics is not land classification *per se*. Preparation of maps by such institutional characteristics as tax delinquency or form of ownership bears little or only indirect relationship to land as a resource or to the production possibilities of land. A map which shows the geographic distribution of crops, while termed a "classification of land by uses," represents land-use classification no more than it represents labor-use capital-use classification; all 3 factors are responsible for the products which exist and can be enumerated for a particular geographic area at one point in time. While classification by institutional characteristics is important in land economics, classification in terms of soil characteristics is more important for analyses in farm management and production economics. Land classification also has been grouped under the following five types.[1]

Type I. Classification in terms of inherent characteristics. This classification system employed by soil scientists deals directly with the soil types, the slopes, the mineral content, and surface and sub-surface features of land. The end results are maps which display the distribution of land in terms of the qualities given it by nature. It will undoubtedly continue to serve as the foundation for land classification and, if integrated with the concepts of farm management and production economics, can best provide the basis for determining the efficiency in the use of capital, labor, and management resources as well as land.

Type II. Classification in terms of present use. This is the procedure indicated above as geographic or historic, and actually involves classification

---

[1] *Land Classification in the United States.* Washington: National Resources Planning Board, 1941.

of products forthcoming from all resources rather than from land alone.

Type III. Classification in terms of use capabilities. This classification procedure has been widely used by the Soil Conservation Service. It is based on slope and productivity characteristics. The system does not recommend any particular use but more nearly suggests the limits in use.

Type IV. Classification in terms of recommended use. Under this system of classification, widely used by the Tennessee Valley Authority and the Soil Conservation Service, land is assigned a recommended use such as rotation, permanent forage, or forestry. The assumption implicit here is that economic appraisal has been made of all production possibilities and the optimum opportunity has been selected. This often is far from the case.

Type V. Classification in terms of program effectuation. This classification procedure uses maps which serve as management aids in showing when and how each alternative follows IV above and is to be carried out.

From the standpoint of physical considerations, the scientist might well place all lands which substitute at a constant and 1:1 ratio in a single class. (Substitution is obviously of this nature if the production functions are identical.) The classification problem may differ from that of livestock, however, since the product of all land is not homogeneous in respect to location, and product price differentials become important. The value production function, rather than the physical production function, is then important from the standpoint of the decisions. Classification in terms of value productivity becomes complex where the prices for both factor inputs, apart from land and commodities, differ between land areas.

Specific Problem in Soil Classification and Supply

While land can be classified purely from the standpoint of geological, physical, economic and institutional characteristics, the important problems of land classification fall largely in the direction of production economics considerations. Two of the most complex problems of land as a factor of production are those which stem from time. For the individual farmer, time involves purchase of land as a factor of production where decisions extend into an unknown and uncertain future. Land classification can do little to lessen the errors associated with these time decisions; they grow in the main out of price changes which are exogenous to the individual farm and the agricultural economy. Soil classification can serve as a decision-making aid, however, in indicating the comparative productivity of different soils. As Kellogg[2] points out, study and classification of "land" has little content, since an aggregate of heterogeneous resources are included in this amalgam resource. Soil has precise meaning as a factor of production; land does not.

---

[2] "Soil and Land Classification," *Jour. Farm Econ.*, Vol. 33.

The supply of soil. The second problem which especially relates soil to time is one of the over-all supply of land relative to the national or world population. Populations of the future determine the "need" or "demand" for land. Improved soil classification can do little to help predict future populations; this is one of the uncertainties which spring from time. Yet soil classification is important in the sense of predicting the supply or stock of this particular resource available for future populations.

Land supply is a subject which has been given little concreteness and meaning. It is true that we know that land employed in United States agriculture totals nearly 1,200 million acres, that cropland totals nearly 350 million acres, and that 1,200 million acres can be classified as arid. Similarly, the approximate acreage of Clarion-Webster silt loams in Iowa, Davidson clay loam in Georgia, Denton Stony clay loam in Oklahoma, and Ochlochonee fine sandy loam in Alabama can be estimated. While we may add these many specific soil types together into an aggregate of "so many" million acres of land, the total number of acres itself has very little meaning. Needed in soil classification is a method whereby the various soils can be added together to give some operational notion of the quantity of this resource available for present and future populations. The problem is one of resources substitution, and is given a conceptional framework in a later section. Enough is known, for example, about the rate of substitution of one carbohydrate feed for another so that an indication of the annual supply of this resource is possible. In other words, soil classification somehow should be extended beyond its present physical basis to indicate the rate at which an acre of one soil substitutes for another. This system of classification, as a means of differentiation between types, would be useful to farmers as entrepreneurs making investment decisions. A very great use would be, however, in establishing the supply of soil resources in a manner more meaningful than a total acreage figure. Classification in the physical terms of soil scientists rather than description in terms of historic and institutional characteristics can best provide this basis for aggregation.

Resource productivity. The concepts outlined above are also important in discussions of soil productivity.[3] If curve C in Figure 4 is taken to represent the input-output curve for Muscatine soils in Illinois, while E represents Cecil soils in North Carolina, can we say that the productivity of the former is greater than the latter? In a purely physical context, we can say that C has greater physical capacity to absorb fertilizer or other inputs and that yield per acre can be extended beyond that for E. The economic productivity is higher for E than for C, however, when the factor/product price ratio is low. When the price ratio is high, Muscatine soil has greater

---

[3] An excellent discussion of productivity concepts can be found in J. D. Black, *et al.*, *Farm Management*. New York: Macmillan, 1947, pp. 407-419. While the concepts outlined there differ somewhat from those discussed above, they have the same general meaning.

economic productivity than Cecil soil. Our use of the terms efficiency and productivity is thus couched in economic import. They allow efficiency and productivity to vary as price ratios change. The term productivity, when used with a purely physical content, has a meaning more or less identical with capacity as outlined above.

Aggregation of Resource Substitutes

Classification of land or judging of animals refers to the productivity of other resources as units of the specific factor (an acre of land or a cow) are held constant. A problem of a somewhat different kind is involved in the classification or aggregation of resources which serve as substitutes within the technical or producing unit. From the standpoint of supply, is it possible to throw all farm workers into a single aggregate of man-years? Is it strictly correct to aggregate corn, oats, prairie hay, alfalfa, beet pulp, and all other feeds into a single national feed supply expressed as feed units? The same question arises for a soil conservation planner who prepares farm feed budgets under different cropping systems and compares total feed unit production under the 2 alternatives. What problems arise when grains and forages are aggregated into a total stock of digestible nutrient? Is it necessarily true that a rotation which produces 6,000 T.D.N.'s will allow a greater output of livestock product than one which results in 5,000 T.D.N.'s? Or at the level of national resource management, how useful is knowledge that the United States possesses an aggregate of 1,060 million acres of farm land of miscellaneous types and quality? Resources can be aggregated in a simple and useful manner only if they substitute at constant rates in the production of each possible product. In Figure 2, for example, iso-product line IS_2 can be taken to indicate the combinations of factors X_1 and X_2 which allow a given output of a homogeneous product. The two factors can be clearly aggregated into a single supply. Since they substitute at a 1:1 rate (the iso-product line has a 45° slope), they are homogeneous and can be classified as a single resource from the standpoint of either factor supply or entrepreneurial decisions. Aggregation does not require that factors substitute at a 1:1 rate, however; as long as the substitution ratio is constant, 2 factors can be added together and the aggregate stock is then a meaningful concept. For iso-line IS_1 in Figure 2, factors X_1 and X_2 substitute at constant marginal rate of $\Delta X_1 / \Delta X_2 = 2/1$ or 2.0. If 200 units of factor X_1 and 100 units of factor X_2 are available, the aggregate stock of resources is equivalent to 200 units of factor X_2 or 400 units of X_1. Similarly, individual stocks of 100 units of X_1 and 200 units of X_2 are equivalent to a composite stock of 500 units of X_1 or 250 units of X_2. Regardless of the proportions, the aggregate stock, expressed either as units of X_1 or X_2 or as a common factor $\overline{X}$, always has exact meaning. Knowledge that the substitution rate of X_1 for X_2 is constant at 2.0 is sufficient information for the entrepreneur; given the price ratio, he can determine whether to use X_1 or X_2. It also provides sufficient information of the factor supply for national planners. Classification of X_1 and X_2 into resource categories at constant conversion rates is thus justifiable. Resource aggregation is effective and simple in the case of two grades of feed which substitute at constant rates. Number 1 corn and number 2 corn fall in this category as do certain other pairs of carbohydrate or protein feeds.

Factors which substitute at diminishing rates cannot be aggregated simply by converting them to a common index at constant rates in the manner of T.D.N.'s or feed units. The difficulty can be illustrated by Figure 3 where the iso-product curve SL indicates diminishing rates of substitution for factors X_3 and X_4. Suppose that SL represents the "average" quantity of commodity produced over time and that 6 units of X_3 and 6 units of X_4 represent the "average" proportions in which the 2 factors have been combined. The resource classifier then attempts to convert the 2 factors into a "common resource" called Z. In order to accomplish this transformation both X_3 and X_4 might be given the constant weight of 1.0 (1 unit of either X_3 or X_4 equals 1 unit of Z). When this procedure of aggregation is used, the several combinations including (a) 12 units of X_3 and none of X_4, (b) 12 units of X_4 and none of X_3, (c) 10 units of X_3 and 2 of X_4, or (d) 6 units of X_3 and 6 units of X_4 all give a 12-unit stock of Z. The dotted line TR indicates all of the combinations of X_3 and X_4 which will give an aggregate stock of Z equal to 12 under this system of classification. The fallacy of the classification procedure is obvious. "Twelve units" of Z made up of 10 units of X_3 and 2 units of X_4 is not identical to 12 units of Z made up of 6 units of each particular factor. The 10-2 combination allows only a smaller output. While any combination of X_3 and X_4 indicated by the conversion line TR suggests a composite "X" stock of 12 units of Z, the many combinations of X_3 and X_4 on TR specify different outputs of product. As the proportion of Z represented by either X_3 or X_4 increases, the product which can be produced from the 12-unit stock of Z becomes smaller and smaller. (Each successive point toward the axes and above or below point a on TR must be intersected by iso-product curves which fall lower in the plane and indicate smaller products.) The 12-unit stock of Z which has been aggregated from X_3 and X_4 at a constant conversion rate does not serve as a homogeneous resource when it is composed of different proportions of the 2 factors because they do not substitute at constant rates.

Where 2 feeds such as corn and hay or protein and corn substitute at diminishing rates, the fallacy of the farm conservation plan which aggregates all feeds into a single stock of feed units based on total digestible nutrients is apparent. The T.D.N. measure is of limited value when used by soil conservation planners or other persons in comparing the potential productivity of rations or feed stocks forthcoming from different rotations. This statement also applies to national feed budgets when the proportions of grains and hay vary considerably between years. Neither can the supply of agricultural labor or the stock of soil be aggregated for all uses by giving different but constant weights to every individual unit if substitution of laborers is at diminishing rates.

Curve SL in Figure 3 provides the basis for aggregating factors which substitute at decreasing rates. To provide the basis for reliable predictions, classifying procedure must be this: (1) The particular use to be made of the resources must be determined; grain and hay substitute for each other at different rates when employed in milk as compared to pork or beef production. As Professor Chamberlin has pointed out, bricklayers and carpenters may not be interchangeable in house construction but they can become homogeneous before an army drill sergeant. (2) The rate of weighting or conversion must vary as the proportions of the resources vary. Since SL represents all of the combinations of X_3 and X_4 which will produce a given amount of a homogeneous commodity, it specifies the number of units of either factor required to replace 1 unit of the other factor and defines the necessary rate of conversions for the particular use. Starting from the combination indicated at point a, the "constant rate method" says that 10 units of X_3 and 2 of X_4 are equal to 6 of X_3 and 6 of X_4. A system of aggregation based on curve SL indicates, however, that 12 units of X_3 and 2 of X_4 must be used to equal the 6-6 combination. In a practical sense, different weights must be applied to individual factors as makeup of the total stock varies.

Classification of complementary resources. When 2 factors are complementary to the extent that they must be used in fixed proportions, they represent, for all practical purposes, a single amalgam factor, and there is little gain in dividing them into separate categories. Water is made up of both hydrogen and oxygen. For purposes of production, however, water alone needs to be considered. There is no basis or reason for considering either of the particular elements in isolation.

Other Stratification Classification Problems

Many other problems in aggregation or stratification are of concern to production economists. One of these is the classification of farms by type of farm or farming system. Knowledge of production situations or adjustment possibilities which face individual types and sizes of farms are important for farm recommendations or national policies which touch upon resource use. Agricultural policies directed at farms in the aggregate without regard to type, size, or income level are likely to be based on conflicting objectives and terminate with confounded results. Classification of producing units for these purposes would be simple if all farms specialized in a single commodity. Since the production possibilities before the farm firm and the adjustments which it makes to price changes are ones of degree, great refinement cannot be given to farm type classifications when several closely competing products can be produced. Historically, farm classifications of this type have been published as studies in "type of farming areas." The type-of-farming-study is descriptive or historic in the sense that it shows product combinations at one point in time (one point on the production possibility curve). The fundamental task is one of isolating the full production possibilities which face the firm in order that adjustment or policy recommendations can be made as prices change or an entirely new economic environment arises. The product-product relationships of Chapter 7 thus provide models or analytical guides for type of farming classifications. In this vein, problems of farm-size and farm-type classification become highly related. Aside from purely descriptive and income distribution aspects of size classification, the important objective of size-type classification should be one of determining how production possibilities and commodity substitution ratios differ between farms of different sizes. The relevant concept here is one of isoclines and is discussed in Chapter 7.

Stratification in Research

Classification or stratification problems are also important in research. They have importance here not in the sense of substitution ratios to be compared with price ratios but in terms of the accuracy with which the inferences of the research worker provides guidance for the resource administrator. As in other lines of agricultural research, investigations in production economics often are based on cross-sectional samples. Time series samples or observations are also employed, and both procedures are sometimes used together. The cross-sectional approach, which has had greatest application, includes estimation of production and efficiency relationships from a sample of farms at a given point in time. Under a cross-sectional study, returns to scale, for example, may be investigated by relating income to different sizes of farms. The attempt is to predict the within or intra-farm relationships (the relationship of returns to scale within a single farm if it were to vary resource inputs over a wide range from observations selected from different farms, an interfarm sample). Under a time series sample, observations would be obtained from a single farm as it changed resources inputs over time. While the sample would include interyear observations, it is of an intra-farm nature alone. The same procedures are followed in physical sciences. Animal husbandrymen attempt to predict the outcome for a hog fed different proportions of corn and protein. Yet he uses "between hog" observations to predict the outcome for a single hog. The agronomist attempts to predict yields from a single acre of land devoted to different rotations of cropping practices.

While he uses interunit observations or samples to predict the outcome for a single acre the agronomist sometimes combines cross-sectional and time-series samples in rotation experiments. Physical scientists ordinarily exercise extreme care in attaining homogeneity of their cross-sectional sample. The animal nutritionist may select litter mates for a protein ration study, while the agronomist may employ small plots of soil which are of the same physical characteristics and have had identical management treatment in the past. A question arises in connection with these homogeneous and highly selective samples, however. To what population does the resulting inference apply? Generally, the results are applied, indirectly if not directly, to an entire species of animals or an entire soil area. If this is to be done, the physical scientist should either increase the number of strata which he investigates or widen the representation of his sample.

At the other extreme the production economist needs to copy the classification procedures of the physical scientist and emphasize stratification and homogeneity in cross-sectional samples to an extent that it enables him to isolate structural relationships in reality. Data for estimation of production or economic relationships have been drawn largely from 3 sources: (a) the complete population of a region, state, or the nation based on census or other secondary data; (b) the complete sub-populations or strata of an aggregate population, based on farm records or block samples; and (c) random samples drawn from a population. While inferences based on any of these sources of data are suited for "census type" or "nose counting" studies in which estimation is of means, standard deviations, frequency distributions, or other statistics for an aggregate population, they seldom provide data needed for estimating production functions or resource-income relationships for particular strata or segments of the overall population.

It is indeed difficult to predict the type of relationship which is traced out in studies based on aggregate samples or census and other secondary data. A large number of investigations based on farm samples have focused on the effect of alternative scales of operation and resource and product combinations on income. These studies often imply increasing returns to scale without limit in agriculture and that complete substitution of factors or products is economic. The "apparent" relationships are inherent in the stratification and sampling procedures wherein it is found that net income, labor income, or other measure of economic profit increases as a continuum and are of the "hybrid" or "mongrel" type illustrated below. Suppose the inferences or recommendations forthcoming from a farm sample, even though they are in terms of income, depend on the nature of the production function. It is known that the production function or input-output curve for a specific resource as fertilizer or seed applied to land follows, over the major portion, the nature of curve A in Figure 5. Data from empirical studies of the type suggested above imply the curve B. Such distorted findings relative to resource productivity may be explained by several factors. One is the possibility that farms with high crop yields also are using large amounts of resources. Another, one obviously expected, is that better farmers (greater management inputs) are on the high-yielding crop land and part of the return from other practices or resources is attributed to crop resources or services. However, another important classification concept is involved. It is the notion that a distinct input-output curve exists for each quality of resource. That "low," "medium," and "high" crop yields will be found on sample farms with land of low, medium and high productivity is almost certain. Figure 6 illustrates the expected outcome when this occurs. Curves A, B, and C represent the assumed production function (yield of crop for varying fertilizer levels, and so forth) on 3 soil types of

"low," "medium," and "high" productivity respectively. The procedure of sorting farms into 3 groups, depending on their crop yields, and computing the mean of each group has the effect of isolating the 3 points a, b, and c on the different production functions. It gives the "apparent" input-output curve (or corresponding profit curve) of abc, which is not a distinct production function, but instead connects 3 points on separate curves. It

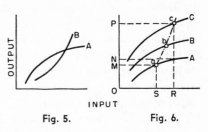

Fig. 5.   Fig. 6.

Effect of sample stratification.

implies that if farmers on soil of "low" productivity increase inputs from OS to OR they traverse curve abc, and yields (or profits) will increase from OM to OP. However, since soil of "low" productivity has the true production function A, an input of OR gives a yield not of OP but only of ON. Extension of inputs with the hope of getting yields of OP may result in less than maximum profits. The procedure used not only distorts the nature of the relationship but overestimates resource productivity even if the apparent curve abc is a straight line or increases at a decreasing rate. This is evidenced in the example since the slope of the "apparent" production function is greater than the slope of any other curve. The "apparent" production function overestimates the average and marginal productivity of resources, and farmer or society decisions based on it will also be in error. Even the farmer on the most productive land would not realize an increase in output per unit of input as great as is implied by the "apparent" curve.

While perhaps the only basis possible for estimates of resource productivity on an overall or regional basis, estimates of marginal productivities based on census or other aggregative data also involve similar distortions of the relationships studied. In some cases the inferences based on such aggregate data are refined enough for the uses to be made of the data. However, their limitations should be recognized and individual or policy recommendations should be so conditioned. There is, of course, opportunity to improve inferences dealing with structural relationships through proper stratification or classification of the sample. The production economist and the technical scientist need to compromise their approaches in the sense that the former provides estimates for homogeneous strata of the population while the latter provides estimates for larger populations which are not based on infinitely small samples or sub-populations.

Micro and Macro Relationships

A further basis for classification in production economics is that of micro and macro relationships. These concepts, while partly inherent in the discussion of aggregation and stratification on previous pages, deserve further elaboration. *Microeconomics* deals with relationships of individual quantities or units such as those for a distinct cow, farm, household, market, or producing area. *Macroeconomics* deals with relationships of mass phenomena or composite quantities and is not concerned with individual producing units, single factors, or markets in a particular area but with broad aggregates of production, income, and other economic quantities. Distinction between micro and macro relationships is important for all individuals concerned with production adjustments and prediction. The individual farm entrepreneur must appraise the prospective action of masses of other farmers if he is to anticipate correctly the use of resources which will maximize future returns. The extension specialist and the research analyst, both of whom are concerned with prediction, also must recognize the differences between the 2 classifications of adjustments if they are to safeguard against erroneous inferences. However, the difference between micro and macro relationships is only one of degree, since aggregation can be at any level; the production from a farm in a specific area can be looked upon as relating to micro relationships, while the aggregate product from the area can be looked upon as involving macro quantities. Even here the product from the single farm is an aggregation of output from many technical or producing units in the form of animals and acres. Conversely, the product from a single area is a part of a whole and can be aggregated with that from other areas into a mass quantity for a state or nation. Where, then, should the line be drawn between micro and macro relationships? From the standpoint of the production economist, the distinction becomes important when the structure or nature of the relationship differs with the level of aggregation in the manner illustrated by this example: If one farmer shifts resources from dairy to beef products, the structure of market prices is not changed and the reorganization may be profitable. However, if farmers *en masse* make a similar adjustment, it is possible that the opposite shift in the resources use by an individual farmer will be more profitable. This is the dilemma which faces either the farm manager or the college specialist who attempts to predict the future and alter resource use. If sufficient numbers of farmers followed the predictions implied in the annual outlook reports, an individual operator could best maximize profits if he adjusted resources in a manner opposite to that suggested by the outlook forecasts. Similarly, while a farm management study based on a sample of 150 farms may infer correctly that these farms can increase profits through a change in their pattern of production, the inference may prove erroneous if thousands of farmers make the adjustment. The most important differences between individual and aggregate relationships are those relating to the structure of demand and prices. The nature of the demand, supply, and revenue curves or functions for an individual farm was outlined in earlier chapters; the demand curve for products or the supply curve for factors is horizontal denoting that regardless of the quantity sold or purchased, the price per unit remains unchanged.

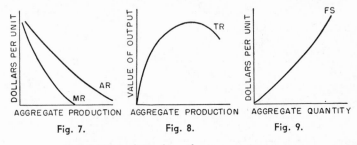

Fig. 7.   Fig. 8.   Fig. 9.

Market relationships of a macro-nature.

The marginal revenue curve for products or the marginal cost curve for factors is identical with the average revenue and average factor cost curves. While no farmer purchases enough of a single factor or sells enough of a particular product to cause the market price to vary, farmers acting *en masse* do have these effects. For aggregate market situations (macro relationships), the demand (average revenue) curve for products assumes the conventional slope illustrated by AR in Figure 7. Since it is negatively inclined, the marginal revenue curve takes the form of MR, and is positive as long as the price elasticity of demand is greater than 1.0 but becomes negative when the elasticity is less than 1.0 in absolute value.[4] The fact that increased production eventually reduces rather than increases total

---

[4] The marginal revenue is again defined as $\Delta R/\Delta Q$, where ΔR refers to the change in total revenue and ΔQ refers to the change in total quantity of product. Marginal revenue can be computed as an "average" over a range of the total or average revenue curve or as the "exact" marginal revenue at a particular point on the average or total revenue curves. The marginal revenue refers to a particular point (the first derivative) only as ΔQ approaches zero. Similarly, the elasticity of demand is given as $\Delta P/\Delta Q$. Q/P where P refers to price per unit and Q refers to the quantity marketed, while Δ refers to change. Price elasticity of demand can also be measured (a) over an arc of the demand curve or (b) at a particular point on the demand curve.

revenue is indicated in the total revenue curve, TR, of Figure 8; the value of output increases as long as the marginal revenue is positive; total revenue then declines as marginal revenue becomes less than zero and elasticity of demand becomes less than 1.0. While the demand elasticity for a few particular agricultural commodities is greater than unity (a greater production results in a greater total income), it is less than 1.0 for the major individual products and for the aggregate of agricultural production. Mass increases in farm output fall in the range of the industry revenue curve with a negative slope, and denote a smaller rather than larger gross return. The production economists must use care in "classifying relationships" in order to be certain that macro changes are not involved when the outcome is viewed in a purely micro nature.

Similarly, while the supply curve for factors which faces the individual farmer is infinitely elastic or horizontal, the supply curve for the agricultural industry is of the nature indicated by FS in Figure 9. Additional quantities of steel and labor resources for tractors can be bid away from other industries only if agriculture pays higher and higher prices.

Later chapters involve relationships of an aggregative or macro character as well as those of a micro nature. Both are important from the standpoint of agricultural production economics research or recommendations. The research worker or extension specialist must distinguish between adjustments by individual farmers and by groups of farmers if his inferences are not to be in error. On the other hand he can predict mass outcomes only as well as he can predict the behavior and action of individual farmers.

Selected References

Black, J. D., *Production Economics*. New York: Henry Holt, 1926, Ch. 13.

————, *et al.*, *Farm Management*, New York: Macmillan, 1941, pp. 407-412.

Goodsell, W. D., Jones, R. W., and Bierman, R. W., *Typical Family-operated Farms, 1930-45*. U.S.D.A. B.A.E. Farm Management Division processed, 1946.

Holmes, C. E., *Economics of Farm Organization and Management*. New York: Heath, 1928, Ch. 12.

Kellogg, C. E., "Soil and Land Classification," *Jour. Farm Econ.*, Vol. 33.

Koopmans, T. C., *Activity Analysis of Production and Allocation*. New York: Wiley, 1951, Ch. 3, "Analysis of production as an efficient combination of activities."

National Resources Planning Board, *Land Classification in the United States*. Washington: U. S. Government Printing Office, 1941.

Osgood, O. T., *Land and Farm Classification*, Miss. Agr. Exp. Sta. Bul. 32.

Renne, R. R., *Land Economics*. New York: Harper, 1947, pp. 40-53.

11

Nature of Costs and Family Farm Theory

UP TO THIS POINT, we have been interested mainly in price ratios as they relate to transformation and substitution ratios and choice between alternatives. We now turn to the nature of the firm's production costs. Since most economists are well versed in cost analysis, this chapter treats only of the fundamentals of costs as they relate to problems in agricultural production. Certain aspects of costs were discussed in Chapter 4. There we indicated that a firm might maximize profits by equating the marginal cost of the factor with the marginal value product of the factor. This chapter treats of costs in a somewhat different manner. Instead of relating costs to units of factor services we now relate costs to units of output. In order to simplify the analysis and conserve space, this presentation is in terms of a single product, a simple production function, and a single time period. This frame of analysis will be relaxed in later chapters. While Chapter 4 dealt partly with the same decision phenomena (the most profitable intensity or level of output), it did not indicate the conditions under which production should be ceased entirely. This problem is important to farm firms which include a high proportion of fixed costs in their plant structure and is analyzed in following sections.

This chapter relates to the structure of short-run costs only. In the accepted terminology of economics, the *short-run* refers to production in a firm (farm) or other technical or economic unit where one or more factors are fixed in quantity. Time is considered only in this manner. Mainly, short-run refers to a production situation where output is varied in the proportional rather than a true scale manner. (See discussion of Chapter 12.) The production function for 1 acre of land as a technical unit or a 160-acre farm as an economic unit refers to the short-run. The number of acres (and buildings or similar resources) are held constant in either case while the amount of labor, tractor fuel, feed, or other resources can be used in varying amounts on the 160-acre farm or on the single acre, and thus changes take place in the proportion of factors which are involved. Analyses which refer to a time period of such length that all resources (the land and buildings, as well as labor, livestock, and other forms of capital) can be varied are ordinarily considered to relate to *long-run* production phenomena. (Distinction between short-run and long-run revolves around fixity of resources rather than time sequence. As will be evidenced later, the long-run actually refers to variations in output relating to scale adjustments.) Chapter 12 deals with problems of returns to scale and hence the nature of long-run costs.

Meaning of Cost

The term cost generally refers to the outlay of funds for productive services. Costs are also involved in the "right or franchise" to carry on the production process. Taxes represent such "franchise" outlays but are in no way related to the physical laws of production. They are important, however, in determining the structure of costs for a farm or other producing unit. Cost outlays for productive services are directly related to the laws of production; their structure is determined by the nature of the production function as well as by the level of prices and the nature of the market for productive services. Costs, like production functions, relate to a specific time period and generally are in terms of homogeneous product and factor. The costs of any production period include the value of the resource service transformed into product in this single period rather than the value of the resource itself. Since a poly-period resource such as a dairy cow or a mower actually represents a stock of resource services, only a part of this stock of services is transformed into product in each "distinct" production period. A mono-period resource such as seed corn also represents a stock of services but the entire stock of services is transformed into product in a single period. Thus, the value (cost) of the resource services transformed into product in any single period from a mono-period resource is identical to the value of the resource itself. This is not true for durable or poly-period resources, however. As was mentioned earlier, poly-period resources may include both stock and flow services. Some services flow from the resource in each period, irrespective of the amount of use. These flow services always are included in costs for each period (except where they are free, as in the case of air). Stock services embodied in poly-period resources do not represent a cost in a particular period unless the resource is used. Then it is the value of the services actually used that is included in the costs of the period.

Categories of cost. Several kinds of costs are involved even in the most simple production processes. Two major categories of cost are (1) fixed costs and (2) variable costs. *Fixed costs* refer to those costs which do not vary with (are not a function of) output. They include (a) real estate taxes and similar "franchise" payments; (b) contractual payments such as rent and interest on capital for the use of certain resources which are fixed over a specified time period; and (c) the value of services from fixed resources which are truly flow services and are given off during the production period regardless of the level of production in a particular period or whether the resources are owned or hired. *Variable costs* refer to those outlays which are a function of output in the production period. They include the value of stock services derived from either mono-period or poly-period resources in a single production period. The resource services which are represented by variable costs differ from those represented by fixed costs in the sense that the latter are given off in a constant flow irrespective of the quantity of commodity produced. The former spring entirely from those stock services which are transformed or "used up" only as the production process is initiated and as a flow of output is forthcoming. Variable costs also include taxes or other non-technical costs which must be paid on a basis of the number of units produced.

Total costs. Total costs of production are made up of total variable costs and total fixed costs (total costs = total fixed costs plus total variable costs). As in the case of other functional relationships, the total cost curve or cost function represents the functional relationship between output and total cost. Cost functions or curves can be presented arithmetically in table form, geometrically in graphical form, or algebraically in equation form. They can be derived for animals and acres as technical units or for farms as firms. The same categories of costs are involved in both cases. In the discussion which follows we first cite examples which apply to technical units. As is suggested later, however, the same considerations apply to the farm as an economic unit.

Nature of Cost Functions

The exact nature (curvature) of the total cost function depends on the nature of the production function which underlies it; factor prices affect the level and slope but not the "curvature" of the total cost curve under competitive conditions such as those in agriculture. First let us examine the nature of the total cost curve or function for a linear production function such as that illustrated in Figure 2 of Chapter 2. A cost function of this nature is pictured as TC in Figure 1. (Cost curves or functions are always graphed with output on the horizontal axis and costs on the vertical axis.) It is linear for these reasons. Each unit of resource can be purchased at the same price under competitive conditions and adds an equal amount to total costs. Therefore, all units of product measured on the bottom axis add the same amount to total cost. In Figure 1, total fixed costs are $50. These costs, such as taxes, cash rent, insurance, and depreciation, which are a function of time and obsolescence only, occur and remain at the same level even if output is zero; total fixed costs (FC) remain as indicated by the dotted horizontal line at $50 as production is raised to 100, 200, or any other level. Since total costs are a sum of fixed and variable costs, the total cost curve originates at $50 on the y-axis. Any increase beyond $50 is due entirely to variable costs such as labor, materials, or depreciation of fixed resources, which is a function of output. A total cost curve always has a positive or upward slope. In Figure 1, total variable costs have been obtained by placing a price of $4 on each unit of the variable factor indicated in Figure 2 of Chapter 2. They are zero for a zero output and increase to $40 for an output of 100 and $120 for an output of 300, and fixed costs represent a decreasing proportion of total costs as output is increased through use of more variable resources. A vertical line can be drawn to the total cost curve for any output represented on the horizontal

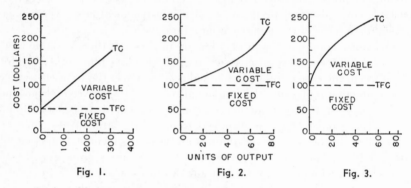

Total cost function under constant, decreasing, and increasing productivity.

axis. The portion falling below the dotted line is the total fixed cost while that lying above is the total variable costs. If the origin on the cost (y) axis is moved up to $50, variable costs are zero for an output of zero.

Figure 2 represents a total cost function where the factor-product relationship is one of diminishing marginal productivity beginning with the first application of the variable factor. It is based on the physical data of Figure 3 of Chapter 2, where fixed costs are $100 and a cost of $25 has been assigned to each unit of the variable factor. Costs have not been computed for that portion of the production function which represents diminishing total revenue. Whereas the production function has an elasticity of less than 1.0 throughout, the total cost curve will curve upward from the outset, because, although each successive unit of the variable factor costs as much as the previous unit, it adds less to total output than the previous unit of resource service. Fixed costs are constant irrespective of the level of output and the curvature of the total cost curve (TC) is due alone to the technical relationship between the variable resource input and the product output. If the origin of the cost axis is moved up to 100 (with the dotted line FC becoming the horizontal or output axis) the total variable cost curve will be identical with the curve TC. Thus it is evident that the slopes of the total cost curve and the total variable cost curve are the same.

Figure 3 illustrates the cost components for a production process reflecting increasing returns throughout. It is based on the data for Figure 4 of Chapter 2, where fixed costs are $100 and the variable factor is priced at $20 per unit. Whereas the production function slopes upward at an increasing rate, the total cost curve slopes upward at a decreasing rate. (The curvature is always reversed between the production function and the total cost function or total variable cost function except in the case of a linear relationship.) Again the mathematical basis is evident. Each input unit adds more units of output than the previous input, therefore each increment to output must add less to total costs than the previous increment.

Generalized cost functions. A production function which includes a range both of increasing and decreasing returns is paralleled by a cost function of the nature illustrated in Figure 4. Here the total cost curve has been derived from physical data of the nature indicated in Figure 5 of Chapter 2. Again total costs increase at (1) a decreasing rate over the range of outputs consistent with increasing returns on the production function, (2) an increasing rate over the range of outputs defining decreasing returns on the production function. The total cost curve also has an inflection point indicating the change in rate of increase (curvature) paralleling the inflection point on the production function. In Figure 4 the inflection point in costs is at an output of 18. The inflection point in product occurs with an input of 3 (an output of 18) in Figure 5, Chapter 2. Previous statements about the relationships between total costs, total variable costs, and total fixed costs (see Figures 1, 2, and 3), also apply to Figure 4.

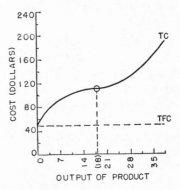

Fig. 4. Generalized cost curve (function).

Costs per unit. Total costs are of interest to the business firm in computing the net gain of the business during the production period. Farm management and accounting experts have concerned themselves with establishing total costs for a farm as an economic unit or for an acre or animal as a technical unit. The interest here is in establishing a single point on a total cost curve, such as $167 for an output of 35 in Figure 4. Ordinarily, variable and fixed costs and their individual components are listed separately on the income statement of farm accounts and then each category is totaled. The total costs (fixed costs plus variable costs) are then subtracted from total revenue (gross income) to determine the net income figure for the farm. For a single farm this number represents one point on a total cost curve and gives no indication of the slope of the curve. While data of this type indicate the surplus value of the output flow over the input flow, they are of limited assistance in decision-making, and do not indicate the optimum amount of variable resources to be applied to a collection of fixed factors. It is the unit (average) costs of production which are helpful in decision-making and resource management.

Four types of unit costs can be derived from total costs. These include: (1) average total cost (AC), (2) average variable cost (VC), (3) average fixed cost (FC), and (4) marginal cost (MC). Numerous methods can be employed in deriving average costs. These vary both in complexity and degree of accuracy. Some of the more elementary methods of calculation are outlined here and are sufficiently accurate for many analytical purposes. The average variable cost (VC) is computed by dividing total variable costs (TVC) by the corresponding total output ($VC = TVC \div$ output). Average fixed cost (FC) is computed by dividing total fixed costs (TFC) by the corresponding total output ($FC = TFC \div$ output).

The average total cost (AC) is derived by dividing total costs (TC) by the corresponding total units of output ($AC = TC \div$ output). Average total costs can also be derived by adding the average fixed cost and the average variable cost. Average total, average fixed, and average variable costs refer (at any single level of output) to *all* units of output. *Marginal cost, however, refers to the amount added to total costs by the last unit of output.* It can be derived from total costs in the manner implied by the definition: where factor inputs and product outputs are continuous, the cost of the last unit, marginal cost (MC), simply represents the amount added to total costs by this unit of output. Where factor inputs are discontinuous and output is, therefore, forthcoming in groups of several or many units, the marginal cost (MC) can be computed only as an average for the last group of output units. Here it is derived by dividing the addition to total costs (the cost of the added input) by the addition to total output. ($MC = $ cost of last unit of input $\div$ marginal product of last unit of input.)

Relationships Between Output Functions and Cost Functions

Unit costs are illustrated in arithmetic form by Table 1, and have been computed by the methods outlined above. Physical input-output data are also included in order that these can be compared with the corresponding cost figures. The important relationships between output and cost functions are these: since the production function (columns 1 and 2) includes a range of both increasing and decreasing returns, the parallel total cost function (column 7) increases, first at a decreasing rate, and second at an increasing rate. The point of inflection comes at the same output for both. These same relationships exist between total output and total variable

Table I.

Output and Cost Relationships (Computed with Fixed Costs at $560 and Each Unit of Variable Factor at $1,000. Data are Hypothetical)

Total input of variable factor	Total output (Product)	Marginal product of input	Average output (Product)	Total fixed cost	Total variable cost	Total cost	FC^a	VC^a	AC^a	MC^b
(1)	(2)	(3)	(4)	(5)	(6)	(7)	(8)	(9)	(10)	(11)
1	500	500	500	$5600	$1000	$ 6600	$11.20	$2.00	$13.20	$ 2.00
2	1500	1000	750	5600	2000	7600	3.73	1.33	5.06	1.00
3	3000	1500	1000	5600	3000	8600	1.87	1.00	2.87	.67
4	4000	1000	1000	5600	4000	9600	1.40	1.00	2.40	1.00
5	4500	500	900	5600	5000	10600	1.24	1.11	2.35	2.00
6	4800	300	800	5600	6000	11600	1.17	1.25	2.42	3.33
7	4900	100	700	5600	7000	12600	1.14	1.43	2.57	10.00

a Computed by dividing the relevant total cost figure by the corresponding total output.

b Marginal cost has been computed by dividing the addition to total cost in each case beyond the first by the marginal product of the particular input. Example for total outputs between 1,500 and 3,000: $1,000 cost of input ÷ 1,500 marginal product of input = .67 average marginal cost of output between 1,500 and 3,000. This procedure provides only the "average" marginal cost (the marginal cost as an average for all additional units of product).

cost. The reason is obvious. Total costs increase only through changes in total variable costs. Average total costs (*AC* in column 10) decrease as long as the decrease in average fixed costs (*FC* in column 8) is greater than the increase in average variable costs (*VC* in column 9). Average variable costs (column 9) decrease as long as average output (column 4) increases; they increase with the decline in average productivity of the variable factor. (3) Marginal costs (*MC* in column 11) decrease as long as the marginal productivity (column 3) of the variable factor increases, and increase with the decline in the marginal product.

Geometric derivation and cost relationships. The rules of tangency which were applied to the physical relationships of Figure 5 in Chapter 2 can also be applied to cost curves.[1] It will be remembered that 2 tangent curves have the same slope and, therefore, represent the same rate of change or

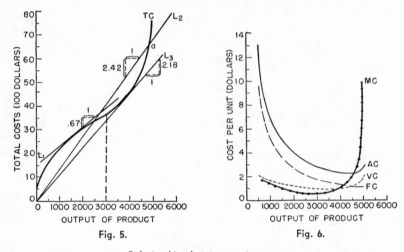

Fig. 5.   Fig. 6.

Relationships between cost curves.

the same marginal quantity. Curve *TC* in Figure 5 is a curve of total costs. The line L_1, which is tangent to *TC* at an output of 1,500, has a slope of .67/1.0; each 1-unit change on the horizontal axis is associated with a change of .67 on the vertical axis. Therefore, the marginal unit cost (*MC*)

---

[1] The system of computing marginal costs outlined here gives the *exact* figure as compared to the *average* marginal cost shown in column 11 of Table 1. The *exact* marginal cost indicates the amount added to total costs by a single unit of output. The *average* marginal cost shows the average addition to costs between two distinct increments of input and output. Thus the exact marginal cost is defined by the ratio $\Delta C/\Delta Y$ where ΔC refers to the change in total cost and ΔY refers to the change in total production. If changes in output (ΔY) become sufficiently small (approaches the limit zero), the marginal cost becomes the derivative of the total cost function. With a total cost function given as $C = \$500 - 10Y - .5Y^2 + .005Y^3$, the marginal cost for any unit of output $\frac{dc}{dY}$ becomes $\frac{dc}{dY} = -10 - 1.0Y + .015Y^2$.

of the 1,500th unit of output is 67¢. Similarly, a line tangent to any other point on TC defines the corresponding marginal cost.

The average total cost (AC), like the average physical product, is defined by the slope of a straight line passing through the origin and intersecting (or tangent to) the total cost curve (TC).[2] In Figure 5, the line L_2 intersects TC at an output of 4,800 (point a). The slope of this line is 2.42/1.0 and denotes an average cost (for all units of output) of \$2.42. Line L_3 both passes through the origin and is tangent to (has the same slope as) the total cost curve TC. Therefore, it defines both the average total cost (AC) and the marginal cost (MC). As indicated in Figure 6, the average and marginal cost curves are equal (intersect each other) at an output of 4,300 (both have a value of \$2.18).

Relationship of average to marginal costs. Relationships between average and marginal costs can now be stated and illustrated in Figure 6.[3] (1) Average variable costs (VC) will decline as long as they are greater than marginal costs (MC). Marginal cost is equal to average variable costs (the curves intersect) when the latter are at a minimum and variable costs increase as marginal cost becomes greater; (2) average total costs (AC) will decline as long as they are less than marginal cost. Marginal cost is equal to average costs when the latter are at a minimum and average total costs increase as marginal cost increases.

Since the slope and curvature of the cost function depends on the nature of the production function, discontinuous input-output relationships are accompanied by discontinuous cost data. As indicated in Chapter 4, discontinuities in costs are not so prevalent as might be supposed. For practical purposes, marginal costs need be provided to managers only in average or discontinuous form. Uncertainty again outweighs any refinements which might be made in cost calculations.

Other unit cost curves. If the production function takes only one form (constant productivity, diminishing productivity, or increasing productivity) the average [unit] cost curves are conditioned accordingly. For a linear production function (such as Figure 2, Chapter 2) and linear total cost curve (such as Figure 1 of this chapter), the marginal and average variable cost is constant while the average fixed and average total costs

---

[2] The average variable cost (VC) also can be derived from a total variable cost curve. Total variable costs can be shown in Figure 5 (top graph) by moving the zero axis up to \$5,600 (since total fixed costs are \$5,600). Tangent lines will then define the marginal cost. Since the slope of the total cost curve is "dependent" entirely on the slope of the total variable cost curve, the marginal cost (MC) so derived would be identical were it derived from a total cost curve. Variable costs (VC) will again be represented by the slope of a line intersecting the cost axis at \$5,600 (since this represents zero variable costs).

[3] These relationships are best presented in Figure 6. Although the basic data are the same, the curves of Figure 6 are plotted from a continuous cost function while the data of Table 1 are computed by arithmetic from the "discontinuous" inputs. Therefore, the equation of marginal and average quantities is not so apparent in Table 1.

will decline throughout all ranges of output. These relationships are illustrated in Figure 7 for a 3-plow tractor, where output is measured as hours of use per year. The total cost curve indicates that each additional hour of use (with the same load) adds the same amount to total costs for fuel,

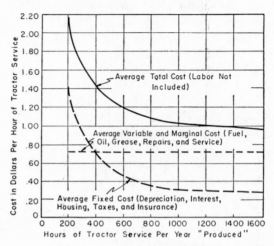

Fig. 7. Three-plow tractor: relation of costs per unit of tractor service to annual use (Source: Iowa Agr. Exp. Sta. project 1135).

grease and similar variable resources. If each unit of tractor service adds the same amount of product to total output (yield per acre is the same for any number of acres operated by the same set of equipment) a graph of tractor costs per bushel of wheat or corn also will display the relationships

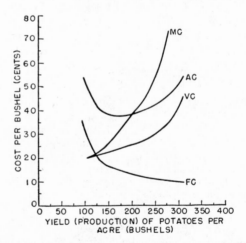

Fig. 8. Unit cost curves relating fertilizer input and potato production on a single acre (Source: derived by application of basic costs to data of Table 1. Because of the discontinuous units of output in Table 1, MC does not intersect AC at the lowest-cost point).

of those in Figure 7. Where each increment of tractor service, because of lack of timeliness of operation and hence a decreased yield per acre as the tractor is used over more acres, adds less to total product, the production function (of tractor service as compared to crop output) will be one of diminishing productivity, and unit (average) crop costs will be of the general nature presented in Figure 8. Where the production function is of the general nature of that in Table 1 of Chapter 2, marginal and average variable costs (diminishing productivity of variable resources from the outset), increase from the outset and fixed costs decline throughout all ranges; average total costs decline as long as the decrease in average fixed cost is greater than the increase in average variable cost and slope upward as soon as the reverse is true. All of the cost situations outlined above have relevance in farm production economic research and recommendations.

The exact curvature or elasticity of average and marginal cost functions depend, under competitive conditions such as those which characterize farming, on the elasticity of the physical production function. If the elasticity of the production function is low and constant, the marginal and average cost curves will have a very gradual upward slope as indicated in Figure 9. Similarly, a high initial production elasticity which declines

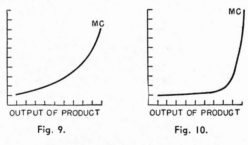

Fig. 9.   Fig. 10.

Marginal costs with different elasticities.

slowly results in these same relationships. If the elasticity of production is first very nearly constant at a high level and then breaks sharply to low levels, the corresponding cost curves more nearly parallel those indicated in Figure 10. Both types of curves exist in agriculture depending on the productivity of the specific resources and the number of resources that are held fixed. (See Chapters 2, 3, and 4.) Some agricultural economists have put forth the hypothesis that only cost curves such as those in Figure 10 exist in agriculture.[4] However, the marginal cost curve for a single technical unit (1 animal or 1 acre) may parallel that of either Figure 9 or Figure 10. When the farm as an economic unit is fixed in size, the marginal cost curve takes on the characteristics of 10. An increase in variable

[4] Wilcox, W. W., "Effects of Price Change on Farming Efficiency," *Jour. Farm Econ.*, Vol. 33, pp. 55-65.

factors, starting from the first technical unit, results in a near-constant marginal cost curve; marginal costs curve up sharply as the limit of technical units has been reached. (This concept is the counterpart of that relating to the production function of Figure 14 in Chapter 3.) However, as indicated in Chapter 12, the marginal cost curve may have only a gradual upward slope when all factors are variable. The nature of the marginal cost curve in agriculture has important implications in farmer response to price, and hence in the nature of the supply function for agriculture as an industry.

In order to save words, reference to costs will hereafter be made in this fashion: Average total costs will be termed average costs, marginal unit costs will be termed marginal costs; average variable and average fixed unit costs will be designated as variable and fixed costs respectively. Total cost functions will be designated by the prefix *total*.

Revenue Relationships and Maximum Profits

Principles of profit maximization can now be outlined in terms of marginal costs and marginal revenue. These principles are the exact counterpart (a different manner of stating the same conditions) as the principles recited in Chapter 4 where the marginal product ratio $(\Delta Y/\Delta X)$ was related to the factor/product price ratio (P_x/P_y). Both methods of stating the principle define the same level of production or resource intensity where a farm with unlimited capital is attempting to maximize profits in a given time period. The present method of stating the principle adds no new knowledge to that outlined in Chapter 4. However, the concepts outlined are useful in an analysis of farm costs.

Marginal revenue. Marginal cost has been defined in a preceding section. We now examine the meaning of marginal revenue. First, however, it is necessary that we examine other revenue relationships for the farm. Under the competitive conditions which characterize agriculture, the amount of product which one farmer sells has no important influence on market price. He will receive the same price per unit whether he sells 1,000 or 10,000 bushels of corn or other product. In other words, each unit of product sold adds the same amount to total revenue or gross income. Accordingly, the total revenue or gross income curve for an individual farm is of the general form presented in Figure 11. With the price of (say) wheat at $1.50, for example, the curve is linear, indicating that each bushel of wheat sold adds $1.50 to gross income. Marginal and average revenue can be derived from total revenue (TR) in the manner already outlined for physical products and production costs. (Any straight line from the origin and intersecting the total revenue curve defines the average revenue while any straight line tangent to the total revenue defines the marginal revenue.) Since the total revenue curve is linear, arithmetic calculations can be used to prove that both average revenue (AR) and marginal revenue (MR) are identical and constant at the market price ($1.50 in the example).

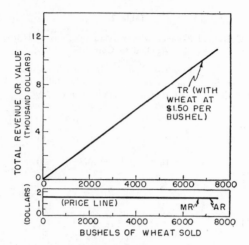

Fig. 11. Relationship between a firm's total sales and revenue curves under competition.

Profits are at a maximum for a producing unit when the yield or output (or factor input) is at a level such that marginal cost is equal to marginal revenue.[5] The reason is evident: the marginal cost and marginal revenue measures indicate additions to total costs and total revenue respectively. Hence, production of 1 more unit of output is always profitable as long as the marginal cost is less than marginal revenue; less is added to total costs than is added to total revenue. Production of 1 more unit is always unprofitable if marginal cost is greater than marginal revenue, since more is

---

[5] That the 2 methods of defining maximum profits (1, the marginal product = the factor/product price ratio and 2, marginal cost = marginal revenue) are identical can be illustrated by this simple example: In Chapter 4 we illustrated that when the marginal product was equal to the factor/product price ratio the maximum profit condition in (I) below is attained:

$$\Delta Y/\Delta X = P_x/P_y \tag{I}$$

From equation (I) we can derive equation (II), which states that the value of the added output is equal to the value of the added input.

$$(\Delta Y)(P_y) = (\Delta X)(P_x) \tag{II}$$

In our definition of this chapter we said that the (average) marginal cost of an increment of output is determined by dividing the addition to total cost from using 1 more unit of resource (the right-hand element of equation II) by the increase in output. Hence equation (III) can be derived from (II), and states that marginal revenue, the selling price of the product, is equal to the marginal cost of the product.

$$P_y = \frac{(\Delta X)(P_x)}{\Delta Y} \tag{III}$$

added to total costs than is added to total revenue. The principle is illustrated arithmetically in Table 2, where costs are attached to fertilizer as a single variable factor, while an acre of land is the fixed factor. With

Table 2.

Corn Yields, Costs and Revenue with Varying Amounts of Nitrogen Fertilizer Applied to Corn *

Lbs. fertilizer per acre	Total yield of corn per acre	Yield of corn per 40 lbs. of added fertilizer	Marginal cost per bushel with fertilizer priced at:		Marginal revenue per bushel with corn priced at:	
			$4 cwt.	$8 cwt.	25¢ bu.	$1.00 bu.
0	0					
		22	.08	.15	.25	1.00
40	22					
		16	.10	.20	.25	1.00
80	38					
		8	.20	.40	.25	1.00
120	46					
		5	.32	.64	.25	1.00
160	51					

* Source of yield data: N. Car. Agr. Exp. Sta. Bul. 366. Yield above production with no fertilizer applied on an individual farm of Norfolk sandy loam at Raeford, N. Car. Marginal cost has been computed by the "average" method. Thus the figure of .04 more nearly describes the marginal cost of the 11th unit of output than the 22nd unit; the figure of 64¢ most nearly defines the marginal cost of the 48.5th than the 51st bushel of corn.

corn priced at 25¢ and fertilizer at $4.00 cwt., the third input of fertilizer is profitable, since each added bushel of corn forthcoming from it costs 20¢ (as an average) and sells for 25¢. The fourth increment of fertilizer is not profitable; since the added cost is 32¢ while the added revenue is only 25¢, 5¢ is subtracted from net return for each bushel added to total yield. With corn at 25¢ and fertilizer at $8, the 51 per acre yield maximizes net returns. The maximum physical output per acre also is profitable when corn is priced at $1 and fertilizer is priced at $4. While the example has been in terms of an acre as a technical unit, it applies similarly to a farm as an economic unit (which includes many technical units).

The principle of profit maximization is illustrated with greater refinement in Figure 12. With a price of $10, marginal cost and marginal revenue are equal at an output of 80, and hence define maximum profits. While the last unit adds the same amount to total costs as to total revenue, any reduction of output below this level subtracts more from revenue than from costs; increase in output beyond this level adds more to costs than to revenue. For example, if output is dropped from 80 back to 70, net profits will be decreased by the amount indicated in shaded area A. If output is extended from 80 to 90, net profit is decreased by the shaded area indicated in *B*. When the price is $13, profits are maximized with an output of 90.[6]

The limitations applied to the principle of profit maximization in Chapter 4 also apply here. Not often is the farmer able to equate marginal cost and marginal revenue, thereby maximizing profits. First, he must operate under imperfect knowledge and can only make estimates of future prices and yields, and those actually realized may deviate widely from expectations. Second, he seldom has the capital to push production to the optimum level even if his foresight is accurate. Notwithstanding these complexities, the conditions outlined above are still those which he would like to attain even if he must "shoot in the dark." (The statements of input-output discontinuities in Chapters 2 through 4 have equal application when profit maximization is in terms of marginal cost and marginal revenue.)

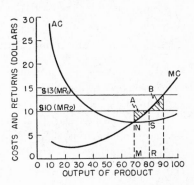

Fig. 12. Graphic representation of profit maximization.

Minimum cost vs. maximum profit. In Chapter 6 we were concerned with problems of choosing between 2 variable factors in producing a given output of product. Under these conditions, minimum cost was always consistent with maximum profit. However, we have returned to a situation of a single variable factor and a single product, the situation of Chapters 2, 3, and 4, to illustrate the nature of production costs. Under the latter situation, minimum cost per unit is not always an indicator of maximum returns. This statement can be illustrated by Figure 12. When selling price is $10 the minimum cost per unit, *MN*, is realized with an output of 70. When output is increased to 80, per unit costs increase to *RS*, but profit also increases by the amount of the shaded area indicated by *A*. With a price of $13 cost per unit is higher, and profit per unit is lower when 90 rather than 70 units are produced. However, since the percentage increase in number of units on which a profit is realized is greater than the decline in the profit per unit (on all previous units of output), total profit over all units is maximized with an output of 90. Only in one case

---

[6] The principle of profit maximization can also be illustrated graphically in reference to the total cost and the total revenue functions. Maximum profits are denoted by an output indicating a maximum distance between the cost and revenue curves. Also, the 2 total curves must have the same slope at the point of this maximum difference since marginal revenue and marginal cost must be equal if profits are to be maximized. These concepts of costs, gross revenue, and profit parallel the computation of farm accounting wherein total cost is subtracted from total revenue to determine net return on the individual farm.

does minimum cost denote maximum profit output. This is the case when selling price and marginal revenue are equal to the minimum average cost. With a selling price of *MN* in Figure 12, marginal revenue and marginal cost are equal at an output of approximately 70. Profits are then at a maximum and average cost is at a minimum for this output.

Decision-Making Costs and Minimum Loss Principles

Only variable costs are important in decision-making, once commitments for fixed costs have been made. Thereafter, fixed costs are of historic importance only. (Fixed costs help establish the level of total costs, but only variable costs affect the rate at which total costs change.) Variable costs alone must be covered by selling price if production is to be profitable in the short-run. Even though the selling price or marginal revenue does not cover average costs (fixed and variable costs), production

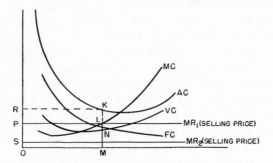

Fig. 13. Graphic representation of loss minimization.

is economic as long as the return is above the per unit variable cost: while losses are realized, they are minimized by continued production. If selling price is below the variable or operating cost per unit, loss can be minimized by ceasing production. The condition of "loss minimization" (actually an element of profit maximization) is attained by equation of marginal cost and marginal revenue (or in the case of discontinuous factor services, by extending output as long as marginal revenue is greater than marginal costs). Minimum loss conditions are illustrated in Figure 13, where the selling price is *OP* (vertical axis) and the output is *OM* (horizontal axis). The average cost is *MK* (or *OR*), as is indicated on the curve *AC*, and the loss per unit is *LK* or *PR*. However, since the selling price of *OP* exceeds the average variable cost of *MN*, losses are reduced as output is extended to *OM*, since the producer now has a total return above out-of-pocket costs equal to *NL* times *OM* which can be applied on fixed costs. Total fixed costs would still have to be paid while no income would be forthcoming if production were ceased.

While production can be maintained in the *short-run* as long as selling price is above variable cost, it cannot be continued indefinitely unless selling price exceeds average total costs. In the *long-run*, fixed factors wear out and cannot be replaced economically unless price is above average cost (including fixed as well as variable costs). In other words, resources and costs which are "fixed" in the short-run become variable in the long-run and all costs must be covered in the long-run before commitments are made for resources which will again become fixed. The conditions outlined are exactly those in which most farmers find themselves during depression periods. Although returns do not completely cover total costs, continued production is economic as long as selling price exceeds cash outlays for variable resources and resource services such as seed, feed, tractor fuel, custom work, and rent. Ordinarily, the farm maintains production with the expectation that prices will rise from depression levels. Unless cash fixed costs are returned over longer periods, the farmer finds that he must either switch to other occupations or experience a continuous decline in living standards.

Changes in Structure of Agricultural Costs

The proportion of total farm costs represented by fixed costs varies with types of farming, the scale of the enterprise and the system of accounting. Variable costs represent a greater proportion of total costs in dairy or poultry production than in forestry or cattle grazing. Fixed costs represent the greatest percentage of total costs for most family farm units if the implicit (opportunity) costs of operator and family labor or other durable resources owned by the family are included in the accounting system as fixed costs. However, where income accounting is in a manner which considers out of pocket costs only, cash variable costs exceed cash fixed costs on the majority of owner-operated farms. (Interest payments cause fixed costs to exceed variable costs on a great number of farms.) Variable costs also represent the greatest portion of the tenant's total costs on share-rented farms while cash rent is often great enough to cause total fixed costs to exceed total variable costs for tenants on cash-rented farms.

The structure of farm costs may change to include a greater proportion of fixed costs because of any one of the following reasons: (1) *The price of variable factors may decrease while fixed costs and techniques remain constant.* This is illustrated in Figure 14, where original costs include fixed costs of OV and variable costs amounting to the distance between the total cost curve TC_1, and line VV'. When output is OR, the total cost per unit is RC and includes RA fixed costs and AC variable costs. The proportion of fixed costs to total costs is RA/RC. If the price of variable factors declines to one-half (total cost curve TC_2), the proportion of fixed costs increases to RA/RB. Even though the proportion of fixed costs has in-

creased, a farmer would be better off under the new situation than previously and would be even less vulnerable to price declines. (2) *The
technique may change to increase the productivity of the variable factor
while factor costs remain constant.* This can also be illustrated by Figure
14. With total costs originally at the level indicated by TC_1, a change in
techniques which doubles the productivity of the variable factor will lower
the total costs to TC_2 (will cause variable costs to drop by one-half for
any one output). Again the proportion of fixed costs will increase from

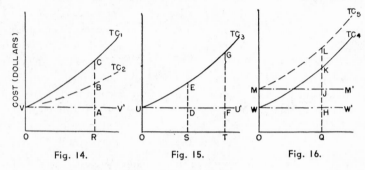

Fig. 14.   Fig. 15.   Fig. 16.

Changes in cost structure.

RA/RC to RA/RB and cost-wise, the farmer will never be worse off than
formerly. (3) *Output may decrease due to a decline in product prices while
other prices and techniques remain constant.* Figure 15 illustrates this
case: as output falls from OT to OS, the proportion of fixed costs increases from TF/TG to SD/SE. (4) *The cost of fixed services may increase while other prices and techniques remain constant.* Figure 16
illustrates this case: originally, total costs are represented by curve TC_4
and include fixed costs amounting to OW. Fixed costs then increase to
OM and total costs become that indicated by curve TC_5. With output at
OQ, the proportion of fixed costs increases from QH/QK to QJ/QL. (5)
*Resources which embody fixed costs may be substituted for resources
which entail variable costs.* This case also can be illustrated by Figure 16,
where the original cost structure is represented by curve TC_5 and includes
fixed costs amounting to OW. Now factors embodying fixed costs are substituted for variable factors while total costs are still represented as TC_5;
fixed costs become OM, while variable costs for any single output decline
by WM. (Ordinarily, the entrepreneur would not substitute one resource
for another unless costs were reduced.) With output at OQ, the proportion
of fixed costs increases from QH/QL to QJ/QL as the substitution takes
place.

Typically, changes in the structure of prices or in the production function would cause several of the above adjustments to come about at the
same time; some would tend to cancel others. In any case, a change *per se*

Table 3.

Effect of Changes in Prices for Fixed and Variable Resources on Cost Structure *

Output (units)	Situation 1 Initial unit costs before change in price of factors (dollars)				Situation 2 Unit costs after price of fixed factor has doubled (dollars)				Situation 3 Unit costs after price of variable factor has doubled (dollars)			
	Fixed	Variable	Average	Marginal	Fixed	Variable	Average	Marginal	Fixed	Variable	Average	Marginal
10	24.00	4.48	28.48	3.82	48.00	4.48	52.48	3.82	24.00	8.96	32.96	7.64
20	12.00	3.96	15.96	2.65	24.00	3.96	27.96	2.65	12.00	7.92	19.92	5.30
30	8.00	3.92	11.92	3.56	16.00	3.92	19.92	3.56	8.00	7.84	15.84	7.12
40	6.00	3.88	9.88	4.04	12.00	3.88	15.88	4.04	6.00	7.76	13.76	8.08
50	4.80	4.00	8.80	5.00	9.60	4.00	13.60	5.00	4.80	8.00	12.80	10.00
60	4.00	4.28	8.28	6.44	8.00	4.28	12.28	6.44	4.00	8.56	12.56	12.88
70	3.43	4.74	8.17[a]	8.36	6.86	4.74	11.60	8.36	3.43	9.48	12.91	16.72
80	3.00	5.32	8.32	10.96	6.00	5.32	11.32	10.96	3.00	10.64	13.64	21.92
90	2.64	5.86	8.50	13.64	5.28	5.86	11.14[a]	13.64	2.64	11.72	14.36	27.28
100	2.40	7.00	9.40	17.00	4.80	7.00	11.80	17.00	2.40	14.00	16.40	34.00

* Costs for situation 1 have been derived from a cost function $C = k + aX - bX^2 + eX^3$.
[a] Output which gives lowest average cost per unit.

sum" form of a 12-month unit of operator labor. (Although operator and family labor can be used in variable amounts, an out-of-pocket cost does not exist for each unit of labor used.) Similarly, some farmers own all of their equipment and thus experience both the fixed costs (depreciation and other flows of services due to time alone) and variable costs (services given off or transformed only as commodities are produced). Other farmers hire the same machines and, therefore, can view machine services in the form of variable costs. Because the costs attached to family-furnished resources do not enter into the marginal cost structure, the hypothesis is often put forth that family farms are less responsive to price changes than large-scale or commercial farms which must pay labor as a marginal or variable cost and non-agricultural firms which also hire large amounts of labor and have a high proportion of variable costs. It is true that the supply of agricultural products does fluctuate less widely between national prosperity and depression than the supply of certain non-farm products. Since such an important portion of labor and other resources is furnished by the farm family and does not require a cost outlay, it is of interest to examine the effect of these differences on cost structures and the manner in which the farm firm might react to changes in price relationships if profits were to be maximized. A more complete analysis of supply responses is provided in a later chapter. Hence the analysis which follows compares cost structure and production adjustment on farms which do and farms which do not consider all costs as out-of-pocket costs. To simplify the discussion we use the term "large-scale farm" and "family farm" for the 2 categories. While the presentation will be in terms of family versus large-scale or commercial farms, it applies equally to all situations (even though the units are of the same size) where the accounting system of some farms includes the cost of a service as variable while others consider it as fixed.

Differences between farms in their adjustment to price change must come about because of differences in either (1) the cost structure, (2) the production function, or (3) their expectations of price changes. The short-run production function may differ between large and small farms depending on the nature of returns to scale and the level at which specific factors are held constant. However, simple production functions such as those which relate fertilizer input to crop output or feed input to livestock output may well be the same on farms which do and those which do not include labor in their marginal cost accounting. There is little reason why family and large-scale farms on the same soil or employing livestock of similar quality should be faced with different production functions for each technical unit. Thus were family or large-scale commercial farms to consider only the marginal cost of fertilizer as it relates to returns, both would operate technical units with equal intensity irrespective of the level of fixed costs for the technical unit (and were capital equally available in either case).

Ordinarily labor is a variable cost on the large-scale farm but often is either "free" or "fixed" on the family unit where it has no alternative opportunity. On a small farm no actual outlay is required for the complementary labor used with the more intensive application of fertilizer to an acre of land, feed to an animal, and similar variable resources for other technical units. Labor used to complement other resources does not enter into marginal costs for a farm where the work is performed by family members but it does, however, enter into marginal costs for the large-scale farm which purchases the services of labor as well as those of fertilizer. This difference has the effect, except in the rare case of constant labor productivity, of decreasing the so-called family farm's marginal cost relative to that of the large-scale unit. Therefore, the small-scale farm should be more responsive, in an absolute sense and apart from considerations to be mentioned later, to price (if both attempt to or do maximize profits).

Intensity per technical unit. These possibilities can be illustrated for the costs of a single technical unit by means of Figure 18. Linear marginal cost curves have been used to simplify the exposition. The marginal cost curve per technical unit for the family farm (or any farm which does not

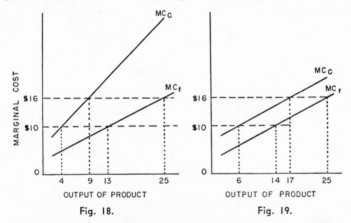

Fig. 18.   Fig. 19.

Family and commercial farms: effect on level of output of converting variable outlays to fixed or "free" outlays.

include the cost of all variable services in its marginal accounting) is MC_f and includes (say) the cost of material, fuel and machinery services required in applying fertilizer, seed, and other materials and in harvesting the greater product. The marginal cost curve per technical unit for the large-scale farm (or any farm which includes all variable services in its accounting) is MC_c and includes the service costs of the small farm plus the costs of labor. Here diminishing returns is supposed for labor as well as other complementary resource services used on each technical unit. We assume identical production functions for each technical unit within the large or small farms. For the sake of simplicity the marginal cost of labor, although it does not represent an out-of-pocket cost to the small farm, is taken to be equal to that of other resource services. Therefore, the marginal cost curve at any output for the large farm has twice the height of the curve for the small farm. Since (a) diminishing returns hold for labor as a direct complement of other inputs and (b) labor is not a cost, the marginal cost curve for the family farm has less slope (does not increase so fast) than that of the large-scale unit which does pay for labor. Not only should it be true that the family farm produces a greater output per technical unit for any one price (because marginal cost is less) but also it should, in an absolute sense, be more price-responsive than the large farm. At a price of $16, the large-scale farm should produce 9 units of output per technical unit if it is to maximize profit; the small farm should produce 25. When price drops to $10, the large-scale farm should contract production per technical unit by 5 units (to 4). The family farm should cut production by a greater amount or by 12. In the case just cited the "commercial farm" would reduce output per technical unit by a smaller absolute amount than the "family farm." However it would decrease output by a greater relative amount; the commercial farm reduces output by 56 per cent while the family farm decreases output by only 48 per cent.[7] The cost elasticity is more important than the presence or absence of labor costs *per se* in determining production response. The marginal cost curve of the commercial farm has greater elasticity than that for the family farm in this case since it originates at a greater level of costs.

This statement holds true where diminishing productivity for the labor parallels that of other complementary services applied to technical units. Commonly, twice as much labor is required for the added feed in carrying an animal from 250 to 300 as from 200 to 250 lbs. in weight. An alternative possibility is that labor productivity is constant while the productivity of other resources diminishes. Here labor costs per unit of output would be constant and the marginal cost for each unit of output on a commercial farm would exceed those of a family farm by a constant amount equal to the labor cost. This situation is illustrated in Figure 19. Both curves have the same slope and each farm should, where profit maximization is either attempted or accomplished, adjust production by the same absolute amount for any given change in commodity price.[8] However, the "com-

---

[7] If the 2 marginal cost curves passed through the origin, an unlikely situation for marginal costs, both firms would reduce output by the same relative amount while the family farm would reduce output by a greater absolute amount.

[8] A second, but still unlikely possibility, is that the marginal productivity of labor might be increasing while diminishing productivity exists for the resources which labor

mercial farm" will reduce output by a greater relative amount than the "family farm." Reduction per technical unit is equal to 8 in either case but this quantity is a smaller percentage for the original output of 25 on the "family farm" than for the original output of the "commercial farm."

Economic units. The analysis of production adjustments wherein some farms have an outlay for specific resources while others do not has been applied to the intensity of output for 2 identical technical units. It also can be applied to 2 farms as economic units (aggregates of technical units) of the same size and with identical production functions. Curve MC_c in Figure 18 can be considered the marginal cost curve for a 160-acre farm which includes labor in its cost accounting while curve MC_f is the curve for a farm of the same size (160 acres) which does not have a cash outlay for labor. The "family-labor" firm will, if profit is maximized, (a) produce more at any given price and (b) adjust production by a greater absolute amount for any price change than a farm of the same size which does pay for all resource services as variable costs.

Now we turn to the outcome for farms as firms where the one with labor costs is larger than the one which need not include labor outlays in its marginal costs.[9] We are, for example, interested in the short-run production and cost functions for a family farm of 400 acres as compared to a large-scale farm of 2,000 acres. Using this example and first considering the case in which production functions are identical for the 2 farms, marginal costs assume the form of those illustrated in Figure 20: the curve MC_f represents marginal costs for a small farm with labor available as a "free" or "fixed" resource. Curve MC_{c1} represents the marginal cost, excluding outlays for labor, for a farm 5 times larger and with an identical production function for each of the five "400-acre portions"; at any level of marginal cost, output is 5 times greater under MC_{c1} than under MC_f. However, if the large-scale, commercial farm considers labor in its marginal accounting, labor costs must be added to the cost of other resources. The curve MC_{c2} represents the situation for the large farm where marginal costs for labor as well as other resource services are included and the per unit cost of labor is equal to the cost of all other variable resource services. (MC_{c2} is twice as high or has twice the slope of MC_{c1}.) With a price of $24 and labor costs equal to the sum of all other variable costs, the large

---

complements. In this case the marginal costs for the farm which does consider labor as a variable cost will not only be higher than for one where a stock of labor is available in free or fixed form but the curve will also have less slope (greater elasticity). In this case the response to price may be greater on a farm which does consider labor as a variable cost.

[9] Each value or horizontal point on curve MC_f in Figure 20 has been multiplied, in the vein of a linear, homogeneous production function, by 5 to obtain curve MC_{c1}. Linear, homogeneous production functions are discussed elsewhere. Linearity of the long-run production function is assumed to simplify the discussion and not as a hypothesis of agricultural production relationships.

farm (MC_{c2}) should produce a greater total product than the small farm (MC_f) if capital is unlimited and profits are to be maximized. Yet production would be less relative to the quantity of resources employed and the size of the firm. (The slope of MC'_{c2} with the addition of labor costs is less than MC_{c1}.) As price drops to $12, the large farm would curtail production both by a larger absolute amount and a larger relative amount than the

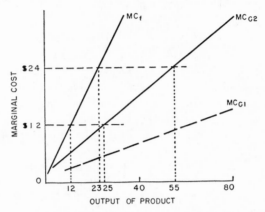

Fig. 20. Effect of accounting procedure (inclusion or exclusion of labor as a variable cost) on marginal costs and production response by large and small farms.

small farm: output should be reduced by 30 units for the former and by 11 units for the latter.

We have employed an example of a linear long-run production function (see next chapter) where the output on the farm with 5 times as many resources is 5 times that of the small farm (also our marginal costs originate at zero). Other types of production functions and scale economies or diseconomies may give rise to other differential production responses. We have been able, however, to illustrate that absence or presence of labor (or other out-of-pocket) costs do not *per se* cause the "commercial" farm to be more responsive in an absolute amount than the family farm.

Maintenance of output in depression. A farm firm which need not consider labor as an out-of-pocket cost can remain in production at a lower level of commodity prices than one which must view the labor outlays and similar services as cash costs. This possibility is illustrated in Figures 21 and 22 for two farms of the same scale.[10] The first illustrates the structure

---

[10] In deriving Figures 21 and 22, diminishing productivity has been assumed for both labor and complementary resource services. The cost per unit of labor has been assumed equal to the cost per unit of variable non-labor services. Thus the marginal and variable cost curve is twice as high for the firm which pays labor costs as for the firm which does not. Since it has been assumed that the total labor supply available on the family farm is great enough to produce OX output, the total outlay for labor is equal at OX for both farms. In the case of the family farm this total labor outlay has been added as a fixed cost to other fixed costs. It has been added as a variable cost to other variable costs for the commercial farm.

of costs for a farm where labor is a fixed cost, while the second represents the nature of costs where labor is a cash variable cost. (The fixed cost curve is not shown. However, the fixed cost for any unit of output is the difference between the variable and the average cost for the same output.) Fixed costs per unit are smaller, while variable unit costs are greater, for the commercial as compared to the family farm up to an output of OX, which the family farm can produce without hiring non-family helpers.

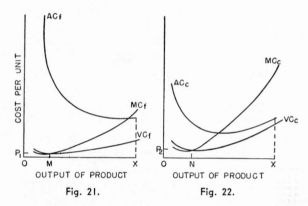

Fig. 21. Fig. 22.

Effect of labor as fixed or variable cost on a firm's cost structure.

When the production functions are identical and the same prices attach to all factors services (including the same value on the labor required to produce OX for the family as well as the commercial farm), both firms will have an identical average cost at the output OX. The marginal cost curve for the family farm again will have less slope than the cost curve for the commercial farm of the same size. Similarly, variable costs will be greater on the commercial farm and will exceed those of the family farm by an amount equal to the labor outlay.

The commercial farm can maintain an output of ON or greater only as long as the product price does not drop below OP_2 in Figure 22; for prices lower than OP_2, losses can be minimized by ceasing production. The family farm can, however, minimize loss by maintaining an output of OM or greater for prices below OP_2 in Figure 22 but greater than OP_1 in Figure 21. While the analysis has been applied to 2 firms of the same size it also applies, with adaptations such as those in Figure 20, to small farms which do not have an outlay for labor and large farms which do view labor as a variable cash cost (or equally for a small farm which might hire all machine services as variable costs as compared to a large farm which owns all machines and, therefore, views some machine services in the vein of fixed costs). The nature of the cost structure on farms where the greatest portion of the labor supply is furnished by the family and does not enter into variable and marginal cost accounting provides one element in explaining why agriculture tends to maintain output and employment during depression while non-agricultural industries do not. If all agriculture were organized on a large commercial basis (if most labor were hired) then perhaps the industry might curtail output and employment to a greater extent during depression. There are, however, other forces which help explain the inelasticity of agricultural production. Evidently these explanations, which will be outlined in a later chapter, are extremely important.

A similar belief found in agriculture is that high real estate taxes, principal payments, cash rent, and similar costs cause farmers to carry on intensive production because of the resulting cost structure which includes a high proportion of fixed costs. This cause-effect explanation in itself is unlikely, however. Farmers with high taxes or cash rent may carry on intensive production but the reason is not likely to be found in fixed costs *per se*. Although average costs differ depending on the level of fixed costs, fixed costs in no way affect the level and rate of change in marginal costs. If short-run profit maximization is the objective, 2 farmers with different levels of fixed cost should produce exactly the same amount of product if (a) the production function and (b) prices for commodities and variable services are the same for both. When production intensity varies between farms with different fixed cost levels, the behavior is more likely explained by one of the following forces, which are analyzed in later chapters: (1) The high fixed cost associated with debt brings forth intensive production because of the complex of risk and uncertainty associated with small equities. (2) Taxes and related fixed costs are likely to be found on intensive farms because of the combination of the nature of the production function and commodity price-factor cost relationships which cause a high output per technical unit to be profitable: the value of the marginal product is great, and when capitalized, gives a high value to land and in turn provides a base for high taxes. (3) Other phenomena falling in the category of firm-household relationships and lack of knowledge explain the behavior of the farm entrepreneur.

Capital limitations and price response. To this point we have compared family and commercial farms (or farms which do as compared to farms which do not make outlays for all resources) which have enough capital to push output to levels where marginal cost and marginal revenue are equated. Great differences exist, however, in the amount of capital which farms employ and hence in the manner in which they might logically respond to farm price change. While it has obvious limitations, the simple graph of Figure 23 can be used to illustrate possible differences in production response on farms where capital is limited as compared to cases where it is not limited. The original price is OP_2. The "family" farm is able to acquire only enough capital to expand output to OX_1, while the "large-scale" farm has enough capital to expand output to OX_3. When price drops to OP_1, the "large scale" farm must curtail production to OX_2 if profits are to be maximized. However, the "family" farm can retain output at OX_1, since marginal cost is less than marginal revenue under either price relationship.

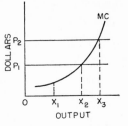

Although the historic definitions of family and large-scale farms may be unimportant and perhaps somewhat useless, differences in capital may well explain why farms with varying quantities of resources do (or should) react differently to price changes. The farm firm with limited capital may, however, still contract output as prices decline. Uncertainty, expectations of further price declines, and other subjective considerations may cause it

Fig. 23. Capital limitations and production response.

to withdraw some resources from production even though marginal revenue still exceeds marginal and variable costs.

Intensity and Time

While the problem does not arise in the customary text book discussion of intensity, the time element becomes important in agriculture.[11] The intensity of production with land serving as the technical unit provides no special problems apart from those already outlined. Regardless of the rate at which variable resources are applied and the amount of product forthcoming from the fixed unit, the production period is terminated at one point in time for the entire product. Whether 40 or 120 lbs. of fertilizer are applied on an acre of Norfolk sandy loam of North Carolina, the corn yield increments of 22 or 51 bushels will be ready for harvest in October (with only slight variations in time of maturity). Similarly, the milk flow from a dairy cow is forthcoming in the same time interval whether it is at the rate of 5,000 or 7,000 lbs. per year. In the case of other technical units such as a hog or beef animal, however, the level of output is a function of time. If the output from (marketing weight of) a hog is increased from 200 to 250 lbs., the increased product will be ready to market only at a later period. Because of seasonal changes in supply and demand, prices differ for meat animals sold at different points in time. The problem of optimum intensity per technical unit is therefore somewhat more complex in meat than in crop production, as is suggested by Table 4.

---

[11] Production analysis usually assumes a homogeneous product. Thus pork marketed at different weights (produced at different times) is not homogeneous in respect to time. It might, therefore, be considered as competitive products in the manner of Chapter 7. In terms of interyear decisions, the farmer with 2,700 bushels of corn might compare production of 150 hogs marketed at 200 lbs. each in July or 100 hogs marketed at 290 lbs. each in September.

Table 4.

Necessary Selling Price for Hogs 1 Month From Now to Permit the Feeder to Break Even in Putting 50 lbs. Additional Weight on Hogs of Different Weights with Different Prices for Corn and Hogs Now *

Dollar Price of Corn per Bushel Now	Price of Hogs in $ Per 100 lbs., Now			
	10.00	15.00	20.00	25.00
	On Hogs Weighing 200 lbs., Now			
1.00	10.25	14.25	18.25	22.25
1.25	10.81	14.81	18.81	22.81
1.50	11.38	15.38	19.38	23.38
1.75	11.94	15.94	19.94	23.94
	On Hogs Weighing 225 lbs., Now			
1.00	10.27	14.36	18.45	22.55
1.25	10.80	14.89	18.98	23.07
1.50	11.32	15.41	19.50	23.59
1.75	11.84	15.93	20.02	24.11

* Source: U.S.D.A., AIS no. 78.

The problem of intensity in meat production is also made complex by the fact that the grade of the product changes as the output of the animal is increased. In terms of market specifications, a feeder steer grades choice or prime only as a certain degree of finish is attained. Similarly, the mar-

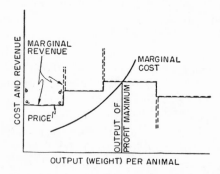

Fig. 24. Cost and revenue relationships for meat animals of different weights.

ket tends to discount the price of hogs weighing under 200 and over 275 lbs. (although the exact weight interval varies from time to time depending on current demand and other forces). If we look upon the output from a steer or hog as constituting a single product, the cost and revenue curves take the appearance of those presented in Figure 24. Here the price changes with weight and, hence, with grade. Marginal revenue is identical to price, except that it becomes very great or very small at breaks between grades. Those pounds which carry the output into each different grade add more to total return than their own price, since they also increase the value of all previous pounds. Here again, though, the analysis of Chapter 7 is appropriate; the different grades are actually different products for which the cost and price relationships must be compared. (In Figure 24 the small dotted rectangles have been left open to indicate that they do not enclose the full area in question. The area or line indicated above d should equal the area of $abcd$ since all previous units of product have their price increased.)

Short-Run Cost Flexibility

The analysis of resource use has been in the context of perfect knowledge up to this point. Under these conditions the firm would always adopt the low cost method of production; the production function and cost structure selected would always be those which give the lowest average cost curve. The entrepreneur may, however, select a short-run producing plant which does not give minimum average costs because of either of two reasons: (1) He may have perfect knowledge and know that prices will vary regularly over the future. (2) He may have imperfect knowledge and anticipate that factor/product price ratios will fluctuate in the future, the direction and extent being uncertain. Thus while the complete analysis of production dynamics and uncertainty is reserved for a later section, we pause here to examine the physical possibilities which exist for incorporating flexibility into the short-run cost structure of the firm. The procedure is to (first) analyze situations where flexibility is desired to meet price variations, and (finally) to examine flexibility under variability of the production function or yields. The analysis relates to size and cost phenomena in this sense: a farmer with funds for 2 tractors may prefer to (a) farm a 200-acre unit with a surplus of machine capacity as a basis for flexibility in meeting year-to-year variability of weather rather than (b) farm a 400-acre unit which taxes machine services to full capacity and does not provide a cushion for unfavorable weather. Another farmer with funds to support a 30-sow herd under inflexible but most efficient (least cost) techniques may rationally select facilities which allow a maximum of 24 litters but result in lower costs when prices are unfavorable and farrowings are restricted to 15 sows.

Flexibility for price variability. An optimum size and form (arrangement or technique) of short-run plant exists for each possible output of product. Plants either larger or smaller or representing a different organization (different techniques) of production could result in higher unit costs. Yet, since the possibility is entirely real that the price of the product (and also of factors) will vary from one producing period to another, the firm may not wish to build plans around an optimum cost structure and a fixed output such as OM in Figure 12. Instead, it may wish to select a producing unit which, although it does not allow the minimum average cost for the average annual output, will allow a minimum cost for the output of any single year. Incorporation of cost flexibility into the plant can allow minimum costs for outputs which fluctuate between years. The firm may select any one of many techniques in its attempt to attain cost flexibility. One alternative is to select a production function (technique) which involves high fixed costs but provides high initial productivity of variable factors. Another is to adopt a plant which involves low fixed costs but at the same time causes low initial productivity of the variable factor. Two alternatives of this nature are illustrated in Figure 25. Curve I represents a short-run production function for variable resources when (1) a large outlay for machines with high fixed costs are employed, and (2) the production function is fairly inflexible in the sense that use of added variable factors adds relatively little to total output in the final range of inputs (as compared to the earlier range of variable inputs). A set of high capacity machines in crop production or use of automatic grain elevators, feed conveyors and other equipment for livestock production partly characterizes this situa-

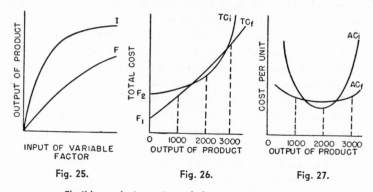

Fig. 25.   Fig. 26.   Fig. 27.

Flexible producing units and short-run cost structures.

tion. The first units of labor (and complementary factors) to operate these implements are highly productive. Use of additional labor with the same machines may add very little to product. Curve F represents the short-run production function for variable resources when (1) little of the factor embodying fixed costs is employed and (2) the input-output relationship is flexible in the sense that although productivity is lower in earlier ranges of input than for I, marginal productivity is maintained at a more nearly constant level for larger inputs. Curves such as F can be brought about through labor-using and similar techniques in caring for livestock, picking potatoes, and growing beets and cotton. For enterprises such as these, production can be organized to include low fixed costs and addition or subtraction of resources (changes in the size of acreage or herd handled) can be made readily without great changes in productivity of labor or other resources.

The total cost relationships arising under the flexible and inflexible production functions of Figure 25 are illustrated in Figure 26. If the output is to be exactly 2,000, then the inflexible production function (I in Figure 25) allows the lowest cost for the output as denoted by total cost curve TC_i in Figure 26. For this output the high fixed cost (OF_2) is spread over a large number of units of product and factor input is not yet great enough to cause sharply rising costs due to the low marginal productivity of the variable factor. However, the flexible production function (F in Figure 25) allows lower total costs for small outputs, as is indicated by the total cost curve TC_f in Figure 26. While productivity of the variable factor is less under F for small outputs, fixed cost is much lower than under I. Again, for large outputs, the flexible production function F allows a lower total cost than the inflexible production function; the marginal productivity of variable resources does not drop so rapidly under the flexible plant. When output varies regularly between 1,000 and 3,000, the flexible cost arrangement allows minimum costs for the average output of 2,000. If output were to remain constantly at 2,000, the inflexible plant would be most desirable.

These same relationships are presented in the form of short-run average cost curves in Figure 27. The inflexible curve AC_i (which corresponds to production function I and the total cost curve TC_i) results in a minimum average cost for an output of 2,000. AC_f corresponds to an entirely different technique (production function F) and, while representing higher costs for an output of exactly 2,000, results in lower costs when output is at the level of 1,000 or 3,000. Now if it were certain that price relationships would not vary between years and that output per year would always be at 2,000 the firm should select the inflexible production function I and hence cost functions TC_i and AC_i. This structure of producing plant with its high fixed costs would be consistent with minimum costs and maximum profits. Yet if the firm knows or expects that, while output, because of fluctuations in price, will average 2,000 over a period of years, it will fluctuate from 1,000 to 3,000 (an output of 1,000 in one year and 3,000 in another year resulting in a 2-year average of 2,000), the flexible plant F should be selected. This choice will be optimum where the producer has funds enough for only a single plant. His selection of a technique which does not give minimum costs cannot be termed irrational.

We have illustrated how flexibility can be incorporated into the cost structure to meet known or anticipated price changes. Similar adjustments can be made to meet variability and uncertainty in weather and yields. We postpone further analysis of these problems until the uncertainty precautions of Chapter 17 are discussed. Under uncertainty the entrepreneur must make a subjective decision in respect to choice of flexibility. He should incorporate flexibility into the firm as long as its value is greater than its cost. If carried too far, flexibility causes undue cost sacrifices for each unit of output attained. In agriculture, "inflexible" costs functions may lie above "flexible" curves mainly in the range of small outputs; they usually lie below "flexible" curves over both intermediate and large outputs. The decision then is whether, with capital limited, a plant should be built which will allow lower per unit costs in case output must be contracted.

Selected References

Allen, R. G. D., *Mathematical Analysis for Economists*, London: Macmillan, 1942, pp. 260-262.

Black, J. D., *et al., Farm Management*. New York: Macmillan, 1947, Ch. 21.

Brewster, J., and Parsons, H., "Can Prices Allocate Resources in Agriculture," *Jour. Farm Econ.*, Vol. 27.

Carlson, Sune, *A Study in the Pure Theory of Production* London: King & Son, 1939, pp. 41-52.

Stigler, G., "Production and Distribution in The Short-run," *Jour. Pol. Econ.*, 1939.

———, *Theory of Price*. New York: Macmillan, 1947, pp. 126-138.

Tarshis, Lorie, *Elements of Economics*. New York: Houghton Mifflin, 1947, Chs. 6, 7, 8, 9.

Weintraub, S., *Price Theory*. New York: Putnam, 1949, pp. 72-77.

Wilcox, W. W., "Effects of Farm Price Change on Efficiency in Farming," *Jour. Farm Econ.*, Vol. 33.

12

Returns to Scale and Farm Size

Pʀᴇᴠɪᴏᴜs ᴄʜᴀᴘᴛᴇʀs have dealt with production relationships when one or more resources in the farm firm are fixed. We are now ready to examine the nature of physical and economic returns when all resource services can be varied. The problem to be analyzed is one of returns to scale or the economics of farm size. The subject is one which is of interest not only to agricultural production economists but also to operating farmers and the general citizenry. Farm operators are interested in the nature of returns to scale from the standpoint of profits; the non-farm population is interested in farm size not only from the standpoint of efficiency in production of food and fiber but also from the standpoint of political and sociological ends. Not all the ends toward which farm size can be directed are compatible. At the farm level the operator must compare the utility from (possible) added profits with the disutility from taking greater risks or expending greater energies in the management function. At the national level society may choose between larger farms as a means of attaining economies in food production and smaller farms as a means of attaining sociological objectives and political stability. The extent to which one end should be extended at the expense of another, either at the farm or national level, depends quite largely on the nature of returns to scale in farming. If scale or size economies are very great, other ends may be extended only at a very great sacrifice. If scale economies are small or non-existent, small farms might be used with little sacrifice in attaining a more nearly equal distribution of farm wealth, political stability within agricultural, and similar ends.

Agricultural production economists have been concerned with farm size since the birth of agricultural economics. Warren included an analysis of returns to scale in his early survey of Tompkins County, New York;[1] in relating farm size to labor income or profit he inferred, through his findings, constant or increasing returns to scale because profits increased continuously over the range of farm sizes studied. Similarly, farm management studies over the past several decades have continued to provide inferences

---

[1] Warren, G. F., *A Survey of Tompkins County, New York.* New York Agr. Exp. Sta. Bul. 295, Ithaca, 1909.

of constant or increasing returns to size. Many hypotheses in respect to scale and cost economies also prevail. Most groups interested in "maintaining and extending" the interests of farming put forth the assumption that great economies exist for large farms and, therefore, the small family farm is on the verge of being eliminated. Although this man-on-the-street speculation has been going on for four decades, major and rapid adjustments have not taken place in farm size. Continuance of the so-called family farm as the main structure of agriculture suggests, on the one hand, that if size economies exist, they soon give way to diseconomies. Concurrently, the continuance of the small farms suggests the hypothesis that economic dynamics or risk and uncertainty may be the final determinant of farm size in agriculture.

In the analysis which follows we set forth the fundamentals of scale or size relationships. Emphasis is focused first on pure scale relationships. Finally, we discuss the nature of cost relationships as they relate in any manner to farm size. Those aspects of capital use and farm size dealing with uncertainty, perhaps the most important phenomena explaining the pattern of farm size, are discussed in Chapter 18.

Pure Scale Relationships

A study of scale relationships is simply an extension of the analysis presented in earlier chapters. Scale relationships can be analyzed from the standpoint of a firm which produces either a single product or multiple products. In order to simplify the analysis which follows we begin with a single product and return to the relationships considered initially in Chapters 2 and 5, which were concerned almost entirely with relationships in proportionality for a single product. We recognized that the production process involved a number of resources but these were considered in the vein of a production function such as

$$Y = f(X_1|X_2, X_3, X_4 \ldots X_n) \text{ or } Y = f(X_1, X_2|X_3, X_4 \ldots X_n)$$

where only the resources on the left of the vertical bar were variable; those on the right were held fixed or constant. Only proportionality relationships were studied, since, as some resources were held constant while others were increased, the proportions of the factors were changed. In studying scale relationships we consider a production function of the nature $Y = f(X_1, X_2, X_3, X_4 \ldots X_n)$ where all resources are variable. Pure scale relationships are involved only if all resources which go into production are increased by the same proportion: if the input of one is doubled, the input of all others must be doubled. If all resources are increased, but some are doubled while others are tripled, the resulting change in input-output relationships involves variable proportions. Under proportionality relationships we were interested in whether the marginal productivity of one factor was of a constant, increasing, or decreasing nature as the factor was added to a fixed collection of other resources. We are now concerned with whether, as all factors are increased by the same proportion, the product increases by (1) the same proportion, (2) a greater proportion, or (3) a smaller proportion. If the first holds true, *constant returns to scale* prevail; the second and third lead to *increasing returns to scale* and *decreasing returns to scale* respectively. Most discussions of scale problems in agriculture actually involve proportionality relationships. Scale relationships are reflected in farming if, and only if, all factors are held in constant proportions as output is increased. This is to say that if an original farm combination includes 160 acres, 15 months of labor, 1 Farmall M tractor, and a given aggregation of other resources, scale relationships are involved if input is increased to include 320 acres, 30 months of labor, 2 tractors, and a doubling of the other resource aggregation. If the first resource combination is accompanied by an output of 3,200 bushels of wheat and the second is accompanied by an output of 6,400 bushels, constant returns to scale prevail. Outputs of more or less than 6,400 bushels for the second combination would denote increasing and decreasing returns respectively. An increase from the first combination to one including 320 acres, 18 months of labor and 1 tractor involves a proportionality relationship. In order to simplify our initial discussion of scale relationships, we will return to a geometric presentation and consider a production function of the nature $Y = f(X_1, X_2)$, where only two resources are involved. The same analysis can be extended to any number of resources.

Proportionality relationships and size of the producing plant. Distinction between proportionality and scale relationships can be made by referring to a product contour (iso-product) map of the nature outlined in Chapter 5 and illustrated again in Figure 1. The four contours illustrate the possible combinations of X_1 and X_2 which can be employed in producing 100, 200, 300, or 400 units of the product, Y_1; a different contour exists for each level of output. Proportionality is illustrated when the input of resource X_1 is held constant at 150 and X_2 is varied from zero to 15, 40, 80, and 140 units. Diminishing productivity holds true for X_2 since, as input is increased from 15 to 40 or by 267 per cent, output increases only from 100 to 200 or by 100 per cent. Similarly, output increases by smaller percentages than factor input as X_2 is increased to 80 and 140 units. Diminishing returns also holds true for X_1 when factor X_2 is held fixed at any one level. This statement becomes obvious when the vertical distances between the iso-product contours are examined. If the input of X_2 is held fixed at 140, the vertical distances between product contours (the dotted line above 140), indicating the input of X_1, become greater and greater as the product contours representing 100, 200, 300, and 400 units of product are reached.

A different relationship in proportionality exists for each level at which resources are fixed. For example, the vertical lines in Figure 1 trace out different productivities for X_1 as X_2 is held fixed at different levels. Output can be varied by increases in X_1 when the "size" of the producing or technical unit (quantity of fixed factors) is defined by 140 units of X_2. Output can also be varied to the same levels when X_1 is increased and size of the producing unit is defined by 80 units of X_2. We thus distinguish between changes in output (1) when variable resources are applied more intensively on a plant of a given size (for example, extending output from 200 to 400 when X_1 is increased and X_2 is fixed at 140) and (2) when size of the plant is increased (for example, a shift from 80 to 140 units of X_2). In agriculture, 8,000 bushels of corn might be produced on a farm unit of 160 acres. Starting from this base with machinery and labor fixed, output might be increased to 9,600 bushels either by (a) applying 20 lbs. of nitrogen on each of the 160 acres or (b) farming 182 acres without nitrogen. Both adjustments result in a change in the "size of the business." In one case, fertilizer is the variable resource. In the other case, land is the variable factor. While farmers often refer to farm size in terms of acres (technical units), changes in size can be made through increases in any resource. For purposes of later distinction, we refer to the first or (a) in terms of "level of output" or "degree of intensity," and the second or (b) as "size of the unit." Size also can be increased in the scale sense indicated below.

Scale relationships and farm size. In contrast to proportionality relationships, scale relationships refer to a simultaneous increase in all resources. Proportionality relationships involve the "short-run" production functions of which one or more factors are fixed. Scale relationships involve long-run production functions of which no factors are fixed. When all factors are increased in fixed proportions, they, in effect, represent one single aggregate resource. This aggregate of resources can be considered as a single homogeneous factor, since the particular factors are combined in the same ratio irrespective of output. Scale relationships can thus be presented in the graphic form of the single-factor production functions illustrated in Chapter 2; Figure 2 in Chapter 2 illustrates constant returns to scale, while Figures 3 and 4 represent decreasing and increasing returns to scale respectively when only one factor is involved in production. However, we return to a contour map in order to distinguish better between proportionality and scale relationships. Scale relationships are indicated by lines OS_1 and OS_2 in Figure 1. The scale line is drawn in linear fashion to indicate that factors are held in fixed proportions. For scale line OS_1, the combination of factors is always in the ratio of 1.25 of X_1 to 1.0 of X_2; for scale line OS_2, the ratio (slope) at any point is 1.0 of X_1 to 1.33 of X_2. Scale relationships are indicated by the intersection of lines OS_1 or OS_2 with the product contours. At the point of intersection of OS_2 with the 100-unit contour, the factor inputs include 30 of X_1 and 40 of X_2. A doubling of the factors extends inputs to 60 of X_1 and 80 of X_2. The product contour which intersects this point on the scale line denotes an output of 200 units of X_2. Thus constant returns to scale holds true: an increase in factor input by 100 per cent has increased the output by the same percentage. A further increase in factors to 90 of X_1 and 120 of X_2 (an increase of 50 per cent for each) results in an increase of product to 300 or by 50 per cent and the elasticity of production is again 1.0. Although figures are not included, the constant returns to scale are also traced out along scale line

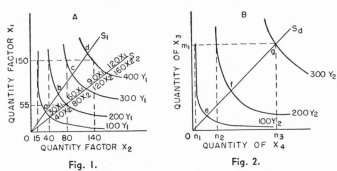

Fig. I.   Fig. 2.

Constant and increasing returns to scale (diminishing productivity for single factors).

OS_1; the vertical distances Oa, ab, bc, and cd on the scale line are all equal between intersections with the contours. The contour map of Figure 1 denotes a *linear, homogeneous production function*.[2]

[2] A production function denoting constant returns to scale is said to be homogeneous of the first degree, denoting that, if input of each factor is multiplied by a constant amount, the product will be increased in a like ratio. The marginal and average productivity of all factors depends only on the ratio between the amounts of the factors and not on the amount of the factors. If a production function is defined as $Y = f(X, Z)$ and the input of both X and Z is multiplied by a constant k, the right side of the equation becomes $f(kX, kZ)$ and the product will be increased by the same proportion (to kY) only if the function is homogeneous of the first degree. In other words, we must have the condition $f(kX, kZ) = kf(X, Z) = kY$, denoting that the product is increased by the same constant ratio as all factors.

We can now illustrate the difference between production functions which denote constant returns to scale and those which illustrate economies and diseconomies to scale. Suppose that the production function can be defined in the manner of (1) below, where Y refers to the product, while L refers to labor, and C refers to capital.

$$Y = 10\,C^{.25}L^{.75} \tag{1}$$

If we multiply each factor by a constant, k, the right side of the equation becomes $10\,(kC)^{.25}(kL)^{.75}$.

Using the rules of simple logarithmic multiplication, we obtain (2) and (3) which can be simplified to (4) and (5).

$$10\,k^{.25}C^{.25}k^{.75}L^{.75} \tag{2}$$
$$= 10\,k^{.25+.75}C^{.25}L^{.75} \tag{3}$$
$$= 10\,kC^{.25}L^{.75} \tag{4}$$
$$= k(10C^{.25}L^{.75}) \tag{5}$$

Accordingly, the product will also be increased by the same ratio, k, since the power of k above is 1.

$$\text{Thus } kY = k(10C^{.25}L^{.75}) \tag{6}$$

Therefore, since $kY = 10(kC)^{.25}(kL)^{.25}$ constant returns to scale hold true.

An important contrast can now be made in Figure 1. While diminishing returns hold true for either individual factor (an elasticity of less than 1.0 when the other is held constant), constant returns to scale hold true when both factors are increased by the same proportion. Returns to a single factor and returns to scale may actually be in opposite directions. This statement is consistent with our earlier note in which we said that the elasticity of production for any individual factor tends to increase as greater numbers of other resources are also increased.

Decreasing returns to scale are illustrated in Figure 2 for the product Y_2. When X_3 and X_4 are held constant in the proportions indicated by scale line S_d, the percentage increase in aggregate input is greater than the percentage increase in output of product. This fact is indicated by the increasing length of the scale line segments, assuming that starting from the origin, O, the distance between the points of intersection of successive product contours with the scale line becomes progressively greater. If output is to be increased from 100 to 200, or by 100 per cent, aggregate factor input must be more than doubled; the distance ef is greater than oe. Similarly, an increase in product by 50 per cent (from 200 to 300) requires an increase in factor input by more than 50 per cent. (For the production function illustrated in Figure 2, diminishing productivity also holds true for single factors. Again, this is evidenced by the fact that when factor X_3 is held constant, at om_1, increasingly greater inputs of X_4 bring about equal increments of product.) Increasing returns to scale might be shown similarly on a contour map. In this case, starting at the origin, O, the distance between the points of intersection of successive product contours with the scale line becomes progressively smaller.

The classical production function which includes a range of increasing returns to scale, a point of constant returns to scale and a range of decreasing returns to scale, would be denoted by scale line segments (between points of intersection by successive product contours) which first decrease and finally increase. The percentage increase in each resource input would have to be related to the percentage change in output to determine whether the segment of the scale line between successive contours fell within an area of increasing or decreasing returns to scale. Obviously, this single point of constant returns to scale would be difficult to locate on a contour map. The investigator concerned with locating points such as these must resort to algebra and calculus rather than geometry.

The scale line need not indicate the path of resource combinations which should be employed (to minimize cost at each level of output and hence maximize profits) were a producing unit to start from zero and increase output to its most profitable level where marginal revenue equals marginal cost for the aggregate resource input. If the marginal rate at which factors substitute differs significantly at varying levels of output, different proportions of factors should be employed at different levels of output. An isocline such as those described in Chapter 5 defines the path which re-source combinations should follow when scale is increased. The isocline to be followed is the one which defines factor substitution ratios, all of which are equal to the factor price ratio. This single isocline is termed the *expansion path,* and, for a single product firm, output should be extended along it until marginal cost is equal to marginal revenue.

Scale relationships and agricultural studies. Scale relationships are basic to certain inferences which are made in the field of agricultural production economics. The conventional procedure employed in farm management wherein residual returns are imputed (1) to management or labor as a basis for efficiency comparisons between individual firms, between regions and between industries imply constant returns to scale (2) to land as a basis of farm appraisal or (3) to pasture as a method of measuring crop returns, assume that if the marginal product is derived for all factors but one, the residue of the product can be imputed to it. Production economics logic justifies this procedure only in the case of constant returns to scale and the conditions of equilibrium and competition to be outlined in Chapter 13.

Scale relationships in agriculture. Although discussions and arguments over farm size have been hot and heavy for several decades, very little is actually known about returns to scale in agriculture. or even about the nature of costs as related to proportionality adjustments in farm acreage or livestock numbers. On the one hand it appears that constant returns to scale should prevail if all factors including management could be increased by equal proportions. On the other hand it appears that physical scale re-lationships should be of an increasing or decreasing nature. It is likely that diminishing returns hold true for a plow which is made bigger and bigger (for example, an increase from one 14-inch plow bottom to 2, 4, 8, or 16 14-inch plow bottoms).[3] Conversely, if the diameter of a silo is increased, volume increases, but limits in strength are reached at a greater rate than the increase in diameter of the structure. The first laws of physics indicate that as an object is increased according to scale, volume increases as the cube of the length, while area increases only as the square. In the case of the silo, proportionately greater inputs of mate-rials would be necessary if additions to the capacity of the silo were made in a purely vertical manner. While engineering phenomena might specify

---

[3] The following quotation (from J. M. Clark, *The Economies of Overhead Costs.* Chicago: University of Chicago Press, 1923) is a classic illustration of this point:

"There is the story of the man who thought of getting large-scale production in plowing, and built a plow three times as long, three times as wide and three times as deep as the ordinary plow and harnessed six horses instead of two to pull it. To his surprise the plow refused to budge, and to his greater surprise, it finally took fifty horses to move the refractory machine. In this case the resistance, the thing he did not want, increased faster than the surface area of the earth plowed, which was the thing he did want."

either increasing or decreasing returns, scale changes need not be restricted to the types of adjustments outlined above. Scale can be increased by the use of 2 4-bottom plows and 2 identical tractors rather
than 1 8-bottom plow and a "proportionately larger" tractor. Silage
storing capacity can be increased to 30,000 tons by building 100 silos,
each of which stores 300 tons, as well as by building 1 silo which holds
30,000 tons. Similarly, scale can be increased for a single farm firm through
addition of duplicate acreages and duplicate collections of machinery as
well as by a spatial expansion of a given unit. If the original farm size
includes 640 acres of wheat land, 12 months of labor, and 1 tractor
with complementary equipment, the farm firm can be doubled in scale
by acquisition of another 640 acres and use of 24 months of labor
and a duplicate set of machinery. Obviously, some degree of decreasing
returns would exist if the farm headquarters were retained at a single
location as acres, labor, and machines are increased. Added time would be
required in mere travel to outlying fields as the farm acreage increased.
Yet the establishment of a second farm headquarters could, conceivably,
reduce travel on the second 640 acres to a point where it equals that on
the first. The same type of scale adjustment can be made in livestock production. A common farmer observation is that the disease hazard in hog
production becomes greater when numbers of litters is increased beyond
18-20 per season. However, even if disease is a function of herd size, the
swine enterprise need not be increased at a single location. Size of the hog
enterprise can be increased in the "true scale" sense while the disease
hazard is controlled by having duplicate units at different corners of the
farm or even on different farms. It seems possible that constant returns
(and very likely that decreasing costs in the proportionality and fixed cost
sense) might hold true were single farmers to double or triple operating
units in the manner outlined here. While not all farmers have managerial
ability to expand scale, certainly a large number of operators have. Perhaps few follow this course because of the uncertainty-capital rationing
complex outlined in a later chapter.

Returns-to-scale relationships are accurately reflected only if all factors
including management are increased in equal proportions. The increased
input of management services can be made in 1 of 2 ways: Management can be increased by adding individuals who also contribute decision-
making or coordinating services (this is the true scale method of adding
entrepreneurship) or by more fully utilizing the capacities (the stock of
managerial ability) of a single individual. In the second case, the farm
entrepreneur may not exhaust his decision-making powers for small-scale
operations. He may, however, draw more heavily on this "stock of ability"
with larger operations by simply devoting more thought to decision-making or by a reduction in the manual labor performed, accompanied by a
greater concentration on managerial functions. While true scale relation-

ships involve increases in managerial services which parallel additions of other factor services, returns-to-scale relationships might also be considered in the light of a fixed stock of management (with different quantities of the "flow" of managerial services being utilized as scale is increased). Actually, a large-scale firm in agriculture could be organized in the manner of current commercial farm management companies. The prevalent system includes the management of rented farms for a fee with each tenant owning his own equipment and acting as a "sub-manager" for the particular unit. A "management firm" also could be organized whereby the single company (a) owns all resources and hires laborer-submanagers; (b) rents land directly, owns machinery, livestock, and other capital, but otherwise follows system (a); or (c) rents the land and sublets it to a tenant who furnishes other resources. Under any of these 3 systems a single supervisor (farm manager) might be employed to provide direct management for each 40 or 50 farms. It appears likely that constant returns might be realized for the first several supervisors if it were possible to obtain (1) large numbers of farms of equal size on similar soil, (2) tenants of equal capital, technical and organizational ability, and (3) supervisors of equal coordinating ability. (See later chapter on uncertainty for a detailed distinction between coordination and supervision.) At least this possibility exists for the first several groups of farms which might be added (and without reference to any decreasing short-run costs associated with the spreading of the fixed costs of office space and other overhead facilities of the central concern).[4]

Possibilities of increasing and decreasing returns to scale. Specialization and division of labor by tasks provide one basis for an hypothesis of ranges of increasing returns to scale in agriculture. With the number of laborers, machines, buildings, and animals increased in identical proportions (with factor homogeneity in the sense that machines are of equal size or laborers are of equal capacity), the greater volume should allow workers to specialize to the extent that tasks can be fitted to ability of the worker and work simplification (labor saving methods) can be extended. With a proportionate increase in all factors, the product should increase because of the greater labor productivity. On a highly specialized duck or poultry farm, these economies are realized where the hatching, growing, and slaughter of poultry is on a scale which allows one man to specialize in preparing feed and another to specialize in feeding operations, while the same specialization extends through the slaughtering stages.

---

[4] Increasing or decreasing short-run costs might occur within each "supervisory unit" as farms are increased from (say) 1 to 40, due to proportionality (or even scale relationships). However, given homogeneity of farms, supervisors, tenants, and other resources, the costs and returns should be duplicated for 4 as compared to 2 supervisory units, each made up of 40 farms (plants). The overhead management of a commercial firm becomes the "eventual fixed factor," and hence may give rise to decreasing returns because of proportionality reasons.

Some dry-lot dairy farms also are large enough to realize these scale economies. However, most farms never have attained a size such that these economies, labor specialization particularly, have been realized to any significant degree. It is not that scale economies are absent from agriculture; the great majority of producing units never attain a volume large enough so that increasing physical returns become important. Even for farms employing 2 or 3 men, the seasonality and the spatial and biological character of agricultural production serve to deter the scale gains realized in small non-farm firms of approximately the same size. While other types of "factor-interaction" exist and lead to increasing returns to scale, these appear unimportant in agriculture. Some writers consider that scale economies exist in this sense: a dairy enterprise of 30 cows which produces twice as much milk as a 15-cow herd will not usually require twice the quantity of materials for barn space, milking machines, and equipment. For example, a dairy barn for 30 cows may be twice as long as one for 15 cows but it will not require twice as much lumber, as will 2 barns with a capacity of 15 animals each; the long barn will require only 2 ends, while 2 small barns of the same length require 4 ends. The same logic can be applied to machines and other buildings. However, this adjustment becomes one of proportionality (the input of buildings is not doubled with cow numbers) unless the 2 barn ends otherwise saved are used for facilities which improve the health and production of the 30-cow herd. If the "saved" lumber is used in a manner to boost milk production of the 30 cows to a level which is more than double that for 15 cows, increasing economies to scale exist. An exact doubling of output (with labor, feed, and other resources as well as farms doubled) denotes constant returns to scale.

Decreasing physical returns to scale in agriculture are likely to be explained mainly in managerial limitations. However, the relationship falls in the realm of proportionality when a single stock of management is limited in the sense that pure supervision becomes less exacting, and coordination (true management or choice-making) becomes less perfect. Management, in the sense of coordination, is limited because of the uncertainty considerations outlined in Chapter 18. Another type of "factor interaction" or physical diseconomy may arise in multiple-enterprise units where the joint expansion in 2 enterprises such as turkeys and chickens may bring forth diseases which would not prevail with small outputs. Finally, distance and travel may cause decreasing returns to scale where acreage is extended contiguously rather than as 2 distinct units each with its own farmstead.

Farm production functions. The only empirical studies which have been made to test returns to scale in agriculture suggest either decreasing or constant returns. Even then these data cannot be taken as conclusive evidence. They are based on samples which include great heterogeneity in the resources employed: management has not been included as an input and perhaps the procedures employed are not most appropriate. Using a logarithmic function which forces a single elasticity for each factor, the writer obtained the data for Iowa farms included below in Table 1. While the function employed allows only elasticity over the range of observations studied, the same function was employed for different segments of the data; all ranges gave elasticities indicative of decreasing returns to scale.

Table 1.

Elasticities Indicating Returns to Scale Relationships for a Random Sample of Iowa Farms.*

Elasticity of particular resource services

Farm Type	Land	Labor	Equipment	Livestock and feed	Other resource services	Total elasticity
Crop farms	.24	.07	.08	.53	.02	.94
Hog farms	.07	.02	.10	.74	.03	.97
Dairy farms	.10	.01	.06	.63	.02	.82
General farms	.17	.12	.16	.46	.03	.94
Large farms	.28	.01	.11	.53	.03	.96
Small farms	.21	.05	.08	.43	.03	.81

* Source: E. O. Heady, "Production Functions from a Random Sample," *Jour. Farm Econ.*, Vol. 28.

The elasticity figure for each resource indicates the percentage by which output increases for each 1 per cent increase in the particular factor. If the sum of the elasticities for all of the factors were exactly 1.0, constant returns to scale would be denoted; an increase in all inputs by 1.0 per cent would increase output by 1.0 per cent. In Table 1 the sum of the elasticities is less than 1.0 for each type of farm as well as for both large and small farms, and thus suggests decreasing returns to scale as an average "over all" inputs. The "degree of increasing returns" is greater for large than for small farms. Decreasing returns holds true for individual resources for all farm types. Until more conclusive data are derived, the exact nature of returns to scale for any segment of agriculture will remain unknown. Some studies have indicated constant or increasing returns to scale.[5]

---

[5] A production function derived for Southern Iowa farms in 1950 gave the following results, where Y refers to the value of farm production, R refers to real estate (land and buildings), L refers to labor, M refers to machine services, F refers to livestock and feed services, and Z refers to miscellaneous resource services:

$$Y = .31R^{.23}L^{.03}M^{.10}F^{.50}Z^{.25}$$

The exponents of this logarithmic function are elasticities: an increase in real estate by 1.0 per cent is accompanied by a .23 per cent increase in product. Since the sum of the elasticities is 1.11, increasing returns to scale should be indicated. However, a test of significance indicated that, at a 5 per cent probability level, the results do not differ significantly from constant returns.

A production function estimated by means of simultaneous equations for cash-crop farms in Central Iowa for 1948 resulted in the following regression equation with inputs aggregated into labor (L), all capital services (C), and land (R):

$$Y = 1.46L^{.06}C^{.47}R^{.57}$$

The data of Table 2 were derived by means of simultaneous equations and give some suggestion of returns to scale in crop and livestock production in Southern Iowa for 1947. The estimates suggest that crop production

Table 2.

Elasticities Estimated for Crop and Livestock Production in Southern Iowa.

Resource	Elasticities in crop production	Elasticities in livestock production
Land	.36	.04
Labor	.44	.17
Capital in equipment, machine services, buildings, crop services, and so forth	.01	.41
Capital in livestock		.49
Total elasticity	.81	1.11

took place under decreasing returns (a 1 per cent increase in all resources gave a .81 per cent increase in output) while livestock production took place under conditions of increasing returns; farms in the area generally have little capital and little livestock. Generally, we would expect the great economies to scale in crop rather than livestock production, however.

Early studies, such as that of Warren, suggested increasing returns to scale or declining average costs through the ranges of farm sizes studied; [6] the relatively greater labor return or management profit on large farms implies, apart from the imputational difficulties mentioned later, some nature of factor or cost savings as output per farm is expanded. More recent studies based on the same technique of estimation suggest the same thing for prosperous periods but imply decreasing returns during periods of unfavorable prices.[7] Much work is yet to be done before any refined knowledge will be had about scale relationships in farming.

Size and Cost Economies

While the size of the firm can be increased through scale adjustments, most changes in farm size and most of the concern about farm size revolve around semi-proportionality adjustments. One farmer operates 160 acres

While the sum of the constant elasticities is 1.1, suggesting that an increase in all factors by 1 per cent results in an increased output of 1.1 per cent, the statistics do not differ significantly from linear. For problems and limitations in estimation of these functions, see the discussion and literature cited in the following: Heady, E. O., "Use and Estimation of Input-Output Ratios," *Jour. Farm Econ.,* Vol. 34, and Heady, E. O., "Production Functions from a Random Sample," *Jour. Farm Econ.,* Vol. 28.

[6] Warren, G. F., *Farming in Tompkins County, New York.* New York Agr. Exp. Sta. Bul. 295.

[7] See studies such as E. F. Carpenter, *Farm size in California.* U.S.D.A. mimeo; W. Ruden, *Farm Size and its Relation to Volume of Production and Costs.* Nebr. Agr. Exp. Sta. Bul. 346; and A. Nelson, *Planning Minimum-Sized Farms in Central South Dakota.* S. Dak. Agr. Exp. Sta. Bul. 341.

with a general-purpose tractor and 15 months of labor; another operates 240 acres with the same complement of machinery and 20 months of labor. A third farmer may operate 420 acres with 2 large tractors and 24 months of labor. In neither of these cases is the difference in farm size reflected by proportional adjustments in all resources or by homogeneity in form of resources. Thus in the remainder of this chapter we use the term "change" or "difference" in size to refer to different firm or plant capacities which are possible through expansion by either the scale or proportionality route or some combination of the two. The discussion which follows refers particularly to size of producing unit as denoted by different levels of fixed factors such as different acreages operated by the same complement of machinery or without proportional adjustments in equipment.

Cost economies and diseconomies. Most concern over farm size has to do with the per-unit costs associated with farms of different magnitudes. The individual operator is interested in the average and marginal costs as they relate to the profitability of acreages or livestock enterprises of different sizes. The popular public concern over farm size has been in terms of the average costs for farms of different acreages and the competitive advantage of large as compared to small units. Hence we pause to examine cost economies and diseconomies from whatever source they may arise. By cost economies or cost diseconomies, we refer to phenomena which cause unit costs to decrease or increase respectively as size of the plant (number of technical units) and output are expanded. We have already discussed changes in unit costs as output is extended to more intensive levels for a plant of given size; this was the subject of analysis in Chapter 11.

Physical scale relationships partly explain why unit costs of production change as firm size and output increases. Increasing physical returns to scale cause declining per-unit costs; decreasing returns to scale have the opposite effect. However, other forces also are important in causing costs to change as size and output are expanded. In fact, certain cost economies are realized only as size is increased in the proportionality sense with some change in the form of machines or other resources.[8] Cost economies or diseconomies may be either internal or external to the individual producing unit. They may also be of a monetary (pecuniary or market) nature or of a physical (technological) nature. Internal economies are those realized

---

[8] The presentation here may appear somewhat unorthodox in the sense that scale relationships have been in terms of increasing and decreasing returns in a physical sense, while cost economies and diseconomies refer to any force which causes unit costs to decline or increase as size and output is increased. The terms "increasing returns to scale" and "cost economies," or "decreasing returns to scale" and "cost diseconomies," are not used as synonyms. The large firm which has expanded in the proportional sense realizes lower unit costs, and we are therefore interested in this avenue of expansion.

from size adjustments within the individual producing unit; they occur irrespective of adjustments in the industry. External economies are those realized entirely outside the producing unit. They depend on adjustments of the industry and relate to the firm only as it is a part of the industry.

Internal market economies. Internal market (pecuniary) economies are those associated with purchase of factors or credit in large scale lots.[9] While some price gains are forthcoming for the agricultural firm as production materials or borrowed funds are acquired in large as compared to small lots, the main cost differences between farms of different size do not appear to grow out of economies of this nature. The relative cost advantages growing out of quantity buying or selling are likely to be in such situations as plantations (with operations performed by hired labor under one management) as compared to straight share-cropper farms in cotton areas.

Internal physical economies. This type of cost reduction arises mainly as the indivisibility of factors is overcome when size and output is increased. Use of work simplification techniques and division-of-labor procedures represents one example. A similar physical economy comes about as size is expanded by use of different levels or forms of fixed factors. The fixed cost phenomenon discussed in the previous chapter is of this nature: a larger volume in a plant of a given size causes declining average costs as long as the decline in per-unit fixed cost is greater than the increase in per-unit variable cost. Indivisibility also is overcome, in the sense that large machines can be used for large producing units but are not economical for small units (the form of the resource can be changed). The farmer with a few bushels of grain or a few head of livestock may use a scoop or a pitchfork, while one with a large volume may employ automatic elevators. Although automatic elevators can be used on very small farms, the fixed costs are prohibitive. Finally, costs of small machines are high relative to their capacity, as compared to that of large machines.[10] Cost advantages of pig and chick hatcheries are mainly of an internal technical nature although market economies are not unimportant.

Internal diseconomies. Internal diseconomies in agriculture are largely of a technical nature. Few farms purchase so much of any factor that its supply price increases with additional use. (This situation does exist, however, for specialized vegetable or other units which employ the entire

---

[9] Ultimately all economies result from physical economies. A large farm may, because of the volume, receive a discount on feed. The feed firm, however, is able to give the price discount because it is able to sell a greater quantity with 1 bookkeeping entry, 1 salesman, and 1 haul, as well as to make other gains through proportionality adjustments.

[10] The shift from 10 acres cultivated by 1 man and a garden tractor to 500 acres cultivated by 2 men and 1 large tractor made up of 50 times more steel does not represent a "pure" scale relationship because (1) the proportion of labor and other resources has changed and (2) the machinery resources are no longer homogeneous.

local supply of day labor and must bid against outside employments and at higher rates as volume increases.) Physical diseconomies are mainly of the nature already outlined in previous sections, where management and space become limiting factors and result in diminishing productivity for other resources. Another physical diseconomy may be of the "factor inter-action" and disease-hazard type already mentioned. When one set of machinery is taken as the fixed resource, cultivation of more and more acres eventually causes factor productivity to decline, because the added acres cannot be cultivated in a timely fashion over the number of working and growing days available in a single year.

External economies. External economies and diseconomies are not wide-spread in agriculture but some are important. External market economies arise in farm costs as the number and size of farms in an area increase to such an extent that feed mills, marketing outlets, and transportation systems are built up to give a lower cost for the products delivered to the market (serve as substitutes for processing and transportation which would otherwise be furnished at a higher cost by the individual). Organization of cooperative purchasing or processing firms also may result in lower factor costs or higher product prices particularly as the scale of single enterprises increases. Technical economies arising outside the individual farm arise where greater acreages under cultivation help eliminate weeds, predatory animals, and other pests, and consequently allow a greater output from given farm resources. Some of the more important external physical economies (although these might be equally classed as pecuniary economies) arise in irrigation and drainage projects. Irrigation ditches to carry water in and drainage ditches to carry it out represent large physical and monetary outlays paralleling those of high-capacity machines on a single farm. With increases in the number and size of farms using services from resources of this nature, the indivisibility of a major ditch and other water installations is overcome and fixed costs also can be spread over a larger output. External economies are possible as size is increased either through scale or proportionality adjustments.

External diseconomies. External diseconomies of a market nature arise as all farms in the industry increasingly bid labor, nitrogen for fertilizer, or other resource services away from competing industries. Use of additional resources by farmers in the aggregate is possible only as higher prices are paid for factors and per-unit production costs increase. Technical diseconomies may arise especially under irrigation projects: a point can be reached at which the use of more water by one farmer causes less to be available to others; difficulties are encountered particularly under pump irrigation, where increasing use of ground water lowers the water level and increases pumping costs to individual farms. Cloud seeding and creation of artificial rainfall may also bring about external diseconomies of a physical nature. In the case of soil erosion, one farm realizes reductions in yield as more or larger farms spring up (or break land out of sod) around it and cause rainwater, as it flows from one farm to another, to wash out crops, remove top soil, or form gullies.

Long-Run and Short-Run Costs and Farm Size

Of all the possible forces which may give rise to cost advantages for large-scale farms, internal physical economies growing out of proportionality relationships are most important. These proportionality adjustments are reflected largely in changes in the level and form of fixed factors rather than in pure scale adjustments (although the latter are partially involved). The historic concern of agriculturists over mechanization and farm size is an expression of the belief that cost advantages are brought about largely by this combination of forces. Ordinarily, it is pointed out that while one farmer using horse power or a small tractor can reduce per-unit costs by cultivating more acres, an operator with a single large tractor and a set of high capacity machines can cultivate even more acres and realize much lower per-unit costs because of smaller labor requirements and the spreading of the high fixed cost over a large output.[11]

The relationship between proportionality, unit costs of production, and the optimum size of the firm, either in a minimum cost or maximum profit sense, in agriculture is best explored through concepts of long-run and short-run cost curves. Again, in the terminology of economics, *short run* refers to a cost structure and time period in which some factors are fixed in quantity and form. The cost schedule or curve for a farm which includes 160 acres and a given set of machinery refers to a short-run cost situation. A second farm with 320 acres and a larger set of machinery has a different short-run cost curve. The term *long run* refers to the cost possibilities which face a producing unit over a period of time of such duration that no factors need be considered fixed.[12] It follows then that the difference between the cost curves associated with the 2 units mentioned above refers to long-run costs.[13] By the term "size of the producing unit or firm,"

---

[11] Both situations involve proportionality relationships. In the first case, the operator and the power and equipment complement become fixed, while land (and complementary seed, fertilizer, and so forth) become variable factors. In the second case, the large tractor and the machine complement represent the fixed factor, while acreage is again variable. The capital used in the one case, even though a multiple of that used in the other case, is not a homogeneous type of resource. In addition, the quantities of capital and labor are not likely to be held in constant proportions as output is increased. Even if capital is measured in terms of dollars and without reference to its form (horses or tractors), a true scale relationship is not involved if the second machine combination uses relatively less labor than the first.

[12] In the long run, all costs being variable, there will be only 1 average cost curve and it will represent both the variable and average total costs.

[13] The "shortest" short run exists when crops for the year are already partly grown and costs have been incurred (and therefore, can now be considered as fixed). A

we refer to the existence of different short-run cost curves resulting from different collections of fixed factors. While output can be increased through more intensive operation of a given size plant (the analysis of Chapter 11), we prefer to look upon this adjustment as one of "level of output" from a plant or farm of a given size (rather than relating to different sizes of plant or firm). For our purpose, adjustment in the size of the firm can come about either in the pure scale sense or in the sense that output is increased through an adjustment in all factors but by different proportions (including a decrease of some factors and an increase in others).

Short-run cost curves. A different short-run cost curve may exist for each level of fixed factors and for each variation in the form of fixed factors (each variation in the technique of production). These possibilities can be illustrated by Figure 3.[14] Curve SAC_1 might be taken to represent the average costs for a farm which can operate a variable number of acres with 1 set of small machines as fixed factors. As in the case of the cost curves discussed earlier, SAC_1 may decline with greater outputs, as increasing productivity is realized for the variable factor, or fixed costs are spread over a greater output. The bases for its eventual rise were explained in Chapter 11. Curve SAC_2 may represent a farm which includes fixed resources made up of 2 sets of small machines or 1 set of large machines.[15] On the other hand, SAC_1 may represent the cost situation on a dairy farm where fixed costs are represented by a barn which houses 15 cows; SAC_2 may represent the situation for a barn of identical construc-

---

"medium" short run (or long run) exists in the sense that, while little can be done to change the current year's cost structure, the acreage and direct costs are entirely variable in the year ahead (but the overhead costs represented by specialized machinery are not variable in the next year). The "longest" long run applies to the time span in which even specialized machines will be worn out and the entrepreneur can consider all costs as variable. The possible number of "lengths of run" is almost infinite. Once a farmer has selected a particular combination and form of resources, an entire series of short runs exist. One may refer to the complete depreciation of cultivator shovels in a year; another may refer to the complete depreciation of the power unit in 10 years and the cultivator in 15 years; but the buildings may not necessitate a "replacement decision" for at least 50 years. What is really important is that the relevant "length of run" be selected for the particular problem under analysis.

[14] These curves also relate to scale relationships if the increase in quantity of factors (the fixed factors represented by SAC_1, SAC_2, and so forth) refer to factors which are homogeneous or are of the same form in all cases. The relationship of short-run cost curves to the product contour map can now be explained. Short-run curve SAC_1 in Figure 3 might be looked upon as representing an increase in X_1 in Figure 1 while X_2 is held constant at 40; curve SAC_2 in Figure 3 represents variations in X_1 in Figure 1 when X_2 is held constant at 80. The long-run curve in Figure 4 may be representative of a scale-line adjustment when all resources are variable (such as S_1 or S_2 in Figure 1). If long-run cost curve LAC in Figure 4 represents a scale adjustment, both increasing and decreasing physical returns to scale must exist in the product contour map.

[15] This family of curves may be taken to mean this also: each short-run curve represents the minimum curve from a family of curves for a given technique. Thus SAC_1 may represent horses as the power unit, SAC_2 may represent a small tractor, and SAC_3 may represent a diesel power unit.

tion housing 30 cows. If the outlay for the barn does not increase in proportion to the number of cows and the output of milk, costs per unit, at some point, must be less for the large as compared to the small unit. For small acreages or outputs, the cost per unit will be greater for the large-unit SAC_2 than for the small-unit SAC_1; the greater fixed costs cannot be spread over a great enough number of units to result in per-unit cost advantages. Eventually though, cost economies result in lower per-unit costs for the resource combination represented by SAC_2. The cost of producing the small output OY_1 is less under SAC_1 than under SAC_2. However, for the larger outputs OY_2, the per-unit cost is less under SAC_2.

While only 3 short-run cost curves are shown in Figure 3, an entire family of these curves exists for each producing situation. A different short-run curve exists for each level at which identical factors may be held fixed (2 or 3 tractors as compared to 1) or for each possible form of fixed factors (a large Caterpillar tractor as compared to a small Ford tractor). If costs eventually increase (cost diseconomies) for any of the reasons already cited, higher short-run curves such as SAC_3 come about. The cost of producing the output OY_4 is greater under SAC_3 than under SAC_2. However, for "very large" outputs such as OY_5, the per-unit cost is lower under SAC_3.

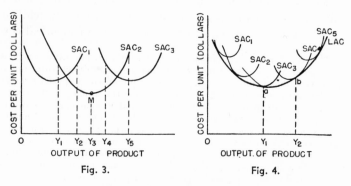

Fig. 3.   Fig. 4.

Short- and long-run cost curves.

Out of an entire family of short-run cost curves, one particular curve has a minimum point which is lower than that of any other curve. SAC_2 represents such a cost curve. At the minimum point, M, the output OY_3 can be produced at a lower cost with the SAC_2 plant than with any other short-run plant. Similarly, the output OY_3 can be produced at a lower cost with plant SAC_2 than can any other output in any size of plant. Using per unit cost of production as the criterion, SAC_2 thus represents the optimum size of producing plant (although the optimum size may be larger under certain short-run price situations and when profit maximization is the criterion).

Long-run costs and planning curves. A long-run cost curve, LAC, can be constructed for any family of short-run cost curves such as those of Figure 3. The long-run cost curve is the "envelope" of the short-run cost curves. This is to say, it is the single curve tangent to the entire family of short-run cost curves. It is tangent to only one point on each single short-run curve in the manner illustrated in Figure 4. The point of tangency is (a) to the left of the minimum cost point on short-run curves denoting firms of a size less than optimum, and (b) to the right of the minimum cost point for plants greater than optimum in size. The point of tangency of the long-run cost curve (LAC) and the short-run curve denoting the lowest possible costs (SAC_3) is at the minimum point on the latter. Conceivably, a short-run cost curve exists for each point on the long-run cost curve. This proposition supposes, however, that fixed factors can be employed in quantities or forms that are entirely divisible. More realistically, the different forms of factors that may become fixed are not entirely divisible. If power units become the fixed factor, then fractions between a small tractor and medium sized tractor may not be possible. Where a dairy barn represents the fixed factor, however, it is entirely possible to build a barn which is 60 feet long, or one which is 60 feet, 6 inches long.

The long-run cost curve can, on the one hand, be looked upon as a planning curve. Were a person ready to start farming, for example, he could consider costs in the sense of LAC in Figure 4, and proceed to build a short-run plant indicated by a particular point such as a or b on the long-run curve. After the producing plant is constructed, the long-run curve becomes of historic interest only. The relevant decision-making cost curve is then of the short-run nature such as SAC_2 or SAC_3. It is not necessary that the firm retain the output (such as OY_1 or OY_2) represented by the particular point (a or b) on the long-run cost curve; given the short-run plant SAC_2 or SAC_4 indicated by the point of tangency, output can be increased by using additional variable resources with the set of fixed factors denoting the particular short-run plants.

Not all farmers can view long-run costs in the sense of a planning curve, wherein they select the most profitable point and collect together the relevant set of resources. Instead, the size of the unit in agriculture is partly a historical phenomenon, wherein a beginning operator acquires a unit of a size determined by the limited resources which he possesses. Following acquisition of the unit, additional output is added as capital accumulates. Opportunity in choice of the particular short-run plant is open to some farmers, however. This possibility exists for those who own or can borrow capital in large amounts. Similarly, it is open to the "financially-able" tenant who can rent farms of various acreages or for corporations which might sell stock and operate on a large-scale basis. The concept of long-run cost curves is most meaningful in agriculture, however, to denote the nature of cost advantage for farms of different sizes.

Other long-run cost possibilities. A long-run cost curve (or family of short-run cost curves) such as that of Figure 4 defines a size situation in which cost economies and diseconomies are both present. There are many other possibilities. One is that lower costs exist for all possible larger sizes of the firm (the long-run curve has a negative slope only). Generally, this possibility must be ruled out on technical grounds. At some size, all indivisibilities are overcome and no other physical economies can be realized. In addition, a volume of output must be attained eventually, at which further pecuniary economies become unimportant. Another possibility is that the long-run curve has a positive slope only. This hypothesis also seems unlikely for any important part of agriculture. Even a hog herd of eight sows, when compared to a herd of four sows, must realize certain economies growing out of factor indivisibility. The discontinuity in factor units or lack of homogeneity in factor form is great enough to result in lower costs over some range of size. A further hypothesis is that the long-run curve is constant in the manner of LAC in Figure 5. Here decreasing

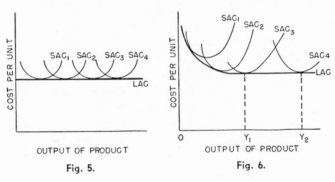

Fig. 5.   Fig. 6.

Alternative long-run cost situation.

and increasing costs would arise for changes in output from short-run plants of given sizes, but a farm with a collection of fixed resources twice as great as that of another would have the same minimum costs (at an output twice as large as that of the smaller unit). This possibility could arise only under a pure condition of constant physical returns to scale where machines and other tools of production were homogeneous in form. Whether or not it represents a true scale relationship (all factors increased in the same proportion) depends on the input of management. If all factors are doubled except management, the relationship is still one of proportionality. If the input of management is not changed, while the input of other factors and the output are doubled, then increasing returns to factors are probably present; a doubling of management along with the doubling of other factors should "more than double" the product. A more nearly acceptable hypothesis is that differences in form of the machines and discontinuities in factor units are great enough to cause lower short-run cost curves in all early farm size ranges. Eventually, though, a point may be reached where economies associated with proportionality and the spreading of fixed costs are completely exhausted. This situation can be illustrated by Figure 6. The short-run curve SAC_1 might represent costs when land is increased relative to a fixed power unit which includes four horses; curve SAC_2 might represent the situation when acres are varied relative to a machinery unit including a Ford tractor and two-row equipment; SAC_3 might represent the costs for a fixed machine unit which includes a general-purpose tractor and four-row equipment.[16] While constant long-run costs may hold true over some ranges of agricultural output, increasing costs undoubtedly occur at some level if management is fixed in quantity.

Agricultural Cost Situation

The structure of long-run costs in various segments of agriculture is a subject of speculation. Although the subject has been the center of debate for several decades, little is actually known about the structure of long-run costs (the level of the various short-run cost curves for units of different sizes) in agriculture. It appears clear that a range of cost economies, growing out of proportionality (different amounts and forms of fixed factors), prevails in all types of agricultural production. How far these decreasing costs extend and whether they merge immediately with increasing costs has not yet been established. Analysis of available engineering and cost data, however, makes it fairly evident that the greatest cost economies associated with units of different sizes are to be found in crop production where power units and machine combinations of high capacities can be substituted for labor and fixed costs can be spread over a large acreage. The relative advantage of the large unit depends, of course, on the cost of labor as compared to the cost of capital in the form of high-capacity machinery. With very low wage rates relative to machine prices, small farms are in a more favorable position. The reverse is true when labor/machine price ratios are high. Large-scale cost advantages stand to be greatest in grain farming regions such as the wheat areas of the Great Plains and the cash crop systems of the Corn belt. Mechanization may lead to important changes in the structure of costs and farm size in the major

---

[16] Strict academic discussion ordinarily assumes that the short-run cost curves from a family representing the same technique all include the same form of resources. Thus SAC_1 would represent a single Farmall M tractor, as the fixed unit, SAC_2 would represent two M tractors, and so forth. However, many of the important farm comparisons must be between cost structures when the form of resource changes (as between a 4-horse team, a Ford tractor, and a Caterpillar tractor). A family of short-run cost curves exists for each form of resources, of course. Hence, if we are interested in different techniques, we might suppose that each short-run curve in Figures 4 or 6 is the minimum curve drawn from its respective family of curves.

cotton-producing regions, depending on the relative adjustment of wage rates to the new situation. Advances in machines which substitute for labor have not been great in animal production. Under existing techniques, the optimum number of animals which can be handled by 1 man is soon attained and further economies are not great when 2 men are employed and twice as many animals are produced. While some further division of labor and specialization in tasks is possible, a 2-man dairy herd requires about double the labor and small equipment (pails, milking units, and so forth) as a 1-man herd. Some savings are made for a barn which holds 32 cows as compared to one which houses 16 cows. However, "length-wise" expansion of the barn saves only the materials required for two ends. Under range cattle or sheep production, labor-saving equipment with high fixed costs, except perhaps in haying, is not important, and a 4-man unit may require almost double the resources and outlay of a 2-man unit. In most types of livestock production, feed represents the major resource employed; there are few if any feed economies as the size of the herd or flock expands.

Competitive Equilibrium and Size

The new techniques of the last two decades (particularly labor-saving machines which have high fixed costs) have caused much concern and alarm; the implied assumption is that minimum long-run costs (the low point on a curve such as LAC in Figure 4 and the "optimum" short-run curve SAC_3) can be realized only by a very great acreage per farm. It is

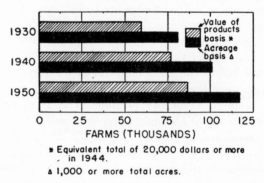

* Equivalent total of 20,000 dollars or more
  , in 1944.
△ 1,000 or more total acres.

Fig. 7. Number of large farms, United States, 1930, 1940, and 1950.

true that small power and machine units are being developed giving cost advantages to small units heretofore available only to large units. The small tractors perfected in the last 10 years characterize this development. Yet the belief still exists that the firm cost structure and competitive nature of agriculture is one which must "force" larger units. The size of the farm measured in acres (the land input) has been increasing steadily over several decades. (See Figure 7.) Concern has not been great over size adjustments through intensification, since (a) census statistics do not record and portray these changes, and (b) the main issue of farm size is one of how many farms can exist; the greater the per-farm acreage, the fewer the farms. While agricultural fundamentalists do not worry about this aspect, it is also true that the larger farms are in terms of the amount of feed utilized on a given acreage, the smaller is the number of farms which can be supported from a given feed supply.

Because of the great public concern over forces which determine farm size, some concepts of size equilibrium are discussed below. Prices for factors and products, along with other forces, help determine the size of the firm which can exist profitably in the long run. In a competitive industry the pressures of market forces are such that the techniques of production (form of resources) and number and size of producing units must result in minimum long-run costs if resource owners are to realize either (a) profit from production (where all resources are hired) or (b) a return on resources as great as possible from alternative investment opportunities (where some resources are owned by the operator or manager). The market adjustment can be in either 1 of 2 directions: prices received for commodities produced may fall to a level which allows only firms of an optimum size and technique to exist; prices paid for resources and resource services can rise to a level which brings about the same equilibrium.

Product prices and size. Figures 8 and 9 illustrate the nature of product-price forces which may force firms to the optimum size in the long-run. In Figure 9 the short-run curves SAC_1, SAC_2, and SAC_3 may be taken to

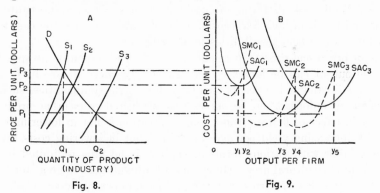

Fig. 8.   Fig. 9.

Equilibrium in size of the producing unit.

illustrate the nature of average costs for three farms of different sizes. The curves SMC_1, SMC_2, and SMC_3 are the short-run marginal costs which attach to each of the average cost curves. Figure 8 illustrates the possible demand and supply situation of the market; curve D is the demand curve, while S_1 is the original short-run supply curve. Under this market situation, price of the product should tend towards OP_3, and farms of the three different sizes can operate at a profit. The small unit (SAC_1) can equate marginal cost and revenue and maximize profits if it produces oy_2 units of product in its fixed plant. The medium-sized unit (SAC_2) can maximize profits with an output of oy_4, while the large unit (SAC_3) can produce oy_5, if profit maximization is the single goal of its activities with the plant indicated by its cost curve.

This cost and price situation results in high profits and should motivate new producers to begin production or cause existing producers to expand size. To the extent that more and larger producers engage in production of the commodity, the short-run supply curve will shift to the right in Figure 8 as indicated by S_2. (The short-run supply curve would, assuming that all producers maximize profits in the short-run, represent the horizontal summation of the marginal cost curves for all individual firms in a static economy.) As this adjustment proceeds far enough, a short-run supply curve such as S_3 is finally attained and the price falls to OP_1. Only firms of an optimum size (minimum average costs) can exist in the long run under this price situation if all costs are to be met (or if the farmer as a resource owner is to realize as much from his own labor and capital as would be possible from their alternative uses). Thus SAC_1 represents a unit which is likely to be eliminated in the long run because it is too small; SAC_3 may be eliminated because it is too large. Only a unit of the size indicated as SAC_2 can exist in the long run. Adjustments of this type have been interpreted by agriculturists to mean that mechanization and similar new techniques must eventually bring about the liquidation of "family farms." While not all forms of mechanization serve as a substitute for labor and result in high fixed costs, many do and thus give the cost relationships adjustment possibilities indicated above.

Factor prices and size. Adjustments from the price direction are possible only as output can be increased (a new supply curve is possible). This type of adjustment is open particularly for single commodities, such as soybeans or onions, where resources can be shifted from other products. The main effect of many forms of mechanization is not in lowering costs through increasing yield per acre or animal but in lowering costs by replacing labor with various forms of capital. Land area is limited in the important agricultural areas. Hence, if cost advantages are great for large acreages, the size of farms in terms of the number of acres can be increased only as some farms are liquidated or decreased in size. In other words, some market force must cause the operators of small farms to relinquish their units in order that farm consolidation can take place. The phenomenon involved here is perhaps important in explaining why farm size in acres changes only slowly. The situation is in contrast to that of other industries where spatial considerations are not the final limitations in determining the number or size of firms which can exist at any one time.

While not all innovations result in a greater output and hence a lower product price, an eventual adjustment in size can be brought about through the prices for the factors. Without a decline in product prices the potentially large unit can, because of cost advantages, bid higher prices for labor or land than can the small unit. An increase in the price of factor services has the effect of forcing production costs and the entire family of cost curves upward. Accordingly, tangency of the minimum cost curve and the firm price line can be brought about as easily through the phenomenon of higher resource prices as through lower product prices. Even under this situation, the income of the small farmer may be as great as previously; the only difference is that the sacrifice in opportunity returns is greater once he has the opportunity to sell his land for a higher price. While adjustments of this nature take place in agriculture, they need not occur "overnight." If a farm of a size paralleling SAC_1, in Figure 9, is operated by an elderly man with limited capital who does not have other skills, he may continue to operate the small farm as long as it returns out-of-pocket costs plus some return for his own labor and capital (and hence provides some funds for living purposes). However, other generations of potential operators may not be so willing to farm under conditions which allow only low returns on resources.

Forces Leading to Varied Pattern of Farm Size

Even though farm size has been a topic of debate and a problem of empirical analysis for several decades, few empirical data are available to indicate the particular forces which determine the pattern of farm size at any one time. It is interesting, however, to "speculate" as to why farms of different sizes persist side by side over time if constant returns to scale do not exist. Some hypotheses follow.

Firm-household relationships. One reason why farms of different size may exist side by side is the interrelationship between the firm and the household in agriculture. Not all operators are engaged in production for the purpose of maximizing profits: many are concerned with the maximization of satisfactions, and dollar returns constitute only one "consumption good." The direct satisfactions from farming as an occupation may be equally as important as money income to some people. Individuals are thus willing to accept somewhat lower returns in operating small farms than could be realized in other industries. In this same framework, persons who are not fitted for work of other types may realize a greater marginal product from their own labor by operating small farm units. Firm-household interrelationships may also explain why some farmers operate units so large that they are inefficient either in terms of cost or alternative investment opportunities. Evidently one "good" in the value system of American people is that of "bigness." Individuals place a high value on the prestige associated with being the owner or manager of a large firm. The eyes of the community often focus on the large-scale farmer as a successful leader. The large estates of the nobility in Europe, the plantations of the Old South, and the current "city or gentleman farmer" unit of America are other expressions of the same motive. Not a great number of operating farmers accumulate enough capital to partake in consumption of farm size as a commodity.

Family-furnished resources. Farm families may have other monetary reasons for operating units of a size which neither allow minimum costs per unit nor return as much on the capital as would alternative investments. Family labor often would have few employment opportunities if the head of the family were to engage in other occupations. While the return on capital and labor of the operator may not be as great as for either large farm units or other employments, addition of the return from the family labor gives a total economic product which compares favorably with other alternatives. On many commercial farms family labor aside from that of the operator constitutes as much as one-fourth of the total labor input. The existence of family labor as a factor input which does not require a cash outlay may allow small units to compete favorably with large units throughout the full range of the business cycle. This statement applies particularly to those economic systems where recurring depression and prosperity periods are the rule rather than the exception. The losses associated with unfavorable product/factor price ratios during depression may be as important as the temporary gains which the large unit realizes from cost economies in short-lived periods of prosperity. The small unit may realize relatively smaller returns during prosperity periods (because it operates too few acres to attain minimum per-unit costs), yet the "non-cost" family labor provides a "depression cushion."

Constant costs and labor techniques. The existence of near-constant costs, and hence the opportunity for small and large farms to exist side by side, with capital limited because of uncertainty considerations, is not inconsistent with varied sizes of farms for livestock grazing and crops with high labor requirement where high-capacity machines are not adopted. In agricultural areas of dense populations, wage rates are extremely low and near-constant costs may prevail in the sense that "high-labor" techniques are more economic than mechanized production methods. The dense population centers and low rage rates which characterize the agriculture of Asia, Europe, and, to some extent, the cotton producing regions of the United States bring about a substitution of labor for capital rather than contrariwise.[17] Under this pattern of resource combination, the long-run cost curve more nearly approaches linearity (constant average costs), and, therefore, gives the small unit a greater relative advantage than does mechanized agricultural production. Costs under the primitive agriculture of many areas of the world are constant for all practical purposes. The large unit, which uses the same labor techniques employed by the small farm, then has little ability to "squeeze" small units from the industry; conversely, there is no limit to the size which might be attained by large units. Perhaps it is here that "historic accident" most nearly determines the pattern of farm size. For generations large estates may exist side by side with small peasant units. Only over long periods of time do enough owners die to leave an opportunity for complete consolidation by large estates or other small holders who may accumulate enough capital. Under the extreme of these situations found in Europe, "the crazy quilt" pattern of ownership results. Interwoven ribbons and parcels of land are held in small acreages and even in fractions of an acre. This pattern of holding further precludes the attainment of the cost economies associated with mechanization and places the owner of a small holding in a position whereby he can compete over time with a large estate which also is divided into small and scattered plots.

Expectations of returns, capital limitations, and size. The long-run hopes or expectations of young farmers also help explain why small units do exist side-by-side with large units even in the face of important cost economies. Even though his first returns are less than might be realized if the same resources were employed elsewhere, the beginning farmer is willing to operate a small unit because he anticipates that his managerial ability is great enough to allow him to accumulate capital in quantity. Under these expectations he hopes to acquire eventually a farm of a size which will enable it to stand on its own competitive feet. These expectations may never be realized, and he may, because of age, immobility, and firm-household considerations, continue to operate a small unit until he retires. The scale of operations is then quite generally limited to the capital which he can accumulate.

Cost, capital, and uncertainty complex. The large power units and machine combinations which were first developed not only substituted for labor at a greater rate on larger farms but also included fixed costs which were prohibitive to the small operator. The divisibility in power and machine units which has been brought about by recent development of small tractors and complementary equipment has also increased the rate

---

[17] The possibility exists that the higher price for land in densely populated areas enters into the marginal cost structure in a manner to cause farms to be smaller in the consuming centers of nations. The possible effects here are outlined in detail in the chapter on production location.

at which machinery substitutes for labor on small farms. Many machine combinations, in respect to size and type, are open to today's commercial farmer. Costs for optimum outputs are not greatly different for many of these. This point is illustrated in the data in Figure 10 from an Iowa study.[18] While there are cost advantages for large scale units, costs per acre for both large and small machine combinations tend to level out; [19] further cost economies become less important as acreage is expanded to a point where variable costs constitute the greatest proportion of total costs. This point falls "roughly" at 80 acres for the 1-plow machine combination, 120 acres for the 2-plow combination, 240 for the combination of a 1-plow and a 2-plow arrangement, and 280 acres for a 3-plow unit. Costs for these combinations are, respectively, $29.47, $27.12, $26.82, and $26.19. The difference between the 2-plow and 3-plow combinations is only $.93 per

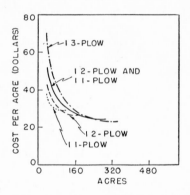

Fig. 10. Per acre cost for different machine combinations in Iowa Cash Grain Production (Source: Iowa Agr. Exp. Sta. project 1135).

acre. This difference probably seems small in the minds of many farmers, relative to the chances of loss associated with an uncertain market and the capital outlay required for the larger unit. The uncertainty may be more important than the cost differences in explaining the final determinant of farm size. An observation of farm management workers is that large farms return more per unit of resources in prosperous periods while small units return more in depression periods. Thus the expectation of recurring prosperity and depression cycles may lead to the selection of small rather

---

[18] The 1-plow combination includes equipment complementary to a 1-plow tractor. The 2-plow tractor combination includes 2-row equipment while the 3-plow tractor combination includes 4-row planting and harvesting equipment. The 1-plow and 2-plow combination includes 1 set of equipment for each tractor.

[19] Each of the curves for a distinct machine combination can be looked upon as a short-run cost curve representing a different technique. The costs include all fixed and variable costs of machinery, labor, power, and crop services for the typical rotation on Clarion Webster soils.

than large units; farmers may believe that the degree of risk associated with large-scale operation is not only greater but also that return per unit of resources may average less over the complete economic cycle.

Low income and small scale farms. Small-scale farms and part-time and nominal units comprise 2½ million farms, or about two-fifths of all farms. These contribute less than 10 per cent of the total agricultural production and only 5 per cent of the value of sales. Generally speaking these farms are of low-income characteristics regardless of the criteria employed. Some of these 2½ million units are retirement farms. Many operators have income from other sources. But the bulk of the small-scale farms shown in Figure 11 furnishes the primary source of income and employment for the farm families concerned. Most of the 923,000 small-scale farming units (gross incomes of $500 to $1,200) are located in the low-income farming areas, such as the Appalachian, southeast, and Delta states. About one-fourth of these are share-cropper units. Few of these small-scale farms

FARMS IN SPECIFIED CLASSES
Percentage, by Regions, 1945

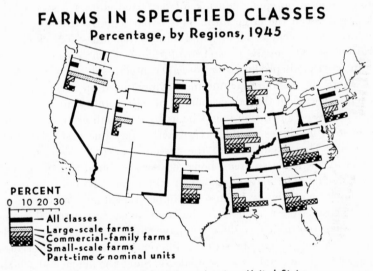

PERCENT
0 10 20 30

— All classes
— Large-scale farms
— Commercial-family farms
— Small-scale farms
— Part-time & nominal units

Fig. 11. Distribution of farms by sizes, United States.

are retirement units, and most of them provide the major source of the farm families' income. Lack of income and capital, imperfect knowledge of opportunities elsewhere, uncertainty involved in changing modes of living, and other mobility barriers prevent operators of these farms from relinquishing control of their units in order that farms can be consolidated. The nature and extent of the economies inherent in mechanized production can have little effect in causing liquidation of these units. Their existence is a major source of under-employment of resources and poverty in agriculture and give rise to certain efficiency problems discussed in Chapter 24.

Resource Indivisibility and Cooperative Resource Ownership

Because of its spatial characteristics and the fact that "many tools of production are on wheels" (in contrast to the fixed nature of machines under the factory production of other industries), opportunities exist whereby small farms can and do realize the cost economies associated with large units. The marginal value productivity of particular resources and the returns to farmers as resource owners can be as great on small farms as on large farms and in other fields of production. Machine indivisibilities can be overcome through the cooperative ownership and use of machines with high capacity and high fixed costs. Similarly, indivisibility is also overcome by the custom market for services of ditching machines, terracing equipment, combines, corn pickers, hay balers, and spraying equipment, and even small implements in many communities. The availability of custom services is another force which tends to give small farms the cost advantages associated with machine indivisibility. The custom machine is used on enough farms so that fixed costs are spread over as many acres as on the large farm. This is particularly true in the case of combines, corn pickers, balers, and similar machines for which custom operation is widespread. Existence of these custom services also helps explain why small producing units can compete side by side with large units. Were the custom machine market organized on a competitive and sufficient scale (such that all economies of indivisibility might be attained and timeliness of operation might be assured), small crop farms operated with custom machines would have exactly the same cost advantages as large units. The potentiality of the custom market in lowering costs on livestock farms is not so great, however, because buildings and equipment are not mobile. The acreage at which major cost reductions are realized differs between machines. Because it can be divided into small sections and the fixed costs are low relative to the labor and power required to operate it, the spike-tooth harrow does not have great cost advantages even on big units. A hay baler represents a different situation because costs fall rapidly with the magnitude of annual use. Since the acreage at which cost per unit of product attains a minimum differs between machines, it is hardly possible to establish a single cooperative embracing one number of small farms which allows all of the cost economies inherent in indivisibility characteristics of machines. Minimum costs per unit of product may be attained on 160 acres for a 2-row corn cultivator, but on 800 acres for a 5-foot combine. Nevertheless, cooperatives embracing different numbers of farms for particular machines can be organized to give the full benefits inherent in overcoming machine indivisibility. A machinery cooperative owning 10 2-row cultivators and 1 5-foot combine might service 40 farms with 40 acres of corn each and 40 farms with 20 acres of small grain each. This logic partly underlies the machine-tractor stations provided in Russia or the machine cooperatives of countries such as Norway. At some level the farmer places a greater value on "independence" as a consumption good than on further income effected through cooperatives and cost economies. Yet, if the threat to "family farms" growing out of cost economies associated with large scale production is as great as suggested in many testimonials and newspaper editorials, and if the values attached to small farms stands high enough in the means-end scale of the American public, an extension in cooperative ownership of the factors of production represents one means of guaranteeing the end of more family farms.

Family Farms and Size Adjustments

One of the popular subjects for debate in agricultural circles is that of family farms. The concept of a "family farm" is one which involves size relationships. The approach to the so-called family farm has been quite different even within the field of agricultural economies. Farm management economists, working almost entirely with units operated by farm families and basing their logic on production or resource efficiency principles, have tried to show how farms can be expanded to the most efficient size in terms of costs, returns, family living and resource efficiency generally. This activity has been inherent in the procedures wherein costs are computed and resource returns (such as labor income) are derived to illustrate the size of the unit which gives greatest profits or gives the farm family an income and living standards as great as would be possible if the same labor and capital were used in non-farm alternatives. In contrast, land tenure economists have operated on the basis of Jeffersonian agrarian principles, wherein it is supposed that more and more families of the nation should operate farms. When followed to its extremes this philosophy leads to smaller and smaller farms with decreasing incomes to farm families. The term "family farm" has no specific meaning in respect to the size or scale relationships in agriculture. Many people have supplied a definition of the family farm; there are about as many definitions as there are special interest groups. The term has great economic-political appeal, and if an individual, economic group, or political party wishes to win the majority favor of farm people, it need only espouse the cause of the family farm. The appeal is similar to those such as "more jobs for laborers," "higher salaries for college professors," or "more profits for industrialists." The subject makes fine material for soap-box oratory. In their varied definitions of the family farm many people, including agricultural economists, imply that it is the most efficient producing unit; then they immediately suggest that it is in danger of being liquidated by large-scale units. The logic employed here is inconsistent; if the family farm were actually the most efficient producing unit, it would be represented by a short-run cost curve such as SAC_3 in Figure 4. Under competitive conditions, it alone could survive in the long run; larger units would be eliminated.

Other definitions suggest that the family farm is one on which (1) all management is provided by the farm family, (2) more than half the labor is furnished by the family, and (3) returns on resources are as great as might be earned in alternative employments.[20] This definition also implies that, in terms of general equilibrium analysis, the family farm is the most efficient producing unit. Accordingly, there is no basis for the further suggestion (and one which almost always follows) that "the family farm is in dire danger of being eliminated by sinister forces."

If the over-all efficiency conditions outlined in previous or subsequent chapters are to be attained in agriculture as a competitive industry, the optimum scale of farm and employment of particular resources is defined in equation I below, where P_y refers to the price of the product, MP refers to the marginal product of the resource denoted by the subscript, and P_l, P_c, P_o, and P_m refer to the prices of labor, capital, land, and management resources respectively. Here the size of the firm must be expanded in such a fashion that (1) the value of the marginal product for any resource unit must equal the price of the resource unit, and (2) this ratio must hold true between all resources.

$$P_y \frac{MP_l}{P_l} = P_y \frac{MP_c}{P_c} = P_y \frac{MP_o}{P_o} = P_y \frac{MP_m}{P_m} = 1.0 \qquad \text{(I)}$$

The family farm definition, which states that the family unit can be only large enough that the management and the major part of the labor resides in the farm family, specifies condition II. Here the marginal value

$$P_y \frac{MP_c}{P_c} = P_y \frac{MP_o}{P_o} = 1.0 < P_y \frac{MP_l}{P_l} \text{ and } P_y \frac{MP_m}{P_m} \qquad \text{(II)}$$

product can be equated with the cost of resources for land and capital, but this condition need not be attained for labor and management. The upper supply of these resources is given in the entrepreneurial and sociological structure of the farm family. With limits on the input of management and labor services, the amount of capital or land services which the farm firm should purchase (to equate value products and factor prices and to maximize returns) depends on the limited supply of the other two resources. The optimum size will differ between farms depending on the stock of labor and management possessed in the household of each and it need not result in the most efficient use of a nation's resources.

It is doubtful that cost economies are great enough in most segments of American agriculture to endanger the units typically operated by farm families. Where these possibilities do exist, society must make choices

---

[20] The elements of this definition can be found in J. Ackerman and M. D. Harris, Editors, *Family Farm Policy*. Chicago: University of Chicago Press, 1946, pp. 385-391.

between alternative ends towards which production and farm size policy can be directed. We have outlined these production policy choices elsewhere.[21] Even then, final choice of farm size in respect to economic efficiency or political and sociological stability will depend on the technical nature of scale relationships.

Selected References

Allen, R. G. D., *Mathematics for Economists*. New York: Macmillan, 1942, pp. 315-322.

Bachman, K., and Jones, R., *Sizes of Farms in the United States*. U.S.D.A. Tech. Bul. 1019.

Black, J. D., *et al.*, *Farm Management*. New York: Macmillan, 1947, Ch. 19.

———, "Scale of Agricultural Production in the United States," *Quar. Jour. Econ.*, Vol. 52.

Boulding, K. E., *Economic Analysis*. New York: Harper, 1948, pp. 672-698.

Chamberlin, E., "Proportionality, Divisibility and Economies of Scale," *Quar. Jour. Econ.*, Vol. 42.

Crum, W. L., and Schumpeter, J. A., *Rudimentary Mathematics for Economists and Statisticians*. New York: McGraw-Hill, 1946, pp. 106-109.

Fellows, I. F., Frick, E. G., and Weeks, S. B., *Economies of Scale in Dairying*, Conn. Agr. Exp. Sta. Bul. 285.

Hahn, F. H., "Comments on Chamberlin's Cost Concepts," *Quar. Jour of Econ.*, Vol. 43.

Heady, Earl O., "Production Functions from a Random Sample of Farms," *Jour. Farm Econ.*, Vol. 28.

Stigler, G., *The Theory of Price*. New York: Macmillan, 1947, pp. 128-145.

———, "Labor Productivity and Size of Farms: a Statistical Pitfall," *Jour. Farm Econ.*, Vol. 31.

---

[21] See Heady, Earl O., "Technical Scale Relationships and Farm Size Policy," *So. Econ. Jour.*, Vol. 19.

13

Time, Factor Rewards, and Resource Valuation

Up to this point, we have made passing references to time as it relates to the life of resources, the flow of productive services, and the nature of costs. We also discussed simple decision-making as it related to 2 points in time; by examining milk produced at 2 times of the year in the vein of 2 different products, we were able to outline the production possibility curve in the conventional manner of product-product relationships. Our first steps in the analysis of resource use have been necessary and useful. However, since time has not been emphasized, they have limited application. They do not come to grasp with problems of planning when knowledge of the future is imperfect. The future has not been tied to the present in any manner except for seasonal production possibilities and seasonal price differentials. We now part from this "timeless" or "single period" consideration of production and consider time *per se* as it relates to resource administration. It is the time considerations in production which give rise to the real difficulties in decision-making. If production were instantaneous, decisions could be perfect, since the production function and the prices for factors and products would be known. This situation is far from reality in agriculture and, therefore, resource management must involve an immense amount of guesswork. With recognition of the real implications of time in production, we postpone the problems of imperfect knowledge until Chapter 15. In this chapter we discuss certain basic concepts for appraising alternative sequences or flows of income over time. The concepts might be termed "static," since they assume future quantities are known with certainty. However, the relationships and choice framework presented are the same, in rough fashion, as those in which the future must be estimated with error. The analysis of this chapter is in terms of a firm and profit maximization. Time considerations involving firm-household interrelationships are outlined in Chapter 14.

The problem. We are concerned with factor inputs or investments which provide income not only in one period but as sequences over time. Should the entrepreneur simply treat a dollar's income in a future period in the same manner as a dollar's income in the present period? If a unit of fertilizer provides an income of $3 in this year, $2 next year and $1 in the following year, should these be added together and treated the same as a marginal return of $6 in the current year? Suppose an investment of the same size can be made in 2 different alternatives, A and B, and that A, a set of cropping machinery, gives off a flow of income equal to $1,000 a year for 20 years, while B, a set of buildings, gives off $400 a year for 50 years. The income in total time span amounts to $20,000 in either case. Can the entrepreneur be indifferent as to the alternative selected? Finally, the problem can be posed this way: With the 2 alternative income flows outlined above, what prices can be paid for the resources under A which will make it a more profitable investment than for the resources under B? From the standpoint of production economics, decisions in respect to production alternatives which give varying flows of income over time are not problems distinct from those of resource valuation. Accordingly our procedure is this: First, analysis is made of choice in production alternatives which involve time. Second, resource valuation is analyzed within a production economics complex. The study of resource valuation is treated only partially in this chapter because uncertainty considerations are included in Chapter 19.

Simple Problems in Time

A simple introduction to decisions in time can be made with the factor-product example in Table 1. The input might be considered as fertilizer

Table I.

Production Function Involving a Sequence of Services and Products over a Three-Year Time Span (Hypothetical Data)

Input of Factor at beginning of Year 1	Marginal cost of input	Marginal product at end of:				Value of marginal product forthcoming during:			
		1st year	2nd year	3rd year	Total of 3 years	1st year	2nd year	3rd year	Total of 3 years
(1)	(2)	(3)	(4)	(5)	(6)	(7)	(8)	(9)	(10)
1	$24	12	8	4	24	$24.12	$16.08	$8.04	$48.24
2	24	9	6	3	18	18.09	12.06	6.03	36.18
3	24	6	4	2	12	12.06	8.04	4.02	24.12
4	24	3	2	1	6	6.03	4.02	2.01	12.06
5	24	0	0	0	0	0	0	0	0

or a similar resource which, when applied in 1 year, gives off services over a 3-year period. The first input unit gives a product of 12 units at the end of the first year, 8 units at the end of the second year, and 4 units at the end of the third year. Similarly, the second input adds 9, 6, and 3 units of product at the end of each year. With each input unit priced at $24 and each output unit priced at $2.01, how many units of fertilizer should be applied? Should the entire marginal value product in column 10 be treated as if it were forthcoming in the year when the factor input is applied? Under this procedure, it is profitable to apply 3 units of factor, since the total marginal value product of $24.12 is slightly greater than the marginal cost of the input (the transformation ratio of 12/1 is greater than the undiscounted price ratio of 24/2.01).

However, is it not true that the marginal cost of each unit of input is greater than $24 over the 3 production periods? The funds used for production of the commodity might be loaned at an interest rate of 5 per cent. A sum equal to $5 put out at 5 per cent interest for a year has a value of $5(1+.05)$, or $5.25 at the end of 1 year and $5(1+.05)^2$ or $5.50 at the end of 2 years. The costs of the present can be put on a basis for comparison with returns of the future by causing the current costs to "grow with time," or returns in the future can be "shrunk with time" by reducing them to a basis comparable to costs of the present. It is possible to bind the future with the present in the first case through the process known as "*compounding*" and in the second case, through the process known as "*discounting*." Here we are interested in discounting in a "perfect knowledge" and "pure firm" sense. Discounting under these conditions is on the basis of interest rates external to the firm (for example, market interest rates). (We outline the implications of uncertainty and internal interest rates in Chapter 18.)

Compounding costs. Compounding of costs represents the process of letting cash outlays "grow" as a function of time. If costs are accumulated over time at compound interest, the compounding equation becomes

$$C = c\,(1 + r)^t \tag{I}$$

where C refers to the compound value of an original cost outlay of c invested for t years. Applying this equation to $1 invested for 4 years, the compounded amount of the cost at the end of 4 years is $C = 1(1.05)^4$, or $1.23. In the case of Table 1, however, resource services are given off not at the end of 1 future year but at the end of 3 future years. Thus the total costs for each input unit (in terms of the time when each fraction of services is given off) can be expressed by the equation

$$C = c_1\,(1 + r) + c_2\,(1 + r)^2 + c_3\,(1 + r)^3 \ldots + c_n\,(1 + r)^n \tag{II}$$

where c_1, c_2, c_3, and c_n refer to the value or cost of the services given off at the end of the first, second, third, and nth years.[1] If the services are given off within the first, second, third, and nth year, and costs are not compounded for a fraction of a year, equation II can be modified as follows:

$$C = c_1 + c_2\,(1 + r) + c_3\,(1 + r)^2 \ldots + c_n\,(1 + r)^{n-1} \tag{III}$$

---

[1] These equations can be summarized as $C = \sum_{i=1}^{i=n} [c_i(1 + r)^i$ where c_i is the cost in the individual year and the period of years includes $i = 1$ to $i = n$.

A large number of farm costs fall in the category outlined above; while seeds, labor, and tractor fuel which go into annual crops represent a transformation period of less than a year; machinery, buildings, livestock and even fertilizers embody stocks of services which must be purchased at 1 point in time but are given off over several production periods. Conservation improvements such as terraces and dams, lime, and many other resource investments also give off a flow of services and products over a series of production periods. In contrast, some types of agricultural production involve cost outlays in each of several production periods while the product is available only at the end of the last period. Production of a dairy heifer, a beef steer, or lumber represents such an example. What, then, is the sum of costs or the total capital investment represented in the product at its time of completion of sale? In this case, the sum of costs (C) up to the single date of sale can be expressed by the following equation when the product is sold at the end of n years and c_1, c_2, c_3, and c_n represent cost outlays at the beginning of the first, second, third, and nth years:

$$C = c_1 (1 + r)^n + c_2 (1 + r)^{n-1} + c_3 (1 + r)^{n-2} \ldots c_n (1 + r) \qquad \text{(IV)}$$

If the cost outlays are made within each production period and interest is not applied for a period of less than a year, then the equation reduces to the following, with the product forthcoming and marketed at the end of n years.

$$C = c_1 (1 + r)^{n-1} + c_2 (1 + r)^{n-2} + c_3 (1 + r)^{n-3} \ldots c_n \qquad \text{(V)}$$

Any one of the above formulas binds present resource costs to their future products and revenues. The first equation supposes an investment at one distinct point in time which will not be transformed into product until the end of a distinct future period. Equations II and III apply to poly-period resources purchased at 1 point in time and with services and products forthcoming in each of several periods of the future. Equations IV and V apply to a sequence of outlays of either a mono-period or poly-period nature, with the product marketed at the end of the last period. In each case, costs are compounded in a manner such that they can be compared with the marginal revenue at the same future time. When equation II is applied to the factor costs in Table 1, total revenue of the 3 years justifies application of only 2 inputs; the compounded cost of an input is $26.03 and is greater than the total marginal return of $24.12 for the third input.

When resources are expended for only a very short period of time, the resultant costs ordinarily are not discounted. Feed purchased today and converted into milk tomorrow is never handled in the manner outlined above. The reason is obvious: the difference between the cost of the feed and its compounded cost tomorrow is an unimportant and insignificant quantity. Only as time differences become sufficiently important does compounding of costs take place. Little is known about the extent to which farmers discount future returns in the static sense outlined here. Farmers do use the procedure, but it becomes intertwined with the uncertainty and firm-household considerations to be outlined later.

Discounting revenue. In the example above we have shown the manner in which present costs can be compounded to show the real costs of obtaining a future revenue when the opportunity of loaning funds at interest is considered. The various equations indicate the amount of capital which will be available at the end of a specified time span, if it is loaned out at compound interest rather than invested in a production process. The procedure also can be reversed and we can compute the present value of a future revenue. We can again use the procedure to answer a decision question such as "Will a marginal return of $1.60 10 years hence justify the marginal cost of $1 at the present?" A return of $1.60 in 10 years is worth no more than 98¢ at present; if a sum of money equal to 98¢ is loaned out at a compound interest rate of 5 per cent, it will amount to $1.60 at the end of 10 years. With profit as his motive and with perfect knowledge of the future, the entrepreneur would be unwise to invest $1 in resource services now in order to get $1.60 at the end of 10 years. Instead he should loan the $1 at the market rate of 5 per cent, since it will amount to more than $1.60 in 10 years. Future revenues can be discounted back to the present to make possible their comparison with present investments in this manner. The present value, V, of future revenue, R, forthcoming at the end of t years in the future can be expressed as follows:

$$V = \frac{R}{(1+r)^t} \qquad \text{(VI)}$$

where r is again the market rate of interest.

When income is forthcoming as a sequence of incomes over a period of years, the equation can be expanded to VII below where R_1, R_2, R_3, and R_n represent revenue forthcoming in the first, second, third, and nth years.

$$V = \frac{R_1}{1+r} + \frac{R_2}{(1+r)^2} + \frac{R_3}{(1+r)^3} \cdots \cdots \frac{R_n}{(1+r)^n} \qquad \text{(VII)}$$

When equation VII is applied to the marginal value products in Table 1, the total present values of the product forthcoming from the first input becomes $44.49 ($22.97 at the end of the first year, $14.58 at the end of the second year, and $6.94 at the end of the third). That is to say, the total return of $48.24 over the 3 years is worth no more than a present return of $44.49 since, if the latter amount is compounded annually at 5 per cent, it amounts to a total of $48.24 over the 3 years. Similarly, the total discounted or present value of the second, third, and fourth inputs is $33.37, $22.25, and $11.13 respectively. It is now evident that the third input is unprofitable because it requires an outlay of $24 at the present.

The marginal cost of time. The example above suggests the manner in which time and the interest rate may condition the level of capital investment for a pure firm with perfect knowledge. The step outlined below can be taken as a further discounting refinement. Here we not only compound costs but also discount net returns back to the present, in order that income of different years can be put on a comparative basis at the outset. Our example, one dealing with the marginal cost of time, considers only 1 level of investment. It best applies to agricultural production such as orcharding and forestry, although the same considerations are involved in all types of production which involve time. It also applies to investment in land where the outlay is made currently and the product is withdrawn or given off at some specified rate in future years. A farmer, for example, may own a piece of land near a city. The land gradually appreciates in value (its site or location "product" may grow) as the city spreads nearer and nearer. How long can the land be held profitably if the purpose of investment is to maximize profits through the appreciating sale value of the farm?

Let us analyze this general problem by drawing upon an example in farm forestry. Suppose that either an individual farmer or a lumber corporation buys a 50-acre tract of land and plants it to trees. The costs per acre include $10 for trees and $10 for land. (To simplify our problem we will disregard annual outlays for taxes, since these can be "compounded forward" quite simply.) Time now becomes an important factor of production, along with land and trees. Since the value of the trees increases with each year, we must decide how far into the future the investment should be extended. Looking forward, when should the trees be harvested and sold? One point in time when this decision may be evaluated is at the outset of planning. The decision also may be reappraised each year. The length of time for which it appears that the resources or product can be held profitably will change with time because of the discounting factor. Hence, we will define the period of investment which, at the outset, appears to be most profitable. This problem may face a firm with the opportunity to contract sale of its future product. Table 2 provides the example. Investment in the first year is the $1,000 for the land, trees, and planting costs. By the second year, the first full year after the cost outlay, compounded costs have grown to 1,000 (1 + .05), or $1,050. Line 1 indicates the total accumulated costs, with an interest rate of 5 per cent, in each year. Line 2 indicates the total sale value of the tree and land resources in each year. If revenue were not discounted, the investment could be held profitably to the sixth year where the marginal cost in time (60.8) is equal to the marginal revenue (60.8). If, however, we are viewing the entire process in an *ex ante* fashion (for example, from the planning data), we must determine whether a dollar in net income in the future is worth a dollar in net income today. It may not be so considered if today's dollar

Table 2.

Maximization of Revenue Over Time (Hypothetical Data) *

Item	Present	Year 1	2	3	4	5	6
1. Total cost	1000	1050	1102.5	1157.6	1215.5	1276.3	1340.0
2. Total revenue	1000	1045	1149.5	1235.5	1297.3	1358.1	1398.8
3. Net revenue to date	0	—5	47	77.9	81.8	81.8	58.8
4. Annual marginal cost		50	52.5	55.1	57.9	60.8	63.7
5. Annual marginal revenue		45	104.5	86.0	61.8	60.8	40.7
6. Rate of cost increase		5%	5%	5%	5%	5%	5%
7. Rate of revenue increase		4.5%	10%	7.5%	5.0%	4.7%	3.0%
8. Discounted net revenue at outset	0	—	42.6	67.3	67.3	64.0	43.9

* The total cost of each year has been compounded at 5 per cent to give the total cost for the next year. The total revenue of each successive year has been divided by the total revenue of the previous year to give the percentage increase in the revenue (line 7). The net revenue (line 3) of each year has been discounted back to the first year by the formula $R/(1 + .05)^n$ where n refers to the number of full years beyond the first.

can be invested at interest. Thus, if the net revenue of $47 for year 2 is discounted back to the planning date in the usual manner, its current or discounted value is $42 \div (1 + .05)^2$, or $42.6. As is indicated in line 8, discounted net revenue is at a maximum between the third and fourth years. The discounted net revenue reaches a maximum a year earlier than the net revenue itself.

Maximization of the discounted net revenue is still a problem of marginality. This fact is illustrated by lines 6 and 7 of the table. The net discounted revenue continues to increase as long as the per cent added to total revenue in each year is greater than the per cent added to costs. Discounted net revenue becomes a maximum when the percentage rate of cost increase is equal to the percentage rate of revenue increase.[2] Undiscounted revenue is at a maximum when the absolute rate of cost increase (the marginal cost) is equal to the absolute rate of revenue increase.

Agriculture examples. While the important problems of decision fall in this framework, not only because time is involved but also because quantities extending into the future fall in the category of expectations rather than known amounts, few studies in agriculture have come to grasp with costs and revenues in the manner outlined above. The data of Figure 1,

---

[2] If the time period of the investment is decided at year three rather than year one, the discounted net revenue will come at a later date than between the fourth and fifth years. The reason is obvious: the income of each future year need not be discounted over so many years as when discounting starts from the outset and therefore the discounted net revenue will not reach a maximum until a later time.

while of a somewhat different form than that presented above, do provide an empirical counterpart. They show costs and returns for apple trees in New Hampshire at prewar prices. The yield curve illustrates the nature of change in each year with returns undiscounted, while the cost curve includes the annual outlays plus simple interest on the original investment.

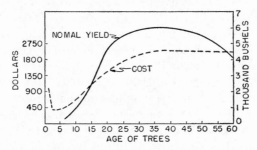

Fig. I. Costs and receipts per 1000 trees (Source: New Hamp. Agr. Exp. Sta. Bul. 323).

At the outset of an apple orchard, costs are incurred but no revenue is forthcoming from apples. A sale value exists for the trees and land, however, and is based on discounted future incomes. Initial costs are high because of tree and planting costs. While some return is realized in a second stage of time, it is less than costs, which rise as labor is required for spraying and picking. While both costs and revenue rise as the productivity of the trees increases up to 35 or 40 years of age, annual costs may, depending on prices, exceed annual revenue for nearly 12 years. Thereafter, annual revenue rises at a faster rate than costs up to the time the trees are about 30 years of age. Annual undiscounted net income is then at a maximum but begins to decrease while costs remain relatively constant; revenue falls below costs somewhere in the neighborhood of 50 or 60 years, depending on the level of prices. For purposes of orchard valuation, future revenues must be discounted back to the year of the investment, in order that the farmer can determine whether purchase of an orchard is profitable or can compare orchard returns with other alternatives for which the same capital might be employed. In addition, future costs and returns are important from the standpoint of orchard valuation at any time within the 60-year span of the enterprise.

Time Views and Decisions

We can now see the differences between historic or *ex poste* as compared to forward or *ex ante* views of the production and decision-making process. Even if the farm were a pure firm with no motive other than profit maximization, and even if it operated in an environment of complete certainty, the decisions it would make looking forward are not the same as those it would make when looking backward if income were related to a single year.

Choice between alternative products in time. This logic becomes apparent with a third example in time. Farmers with given funds often must choose between alternative investments which involve an altogether different timing of returns. Funds may be invested in terraces which bring in no returns now, but, in the sense that they prevent erosion, will bring in income at a later time. This alternative competes with an investment in hogs or cotton which brings in a return during the year. Likewise, the farmer may choose between machinery for cash cropping which will bring in a return over the next few years and a young orchard or dairy breeding stock which will not give returns for 10 or 15 years. Which is most desirable in a pure firm context? Suppose $70,000 is available for investment. One alternative, A, will give immediate returns amounting to $4,000 at the end of each year for 10 years, a total future income of $40,000. The second alternative, B, will give a return of $5,000 at the end of each of 10 years starting with the 11th year, a total future income of $50,000. Using an interest rate of 5 per cent and the discounting procedures outlined above, the present value of income from alternative A is $30,916. The present value of income from alternative B is $23,602. Although it can be said historically that B returns more than A, the second alternative is most desirable from an *ex ante* standpoint where returns of the future are discounted back to the date of investment. Even aside from tenure and uncertainty considerations, the farm operator may have sufficient logic for investing in cash crops rather than long-term conservation improvements. In terms of the logic outlined above, profit maximization decrees that, from all the alternative investments possible, the entrepreneur should select the one which gives the greatest capital value (present value of discounted future earnings).

Time and Substitute Resources

The example above, a product-product decision, illustrates how one enterprise may be selected over another because of difference in timing. We now employ the same logic for some factor-factor decisions. An important factor-factor problem in agriculture is that of the selection of methods of production or resources which serve as substitutes in the future but require investments of varying time periods. Suppose that in dairy farming alternatives exist for use of a $7,311 "inflexible" barn which will last 60 years or a $5,063 "flexible" barn which has a life of only 30 years. For the sake of simplicity we can suppose depreciation or transformation is at constant rates. Without compounding of costs, the annual depreciation amounts to $233 for the first and $243 for the second barn. We will further assume that the 2 barns are perfect substitutes in the sense that both allow the same annual output of livestock when used with equal inputs of complementary (non-barn) resources. Should the farmer not select the first since its depreciation cost is less per year? Questions such as this are particularly complex when they must be decided for an uncertain future. Under the uncertainty and capital limitation analysis presented later, it becomes apparent that the farmer may rationally select the high-cost barn because of (a) time flexibility considerations and the ability to shift to different lines of production without losing a large investment in an obsolete barn, or (b) limited capital and the opportunity to realize greater returns through alternative investments rather than to have large funds tied up in buildings. Still, the importance of time can be illustrated in the perfect knowledge followed here. While it might first appear that the 60-year barn represents the low-cost method of producing the given annual outputs, the perspective changes as time is considered. At a 5 per cent interest rate, the total cost of barn services under the 2 systems can be compared. If the 2 barns give off identical flows of revenue over time, and costs other than building services are the same, we can compare the 2 cost quantities as (a) \$7,311 and (b) \$5,063 + (5,063)/(1.05)^{30}. In other words if we plan to carry on production for 60 years, we will need to invest \$7,311 in the long-lived barn or \$5,063 in the short-lived barn and lay away an amount equal to (\$5,063)/(1.05)^{30} in order to purchase a second short-lived barn at the end of 30 years. The quantity (\$5,063)/(1.05)^{30} is \$1,151; we must, at the outset, lay away \$1,151 at compound interest if we wish to replace the first 30-year barn at the end of its life. Since the sum \$5,063 + (\$5,063)/(1.05)^{30} becomes \$5,063 + \$1,151, or \$6,214, the 2 short-lived barns give a 60-year cost which is less than the \$7,311 for the more permanent structure.

It is then obvious that if the 2 barns produce the same physical and value product over time, the short-lived resource should be employed because the total cost of its services is less over the 60-year period. As is brought out subsequently, this aspect of decision-making becomes even more relevant where entrepreneurs have limited capital and the "opportunity rate" at which costs are compounded or income is discounted becomes the return possible in alternative enterprises rather than the market interest rate. Comparison may be made in the same manner between "high-machine" and "high-labor" producing techniques. The present value of costs, PC, can be computed in the manner below for each technique where I refers to the investment in machines at the outset and c refers to the labor and machine service costs made in each year, i, of the future.

$$PC = I + \sum_{i=1}^{i=n} [c_i/(1+r)^i]$$

The farmer who has ample capital and uses this procedure may, if he uses a discount rate of 5 per cent, find the machine method of producing cotton to be least costly; a high initial machine investment will cause lower labor costs in the future. The farmer with limited capital who must discount at

20 per cent (see Chapter 19) may find the labor method to involve less cost; it does not initially tie up funds which could be used elsewhere.

Divergence between the actions of farmers and the recommendations of specialists may occur for other resource substitutions which concern time. For example, the farmer may rationally select superphosphate over rock phosphate where applications are regulated to provide equal amounts of P_2O_5. Even if the original costs are less for each P_2O_5 unit through rock phosphate, the longer term investment (plus the possibilities of price declines) can throw the economic balance in the direction of superphosphate. Similarly, the farmer may be sound in his decision to buy 2 consecutive second-hand tractors, which last 5 years, at a price of $1,000 each, rather than a new tractor with a life of 10 years and a price of $2,000. The same considerations apply to pasture improvement. A lespedeza mixture which involves an investment over a 20-year period may appear less desirable than a brome and clover mixture which involves an investment extending only 4 or 5 years into the future.

Level of interest rate. The effect that the level of interest rate might have on total capital investment in an economic environment of perfect knowledge is now apparent. (Questions of the efficacy of the market interest rate in determining investment policy under uncertainty are discussed in Chapter 19). Changes in interest rates cause the scale of capital employed to change in the same manner as changes in costs of factors within a single production period. Costs grow at a slower rate with time as the interest rate declines. Similarly, future revenues are discounted by smaller amounts with time. The level to which capital investment can be pushed profitably thus becomes a function of the interest rate. Different rates of interest not only affect the level of investment which is profitable, but also affect resources value when valuation is in terms of a static framework. While professional appraisal work involves great detail in preparation of cost and income budgets, differences in the interest rate selected for capitalization can cause estimated present values to vary immensely. Use of an interest rate of 4 rather than 5 per cent will cause a perpetual income flow of $10 to have a present value of $250 rather than $200.

Transformation, compounding and productivity comparisons in research. Farm management economists have partially recognized time in their computation of net profit (ordinarily expressed as management return or as a residual to labor); in addition to deducting depreciation as an annual expense, they charge interest on the beginning-of-the-year value of resources. The interest which might be earned in an alternative employment of funds is thus added to depreciation costs. However, the amount and distribution of "compounded costs" are different under this system of accounting from those under that suggested by equations II and III. Under the customary farm accounting procedure, services given off from a resource with limited life come at a greater cost in early than in later years.

The reason is obvious: if a machine costs $1,000 and depreciation *per se* amounts to $100 per year (assuming straight line depreciation), depreciation during the second year plus 5 per cent interest charges on the value of the machine at the beginning of the second year totals $145 ($100 depreciation plus 5 per cent of $900). Similarly, the total cost becomes $110 in the tenth year ($100 depreciation plus 5 per cent interest on the $100 value of the machine at the beginning of the year) and annual machine costs decline with the age of the machine. If equations II and III are employed in the accounting procedure, costs of services in the tenth year are greater than those for the second year when compounding is carried forward from the date of the investment (see columns 4 and 7 in Table 3). Thus, while the research study may show that the costs of a machine are less than the value of the product which it produces in the tenth year, the farmer may rationally refrain from the investment, since his decisions are entirely from an *ex ante* standpoint.

Depreciation or transformation procedures also have other implications in production economics research and the recommendations based on it. An interfarm efficiency measure discussed in later chapters involves the comparison of output/input ratios for different farms and farming regions. Farm production economists have made these types of comparisons since the birth of agricultural economics.[3] They are used to suggest where resources can be used most economically. Ordinarily, these efficiency ratios are computed in a manner to approximate the value of services transformed into product in a single year (the procedure of charging an interest rate on capital and a wage rate for family labor, in computing "management" or "labor" returns for different farms to indicate which is using resources most efficiently). In some instances, however, the value of *resources* used, rather than the value of the resource *services* transformed in a single year, has been used to estimate the "average" productivity of resources employed in different lines of agriculture.[4] This procedure leads to erroneous productivity comparisons if the resources employed by different farms or areas do not give off services at the same rate (for example, do not have the same transformation or depreciation rates). Suppose that a $10,000 dairy barn employed by one farmer gives off services at the rate of $200 per year. Another farmer employs fertilizer valued at $100 which gives off services for 1 year only. If the value product of the barn in a single year is $2,000 while that of the fertilizer is $1,000, the barn investment appears to have a low productivity when total capital is compared to the value product of a single year. In this setting the value

---

[3] For an early use of this procedure, see G. F. Warren, *Farming in Tompkins County, New York*. New York Agr. Exp. Sta. Bul. 295, 1908.

[4] This is the procedure employed by C. Clark, *Conditions of Economic Progress*. London: Macmillan, 1940; and T. W. Schultz, *Production and Welfare of Agriculture*. New York: Macmillan, 1949, pp. 49-57.

product for each $1 invested in barn is only 20¢ (2,000/10,000) while that for fertilizer is $10 (1,000/100). If the resource services alone are compared, however, the value of product in both cases is $10 for each $1 of services (2,000/200 for the dairy barn and 1,000/100 for the fertilizer). Income accounting to guide individual farmers or to gauge regional or national resource efficiency are thus not distinct procedures; they involve the same basic principles and appropriate depreciation or transformation estimates must be used in either case.

The Valuation of Resources

The procedures outlined above for compounding costs into the future or discounting revenues back to the present have their counterpart in resource valuation. The 2 procedures are not distinct, as some agricultural economists suppose, but are simply different shades of the same thing. On the one hand, the entrepreneur can compare present costs with future incomes to see if an investment is justified; on the other, he can compute the present value of future incomes to determine whether investment in the resource will return as much as when the same fund is invested in another alternative. Production economists specializing in resource valuation ordinarily follow procedures stemming from the discounting systems outlined above. Here again, it is assumed that (a) knowledge of the future approaches perfection, (b) capital is unlimited, and (c) motives of the firm are purely those of profit maximization. Under these assumptions, an external or market interest rate can be used in the capitalization process. (More realistic assumptions for resource valuation are provided in Chapters 14 and 19.)

While not all persons who purchase land or other farm resources expect to or do become "farmers," they do actually represent "firms." Operating farmers represent firms which own resources and themselves convert resource services into products. Landlords who are not operating farmers represent resource-owning firms which sell factor services to other agricultural firms. A grain farmer represents a business firm, even though the corn which he sells represents resource services which are purchased and converted into beef by a feeder. Landlords who invest in farm resources fall in a like category in the sense that resource investment represents a firm or profit decision.[5] Hence, there is little if any reason why, in a static

---

[5] As mentioned at another point, the main purpose of resource appraisal or valuation is to aid managers or firms in decision-making. Were this not true, market values alone would be relevant. Appraisals are made for many other purposes. They may be made as a basis for settling estates, or for purposes of compensation where the governments condemn the land of an individual land-owner. In cases such as these, the relevant appraisal problem is one of estimating market prices for a piece of real estate which will not be sold in the market. Loan firms are also highly concerned with resource appraisal and valuation. Again, however, the concern is one of decision-making

framework, valuation principles or recommendations to operating farmers should differ from those for landlords. We continue the method of this chapter and analyze resource valuation under the traditional appraisal assumptions of certainty and profit motivation. These assumptions are dropped in later chapters.

Realization and use value. The value of resources might be classified as either (1) realization or market value or (2) use or productivity value.[6] In reality, of course, only 1 unique value, the market value, exists; any other value attached to resources is merely an expectation based on anticipations of the future. From a pure firm and profit standpoint the use or productivity value of resources must exceed the realization or market value.[7] Otherwise the firm should, if profits are to be maximized, sell its resources, cease production, and loan the funds at interest. Under the situation of capital limitations outlined later, the problem of investment in durable resources becomes more nearly a question of the comparative returns to be realized on other resources, such as livestock and crop improvements, and the expectations of changes in land values. The use or productivity method of resource valuation involves computing the present value of a future stream of incomes. Present values differ greatly, depending on the number of years over which the income flow is forthcoming, and on whether the flow is terminable or one in perpetuity. In the conventional farm appraisal techniques wherein future incomes are discounted back to the present, the procedure is one of determining the quantity of money which, if loaned at compound interest, will return an amount equal to the investment at the end of the relevant time period. The process, known as

---

on the part of the credit firm: Should a loan be made? How much should be loaned per acre? The decision then revolves around estimates of either (a) market values, or (b) present values of future incomes in the "use value" sense. The latter again implies estimates of the value productivity of the specific resources, and hence its present or future sale value. Thus appraisal for many purposes involves the same basic principles and considerations.

6 See Sune Carlson, *Pure Theory of Production*. London: King & Son, 1939, p. 119. The use or productivity value is normally termed the *capital* value in economic literature.

7 Other methods of farm appraisal are sometimes employed in addition to the market or use value of resources. It is the market and use values alone which are important from the standpoint of choice and decision-making. The obvious comparison is that of whether a given fund will return more if invested in resources at market values and used to produce products in the future or in alternative opportunities. "Normal" values may be established as historic quantities but these are of value mainly as expectations of future use values. German farm economists use the market value of "central farms" as a basis of establishing the value of other farms which have not changed ownership at market prices. This system is of little value in decision-making (the major or perhaps sole function of resource valuation) unless it gives an estimate of the use value as compared to the market value. Generally, the comparison (between farms) suggests what the market value of one farm would be if it were to change hands. It does not represent a comparison between the productivity and market value of a given farm.

capitalization, is sometimes termed the "productivity method" of farm valuation.

As has been indicated previously, the services embodied in resources are of a pure stock nature when their use need not relate to a specific time interval; the quantity used in one period competes with or determines the amount to be used in another period. Feed grain is an example. Services are of a pure flow nature when only a limited quantity of services is given off in one period and the use of the flow in this period does not affect the services forthcoming in another period. Sunshine, rain, and the spatial aspects of land are examples. Resources such as machines or buildings involve both stock and flow services. In not all cases can a distinction be made between resource services which flow forth and provide income in perpetuity and those which provide income over a limited or terminable time period. In terms of the nature of the services and income given off, alternative systems of resource valuation become those outlined below.

Case I: Perpetual flows of resource services and incomes. Where the flow of resource services and income is at a constant rate over an indefinite period of time, the following equation defines the present value of this sequence of incomes which supposedly is known with certainty into perpetuity.

$$V = \frac{R}{r} \qquad (X)$$

Here R refers to the annual net income and r refers to the market interest rate.[8] (R also can be the value product of the resource if it does not involve taxes and other "non-production" costs.) If an acre of land gives off an

---

[8] The formula $V = \dfrac{R}{r}$ is derived from the constant income stream by compounding it annually. As is indicated in the text, the present value of any income in a future year is given by the formula:

$$V = \frac{R}{(1+r)^n} \qquad (1)$$

An income stream in perpetuity thus involves capitalization of the income in years 1, 2, 3 .... n. Thus the value of R annual income in perpetuity is

$$V = \frac{R}{1+r} + \frac{R}{(1+r)^2} + \frac{R}{(1-r)^3} + \frac{R}{(1+r)^4} \cdots \frac{R}{(1+r)^n} \qquad (2)$$

The mathematical limit of this algebraic quantity is

$$V = \frac{R}{r}\left(1 - \frac{1}{(1+r)^n}\right) \qquad (3)$$

which reduces to the following as n approaches infinity

$$V = \frac{R}{r} \qquad (4)$$

From (2) it is obvious that very distant incomes can have very little import in establishing present values. (This point has even greater application under uncertainty.) Thus even though a tract of land will be giving forth income 200 years hence, the income of the 200th year adds a negligible amount to present values. An income of $2,500 in 100 years has a current value of only $20.00.

annual flow of productive services such that the yearly net income is $15, the capitalized value of the acre (of the income in perpetuity) is $300 when the interest rate is 5 per cent. In other words, an acre of land which gives an annual income of $15 in perpetuity has a value no greater than a cash fund of $300 which might be loaned at 5 per cent interest compounded annually.

There are few, if any, instances in which a resource provides a constant income stream in perpetuity. Still, equation X is employed in appraisal as the "normal" or "productivity" method of farm real estate valuation. Although the term "normal" has little operational meaning in an uncertain economy, farm prices, costs, and yields for some period are taken as "normal"; net income for the farm is computed on the basis of these and is divided by an arbitrary interest rate to establish the "normal value" of the farm. Of course, many other models of perpetual income flow can be employed. Occasionally, the net rental is taken as the basis for capitalization.[9] The perpetuity method of valuation, where it is useful, best applies to the land resource since it is about the only factor which embodies continuous flow resources. However, the total of resources represented in soil as an aggregate factor do not fall in the category of perpetual flow services; the location and the spatial characteristics of land alone represent continuous flow services. Only a "pure sand" lends itself to unqualified use of equation X. Phosphate and potash or nitrogen and organic stocks in most soils often are capitalized as if they provided income in perpetuity. Ordinarily they do not, and the valuation equations which follow are more nearly appropriate than equation X, the "normal system." Original deposits of certain chemical elements were great enough for some soils that an annual flow of services could be made available over a long period of time. Thus exhaustion of supplies in the very remote future had little importance in farmers' planning horizons, and they could, in a sense, view the services in a perpetual flow manner. With continued farming, the original deposits of elements in many of these soils have been depleted to a point where they more nearly fall in the category of stock services and terminable income sequences. Equations such as XVI and XVIII then become more nearly applicable than equation X. Although a tendency exists to treat them in this manner (when current or "normal" rentals are used as the basis of capitalization), farm buildings attached to land cannot be valued in the manner of perpetual flow service.

Case II: Stocks of resource services and terminable incomes. Although land is the one agricultural resource which most nearly embodies service flows

---

[9] The R item of formula X may also include a "subjective product or income," which is in the form of the value which farm operators attach to living in communities of particular nationality, religious or other groups. This income can hardly be capitalized in the "pure firm," "external interest rate" context of this chapter. Rather it more nearly becomes a facet of that phenomenon analyzed in the next chapter.

with perpetuity characteristics, breeding stock, buildings, machinery, trees, and most soil improvements embody stocks of resource services which are given off in each year over a definite period. The equation below defines the present value of a terminable income bearer (a resource which gives off services over a limited time period) where future income is known with certainty and the income is the same in each year.

$$V = \frac{R}{r}\left(1 - \frac{1}{(1+r)^n}\right) \tag{XI}$$

Again, R refers to the annual net income, r refers to the rate of interest, and n refers to the number of years for which the constant income runs.

Although certain buildings and machines approximate the conditions of (a) a stock of resource services given off over a definite time period with (b) an even flow of services in each year, most terminable income bearers give off services and income at different yearly rates throughout their life. Soil improvements such as fertilizer and lime are of this nature. Services given off by many major machines and by breeding stock are of this nature. When the income or value product differs in each year, the present

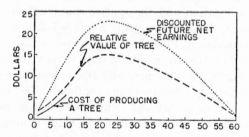

Fig. 2. Present value of future income per 1000 trees (Source: New Hamp. Agr. Exp. Sta. Bul. 323).

value of the resource is better expressed as in the manner of equation VII outlined previously.[10] Equation VII is appropriate for the orchard example illustrated in Figure 2. Using these data, research workers making the study obtained a present worth of discounted future net earnings, as indicated in Figure 2. The orchard values obtained are in terms of an external market rate of interest and do not include the uncertainty discounts included in Chapter 19. The value of the orchard rises sharply to a maximum at a time when the trees are between 20 and 25 years of age.

---

[10] The equation can be written as

$$V = \sum_{t=1}^{t=T} \frac{R_t}{(1+r)^t}$$

where R_t represents the value product forthcoming at the end of the tth year and the income continues for T years.

This maximum comes nearly 10 years before net earnings reach their peak. An orchard has its greatest value, not when net earnings are greatest, but at an earlier age as it enters the stage of increasing productivity and a longer sequence of annual incomes lies ahead. As the chart also suggests, the value of a growing tree, which is based on the discounted returns of the future, is greater in the early stages than the replacement cost. Also, the value for a newly planted tree is less than the value of a tree which will begin bearing in a few years because the "waiting" or "discount" period is longer. The same logic applies to forests and breeding (as against fattening) livestock. The "use" or "productivity" value of a dairy or beef cow is greater, where her productivity is known with some degree of accuracy, at the beginning of her productive life than at the peak of her production. Again the reason is that a longer sequence of incomes lies ahead.

Case III: Flow services with perpetual income and stock services with changes in income. Land and other resources embody both flow services which will be given off in perpetuity and stock resources which will be used up in some definite period of years. Under this situation, total income from the resource includes components with both terminable and perpetuity characteristics. If the terminable portion is certain and runs at a *constant* rate for exactly n years, the present value is given as follows, where R refers to income in perpetuity and R' refers to the terminable income of each year:

$$V = \frac{R}{r} + \frac{R'}{r}\left(1 - \frac{1}{(1+r)^n}\right) \qquad \text{(XIII)}$$

More often, resources of this nature include a terminable flow of services and a *variable* income which decreases or increases with time. In the case of land, decreases in income may come about as virgin stocks of fertility are used up, as soil erosion takes place, or as prices decline; increases may take place as prices increase. Where prices are known with certainty and the increase or decrease in income is at a constant arithmetic rate, the present value can be expressed as

$$V = \frac{R}{r} \pm \frac{I}{r^2} \qquad \text{(XIV)}$$

where I refers to the annual increase or decrease in income. This equation can be modified as follows where the decline or increase will last for n years:

$$V = \frac{R}{r} \pm \left(\frac{1}{r^2}(1 - \frac{1}{(1+r)^{n-1}}\right) \qquad \text{(XV)}$$

If the annual increase or decrease is expected to vary by years and to last for n years, the present value can be expressed best as

$$V = \frac{R}{r} \pm \left(\frac{I_1}{(1+r)^1} + \frac{I_2}{(1+r)^2} + \frac{I_3}{(1+r)^3} \cdots + \frac{I_n}{(1+r)^n} \right) \quad \text{(XVI)}$$

where the increment or decrement is indicated as I_1 for the first year, I_2 for the second year, and so forth. Equation XVI best represents the realistic situation in which changes in prices are expected to take place between years due to depression or inflation.[11]

While equation X is one employed by many academic appraisers, farmers have at times employed others of the models outlined as if the future were known with certainty. Farm values rose steadily in the manner of equation XIV in the years prior to World War I. The increasing values were based on several forces including (1) the clearing, improving, and settling of land; and (2) a growth in domestic and foreign demand for U. S. farm products. Estimates have been made to suggest that in 1910 Iowa farmers, in the prices which they paid for land, approximated equation XIV, wherein the R/r portion of the equation amounted to $78 per acre while the I/r^2 portion amounted to $21 (a total value per acre of $99).[12] By 1920 the first portion had risen to $139 and the second portion to $114 (a total of $253 per acre). Of course, it is now a historic fact that the "present values of future incomes" placed on farms in 1920 were inconsistent with the incomes actually realized. Farmers evidently capitalized the "terminable" incomes of the war period into values as if the annual increments would continue to increase (equation XIV). During and after World War II, farmer land purchases more nearly approximated

---

[11] Or, if we apply the equation to valuation of farm as a whole (under suppositions of constant prices and a known future), it also becomes applicable in the sense that both perpetual flow and stock resource services are included. If we employ equation XVI to place a use or productivity value on a farm which (say) includes only two factors (although a multitude are embodied in land alone) as land (L below) with pure flow services and fertility deposits or buildings (noted as B below) as a stock of services given off over time, the process of valuation would include the following steps under perfect knowledge and competitive conditions: First, the annual value product of land would need to be estimated to give the perpetual flow portion of the income as $\left(\frac{\Delta P}{\Delta L} \cdot L - C \right) \div r$ where C is the annual tax. (In the notations, ΔP refers to the change in value product, ΔL refers to change in land input, ΔB refers to change in building input, and L and B refer to land and building quantities.) The marginal value product of the resource containing the stock services must also be derived for each year to give a present value of

$$\sum_{t=1}^{t=T} \left[(\frac{\Delta P}{\Delta B} \cdot P - C) \div (1+r)^t \right]$$

where t refers to the particular year and the income extends T years. The present value of the farm including both land and buildings then would become:

$$V = \left[(\frac{\Delta P}{\Delta L} \cdot L - C) \div r \right] + \sum_{t=1}^{t=T} \left[(\frac{\Delta P}{\Delta B} \cdot B - C) \div (1+r)^t \right]$$

[12] See J. D. Black, *et al.. Farm Management.* New York: Macmillan, 1947, p. 738.

equation XVI. While incomes increased with the warborne inflation, land values did not increase proportionately, since farmers expected the inflated returns to terminate. Upon outbreak of the Korean conflict, however, farm real estate values took a sudden spurt, suggesting that farmers more nearly looked upon the higher income as (a) a perpetual flow (equation X), or (b) as likely to continue the rate of increase (equation XIV). The system employed undoubtedly was a combination of those outlined above and included aspects of the uncertainty models explained in Chapter 19.

When the land of newly purchased farms has been heavily exploited and requires large outlays in early years in order that productivity can be built up and income can be stabilized at higher levels, either equation XV or XVI is more appropriate than equation X as an appraisal model. Conversely, if farms have been over-improved in the sense of buildings and soil amendments, these surplus improvements provide a stock of services to be used over time but which cannot be replaced economically. The excess improvements provide an added return in the first few years, however, which gives a present value in the manner suggested by equations XV or XVI rather than equation X, the academic appraiser's favorite model.

Costs, revenue, and farm appraisal. Under the so-called productivity or use method of farm valuation, the yields and product prices of the future are first estimated (as indicated in Chapter 19, these are pure expectations subject to error and uncertainty). Inputs and costs are then estimated in a similar manner. In this procedure, known historically by farm management workers as budgeting, annual costs are subtracted from annual gross revenue to give net income estimates. In reality equation X, the productivity equation most often employed, represents a budgeting procedure involving both costs and revenue and can be represented as

$$V = \frac{R' - c}{r} \tag{XVII}$$

where R' represents the gross revenue and c represents the costs per year. This equation assumes equal revenues or costs in each year. When the revenues and costs of each year differ for a business, the present value of its resources becomes

$$V = \left[\frac{R_1'}{1+r} + \frac{R_2'}{(1+r)^2} \cdots + \frac{R'_n}{(1+r)^n} \right] -$$
$$\left[c_1 + \frac{c_2}{1+r} \cdots + \frac{c_n}{(1+r)^{n-1}} \right] \tag{XVIII}$$

where R' represents the gross revenues at the end of each year and c represents the cost at the first of each individual year. Since newly purchased farms often involve larger cost outlays at the outset for terraces, soil improvements, and other inputs which do not later necessitate annual costs, there exists basis for computing use or productivity values in the manner of equation XVIII. Equation XVIII suggests that a single budget, the assumption of equation XVII and common appraisal procedures, does not suffice, and while one budget may be computed as an average estimate for remote years, separate budgets should be made out for early years.

Valuation through depreciation. In contrast to procedures which place a present value on income extending into the future, resources sometimes are valued in terms of their depreciation or transformation in the past. This system is of limited value from the standpoint of decision-making, except as it allows an estimate of the unexhausted services embodied in the resource, and hence provides expectations of income to be forthcoming in the future.[13]

Imputation, Productivity Comparisons, and Valuation Accuracy

The remainder of this chapter is devoted to problems of product imputation in agricultural production economics. The production economist is interested not only in the return to a single factor, such as wages to labor, interest to capital, rent to land, and the entrepreneurial returns to management, but simultaneously in the reward to all factors. This study has emphasized that production or resource use always involves more than one factor. Some resources are pure complements; others are pure substitutes; some act both as complements and substitutes. In no case can the return imputed to or the value placed on one resource be accurate unless the several resources are considered at the same time. Production economists are interested in product imputation in the 2 interrelated processes of (1) productivity or efficiency comparisons between farms, regions, and industries; and (2) resource valuation as a basis for managerial and administrative decisions. First, we explain the importance of imputation principles to these 2 problems. Next, we examine the fundamentals of product imputation.

Imputation and value estimates. Not only does the individual operator have an important stake in farm asset valuation but society also stands to gain or lose depending upon the accuracy with which expectations in this important area are fashioned. The problem of resource valuation is

---

[13] When depreciation is of a straight line nature, the value (V_t) of the resource in t years after its purchase can be explained by the formula

$$V_t = \frac{P(n\text{-}t) + St}{n} \tag{1}$$

where other notations have the same meaning as in equation VIII and the corresponding footnote. If an exponential system of depreciation (a given percentage decrease in value each year from the value at the beginning of the year) is used the formula becomes

$$V_t = (\frac{S}{P})^{\frac{t}{n}} \cdot P$$

basically and fundamentally one of allocating or imputing the total product forthcoming in a single production process to each of the several resources involved. The product or reward to one factor of production cannot be established accurately except as the rewards for other factors are accurately reflected. Problems of valuation are first those of marginal productivity analysis, and only second those of "placing a price tag" on specific factors.[14] The appraiser does not accept the market price for land, but instead formulates his own expectation of the physical and value productivity of the resource. Yet in doing so he accepts the market estimates of productivity and value (price) for labor, feed, tractor fuel, and so forth; he simply subtracts the market price (expense) of these resources from the total product and imputes the residual to land. Why should he not be satisfied with the market value of land if he accepts the market value of other resources? The "value" he places on land can be no more accurate than the share of the product which he imputes to labor, and farm machinery, fertilizer, livestock, or other forms of capital. If his estimates lead farmers to follow a similar course of action and impute the product of labor or capital to land and capitalize or remunerate each factor accordingly, the possible results become apparent: labor and capital may receive a reward out of line with their value productivity and they will be under-used; the capitalized value of real estate may be too high and farmers may be led to invest a disproportionate amount of their limited capital here rather than in livestock and soil improvements.

Rent and residual returns. Some writers consider the return to land purely as a surplus or residual return.[15] The notion here is that any return above the amount necessary to retain the factor in production is a "surplus" or "residual." There is nothing unique in production economics, however, about the imputation process as it relates to the land resource; the principle is the same for all factors of production and mistaken inferences in factor valuation grow out of the misconceptions that land can or must be treated apart from other resources. Any factor can receive a return greater than the minimum payment necessary to maintain it in production. This

---

[14] Appraisers have sometimes termed equations X through XV on previous pages as productivity appraisal methods when applied to farm land because the physical productivity of a farm is first estimated, then price expectations are applied. The system is contrasted to "market value" or similar methods of appraisal. The real difference is not one of "productivity" versus "non-productivity" methods of valuation. Instead, the question is one of who makes the productivity estimate. In the first case an individual appraiser (farmer, agricultural economist, loan official) makes the estimate of value productivity. In the second case a large number of investors and would-be investors make the estimates of value productivity; these are reflected in the prices which they pay, offer, and estimate for farm resources in the market.

[15] This is a notion of R. R. Renne, in *Land Economics*. New York: Harpers, 1947, p. 204; and is taken from Marshall's distinction between rents and quasi-rents, in *Principles of Economics* (8th Edition, Ch. IX). The notion originated with Ricardo (*Principles of Political Economy and Taxation, 1817*).

condition applies to family labor and other resources in agriculture where the short-run supply price is only slightly greater than zero. A more accurate statement is this: Resources such as land which embody a perpetual flow of services may be retained in production as long as returns are greater than zero. Resource embodying only stock services may also be retained in production at a price greater than zero, until the services are completely transformed into product and the return, however small also is a "surplus" during this period. No further units of the stock-service resource will be produced, however, if the price of (the return to) the resource is not greater than its cost. Even land includes stock services which, once they are transformed into product, will not be replaced unless the return imputed to them is greater than their market price or cost. Land return is analyzed below as a marginal product in the manner of the product to any resource, the frame of analysis of the agricultural production economist.

Farm efficiency comparisons. The second facet of the imputational problem is that of resource efficiency comparisons. An early problem which faced students of production economics was measurement of resource efficiency and farm profits.[16] Recent aggregative analyses in production economics have encountered the same problem. Pioneer production economists soon found that net farm income served unsatisfactorily as an index of resource or production efficiency, since (1) one farm uses unpaid family labor while another pays a wage for hired labor; (2) tenants share farm income with the landlord, while the owner-operator receives the full amount, (3) interest is a debit in the accounts of the farm with borrowed capital; and (4) reflections of efficiency may be obscured on small farms because of a small volume of output. Accordingly, 2 measures of profit, management return, and labor income were substituted for net income as an index of efficiency of resource combination.[17] While there are slight differences in computation, both involve imputation of the total product and are residual quantities computed by subtracting from net farm income a charge for all resources except labor or management (or from gross profits with allowance for operating costs depending on the computational procedure). Resources, except the one given the residual, are charged at market rates. If the residual quantity to labor or management is greater for one farm or region than for another, the conclusion is that resource combination is most efficient in the first. This procedure assumes that the

---

[16] See G. F. Warren, *op. cit.*, for an early use of residual returns for measurement of efficiency. See T. W. Schultz, *op. cit.*, for use of the same general procedure as Warren's except that it imputes the full product to labor.

[17] For details on the method of imputing residual products to various factors see Hopkins and E. O. Heady, *Farm Records.* Ames: Iowa State College Press, 1949. For other notes on limitations of the methods see E. O. Heady, "Elementary Models in Farm Production Economics Research," *Jour. Farm Econ.*, Vol. 29, and "Production Functions from a Random Sample of Farms," *Jour. Farm Econ.*, Vol. 27.

Table 3.

Farm Efficiency When Measured by Rates Earned and Market Rates *

| | | Net income | | | "Net profits" when resources charged at 5 per cent | | "Net profits" when resources charged at rate earned | |
| | Resources employed | Situation A | Situation B | Charges at 5 per cent | Situation A | Situation B | Situation A | Situation B |
Farm	(1)	(2)	(3)	(4)	(5)	(6)	(7)	(8)
A	10,000	800	200	500	300	− 300	0	0
B	20,000	1600	400	1000	600	− 600	0	0
C	30,000	2400	600	1500	900	− 900	0	0
D	40,000	3200	800	2000	1200	− 1200	0	0
E	50,000	4000	1000	2500	1500	− 1500	0	0

* Column 5 is column 2 minus column 4. Column 6 is column 3 minus column 4. Column 7 is column 2 minus charge for resources at 8 per cent. Column 8 is column 3 minus charge for resources at 2 per cent.

market price for resources, except for the one receiving the residual share, coincides with the value productivity of the same resources. Market prices might be expected to equal the value productivity of resources in the long run under competitive conditions. However, this condition need not hold true in the short run or in a dynamic economy in which expectations are imperfect and where competition does not have full reign. Even farm rental rates, a competitive resource price determined in the agricultural industry, may deviate rather widely from the marginal productivity of land at any given time.

In the sense that a single index of efficiency (otherwise the marginal value productivity of each resource might be used) is needed for judging resource efficiency on individual farms or groups of farms, the most accurate single criterion would be a net profit figure computed on the basis of the actual marginal productivity of resources rather than on the basis of the market price. Otherwise, the relative profitability of different enterprise and resource combinations cannot always be appraised properly. This is illustrated by the hypothetical data of Table 3. Column 1 shows the quantity of resources employed by each of 5 operators. Column 2 indicates their net incomes under a high level of prices (situation A) and column 3 indicates incomes under a low level of prices (situation B). Under situation A the "actual" rate earned is 8 per cent, while under B it is 2 per cent (average and marginal productivity per dollar equal to .08 and .02 respectively). Column 4 indicates the total charge against resources when an assumed market rate of 5 per cent is used in computing "net profit" (labor income or management return). Columns 5 and 6 indicate the residual "net profit" when resources are charged at the market rate under situations A and B respectively. The data have been established so that resource combination is equally efficient on all farms (the productivities or rates of return for individual farms are identical under each of the income situations). However, if resources are charged at market rates and the "net profit" so computed under situation A is examined (column 5), resource combination appears most efficient for farm E. If the same method is applied and the data for situation B is examined (column 6), the resource combination of farm E appears most inefficient. Such conclusions are obviously incorrect. When the market rate is less than the actual productivity of resources, part of the return to other factors is imputed to the one receiving the residual. If the market rate is greater than the productivity, the reverse holds true. For the example under consideration, columns 7 and 8 indicate the "net profit" computed by using the "actual productivity" rates. In both cases "net profit" is zero and the correct conclusion is drawn that resource use is equally efficient on all farms. When the marginal productivity and market prices differ, the "net profit" figure used in making efficiency comparisons should be based on the former rather than the latter if a true index of efficiency is to be obtained.[18] It is now apparent that resource efficiency comparisons and factor valuation both revolve around imputation of a total physical or value product to the respective factors.

Leasing and other imputational problems. There are many other areas of agricultural economics which involve problems of imputation. One is pasture valuation. Agronomists borrow the residual procedures outlined above when they subtract out the value of corn and protein (on the basis of market prices) and impute the remaining value of livestock production to pasture. Imputation problems are also involved in those tenure arrangements devised by farm management specialists whereby the total income is imputed to a father and son on the basis of resources furnished under a labor-share agreement. Similar problems arise for share leases of other types.

Assumptions in residual imputation and the Euler theorem. The residual imputational procedures outlined above for farming efficiency comparisons and resource valuation imply both (1) that except for 1 factor, the market price of a resource is equal to its marginal value product; and (2) that the total physical or value product can be broken up into shares such that (a) the reward to each factor is equal to its marginal productivity, and (b) the rewards so computed just exhaust the total physical or value product. In summary, the residual imputations of agricultural economics assume that no residual can remain and that each factor can be imputed its exact reward. This assumption is implicit in the procedure; otherwise the appraiser would have no reason to impute the residual to land rather than labor, seed corn, or other capital item, while the efficiency analyst would have no reason to impute the residual to labor rather than capital or land. Early economic theories did premise that one or more residual shares of the total product exist; profit to management and rent to land were taken to be such residuals.

In contrast to the early residual theories, more recent production principles state that each resource may receive its marginal product as a reward and therefore, that no factor need receive a residual reward. This

---

[18] The rate at which resources are charged is not a problem in all cases where a residual "profit" figure is used. The market rate is, of course, the proper one if the income figure is to indicate the profitability of managing one's own resources as compared to hiring them out to other firms in the manner of the resource valuation procedures outlined later. The problem of the rate would also be unimportant if one were comparing farms which used approximately the same quantities of the various resources. It is a very important consideration, however, if management or labor income is being used to indicate the profitability of individual practices and if there is a considerable variation between farms in respect to scale of operations. Many studies have shown a high association between scale of operations and the extent to which individual practices are adopted. Accordingly, a management or labor return figure based on market prices for resources can easily overestimate or underestimate the profitability of individual practices, the relative returns from different scales of operation, or the value of specific resources.

condition applies to the long-run situation in a competitive market. One question which may arise in the reader's mind is this: if each factor receives its marginal product as a reward, will the total product be just exhausted or will it be smaller or larger than the sum of the shares to the individual factors? The answer is given in an econometric principle known as Euler's theorem. In contrast to the early residual theories, this principle states that if each factor is imputed its marginal product, the total product will, under specified conditions, be exactly exhausted. Under the residual imputational system, factor shares in correspondence with marginal products would not be consistent with "exhaustion of the total product." Euler's theorem has come to be considered as a central tenet of production economics. The theorem need not be looked upon as proof that every factor in the economy receives its marginal product as a return. (Actually it is the discounted value of marginal products which must be imputed to factors.) Rather it can be used as simple proof that a total physical or value product can be distributed to the factors by which it is produced in a manner to exhaust the total amount or the total value of output. We thus proceed to illustrate 2 principles which are important for the imputational problems of production economics: (1) each factor can receive the marginal product as a reward, and (2) the total product can be equal to the sum of the shares to the individual resources. The implications of resource rewards in terms of marginal products as a basis for establishing factor prices and in facilitating resource efficiency is brought out in a following section. The Euler principle applies to producing units of any magnitude, whether they be an acre of land, a farm, or the agricultural industry. It has been grossly neglected in agricultural economics.

Exhaustion of the product. First, let us examine the division of the total product among the factors with which it is produced. Elementary methods of estimating the marginal product of a single factor were explained in Chapter 6 (Figure 1). When input of X_2 was held constant at 80 and input of X_1 was increased from 55 to 150, the output of product increased from 100 to 300. The 200 unit increase in output represented the product from the additional 99 units of factor X_1. The value productivity of the 99 units of X_1 is established when prices are attached to the output. If we had held X_1 constant and varied X_2, we could have measured its marginal product in the same manner. If we multiply the marginal products so determined by the total number of units of X_1 and X_2 employed, we obtain the share of the total product attributable to (contributed by) each factor. Do these contributions to each factor add up to the total product? The total product is just exhausted when the marginal product is imputed to each factor under one condition: the elasticity of production must be equal to 1.0. While a production function which is characterized as linear and homogeneous throughout (for example, a straight-line, input-output curve) gives this condition, other production functions may also allow exhaustion of the product. The condition, that the elasticity of production equals 1.0, is also attained for a production function where diminishing marginal resource productivity holds true. As outlined in Chapter 2, the elasticity is equal to 1.0 at the point where the marginal physical product is equal to the average product of the resource (where the marginal curve crosses the average curve). Using a simple 1 factor-1 product example, we can illustrate the principle in Figure 3. Curve M defines the marginal product of the single resource, while curve A defines its average product; the total product curve is not shown. As we already know, the elasticity of production is 1.0 when OE of resources are used, since marginal and average products are then equal. Suppose then that we reward the OE units of resource by giving them a return of OG each, an amount equal to their marginal product. The total reward to the factor is then $OE \times OG$, or $OEFG$. This quantity is equal to the total product, as denoted by the average curve, and, therefore, a reward

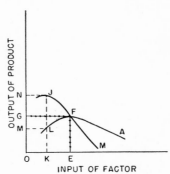

Fig. 3. Imputation of total product.

to each unit of the factor equal to the marginal product of the last unit exactly exhausts the total product. Suppose that only OK units of resource are used, however. Here the elasticity of production is greater than 1.0. If we reward each unit of factor by an amount ON, the marginal product of the last unit, the total return to all units is $OK \times ON$, or $OKJN$. This amount is greater than the total product of $OKLM$ and our condition, that the share imputed to a factor should equal the total product, is not attained. If factor rewards of less than OG were made for inputs greater than OE, the total product would exceed the share imputed to the resource. Only the reward of OG to OE units of factor exhausts the product; the production function is linear and homogeneous of the first degree at this point.[19]

---

[19] A simple algebraic presentation can illustrate the case (elasticity of production different from 1.0) when the share to the factors need not exhaust the product. We will employ only 1 factor in our production function although the same principle applies to more than 1 factor. Thus our production function is $P = f(L)$, where P is the product and L is labor. Let us "start out backwards" and set down a situation where the share of the product to factors is less than the product. We will then work to the elasticity condition which holds true for this situation. In (1) below we have indicated that the total share to a single factor labor (the only resource considered for the production function) is equal to its marginal product $(\Delta P/\Delta L)$ times the quantity of labor (L) and this share to labor $(\Delta P/\Delta L) \cdot L$ is less than the total product P as indicated in (1).

$$(\Delta P/\Delta L)L < P \tag{1}$$

In (2) below we divide each side of (1) by L. The L's cancel out on the left hand side leaving (3)

When labor, capital, land, and management are all used in the production process, the Euler theorem states that the condition of equation XIX is attained for a linear homogeneous production function (an elasticity of production equal to 1.0). Here P refers to the total product (measured

$$P = \frac{\Delta P}{\Delta L} \cdot L + \frac{\Delta P}{\Delta C} \cdot C + \frac{\Delta P}{\Delta S} \cdot S + \frac{\Delta P}{\Delta M} \cdot M \qquad \text{(XIX)}$$

in this case in physical terms) $\frac{\Delta P}{\Delta L}$ refers to the marginal product of labor and L refers to the quantity of labor, $\frac{\Delta P}{\Delta C}$ refers to the marginal product of capital, while C refers to the quantity of capital, and the S and M symbols refer to the marginal products and quantities of land and management respectively. The principle of product exhaustion can also be shown for several factors of production in algebraic or arithmetic terms and none need receive a "residual share." We illustrate it below in arithmetic form for a simple, linear, homogeneous production function where constant returns to scale (an elasticity of 1.0) exist for all units of input and of the several factors. Suppose that a product is produced with land, labor, and capital. The production coefficients (the regression coefficients or the amount of product forthcoming from each unit of factor) are 10 for labor, 2 for capital, and 5 for land.[20] If we use 1 unit of each factor, the total product is 17; since the average and marginal

---

$$1/L(\Delta P/\Delta L)L < \frac{1}{L} P \qquad (2)$$

$$\Delta P/\Delta L < P/L \qquad (3)$$

If we now multiply each side by ΔL we obtain (4) and the ΔL's cancel out on the left side leaving (5)

$$\Delta L(\Delta P/\Delta L) < \Delta L(P/L) \qquad (4)$$

$$\Delta P < \Delta L(P/L) \qquad (5)$$

By dividing both sides by P we obtain (6) and the P's on the right cancel out to give (7)

$$1/P(\Delta P) < 1/P \cdot \Delta L(P/L) \qquad (6)$$

$$\Delta P/P < \Delta L/L \qquad (7)$$

Therefore, we have shown that the total product imputed to labor (by multiplying the quantity of labor by its marginal product) is less than the total product (equation 1) when the percentage change in the product is less than the percentage change in the factor (equation 7). In other words, the total product is not exhausted by using the marginal productivity of labor as the basis for rewarding labor when the elasticity of production is less than 1.0.

[20] Limitational factors (those which must be combined in fixed proportions if product is forthcoming) give rise to particular problems in imputation. However, as was indicated in the chapter on factor classification, when two strictly limitational factors are concerned, the two factors can be considered as a single resource. For more detail on the problems outlined here see Heady, E. O., "Use of Input-Output Ratios," *Jour. Farm Econ.*, Vol. 34.

products are equal, a return to each factor equal to its marginal product just exhausts the total product. If we increase labor to 2 units, the total product becomes 27, and again is "just exhausted" if we impute to the 1 unit of land its marginal product of 5, to the 1 unit of capital its marginal product of 2, and if each of the 2 units of labor receives the marginal product of 10.

While a competitive market would (in the long run and in the absence of imperfect knowledge) result in factor prices equal to the marginal products of resources, it is not true that all factors actually receive their marginal products as rewards. One of the extreme condition forces is the dynamics-uncertainty complex outlined in Chapters 15-19. When the elasticity of production for each resource is other than 1.0, the "exhaustion of the product" cannot apply, but, as brought out below, there is no basis for allocating the residual surplus or deficit to land or any other single resource.

Imputational procedures in agricultural economics. In both of the major areas wherein production economists are concerned with product imputation, they assume conditions of competition such that the market price for factors or factor services approximates the value productivity of resources, except for the one to which the residual is imputed. In other words, the analyst who makes a farm management or national efficiency study and imputes a return to all resources except labor at market prices is saying that equation XX serves as the appropriate imputational procedure. Here RL denotes the residual return to labor, V denotes the total value product, and the other terms denote the share of the total product attributable to capital, management, and land. (The term $\frac{\Delta P}{\Delta C}$ is the marginal product for capital and P_p is the price of the product, while C represents the quantity of capital, $\frac{\Delta P}{\Delta M}$ and $\frac{\Delta P}{\Delta S}$ refer to the marginal products, and M and S refer to the quantities of management and land respectively. If he assumes that the market price of the factors is equal to their marginal value products, then he assumes formulas XX and XXI to be identical where P_c, P_m, and P_s refer, in equation XXI, to the prices and C, M, and S refer to the

$$RL = V - \left(P_p \frac{\Delta P}{\Delta C} \cdot C + P_p \frac{\Delta P}{\Delta M} \cdot M + P_p \frac{\Delta P}{\Delta S} \cdot S \right) \qquad \text{(XX)}$$

$$RL = V - (P_c \cdot C + P_m \cdot M + P_s \cdot S) \qquad \text{(XXI)}$$

quantities of capital, management, and land respectively. The appraisal expert reverses the procedure and assumes that the market prices of resources serve as an accurate estimate of management, labor, and capital productivity but that the return of land (S) must be estimated as a residual in the manner of equation XXII. (Land, L, and its marginal product, $P_p \dfrac{\Delta P}{\Delta L}$, have now been included on the right, while we attempt to

use RS, the residual return to land, as an estimate of $P_p \dfrac{\Delta P}{\Delta S} \cdot S$.)

$$RS = V - \left(P_p\frac{\Delta P}{\Delta C} \cdot C + P_p\frac{\Delta P}{\Delta L} \cdot L + P_p\frac{\Delta P}{\Delta M} \cdot M \right) \qquad \text{(XXII)}$$

These residual methods again give the actual marginal productivity of only 1 factor if market prices actually do reflect (coincide with) the marginal productivity of other factors and if the elasticity of production is 1.0 for all factors.

Management and resource valuation. The total product can be exactly exhausted (a) when the share imputed to each resource is equal to the number of units of the resource multiplied by its marginal product, and (b) even when the production function is homogeneous and linear, only if all resources are included in the imputational process. To the extent that management represents a distinct factor of production, it also must be given a share of the total return, if farm valuation estimates are not to be in error. Common appraisal techniques, as the budgetary process is carried out and the estimated residual return is capitalized, give management only a fleeting consideration. If the budgetary or appraisal process assumes large management inputs while no return is imputed to management, the farm becomes overcapitalized. The average or less-than-average manager thus may be led to financial disaster if he accepts the appraisal expert's prediction of value.[21]

The residual imputational process has no basis unless the production function is homogeneous of the first degree; without an elasticity of 1.0, there is no more basis for leaving the residual to one factor than for leaving it to another. The Euler system suggests that if the value or marginal productivity of one factor is to be estimated apart from the market, the reward of other factors might equally be estimated apart from the market. In case the agricultural production function is non-linear throughout a relevant range of resource use, or the majority of individual farms have not attained a scale of minimum long-run costs (the linear portion of the production function), the elasticity of production may be greater than 1.0 and imputation of the marginal product to each factor need not add to the total product. In this case, an alternative assumption of the residual appraisal systems, there is little if any logic in production economics to

---

[21] Farm families may also capitalize direct utilities from resources into real estate. Members of certain church or nationality groups will pay a higher price than others for farms within the ethnical or religious group. Higher prices may prevail for farms near town and school or on a paved road (and apart from market advantages). These considerations are additional firm-household interrelationships and the individual must make a subjective estimate of the value of the direct utility which he derives from the particular set of resources.

justify allocation of the excess to land rather than any other factor of production.[22] Labor or capital might equally well be given the residual after the market price ("market estimate of productivity") for land services has been subtracted.

Determination of rent and wages and allocation of resources. Relationships in production economics can also be used to show that if resources in a competitive industry such as agriculture are priced in terms of their marginal value productivity and allocated between opportunities in the same manner, a maximum product will be forthcoming from a given quantity of resources. The elementary examples of Chapter 4 illustrated that a total product, whether measured in value or physical terms, can be maximized only if mobile resources (for example, labor and capital) are allocated between producing units in a manner to equate their marginal products.[23] Without going into detail on uncertainty and household aspects of production, we use the static models of Figures 4, 5, and 6 to illustrate the effect factor pricing may have on production and resource allocation in a

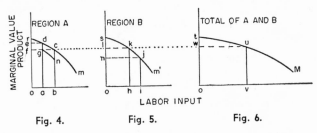

Fig. 4.　　　　Fig. 5.　　　　Fig. 6.

Factor prices and resource use.

competitive market. Let us suppose that 2 farms or 2 agricultural regions with similar production functions exist as indicated as Figures 4 and 5. When the 2 regions are added together they give the aggregate marginal value product curve indicated by M in Figure 6. The total supply (stock) of labor available in the 2 regions is ov. If the marginal value product serves as the demand for labor, M is the labor demand function in the 2 regions. With supply (stock) and demand for labor equal in the 2 regions (Figure 6), the total product is $ovut$, the share of the total value product imputable to labor is $ovuw$, and the rent to land is wtu. Under this imputa-

---

[22] Aside from implicit assumption in traditional farm appraisal systems that the elasticity of production is greater than 1.0 or that farmers have not estimated use of capital in the direction of minimum costs, theory of competitive industry would suppose that the product could be exhausted by imputing the share of each factor to the particular resource.

[23] While the discussion of these figures was in terms of the application of resources to technical units, the principle applies equally to any other unit as is brought out in later chapters.

tion of the product and a wage rate of *ow* (equals *ol* and *of*), the marginal value productivity of labor is equal to the wage or marginal cost of labor when region (or firm) A employs *ob* workers and region B employs *oh* workers. With mobility of labor, the total products in regions A and B respectively are *obcr* and *ohks*, the total returns to labor are *obcf* and *ohkl*, and the rents to land are *fcr* and *lks*.

If labor is not mobile or is not priced according to its productivity, a different resource allocation pattern may result and a smaller product may be forthcoming. For example, suppose that of the total labor supply *ov*, a quantity equal to *oi* is "frozen" in region B, while only *oa* is available in region A. With competition within both regions, the wage rate becomes *on* in region B and *oe* in region A, while rents are *njs* and *edr*. Thus the total product from the same quantity of resources is now less than that outlined above, the decline in product amounts to *hijk* minus *abcd*. Similarly, if labor is mobile but for institutional or other reasons the wage is established at the level *oe* in region A, only *oa* labor can be employed if the marginal cost of the labor is not to exceed the marginal value product. An amount of labor equal to *oi* must be employed in region B, and the wage rate cannot exceed *on* if the return is to be as great as the cost of labor. Again the total product forthcoming from the 2 regions is smaller than if A employs *ob* and B employs *oh* of labor.

The possible effects of an appraisal method or a market mechanism, when they do not allow a price for factors equal to their marginal value productivity, on the use and inefficiency are now obvious. If the valuation procedure imputes part of the real reward of labor to land, too little of the former may be employed in agriculture. Failure to impute full rents to land may result in an excessive use of labor and capital.

Selected References

Allen, R. G. D., *Mathematical Analysis for Economists*. London: Macmillan, 1942, pp. 249-251.

Black, J. D., *et al.*, *Farm Management*. New York: Macmillan, 1947, Chs. 32, 33.

Boulding, K. E., *Economic Analysis*. New York: Harper, 1948, Ch. 35 (Time, Production and Valuation), Ch. 36 (The Equilibrium of the Enterprise in Time).

Carlson, Sune, *The Pure Theory of Production*. London: King & Son, 1939, pp. 119-126.

Heady, Earl O., "Use and Estimation of Input-Output Coefficients," *Jour. Farm Econ. Proceedings*, Vol. 34.

Hopkins, J. A. and Murray, W. G., *Elements of Farm Management*. New York: Prentice-Hall, forthcoming, Ch. 4.

Hopkins, J. A., and Heady, Earl O., *Farm Records*. Ames: Iowa State College Press, 1949, Chs. 7, 8.

Ibach, D. B., "Role of Soil Depletion in Land Valuation," *Jour. Farm. Econ.*, Vol. 22, p. 460 ff.

Keynes, J. M., *General Theory of Employment Interest and Money*. New York: Harcourt, Brace, 1936, pp. 132-136.

Murray, W. G., *Farm Appraisal*. Ames: Iowa State College Press, 1940, Ch. 11.

14

Firm-Household Interrelationships and Efficiency Within the Farm

Preceding chapters have supposed that the farm as a business firm has profit maximization as its objective. We drop this condition of analysis in this chapter and consider the farm family and the farm firm as a single composite unit. Maximization of satisfaction or utility (welfare) of the family then becomes the goal, and choice indicators must be altered accordingly. These modifications are important in that portion of production economics research directed towards the intra-farm use of resources. No longer can it be said that the individual farmer uses his resources irrationally when he does not maximize profits in a single time period. Motivational forces behind the farm producing unit are consumption-inspired as well as profit-inspired. The farm manager is not transformed as he arises from his breakfast table and goes to the barn to begin the day's routine. It is probably true that production decisions were made in the routine of consumption activity at the breakfast table. His decisions as a consumer may be partly a product of habitual behavior, and his decisions as a producer may be similarly conditioned.[1] Applied research in agricultural economics has emphasized production almost entirely as it relates to maximization of profits or other ends on the firm side of the farm. Analysis of consumption has been looked upon as a field distinct and apart from the problems of resource allocation, and studies in household economics have been delegated largely to home economists. There is little rhyme or reason in this segregated approach. Although its limitations have been overcome partly in extension education by integration of farm and home planning, not enough recognition has been given to the interaction between the firm and the household in agriculture. As later chapters unfold, it will be possible to illustrate how household considerations, such as the level of income, affect the efficiency and quantity of resource use. Erroneous inferences on how the agricultural firm either does or should act may arise where profit maximization rather than utility maximization

[1] C. F. Katona, *Psychological Aspects of Economic Behavior.* New York: McGraw-Hill, 1951, Ch. 9.

is taken as the goal. Some agricultural economists have even gone so far as to say that the motives behind farmer decisions are mechanistic rather than economic.[2] These inferences are based on the supposition that the firm unit of the farm is dominant. In actuality, when the farm is considered an over-all economic unit encompassing both firm and household units, the optimum use of resources in production or the optimum allocation of income in consumption cannot be defined until the 2 basic sets of economic relationships (production and consumption) are related. Production and consumption economics fall in one framework.

Farm setting. In no other industry is the interdependence between the household and firm so strong as in agriculture. While the close relationship may be approximated in some small-scale service or handicraft industries, it is quite alien to major industries, where corporate business organization predominates. Households which contribute capital to the corporation are often remote, both in a physical and a decision-making sense, from management which determines the production and resource use policies of the firm. While the stockholder exercises some control through his voting privileges and willingness to invest in stock, decisions on capital accumulation and similar policies are made without direct regard to the consumption patterns of the many consuming units which contribute capital.[3] The farm is a complete economic unit in itself. Not only does each member share in the work and the decisions, but all of the problems of income distribution and resource allocation involved in a national economy are involved in the farm-family unit. "Farming and living" are more nearly identical in agriculture than "working and living" in non-agricultural occupations. Some operators look upon themselves as "stewards of the soil," and good husbandry becomes an ultimate consumption goal. Farming is chosen as an occupation by many operators because of the values which they attach to farm work, including the opportunity to be one's own boss. Operators of specialty farms, particularly, have a liking for the type of enterprise with which they work. A small patch of wheat is grown on numerous farms of the winter wheat belt because of "sentimental" reasons alone, in spite of the fact that other crops now have a profit advantage. The leisure and simplicity which characterize subsistence and "mountain" farming have been so ingrained into the value systems of many older farm couples that a non-farm alternative with higher money income is not a force great enough to uproot them. Not only are the firm and household intertwined in terms of physical location and economic decisions, but

---

[2] See J. N. Brewster and H. L. Parsons, "Can Prices Allocate Farm Resources," *Jour. Farm Econ.*, Vol. 28.

[3] Consumption-production interrelationships within the corporation may be important, however, in the sense that they relate to decisions by executives. Personnel with whom decisions actually rest may choose capital accumulation and expansion in the scale of the corporation, in order to satiate their personal wants. Being looked up to as the president of a large corporation represents a good in consumption.

the supply of labor to the firm is provided partly through the particular household.

Profit and decision-making. Not only do price relationships fail to serve as the ultimate choice indicator or criterion for the allocation of recourses and income in agriculture, but, also, profit is not the ultimate end or quantity which the farm family attempts to maximize. Within a range, greater profits are complementary with greater family satisfactions. At some level of income, however, profits become competitive with the direct utility which can be derived from farm income and resources. Some of the non-profit ends or non-price choice indicators are outlined in this chapter. Others are discussed in Chapter 17, and are particularly relevant to production choices under uncertainty. It can even be postulated that the farm manager must make a choice between money income and entrepreneurial inactivity.[4]

Production and profits are, within themselves, only intermediate ends of farming. In the means-end chain they represent means to more ultimate ends rooted in consumption and utility. While some farmers attempt to increase income because they attach values to profits as a good *per se*, most farm families work toward profits in order to consume the products which money returns will buy. The selection of production processes which allow an income flow consistent with the need for cash withdrawals to be used in consumption stands at a level with pure profit maximization in determining the manner in which resources can be and are used. This firm-household complex is important not only in defining the organization of resources and family activities which will maximize utility at a given point in time, but also in helping to explain uncertainty precautions, capital accumulation, soil conservation, and other production-consumption decisions which relate to time.

Basic Theory of Subsistence Farming

A "pure type" of firm-household interrelationship is that of subsistence farming, in which the family neither sells nor buys products in the market. This "Crusoe-type" economy is perhaps never actually attained. However, goods derived from subsistence products on the farm are more important than those purchased with income through the market for an important group of the nation's farmers. The 1950 census listed 1,250 million families with an income of less than $500, while the figure for 1940 was 2,360 million. These farms are concentrated in the Appalachian, Ozark, and Ouchita Mountains; the cotton areas of the South; and the Lake States cut-over region, but are also sprinkled throughout the nation's agriculture. Garden products and housewife services provide an element of subsistence

---

[4] See T. Scitovsky, "A Note on Profit Maximization," *Rev. of Econ. and Stat.*, Vol. 11, pp. 57-60.

production even on commercial farms. Because its prototype is more important in agriculture than in any other single industry, we employ the pure "Crusoe-type" of subsistence farming as the first simple model to be examined in explaining how household considerations condition choices in production.

The principles of pure subsistence farming are illustrated in Figures 1, 2, and 3. Since the end toward which resource used is directed has changed, we must now examine the nature of the appropriate choice indicator. The consumer indifference curve is the relevant choice indicator when the objective of resource allocation is one of maximum satisfaction. The indifference curve in consumption is the counterpart of the iso-product contour in production. It suggests the relative values which the consumer attaches to different goods and services (including such intangibles as leisure and freedom) and illustrates all possible combinations of 2 products which will result in equal satisfaction (utility) for an individual. Indifference curve I_1D_1 in Figure 1 indicates all of the combinations of

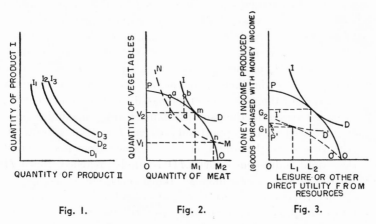

Fig. 1.   Fig. 2.   Fig. 3.

Simple firm-household interrelationships.

goods I and II which give equal utility. Curve I_1D_1 is convex to the origin, indicating that the goods I and II substitute at diminishing rates; if total utility is not to be lessened, increasing quantities of product II must be taken on to compensate for each successive unit of good I sacrificed. Indifference curves generally have the same properties and implications as iso-product curves in respect to linearity, complementarity, and substitution rates. The curves which constitute one person's indifference map never cross (intersect) each other. The distance between the curves does not signify a cardinal relationship, and, therefore, the distance between curves on an indifference map does not justify an interpretation of any (comparative) quantitative relationship between the "amount" of utility which each represents. All that can be said about the indifference curves is that they increase monotonically from the origin, the ordering being indicated by ordinal numbers. In consequence, any specific indifference curve represents (a) greater total utility than does any other indifference curve closer to the origin and (b) less total utility than any indifference curve further from the origin. Curve I_2D_2 represents greater total satisfaction than I_1D_1 but less than I_3D_3.[5] It follows that an individual who is striving to increase his total satisfaction will in effect be tempted to advance to indifference curves more distant from the origin than the one on which he is now located. His goal is to attain the highest possible utility level from given funds or resource (or minimize the outlay for a given utility level) in the same fashion that the goal of the pure firm is to maximize the product from given resources or minimize the input for a given product.

The pure subsistence farmer again has limited resources with which he can produce alternative commodities for direct consumption. Line PO in Figure 2 represents such an opportunity curve for vegetables or meat, 2 products produced in the same time period, and is based perhaps on 15 months of operator and family labor, 10 acres of mountain land, and $100 dollars of capital. What combination of meat and vegetable will maximize utility in this single period? One possibility includes OV_1 of vegetables and OM_2 of meat. However, this combination of products, consumed directly by the household and not exchanged in the market, allows attainment of the utility level indicated by indifference curve NM only. It does not represent the use of resources which maximize satisfactions since it intersects the opportunity curve, PO. Higher total utility curves, with respect to the origin, can be attained from the given stock of resources until indifference curve ID is finally reached. Since ID is tangent to PO, utility is maximized.[6] Indifference curves higher in the plane (further from the origin) than ID cannot be attained from the opportunities (resources) represented by PO. Indifference curves lower in the plane intersect OP and do not define a maximum utility. The marginal rate of substitution of goods in consumption is equal to the marginal rate of substitution of goods in production. The combination m thus denotes

---

[5] The reader need only transform the discussion of Chapter 5 into the terms of consumption and indifference curves. If further background is needed, it can be obtained in K. E. Boulding, *Economic Analysis*. New York: Harper, 1948, pp. 735-780; or S. Weintraub, *Price Analysis*. New York: Pitman, 1949, pp. 6-30.

[6] The fact that any combination of products other than m cannot be attained is illustrated geometrically. If the combination of products on the indifference curve were to be changed from point m to point b, the individual as a consumer is willing to sacrifice only md of meat to gain db vegetables if his total utility is not to be lessened. But, as can be seen on the opportunity curve, an increase in vegetables by ca (which is equal to db) necessitates sacrifice of an mc (which is greater than md) quantity of meat. The amount of meat (1) sacrificed on the opportunity curve is greater than (2) that which can be sacrificed on the utility curve if total utility is not to be lessened.

maximum utility and the optimum allocation of resources under a pure subsistent type of farming; resources must be used in a manner to allow an output of OV_2 of vegetables and OM_1 of meat.

Commercial farms and subsistence production. The principles outlined above apply similarly to the subsistence segment of the commercial farms. The "equal or given" outlay of resources can now refer to a small garden plot, the time of the husband and machine services devoted to gardening, or the labor of the housewife and the children in planting and harvesting vegetables. Decisions are then in reference to the number of rows of tomatoes or cabbages to be planted. A more important "subsistence" decision on the commercial farm is the allocation of the housewife's time between competitive alternatives, such as gardening as compared to household duties. With household duties expressed on the x axis of Figure 2 and "outside" work on the y axis, the time and ability of the housewife determine the opportunity curve and an optimum allocation of her efforts is expressed in the manner outlined above.

The rationale of many farm decisions can be explained in the firm-household or subsistence farming model of Figure 3. The mountain farmer may view the allocation of his time in the context of an opportunity curve such as PO and an indifference curve such as ID. The opportunity curve can be taken to indicate production of money income which can be obtained from producing more product for the market as compared to using labor for leisure or fishing.[7] The indifference curve shows the relative value which is placed on goods purchased with money income as compared to the direct utility from using labor or other resources for fishing. If the farmer does nothing but fish, he can't produce a money income. He may, however, divide his time between fishing and producing money income, in line with the opportunities expressed by PO. The optimum, defined when goods in consumption substitute at the same rate as goods in production, is again denoted by tangency of curves PO and ID for outputs including OG_2 of money-income and OL_2 of goods such as leisure and fishing which provide direct utility from resources. The farmer is not then a "shabby operator" or an "irrational producer" because of his failure to "fish less and farm more." Similar logic applies to other farm decisions intertwined in the firm-household complex. The farmer rationally may choose fancy buildings at the expense of productive livestock since the combination

---

[7] The opportunity curve comparing money income and utility which can be derived from other things than money may also have a range of complementarity such as that indicated by curve IP in Figure 15 of Chapter 7. Here we need only assume that money income is measured on the vertical axis while goods which provide utility derived directly from farm resources are measured on the horizontal axis. If the direct utility expresses the enjoyment of farming *per se,* it then becomes conceivable that the "enjoyment from farming" increases with income up to a certain point. Beyond this point, more profits (from harder work and longer hours for the family) decrease the "enjoyment of farming."

selected may be the one which maximizes utility rather than profit. This possibility exists, and falls in the context of economics in spite of the fact that the motives of farming are sometimes termed "mechanistic" rather than economic.[8]

Family democracy and decisions. The simple models above employ the indifference curve or the preference system of a single individual in specifying the optimum organization of resources between profit, subsistence, leisure, and other competing alternatives. In many families, choices are made in this context and the values of the operator rule supreme in decision-making. This procedure does not guarantee maximization of family welfare or satisfaction, however. Maximization of family utility becomes a complex process, especially because the desires and values of each individual cannot be weighed through a pricing mechanism but must be expressed through a voting procedure. Resolution of these family problems is possible within the context of welfare economics and social choice.[9] Because of space limitations, these farm-household elements are not outlined in detail here. This point should be emphasized, however: the optimum allocation of resources within the firm-household complex will differ, depending upon the indifference curve which serves as the choice indicator. When a democratic family can resolve its conflicts, and expresses the relative values of each individual in a group indifference curve, the optimum allocation of the housewife's time between farm or subsistence production and household work is one which will maximize the family's welfare when weight is given to the preference system of the wife as well as those of other members of the family.[10] However, if the indifference

---

[8] The old notion that the farmer builds the barn first and the house second is consistent with maximum family welfare when the choice is a reflection of the "family" indifference curve. Of course, if it is the choice indicator of the farmer as a "family dictator," the decision need not be compatible with maximum family welfare. Decisions of this nature within the family involve all the complexities of welfare economics. Utility of the two individuals cannot be increased unless (1) the investment in the barn makes both the husband and wife "better off" (perhaps both prefer a bigger barn to a bigger house for "show purposes"), or (2) compensation can be arranged whereby a greater product is forthcoming and allows a form of compensation to be made to the wife to guarantee that she is "no worse off" while the husband is "better off." Compensation may be indirect in the sense that the barn (at the expense of the house) not only has "show value" but brings in greater income to be used for a dish-washer.

[9] See K. J. Arrow, *Social Choice and Individual Values.* New York: Wiley, 1951; and M. Reder, *Readings in the Theory of Welfare Economics.* New York: Columbia University Press, 1947.

[10] Although some notion of a family or community indifference curve can be set forth, the step is not taken here because of space and time limitations. Generally, throughout this study, the use of the indifference curve can be supposed to represent the relative values of either (1) a single individual as a family member, (2) a family composed of members with identical values, or (3) a family in which values differ but the group indifference curve is capable of resolution and expression. The concept is useful in any case. It is true, of course, that economic theory gets around these problems, either by assuming that choices made by individuals alone are relevant

curve used in choice (*ID* in Figure 2) is for the husband of a patriarchal family, decisions are made in the vein of a "dictator's choice indicator." The allocation of resources between leisure and production or other competing alternatives, while maximizing utility to the patriarch, need not maximize satisfaction to the wife or to the family as a unit.

Capital Accumulation

The firm and the household come into conflict particularly over the portions of the income flow to be allocated between (a) current consumption or (b) re-investment in the business as a basis for later income and consumption. Conflicts are expressed in use of income for either a refrigerator or a boar, a family vacation or a manure loader, or false teeth for the husband versus fertilizer for the cotton.

The important elements of firm-household relationships spring from time, uncertainty, and capital limitations. If it were not for the time-uncertainty complex explained in detail in later chapters, capital limitations would not arise and the firm-household interaction would be unimportant. Both units would have unlimited funds and either could be treated as an economic entity apart from the other. Where capital limitations exist, the closeness of firm-household interrelations depends on the severity with which funds are limited. The problem is greater on a small low-income farm of the Appalachian highlands than on the King Ranch in Texas. Time and the household bring an added type of discounting into effect. In Chapter 13, discounting was in terms of a pure firm attempting to maximize profits, and discounting was based on the market interest rate. When maximization of household satisfactions becomes the criterion by which farm resources are gauged, however, the market rate of interest (which compares the profitability of investing a sum of money which will bring in income at a later time with loaning it at interest) is no longer relevant. The household unit is concerned with the utility to be derived from income now as compared to that forthcoming in the future. The problem is one of allocating resources and income in a manner to maximize utility over time. By treating income, or the goods purchased with it, at 2 points in time as 2 different goods, we can specify an optimum in the manner of the elementary illustration below. The farm family's decisions are even more complex since they must make choices in respect to many time periods.

Production and consumption over time. The optimum allocation of income between consumption and capital accumulation depends on the nature of the time-opportunity curve facing the individual (or family) and the

---

or that differences in values can be resolved in the welfare context in which some members of a group are made "better off" and none are made "worse off" (or that exchanges and compensation can accomplish this).

time-indifference curve which he possesses. The time-indifference map shown in Figure 4 is probably an hypothesis of the manner in which consumption goods of one time period substitute for those of another when income is at various levels.[11] The t_1 axis measures income for consumption at the present, while the t_2 axis measures that for the future. Indifference curve T_1I_1 is for a low income or consumption level; the curve is relatively flat, suggesting that a high value is placed on present consumption as compared to saving or later consumption. A large amount of future income is necessary to substitute for current sacrifices in consumption

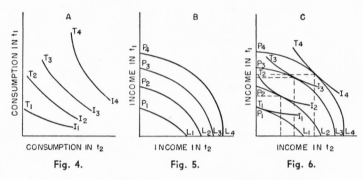

Inter-temporal indifference curves and production possibilities.

under curve T_1I_1. As income or consumption possibilities climb to higher levels as suggested by curves T_2I_2, T_3I_3, and T_4I_4, the slope of the indifference curve increases, indicating that the individual places less value on current as compared to future income and consumption.[12] The person with an income at the subsistence level places little premium on foregoing current consumption in order that his income and consumption of the future

---

[11] Alternative hypothesis are that the time-indifference curve is (1) linear with a slope of (a) less than 45°, denoting a discount on all future consumption as compared to present consumption; (b) exactly 45°, indicating equal values on or indifference between present and future consumption; or (c) greater than 45°, denoting a premium on all consumption of the future; and (2) convex with slopes of (a) less than 45°, or (b) greater than 45° with similar implications. Any of these possibilities have implications which are apparent in defining the optimum rate of saving and capital accumulation, and the basic principles presented in the analysis are not changed.

[12] Again, there might be exceptions, such as "steeper" indifference curves at "low" as compared to "high" levels of consumption. These exceptions do not change the basic logic and are not presented in detail because of space limitations. It should also be indicated that the individual indifference curves are not those drawn from a family representing a single preference function. When used to represent the situation for different individuals (or for the same individual with different amounts of capital in time), the separate curves are all representative of different preference functions.

will be increased. The same person (or different persons with similar preference functions) is thought to place greater premiums on saving and accumulation as income and consumption levels increase. The time-indifference curves have been drawn convex to the origin rather than linear, suggesting that a different discount or premium is placed on each increment of saving. This is in contrast to the pure firm approach of discounting in Chapter 13, where all of the income of one time period was discounted at a single rate, although the extent of discounting increased with time. Premiums required on future income for each dollar of current consumption sacrificed may be at the rate of 4¢ on the first $500, 75¢ on the second $500, and $2 on the eighth $500. The individual may even be willing to pay to save the first $500 if it provides for retirement.

The nature of time production possibilities are shown in Figure 5.[13] As long as any economic product or interest is forthcoming from capital re-invested, the time-possibility curve may have a slope of less than 45°, indicating that each dollar re-invested will return itself, plus a net addition to income of the future. On most farms the time-possibility curve for large amounts of capital will be concave to the origin, due to the diminishing productivity of resources for a particular time period of the future. For the same reasons, the slope or curvature of the time possibility curve may be greater for farms with larger amounts of capital, as illustrated by P_1L_1, P_2L_2, P_3L_3, and P_4L_4. Figure 6, which combines Figures 4 and 5, illustrates the equilibrium position or optimum rate of capital accumulation for different income possibility levels. With income at a very low level, all current income may be consumed as is denoted by intersection of curves T_1I_1 and P_1L_1 at the t_1 axis. At the highest level of income, savings account for disposition of the greatest portion of current income as indicated by tangency of T_4I_4 and P_4I_4. The disparity between capital accumulation and income for low and high income farms may thus become greater over time even though each attains an optimum position from its limited resources. This tendency for the "propensity to consume" to decline with income level was partially substantiated in a 1950 Iowa survey. While it involves interfamily complexities, the study showed that farm families with average incomes of $1,500 saved 14 per cent, those with incomes of $3,000 saved 31 per cent, and those with an income of $4,500 saved 52 per cent of their income.

---

[13] When time and uncertainty are taken into account, the slope of the indifference curve is not independent of the expected slope for the opportunity curve. If the individual "believes" future returns to be high, he may put a relatively low value on the transfer (saving) of income from the present to the future. If he "believes" the future may give very low returns (or will result in a low value on assets carried into the future), he may place a relatively high value on saving. Or, exactly the reverse may hold true for other individuals. The phenomena here best relates to uncertainty and the nature of expectations and is discussed in detail later.

Basis of Discount and Farm Retirement

The slope of time-indifference curve reflects the value or discount which the consumer places on current income and savings. It is likely that farm families do place a premium on saving some of their income for the future. Indifference curves, such as those of Figure 4, may take on a slope of more than 45° over some portion, indicating that a sacrifice of $1 in current consumption is rational, even if the return on the $1 is negative.

Numerous forces condition the values which farm families attach to future as compare to current income (explain the slope of the time-indifference curve). While low income or great economic uncertainty may cause current consumption to have a high value relative to future consumption, retirement considerations and the value systems of farm families *per se* may have the opposite effect. Evidently, farmers put a high value on capital accumulation. The Iowa survey, mentioned previously, found that saving, capital accumulation, and expansion of the farm business very nearly become ends in themselves for many farmers. (While satisfaction is the more ultimate end, capital accumulation is the direct means or manifestation of attaining this end.) Numerous farmers in the study indicated that they would save even if it were necessary to pay for the privilege. When they do not have other means for providing retirement income, most individuals would react in this manner.

The premium or discount placed on the future (the slope of the time indifference curve) varies between individuals; while some would rather live at high levels now and at low levels later, others prefer the opposite. It is conceivable that many individuals have in mind some optimum level toward which they strive, and which, if realized, they attempt to maintain into the future. Other forces affecting the values attached to saving include uncertainty, inheritance customs, and the mores of the community. Uncertainty enters into the savings and capital accumulation picture in several ways: saving is one way of increasing operator equity and hence of insuring against insolvency under price declines, sickness, casualties, and other unforeseen causes of decreased income or increased outlay. Also, it may insure that future price declines will not lower living to unacceptable levels during retirement. Where capital accumulation is purely a retirement consideration, the anticipated optimum depends on whether the individual expects to (1) retire on the flow of income from savings or (2) retire on the stock of capital itself.[14] The implications are apparent for a situation where knowledge might be perfect (as implied in the sense of Figure

---

[14] A survey of central Iowa farmers by the author indicated that 13.9 per cent expected to retire on a capital fund, 66.7 per cent expected to retire on earnings from savings, and 19.4 per cent expected to use a combination. These farmers estimated that savings of $21,937 would be necessary for retirement on a fund basis, while $56,925 would be necessary for retirement on an earnings basis.

6). Suppose that a farm family anticipates a retirement period extending over 10 years and that $2,000 per year is necessary for living during retirement. The capital to be accumulated must amount to (1) $20,000 if the capital stock is consumed during retirement, or (2) $50,000 if income during retirement is in the form of interest at 4 per cent on the capital stock. Two types of uncertainty may cause a premium to be placed on the latter method, however. One element of uncertainty is the length of life remaining after retirement for the operator and his wife or other dependent. If he lives more than 10 years, he must find subsistence from other sources if he originally has selected the stock or fund retirement system. The other element of uncertainty is the level of prices. If a state of depression exists during retirement, the stock system will necessitate a level of living lower than anticipated. The flow system provides a hedge for either type of uncertainty. If the retirement period stretches over a longer period than anticipated, the flow of income will continue, and living can also continue. If depression comes about, part of the greater capital can itself be consumed. Because of these 2 uncertainties, it is also possible that the farm family attempts to "over-save" or provide some "cushion."

A formal retirement program for farmers fashioned after the social security system of the federal government or the retirement plans of private firms might have important effects on capital productivity and capital accumulation in agriculture. First, because their future is secured, young farmers might operate with less caution and invest in more productive ventures, rather than in real estate to provide retirement *per se*. Second, because their livelihood is also guaranteed, widows and others with meager incomes might place less pressure on exploitive farming systems for rental farms. Because of other forces and objectives which encourage saving, it is not likely that a designed farm retirement policy of this nature would have important effects in reducing savings in agriculture. The Iowa study cited earlier found that many families value (a) farming as an occupation, or (b) ownership of farms to an extent that they accumulated savings in order to pass along farm property to their children. For other farmers, capital accumulation and debt retirement is dictated by custom. They feel that their neighbors expect them to save, and consequently take this as one of the direct or indirect goals of farming. This end, intermediate or ultimate, as the case may be, also may be built into value systems through early training and attitude of family members. The individual may be trained in the use of credit and be fully aware of profits to be gained, but may still be unwilling to exchange for them the satisfaction and peace of mind realized by paying cash.

Capital accumulation and conservation. Firm and household competition comes into focus for all choices which involve time. Under low incomes the pressure to live currently stands in the way of such long-term investments as buildings, improved breeding stock, and important conservation improvements. Rather than curtail consumption in order to accumulate capital for a barn or dairy stock which will increase income several years hence, the low income farmer may prefer or be forced to invest in hogs or in cash crops which give returns within the year. The same problem arises in connection with soil conservation practices and farming systems which, though they eventually lead to an increase in income, curtail income in the immediate future. The dilemma here is posed for a group of Iowa farms in Table 2. While changes in income are positive as an average over time, the negative change in income during the first few years keeps many farmers from adopting farming systems of the nature proposed.

Table 2.

Changes in Capital Requirements and Income in Adopting a Soil Conservation Farming System. Average for 160-acre Farms on Marshall Silt Loam in Iowa.*

	Year after start of conservation farming system				
Item	first	second	third	fourth	fifth
Additional capital	0	$869	$500	$603	$426
Change in income	− $387	− $242	− $122	+ $269	+ $804

* Source: E. O. Heady and C. A. Allen, *Returns from and Capital Required for Soil Conservation.* Iowa Agr. Exp. Sta. Bul. 381.

Utility of Uncertainty Bearing

Any analysis dealing with the rationale of farmer production response must concern itself with the utility of choices involving risk or uncertainty. The paragraphs below not only extend further our study of firm-household interrelations but also serve as an introduction for the chapters on uncertainty which follow. Individuals must and do choose, on a utility or consumer satisfaction basis, among alternatives between which the important difference is in degree of risk or uncertainty. Insurance and gambling are everyday examples. The farmer who buys fire insurance for his buildings chooses a small certain loss (the annual premium) in preference to a small chance of a large loss (the value of the buildings should they burn) and a large chance of no loss (if the buildings never burn). Contrariwise, the individual who plays a slot machine or buys a ticket in a football pool subjects himsef to a large chance of losing a small amount and a small chance of a large gain.

Choice, on a utility basis, among different degrees of risk is not restricted to gambling and insurance. Most farmers have some preference for a small amount of risk.[15] If this were not true, few persons would be

[15] Economic action, after all, is only a small part of an individual's total behavior. It is likely that everyone gets direct satisfaction out of risk-taking. Otherwise, life would be very unpleasant, because the future is studded with risks. However, not all persons want to assume economic risks. An individual showing caution with respect to the use of money might risk his life in a fighter plane or his health in a jungle.

farmers; the variability of farm income is much greater than the variability of wages in many other occupations. Even differences in the degree of uncertainty which attaches to investments are high within agriculture.

There are great differences between individuals in their willingness to undertake risky enterprises. These differences exist where capital positions and information are similar but the "sporting instinct" (utility or disutility of assuming risk) varies between individuals.[16] Very great profits in farming were made over the last decade by individuals willing to undertake investments with high risks or uncertainty. Farmers who disregarded the advice of "specialists" and purchased land or feeder cattle in the immediate postwar years, for example, realized a "speculative gain" which was not forthcoming to their more conservative neighbors. At the other end of the scale these same persons, characterized by a high risk preference, were not favored by an advantageous environment during the late 1920's and early 1930's. Cattle feeding, a high-risk enterprise, is undertaken particularly by farmers with a high risk preference; they derive satisfaction from the adventurous enterprise, and, as they say, "never lose anything feeding cattle but in some years the manure proves to be a costly fertilizer." Farmers who find risk and risk-bearing to be highly distasteful may select an enterprise such as dairying in preference to cattle feeding even though the expected "most profitable" returns are higher for the latter. Thus, where resource use is being studied as related to the combined farm unit, net income need not reflect efficiency when utility maximization is the farmer's ultimate goal. An operator who feeds lambs may realize a smaller income over time than his cow-milking neighbor, yet his total consumable product (money income plus direct utility from, in his opinion, a more "enjoyable" enterprise) may be greater than were he to milk cows or raise chickens.

Figure 7 provides an hypothesis of the indifference curve when the utility of uncertainty bearing is compared to utility from money income.[17]

---

[16] At the same time, as indicated in a previous footnote, risk preference is not an exclusively economic phenomenon. It can assume non-economic forms which may have indirect economic effects. It is all part of the managerial concept. A farmer who drives dangerously on the highway, or who overtaxes his strength and health in an attempt to make more money, may be indirectly taking a bigger chance of gain or loss than if he bet on horse races.

[17] The ordinates of Figure 7 might be looked upon as ordinal rather than cardinal measurements. For example, movement along the horizontal axis may simply represent "more uncertainty" rather than an "exact amount" of uncertainty, or the ordinates might measure the "mean" probable outcome of various ventures on the vertical axis and the variance, standard deviation, or other measures of dispersion on the horizontal axis. While these statistics might be purely in the form of "subjective expectations," they might also be historic measurements which serve as an inference for the future. Also, it should again be pointed out that the 2 indifference curves in Figure 7 are drawn from different preference functions for different individuals. Two of a family of indifference curves drawn from a single preference function for 1 individual would never cross.

Curves A and B are for 2 individuals with different preferences for risk. Money income and uncertainty bearing are substitutes up to a point for both individuals. For B, all combinations of the 2 products (money income and uncertainty bearing) between (a) om_4 of money income and zero uncertainty and (b) om_1 of money income and ou_2 of uncertainty, give equal satisfactions or utility. He is willing to sacrifice the prospect of decreased money income in order to take on added risk and the utility which accompanies it. Beyond ou_2 of uncertainty, however, individual B is unwilling to accept greater uncertainty unless there is promise of rewards in the form of greater, rather than less, money income. Greater risk-taking becomes sufficiently unpleasant that total utility can be maintained at a given level only if the possibility of high monetary returns is great. In the alternatives along the positive slope of curve B, risk and money income are complementary goods, and the entrepreneur is willing to shoulder greater uncertainty only if he has prospects of great monetary rewards. The fact that indifference curves A and B slope upward at an increasing rate suggests that as uncertainty becomes greater, increasingly large money incomes must be in prospect if the individual is to place these possibilities at a level as desirable as a lower but more certain income.

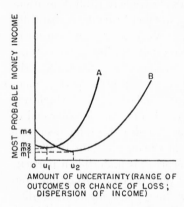

Fig. 7. Indifference curves indicating substitution between possible profits and prospective losses.

The individual represented by indifference curve A gets less enjoyment from undertaking risk than does B. This is evident from the fact that he would substitute uncertainty for money income only up to ou_1. Beyond ou_1, increased uncertainty must be accompanied by increasingly great prospects of high money returns. (A "curves upward" at a much faster rate than B, and thus indicates a lower risk-preference for the farmer.)

Ownership and Other Ends in Farming

Numerous other competitive ends involve choice by the farm family in the context of utility rather than profit maximization. Again, many of these prove to be intermediate ends, goals which are achieved only as a means to more ultimate ends. One such intermediate end is farm ownership. Attainment of ownership is an end *per se* to some families, but it is a step to other goals for most. Many families willingly sacrifice somewhat higher incomes as renters for the alternative of operating an owned farm; ownership may be selected because of the social status in the community which it bestows upon the family; it may serve as a means of lessening tenure uncertainty or in increasing security for old age; some farmers wish to pass an acreage along to their children. Not all farmers attach the same values to ownership, however, and there is no reason why ownership should be placed, as is often done by tenure economists, at the top of the hierarchy of ends. The economic problem is one of getting the optimum combination of money income and security of tenure or other competing alternative (such as m in Figure 2, when the x axis represents security of tenure and the y axis represents money income.) Money income and security may be complementary through some range. The implications of this possibility are evident and need not be explained in detail here. These points are discussed further in a later chapter.

Life Cycle of the Firm and the Household

Another important element of the firm-household interrelationship, and one which especially affects resource efficiency, is the life cycle of the combined unit. While the two are not perfectly interlocked, the life of the firm in agriculture closely parallels the life of the household. The cycle interrelationship is partly depicted in Figure 8, which shows the relationship of acres operated and output of livestock product to operator's age. The situation is in contrast to industries organized on a corporate basis, in which the perpetual life of the corporation makes it unnecessary that the capital stock be liquidated as each of the capital-contributing households "dies off." The problem is accentuated in agriculture because the surplus of deaths

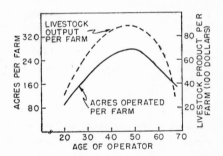

Fig. 8. Growth and decline of acres operated and livestock production per farm (Source: Iowa Agr. Exp. Sta. project 1135).

over births results in a net migration of people out of agriculture. Since estates are most often (although recent effort is in a different direction) divided equally among heirs, a portion of equity in agricultural capital is continually flowing out of the industry. Herein lies the crux of an efficiency problem in agriculture: Since firms die with the household, it is necessary that each new firm-household combination furnish its own capital, although there may be an overlap wherein an "old" firm-household combine furnishes capital to the "new" combine through a partnership arrangement.

Farm cycles. The farm firm goes through phases of a life cycle in much the same manner as the household.[18] During the first stage of the house-

---

[18] A second interesting socio-economic aspect of the life cycle is this: Ordinarily, a new family (marriage) will arise only if the tastes or values (the slope of indif-

hold, marriage and the birth of children, the beginning family is short on capital and competition between the firm and household for funds is probably greater than at any other time. The addition of individuals to the household through births increases the outlays needed for living, but, in many cases, the growth of the firm is not great enough to provide additional income. During the second period of the family, growth of the children, the household furnishes resources in the form of labor to the firm. In the third stage of the family, exodus of the children from the household with continued farm operation by the parents, the firm "comes into its own" in terms of available capital and owner equity. These several stages in the life of the firm and the repetitive capital accumulation process by each generation of households cause over-all inefficiencies. In the early

Table 3.

1950 Resource Combinations and Productivity for a Sample of Iowa Farms *

Operator Age Group	Capital Operated per 12 month labor	Value of product per 12 month labor	Return on Capital (per cent)
Under 35	35,980	$2,234	6
35-49	44,683	1,840	5
50-59	40,043	1,446	3
60 and over	31,738	1,457	2

* Source: Unpublished data from Iowa Agriculture Experiment Station, Project number 1135.

stages of the cycle, the firm combines small proportions of capital with each quantity of labor, and resource productivity is great because so little capital is available. Somewhere over the middle stages, capital and labor are combined most nearly in the manner suggested by price relationships,

ference curves or the nature of the preference function) are sufficiently similar for two people. Thus decisions on the allocation of resources between the farm and household (or the allocation of resources within either unit) does not give rise to great conflict in firm-household decision-making. (If the couple find their indifference curves actually have very great differences in slope, the wife will "go home to mother.") The birth and growth of children (the middle of the cycle) will (a) give rise to additional choice or indifference curves to be accounted for in decision-making if the parents do not inject "exactly their own" value system into the children, (b) give rise to additional but identical indifference curves if the parents do embody their own value system into that of the children. In the first case, decision-making will become much more complex in a democratic family and the allocation of resources between firm and household may merge into different patterns. However, as the stage of the family is reached at which the children leave home, the value systems which relate to decisions will again revert to the husband and wife (the original pair of indifference curves), and decision-making will again be simplified. (Supposedly, the preference functions or indifference curves should be even more nearly identical now. The fact that the couple have lived together for many years should bring their indifference systems more nearly into conformity.)

but resource productivity may decline as more resources are put into use. In the last phase, the operator sometimes invests in enterprises and production methods which require less strenuous labor and management outlays; resource productivity declines both because of the manner in which resources are combined and because labor is less productive. The total product forthcoming from the resources used in agriculture might well be increased if the first and last stages of the firm cycle could be merged. The equity and capital possessed by older operators would produce a much greater product if employed on beginning farms where the operator is short on resources and possesses sufficient managerial ability. These possibilities are partly reflected in the Iowa data of Table 3.

Means of lessening inefficiency. Numerous schemes might be used to offset the process wherein each generation of farm firms must accumulate a large portion of the equity capital employed in the industry. Under one extreme, society might own all of the resources employed in agriculture. A franchise could then be given to each generation of firms, and they could operate with public-owned capital. Under this system, one obviously attended by its own complexities and limitations, the continuum of capital accumulation-capital liquidation would be eliminated. Corporation farming with stock owned outside of a single family is another possibility. A common mechanism which can help remove inefficiency is the farm-business or (father-son) arrangement developed by farm management specialists. Here the new firm gradually merges with the old firm and transfer of capital can be made in a manner which alleviates large fluctuations in factor proportioning and productivity. Other possibilities (where they are not used to substitute for other more efficient means or do not conflict with other economic goals) are provided in low-equity loans now provided by the Farmers Home Administration.

Integration of Education

Firm-household interrelationships in agriculture have important implications for extension education. Production and family aspects of extension education should be integrated in a manner which aids the farm family in attaining those more ultimate ends toward which they direct their decisions. In the first place there is little basis for taking single enterprises or factors out of the farm business context and extending them apart from other choices. The technical specialist in agriculture should devote his time to explaining the input-output relationships of the single product or products in which he specializes. Problems in farming which involve choice fall in the realm of economics. However, the production economist cannot restrict his recommendations to choice based on price relationships and profit. We must look upon indifference curves and utility maximization as tools of choice in production standing at a level with price relationships and profit maximization.

Extension education can best be carried on in the form of farm and home planning. Two steps are important. The first should include aid to the farm family in outlining its physical production possibilities (curve *PO* in Figure 3) as they relate to both the firm and the household. The second shoud include aid to the farm family in delineating its goals or objectives (curve *ID* in Figure 3) and the rate at which one choice in consumption substitutes for the others. The end here is not one, as many extension workers suppose, of "establishing goals for farm people" but of providing more complete information so that families can better formulate their own scale of values. Once farm families know the production possibilities which are open to them and have clearly formulated their own pattern of values, they can decide the manner in which limited human and capital resources should be used to maximize family satisfactions. Maximum welfare (satisfaction), rather than maximum yields per acre or maximum profits for the farm, is the goal towards which extension education should be directed.

Underemployment and value systems. Interrelationships between production and consumption should be especially emphasized in education or public policies directed at low-income farm families. Because the market product produced by farm people in such regions as the Appalachians highlands is very small, many agriculturists suggest that these mountain people be moved to nonfarm industries or other agricultural regions where their productivity might gain more from the added product forthcoming from the labor resources represented.

However, when low-income families are producing at boundary positions and select, because of their customs and particular value systems, a subsistence farming system and their existing level of living in preference to other alternatives, the question arises whether or not they should be shifted to other alternatives. Questions such as these are difficult to handle in an empirical sense and involve those arbitrary welfare judgments in which utility gains to some members of society must be compared with losses to other members of society. Compensation can be arranged whereby the subsistence farmer is left "equally well off" as he moves to other lines of work. However, other possibilities are also open: (1) The low-income farmer can be given information on the level and nature of living elsewhere. He is then free to change his values (the slope of the indifference curve) in a manner consistent with his own likes or dislikes. (2) He can be given training to increase his ability to produce money income in nonfarm occupations. The opportunity curve will then have a greater slope and, with no change in the relative values attached to money income as compared to leisure, equilibrium will be noted as the individual devotes a greater portion of his efforts to market production and money return.[19] The value systems of older persons may change little under education of this nature but important changes may be brought about for their children. Education in these respects need not involve the "forcing of a value system" upon the individual. It simply represents an attempt to inventory opportunities for the individual and to let him form his own value system.

[19] This possibility can be illustrated in Figure 3, where line P^1O^1 is the individual's original production possibilities. Training and education shifts the production possibilities to PO; hence the individual increases production of market services and money income to the level OG_2 (from an original level of OG_1) and his total utility is increased at the same time.

Selected References

Arrow, K. J., *Social Choice and Individual Values*. New York: Wiley, 1951, Chs. 1, 2, 3.

Back, B., "Firm-Household Aspects of Low-Income Farms," Ph.D. thesis, 1952.

Friedman, M., and Savage, L. J., "Utility Analysis of Choice Involving Risk," *Jour. Pol. Econ.*, Vol. 56.

Heady, Earl O., Back, W. B., and Peterson, G. A., "Interrelationships of the Farm Business and Household," *Iowa Agr. Exp. Sta. Bul.* 395.

Heady, Earl O., "Fundamentals of Farm Ownership Policy," *Jour. Land Econ.*, 1953.

Katona, G., *Psychological Analysis of Economic Behavior*. New York: McGraw-Hill, 1951, Chs. 5, 9.

Loomis, C. P., *Growth of the Farm Family in Relation to its Activities*. North Carolina Exp. Sta. Bul. 298.

Loomis, C. P., and Hamilton, C. H., "Family Life Cycle Analysis," *Social Forces*, Vol. 15.

Machlup, F., "Marginal Analysis and Empirical Research," *Amer. Econ. Rev.*, Vol. 36.

Monroe, L., "Patterns of Living of Farm Families," U.S.D.A. Yearbook, 1940, pp. 848-869.

Peterson, G., "Firm-Household Interrelationships in Iowa Agriculture," M.S. thesis, 1951.

Reder, M. W., "Reconsideration of Marginal Productivity Theory," *Jour. Pol. Econ.*, Vol. 55.

Scitovsky, T., "A Note on Profit Maximization and its Implications," *Rev. Econ. Studies*, Vol. 11.

Studley, L. A., *Relationship of Farm Income to Farm Business*. Minn. Agr. Exp. Sta. Bul. 279.

Wilcox, W. W., and Pond, G. A., "The Human Factor in Farm Management," *Jour. Farm Econ.*, Vol. 14.

PART III

Planning under Imperfect Knowledge

T HE CHAPTERS of this section deal with the planning of production and resource use when knowledge is imperfect and considerations of risk and uncertainty become important. The analysis is focused on the farm as a firm. However, certain aggregate and policy aspects of production planning are also discussed.

15

Risk and Uncertainty in Agricultural Production

Except for Chapter 13, our analysis has referred only indirectly to time. Chapter 13, like many analyses in agricultural economics, related to choices in time with the future known with certainty. We now drop this unrealistic assumption and examine problems in production and resource use when the future can only be estimated. When time considerations are associated with perfect knowledge of the future, problems of error in decisions and planning do not arise and use of concepts in addition to those already outlined is not required in analysis of production problems. In most cases, however, the time involved in agricultural production does preclude perfect knowledge of the future; and therefore, decision-making must take place in an environment of uncertainty. Plans in agriculture must be made at one point in time for a product which will be forthcoming at a future point in time.

A discussion of uncertainty is not "theoretical and impractical"; the major decisions of individual persons and nations fall in this framework. Decisions must be and are made about the future, and courses of action are designed, even though they are based on mere "hunches." The economic and social organism, whether it be a business firm, a family, a peaceful state, or a warring nation, must in some way chart a course of action into this hazy horizon. What are the characteristics which denote the degree and nature of the uncertainty inherent in production processes where knowledge and prediction are imperfect? What are the available means, whether successful or unsuccessful, in fashioning resource use to meet an uncertain future? How do uncertainty considerations condition the efficiency of resource use? These are the questions with which the next several chapters are concerned.

Risk and Uncertainty

The producer is faced with 2 types of eventualities or outcomes which have bearing on plans for the future. One of these is *risk;* the other is *uncertainty.*[1] Farmers are prone to class all outcomes which lead to losses (or deviations of realizations from expectations) as risks. However, a useful distinction can be made between the 2 concepts. Each has different implications on how resources should be or are used.

Risk and empirical prediction. Risk refers to variability or outcomes which are measurable in an empirical or quantitative manner. The outcome for each particular item (for example, the particular hog which will die or the exact yield of wheat in a single specified year) need not be predictable. It is only necessary that the probability of outcome or loss can be established for a large number of cases or observations. Empirical probabilities of outcome or loss can be established in either 1 of 2 manners. (1) The *a priori* probability of outcome can be established when the characteristics of the eventuality are known beforehand. It is not necessary that a continuous drawing of cards be made to determine that the chance or probability of drawing the ace of spades from a deck of cards is 1/52. In the same manner we can predict with certainty that with continuous rolls of a perfect dice, a 6 will occur 1 out of 6 times. (As the number of throws of the dice increases, the relative frequency of a 6 approaches 1/6.) It follows that the person who continually entertains himself with games of chance is not faced with uncertainty; he is faced with risks. Although the outcome of a single game cannot be predicted without error, the outcome over a large number of games is certain. The habitual player of slot machines is faced with the certainty of loss over time. (2) The statistical probability of outcome can be established when (a) the sample of cases (observations) is large enough, (b) the observations are repeated in the population, and (c) the observations (cases) are independent (are randomly distributed in the manner of a stochastic variable). Insurance companies can predict the statistical probability of deaths, fire losses, and similar outcomes with a degree of certainty such that phenomena under consideration can be classed as a risk. Risk is insurable in an actuarial sense; uncertainty is not. However, the actuarial value (probability) of deaths, fire losses, and similar outcomes is measurable (and hence insurable), only when the number of cases or observations is sufficiently large and randomly (independently) distributed. The probability that a single house will burn cannot be established, but insurance companies can predict, with small error, the number of houses out of 100,000 which will burn.

Refinement can be added to the concept of risk in this manner: the parameters of the probability distribution (frequency distribution of out-

---

[1] Rather than spend time distinguishing between such terms as "dynamics," "statics," and "stationary," we recognize four categories of time problems: (1) where change does not take place, (2) where change takes place but each outcome can be predicted, (3) where change takes place, and while each outcome cannot be predicted, the price and production parameters can be predicted, and (4) where change takes place but parameters cannot be predicted in an empirical sense.

comes) can be established for outcomes that involve risk. In other words, the mean, mode, skewness, kurtosis, and variance (first, second, third, and fourth moments, or other measures of dispersion) can be established with an empirical probability of 1.0 (certainty) for the particular distribution.[2] Risk is present when the modal and mean wheat yield can be predicted over a period of years, along with the variance from the mean, and the number of years in which the yield will fall in each yield interval (for example, 0-5 bushels, 6-10 bushels, or 11-15 bushels).

Which eventualities on the farm may be classed as risks? The number of eggs lost through breakage is a risk for most farm flocks; the number of eggs produced is great enough and the frequency of breakage within a limited time period is of a magnitude such that most farmers are able to establish the probability of loss (the percentage of eggs which will be lost through breakage). Some farmers feed enough cattle over time that they can fairly well establish the probability of death loss; some place it at 1.5 per cent. Outcomes such as mastitis, hog cholera, theft, and other major livestock losses do not fall in the same category, however. The individual farmer's "sample" is not great enough over time and the losses are not randomly distributed among animals in a manner so that he can establish the probability of the outcome. Normal wear, depreciation, and breakage on farm equipment can be predicted with enough accuracy to be classed as risks, but large and infrequent occurrences, such as fire and tornado damage, cannot be so defined from the individual farmer's standpoint. Although the farmer must consider the latter outcomes as uncertainties, insurance firms can treat them as risks. The year-to-year variability in crop yields associated with fluctuations in the weather may be classed as risks on farms (a) where climate is highly stable, (b) where small random variations occur from year to year, and (c) where the complete range of yield outcomes is repeated frequently enough that the farmer operator can establish the mean or modal outcome and the range (variance) of outcomes. This situation perhaps typifies the climate and yield fluctuations in a few areas of the eastern Cornbelt and the southeastern United States. It is less applicable to the western Cornbelt and the Great Plains. It is not known, for example, whether a 7-year drought such as that of the 1930's occurs once in each 30 years or once in each 200 years, or if any regularity of occurrence or duration exists. Our sample of yields over time simply is not great enough to justify any very definite statements about yield expectations over longer periods. At best, year-to-year statistics on wheat yields are available for a 60-year period in many semiarid farming regions. (While some people have examined tree rings for a

---

[2] Obviously, the definition of risk does not refer only to single-value distributions but allows an array of values (outcomes) which can be estimated empirically. Perhaps risk should be defined in the terms of statistics; the parameters can be estimated empirically, but still involve errors of prediction in the fiducial limit sense.

longer period and attempt to use them in predicting the long-range distribution of yields, it appears that the errors attached to these inferences either (a) are very great or (b) cannot be established.) Even if it could be established that a 7-year drought occurs once in each 100 years (crop failure has a probability of .07), its possibility is still an uncertainty in the planning of the individual farmer if he cannot tell whether it will occur once, twice, or not at all in his lifetime. Many people have been advising farmers over the past several years as if a 7-year drought were known with certainty to occur once within every 30 years. While there is some basis for this action in terms of conservatism, existing probability and yield statistics do not provide the basis for this type of inference.

Risk as a cost. Pure risk does not, or need not, have impact of a nature to affect decision-making and resource use. Since pure risk involves complete knowledge of the mean and modal outcome, the range and dispersion of outcomes (all parameters or moments of the distribution can be estimated in a statistical sense) losses and gains which grow out of risk phenomena can be incorporated into the firm's cost schedule, and have the bearing on decision-making outlined in previous chapters. For example, if the poultry farmer loses 1 egg out of each 200, the cost of the egg lost from breakage can be added to the cost of the remaining 199 eggs and the marginal returns from poultry production can be so reckoned. Incorporation of losses growing out of pure risk into the firm's cost structure is possible only in the case of egg breakage or similar phenomena where the number of occurrences is great enough within the firm that the probability of loss can be established. In some few localized areas, hail damage occurs so frequently and regularly (the number of observations is great enough that the mean expected loss can be established for a single farm over a short period) that farmers simply consider the loss as a cost inherent in the producing environment and do not bother to insure (particularly where insurance costs are at a level approaching uninsured losses). Risk also can be incorporated into the cost structure of the farm business even where the number of cases is not great enough to allow prediction of loss on the single farm. The probability of loss of a barn through fire often is in the nature of an "uncertainty" for a single farm; whether or not the barn on a particular farm will burn cannot be predicted with an empirical probability of 1.0. However, because commercial insurance firms write policies on a large number of barns, they can establish the probability of losses over the complete number of farms. The individual farmer thus is able to insure his barn through paying a premium which becomes a known cost for his own business organization.[3]

---

[3] Insurance for fire and similar damage does not entirely eliminate uncertainty, however, where the loss disrupts the production process. This is particularly true in whole-milk retailing, where a temporary curtailment of production by one dairy farmer may cause some of his customers to transfer to other producers.

Risk, then, relates to variability phenomena which can be incorporated into costs. It does not alter decision-making from those conditions of equilibrium already outlined. It is uncertainty which gives rise to the need for an entirely different framework for decision-making and resource administration.

Uncertainty and subjective prediction. In contrast to pure risk, the probability of an outcome cannot be established in an empirical or quantitative sense for uncertainty. Uncertainty is always present when knowledge of the future is less than perfect in the sense that the parameters of the probability distribution (the mean yield or price, the variance, range or dispersion, and the skewness and kurtosis or shape of the distribution) cannot be determined. Uncertainty is, therefore, entirely of a "subjective" nature. It simply refers to anticipations of the future and is peculiar to the mind of each individual producer. Uncertainty arises because the entrepreneur must formulate an "image of the future" in his mind but has no quantitative manner by which these predictions can be verified. In the egg (risk) example cited above, the farm operator can, because he has enough previous experience or observations, estimate the percentage of eggs which will be broken. The prediction of breakage is not so highly subjective, but is based on quantitative experience. For prediction of future prices, however, there ordinarily is no historic or quantitative base upon which expectations can be established. The structural variables which relate to or determine price are themselves subject to change and a single economic environment is not repeated often enough (if at all) to establish an outcome which can be viewed in the sense of repeated trials. The same applies to physical yield phenomena where the number of observations over time (historic yield measurements) is not great enough to establish the mean, variance, and sequence of yields.

In summary, *uncertainty* refers to future events where the parameters of the probability distribution cannot be determined empirically. It involves the making of decisions with less than perfect knowledge. Anticipations of the future can be formed but there is no way that the entrepreneur or administrator can assemble enough homogeneous observations to predict the relevant probability distribution. While subjective probabilities (either in an ordinal or cardinal sense) may be assigned to these anticipations, no method exists by which actual numerical values may be assigned these. Uncertainty is not insurable; it cannot be reduced to a cost in the manner or risk. The term can be used in a very broad sense to include all circumstances in which decisions must be made without perfect knowledge of significant future events. Significant events are all occurrences which if foreseen perfectly would have influenced a particular decision.

Yield and technical uncertainty. Phenomena which can be treated under the heading of pure risk also give rise to uncertainty and imperfect knowledge in planning. Although previous chapters usefully employed the concept of a production function known with certainty, we have broken with this postulate in order to analyze more closely the agricultural production and decision-making environment as it actually is. The farm producer is not faced with a single production function. Instead, he is faced with an entire distribution of production functions. The year-to-year variability in the production function may be classed as risk phenomena over longer time periods. However, in making year-to-year decisions, the farmer must still estimate or form expectations of the yields (points on the production function) to be expected in the immediate year ahead. In a pure risk con-

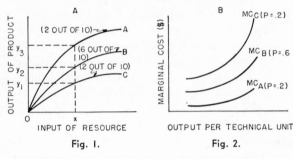

Fig. I. Fig. 2.

Yield or technical variability.

text, he may view the production process in the vein of Figure 1 and the marginal cost probabilities in the form of Figure 2. As an overly simplified case, we assume that production functions A and C occur twice in each 10 years (the probability for either is 2 in 10 or .2), while production function B is realized in 6 out of 10 years (a probability of 6 in 10 or .6). Thus B is the modal and mean outcome, while A and C suggest the dispersion or range of outcomes. If ox of resources are always applied, yields over 10 years will include 2 of oy_1, 6 of oy_2, and 2 of oy_3. Yet with this information, and even if prices are known with certainty, ex $ante$ decision-making is still complex when the exact sequence of yield outcomes is not known. (Knowledge still is not perfect.) Where yield fluctuations are random, the farmer can never maximize profits if he always applies resources as if average yields were to be realized in each year. In 2 out of 6 years he will apply too many resources; he will apply too few resources in 2 other years of the 10. The error will be even greater if he expects and plans for production function C in the year ahead but realizes A. Thus the presence of enough cases so that the parameters of the probability distribution can be established does not preclude imperfect planning by the individual entrepreneur. While the distribution of yields over 10 years allows measurement in the vein of a risk, uncertainty is involved in predicting the yield of any one year. If yield outcomes were of the purely random manner outlined here, the individual farm would undoubtedly be able to insure yields through commercial insurance companies. However, he is still faced with the possibility of errors of 2 sorts: (1) He may insure against low yields; if he has a high yield he has lost the premium invested in insurance. (2) He may fail to insure; if he has a low yield he loses the indemnity which would have been forthcoming under insurance.

Data provided by agricultural scientists on crop yields for different rotations and fertilizer applications or for livestock production under different rations ordinarily are in the form of averages such as production function B in Figure 1 (or even more discrete data such as an ox input of fertilizer and an oy_3 yield of crop). These experimental inferences are of limited application, when the mean outcome is provided without some notion of the error, or "degree of uncertainty" (in a purely statistical sense), which applies to a single year. An improved planning base might be relayed to the farmer, however, if the yield or production function estimates were given in the form of a frequency or probability distribution.

Single valued expectations. Under uncertainty, the farm operator, planning his next year's operations, might suppose that only 1 price is possible in the year ahead. This anticipated price might be $1; prices neither higher nor lower are expected and no "weight" is given the likelihood that prices above or below $1 may occur. The $1 price expectation thus is single-valued (in contrast to the multi-valued expectations and distributions outlined below). It is extremely doubtful, however, that single-valued expectations of this sort are employed by many managers. Generally, the entrepreneur recognizes that while a $1 price for corn may be more likely than prices of 80 cents or $1.20, the possibility always exists that either of the latter prices will come about.

Where the entrepreneur forms a single-valued expectation, he must indeed feel confident about his estimate of the future; in effect he says that he is subjectively certain of the future. In this case (single-valued expectations and subjective certainty), he would plan his operations in the static or timeless vein outlined in earlier chapters. There have been periods in which price expectations may have been formulated in this single-value manner. For exampe, during wartime when ceilings are in effect, or during depression when floor prices are in effect, it may be "obvious or certain" to the entrepreneur that prices will be at this one and no other level. Uncertainty exists in the mind of the entrepreneur only if expectations of future prices, yields, and capital allowances are not single-valued (if some range of results is considered possible or likely by the entrepreneur).

Since knowledge of the future is so imperfect, entrepreneurs normally expect that a range of outcomes, rather than a single outcome, is possible. Accordingly, they may formulate these multi-valued expectations in either an ordinal or cardinal sense. If the framing of expectations is in an ordinal (ranking or ordering) sense only, then a farm manager, in making up his corn production plans for the next year, may simply say to himself that although prices may fall anywhere in the range from $1 to $2, a price of $1.50 is most probable and more likely than a price of $1.60, which, in turn, is more likely than a price of $1.40, and so forth. After interviewing a large number of farmers on an expectation study, the writer is convinced that a great number view the future in this ordinal sense. With the framing of the expectations in a cardinal sense, an exact but subjective probability value would be attached to each possible price. Here the farmer might visualize the future price of corn in the manner of the frequency or probability distribution outlined below.[4] Each of the prices indicated is considered to be a possible outcome and the subjective probabilities shown are attached to each value. Here the price of $2 is held as more likely (in fact, twice as likely) than a price of $1.50 or $2.50.

Expected price for corn	Chances out of 10 for realization	Probability
$1.00	1	.1
1.50	2	.2
2.00	4	.4
2.50	2	.2
3.00	1	.1

For the expectations outlined above, one set of expected prices, a single probability distribution is supposed. Here the assumption is that the probability distribution is itself held with subjective certainty in the mind of the entrepreneur. This "uncertainty case," in which a single probability distribution is visualized by the entrepreneur, has been termed "subjective risk" by some writers.[5] It is called "subjective risk" to distinguish it from the pure empirical risks outlined previously and the "pure uncertainty" outlined below.

Pure or subjective uncertainty might be characterized by expectations which involve a distribution of distributions; the entrepreneur, in attempting to gain a mental vision of the future, foresees not one distribution of possible prices but several of these possible distributions. In other words, the resource administrator, in designing a course of action to meet future prices and yields, first may formulate a subjective prediction of the out-

---

[4] Probability distributions are seldom discrete in the manner of the example cited. However, the example illustrates the nature of the consideration and can serve as a step to graphic presentation of frequency or probability distributions for those readers unacquainted with this area of statistics and mathematics: The geometric probability distributions presented later can be approximated if the prices are recorded on the horizontal, while the "chances out of 10," or the probability values, are recorded on the vertical axis.

[5] See G. Tintner, "The Theory of Production Under Nonstatic Conditions," *Jour. Pol. Econ.*, Vol. L. The term "subjective risk" is employed because the parameters of the distribution involved are not measurable in an empirical sense. Thus it is not "pure risk" in the manner outlined previously, but is again subjective anticipation of the future, where a single distribution of outcome is "anticipated" with certainty (a single-valued expectation of the probability distribution) although the expectation for each individual yield or price item is not single-valued.

come (probability) of certain major events which affect the structure of the economy. Given 3 major possibilities such as depression, continuance of existing prices, and war, he may attach probabilities of .1, .5, and .4 respectively to each. He judges that there is 1 chance out of 10 that depression will come about. Under this possible outcome, should it be realized, he may expect possible prices for corn of $1, .80, .40, and .10. Similarly, a probability distribution may be anticipated under both war and the continuance of present prices. This system of expectations gives a probability distribution of probability distributions in the manner shown below:

Depression (P = .1)		Normal prices (P = .5)		War (P = .4)	
price : probability		price : probability		price : probability	
.10	.3	.10	0.0	.10	0.0
.40	.6	.40	.1	.40	0.0
.80	.1	.80	.1	.80	0.0
1.00	0.0	1.00	.5	1.00	.1
1.50	0.0	1.50	.2	1.50	.2
2.50	0.0	2.50	.1	2.50	.6
3.50	0.0	3.50	0.0	3.50	.1
Total	1.0		1.0		1.0

The operator of a producing firm might follow either 1 of 2 courses of action in formulating his plans under a probability distribution of probability distributions (subjective uncertainty) such as that illustrated above. (1) He may say that a continuance of the existing situation is "most likely" (has the greatest subjective probability) and consider this eventuality alone as relevant for planning purposes. Then he might say that, since a corn price of $1 is most probable (P = .5) under this distribution, plans can be formulated accordingly (with discounting of costs and outcome to conform to the fact that expectations are not single-valued). (2) He may merge or compound the probability distributions by multiplication (multiply the probability of each major contingency by the probability of the prices listed under it). The resulting compounded distribution appears as follows for the distribution shown above:

Price	Depression (probability)	Normal (probability)	War (probability)	Total (probability)
.10	.03	0.0	0.0	.03
.40	.06	.05	0.0	.11
.80	.01	.05	0.0	.06
1.00	0.0	.25	.04	.29
1.50	0.0	.10	.08	.18
2.50	0.0	.05	.24	.29
3.50	0.0	0.0	.04	.04
Total	.10	.50	.40	1.00

The compounding of the several probability distributions gives the simple total probability distribution listed at the right. Here prices of $1.00 and

$2.50 appear "equally likely" (have the same subjective probability). Consequently planning and the course of action selected may differ markedly from that were the first procedure employed (where "normal" prices were selected first, and then the price of $1.00 under this distribution was selected as "most probable").[6] The compounded probabilities give the "weighted" estimates of price outcomes.

The writer's experience with expectation studies suggests that few, if any, farmers go to the effort of formally writing down, first, the major outcomes (and their probabilities) to be expected and, second, the likely outcome (and probability values) under each of these. However, many go through a mental process whereby outlook material, newspaper dispatches, and other sources of information are analyzed to suggest the possible major trends in future events. Then each of these (at least the one appearing "most likely") is scrutinized with even greater detail to suggest some rough estimate of probable price or yield outcomes. Whatever the system followed, farm managers, or professional economists who advise them, must delve into the details of the forces which affect future prices. While the compounding of probabilities may not be followed with the refined detail outlined above, the general procedure helps to isolate or include significant variables affecting future prices and yields. Economic activity must go forward and predictions of the future must be made, whether they are pure hunches, ordinal expectations, or refined cardinal anticipations. Although fine lines can be drawn between pure risk, subjective risk, and subjective uncertainty, we return to our previous single distinction and group all uncertainty under the heading of decisions which must be made with less than perfect knowledge (a framework of incomplete knowledge).

The Degree of Uncertainty

Uncertainty, as explained earlier, is a purely subjective phenomenon and is peculiar to the mind of the individual. Two persons may view the same event; one considers it to involve great uncertainty while the other views it to be highly certain. The event itself does not specify the amount of uncertainty involved. The uncertainty is characterized by the nature of

---

[6] See A. G. Hart, *Risk, Uncertainty, and Unprofitability of Compounding Probabilities. Studies in Mathematical Economics and Econometrics.* Chicago: University of Chicago Press, 1942. As Hart points out, some knowledge is lost by the compounding of probabilities because of the irreversibility of the merger. While the final or total probability distribution of component distributions has but one sum, any total probability distribution may represent the sum of an infinite set of component distributions. The final or total distribution does not indicate whether the sum represents (a) a large number of component distributions each with a small dispersion, (b) a small number of component distributions with a large dispersion each, or (c) a large number of component distributions very much alike and each with a wide dispersion. The "degree of uncertainty" differs under these arrangements and differs substantially for planning purposes.

expectations which each entrepreneur must formulate as a basis for his plans.

Farmers have definite notions that, price-wise, some enterprises involve greater "risk" or uncertainty than others.[7] The same notions apply to physical yields. The manner in which farmers interpret the degree of "risk" or uncertainty is difficult to ascertain. Evidently the magnitude of variation in yield or price is one basis. Another basis is that of loss; enterprises which result in frequent losses are looked upon as being more "risky" (uncertain) than those which less frequently result in losses (even though variability may be greater for the latter). From the study conducted on expectations and uncertainty, the writer is prone to believe that farmers do associate uncertainty with "historic" parameters of price and yield distributions. There is evidence that the past forms an important foundation upon which expectations of the future are based. (See later discussion of expectation models.)

Because the concept of "degree of uncertainty" is important for planning purposes, it is of interest to examine the characteristics of probability distributions which may suggest the degree of uncertainty (or, conversely, the degree of confidence) which surround yield or price expectations. The several parameters of the expected or subjective probability (frequency) distributions can serve as important measures of uncertainty (chance of loss). It should be emphasized again that probability or frequency distributions relating to events of the future are not empirical structures but only subjective or imagined.

One measure of uncertainty for a subjective probability distribution is the dispersion of expectations. In a statistical context dispersion may be represented as (or be measured by) the variance, standard deviation, or range of expected (or realized) values. If the dispersion, range, standard deviation, or variance of expected prices for a commodity is zero, the entrepreneur is certain about his estimate of prices or yields; his expectation is single valued since he considers that only 1 price or yield is possible. If the dispersion of expected outcomes is very great, anticipations are multi-valued and the degree of uncertainty, in the mind of the entrepreneur, is very great. The skewness of the distribution may also reflect the degree of uncertainty or loss prospects. *Skewness* indicates whether the various possible expected prices are arranged symmetrically about the mode (most probable or likely price) or are dispersed in some uneven or asymmetrical manner. Differences in uncertainty or loss prospects can be pictured in a set of probability distributions such as those indicated in Figure 3; the expected price (or yield) is plotted along the horizontal axis

---

[7] We put the term "risk" in quotation marks here to differentiate it from the more formal or academic meaning outlined previously. While farmers ordinarily speak in terms of "risk," they are referring to the phenomenon which we have defined as uncertainty.

while the "subjective probability" (the expected values of prices or yields in the future) are plotted along the vertical axis.[8]

Figure 3A illustrates a normal distribution of expectations. It would represent greater uncertainty than a second normal curve with less variance (for example, a bell-shaped curve with a smaller spread, if units of measurement are the same). However, the right-skewed distribution of expections illustrated in Figure 3B represents less uncertainty or prospect

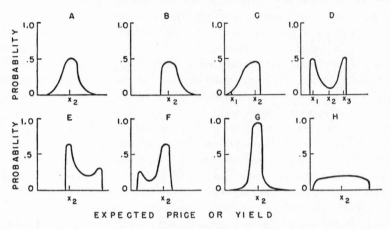

Fig. 3. Relation of subjective probability (frequency) distributions and uncertainty.

of loss than 3A. Suppose that Figure 3A represents a product such as wheat while 3B represents soybeans. A price of x_2 (perhaps $2) is anticipated as the most likely price for both crops, yet the uncertainty is much less for soybeans; if prices other than the modal one (x_2) come about, expectations are in the direction of higher prices.[9] In the case of wheat, however, if prices are to deviate from the modal expectation (x_2), there is equal chance that the price will be either higher or lower (than x_2). An even greater contrast is illustrated in Figures 3B and 3C, which are skewed to the right and left respectively. While the 3B distribution suggests prices mainly higher (if they are to deviate from the most probable or modal

---

[8] The reader who is unacquainted with the concept of a probability distribution may become acquainted with its characteristics in any elementary statistics book. He may also think of the curves in Figure 3 as representing frequency distributions. If the several following distributions (the price listed first and its frequency of occurrence listed last) are graphed, they will give the reader some further notion of the characteristics involved as well as indication of approximation of properties involved: A (normal) $1-1, $2-2, $3-3, $4-4, $5-6, $6-4, $7-3, $8-2, $9-1; B (skewed right) $4-5, $5-7, $6-5, $7-3, $8-2; C (skewed left) $1-2, $3-3, $4-5, $5-7, $6-5; G (peaked top) $3-1, $4-2, $5-16, $6-2, $7-1; H (flat top) $4-7, $5-8, $6-7. (The U and J and inverted J have not been included since the reader can easily devise examples of this nature.)

[9] See footnote 8 for an arithmetic expression of the same points.

value of x_2), 3C suggests that the probability is almost entirely in the direction of lower prices. An Iowa study gave expectations of these contrasts in 2 separate years for corn. In 1947 the majority of farmers were still expecting a depression and thought the most likely value of corn in 1948 might be $1.10; they attached only low probabilities to higher prices but fairly high probabilities to lower prices. In 1949, however, the growing possibility of war and the drought-inspired prices of 1947 had dispelled the expectation of depression. The majority expressed expectations suggesting that greatest probabilities were in the direction of prices above the modal expected price of $1.25.

The kurtosis (degree of "peakedness" or "flat-toppedness" of the yield or price distribution curve) also expresses the degree of confidence in price or yield expectations. While the "chance" of prices either higher or lower than the modal value (x_2) are equal in Figures 3G and 3H, the probability attached to the modal expectation is very much greater for 3G than for any other distribution shown. In Figure 3H, the (subjective) probability of a price equal to x_2 is only slightly greater than prices much lower or higher. In the case of Figure 3G, the entrepreneur would feel "highly certain" about his anticipations; under 3H, he would hardly know whether to make plans based on a price of x_2 or on the basis of very high or very low prices.

Similar differences in degree of confidence in expectations or expected possible loss are expressed in the U-shaped distribution of Figure 3D, the J-shaped distribution of 3F, and the "mirror" J of 3E. The U distribution suggests that the probabilities are about equal for extremely high or low prices (or yields) with few chances for intermediate prices. The J distribution of Figure 3F generally has connotations similar to those of Figure 3C, while the "mirror" J has implications somewhat similar to those of Figure C.

The discussion above has been in terms of uncertainty of price or yield expectations. Similar properties of the probability distribution (for expected or anticipated values) may characterize the income of the enterprise. However, the frequency (or probability) of loss *per se* (rather than the full array of positive incomes) may be equally important.[10] For example, yield and price expectations such as those illustrated in Figure 3B may attach to one enterprise. A second enterprise may be characterized by price and yield distributions (expectations) such as those suggested in Figure 3C. If chance of loss also denotes the degree of uncertainty, it is possible for the enterprise represented by Figure 3B to involve greater

---

[10] The parameters or the moments of the distribution such as those suggested by Figure 3 become relevant in a loss sense if x_2 is taken to represent a zero income. Uncertainty may thus be defined in respect to the probability that a relevant variable, such as profit or cash reserve, falls below zero. See H. Cramer, *On the Mathematical Theory of Risk.* Centraltryckeriet, 1930, pp. 7-84.

uncertainty than enterprise 3C. Loss may attend Figure 3B when prices or yields fall at x_2; they may not occur under 3C unless prices or yields are less than x_1. Thus, while the Figure 3B distribution includes probabilities suggesting outcomes mainly greater than the modal expectation (most probable price as indicated at x_2), expectations under 3C (with probabilities suggesting outcomes less than the modal value) allow for greater probabilities of profit. Similar contrasts also might be made in terms of income under extreme pairs of distributions such as Figures 3E and 3F or 3G and 3H. The nature of the entrepreneur's expectations or subjective probability distribution has greater relevance than expected or known loss in characterizing uncertainty, however. Loss itself may involve no uncertainty; it is known that production of rubber trees in Wisconsin will involve loss.

One more point should be emphasized in respect to expectations, subjective probability distributions, and the degree of uncertainty. The distributions, to the extent to which they are used by farmers, which characterize expectations do not have the same connotations as empirical distributions which define games of chance, quantitative yield distributions, or sample observations from an existing population of events. The latter phenomena imply repeated trials. Under economic planning and expectations, there may be no opportunity for repeated trials. If the entrepreneur goes broke, when plans are fashioned on the basis of a subjective probability distribution defining his expectations, he may not be able to obtain funds to "make another trial."

Degrees of belief. We have outlined some of the logic relating to degree of uncertainty and manager expectations in the previous sections. These various elements all have their place in a systematic analysis of decision-making and uncertainty. Undoubtedly, a large number of businessmen and farm managers are as systematic as the scientist and the statistician in their formulation of hypotheses and the actions based on them; the scientist must choose, on the basis of limited information, among the innumerable logically conceived laws of nature a limited few which are relevant. The statistician, before performing an experiment, must decide what experiment to perform, how to conduct it, and the action to be taken for alternative outcomes. But indeed there must be a large number of managers whose expectations and planning have little of a systematic nature.

Much of the literature dealing with uncertainty treats it in the manner of simple probability description. Some of the concepts in probability do not assume great precision in expectation formation. They only assume that probability is involved as the individual forms judgments through the ordering of probabilities of different outcomes. They say nothing about the actual values of the probabilities (see earlier discussion). Other concepts of uncertainty go beyond this notion and argue that if the individual does not have the ability or opportunity to repeat the experiment indefinitely often, the probabilities, since they are long-run frequency ratios, are irrelevant for his conduct; for the large investments made by individuals, the number of comparable events in an individual's life is likely to be very small. Probability can, however, be viewed in the form of a "degree of belief." If we look upon expectations or uncertainty as a degree of belief, probability is a relation between the evidence and the event considered, but it is not necessarily measurable. Here the evidence must be given some weight; weight increases as the amount of evidence grows larger. This is the Keynes concept in which uncertainty has the 2 dimensions of weight and probability, neither of which needs to be measurable; as the entrepreneur gains greater information he can give greater weight to some prospective outcomes than to others. Some writers and probably a large number of entrepreneurs view uncertainty purely in a "degree of belief" manner.

Types of Uncertainty

Several types of uncertainty are important to the producer as he formulates plans and courses of action which commit resources at the present (t_1) for a product forthcoming at a future date (t_2). One is *price uncertainty* for products or factors. The individual farmer, as the entrepreneur of a competitive firm, has no control over prices. Prices to be realized vary in accordance with actions of other producers, the degree of national prosperity, changes in consumer tastes, the vagaries of the weather, and other miscellaneous happenings. As an "exogenous" or "outside" variable, price instability or unpredictability is never quite as great in other industries. Although the same set of national income and consumer choice considerations affect agriculture and non-agricultural industries alike, the latter are not so greatly affected by weather-generated price variations; monopolistic firms in non-agricultural industries also have greater control over product or even factor (raw material) prices. Price variability and uncertainty arise in agriculture particularly from (a) the fluctuations in national income and prosperity, (b) the recurring commodity cycles for farm products generated by discontinuous production cycles (the hog cycle, and so forth), and (c) random disturbances growing out of weather fluctuation. (Seasonal price cycles are less important from an uncertainty standpoint.) The first source of variability is by all means the most important from the standpoint of long-run production or investment decisions.

A second type of uncertainty (variability) affecting resource returns and important to decision-making can be termed *technical or yield uncertainty*. Technical uncertainty refers to variation in the production coefficients for a given technique. It is absent in some non-agricultural industries but is almost universally present in the various lines of agricultural production. Even in the non-farm industries where it is present, its magnitude is not as great as for particular agricultural crops or for agriculture as a whole. Thus the farm manager is faced with a complex task in formulating plans for use of resources: he must reckon in terms of uncertain yields as well as uncertain prices. The non-farm producer, since he is not so pressed on the side of technical uncertainty, often can devote a greater portion of his entrepreneurial efforts to formulating price expectations and planning.

The greater technical uncertainty to be found in farming may be offset, however, by greater *technological* uncertainty, a third possible source of uncertainty, in non-farm industries. Technological change leads to variability, which in turn gives rise to uncertainty in both agricultural and non-agricultural industries. It is of particular import in industry, where trade names and processes can be patented; a new discovery or invention by a rival firm may sharply lessen the demand for the particular tradename product of a second firm. Farm and non-farm firms are faced with similar uncertainties from technological change, however, when investment questions must consider whether the form of resources or technique adopted will give costs as low as a new technique which may come on the market in the near future. (Uncertainty relates to possibilities of plans which do not maximize profits as well as to courses of action which result in losses.) Both sets of producers have the effects of technological change (including new sources of products) reflected to them as market or price uncertainties: the development of, or reduced costs of production for, an entirely separate but rival commodity affects the demand for the product in question.

A fourth major source of uncertainty is the sociological and legal framework in which the firm operates. Contracts of employment give rise to uncertainty for the industrial firm but are unimportant in agriculture. Farm firms possess their counterpart in this problem through tenure, purchase contracts, and related types of uncertainty. The character of individuals is also a phenomenon which must be predicted and may lead to errors of decisions in employer-employee relationships, and in loan success. Uncertainty and lack of predictability which attach to government programs might also be thrown in this category.

The costs of fluctuations—as compared to an ideal (and perhaps unachievable) situation in which fluctuations do not exist—include the costs of adjusting activity to change. If the nature of change could be predicted, the course of action could be charted for the future once and for all in advance, and following this course would be a routine operation. That it is found desirable to employ a considerable proportion of the resources of any contemporary economic unit (including the economy of Russia) in making decisions in response to (or in the expectation of) change, attests to the importance of uncertainty.

For our purposes, the over-all kinds of change which take place in the economy may be classified as follows:

(1) Exogenous changes, or those changes which are not inherent in the system itself but come about as a result of outside forces. Weather changes, insect and disease plagues, forest fires, changes in consumers' tastes, and population growth are examples. It is assumed that the magnitudes of such changes are given and cannot be changed.

(2) Change inherent in the system itself and not dependent upon a particular legal, political, or economic framework. Capital accumulation and the improvements in technology might be considered as examples, although changes in these variables at given values for other variables might be classified as exogenous changes.

(3) Change inherent within the system but dependent upon a particular legal, political, or economic framework. Changes in the quantity of money in response to changes in total money expenditure for goods and services, changes in tax collections in response to changes in income or expenditure, and changes in storage stocks in response to shifts in supply are examples.

Variability in Agriculture

Physical variability, an exogenous change, is more important in crop than in livestock production and is concentrated particularly in those areas where weather is unstable. Major problems of technical uncertainty are to be found in the Great Plains wheat producing regions, the arid and semi-arid grazing areas of the United States, and on scattered soil and climatic areas in other major producing regions. Although the Cornbelt falls in an intermediate position in respect to yield variability, risks and uncertainties are great for particular soils located in river bottoms, on sandy areas, and in similar hazardous locations. The complete weather cycle is perhaps of a shorter time span in the major portion of the corn states than for grain regions west of the 100th meridian (certain Pacific coast areas excepted). Yield variability is lowest in those parts of the southeastern United States where rainfall is ample and more evenly distributed throughout the year. Of course, fluctuations in rainfall and climate are not the only causes of yield variations; insects, diseases, and other biological pests also cause variations which cannot be predicted. Although rainfall is generally quite stable in the old cotton areas of the United States, the boll weevil is indeed an uncertainty phenomenon. Similarly, while irrigation farming west of the 100th meridian is extremely stable from a moisture standpoint, infrequent and unpredictable freezes or insect attacks give rise to important production uncertainties.

Some notion of the degree of risk or uncertainty involved in farming can be had by examining variability figures for crop yields and production. It should be remembered, of course, that technical variability gives rise to either risk or uncertainty. No attempt has been made to distinguish between the two in figures presented. It can hardly be questioned, however, that technical uncertainty is greatest for primary products in which yield variability is greatest. Table 1 provides a few interesting comparisons here. These data are from experimental plots, and their variability will be slightly greater than that for larger fields or farms. The rank (order) of variability would be similar, however, even were the ideal sample available.[11] Although not entirely representative of the degree of variability for major geographic regions, the figures are suggestive of the variability in yield or production coefficients which face farmers at particular locations. The coefficient of variation (standard deviation divided by the mean) can be used as suggestive (although not a perfect index) of the degree of variability. It suggests the percentage deviation from the mean. The last column indicates year-to-year change in yield. Variability is greatest for the plains crops. However, hay yields show great variability, even in the Cornbelt.

Table I.

Variability in Yield for Specified Crops and Locations *

Crop, location, and period	Mean yield	Coefficient of variation	Year-to-year change as per cent of mean
Corn: Ames, Iowa, 1915-50	56.2	25	26
Oats: Ames, Iowa, 1915-50	36.1	25	24
Hay: Ames, Iowa, 1915-50	1.8	51	62
Wheat: Akron, Colorado, 1909-50	16.3	60	62
Milo: Akron, Colorado, 1909-50	5.7	94	105
Wheat: Fort Hays, Kansas, 1910-50	22.5	63	88
Milo: Fort Hays, Kansas, 1910-50	11.9	124	118
Cotton: Keitt, South Carolina, 1921-50	504	30	24
Tobacco: Oxford, North Carolina, 1913-51	1101	46	35
Potatoes: Aroostook, Maine, 1930-51	351	19	20

* Source: Experimental data from the respective Land Grant Colleges. Trend has been removed.

In addition to interregional differences, the data also are suggestive of intercrop differences which exist at given locations. The percentage deviation of yields from the mean is greater for milo than for summer fallow wheat at Akron, Colorado. Similarly, hay shows greater variability than corn (in the same rotation) at Ames, Iowa. Thus differences in degree of risk or uncertainty for different crops are not to be attributed to regional

---

[11] Other limitations of the data are also recognized by the writer. The infinitely small sample unit represented by the experimental plot does not give a sample representative of the relevant region. The samples do not represent the same period in time. It is recognized that the ideal comparisons would include a geographic sample as well as a sample over time selected in such a manner that unbiased (in a probability sense) comparisons could be made between enterprises on farms (for example, a random sample of the same farms with information over a 30-40 year period). The reader is, of course, aware of the fact that information of this type is not available and will probably never be available for interregional comparisons.

climatic variations alone. Differences in risk and uncertainty (variability) exist between crops even for a given location; the boll weevil did not attack other crops when it first swept the Southeast.

The coefficient of variation figures tell nothing about the sequence of crop failures or successes. These "runs" in yields are more important to decisions than the variability figures themselves. Had farmers known with certainty that wheat yields at Akron would have averaged 4.0 (a range from 1.3 to 8.3) bushels in the 4-year period 1932-1935, and 28.2 (a range from 15.0 to 41.7) in the 4-year period 1912-15, they could have made far better decisions than they actually did. (Price uncertainty was an equally complex force.)

The data of Table 2 provide a second set of yield variability figures which give additional insight into regional patterns of crop instability. These data are for the single crop, wheat, and, although the pattern of variability may differ somewhat for other crops, they do illustrate major differences between geographic locations.

Table 2.

Variability in Yield of Wheat for Selected Counties, 1926-48 *

County and state	Average yield	Coefficient of variation (per cent)	Wheat acreage as per cent of all crops
Baca, Colo.	7.7	92	34
Sully, S. Dak.	7.6	84	28
Decatur, Kan.	10.6	70	56
Sheridan, Mont.	11.3	62	69
Gray, Tex.	10.4	57	68
Pawnee, Kan.	11.5	47	84
Jefferson, Ore.	11.8	45	78
Ringgold, Ia.	12.9	36	10
Champaign, Ill.	20.2	27	11
Decatur, Ill.	16.6	26	26
Christian, Ken.	13.3	24	20
Hamblen, Tenn.	13.5	23	18
Green, Ga.	7.9	22	7
Randolph, N. C.	12.2	17	24
Yates, N. Y.	21.6	17	16
Lee, Iowa	16.0	17	4
Coahoma, Miss.	18.1	17	2
Richmond, Va.	17.0	16	11
Kent, Del.	16.9	15	22
Kent, Md.	18.8	15	29
Berrien, Mich.	19.3	14	8
Hunterdon, N. J.	21.4	11	14
Montgomery, Penn.	20.8	9	16

* Source: L. E. Barber, *Variability of Wheat Yields*. B.A.E. Mimeo., Sept., 1951.

Technical variability in secondary production. Non-agricultural industries as a whole are faced with less technical variability and uncertainty than agriculture because the former engage mainly in secondary and tertiary production.[12] Agriculture is based upon primary (crop) production and thus is subject to all climatic and biological vagaries which affect the production function; these forces are mainly out of range of entrepreneurial control. Whereas the non-agricultural firm can exercise great control over production of secondary commodities, the farm firm has somewhat similar opportunities in livestock, a secondary type of farm production. The yield or production coefficient in livestock is also subject to variability, but control of the production process is generally greater than for crops. Technical variability and uncertainty in the livestock production process *per se* is not so much a matter of regional location as is the case of primary farm commodities. Variability may occur in a beef herd in western North Dakota even if pastures are fully stocked each year, because drought causes grass and hay production to expand and contract, but the beef herd itself may not give rise to greater uncertainty, with ample feed, than the same enterprise in northern Maine. While few data are available, it appears to be a strong hypothesis that the greatest variations in death losses, those which are of important magnitude and cannot be classed as pure and simple risks, are to be found in such enterprises as turkeys and feeder lambs. Beef cows are perhaps at the other extreme, and are followed closely by supplementary dairy enterprises which provide a small butterfat output on many farms. Table 3 compares pork and milk variability on some Iowa farms where dairying proves more stable. A commercial egg flock also gives relatively small variability in yield per hen, although variability is great for many farm flocks. Cattle feeding, pork production, and range sheep production provide intermediate cases. However, those truly great and unpredictable variations (for example, loss of range cows and ewes by blizzard or mastitis in a whole-milk dairy) are not unique to any particular enterprise.

Important differences do exist between livestock in the amount of predictable (risk) and unpredictable (uncertainty) variation which occur in livestock yields over time. While technical variability is greater for crops than for livestock (when each production process is viewed independently) over the entire United States, there are exceptions. In some of the more stable climatic areas, technical uncertainty involved in crop production is no greater than that involved in livestock farming. Also, the variability of crop production becomes interwoven with fluctuations in livestock production in many arid farming areas; cattle often are stocked with such density that short pasture and hay yields cause parallel variations in grass and beef or sheep production.

---

[12] There are major primary industries which are not agricultural. Mining and fishing are examples. In some of these instances, production does not involve great technical variability of the production process. This situation is true of mining, where the stock of materials is large and known. As has already been indicated, other forms of (non-agricultural) primary production do involve great variations in yield and production.

Table 3.

Yield Variability for Two Types of Livestock in Iowa. Frequency Distribution
of Annual Yields as Per Cent of Mean *

Intervals for frequency distribution (deviation from mean expressed as a per cent of the mean)	Pork production per sow with pigs at constant market weights	Milk per cow
152.5 and over	1.6	0
137.5-152.4	2.7	.7
122.5-137.4	7.4	3.2
107.5-122.4	22.8	21.5
92.5-107.4	33.7	48.2
77.5- 92.4	20.6	21.7
62.5- 77.4	7.2	4.6
47.5- 62.4	2.2	.1
less than 47.5	.8	0
Range as per cent of mean	73	49
Coefficient of variation	18.3	12.1
Coefficient of skewness	.13	.17
Year-to-year change as per cent of mean	17.8	9.1

* Source: Derived from a sample of 36 record-keeping farms in Iowa with records of 20 or more consecutive years. Trend has been removed where it proved significant for any individual farm. The data are means of statistics computed for each individual farm

Variability in farm commodity prices. The zenith of uncertainty is to be found in farm commodity prices. Historically, farm prices have been highly unstable, and great fluctuations have taken place from year to year. The pattern of production in one year, therefore, often deviates widely from that which would give the most profitable or efficient use of resources. While there is little basis for predicting major short-run price changes, important differences exist between farm commodities as is illustrated by Table 4. These data are aggregates (of different markets and location, different months of the year, and, in some cases, different grades and qualities of product) and underestimate the price uncertainty which faces the individual farmer who must make production decisions in terms of price expectations for particular kinds and grades of products marketed at a specific market and on a single day. Using these data as a rough indication of the price uncertainty which has faced farmers in the past, it is evident that production and investment decisions must be more complex for some commodities than for others. Again dairying falls at the lower end of the variability scale and when individual commodities are considered, potatoes, hogs, and wheat are at the other extreme. Potatoes and hogs are influenced not only by the general economic fluctuations (prosperity and depression) which affect all commodities but also by the short-run commodity cycle resulting from changes between years in the number of technical units (sows and acres). Variation in the quantity of resources devoted to wheat is much less between years; variability comes more nearly through year-to-year changes in yield per acre. While the

Table 4.

Year-to-Year Variability in Prices for Major Farm Products, United States, 1910-45, No. Years and Per Cent

Commodity	Change in price between years as per cent of previous years							Average year-to-year change in per cent
	+31 & over	+16— +30	+6— +15	0— ±5	—6— 15	—16— 30	—31 & over	
All dairy products	1	6	7	15	2	3	0	10.2
Milk, wholesale	2	6	7	14	2	3	0	11.6
All livestock and livestock products	2	6	7	14	1	3	1	12.0
All crops	3	4	8	14	1	2	2	14.2
All farm commodities	2	7	7	14	2	2	1	12.3
Meat animals	3	4	8	12	2	4	2	15.1
Feed crops	3	6	9	11	1	1	4	17.8
Poultry and eggs	1	6	8	11	3	4	0	12.2
Cotton	10	1	4	10	0	3	4	22.1
Tobacco	5	7	3	10	1	5	0	18.2
Fruits and tree nuts	3	7	6	10	2	4	2	15.6
Cattle and calves	1	6	8	10	3	3	1	13.1
Eggs	1	6	9	9	2	3	1	13.2
Hay	2	5	7	9	5	4	1	13.9
Corn	3	7	9	7	3	1	4	21.0
Sheep and lambs	2	4	12	7	3	4	2	15.2
Food grains	4	5	10	6	2	2	3	17.9
Wheat	4	4	9	6	2	2	3	18.0
Hogs	5	2	10	5	2	6	3	22.1
Oil crops	7	3	9	5	3	5	2	20.6
Potatoes	11	3	4	3	3	4	7	35.2

past need not reflect the degree of price uncertainty likely to prevail in the future, these figures do emphasize the uncertain decision-making environment which faces farm firms. Prices of one year generally provide poor indicators of how resources should be administered in a second year.

Changes in production and decision-making. The degree of uncertainty facing farmers as a result of combined price and technical variability also is reflected in year-to-year changes in agricultural production. The magnitude by which total output of a commodity fluctuates suggests the degree to which farmers' plans are unstable and must be adapted to changes in prices, techniques, and yield. If changes in production were always made with perfect insight into the prices and yields to be realized, variability of production could not be taken to indicate uncertainty and errors of decision. This situation is far from true, however, and the figures of Table 5 can be taken as further rough approximation of uncertainty and complexity in the decision-making environment. Again, the aggregative figures underemphasize the degree of instability in individual producing areas and on individual farms. This great variability in production has come about (a) through individual farmers' attempts to meet technical, technological, and price uncertainties by redirecting resources between commodities; and (b) as yield or production coefficients have varied between years. The major phenomena behind these fluctuations in production are of an uncertainty nature; many of those random and measurable disturbances or variations (egg breakage, unfavorable farrowing experience, and so forth) which can be classed as pure risks have been eliminated in an actuarial sense through the large numbers of farms included in data of Table 5. The data again place dairy products and potatoes in contrasting positions, while other products follow the order already suggested.

Variations in net income also serve as barometers of the degree of uncertainty involved in production.[13] From this standpoint, Cornbelt farmers would be quick to add that cattle or sheep feeding are highly "risky" (uncertain) enterprises. Farmers on the periphery of the Great Plains and even in the Great Plains proper would suggest that corn often involves greater uncertainty than wheat. From an income variability standpoint, certain fruits and vegetables would rank above broilers, which in turn would rank above dairy products in the degree of uncertainty encountered in New England milksheds.

Variability of factor prices. The prices of certain factors used in production display less variability than the prices of farm commodities. A sore point in agriculture has been that, while the price of farm commodities is very flexible, the prices of farm machinery, equipment, and supplies is not so variable. Differences here are illustrated in Table 6, which illustrates

---

[13] Loss is not itself a criterion of uncertainty. For example, oranges might be grown on the plains of western Kansas. Losses would result every year. Thus the probability of loss is not unknown. It is a *certainty* (a probability of 1.0).

Table 5.
Year-to-Year Variability in Production of Selected Commodities, United States, 1910-49. Per Cent

Commodity	Change in total production of commodity as per cent of previous year							Average year-to-year change in per cent
	+31 & over	+11 to +20	+6 to +10	0 to ±5	-6 to -10	-11 to -20	-21 & over	
Dairy products	0	0	0	36	0	0	0	2.1
Poultry and eggs	0	2	8	25	1	0	0	4.1
Cattle and calves	0	0	8	22	4	1	0	4.6
Sheep and lambs	1	3	6	18	4	3	0	6.7
Hogs	3	5	2	18	4	2	1	8.6
Wheat	4	6	3	14	1	5	3	13.1
Corn	4	8	3	9	3	5	4	16.1
Tobacco	6	7	4	7	3	2	4	15.3
Cotton	5	7	4	7	3	3	7	16.2
Potatoes	5	7	2	5	5	9	2	14.5

Table 6.

Year-to-Year Variability in Selected Factor Prices, United States, 1914-49. Per Cent

Factor	Change in price of factor as per cent of previous year							Average year-to-year change in per cent
	+21 & over	+11 to +20	+6 to +10	0 to ±5	−6 to −10	−11 to −20	−21 & over	
Farm machinery (new)	0	1	0	32	0	1	0	3.5
Equipment and supplies (new)	0	1	4	24	2	2	0	5.4
Land (value per acre)	0	1	5	20	2	3	0	5.9
Fertilizer	0	3	7	19	2	3	0	6.1
Buildings	0	5	7	19	2	1	1	6.2
Labor	5	7	4	15	1	1	3	11.1
Land (rent)	4	7	6	11	0	2	4	13.2
Feed crops	7	8	3	11	1	1	5	17.8

short-run variability in selected factor prices. Low short-run variability is illustrated for new farm machinery; high variability is expressed for farm labor and feed crops. Although the form in which the data are presented (year-to-year changes) emphasizes differences in short-run variability, similar patterns exist for the total variability (as measured by deduction from the mean for the entire period) over the period examined. Instability in prices of feeds, labor, and land (rental rates) is great because variability of the price of farm products is great. Feed crops are products to some farmers, but are factors to other farmers. Hence price variability for feed both as a resource and as a commodity is equal. Variability in the price of land or land services (rent) parallels that of farm products. (The greatest portion of farms are rented on a share basis.) Similarly, the prices of resources and services represented by second-hand machinery and equipment are nearly as variable as farm commodity prices.

Stability in the price of selected factors might appear to decrease the complexity of decision-making; with stable resource prices, the process of expectation formation might center almost entirely around product yields and prices. This statement is hardly true, however. Flexibility in product prices and stability of factor prices adds to uncertainty of choice in use of resources. The fact that farm commodity prices may fall or rise while factor prices remain stable (or change by a lesser amount or rate than commodity prices) causes the variance in net income to be accentuated. The extreme decline of net farm income in the depression of the 1930's and the equally sharp rise during the early years of World War II were brought about by differences in short-run price changes between farm commodities and farm factors.

Selected References

Arrow, K. J., "Alternative Approaches to Theory of Choice," *Econometrica*, Vol. 19.

Hart, A. G., *Anticipations, Uncertainty and Dynamic Planning*. Chicago: University of Chicago Press, 1940, Ch. 1.

———, *Risk, Uncertainty and Unprofitability of Compounding Probabilities in Studies in Mathematical Economics and Econometrics*. Chicago: University of Chicago Press, 1942.

Heady, Earl O., and Kehrberg, Earl W., *Uncertainty and Variability in Primary Production of Iowa*. Iowa Agr. Exp. Sta. Bul. 394.

Johnson, D. G., *Forward Prices for Agriculture*. Chicago: University of Chicago Press, 1947, pp. 38-39.

Knight, F. H., *Risk, Uncertainty and Profit*. Boston: Houghton Mifflin, 1921, Chs. 5, 7.

Shackle, G. L. S., *Expectations in Economics*. Cambridge: Cambridge University Press, 1949, Chs. 1, 2.

Schultz, T. W., *Production and Welfare in Agriculture*. New York: McGraw-Hill, 1949, Ch. 8.

Tintner, G., "The Theory of Production Under Non-static Conditions," *Jour. Pol. Econ.*, Vol. 40.

16

Role of Management and Expectations in Resource Administration

AMERICAN society has vested control of resource allocation for agriculture in the hands of millions of individual farm managers. Herein lie the ultimate decisions on how farm resources will be used between alternatives at a given point in time and between alternatives over time. In terms of numbers, management is nowhere near so important in non-agricultural industries. It is our purpose in this chapter to examine the basic role and nature of management in resource administration. All consumer choices, national programs, and other economic influences which have impact on agricultural production must thread through the management of the farm firm. How does management function where the future is uncertain and plans are at best based on guesses?

The Function and Meaning of Management

The term management has many connotations. Sometimes it is used to include the officers of the business firm or to refer to the tasks of a farm operator. In other cases, it is used to include any person with the rank of foreman or better. Management, as the term is popularly employed, can be broken down into 2 distinct activities. One is *coordination*. Need for it grows out of change and inability to predict the future with certainty (or even because of inability to make empirical prediction with acceptable error limits). The other phase is *supervision*. We prefer to look upon management as being synonymous with coordination. Supervision is a somewhat distinct human activity of the "lower order" nature indicated below. Unpredictable change causes firms as well as nations to keep a portion of their resources invested in decision-making activities.

Coordination, a function of uncertainty. The existence of the firm as a planning entity and the need for coordination grows out of dynamic conditions and change or variability (of price and production quantities) which can only be estimated subjectively for the future. Change or variability of production coefficients and prices do not alone give occasion for

465

the use of entrepreneurship; the firm itself has roots only in imperfect knowledge. All economic units involve decision-making or coordination bodies. The firm is the decision or choice-making unit on the side of production. It is paralleled on the consumption side by the household. There is nothing unique about management and the problems of decision-making (alias management or coordination) or forces which give rise to the need for coordination; they are the same at the level of individual firm and household as at the national policy level. The need for management (administrators) in the form of coordination arises only because of change and incomplete information about the future.

The fundamental role of the coordinating unit, management in its true sense, is this: First, it must formulate expectations of the conditions which will prevail in the future. This task ordinarily is encountered before investment is made or production plans are ready to be committed. It involves the anticipation of future prices and production rates. Second, and after expectations of the future have been established, a plan of production (investment) must be formulated which is logical and consistent with expectations. Decisions must be made. Third, the production plan must be put into action. An auxiliary responsibility of management is the acceptance of the economic consequences of plans. In summary then, the important steps in coordination include expectations, plans, action, and acceptance of consequences. We shall see later how the acceptance of the consequences has the effect of conditioning plans and, in turn, is conditioned by the nature of expectations. Learning, obtaining information, and weighing alternatives are fundamental to each of the above steps.

Without the combination of time, change, and the inability of perfect prediction, there would be no need for management, or perhaps more accurately, the need for management would arise only as the firm was initially established. Given time and change which can be predicted with certainty (perfect knowledge of the future), management in the coordination sense would be needed only to formulate a single plan for the future. With perfect knowledge of prices and yields in the years ahead, a single perfect plan could be laid out for all time. It would specify the manner in which resources should be combined at each point in time, for each variation in the production function, for each change in techniques, and for each price situation. (Each of which would be known with certainty when plans were initially considered.) After this plan was drawn up and put into effect, coordination would no longer be needed; supervision alone would be required. Supervisors would see that the plans laid out for each condition specified in the original plan (already known and predicted with certainty) were put into successful operation and terminated as each predicted change in market or physical quantities comes about.

Certainty or perfect knowledge and lack of need for management would not preclude weather fluctuations, technological change, or price variations. Good and bad weather with varying amounts of drought, hail, frost, or insect damage might still come about but the exact yield for any one year would be known at a previous time (when plans were originally drawn up). There would be no further need for decision-making. Once the initial plan had been devised, the entrepreneurial activity could be reduced to routine supervision. If the entrepreneur not only knew that wheat yields would vary but that the yields in the 3 years ahead would be zero, 15, and 40 bushels, his initial plans would account for these known variations. The instructions "from management to supervisor" would include operation of no land in the first year and an acreage consistent with a 40 bushel yield in the third year. The firm itself would not arise in the absence of change and imperfect knowledge (only a physical producing plant would be required).

The rewards for management. Gains from efficient management are realized by society and the individual entrepreneur when production must take place in an uncertain world. Gain accrues to both if the farm manager correctly anticipates that beef supplies will be long (prices will be low) and pork supplies will be short (prices will be high) relative to consumer preferences in the year ahead; the manager's action in investing resources in pork production and withholding them from beef production adds to total utility of consumers. The ability of a farm operator to anticipate correctly the productivity of advanced techniques in cotton production adds similarly to the income available to society as well as to his own returns. Returns to management are premiums in income which accrue from correct anticipation of the future and from plans which are fashioned to conform to expectations. Pure windfall gains which arise from outcomes which were not anticipated and planned can hardly be classed as returns for coordination. Large returns may be forthcoming from pure chance decisions (flipping a coin to see which plan to follow or buying a ticket for the Irish sweepstakes), but these prizes can hardly be looked upon as a function of learning and planning. However, losses or failure to realize large gains cannot be dissociated entirely from the entrepreneur's capital position. While the individual may have the ability to guess the future, a shortage of capital may cause his tenure as an entrepreneur to be terminated after one unforeseen setback. The manager with sufficient capital can survive a single loss and is on hand to profit from later planning successes, even though his innate ability may be no greater than that of the farmer who was forced to withdraw from the game.

Gains or losses also accrue from the supervisory aspects (pure technical skills and the carrying out of plans prescribed in the decision-making process) of farming. Some farm operators do not possess enough skill to drive a tractor down a crooked contour row; corn plants may be torn out and yield reduced. Other farmers who do not have the physical stamina for getting crops cultivated and animals housed in the day before a rain may realize lower yields than their more punctual neighbors. Yet these aspects of work and practice arrangement are more nearly a part of the technical production process. They definitely do not belong in the same category as the coordinating or decision-making aspects of management.

Properties of efficient management. Outstanding farmers must have scientific and analytical minds and must have mental capacities to "think outside" of the narrow environment of their own experiences. They form hypotheses of technological outcomes to be realized when resources are organized to result in new farm practices, and test these hypotheses with their own capital at stake. While many farmers think empirically and gather their information on new techniques after it has been proven by neighbors, educational channels, and commercial sources, the foremost manager even keeps ahead of scientists in the Land Grant Colleges and the Department of Agriculture. Many technical improvements are developed on the farm. Even if the findings are from experimental plots, the farm manager must still infer from these to his own farm; the error in predicting from experimental results to farms is often great because the research findings refer to a highly restricted population of plants, animals, or soils. (The population for which applied physical research in agriculture is appropriate cannot be specified in any objective sense.) Perhaps one characteristic of the outstanding farmer is possession of a mind which can view phenomena in a deductive and analytical manner. This ability allows him, after gathering together relevant data and principles, to extend his though to hypotheses (expectations) about future outcomes. By gathering still more data, he comes to believe in the "subjective verification" of his hypotheses, and is willing to test them on his farm as the plan for the next year. These steps are about the same as those which are followed by the systematic scientist, who must be able to think deductively if he is to formulate new and useful hypotheses for predictive purposes. Managers also think inductively in the sense that they take the data from college experiments or use neighboring farms as case studies for the purpose of generalizing to their own farm. When this process is carried to the extreme, it gives rise to the pure imitator-type of managerial activity; an important number of farmers do follow this procedure perhaps because they lack an imaginative mind. Many farmers, transplanting a plan from another farm onto their own unit, have found that pure induction of this type also results in extreme errors of inference and may cause liquidation of their firms.

Coupled with ability to infer on technological outcomes and the ability to survey and anticipate prices and other phenomena of the future, management may interact with other resources to give a type of increasing returns. Many financially successful farmers are found on highly productive soils. This situation has led some persons to pose the hypothesis that good managers can get relatively more from good soils than poor managers; therefore, the good managers migrate to highly productive soils while poor managers migrate to poor soils. It is true that in the most productive and highest priced soil areas, fewer farm people are found in low income strata. Yet the explanation here is not entirely clear. With increasing knowledge of possible techniques in the more complex soil and economic environments, agricultural specialists have come to believe that the very great rewards to management are to be had in areas which have previously been considered "low income" or "poverty" belts. Developments in the old cotton areas, the northern and southern fringe of the Cornbelt, and the problem soils of New England suggest that the difference in resource productivity under good and poor management is greater than for the more stable economic environments and highly productive soil areas.

An efficient manager or coordinator must have imagination, insight, and the willingness and ability to learn. It is necessary not only that he be able to grasp quickly the implications of information made available to him, but also that he have the mental capacity to glean and cover wide ranges of information. Managers who have proven their abilities over time as co-ordinators (we do not include as successful managers those operators who have inherited wealth, although a set of expectations based on marrying the daughter of a wealthy farmer cannot be entirely excluded) are generally characterized as individuals with high mental abilities and perhaps a dash of sporting blood in their veins. A successful manager must be an efficient learner and possess the tools of learning. (The farmer who cannot read is severely limited in his ability to obtain information and "weigh it" for planning purposes.) Business operations always require the formation of hypotheses about the future. The operator can reduce one of the many hypotheses of the future to a point at which he is willing to test them in production plans only as he is able to integrate facts and expectations in such a manner that his "degree of belief" in one hypothesis is greater than for another. The greater the amount of literature which the manager can cover in the form of outlook materials, bulletins on technological innovations, and weather-yield predictions and correlations, the greater are his chances of formulating hypotheses or images of the future which have a minimum error. He must not only be able to survey a large amount of literature, but also must be able to assimilate information in such a manner that conflicting and consistent inferences can be integrated. Farmers obtain information by reading newspapers, listening to the radio, viewing television, attending fairs, visiting each other, gleaning experimental results, attending extension meetings, and by traveling about the country. While these sources provide vast amounts of information about yields, technologies, prices, governmental policies, and personal relationships, none of them provide perfect knowledge.

Assembling data as a basis for formulating expectations and reducing the subjective uncertainty in the operator's mind requires either 1 or all of 3 types of cost. One cost is the time which the manager may himself devote to the assembling of information and data for estimation of the future. Another cost may be represented by the inefficient use of resources or the unwillingness to commit resources (and hence the passing up of returns which might be forthcoming) until enough time has passed so that the operator can obtain and evaluate the information at hand. The final cost of refining expectations is represented when the business firm hires a staff of economists and other experts to glean all reports, forecasts, and unanalyzed phenomena which may have a bearing on future prices or production coefficients. To collect from college and government bulletins and outlook reports, newspapers, magazines, correspondence, individual communications, and radio comments calls for a vast clerical force. The task of analysis and interpretation is even more profound. While analysis staffs are to be found in many corporate firms, few farm firms have funds great enough for investment in this activity.

The fullest information which the firm can hope to obtain about the future is incomplete and unreliable. Unfortunately, it is a matter of guesswork about just where the margin of profitable estimation and planning lies. It is impossible to determine whether the assembling of added data and more careful planning will yield enough improvement in expectations (enough reduction in uncertainty to more nearly provide the groundwork

Table I.

Mean Price Expectations for a Random Sample of Iowa Farmers in 1948 and 1949 *

Commodity and month in year ahead for which expectation was obtained	Prices expected for 1948		Actual price realized in 1948	Price expected for 1949		Actual price realized in 1949
	In Dec. 1947	In June 1948		In Dec. 1948	In June 1949	
Corn, Dec.	1.51	1.52	1.19	1.07	.94	1.06
Soybeans, Nov.	2.71	3.04	2.32	2.08	1.94	1.99
Fat cattle, July	30.54	32.92	35.19	25.57	25.82	25.14
Feeder cattle, Oct.	20.75	20.47	24.71	20.91	20.64	22.57
Hogs	22.26	20.19	20.00	17.12	15.85	14.70

* The study was designed to determine farmer expectations in the year previous to production and marketing plans. Two surveys (December, 1947 and June, 1948) were made to determine price expectations for the 1948 production year. The same procedure was repeated in respect to expectations for 1949 (with surveys in December of 1948 and June of 1949).

for profitable planning) to pay for itself. The problem involves choice: to what extent should less reliable expectations at lower costs be substituted for more reliable expectations at higher costs? Again, the entrepreneur has decided this question when he is ready to put a plan into action. Obviously, though, prices and yields actually realized may and will deviate from the farmer's expectations, even though he believes subjective uncertainty to be low enough to merit production. For example, the farmers from whom the data in Table 1 were obtained carried on production of the commodities indicated, yet the average error for the group was considerable for individual commodities and in individual years. (The expectational errors were, of course, much greater for individual farmers.)

Convergence and revision of expectations. Flexibility is the keynote of resource administration when uncertainty is great. Adaptations in plans can be made in a manner to augment impending profits or lessen impending losses even up to the time crops and livestock are marketed. Thus the continued need exists for marshalling data throughout the production period. While the entrepreneur must never place himself in the indecision category of Buridan's ass, neither must he forget the proverb, "Haste makes waste."

That the farmer does not formulate a definite set of expectations at an early point in time (t_0) for a later point in time (t_4) which is held at all intermediate points in time $(t_1, t_2,$ and $t_3)$ is illustrated in Table 2. These data were obtained by the writer and others from a random sample of 185 Iowa farms. It is of interest to note that not only did modal expectations (most likely outcomes in the farmers' minds) change, but also the range of outcomes lessened as the end of the production period and the marketing

Table 2.

Mean Price Expectations, Price Limits, and Changes in 1949 Expectations for a Sample of Iowa Farmers

Commodity and month in 1949 for which expectation was obtained [a]	Price expectations indicated in Dec. 1948 (*dollars*)				Price expectations indicated in June 1949 (*dollars*)			
	Modal or most probable price	Lower limit [b]	Upper limit [b]	Range of possible outcomes	Modal or most probable price	Lower limit [b]	Upper limit [b]	Range of possible outcomes
Corn, Dec.	1.07	.77	1.58	1.07	.94	.73	1.30	.59
Hogs, Dec.	17.12	13.50	23.38	9.70	15.85	13.54	20.17	6.97

[a] The first survey was taken in December, 1947 and questioned farmers on their expectations of prices for the year ahead (1949) and for the mean of the months indicated by each commodity. The second survey was taken in June, 1949 and referred to expectations for the same months (indicated in column 1) of 1949 as the December 1947 survey. The same survey was repeated in 1948 and 1949 but only the first year results are shown.

[b] The lower and upper limits were the extreme price ranges within which each individual farmer thought prices would fall with a probability of .99. (The range has been computed from the limits indicated.) However, it is doubtful that the majority of the farmers were thinking over a range of a price distribution which included a probability of .99.

date were approached. Farmers generally expressed greater confidence (less uncertainty for prices at the specified future time) in their June expectations than in the previous December estimates. The length of time for which estimates had to be made and the possible number of forces which might alter expectations was less at the time of the second expression. While feeder cattle cannot be put in the lot in June (the second period of expectation indications) for finish in July (the marketing month specified in the case of feeders), revision of finishing plans can still be made. Even greater adjustments in production plans can be made in the case of hogs: spring pigs on hand in June can be sold as feeders or kept and carried to heavier weights, depending on the outlook; added fall or summer pigs can be farrowed or the brood sows can be sold. Adjustments in resource use might be made for crops even though plantings are in the ground; corn can be side dressed with nitrogen fertilizer, soybeans can be cultivated a third time, or crops can be left unharvested, if unfavorable yield or price situations develop. Thus the efficient manager must not only be mentally competent as an observer, analyst, and planner but he must also have the ambition and initiative to continue the learning process both within and between production periods.

Theoretically and practically, the entrepreneur must recognize that time can involve dispersion and convergence of expectations. As a general rule, the range or dispersion of possible outcomes for prices or yields is greatest for dates more remote from the harvesting or marketing time. The possible range within which prices or yields may fall quite often narrows as the relevant future date is approached. The hog producer, surveying plans in the fall of 1954 for farrowings in the spring of 1955, may have little knowledge of both supply and demand conditions in the year ahead; or if he has knowledge of demand conditions, he still does not know the number of spring sows that will be farrowed. He can only guess. By spring, however, estimates are available on the number of spring sows farrowed the nation over; by midsummer, information is available on the number of spring pigs saved. Thus knowledge of supply and demand conditions (for hogs to be marketed in November of 1953) is likely to be more complete and uncertainty (dispersion of expectation) less in June 1955 than in September 1954. Accuracy of expectations tends to increase up to the time of marketing. On the day before marketing, the farmer may estimate the prices to be received within a range of $1 (although he can err by greater amounts if unforeseen market breaks occur). On the morning of marketing, the range of dispersion of expected prices may converge to a range of 25¢.

The statements above should not be taken to infer that the range or dispersion of expectations (the degree of subjective uncertainty or the ability to predict) consistently and unalterably reduces as the production period draws nearer and nearer to termination. This point is illustrated in Figures 1 and 2. Initial planning is at date t_0, and marketing is at date t_4. The range of possible outcomes (the lower and upper limits within which the operator might expect prices to fall with a probability of 1.0) is ab when plans are laid at date t_0, reduces to cd, ef, and gh at dates t_1, t_2, and t_3, and falls to zero at the marketing date t_4.[1] It is entirely possible, how-

---

[1] Since the change in range does not give any notion of changes in kurtosis or skewness (or even the variance) of the subjective probability distribution, it is an imperfect measure of the degree of uncertainty which exists at any planning date.

ever, that as a date such as t_1 is reached an entirely different set of price or weather forces comes into prospect and conditions expectations accordingly. The possibility of war or drought may arise in the midst of a production period, for example. As is illustrated in Figure 2, the level and range of expectations will take on an entirely different nature as the new information appears; the range of possibilities may narrow from date t_0 to date t_2, but mushroom into an entirely different structure. However, unless new revealing information is obtained (including absence of forces

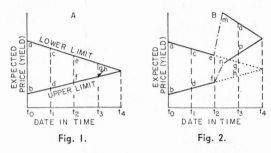

Fig. I.   Fig. 2.

Relationship of time to dispersion of expectations.

which prove original expectations to be erroneous), the new expectation framework should again display the convergence characteristic.[2]

Differences in expectations and rationality. Since the expectations of future prices and production rates are only subjective guesses, 2 managers need not have the same framework of possible outcomes in mind. If, after both farmer A and farmer B have scanned all information available and sought the limits of interpretation forthcoming from outlook experts, A attaches a high subjective probability to an increase in hog prices while B foresees an opposite outcome, the validity of the conflicting hypotheses can be tested only with time. Since both producers must commit their resources in the planning period, the only alternative for either is to follow the course (farrow more or fewer litters) dictated by his expectations. Only one can be right in the end. The agricultural expert can tell with *ex poste* certainty (after the commodity has been produced and marketed) which was correct yet he has no basis for advising the operator who has been proved by history to be wrong, to "go thou and do likewise." Given the *ex ante* nature of production plans, both operators have been "rational" in terms of their expectations; each has been "subjectively correct" in his own mind and as far as experts can inform him.

The extent to which farmers in a similar producing area may formulate

---

[2] In the example of Figure 2, the original hypotheses (the latter portions of the converging line) are no longer relevant at date t_2, and the new (upper) range becomes important for any changes which can be made in plans. At a date even beyond t_2, the possible dispersion or range of outcomes (as suggested by mn) is as great as or greater than at the outset.

conflicting expectations is illustrated in the data of Table 3. These again are taken from the Iowa expectations study. The data are broken down to show the average expectation errors of farm operators who expected prices either to rise or fall above the level existing at the time of the surveys. (These averages obscure the extent to which expectations of individual farmers are in error. The negative error for corn was 95¢ for one farmer who was "subjectively certain" of depression by December of 1948; it was $3 and positive for another farmer who viewed war with Russia and inflation as inescapable.) In terms of their individual beliefs, these 2 groups of farmers with conflicting expectations were each rational in planning a different course of action in the year's production plans.

Table 3.

Price Expectation Errors for a Sample of Iowa Farmers *

Commodity and month in year ahead to which expectations apply	*Errors between Dec.* 1947 *expectations and* 1948 *realizations*			*Errors between Dec.* 1948 *expectations and* 1949 *realizations*		
	Farmers expecting price rise	Farmers expecting price decline	All farmers	Farmers expecting price rise	Farmers expecting price decline	All farmers
Corn, Dec.	.44	.32	.43	.17	.25	.23
Soybeans, Nov.	.67	1.20	.95	.20	1.33	.66
Butterfat	.04	.27	.25	.06	.23	.19
Fat cattle, July	3.44	12.13	9.43	5.04	9.66	7.23
Feeder cattle, Oct.	1.05	8.48	8.32	2.41	7.82	6.55
Hogs	5.52	3.78	4.69	2.49	5.43	3.77

* Error figures refer to the most probable price expected by farmers as compared to the price actually realized. See Tables 1 and 2 for other details on the survey.

The Planning Horizon

The necessity for making subjective forecasts places a limit on the distance into the future for which producers can plan in a meaningful manner. The fact that uncertainty is greater as the time period is extended causes the clear facts of today to shade off into the haze of unknowns which characterizes the more distant future. At what point or distance in time does the individual "chop off" his expectations and planning? The length of time over which individuals plan economic activity is termed the *economic horizon*. Were prices and yields of the future known with objective certainty, the span of the economic horizon would be indeterminant. The distance of the economic horizon differs between individuals and is determined by the length of time for which they can formulate useful expectations and plans. Expectations, again, are "useful" to the individual only when he views them with a degree of "subjective certainty" which merits action and planning (for example, if discounted returns are greater than discounted costs).

There is evidence that the planning horizon is not greatly distant for the majority of farmers and is particularly near at hand for those operators who have unfavorable equities and are beginners or are otherwise short on capital. It is common knowledge that the distance into the future for which useful expectations can be and are formed is characteristically situational and varies greatly between individuals. At one extreme, crop yield expectations are relevant only over a 1-year period for the tenant with an annual lease. Contrariwise, his owner neighbor may have based his most important decision, the purchase of the farm, on much longer-run yield expectations. The beginning farmer or established operator may see the distant future as a complete haze: uncertainty surrounds the life of his business in the short run; the long run is relevant only if he can survive the first few years ahead. In contrast, the operator with a safe equity ratio can see beyond yield or price setbacks of 1 or a few years' duration, and hence a longer time span becomes more important. Obviously, the relevant economic horizon for planning differs between commodities: apple orchards require that useful expectations must be formed over a 25-55 year period. Feeding of heavy cattle (where long term investment in buildings is unimportant) requires that the farmer be able to formulate expectations with sufficient certainty for as few as 60 days.

Expectation Models

Many different models are used in formulating the expectation upon which decisions in agriculture are based. Those employed by farmers are simple and often inadequate. Sometimes several are used in combination. Government and college personnel who attempt to aid the farmer in molding his outlook of the future employ both elementary and complex systems. These expectations, in turn, are used by farmers. The writer knows one competent hog farmer who claims to include all possible variables in his system down to and including the temperature in Washington ("the temperature may affect the temperament of Congressmen and hence the legislation which they enact"). All farmers formulate hypotheses or expectations of the future, whether these be rough or refined. It might be suggested that the operator who adopts a rigid or habitual farm organization and follows it down through time (for example, one who does what his father and grandfather did) does not take the steps of forming hypotheses and planning accordingly. However, aside from the person whose actions are steeped entirely in habit, the operator who follows this course does have a set of subjective guesses about the future in his mind; he simply assumes that the set of expectations with which he started farming (or those employed by his father or grandfathers) is most adequate for all time into the future. Or, he may assume that prices and yields are so erratic that one plan is as good as another. History has proven the inadequacy of this system as applied to all price and yield outcomes.

It is also true that there can be and are many degrees of refinement with which farmers formulate expectations. Some of the more competent farmers do visualize prices of the future in the form of a probability distribution (at least in the sense of a modal or most probable price and a possible range of outcomes). This degree of refinement applies especially to yield expectations. Iowa farmers were found to have definite notions of the "number of years in 10" that they have seeding failures or can expect corn and oats yields falling at specified levels (they see the set of possibilities as a frequency distribution). While many farmers do not visualize all values of a price distribution, a great number have some cardinal notion of the "most probable" price outcome and the range (or some "practicable" lower and upper limits) within which price is expected to fall. Others never place cardinal values on the quantities expected, but do think in an ordinal sense; one price outcome is considered to be "more likely" than a second, which in turn is "more likely" than a third. Often the "tails of the distribution" are simply "left open" under this system, and the ordinal notions of changes refer only to whether prices will remain the same, go up, or go down.

Although much is still to be learned about farmer expectations, the Iowa study cited earlier did indicate that the ranges or limits of expectations seem to serve as an indication of the degree of uncertainty which farmers attach to their expectations. Farmers who have an "intense belief" in their estimates give very narrow limits within which future prices may fall. (A price of $1.50 may appear most probable while the expected range is $1.25 to $1.50.) Those with less confidence indicate wide ranges. (A price of $1.50 may appear most probable but limits may vary from 50¢ to $3.00.) Unwittingly, the skewness is also taken into account by some farmers in establishing degrees of confidence in their expectations. One farmer may feel that the most probable and the minimum price may coincide at the government loan level, while other price possibilities exist only above the loan level. Another farmer may have the opposite view. He may feel that the most probable and maximum price which can be realized is a government loan price of $1.40, while other alternatives include prices in the open market as low as 75¢.

If it could be measured, Shackle's "degree of surprise" might serve as an indication of the degree of uncertainty with which farmers hold expectations and the accuracy with which expectations were formulated.[3] The farmer who foresees a very narrow range of price outcomes (for example, a probability of 1.0 that wheat price will fall between $1.50 and $1.70) is not "surprised" if the price is $1.60. However, he is highly but pleasantly surprised (with the same range expected) if price falls at $2.00. He is unpleasantly surprised if it falls at 45¢. In contrast, the operator who fore-

---

[3] G. L. S. Shackle, *Expectation in Economics*. London: Cambridge University Press, 1949, Chs. 1, 2.

sees a very wide range (say $1 to $3) at the time expectations are formed is not so greatly "surprised" if a $2 price is realized. Similar elements of surprise attach to the skewness of expectations. If original expectations include a most "likely price" of $1.50 with no possibilities of anything lower, but include the possibility of higher prices, the surprise upon realization may be low if price is actually above $1.50, and high if price is actually below $1.50. While the degree of surprise (disappointment or elation) over price outcome can serve as an indication of both the degree of *ex ante* uncertainty and *ex post* accuracy with which expectations are held, it is possible for one to attach high confidence to his forward estimates but be greatly surprised by the actual outcome.[4]

It must also be recognized in the case of uncertainty that whether or not the entrepreneur sees the future in terms of an array of possible outcomes with a different likelihood attached to each, these possibilities cannot be treated in the "repeated trial" sense which characterizes risk. Under a "pure risk" situation, 2 dozen eggs may be broken in a single day, but in 365 days there are opportunities for repeating the activity and gaining from outcomes in the opposite direction. This opportunity does not exist for many production and investment decisions, however. An operator may plan to or have funds for purchasing only one farm during his lifetime. If the decision does not result in realizations which square with expectations, the opportunity for repeating the process is not likely to present itself again. The outcome is an "either or" contingency; the outcome is either successful or unsuccessful if it cannot be repeated as the outcome departs from expectations. Since the future cannot be viewed as a "series of repeated trials," intense consideration must be given to the expectations and information upon which major decisions (whether to buy a farm,

---

[4] *Ibid.* Shackle proposes "surprise" as the prime indicator of the level of uncertainty with which expectations are held. While the notion has merit, qualifications must also be made.

See also A. G. Hart, "Anticipations and Business Planning," *Quart. Jour. Econ.*, Vol. LI. He has the following to say about fulfillment of expectations:

"The first thing required for such a study (non-fulfillment of expectations) is a specification of what is meant by fulfillment of anticipations. If we consider two points of time, the original moment of planning (called t_0) and a date slightly later (called t_1), we may describe the fulfillment of anticipations for any enterprise between these dates as follows:

"(a) Events between t_0 and t_1 must have followed the expectation-values of the t_0 anticipations.

"(b) The expectation-values of t_1 estimates for dates later than t_1 must be the same as the expectation values of t_0 estimates for the same dates.

"(c) The dispersion of t_1 estimates for later dates must be less than that of t_0 estimates for like dates, and the shrinkage of dispersion must be in accordance with the anticipations of convergence held at t_0.

"Failure of any of these conditions will be called a surprise; and surprises may be agreeable or disagreeable. If condition (a) does not hold, this constitutes a primary surprise. If condition (b) does not hold, this constitutes a secondary surprise with respect to expectation values, and if condition (c) does not hold we have a secondary surprise with respect to convergence."

whether or not to select farming or another occupation, and so forth) are made. In few cases can a single price distribution be projected with confidence into the future with the expectation that the outcome of a single period or year is but one random value of the probability or frequency distribution which will be repeated in subsequent years.

Alternative systems of expectations (naive procedures). Perhaps the past more than any other thing serves as the root of price and technical or yield expectations in agriculture. Many models for gaining an image of the future have been employed by or proposed for farmers. Some of these are outlined below in brief form. Some are known to be used by farmers; others are explored as "rule of thumb" or "naive" procedures which might be used by farmers and are largely of a mechanical nature. (The models mainly express subjective expectations based on objective data.[5]) While the number of possible methods of prediction is infinite and may range from pure hunches and superstitious fortune-telling to refined scientific prediction, the number of useful and practicable methods available to farm entrepreneurs is relatively small. For most "rule of thumb" or "mechanical" systems, expectations might be considered either as the most probable value of an entire imagined distribution or the one of a set of ordinal comparisons which seems most likely. Uncertainty is still involved, because the possibility of other price outcomes is always present. While a few scattered studies have been made of farmers' expectations, the field is still little explored. A complete inventory of the methods employed in agriculture and non-farm industries is not available.[6] Some farmers simply "borrow" the expectations of their neighbors. In other cases they accept the county extension agent's opinion. Perhaps a few submit to frustration and chart a course into complete darkness (refuse to formulate expecta-

---

[5] See J. Steindl, "On Risk," *Oxford Economic Papers,* No. 5, 1941, pp. 43-53.

[6] *Ibid.,* pp. 44-45. Steindl places expectation models in these broad categories:

"a. *The stationary type.* The value of the variable has been observed during a certain period repeatedly (say each year) and the average of these values is the predicted value for next year and also for further years.... The degree of uncertainty depends largely on fluctuations around the average.

"b. *The continuity type.* The last observed variable is the value predicted for the future.... This method is based on the assumption of continuous development of the variable in question.

"c. *The quasi-scientific type.* The value of the variable is predicted from other variables ... in much the same way as a scientific prediction from correlation."

See also G. Stigler, *Theory of Competitive Price.* New York: Macmillan, 1947. Stigler classes expectations as *extrapolative* (extending trends into the future) and *analytical* (relating contemporary or probable future conditions to prices).

See also A. G. Hart, *op. cit.* He classifies methods of anticipations as based on assumptions that (1) the recent level of the variable will continue, (2) the recent rate of change will continue, and (3) the variable will tend to some "normal" level.

See also L. Hurwicz, "Theory of the Firm and of Investment," *Econometrica,* Vol. 14. He places the systems of predictions under which expectations can be formed as those adapted to (a) least squares regressions and (b) simultaneous equations.

See also G. L. S. Shackle, *op. cit.* He does not concern himself with the basis and source of expectations, except for incidental suggestions.

tions even in simple form). We present a few of the many possible mechanical models to illustrate how their relative errors may differ for different price and yield situations.

1. **Mean yields and prices.** One simple expectation model is given in mean yields or prices. Several alternative models can be based on mean or average outcomes of the past: the mean of price or yield for some long period of the past (for example, the previous 30 years) can be used as the expectation for each year ahead; or, if the operator is just beginning, he might employ a cumulative average wherein the first year serves as the basis for expectations in the second, the average of the first 2 is used for the third, and so forth, until, finally, the mean of the last 25 years is used as the expectation figure for the 26th year. While the previous 5 years can also be used as the expectation model, it is more nearly of the trend nature outlined below.

The farmer is interested in the deviation between the price he predicts and the price actually received in the year ahead (the expectational error or the absolute deviation between expectation and realization). Two types of deviation or error are important: (1) the error in a single year, and (2) the average of errors over time. The beginning operator with limited capital may place first emphasis on a single year's expectations; great error in prediction may bankrupt him, and he can no longer view the future in the manner of a distribution of repeated outcomes. The farmer with ample capital, since he can "stay in the game" in the case of one or a few losses, may be interested in the system which gives the smallest average error over his operating career. Let us first view expectations from the standpoint of the latter farmer. We can make certain theoretical statements about the expected error if he persistently used the mean system. While his interest is in the average deviation between expectations and realizations over time (the expectational error), we may present some of the logic by referring to variance terms.[7] While the expectational error

---

[7] Over a period of years the farmer's expectational error can be computed as

$$\sum_{x=1}^{x=n} \frac{(x_i - x_e)}{n}$$

where the sign of differences is disregarded, x_i is the price or yield realized in each year, x_e is the expectation value, and n is the number of years. The variance of the mean for a price or yield population is computed as

$$\sum_{x=1}^{x=n} \frac{(x_i - \overline{x})^2}{n}$$

where x_1 is again the yield in any 1 year, x is the mean, and n is again the number of years. The variance for an expectational model can be computed as

$$\sum_{x=1}^{x=n} \frac{(x_i - x_e)^2}{n}$$

where all terms are the same except that x_e again refers to the expectation for the single year.

refers to the average amount by which the farmer would be in error (with plus and minus signs disregarded), the expectational variance is a somewhat different measure of "error." It can be computed by subtracting the expected price or yield for each year from the actual price or yield for the particular year; these differences for each year are then squared, summed, and divided by n, the number of years (or by $n - 1$ for a sample). The expectational variance is used below for certain comparisons since it allows a standard of comparison between expectation models. By using this measure of error in expectations, we can make *a priori* or theoretical statements about relative errors if we know certain properties of our data (correlations between prices or yields in the series). While, historically, the measures are valid, certain qualifications can be made for autocorrelations. The "expectational variances" can be compared with the "standard variance" to indicate the relative magnitude of errors under each expectational model. The "standard variance" (that defined in elementary statistics books) is denoted as σ^2 and is computed in the manner outlined above, except that the mean of the series is used as the base. Thus, if one expectational model gives an expectational or expected variance of σ^2, we know that the "error" is less than for one which gives an expected variance of $6 \sigma^2$ or $2 \sigma^2$. The "standard" variance term, σ^2, simply becomes our "standard of measurement." While the expectational error and the expected variance are in different units (or different magnitudes) for each of the various models, the relative magnitudes of the expectational (expected) variances between expectation models will be the same as the relative magnitudes for the expectational errors between the same models.

In terms of expected values for repeated outcomes, the mean expectation model gives an error smaller than for any other naive model when yields or prices of different years are independently and randomly distributed. The "mean system" has an expected variance of σ^2 when the mean of a full period of years is used as the basis of expectations (and if the "population" of outcomes is repeated). If the manager starts with the first year and uses a "cumulative mean system" over a year of (say) 25 years, the expected variance will also approach the value of σ^2 for the full 25 years over which means are accumulated.

For prices the "mean system" does not serve as well as extension of the previous year's price into the following year. (See Tables 4, 5, and 6.) This is true because price swings due to the general business cycle cause the price of one year to correlate more nearly with that of the past year than with the average of the past several years.

The mean system evidently is used widely by farmers for yield expectations; planning is often in terms of the mean outcome over some previous period. The system, when applied to yield alone, serves fairly well for long-term decisions such as the purchase of a farm (particularly where the period of years is great enough and the parameters of the yield distribution can be estimated in the sense of risk). Trends are more important and must be considered where new techniques are being applied. If enough "draws" (for example, if the manager farms enough years) are taken under the mean system, the average yield expectancy over the full period will be the mean (the mathematical expectation) of the population. However, the system serves less effectively as a basis of prediction when only 1 or a few years are concerned. While the expected variance of the population is σ^2, the variance for a sample of a few years can be either smaller or greater; the manager fears "the sample" with the greater variance.

We should emphasize again that many decisions such as whether to farm or whether to buy a farm hardly adapt themselves to any type of expectational model. The decision may be made only once in the operator's lifetime, and if he is in error the opportunity to repeat the decision may never present itself again.

2. **Random outcomes.** The most naive model open to producers is the random method. The yields or prices from each individual year in the relevant period of the past could be put into a hat and drawn at random and the resulting figure would serve as the expectation or likely outcome for the year or period ahead.[8] For prices or yields actually falling within this framework of stochastic or random variables, the system outlined would give as small an error in expectations (as small an average difference between expected and realized price and yields) as some other systems. Some workers suggest that this system would have given, over a period of 30 years, expectations as accurate as the price outlook recommendations available to farmers in the same period; our experience does not support this suggestion. (See Table 6.) The "random system" is one of the least efficient methods of framing price expectations. Individuals who have lived through the last decade are aware that the economic environment determining prices at different points in time is not a reflection of the past and is hardly a random occurrence. In addition, prices from one year to the next are correlated because of the general fluctuations in the price level.

The system is more nearly applicable to yield expectations. In some agricultural areas this system of expectations works relatively well for certain crops if account is taken of technological trends (for example, if trend is removed). Meteorologists have not been able to establish definite weather cycles in parts of the Cornbelt and Southeast, and speculate that each year's weather must be viewed "randomly and independently."

---

[8] This system, as well as others posed, supposes that a set of observations from the past is available to the manager. This condition does not always hold true, as is pointed out later. Also, while the full distribution has been used on later pages for testing certain of the mechanical models, the observations of recent years would not have been available to farmers making estimates in earlier years. We use the system to illustrate the outcome of "one sample" if the operator had this range of data before him and if outcomes over time did not include other values.

Although there is considerable speculation, knowledge that yield sequences come in definite cycles has not been "firmly established" even in parts of the Great Plains. The sample over time is still inadequate to indicate whether a 7-year drought period (such as the late 1930's) occurs once in 40 or once in 200 years. (Greater evidence exists, however, that year-to-year yields are correlated in the sense that high and low yields are bunched together over 2- and 3-year periods.)

Where yield expectations are based on the "random system" (and if yields do represent a random distribution), accuracy in organizing resources would not be as great, as an average over time, as those based on the mean system (although "by chance" the random method might be more accurate in individual years). Theoretically, it can be said that the random model always gives a greater expectational error than the mean system. While the expected variance under the mean system is σ^2, the expected variance under the random system is $2\sigma^2$, or twice as great. The mean system has an advantage over the random system, not only in the sense that its expected variance is only one-half as great, but also in that the negative errors in individual years can be smaller.[9] The farmer short on capital, particularly, may wish to plan in terms of the mean system rather than the random system, since the former, while it results in smaller gains in individual years, also results in smaller losses in the other years. Of course, use of an expectation model does not cause the anticipated yield to be realized in any case. Under the random system outlined below, the farmer would have occasional expectations of the highest yields, and if he planned accordingly, he would apply labor, fertilizer, and other resources along these lines. If the opposite yield level were actually realized, the intensity of resource application would be far too great. It would never be extended to such great levels under the mean method.

3. **Projection of current yields and prices or their opposite.** This system, particularly as it relates to price expectations, evidently is employed by a great number of operators. Many farm families recall the system (and closely related ones) with sorrow. Witness the great losses which were suffered from the depression of the 1930's because managers extrapolated 1929 (or the average or the trend of the few previous years) into 1930. On the other hand, it would have served favorably in the past as compared to most other simple systems (or perhaps better than all practicable or

---

[9] Suppose a very simple distribution in which yields are 0, 50, and 100 bushels. The mean yield is 50. Under the mean system, the expectational error can never be greater (or less) than 50 bushels. Under the random method, however, the error can run as high as 100 bushels (or as low as zero). Under the mean method, plantings would be made every year (since a yield of 50 bushels is always assumed). Under the random method, ground would be left idle when a zero yield was drawn as the basis of the next year's expectation. Although the mean of the expectational error will be the same under the 2 systems, the variance of the mean (of the expectational error) will be smaller for the mean method.

manageable models in the hand of farmers except for agricultural outlook information) for year-to-year prediction of crop or livestock prices. The system obviously leads to expectational errors. However, its greater accuracy (see Table 4) than numerous alternative systems relates to business cycle phenomena and the fact that years of high and low prices are grouped together in the prosperity and depression phases of the cycle. The expectational variance under the "current" model is $2\sigma^2(1 - \varrho_1) +$ b^2 for linear trends. It is twice the "standard" variance, σ^2, under the mean model multiplied by the term $(1 - \varrho_1)$ where ϱ_1 is the correlation coefficient for prices or yields lagged 1 year, plus the square of the trend value (regression) coefficient between price or yield and time). If ϱ_1, the correlation coefficient, is zero, the expectational variance becomes $2\sigma^2(1 - 0) + 0$; the term b^2 will also be zero if ϱ_1 is zero, since no year-to-year trend exists. The expectation error or variance of $2\sigma^2$ is then the same as under the random system. If ϱ_1 is equal to 1.0, the trend term (b) then has a value and the general equation takes on the value of $2\sigma^2 (1 - 1) + b^2$ or $2\sigma^2 (0) + b^2$. Thus the expectational variance or error is only b^2; in absolute amount, extension of this year's price or yield slightly underestimates or overestimates that of the next year by the amount of the trend.

When a large number of farmers employ this model and base plans upon it, their mass action gives rise to commodity cycles for hogs, cattle, potatoes, and other commodities. The cobweb supply response illustrated in Figure 3 is the result of this type of expectation. With price originating at the level OP_3, in the first year (and with the production function and supply curve known with certainty), the expectation of the same price in the second year would lead to an output of OQ_2 and a realized price of OP_1. Projecting of the current year's price into the future by all producers would then result in an output of OQ_1 and a realized price of OP_2.[10] Commodity cycles in agriculture do not follow the regularity expressed

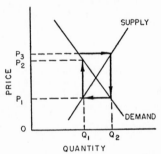

Fig. 3. Cobweb supply response under expectations projecting current prices.

in Figure 3 because production and supply functions also involve variability and uncertainty. However, presence of commodity cycles is proof that the majority of farmers do employ the extension model.

Given the situation where the majority of farmers use the current model

---

[10] The cobweb response shown indicates a "dampening" cycle in the sense that an equilibrium is approached over time. This is the situation because the elasticity of the supply curve is low relative to the elasticity of the demand curve. The response is "explosive" and moves farther and farther from equilibrium when the elasticity of supply is great relative to the elasticity of demand.

and commodity cycles result, individual farmers would do better by supposing that the price in the period ahead will be the opposite or negatively correlated with this period's price; a high price this year would mean a low price the next year (because the majority of producers would assume the opposite) while a low price this year would mean a high price the next year. The farmer expression "when no one else wants hogs, that's when I want 'em, when everyone else gets in, that's when I get out" is a reflection of this type of expectation model.

There is not great evidence that the "opposite" model is most efficient for crop yields even in the Great Plains where it is sometimes supposed that good and poor years come in clusters.[11] While evidence is scanty there seems to be some reason to believe that "below average" hay and pasture years tend to be followed by similar years. One writer has observed that if a year is average or drier, only unusually favorable moisture in the following year will produce "above average" range conditions.[12] When applied to central Cornbelt corn yields, there seems to be little reason why the "extension" method of yield expectations should serve as well as the "mean" system.[13] Yields of apples and certain other fruits do follow a

---

[11] The extent to which yields occur in fairly definite sequences of good and bad years has not yet been determined for even the semi-arid regions of the Great Plains. Yield fluctuations in agricultural areas east of the Missouri River display a more nearly random pattern and normal distribution without definite year-to-year correlations in yields. (The distributions are prevented from being entirely normal because they are bounded by zero at one limit.) Variations also exist in Great Plains Areas as is suggested by the following examples:

Example I (Source: W. L. Cavert, *Long Term Wheat Yields.* N. Dak. Agr. Exp. Sta. Bimonthly Bul. Vol. 11. Period includes 1924-48.)

No. years a "less than average yield" followed by "less than average yield"	8
No. years a "less than average yield" followed by "greater than average yield"	5
No. years a "greater than average yield" followed by "greater than average yield"	5
No. years a "greater than average yield" followed by "less than average yield"	2

Example II (Source: Bureau of Plant Industry, U.S.D.A. Fort Hays, Kans., Exp. Sta. Period includes 1908-50.)

No. years "less than average yield" followed by "less than average yield"	8
No. years "less than average yield" followed by "greater than average yield"	12
No. years "greater than average yield" followed by "greater than average yield"	9
No. years "greater than average yield" followed by "less than average yield"	13

Example III (Source: Bureau Plant Industry, U.S.D.A. Akron, Colo., Exp. Sta. Period includes 1909-51.)

No. years "less than average yield" followed by "less than average yield"	13
No. years "less than average yield" followed by "greater than average yield"	10
No. years "greater than average yield" followed by "greater than average yield"	10
No. years "greater than average yield" followed by "less than average yield"	9

[12] M. Clawson, "Range Forage Conditions in Relation to Annual Precipitation," *Land Econ.,* Vol. 24.

[13] See J. Foote and L. Bean, "Are Yearly Variations in Crop Yields Really Random?" *Agricultural Economics Research,* Vol. 3. They found, after adjusting for trend, that United States corn yields give no evidence of departing significantly from a random series. Defining a phase as the interval between consecutive turning points in

Mean Expectational Errors (Absolute Errors Computed as Simple Mean of Difference Between Actual Price and "Expected Price") for Farm Product Prices Based on Simple Mechanical Models. United States, 1910-50 *

Product	Average expectation error under model							Error as per cent of mean under model							No. years error greater than 70 per cent under model						
	a	b	c	d	e	f	g	a	b	c	d	e	f	g	a	b	c	d	e	f	g
Cotton (¢/lb)	7	4	8	13	6	8	7	39	22	48	75	33	44	39	4	1	11	17	4	8	7
Tobacco (¢/lb)	9	4	13	16	6	12	9	41	16	59	72	27	56	38	7	0	16	18	2	11	8
Peanuts (¢/lb)	2	1	2	3	1	2	2	34	15	40	62	25	32	32	5	1	9	16	10	6	5
Potatoes (¢/bu)	36	32	52	63	34	49	44	36	32	52	65	34	50	44	2	4	15	15	3	14	11
Apples (¢/bu)	44	32	45	81	37	48	47	36	26	37	67	31	39	39	5	1	6	13	4	8	7
Corn (¢/bu)	31	21	46	53	30	31	39	35	24	52	61	35	36	33	4	2	12	15	4	7	5
Oats (¢/bu)	14	11	21	26	13	14	14	31	23	46	57	29	31	31	3	1	10	16	2	5	5
Flax (¢/bu)	82	53	99	149	76	86	80	35	23	43	64	33	37	34	4	3	7	14	4	6	6
Wheat (¢/bu)	41	19	57	74	39	42	39	35	16	48	63	33	36	33	4	0	10	16	3	8	8
Hay ($/ton)	3	2	3	5	3	3	3	23	16	27	42	23	23	23	10	0	3	10	0	1	1
Hogs ($)	4	12	5	7	4	4	4	36	18	53	65	34	39	35	1	0	3	10	0	1	1
Finished cattle ($/cwt)	5	3	6	9	4	1	5	33	17	41	59	28	21	32	4	0	12	14	2	6	6
Feeder cattle ($/cwt)	4	2	5	7	3	1	4	35	14	37	61	27	20	31	3	1	4	8	2	0	3
Finished lambs ($/cwt)	4	2	6	7	3	4	4	31	12	44	58	24	34	32	3	0	3	8	1	0	4
Butterfat (¢/lb)	11	6	18	22	9	14	13	29	13	47	57	24	35	34	2	0	10	11	0	5	5
Eggs (¢/doz)	7	4	9	14	7	8	7	26	15	34	51	25	31	29	1	0	7	10	0	4	4

a. Next year's price is expected to be the average of the period.
b. Next year's price will be the same as this year's price.
c. Expectation drawn randomly from complete distribution.
d. Expectations are based on the "opposite model."
e. The average of the past five years used as the following-year expectation.
f. 1910-14 taken as normal and used as expectation in each year ahead.
g. The modal price is used as the expectation for each year.

* Numerous of the models do not have great practical importance but have been used for illustrative purposes. The writer has data for numerous other systems which are not included for lack of space. These include variations such as starting with the mean of one year, two years, and so forth, as knowledge is accumulated; the use of a "parallel period"; prediction from this year's national income; and others.

definite pattern wherein heavy and light production come in alternate years, but there is no evidence that this is true in cranberry production, even though growers have a general belief that the size of the crop in one year has a definite bearing on the size of the crop in the next year.[14] About one-half the operators interviewed by the writer in 1947 used the "opposite system" for corn yields, and expected a bumper crop in 1948 because of the drought in 1947. Obviously, this system is highly inefficient for prices, because the values in successive years are positively correlated.

4. Modal yields or prices. Under this system the most frequent (probable) outcome of the past would be taken as the expectation for the planning period ahead. This system is identical with the mean method when yields or prices are normally distributed. It gives an expectation pattern for planning which differs from the mean system when the distribution is skewed or J-shaped, as many price and yield series for agriculture are. The average expectational error can be less under certain distribution of the mode system than when the mean system is used. The number of years in which expectations have a zero error always will be greatest under the mode system but the average error over a period of years will often be less under the mean system where distributions are skewed.

The nature of errors in resource use which might grow out of the mean and mode methods can be illustrated in Figures 4, 5, and 6 for yield variations. (The price is held constant or "certain" in order to simplify the presentation.) Here we suppose that the yield distribution for any one level of resource application (such as OX_4 in Figure 5) or the distribution of production functions is skewed in the nature of Figure 4. The production functions are distributed between years as illustrated in Figure 5. (An input-output relation exists for the weather of each particular year.) Of the 3 possible production functions indicated as E, F, and H, the probability attaching to the first is .1 (1 year in 10) while those for the second and third are .6 and .3 respectively. While F is the modal outcome, the mean outcome (which is never realized in a single year) is that suggested by the line M; it is lower than the mode (F), since the probability attached to (the frequency of) H is greater than for E. The marginal cost curves in Figure 6 parallel the production functions of Figure 5. Differences in outcome under the mean and mode methods of expectations can now be illustrated. (We do not bother with the details of discounting at this point.) Under the mean method the manager would always count on a production function such as M (Figure 5), and hence on a marginal cost

yields, they found phases of 1 year to have occurred 35 years, phases of 2 years to have occurred 18 years, and phases of 3 years or more to have occurred only 5 years out of a 58-year period.

For other notes on the nature of yield variations, see L. Bean, *Crop Yields and Weather*. U.S. Dept. Agr. Misc. Publ. 471, Wash., 1942.

[14] See *Weather and Cranberry Production*. Mass. Agr. Exp. Sta. Bul. 433.

Table 5.

Mean Expectational Errors (Absolute Means Computed as for Table 4) for Crop Yields, Based on Five Simple Mechanical Models for the Crops and Locations Specified *

	Average expectational error under model						Error as per cent of mean yield for model						Per cent years error greater than 50 per cent under model					
	a	b	c	d	e	g	a	b	c	d	e	g	a	b	c	d	e	g
Akron, Col., 1908-48																		
Wheat (bu.)	9	10	11	12	8	8	48	61	66	72	51	52	47	55	60	55	52	47
Corn (bu.)	9	13	14	10	8	10	69	103	110	79	60	79	60	72	80	48	48	50
Fort Hays, Kan., 1908-48																		
Wheat (bu.)	12	20	16	13	12	12	51	88	69	57	54	52	51	74	56	50	47	51
Milo (bu.)	15	15	17	22	16	15	97	97	115	146	107	100	85	52	64	75	69	49
Ames, Iowa, 1917-48																		
Corn (bu.)	11	15	17	15	13	11	19	27	30	26	23	19	6	18	18	15	10	6
Oats (bu.)	10	14	12	14	11	9	18	25	20	24	20	17	6	12	9	9	14	3
Hay (ton)	.1	1.1	1.0	1.0	.8	.8	40	67	55	55	44	42	32	55	41	42	31	32
Mobile, Ala.																		
Cotton (lbs.)	187	173	155	130	118	126	37	34	31	26	23	25	10	22	20	0	0	10
Orono, Maine																		
Potatoes (bu.)	49	71	72	63	71	48	14	20	21	18	20	14	0	0	0	0	0	0

* See footnotes to Table 4 for an explanation of the models. The same procedures have been applied to the experimental crop yields indicated.

such as MC_M (Figure 6). Faced only with yield uncertainty and with prices known, he would always count on producing OY_2 (Figure 6) and use OX_2 resources (Figure 5). This procedure would be wrong in every individual year. In 6 years out of 10, OX_3 units of resources should be used and OY_3 units of commodity should be produced for the mode system. For the mode system (marginal cost curve MC_F), "under use" would occur only once in 10 years. Both systems would result in an "over use" of resources in 3 out of 10 years. The reduction in income or loss from over

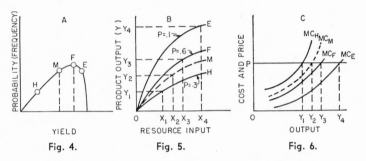

Fig. 4.   Fig. 5.   Fig. 6.

Effect of mode and mean expectation on use of resources.

use of resources in the 3 years of low yields would be less, however, under the mean system than under the mode system. The average income over all years would be greater under the mode system, since it does not restrict resource use so greatly in years when yields are above the minimum. The exact outcome will depend, of course, on the exact nature of the distribution.

The question of whether mean or modal yield data should be provided as expectations applies to the recommendations of technologists. Agronomists, engineers, and animal scientists often compute yield responses over several years (for example, fertilizer experiments) and then publish the average or mean outcome for farmer use. Perhaps even more misleading is the instance in which the trial is run in a single year and then provided to farmers as the mathematical expectation; if the weather is abnormal in the particular year of the trial, the resulting data is highly misleading for years in which weather is average or falls at other extremes. It is little wonder that the farmer often looks upon experimental data as being highly uncertain; in their conventional form, experimental results provide him with little knowledge of the possible range of outcomes. Even the most probable outcome is not indicated for distributions that are skewed. Estimates for the entire set of population parameters (mean, mode, range, variance, and so forth, translated into "farmer language") often would serve better for farmer decisions than a single mean. The beginning farmer with limited capital perhaps should gamble on modal rather than mean experimental results when yield distribution is skewed.

Crop yields in some farming regions are bimodal. In these cases, neither a mode or mean serves efficiently in predicting future outcomes. Use of one of the modal values will result in either very great losses or very great profits in individual years. Use of the mean can result in smaller losses but it will be accurate in fewer years.

5. **Extension of linear trend.** Rather than extend the current price or yield or the mean of several years into the next production period, the producer may project the trend into the future. If prices have been increasing for a few years, then next year's price simply might be taken to exceed this year's price by the same amount (absolute or relative) as the current price exceeds that of the previous year. (The amount by which prices are increased or decreased should depend on the nature of expectation elasticities.) The trend of the past several years also can be used as the basis for expectations over the period ahead; the expectation may be based on a simple unweighted trend line or it may be a weighted trend in the sense that the most recent year is given the greatest weight, while smaller and smaller weights are attached to years more distant in the past; or some rough method of recognizing the trend while discounting it for extreme fluctuations can be used. Formal regression analysis might also be employed by the person who possesses the required knowledge of data and techniques. The general formula for the expectational variance under a simple linear trend is $6\sigma^2 - 2\sigma^2(4\varrho_1 - \varrho_2)$, where ϱ_1 again refers to the correlation coefficient between the price of this year and the price of last year, while ϱ_2 refers to the correlation coefficient between the price of this year and that of 2 years previous. If ϱ_1 and ϱ_2 are both equal to 1.0 (the trend upward or downward is purely linear), the formula takes on the value of $6\sigma^2 - 2\sigma^2(4 - 1)$ or $6\sigma^2 - 2\sigma^2(3)$ or zero and expectations will have no error. If the series of prices or yields are random (ϱ_1 and ϱ_2 are zero), the formula takes on the value of $6\sigma^2 - 2\sigma^2(0)$ or $6\sigma^2$. While the linear trend model gives a minimum error as compared to other naive models when a linear trend exists, it gives a larger error than the mean, random, or current models when the series is random.

If the manager uses a moving average as a trend model (uses the last five years as a basis to establish and predict the trend), the expectational variance is

$$[\sigma^2 \{(N^2 + N) - 2(\varrho_1 + 2\varrho_2 \ldots + N\varrho_n)\} +$$

$$\{N + (N - 1) \ldots + (N - N + 1)\} \, {}^2b^2]/N^2,$$

where the terms have the same meaning as indicated previously, except that N refers to the number of years included in the moving average. For a random series of data, the equation takes on the value $\sigma^2(N^2 + N)/N^2$; if N is sufficiently large, the term approaches the limit σ^2. (It is $2\sigma^2$ when $N = 1$, $1.25\sigma^2$ when $N = 2$, and $1.04\sigma^2$ when $N = 5$.) If there is a linear trend and all of the ϱ values are 1.0, the value of the expectational variance becomes

$$[\{N + (N - 1) \ldots (N - N + 1)\} /N]b,$$

an amount which will again vary with N.[15]

The trend system has been employed both to the joy and regret of farm operators. It was evidently the system employed by a large number of farmers in the 2 decades 1910-30. Until the end of World War I, farmers had experienced a secular increase in land values from the time new farming areas were settled. These increases in land prices resulted as agricultural regions were developed, as the population of the nation grew, and as the foreign demand for United States farm products increased. With the trend of the previous half century in mind, many farmers made investments in real estate with the expectation that values could only climb upward. The trend method is most efficient for short-run price expectations and decisions. Because of wide swings in national prosperity and the clustering of high and low price years, prices of the year ahead often are an extension of those in the past few years. A price expectation model of this nature would have proven quite efficient through the period 1934-52 both for short-run and long-run investment decisions.

Undoubtedly, the trend system of expectation has been a partial explanation of the momentum of the business cycle in capitalistic economies. While the force which sets the economic mechanism on the way to inflation or deflation cannot be isolated, the expectations of entrepreneurs in all industries (that the price trends of the recent past will continue into the future) are extremely important in causing these trends to be realized in fact and even accentuated over short periods (until forces which cause expectations to twist in the opposite direction become operative). The extent to which entrepreneurs lay in stocks, make investments, and hire additional labor or capital in anticipation of rising prices (or the opposite during periods when mass expectations are in the direction of falling prices) depends on the elasticity of their expectations. The elasticity of expectation relates the expected change in future prices to the actual change in current prices.[16] If prices are rising and the elasticity of expec-

---

[15] The quantities shown in Tables 4, 5, 6, and 7 are derived under the supposition that the farmer follows the same model over the entire period. More likely he may employ several models over a long period. However, our estimates are provided only to show the outcome under particular models and specified conditions (random series or a linear trend series). While many other models and conditions could be outlined, we do not have space for their presentation.

[16] The elasticity of expectations (E_e) defines the percentage change in expected prices as compared to the percentage change in current prices with P_o indicating the current price, ΔP_o indicating the change in current prices, P_t indicating the previously expected price, and ΔP_t indicating the change in expected price the elasticity equation, can be expressed as follows:

$$E_e = \frac{\Delta P_t}{P_t} / \frac{\Delta P_o}{P_o} = \Delta P_t / \Delta P_o \cdot P_o / P_t$$

Table 6.

Summary of Expectational Variance for Selected Models

Expectational model	General formula for expected variance	Value of expectational variance when series is random	Expected variance when correlation coefficient between year-to-year values is 1.0 and trend is linear
Mean	σ^2	σ^2	σ^2
Random	$2\sigma^2$	$2\sigma^2$	$2\sigma^2$
Normal	$\sigma^2 + C^2$	$\sigma^2 + C^2$	$\sigma^2 + C^2$
Project current value	$2\sigma^2(1-\rho_1) + b^2$	$2\sigma^2$	b^2
Linear trend	$6\sigma^2 - 2\sigma^2(4\rho_1 - \rho_2)$	$6\sigma^2$	0
Reverse linear trend	$2\sigma^2(1-\rho_2) + 4b^2$	$2\sigma^2$	$4b^2$
Moving average	$[\sigma^2 \{(N^2 + N) - 2(\rho_1 + \rho_2 + \ldots N\rho_n)\} + \{N + (N-1) + \ldots (N-N+1)\}^2 b^2]/N^2$	$\sigma^2(N^2 + N)/N^2$	$[\{N + (N-1) + \ldots (N-N+1)\}/N]b$

tation is greater than 1.0 (suggesting anticipations of greater changes in the future than at the present), the trend system of expectations may cause entrepreneurs to rush their acquisition of resources with the aggregate effect that expectations are realized. Under falling prices, an elasticity of expectations less than 1.0 (suggesting anticipations of greater change in the future than in actual change at the present) can cause the mass liquidation of inventories and bring about rapid downward adjustment in prices. The trend system is not well adapted to yield expectations when weather fluctuations are random. It can be used with some degree of success where weather is found to turn in cycles.

6. **Use of a normal or parallel period.** Yield or price expectations may be based on a previous year or period which is looked upon as normal. The period 1910-14 was taken as a normal price base by individual farmers and by farm organizations over a long span of time. Some individual farms perhaps planned in this vein and farm organizations tried to get the government to guarantee prices at these levels in order that they might plan in terms of 1910-14 prices (as well as receive prices higher than those prevailing in the market during the 1930's). Agricultural economists even extended this system of "normal period" expectations to farmers. Experts in farm appraisal long used 1910-14 as a price base for figuring land values. The weakness of basing expectations for long-run decisions (such as investment in farm real estate) on a normal price which extends far back into history have been evident over the last decade. Individual farmers undoubtedly think back to earlier periods as normal during major fluctuations in yields and prices (as occur in drought and wars). Farmers who expected prices to drop back to a normal level of 1935-39 after World War II sacrificed great profits if their planning was geared accordingly. The expectational error for the normal model is $\sigma^2 + C^2$, regardless of whether the series of prices or yields is random or correlated. The term C^2 is the square of the difference between the mean yield of the price or yield of the period and the value taken as normal. "Normal periods" have been used as attempted bases for "parity pricing."

Rather than a normal period, the manager also may take some period or point in time as the basis of expectations which *parallel* those for a future period. In 1941, a farmer might have supposed that prices during the next 6 years would parallel those of the period 1914-20. Had he acted accordingly (and many did) in making investments and extending production, the expectation model would have served efficiently in terms of the profits forthcoming. However, this parallel system was inefficient in the period following World War II. The obvious expectation of many farmers and economists was that this period would parallel the period from 1920 to 1923. Many operators refrained from feeding cattle or buying farms because they employed this expectation model.

In examining historic crop yield data, Bean has suggested that yields for some crops do go through definite cycles of an extended duration.[17] To the extent that this observation might be proven over time, the farm manager could use the parallel system of expectations. Year-to-year changes in the direction of cotton yields in the 10-year period starting in 1880 directly paralleled those of the 10-year period starting in 1870. However, after examining a second set of years (1916-37) Bean concluded that the years 1926-37 repeated those of 1916-27 but in an inverse or opposite fashion. (The years in the period 1916-27 with positive changes tended to parallel those with negative changes in the period 1926-37). If the expectation of parallel changes had been employed in 1926-27 important planning inefficiencies would have arisen. The accuracy of expectations under this yield situation depends on the ability of the farmer to predict correctly whether to use the opposite or parallel method.

7. Use of futures prices. Another mechanical device which the farmer might borrow from experts in price expectation is the futures prices published for grains, butter, and other farm commodities.[18] Futures provide the basis for short-run production decisions only. They are not available for prices extending over a period of several years. To the extent that the market in futures is effective in accurately anticipating supply and demand conditions, the price quotations should serve as a guide to farmers in forming expectations. However, trading in futures transactions does not exist for a large number of farm commodities. Where futures quotations are available they are closely tied to spot (current) prices. Futures prices tend to equal present prices plus allowances for services of holding. (The margin is not constant because the individuals in the 2 markets do not have the same anticipations and the costs of holding vary.) Accordingly, spot prices become nearly as efficient as the futures prices in forming expectations for production in the year ahead. In many futures markets, a futures quotation is not available from planting to harvesting time. The December corn futures is usually inactive until June and the July wheat futures is usually not active until late October. Futures perhaps serve best for those very short-run or spot decisions relating to storing of crops until later months or selling immediately.

8. Outlook and formal methods of prediction. While the entrepreneur may employ any one of the mechanical models outlined above in a simple or "rule of thumb" manner, he can also employ more sophisticated or complete models (which also include certain of the general methods outlined above). He can attempt to measure the variables which affect price or yield and predict the future through simple (least squares) or complicated (simultaneous equations) regression systems. This statement supposes that the variables used to predict price and yield or production coefficients are

---

[17] U.S.D.A. Misc. Publ. 471.

[18] For a study dealing with expectations and cotton futures, see J. C. R. Dow, "The Inaccuracy of Expectations," *Economica,* Vol. 8.

observable in samples of sufficient size from some past period. If the parameters of price and yield distribution could be isolated or predicted in a statistical sense, the problem would be reduced to one of risk. Corporations have sufficient resources for investing in predictions and estimates of this nature. Very few farmers have either the technical knowledge or the funds for deriving these more detailed expectations. At best they can turn to the land grant colleges and other organizations (including commercial farm management companies or other firms which furnish expectations for a fee) which either employ formal methods in their own predictions or interpret information obtained from other individuals who concentrate on estimating demand and supply functions. Most farmers recognize economic phenomena as being so complex that the outlook predictions obtained from extension workers or commercial agencies is subject to error and therefore must be viewed as subjective estimates for planning purposes. With funds too short for establishing research departments of their own, farmers must continue to draw on public and private outlook services in forming expectations. At the minimum, services of this nature do provide information which farmers can incorporate with other estimates in gaining an "image of the future" such that subjective uncertainty is reduced to a point calling for production plans and action. The writer found that if the directions suggested in outlook over the period 1922-50 had been used as a basis for expectations, this system would have been more efficient for

Table 7.

Mean Expectational Errors (Absolute Mean Errors as in Tables 4 and 5) for Prices of Steers, Hogs, Lamb, Eggs, and Butterfat. Iowa, Specified Expectational Models

Price	Model A	Model B	Model C	Model D	Model E	Model F	Model G	Model H
Steers ($)	6.80	3.10	4.27	3.41	4.62	4.05	2.96	3.40
Hogs ($)	5.00	2.19	3.61	2.81	3.16	3.63	2.24	2.36
Sheep ($)	3.76	1.64	2.77	2.20	2.23	2.60	1.51	2.30
Eggs (¢)	9.1	4.0	6.0	4.6	5.6	6.0	3.1	4.3
Butterfat (¢)	11.3	6.5	9.6	7.7	11.6	11.1	5.3	6.8

A: Random. B: Current year extended into next year. C: Five-year moving average. D: Weighted five-year moving average. E: Linear trend. F: Reverse of linear trend. G: Use of outlook where outlook statements interpreted to mean no change or changes of 5, 10, or 20 per cent in price. H: Parallel model starting supposing that each period in time will have price changes similar to a previous period in time (for example, that 1940-45 will be similar to 1914-19, and 1946-50 similar to 1920-24).

selected Iowa livestock prices than any of the models mentioned here. As Table 7 shows, the use of a particular outlook interpretation over the period 1922-50 would have been more accurate than any other simple model over a somewhat similar period except in the case of hogs. Extension of the current year's price would have served most accurately for hogs and second-best for other products. The parallel model would have been third-best for all types of livestock, while the random system would have had the greatest absolute errors.

The structure of the economy remains unchanged for only very short periods if at all, and therefore price predictions, based on measurable observations, are always subject to wide error. Where structural changes are known or expected, more complex estimation procedures are required. Only the more advance mathematical economists are versed in advanced techniques for predicting economic quantities and few results have been forthcoming thus far. Some of the major variables such as moisture can be used as aids in predicting physical yields in areas such as the Great Plains. The farmer can measure the amount of soil moisture at planting time and predict, with some degree of accuracy, whether wheat should be planted on stubble ground or whether the land should be fallowed in the year ahead. In most sections of the Cornbelt, the New England States, and the major cotton areas, the amount and distribution of moisture after planting is more important for yields than that previous to planting. Since the relevant quantity of moisture cannot be observed at the time of planting, prediction of yield outcome at planting time is open to greater error in some Cornbelt regions than in certain wheat areas.[19] In cranberry production, the moisture and sunshine in the summer previous to the crop and the extent of winter killing and spring frosts appear to be important in predicting the yield in any single year.[20]

Naive and econometric models. Expectation models of the type outlined above have been given the term *naive*.[21] Naive models such as those which the small-business entrepreneur might use have been compared with more sophisticated econometric models for non-farm expectations. Econometric models are those that might be used by the business firm or the Land Grant College which has funds enough to invest in complex research and predicting activities. The econometric models concerned (called thus because of the combination of economic logic and mathematical and statistical techniques) involve simultaneous equations to estimate the structural relationships between many variables and hence to predict disposable national income from 15 endogenous variables (jointly dependent variables for the period of estimation and determined by the economic process to

---

[19] See C. Cole and R. Mathews, *Relation of Depth to Which Soil is Wet to the Yield of Spring Wheat on the Great Plains.* U.S.D.A. Circ. 563, Wash., May, 1940. They have the following to say: "Under the limited precipitation of the Great Plains, the initial water content of the soil, which can be approximated by the depth to which the soil is wet, a strong determinant of the yield that will be produced. Seeding on soils wet only 1 ft. deep is not warranted, on soils 2 ft. deep results are more favorable, and good yields are assured on soils 3 ft. deep or more."

[20] H. Franklin and R. Stevens, *Weather and Water Factors in Cranberry Production.* Mass. Agr. Exp. Sta. Bul. 433, Amherst, 1946.

[21] For an account of these models as compared to econometric models, see Carl Christ, "A Test of an Econometric Model for the United States, 1921–47," in *Conferences on Business Cycles.* New York: National Bureau of Economic Research, 1951. See also discussions by Milton Friedman, L. R. Klein, G. H. Moore, and Jan Tinbergen in the same volume.

be described) and 14 exogenous variables (predetermined variables or those determined in a previous time period or outside the process to be described). Fifteen equations were involved in the estimational procedure. This estimational process was compared with 2 naive models, naive model I saying that next year's value of any variable will equal this year plus a random normal disturbance, and naive model II saying that next year's value will equal this year's value plus the change from last year plus a random normal disturbance. For certain conditions the more complex device failed, for the single year 1948, to be a better predicting system than the less costly naive models.

Farm estimates of price and yield might also be made by these extreme predicting methods. No comparisons have been made of their relative inefficiencies. Land Grant Colleges do need, however, to invest resources in testing these procedures and to determine how improved price expectations can be furnished to farmers. Any improvement in predictions over those of naive models must add to the welfare of farm people and society generally. The naive models provide a benchmark or null hypothesis against which more sophisticated techniques can be compared and their use by farmers will continue to be important until the tools of prediction have been improved by research workers.

Decision-Making and Efficiency

Society has a stake in the expectation-forming and decision-making ability of farm families. Farm families make decisions as (a) consumers, (b) entrepreneurs, (c) suppliers of factors of production and finally, and (d) voters in government decision-making. Society has a stake in decision-making in all of these areas and education should be so oriented. Consumer welfare can be maximized only as consumers do, in fact, make correct decisions. Social and political stability themselves depend on the decisions and actions taken by people through voting or other mechanisms. On the side of production, decision-making is inefficient if it causes factors to be employed in a manner which results in less than a maximum product (as measured in value or other preference indicator by consumers) from a given resource outlay. Production economists have long addressed themselves to efficient farm management. Concepts of inefficient management imply at least 1 of 3 things: (1) that within a given environment, people who are now making decisions could learn to make them better; (2) that, if the environment of the people making the decisions were changed (for example, through reduction in uncertainty or investment in the individual's decision-making ability), better decisions could be made; and (3) that people other than those now making decisions could make them better.

Role of research and extension in better decision-making. The services provided by the experiment stations and extension departments of the Land

Grant Colleges can be looked upon as one basis for improving farmer expectations and decision-making. On the one hand, technological research and education provide the basis for yield expectations under different forms (and organizations) of resources. These data are ordinarily provided in the form of single valued expectations; the mean yield over a period of time alone is relayed to farmers without indication of the experimental error which relates to them. (The information relates to a single year or represents averages for a number of years with no indication of the range, variance mode, and sequence of outcomes.) Similarly, farm management surveys which analyze the profitability of various farm and resource organizations in a past year or period are designed to provide income expectations which extend into the future. They assume, of course, that the future will prove to be a duplicate of the past, and thus they serve ineffectively when great variability in price or yield is experienced. They give little attention to the varying degrees of uncertainty which face farmers with different amounts of capital or with different capital equities. The greatest concentration of resources designed to provide farmers with the basis for expectations *per se* is to be found in economic outlook services provided in the various states. The outlook specialist is first charged with forming his own subjective anticipation of the future. He accomplishes this through the predicting tools which are at his command and with the information which he can obtain from the Bureau of Agricultural Economics. His second charge is that of relaying these formal expectations to farmers in a manner useful for production decisions. The expectations extended by college outlook personnel are mainly suggestive of the direction of price trends. They seldom indicate the most probable or most price or the range of outcomes to be expected. Evidently only a minority of farmers base their future anticipations on outlook information (or only a minority have access to or can translate the information into useful expectations). Were it true that farmers in the aggregate heed outlook suggestions and plan accordingly, the very opposite of the price expectations posed in outlook suggestions would come to exist. Perhaps the number of farmers using outlook information will grow to a point in the future where this macro consideration will become extremely important to college farm management specialists.

Improving the decision-making environment. A chief function of market prices is that of guiding resources into lines of production which conform to the choices of consumers. The great variability of farm commodity prices and the lack of any simple and effective system which farmers can use in forming price expectations causes market prices to serve inefficiently in this respect. The expectations formulated by farmers are subject to such great errors that production is guided into the wrong alternatives and resources are organized inefficiently as precaution to uncertainty. (See Chapter 17.) The ability of farmers to formulate accurate price expectations and to plan accordingly must await reduction in general market instability. Several alternatives are available at the national policy level. One is to reduce major economic fluctuations through fiscal policy and related national programs. Another is use of forward prices to serve as guides in future production.[22] Forward pricing systems must in turn be integrated with storage policies which remove year-to-year fluctuations in yields and production. The extent to which resource efficiency can be increased through forward pricing schemes depends on the ability of national planners to formulate more efficient price expectations than individual farmers. Unless this step can be accomplished, several million farmers, as resource administrators, can plan as effectively on the basis of their own expectations as on the basis of those furnished in the form of forward prices by national planners. These points are discussed further in the following chapter.

Changing the area of decision-making. Many precedents exist in the United States wherein decision-making has been transferred from the individual to society or a community of individuals. On the side of consumption, bans on narcotics and similar legislation have placed limits on the decisions which the individual may make. These limitations evidently have social sanction even though they run counter to liberal economic tradition. Decision-making limitations have also been imposed in the entrepreneurial area. Anti-trust legislation and the Pure Food and Drug Act limit firms in their action to pursue monopolistic price and production policies or create demand through false advertising. These limitations on decision-making apply to areas where the impact of the individual's action, particularly, is in conflict with the value system of society. Freedom in the form of entrepreneurial action, as long as it does not result in monopoly gains or conflict openly and directly with the interests of others, evidently ranks high in the value system of the American Society. Since this is true, improvement in decision-making must come mainly through increasing the decision-making ability of individuals and in improving the environment for decision-making.

Both the entrepreneur concerned and the whole of society must bear the penalties of inefficient decision-making at the individual firm level. The penalties which impinge upon other members of society are less evident here than in entrepreneurial activity directed at false advertising and similar activities. But again the American concept of justice is one of allowing the market mechanism to eliminate the inefficient manager. He is allowed to exercise decision-making activity until his income has been driven to a level which no longer merits further managerial effort. This is in contrast to British wartime and postwar agricultural policy; the inefficient manager was given the opportunity there to draw upon the decision-

---

[22] See D. G. Johnson, *Forward Prices for Agriculture.* Chicago: University of Chicago Press, 1947.

making ability of others and to improve the efficiency with which his resources were used. In case he failed, decision-making powers were withdrawn from him and vested in the local agricultural committee or other individuals. Vesting of the management function in public administrators cannot eliminate all inefficiency growing out of instability and imperfect knowledge of the future. As long as wars, major changes in technology, or consumer tastes and other unpredictable fluctuations in supply and demand forces occur, public managers also are subject to error in their anticipations and plans. Even the Russian state planners for agriculture can attest to this fact.

Selected References

Ball, Gordon, "A Study of Farm Expectations. Master's thesis, Iowa State College, Ames, 1950.

Brownlee, O. H., and Garner, W., "Farmers Price Anticipations and Planning," *Jour. Farm Econ.*, Vol. 31.

Coase, W., and Fowler, G., "The Analysis of Producers' Expectations," *Economica*, Vol. 2, pp. 280-292.

———, "The Pig Cycle in Great Britain," *Economica* (n.s.), Vol. 4, pp. 55-82.

Hart, A. G., "Anticipations, Uncertainty and Business Planning," *Jour. of Business*. Chicago: University of Chicago Press, 1940, Vol. 11, Chs. 1, 4, 5.

Hicks, J. R., *Value and Capital*. Oxford: Clarendon Press, 1939, pp. 205-206 and Ch. 16.

Johnson, D. G., *Forward Prices for Agriculture*. Chicago: University of Chicago Press, 1949, Chs. 6, 12.

Kaldor, N., "The Equilibrium of the Firm," *Econ. Jour.*, Vol. 44, pp. 60-67.

Lange, O., *Price Flexibility and Unemployment*. Bloomington: Principia Press, 1944, Ch. 5.

Schultz, T. W., and Brownlee, O. H., "Two Trials to Determine Expectation Models in Agriculture," *Quar. Jour. Econ.*, Vol. 56, pp. 487-496.

———, "Theory and Measurement of Expectations," *Amer. Econ. Rev.*, Vol. 39, pp. 135-150.

Shackle, G. L. S., *Expectations in Economics*. Cambridge: Cambridge University Press, 1949.

Stigler, G., *Theory of Price*. New York: Macmillan, 1947, pp. 166-171.

Tinbergen, J., "Notions of Horizon and Expectancy in Economics," *Econometrica*, Vol. 1, pp. 247-264.

Tintner, G., "A Contribution to the Non-Static Theory of Production," in *Studies in Mathematical Economics and Econometrica*. Chicago: University of Chicago Press, 1942, pp. 106-107.

Williams, D. B., "Price Expectations and Reactions to Uncertainty by Illinois Farmers," *Jour. Farm Econ.*, Vol. 33, pp. 20-40.

Working, H., "Investigation of Economic Expectations," *Amer. Econ. Rev.*, Vol. 39, pp. 151-170.

17

Adjustment of Production and Resource Use to Uncertainty

O NCE management has completed the first (formulation of expectations) of its several functions, it is ready to plan a course of action or pattern of production which is consistent with its expectations. Of course, plans are not in order until the entrepreneur has obtained sufficient information and reduced subjective uncertainty to a point where he is ready to act and accept the consequences. When the future appears certain enough for action, the plan of production will in fact still depend on the amount of doubt or uncertainty which attaches to anticipations of future prices and yields. Few people are willing to act early and in a rash manner when they are highly uncertain; plans tend to be cautious and conservative. If the producer has complete confidence in his predictions (for example, a subjective probability of 1.0 or a single hypothesis which "he believes") he may, of course, adopt a rigid plan and bet a large stake on the eventual outcome. If he is uncertain about outcomes, he may select a moderate course of action which guarantees against bankruptcy if his expectations prove incorrect.

The course of action which is or should be followed by the entrepreneur is conditioned not only by the nature of his expectations but also by the surrounding entrepreneurial framework. Two managers with identical expectations and viewing the future with similar degrees of uncertainty may rationally follow different courses of action because the framework in which decisions are made differs. The farmer with small capital may justifiably use his resources differently than the operator owning many assets. The pure manager who does not accept the full consequences of outcome may select a different course of action than the owner-manager. Traditional principles of profit maximization (for example, the "perfect knowledge" or "static" type of returns maximization) used as a tool in early chapters and which serve as the basis for many analyses in agricultural economics) are subject to attack from several directions when these several elements are taken into consideration. Given an uncertainty setting, the optimum plan for any individual depends on his psychological makeup, his capital position, and the ends to be maximized.

The Ends of Production

Before it is possible to discuss the production and resource use strategy which may appear as an *ex ante* optimum to the entrepreneur, it is necessary to explore the psychology of the entrepreneur and the ends of the firm.

While the conditions of efficiency outlined in earlier chapters (equation of price ratios, transformation ratios, and substitution ratios) can never be attained in an environment of uncertain prices and production coefficients except by pure chance, these maximizing conditions are, however, the ones which the majority of firms would like to attain; ultimate excellence in prediction and management would be denoted by realizations which just exactly equate marginal costs and marginal revenue or price ratios and substitution ratios discounted only for time. Except for persons with high risk preferences, most managers would like to predict the future in a manner which "squares" with historic attainment. Still, in an environment of uncertainty, the direct ends of production planning may not be that of immediate profit maximization.

The individual. Some people have a high risk-preference and will react in one way to an uncertain situation. Persons characterized by risk-aversion may react in an entirely different manner.[1] These differences are reflected in the willingness of some people to feed cattle while their neighbors go into a "more certain" enterprise such as dairying. Differences between Cornbelt farmers in their willingness to accept uncertainty has been suggested in 2 studies. Farmers were asked to indicate whether they would select a sure return to an alternative involving a 50-50 chance of realizing a larger or a smaller income. In a Southern Iowa study by the writer and others, only 10 of 107 farmers indicated that they would choose the alternative of (a) flipping a coin with a chance of getting either $1,950 or $2,050 for a load of cattle to the alternative of (b) taking the $2,000 value

---

[1] Better terms might be uncertainty-preference and uncertainty-aversion. However, to maintain the tradition of economic terminology, we retain the terms risk-preference and risk-aversion. The terms refer to different degrees of the same thing. By risk-preference we refer to the person who enjoys or attaches utility to courses of action which involve chance or uncertainty; by risk-aversion we refer to the person who prefers security and safety in his actions. The 2 terms can be considered to refer to the slope of the individuals' indifference curve wherein uncertainty competes with income or other goods. The marginal rate of substitution of money (or other goods) for uncertainty is high for the individual denoted by the term risk-aversion. Risk-preference denotes a high rate of substitution of uncertainty for other possible alternatives.

of the cattle.[2] An Illinois study indicated that only 38 out of 161 farmers expressed choice of a plan with a 50-50 chance for a return of $2,500 or $7,500 as compared to a certain return of $5,000 from another farm plan. These figures have not been related to the capital position of farmers and involve the limitations outlined elsewhere.[3] However, they do suggest differences in farmers' risk-preferences and that farmers with different makeups in respect to the enjoyment or disenjoyment of undertaking "risk" in business adventure may adjust differently to uncertainty situations. Studies of planning by businessmen indicate that uncertainty plays a major role in decision-making.[4] In summary, it can be said that the majority of businessmen abhor large amounts of uncertainty and therefore try to avoid decisions for which they cannot foresee the consequences. Perhaps adjustments of this type give rise to behavior patterns which appear to be habitual. Rules of thumb may be employed which do not require the processes of obtaining and weighing information, choosing and deciding. These procedures may be employed where the entrepreneur believes past experience, which has been successful, provides the best basis for action: doing the thing which was done well before may appear to be the safest way to proceed and to involve the least risk.

Capital stake. The amount of capital and the income (the "stake" which may be lost in case the outcome is unfavorable) involved are also important in determining a person's selection of chance outcomes over more certain returns. The farm operator may be willing to take a chance on planting a few acres to a new crop where he would be entirely unwilling to devote the entire farm to the innovation; he may be willing to feed a few cattle in order to enjoy the venture of guessing the market or to run a chance of making a big return from a small investment but he may select a more stable enterprise such as dairying as the core of his investment and income source.

Figure 1 suggests hypotheses of the manner in which people with differ-

---

[2] For details of this study, see E. R. Swanson, "Agricultural Resource Productivity and Attitudes Toward the Use of Credit in Southern Iowa." Ph.D. Thesis, Iowa State College, Ames, Dec., 1950. Studies of this nature may be biased in the sense that (a) farmers looking upon outright gambling (as compared to "betting on farm outcomes") as "morally undesirable" would refuse to flip a coin or (b) react differently when presented with a hypothetical situation than with one where they actually bear the economic consequences. It is doubtful that the first bias entered into the answers, since the question was phrased in a manner to eliminate any stigma. The second bias, to the extent it is present, probably causes the study to underestimate the conservativeness of farmers.

[3] The questions asked in the Illinois study (D. B. Williams, "Price Expectations of Illinois Farmers," *Jour. Farm Econ.*, Feb., 1951) was worded as follows: "If you were given the choice of 2 plans for your farm as a whole, would you prefer to be sure of one with $5,000 or would you try an alternative plan which might return either $7,500 or $2,500?"

[4] Some of these studies have been summarized in L. Katona, *Psychological Analysis of Business Behavior*. New York: McGraw-Hill, 1951.

ent quantities of capital (or even the same person for different quantities of capital) might react to a given setting of uncertainty and chance.[5] It again illustrates indifference curves in the manner of Chapter 14 and relates the utility of expected money income and the utility of uncertainty bearing. The person with a very small amount of capital (curve C) may be, within a limited range, willing to take a long chance (particularly if he has income from a salary and his entrepreneurial activities are a sideline). The absolute loss may be small if his income and capital are already near the zero level; his gain may be great if the long chance comes through. Similarly, the person with a large amount of capital and a high income (curve A) may be willing to substitute chance and uncertainty for likely money income possibilities throughout

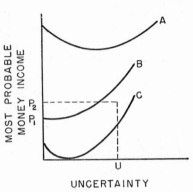

Fig. I. Relationship of capital and willingness to invest in chance incomes.

a greater range. Business ventures which include chances of large gains may provide satisfaction and utility even if they result in small losses and money returns of less-than-maximum. The fun or thrill of attempting to outguess the market may outweigh the income from and security of investment in sure things, such as government bonds or real estate mortgages. Persons in an intermediate capital position and of a particular age and psychological and family makeup, as denoted by curve B, may be unwilling to take any chances if their total capital is involved, particularly if their living depends entirely on the outcome. Perhaps few if any persons in agriculture require prospectively certain incomes. All farmers undertake uncertain ventures. The variability and uncertainty of agricultural production and income does not provide an environment favorable to the person characterized by great risk aversion. This person invests his capital in government bonds and works as a postal clerk.

---

[5] Any number of indifference curves are possible, depending on the individual and his capital. Perhaps the indifference curve never slopes downward for most people with small incomes, the point illustrated here. Obviously, each of a family of indifference curves will differ in slope even for the same individual depending on his capital position, whether the odds involve a large chance of losing a small amount and a small chance of losing a very large amount, and so forth. As in the earlier chapter, it should be emphasized that the indifference curves presented represent individual ones from families for different preference functions (for example, different preference functions or utility surfaces for different people or for the same person with the different amounts of capital). The preference function ordinarily will change with the amount of capital. Curve C supposes a person with a very low income ("starvation level") who has everything to gain and nothing to lose, since his assets and income are nearly zero.

Survival and ends of the firm. Uncertainty itself gives rise to intermediate ends which are cast in a short-run planning perspective. One of the basic motivational forces in human behavior and economic activity is relief of anxiety, which, in the case of business activity, leads to the striving for security. In an enterprise economy, one possible way of achieving security is through profits or income. Entrepreneurs engage in production to make money which they desire, need, and plan to use for the sake of other more ultimate ends (for example, in providing family utility and satisfactions). Because of uncertainty and insecurity, these means become ends, and farmers may strive for profits for the sake of profits. More generally, however, the desire for security gives rise to an attempt for continuous or regular income rather than the possibilities of short-run, maximum profits. Avoidance of losses and bankruptcy may provide a strong basis for attempting to avoid declines in profits rather than an attempt to increase profits.

When, for the beginning operator with little capital, short-term survival has precedence in business planning, management has little interest in long-range investments which will pay out only over an extended period. The means to the end of survival may rest in quick profits, even though these are lower than possible profits extending further into the future. The beginning farmer, the retired operator, or the middle-aged owner with a low equity may rationally select a farm plan with a prospective return of $2,000 which may vary only between $1,200 and $2,800 to one such as cattle-feeding for which modal income anticipations are $4,000 with possible outcomes ranging from a loss of $9,000 to a profit of $14,000. Even after sacrificing large returns from cattle feeding in one year, the same operator may still choose dairying, even though the expectations and uncertainty in the period ahead exactly parallel those of the previous year. Production may also be directed towards an income stream which does not allow profits to fall below some minimum level. (More exactly the problem is one of minimizing the probability that income does not fall below some critical level.) Zero profits or losses become a barometer of danger to many firms. Some farm families are concerned that income should not fall below a level necessary to allow acceptable living standards. Heavily encumbered farms emphasize use of resources to hold income above living expenses and allow for principal and interest payments.

Survival as a means. Survival is only an intermediate end of the agricultural firm: it is not an ultimate end. The immediate objective in planning is one of "staying in the game" in order that profits can be realized over an extended period.[6] The entrepreneur may be influenced not only by the

---

[6] The reader interested in the economics of agricultural production should certainly become acquainted with such works as J. Von Neuman and O. Morgenstern, *Theory of Games and Economic Behavior.* Princeton: Princeton University Press, 1947.

mean or most probable value of future outcome but also by the time distribution of income.[7] A high expected value of future income over thirty years is not the only consideration relating to selection of investment; large losses in early years can bring the opportunity to make decisions to a halt by causing liquidation of the firm. If early losses make continuation of the firm impossible, the value of the future income stream, even if it is expected to be extremely high in later years, then falls to zero. Survival of the firm in the short-run is a means to maximization of returns over a period covering a greater number of years. Entrepreneurial behavior which seemingly contradicts profit or utility maximization postulates should cause the production economist to examine the decision-making framework with greater precision. The manager's "apparent irrationality" (his failure to adopt the specialist's recommendations) may actually be a manifestation of his highly rational concern for the long-run standing of his firm.

Precautions for Uncertainty

While survival as an end may be competitive with maximum profits as an end in the short-run, short-run survival is complementary with profit and utility maximization in the long-run. The precautionary measures which the entrepreneur can employ in attempting to guarantee survival of the agricultural firm are outlined in subsequent sections of this chapter. These precautionary measures as conditioned by the farmer's venturesomeness, his confidence in his expectations, his family responsibilities, and his capital position, may outweigh small changes in price relationships in conditioning use of resources; prices or price prospects may change 20 per cent without causing the pattern of production to change when it is designed to cope with uncertainty. Precautionary measures to meet uncertainty can take one or all of 3 related but somewhat distinct forms: (1) measures can be adopted to reduce the variability or dispersion of income; (2) measures can be adopted to prevent profit from falling below some minimum level such as zero, family living plus debt repayment, and so forth; and (3) measures can be adopted to increase the firm's ability to withstand unfavorable economic outcomes. The first and second measures may be considered as attempts to ward off or "arm against" variability and uncertainty. The third is more nearly one of getting the firm in a position to meet uncertainty. Precautionary measures to lessen the dispersion of outcome or to lessen the chance that it will fall below a minimum level can be introduced in choice of product-product combinations, factor-

---

[7] While consideration here is largely one of the capital market (for example, the farmer who is unable to borrow during setbacks to "tide him over" to more favorable income situations), the time distribution of income becomes a household or "utility" decision too. The problem is a producing plan which will allow cash withdrawals to the household in each time period to allow a maximization of utility. See L. Hurwicz, "Theory of the Firm and of Investment," *Econometrica*, Vol. 5.

factor combinations, and factor-product transformations. Precautions to increase the firm's ability to withstand economic setbacks involve liquidity, capital structure, and scale of operation. One of these measures may also contribute to the attainment of another. They are discussed below in approximately the order presented.

Selection of products and production processes with low variability. To the extent that the past serves as a basis for expectations of the future, enterprises can be selected which have expressed small variability in the past. Farmers tend to class those enterprises which have resulted in the greatest fluctuations in the past as the most "risky" or uncertain. The data on yield and price variations from previous chapters give suggestion of the riskiness or degree of uncertainty involved in this sense for different enterprises.

Table I.

Income Distribution and Variability Over Time for Iowa Livestock Enterprises. 1918-49 (Income Above Each $100 in Feed and Labor Cost) *

Income interval and variability	Type of livestock enterprise						
	Dairy cows	Feeder calves	Yearling feeders	Two-year old feeders	Hogs	Feeder lambs	Hens
0- 39	0	0	0	1	0	2	0
40- 79	0	5	2	3	1	3	1
80-119	16	6	12	10	7	9	16
120-159	16	17	10	7	14	6	14
160-199	0	4	7	5	7	6	1
200-239	0	0	0	3	3	3	0
240-279	0	0	1	3	0	3	0
Variance	300	1462	2045	1926	1159	2150	415
range	56	141	211	170	141	214	62
coef. of var. (%)	14	32	34	34	24	39	19
maximum loss	13	56	59	59	26	72	15
maximum gain	57	96	121	117	110	131	62

* Source: Iowa Agr. Exp. Sta. Bul. 390.

However, when uncertainty is considered in terms of income variability, and particularly the possibility that income will drop below zero or even under a level necessary to provide family living, the farmer must consider attributes of uncertainty in addition to those presented in tabular form. He must consider the compounded and additive properties of the variance for possible price and yield series. The farmer concerned with stability of income might do well to select a dairy or poultry enterprise over lamb or cattle feeding. While he would forego the possibilities of reaping big gains in some years, he would also minimize the possibility of large losses in other years. (See Table 1.) In fact, if the future parallels the past (which it obviously need not do) the expectation of large losses would not exist for dairying. Production methods or resource combinations can also be selected which, even though they do not result in maximum returns, have the effect of stabilizing income or minimizing the probability of variable returns. The farmer may invest in irrigation for this purpose even though its economic benefits do not justify the practice. Great Plains farmers, rather than following a wheat-wheat-fallow rotation, sometimes employ a wheat-fallow rotation for the specific purpose of reducing income variability. Agronomists have tried to devise, because of farmer interest, pasture systems which provide both intra-year and interyear stability of yield; while these systems may involve a sacrifice in long-term profits, they may allow a gain in the form of more stable income.

Single valued expectations and discounted returns. Even if they select the subjectively most promising course of action, it is doubtful that many entrepreneurs treat expectations as if they were *single-valued* (or, if the entrepreneur views uncertainty in the "degree of belief" manner, he is unlikely to hold only 1 hypothesis about the future). To handle expectations in a *single-valued* manner would mean that the decision-maker picks out some particular expected price or yield and supposes that "exactly this and no other" value will be realized; he views the future with subjective certainty. If he stubbornly holds to this hypothesis, he will probably act in the static or perfect knowledge sense outlined in previous chapters. Even if he thinks in terms of a distribution of possible outcomes or alternative hypotheses, he is not likely to select the modal expectation (most likely hypotheses) and treat it as if it were certain. Most managers realize that prices or yields other than the modal or most likely expected value may come about. When uncertainty is recognized in this form, a precaution which the entrepreneur can use is that of discounting future prices, yields, and income. Here discounting is a function of uncertainty rather of time *per se*, as outlined in Chapter 13. The farm manager may imagine that a wheat price of $1.75 is most likely but that it may range anywhere from 78¢ to $2.11 in the year ahead. However, rather than gear plans to a price of $1.75, he may discount the price back to $1.40 or subtract a safety margin and make decisions accordingly. (Techniques of discounting are discussed further in Chapters 18 and 19.) The extent of the price or yield discount may depend on the degree of uncertainty in the mind of the entrepreneur (as reflected by the skewness, dispersion, and other relevant properties of the expectation schedule). Discounting as a precaution to uncertainty denotes pessimism and conservatism. Taken alone, it causes the entrepreneur to plan in terms of price and transformation ratios less favorable than modal expectations; resource use would always be restricted short of that consistent with modal expectations. Discounting does not allow flexibility for taking advantage of more favorable outcomes. Subjectively, the entrepreneur should discount only as long as the marginal value of further discounting is greater than the marginal cost of further discounting. If discounting is carried too far, the individual restricts his opportunities to realize profits; if it is not carried far enough, he subjects himself to possible large losses. The farmer may know that fertilizer will cost $2 per cwt. and "expect" that the cotton price will be $15 while the yield will be normal. In terms of these bits of knowledge and expectations, 1,200 lbs. of fertilizer may "appear" profitable. Yet, to guarantee a safety margin, the farmer may apply only 800 pounds of fertilizer.

While discounting represents one aspect of farmer reaction to uncertainty, we view the precautions outlined on the following pages as more specific arrangements of resources, products, and assets to meet an unpredictable future. Selection of products with low variability, use of formal insurance plans and forward contracts, and selection of stable production processes (irrigation) become attempted methods of warding off uncertainty or unfavorable incomes; flexibility and liquidity considerations become means of preparing for change and uncertainty. However, lack of any type of adjustment may also represent an adjustment to uncertainty. The farmer who employs the "billiard table" expectation model and believes the future to be too changeable and uncertain to allow accurate forecasts may simply select an inflexible plan and stick to it.[8] This type of planning is partly consistent with a set of expectations which suppose disturbances are purely random and cannot be predicted.

Formal insurance. A simple means whereby the entrepreneur can attempt to lessen income variability or minimize the probability that it will not drop below some minimum level is formal insurance. For phenomena which can be insured, uncertainty or possible magnitude of loss is lessened through converting the chance of a large loss into a certain cost. Even though the entrepreneur may "feel confident" that the costs will exceed the returns in the long-run, he may insure to guarantee that early large losses will not result in the premature death of his business. Uncertainty is not completely removed by accepting the burden of an annual fixed cost (the insurance premium) in preference to a possible but uncertain loss from hail, fire, or other contingency. Two types of errors are involved in insurance. If the damage does not come about, the insurance premium is sacrificed. If the farmer does not insure and the damage does come about, the value of the asset is sacrificed. (Most persons pay out a greater amount in premiums than they receive in indemnities.) Insurance is not available to meet the more important uncertainties in agriculture: The most important type of uncertainty, that growing out of price, cannot be lessened by formal insurance contracts; neither can those very great variations in yield which are brought about by drought, insects, frosts, and other natural hazards be eliminated through insurance principles.

---

[8] Under this expectation model the individual assumes that "prices, after moving in one direction, simply bounce back." See P. Samuelson, *Foundations of Economic Analysis.* Cambridge: Harvard University Press, 1948, p. 340.

Forward contracts. An uncertainty precaution which is akin to insurance is that of forward contracts whereby future prices of factors or products can be reduced to certainty.

Contracts in money. On the product side; forward contracts in money can be made by the rancher for feeder lambs and cattle; by the Cornbelt farmer for sweetcorn, peas, or other vegetable crops; and by organizations of dairy farmers for milk prices. The producer of commodities with forward markets can also contract by selling futures. The wheat farmer can take out a futures contract in December for "delivery" of 5,000 bushels of wheat in July. (The forward contract and the futures contract differ in the sense that an agreement for actual physical delivery is made for the former but ordinarily not for the latter.) Forward contracts for resources are also quite common. Cash rent represents a method of introducing certainty into the price to be paid for real estate services (rent in the form of a share lease is unknown until yields and prices are known); the feeder can contract 6 to 9 months ahead for steers or lambs; help can be hired on a yearly basis. Finally, long-term contracts are made for land purchased either on contract or under a mortgage (with fixed and specified interest and principal payments). While a forward contract introduces certainty into the price of the factor or product, it may increase uncertainty of farm income itself. The farmer in a stable climatic area removes the great uncertainty, that of commodity price, when he contracts to grow and sell sweetcorn for a specified return per acre or ton. A rancher with an ample supply of pasture and feed does the same when he makes out a forward contract in April for sale of his calves in September. On the other hand, the cattle feeder who buys the calves on contract may introduce possibilities of large losses. A plains-state wheat farmer taking out a futures contract will, if his crop fails, find that he must fill the contract at a higher price than anticipated. His loss will then be greater than if he had not purchased a futures contract. Forward contracts are most effective in reducing uncertainty and the possible range of outcomes in cases of products with stable yields. They increase the magnitude of possible loss and decrease the size of possible profits when yields and production are highly unstable.

Contracts in kind. Contracts in kind represent another means of reducing income uncertainty or dispersion of income in situations where contracts in money have the opposite effect. Share renting as compared to cash renting or purchase of land is illustrative of this possibility. Some operators hire help on a "labor-share" basis rather than on the basis of a year-round salary contract. Young farmers frequently obtain brood sows from neighbors and return a portion of the litter; others pasture cattle for a share of the increase. Contracts in kind can be designed to lessen the consequences of both price and production variability. Where forward contracts do serve effectively in reducing uncertainty, they also stand to restrict incomes below levels otherwise possible.

Forward contracts for products are generally available for short periods only, such as a year or less. Accordingly, they can hardly be used to circumvent the major uncertainty in farming general inflation and deflation. Perhaps more farmers would use the system were it available for longer periods. There is indication that managers in agriculture prefer some income uncertainty to the contracting of commodity sales, however. In the Iowa expectations study mentioned earlier, a large number of farmers indicated in December that they would contract for corn sales in the year ahead only if the contract price was above what they anticipated as the most probable market price. Williams found a somewhat similar situation to exist in Illinois.[9] The Iowa farmers indicated that, on the average, however, they would accept a contract price of $20.30 for finished cattle in lieu of their (average) modal expectation of $30.54. (Even then, a few indicated that they would contract only for a price somewhat higher than their expected modal price.) The degree of uncertainty in the farmer's mind obviously affects his willingness to contract at any one time. If his expectations are skewed entirely in the direction of prices higher than the contract price, he would frown upon forward commitments. If he expected all possible prices in the future to fall below contract prices, he would rush to sell forward (unless his psychological makeup emphasizes betting on long odds).

Diversification: selection of multiple products. Diversification was discussed previously as a means of profit maximization through reaping the gains of complementary relationships and in equating substitution and price ratios for competitive products. It also can be employed as an uncertainty precaution where the immediate objective is not so much one of profit maximization but one of stability of income. The entrepreneur may chose not to specialize in a single product over time, even where substitution ratios and price ratio expectations would so dictate; he may not even elect not to build a flexible multiple-product plant which allows specialization in a different product each year as price ratios change (or are expected to change). Instead, plans may be laid for producing several products in somewhat fixed proportions over time. The "hope" of the farmer is that if the return from one product is low, the return from another will be high when the "eggs are not all in one basket."

Diversification can be accomplished in 2 quite different methods: (1) The amount of resources can be increased. Under this system a farmer producing product A with $15,000 of capital might diversify by adding another $15,000 in order to produce both A and B; (2) The amount of resources can be held constant while part of them is shifted to other

---

[9] D. B. Williams, "Price Expectations and Reactions to Uncertainty by Illinois Farmers," *Jour. Farm Econ.*, Vol. 33.

products. If the firm has $15,000 and is producing A, it might shift $7,500 to B and produce both. The first system has ramifications highly related to the capital and increasing risk considerations outlined in the next chapter. The system is sometimes suggested by bankers who would like to see farmers use more capital while "spreading their risks." The second system has a more widespread application since most farmers are limited on capital because of their own or other restrictions. The first merits attention but, before it is discussed, we can set up some criteria to serve as a guide in all instances. Income variability can be lessened through diversification only if the prices or yields of the products bear the proper correlations. If the prices, yields, and incomes have a correlation coefficient of $+1.0$, combination of 2 products need not reduce variability. If the correlation coefficient is -1.0, the 2 enterprises serve optimally as an uncertainty precaution. A correlation coefficient of zero is preferable to greater correlation coefficients.

Diversification may be employed as a method of handling 2 aspects of income variability. First, the operator may think in terms of the variability of income over his entire operating career. In this case the number of years involved becomes a population of production periods from which he may wish to minimize the variability of income. Second, the operator may think in terms of possible large profits or possible large losses in a single year. In the latter case he may attempt to treat the single year as a "sample" and organize his resources to minimize the chance of a large loss. While similar, the 2 considerations are not identical, and need not lead to the same course of action. A system of farming may allow low variability of income over the farmer's career, but it also may allow infrequent large losses. We will discuss both cases, but first we consider diversification as an attempt to minimize income variability over the entire population of years in which the farmer operates. We will use variance as a measure of variability.[10]

---

[10] Farmers are not interested in the variance figure *per se* since its computational details are not directly related to the variability figure which concerns them. In statistics the variance σ^2 is defined by dividing the sum of the squared deviations between the individual observations (x_i) and the mean $(\bar{x})$ by the number (n) of observations included in the population (or by $n-1$). Thus while

$$\sigma^2 = \sum_{i=1}^{i=n} \frac{x_i - \bar{x})^2}{n},$$

the farmer more nearly views variability over his operating career in the sense of the figure obtained as

$$\sum_{x=1}^{x=n} \frac{(x_i - \bar{x})}{n}$$

where positive and negative signs are disregarded. We use the variance concept because we can make more precise statements about its expected value for a population

Aside from the "sampling considerations" outlined below and with exceptions for autocorrelations, and considering that different income populations are represented by different enterprises, the first system of diversification, adding an enterprise through additional resources, outlined above often will increase income variance. When 2 enterprises, A and B, with variance σ_A^2 and σ_B^2 respectively are combined, the variance for the total operation, σ_T^2, becomes $\sigma_T^2 = \sigma_A^2 + \sigma_B^2 + 2\varrho\sigma_A\sigma_B$. This equation states that the variance for the combined operation is equal to σ_A^2, the variance for enterprise A, plus σ_B^2, the variance for enterprise B, plus the covariance which is defined as $2\varrho\sigma_A\sigma_B$, where ϱ is the correlation coefficient for the 2 enterprises and $\sigma_A\sigma_B$ represents the standard deviations (the square roots of the variances) for the income of each respective enterprise. Now if incomes from the 2 enterprises have a zero correlation coefficient (ϱ is zero) the equation becomes $\sigma_T^2 = \sigma_A^2 + \sigma_B^2$. Hence the addition of enterprise B to enterprise A will always increase variance (for the combined operation as compared to specialization in A alone). If ϱ, the correlation coefficient, is $+1.0$ the equation becomes $\sigma_T^2 = \sigma_A^2 + \sigma_B^2 + 2\sigma_A\sigma_B$ and variance will be increased by even more than in the previous case. If, however, the correlation coefficient is -1.0, the equation becomes $\sigma_T^2 = \sigma_A^2 + \sigma_B^2 - 2\sigma_A\sigma_B$. The variance under the combined operation can now be less than for A alone; addition of enterprise B will reduce the total variance if the quantity, $2\sigma_A\sigma_B$, is greater than σ_B^2, the variance for B alone. That is to say, total variance (σ_T^2) will remain unchanged if the ratio $2\varrho\sigma_A\sigma_B/\sigma_B^2$ is equal to 1.0, decrease if it is greater than 1.0 and increase if it is less than 1.0. Since this term reduces to $2\varrho\sigma_A/\sigma_B$, the quantity becomes $2\sigma_A/\sigma_B$ when ϱ is equal to -1.0 and total variance will be reduced as long as the standard deviation (the square root of the variance) for B is less than twice as great as the standard deviation of A. If ϱ is equal to -5, the term becomes σ_A/σ_B and total variance is reduced if the standard deviation of B is not greater than the standard deviation of A.[11]

The outcome can be quite different under the second method of diversification, diversion of part of the resources from one enterprise to another. Let us examine the case where the nature of returns to scale need not be considered (for example, we might postulate constant returns within the short-run plant, a realistic situation, as indicated in Chapter 2). We have a given quantity X of resources which has been used for enterprise A. We now decide to use only one-half of this for A and to use the remainder for B. (A quantity of resources equal to $.5X$ is now used for either enterprise.)

---

of incomes. However, the inferences drawn from the magnitude of the variance will be in the same direction as the inferences which might be based on the average deviation from the mean measured in the simple manner above.

[11] For additional details on these relationships, see E. O. Heady, "Diversified Use of Resources in Stabilizing Income," *Jour. Farm Econ.*, Vol. 34, 1952.

The equation for the total variance now becomes $\sigma_T^2 = .25\sigma_A^2 + .25\sigma_B^2 + \frac{\varrho\sigma_A\sigma_B}{2}$.[12] Total combined variance may now be decreased even if the variance of B, the added enterprise is greater than the variance of A, the original enterprise. When ϱ (the correlation coefficient) is zero, the equation reduces to $\sigma_T^2 = .25\sigma_A^2 + .25\sigma_B^2$; total variance will be decreased if .25σ_B^2 is less than .75σ_A^2, the amount by which variance for enterprise A is reduced. In other words, total variance decreases if $.75\sigma_A^2/.25\sigma_B^2$ is greater than 1.0. Since the ratio reduces to $3\sigma_A^2/\sigma_B^2$, total variance will decrease as long as variance for enterprise B is not three times greater than the variance for enterprise A. When ϱ is $+1.0$ the equation reduces to

$$\sigma_T^2 = .25\sigma_A^2 + .25\sigma_B^2 + \frac{\sigma_A\sigma_B}{2},$$ and the combined variance will be in-

creased if the sum $.25\sigma_B^2 + \frac{\sigma_A\sigma_B}{2}$ is greater than .75σ_A^2, the reduction in variance of A. When ϱ is equal to -1.0, the equation reduces to $\sigma_T^2 =$

$.25\sigma_A^2 + .25\sigma_B^2 - \frac{\sigma_A\sigma_B}{2}$ and diversification leads in the direction of a

lowered variance. (Diversion of one-half the resources from A to B will

increase variance only if .25σ_B^2 is greater than the sum, $.75\sigma_A^2 + \frac{\sigma_A\sigma_B}{2}$.)

The nature of returns to scale also has some effect on the quantity by which variance will be reduced as 2 enterprises are combined. If we ex-

amine only the one equation, $\sigma_T^2 = .25\sigma_A^2 + .25\sigma_B^2 + \frac{\varrho\sigma_A\sigma_B}{2}$, from above

we also can make statements in this direction: Reduction in variance will be somewhat less than that specified previously if A is produced under conditions of decreasing returns compared to constant returns scale; diversion of one-half the resources from A to B will reduce output in each production period by less than if the enterprise is produced under constant returns. Increasing returns, as compared to constant returns, will have an opposite effect. Other qualifications also must be made in terms of the nature of returns for enterprise B as well as enterprise A. Also managerial limitations may give rise to some increase in variance as enterprises are added; the entrepreneur may be able to make less efficient decisions as he spreads thinner in obtaining added information and in making more decisions for an increased number of crops or livestock enterprises. In the same direction, enterprise complementarity and interaction may cause variance reduction to fall by somewhat less than under independent competitive enterprises.

[12] The coefficient for the A and B variance terms becomes .25, since variance is computed from the square of the deviations. Thus the square of the constant .5 becomes .25. The covariance term is computed from the cross-products of the standard deviations. Hence it is actually $2\rho(\tfrac{1}{2}\sigma_A)(\tfrac{1}{2}\sigma_B)$ which simplifies to $\frac{\rho\sigma_A\sigma_B}{2}$.

Diversification Fundamentals

Some added notes make possible a systematic treatment of diversification principles. These will be treated in brief fashion for the sake of readers who are interested (persons less interested in algebra may wish to skip to the next section). When resources for diversification are limited we can write, where autocorrelation is not a problem, the general equation defining variance for the farm as a unit in the manner of (I) below where q refers to the proportion of resources allocated to enterprise A while $1 - q$ refers to the proportion of resource allocated to enterprise B. From this equation we can derive (II), which defines the marginal variance for each

$$\sigma_T{}^2 = q^2\sigma_A{}^2 + (1 - q)^2\sigma_B{}^2 + 2\varrho q(1 - q)\sigma_A\,\sigma_B \qquad (I)$$

value of q, the proportion of resources allocated to enterprise A. By computing marginal variance we are able to estimate the change in variability accompanying each change in resource allocation to lower or increase income; conversely, we are able to show the sacrifice in income which accompanies each gain in stability (reduction in variance) of income. By setting equation (II) at zero we can derive (III), which defines the value

$$\frac{d\sigma_T{}^2}{dq} = 2q\sigma_A{}^2 - 2(1 - q)\sigma_B{}^2 + 2\varrho(1 - 2q)\sigma_A\sigma_B \qquad (II)$$

of q, the proportion of resources allocated to enterprise A, which minimizes income variance. If we know the value of q which gives the *greatest stability of income*, we can examine the corresponding *level of income* and determine the sacrifice in returns necessary to minimize variance.

$$q = \frac{\sigma_B{}^2 - \varrho\sigma_A\sigma_B}{\sigma_A{}^2 + \sigma_B{}^2 - 2\varrho\sigma_A\sigma_B} \qquad (III)$$

Similar equations can be derived which show marginal quantities for the standard deviation and the value of q which minimizes the standard deviation of income. Since the value of q which minimizes variance is identical with that which minimizes the standard deviation, the details will not be outlined; the standard deviation of income under diversification is simply the square root of equation (I). From this we can derive the coefficient of variation and examine the relative variability of income under different allocative patterns. For example, one combination of resources may give a low absolute variance but variability may be high relative to the level of income. Equation (IV) below defines the coefficient of variation, CV, in the conventional manner wherein the standard deviation is divided by the mean income. Here I_A and I_B refer to income from enterprises A and B respectively, while I_T is the total farm income and σ_T is the standard deviation of farm income.

$$\frac{\sigma_T}{I_T} = \frac{\sqrt{q^2\sigma_A{}^2 + (1 - q)\sigma_B{}^2 + 2\varrho q(1 - q)\sigma_A\sigma_B}}{qI_A + (1 - q)I_B} \qquad (IV)$$

If we now use the square of the coefficient of variation as our measure of relative variability, we obtain equation (V), which can be manipulated

$$(CV)^2 = \frac{q^2\sigma_A{}^2 + (1-q)^2\sigma_B{}^2 + 2\varrho q(1-q)\sigma_A\sigma_B}{[qI_A + (1-q)I_B]^2} \tag{V}$$

with greater facility. From this equation it is possible to derive (VI) below, which specifies the marginal $(CV)^2$, and therefore indicates the change in level of relative variability for each change in q, the proportion of resources allocated to enterprise A. This equation can be simplified and

$$\frac{d(CV)^2}{dq} = [qI_A + (1-q)I_B][2q\sigma_A{}^2 - 2(1-q)\sigma_B{}^2 + 2\varrho(1-2q)\sigma_A\sigma_B] \tag{VI}$$

set at zero to specify the value of q which minimizes the square of the coefficient of variation and which also will minimize the magnitude of the coefficient of variation (the relative variability of income) as is illustrated in equation (VII):

$$q = \frac{I_A\sigma_B{}^2 - \varrho I_B\sigma_A\sigma_B}{I_A\sigma_A{}^2 + I_A\sigma_B{}^2 - \varrho\sigma_A\sigma_B(I_A + I_B)} \tag{VII}$$

Magnitude of correlation coefficient to lessen variance. From previous equations we can specify, for certain conditions and with the autocorrelation exceptions mentioned, the value of the correlation coefficient which will allow diversification to lower income variance. From equation (I) the value of ϱ, the correlation coefficient, can be stated in the manner of (VIII):

$$\varrho = \frac{\sigma_T{}^2}{2q(1-q)\sigma_A\sigma_B} - \frac{q\sigma_A}{2(1-q)\sigma_B} - \frac{(1-q)\sigma_B}{2q\sigma_A} \tag{VIII}$$

For different values of variance for either product we can now state the magnitude of the correlation coefficient necessary before diversification will lessen variability for the farm as a whole. Let us suppose that the variances are equal for the two enterprises and therefore that $\sigma_A{}^2$ is equal to $\sigma_B{}^2$. Equation (VIII) then reduces to (IX), which can in turn be expressed in the manner of (X). From the last equation it is evident that

$$\varrho = \frac{\sigma_T{}^2}{2q(1-q)\sigma_A{}^2} - \frac{q}{2(1-q)} - \frac{(1-q)}{2q} \tag{IX}$$

$$\frac{\sigma_T{}^2}{\sigma_A{}^2} = \left[\varrho + \frac{q}{2(1-q)} + \frac{(1-q)}{2q}\right]\left[2q(1-q)\right] \tag{X}$$

total variance, $\sigma_T{}^2$, will be reduced only if the right hand side of the equation is less than 1.0 (the ratio $\sigma_T{}^2/\sigma_A{}^2$ is less than 1.0); in other words the condition of equation (XI) must hold true. From equation (XI) it is possible to derive (XII), indicating that, given equal variances for the 2

$$2\varrho q(1-q) + 1 - 2q(1-q) < 1.0 \tag{XI}$$

$$\varrho < \frac{2q(1-q)}{2q(1-q)} \text{ or } 1.0 \tag{XII}$$

enterprises, variability will be reduced for any correlation coefficient less than 1.0. Under the first system of diversification, doubling of resources and addition of a second enterprise, the value of ϱ can be specified in the manner of (XIII). If the variances for the 2 enterprises are equal, this equation in turn gives rise to equations (XIV) and (XV), and finally (XVI) and (XVII) stating that, if total variance is to be less than the variance for A alone, income variance for the total farm business will be reduced only if the correlation coefficient is less than $-.5$.

$$\varrho = \frac{\sigma_T^2 - \sigma_A^2 - \sigma_B^2}{2\sigma_A\sigma_B} \tag{XIII}$$

$$\varrho = \frac{\sigma_T^2}{2\sigma_A^2} - 1 \tag{XIV}$$

$$\frac{\sigma_T^2}{\sigma_A^2} = 2(\varrho + 1) \tag{XV}$$

$$2(\varrho + 1) < 1.0 \tag{XVI}$$

$$\varrho < -.5 \tag{XVII}$$

Knowledge of variances and correlation coefficients also allows us to make statements about the effectiveness of numbers of enterprises in reducing income variance, while predictions can be made for variances and correlation coefficients of any magnitude, let us examine the possibilities of combining enterprises with equal variances where each pair has a correlation coefficient of .6. If σ_A^2 is the variance for 1 enterprise produced alone, then variance for 2 enterprises produced in combination will be $.8\sigma_A^2$, while it will be (on the basis of calculations from a formula such as (I) above expanded to include covariance terms for each pair) $.72\sigma_A^2$ for 3 enterprises and .70 for 4 enterprises. In other words, added enterprises reduce farm income variance by smaller and smaller amounts.

Empirical data. Table 2 and Figure 1, suggesting relationships in diversification, can be derived from simple information by means of the algebraic models such as those on previous pages where autocorrelation is not important. These data show that, as resources are shifted from oats to corn (a q value of zero refers to 60 acres in oats and none in corn, a q value of .5 refers to 30 acres each in corn and oats, and so forth), each increase in the value of q, the proportion of land in corn, a positive quantity is added to variance (the column of marginal variance). Thus income is increased at the expense of stability because total variance also increases; or starting from corn alone, a shift of resources to oats increases stability

Table 2.
Marginal Variance, Level of Variance, and Magnitude of Net Income from 60 Acres of Land.
Troy Township, Clark County, Iowa, 1914-50 (Variance Figures in 1,000 and Marginal
Variance in 10,000)

	Corn—Oats			Corn—Soybeans		
Value of q	Marginal Variance	Variance	Income	Marginal Variance	Variance	Income
1.0		698	865		698	865
.9	78	615	804	30	693	849
.8	70	541	743	7	691	833
.7	62	475	681	—3	693	817
.6	53	417	620	—5	696	801
.5	45	367	559	—8	704	786
.4	37	326	498	—11	714	770
.3	29	292	437	—14	726	754
.2	21	267	375	—17	741	738
.1	13	250	314	—20	780	706
0		241	253			

of income (reduces variance) but causes a sacrifice in the quantity of income. For corn and soybeans, stability of income and level of income are complementary over a range (hence the negative marginal values); as resources are shifted from beans to corn, level of income and stability

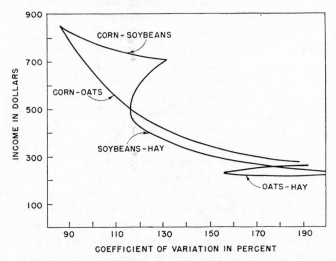

Fig. 2. Production possibilities showing relationship between level of income and relative variability of income, Troy Township, Clark County, Iowa, 1917-1949.

of income both are increased. However a point is finally reached where greater income can be attained only if stability of income is sacrificed (total variance is increased). The farmer must make a choice between these 2 production possibilities. The value of q, the proportion of resources allocated to corn, which will minimize variance is .79 for corn-beans; it is zero for corn-oats, but few farmers would select to minimize income variance because of the *very* low level of income itself. For wheat-milo combinations at Ft. Hays, Kansas, q, the proportion of land to wheat, is .20, while it is .23 and .32 for wheat-barley and barley-milo respectively.

Figure 2 shows that level of income and relative stability of income are complementary throughout for corn-oats combinations; both are increased as resources are shifted from oats to corn. (The uppermost point on each curve represents the income and its relative variability when the entire acreage is in the first mentioned crop while the lowermost point is the case of all resources used for the second crop; in-between points represent combinations of products ranging over these two extremes.) Soybeans and hay are complementary over a range because a shift of resources from hay to beans increases both income and relative stability of income; eventually, a further shift allows income to be increased only at the expense of relative stability (causes an increase in the coefficient of variation). The "turning point" on each of the curves corresponds to the value of q which minimizes the coefficient of variation. Oats and hay have long ranges of complementarity but income is low in all cases.

Minimizing loss in a single year. We now turn to diversification as a "safeguard" for a single year or 2. The analysis above supposed that alternative open to the operator was minimization of income variance over some period, perhaps his operating career. Since unfavorable outcomes in a single year may bankrupt the operator with little capital or a low equity, he may diversify in order to increase the chance that high incomes as well as low income may be realized. The logic used can be that of sampling theory where it is known that as the number of observations drawn from a single population is increased, the variance (and also the average deviation) will decrease. The farmer may simply view different enterprises as if they were different observations drawn from a single population of incomes.[13] With an increased number of enterprises, the chance is increased that a high income for one will accompany a low income for another if returns for different enterprises do not have a high positive correlation. (Previous statements about the magnitude of the correlation coefficient apply here as well as in the earlier example of diversification. Two negatively correlated enterprises guarantees some income in a single year.) This logic of diversification and its implications for profits can be illustrated partly by means of Figure 3, where the production possibilities for products Y_1 and Y_2 are represented by curve AB. Among his expectations the farmer includes 2 hypotheses for price relationships of the future. The first hypothesis, H_1, supposes the price relationship indicated

---

[13] Sampling theory also states that variance can be decreased as homogeneity of the population is increased. Hence our earlier statement that the farmer interested in stability should select single enterprise with few fluctuations can be justified in the logic of statics.

by iso-revenue line DB: it calls for specialization in Y_2. The second hypothesis, H_2, postulates price relationship indicated by AC: it calls for production of Y_1 alone. If the entrepreneur produces Y_2 alone, the action consistent with H_1, and the price relationship of H_2 is actually realized, income is at the low level indicated by revenue line ef rather than at the maximum denoted by AC and by specialization in Y_2. (The 2 revenue lines have the same slope and denote the same price relationship.) If plans are in term of H_2 only, and Y_1 alone is produced, income will be that indicated by gh (rather than that indicated by DB). Hence, to help minimize the chance of income as low as ef or gh, the entrepreneur may select a combination of the 2 products such as that indicated at S. While income will be only at the level db or ac if hypotheses H_1 or H_2 re-

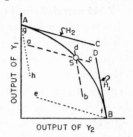

Fig. 3. Allocation of resources to minimize chance of large loss.

spectively come about (rather than at the maximum of DB or AC), the probability of incomes as low as gh and ef has been lessened. While the chance of low income has been lessened, the chance of high income has also been lessened under diversification.

The farmer can diversify not alone to reduce income variance but he can also use more resources and add a stable enterprise to an unstable one. The lowest income in a single year for a combination of 50 acres each of wheat and milo at Ft. Hays, Kansas, over the period 1910-50 would have been $53; it would have been zero under 100 acres of either wheat or milo alone.

Price correlations. As is indicated in Table 3, price correlations for all farm commodities are positive over periods of any length. Ability of

Table 3.
Correlation Coefficients of Annual Prices for Pairs of Products. United States, 1910-50

	Hay	Wheat	Cotton	Potatoes	Hogs	Eggs	Butter-fat	Tobacco	Pea-nuts	Fat cattle
Corn	.84	.91	.83	.68	.87	.84	.84	.83	.87	.76
Hay		.90	.85	.77	.83	.86	.89	.82	.91	.75
Wheat			.87	.81	.94	.90	.93	.85	.92	.85
Cotton				.65	.78	.82	.87	.77	.91	.72
Potatoes					.77	.80	.77	.68	.73	.63
Hogs						.93	.94	.87	.90	.93
Eggs							.95	.83	.89	.84
Butterfat								.83	.93	.91
Tobacco									.92	.82
Peanuts										.86

farmers to stabilize income through diversification is limited for this reason. The implications of these differences are as follows: Diversification is a more effective means of lessening income variability for those price fluctuations growing out of individual commodity cycles, annual variations in the yields of individual crops, and other very short-term changes in supply or demand. It is much less effective in lessening income variability which grows out of the wide swings in national prosperity.

Yield correlations. Diversification to lessen income variance or to prevent "having all eggs in one basket" is more effective as a means of combating yield variability than in meeting price variability. While the empirical statements and general logic outlined above apply to output variations in the same way as to price variations, important differences exist between regions. In areas where moisture is the limiting factor in production, yields of alternative crops are positively related and diversification is not so effective in reducing either wide swings in income which arise from complete droughts or bumper crops of less extreme variations which occur in annual rainfall. In areas such as the central Corn Belt, the eastern United States, and irrigated farming areas, moisture is not so much the single limiting factor in production and a greater number of other forces affect the yields of individual crops. Yields of some crops are therefore not so highly correlated and diversification is more effective in reducing the income variance. These differences are partly illustrated in Table 4, which shows yield correlations for selected states and selected crops. (Variability

Table 4.

Yield Correlation Coefficients for Specified States and Crops, 1920-50

Colorado	Wheat	Corn	Oats	Grain sorghums	Hay
Wheat	1.00	.68	.76	.22	.39
Corn		1.00	.62	.76	.51
Oats			1.00	.56	.51
Grain sorghum				1.00	.70
Hay					1.00

Illinois	Corn	Oats	Soybeans	Wheat	Hay
Corn	1.00	.71	.73	.35	.23
Oats		1.00	.42	.34	.50
Soybeans			1.00	.43	.70
Wheat				1.00	.35
Hay					1.00

Georgia	Cotton	Tobacco	Peanuts	Corn	Hay
Cotton	1.00	.67	.39	.20	.42
Tobacco		1.00	.65	.61	.23
Peanuts			1.00	.69	.30
Corn				1.00	.30
Hay					1.00

in yields is greater and correlations are much less for areas as large as a state than for individual farms within a state. The examples are used for illustrative purposes and not to suggest the specific situation facing individual farmers.) Variance in income growing out of crop yield variability can be most effectively lessened by combinations of crops which have critical needs for moisture at different times of the year. Soybeans and corn have growing seasons of approximately the same length and both use moisture beyond August 1, while small grain such as oats or wheat has its greatest demands for moisture early in the summer. Fruit trees draw on moisture at different times of the year and are affected by quite a different set of insects and diseases than annual crops.

Output variations in livestock, aside from those related to crop yields, are less correlated than crop yields since moisture is not the central variable in livestock production. The diseases or pests which attack individual classes of livestock are not often the same. If the milk cows get mastitis, erysipelas is not also likely to strike the hogs while the feeder cattle come down with black leg and the hens get diarrhea.

Extent and limitations of diversification. The extent to which diversification is practiced as a means of reducing income variability is unknown. However, it is evidently of importance for beginning operators and established farmers in a weak financial position and for some operators in all areas where weather gives rise to gains from diversification. Not only do farmers attempt to avoid "putting all the eggs in one basket," but also farm leaders (bankers, college personnel, newspaper editors, and others) in areas such as the Great Plains and the Southeast clamor for a "diversified agriculture." The motivation in the plains states grows out of the vulnerable position in which farmers, particularly wheat producers, have found themselves during extended droughts. (See Table 2.) While interest is on "getting away from a 1-crop economy" in the old cotton producing regions, emphasis on diversification should more nearly be one of allocating resources between products in a manner to equate substitution and price ratios. One reason why greater diversification has not arisen may itself be a phenomenon of uncertainty; adjustment in the direction of greater feed and livestock production requires greater capital than current cotton farming systems. Because of the "increasing risk principle" (see discussion in following chapter), use of additional borrowed capital proves to be a limiting factor in shifting resource use for such areas as the cotton South.

The opportunities for diversification are much greater than the extent to which these practices are followed in most farming areas. Diversification, where it is found in agriculture, is mainly a function of technical product-product relationships and to a lesser extent a function of income variability. Farmers generally are unwilling to make extreme income sacrifices over time for the gain of a more stable income in the same period. Even in the Plains States, the value which farmers place on income as compared to stability is high enough (or their risk-aversion and gambler preference are of a nature) to cause most to specialize in wheat production rather than a complete system of diversified livestock farming. The addition of a small "stable" livestock enterprise (such as the family poultry or dairy enterprise) may carry them sufficiently into the area of "safety." Beyond these limits they desire to take the chance on higher incomes. Diversification to increase income stability *per se* lessens the opportunity to gain premium incomes from a given resource outlay since it does not allow equation of substitution and price ratios. Another cost in diversification may be the possible sacrifice of gains from increasing returns to scale or size.

Lessening variability of production. While the problem of diversification or selecting products with low price variability, given the immediate end of minimizing income variance, is most important in some farming regions, selection of enterprises with low yield variability becomes the dominant problem in areas of low rainfall and unstable climate. A pressing question in the Great Plains is one of whether or not livestock enterprises should be incorporated with wheat farming as a method of lessening income instability. The selection of a livestock farming system may or may not lessen income variability depending on the location and the organization of the enterprise. In some areas a livestock farm can be created by producing corn and other feed grains in the place of wheat; hogs or other livestock can then be produced with the feed grain. However, where grain-consuming livestock are organized to fit the grain production on the farm, variability in income can be greater under this system of farming than under wheat farming.[14] A farm organized in western Kansas to grow only milo, with a hog enterprise geared exactly to the grain output of the farm, would have greater income variability than one producing only summer fallow wheat. Wheat yields are less variable than milo yields in most of Kansas.

Another possibility in these areas is a shift of resources from wheat to pasture and livestock grazing. Depending on the climate, the type of forage grown, and other factors, the variability of grass yields is less variable than wheat yields in some semi-arid farming areas. This condition is not true in all areas, however, and in some where it is true, variability in pasture-livestock farming systems is still very great. In others the gain in the slightly greater stability introduced by a livestock farming system causes too great a sacrifice in income. In still other instances grazing allows about the same average income over time as grain farming and any slight reduction in income variability is an important criterion of selection. Jones has estimated that a shift from wheat to more grass on a southwestern North Dakota farm would have reduced income per year by only $84 over the period 1929-42.[15] On the other hand, it would have

---

[14] Perhaps the best manner to guarantee minimum variability of income growing out of yield in the Great Plains is this: No crops need be grown and a few acres might be devoted to dry-lot feeding systems where all feeds are purchased. (Livestock yield variability would still occur but crop yield variability would no longer be a worry.) Undoubtedly farmers have thought of this possibility but are not willing to (a) go so far in sacrificing income for stability or (b) would rather move to an agricultural area where feed livestock price ratios are more favorable.

[15] Lloyd E. Jones, "Stabilizing Farming by Shifting Wheat Land to Grass in the Northern Great Plains," *Jour. Farm Econ.*, Vol. 32

reduced the range of outcomes by $1,834; the number of years in which costs exceeded income from 4 to 2 years; and the number of years in which income fell short of costs, debt payments, and family living from 9 to 7 years.

Of course, if the individual's risk aversion is so very great that stability of income becomes the foremost objective of farming, livestock production systems can be initiated which do allow complete stability. Figure 4 suggests possibilities: Line V illustrates the variability in year-to-year yields in forage production. If beef cattle numbers and production were fitted exactly to hay output, they would display a parallel year-to-year variability; the herd could be expanded and contracted in line with yield sequences. If stability is the paramount objective, livestock numbers can be fitted to the lowest yield (line L) and variability (as a result of crop variability) will then drop to zero. Income will always be as low as in the poorest year under the first alternative (V), however, and the opportunity for capturing the profits of the bumper years is never present. While variability of

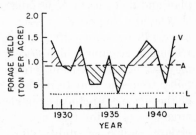

Fig. 4. Hay yield variability and basis for stability in livestock production (yields from Jones, op. cit.).

income under the V alternative will always be greater than that under the L alternative, the greater variability seems preferable in all respects (except for the goal of stability *per se*); family living and debt repayment ability as well as mean income over time is never less than under L, while it would be greater in most years. Selection of a type or form of enterprise which minimizes income stability cannot be justified in this case unless capital is not available. A second alternative in selecting or organizing an enterprise for a minimum variability is suggested by line A which expresses the average forage yield (.9 ton per acre) over the period. Here yields or production above the average could be harvested and stored until years in which yields were less than average. The forage in question is crested wheat grass and, while it might be harvested and stored, costs would be involved in providing storage facilities. (Not all of the surplus grass could be stored until later seasons.) An important question is whether a smaller income under the storage system would be worth the greater stability which it provides. Greater income over the entire period of time might be forthcoming if livestock production were adapted to annual fluctuations in forage production. The difficulty here is that forage output for a single year cannot be predicted without error even at the beginning of a pasture season; the necessary number of cattle cannot always be on hand to allow full utilization of annual surpluses. Then, were all farmers to follow similar adjustments in cattle numbers (so that each one could not "collectively" buy stock from others), the only alternative for individuals would be to build up herds by holding back young stock. The "lush" year or years might thus be past before herds could be expanded from the lows of drought years. Perhaps many ranch managers compromise these alternatives and, while they never build herds to the point of maximum forage production in individual years, some harvestable surplus is stored as hay and some variation in livestock numbers is attempted.

Flexibility. Diversification may be followed as a fixed or inflexible plan for production (the farmer-directed bit of advice to "adopt a well-rounded plan and don't be an inner and outer"). As an uncertainty precaution it is generally followed to lessen income variability or the probability of income below some critical level; it incorporates no special provisions for reaping large gains if high prices should come about. In contrast, flexibility may be incorporated into production plans both to lessen income variability from one year to the next and to increase the expected total value of the income stream. Diversification is mainly a method of preventing large losses; flexibility is more nearly a method of preventing the sacrifice of large gains. Flexibility allows for changing of plans as time passes, added information is obtained and ability to predict the future improves. Flexibility also allows "quick changes" at a lower cost sacrifice than a rigid plan since flexible producing plants are adaptable to a wider range of opportunities than inflexible production processes. Flexibility provides turning points in time for redecision; a plan need not be worked out for the life of the firm. Not only is a "fixed plan" policy unnecessary but it may also prove to be "foolish business procedure" under uncertainty. (See Chapters 9 and 11.) Flexibility can be of three types: (a) time, (b) cost, and (c) product.

Time flexibility. Time flexibility can be introduced into the production plan either through the selection of products or the selection of production processes. Orcharding represents an inflexible intertemporal production plan. In contrast, broiler production or the feeding of heavy cattle represent highly flexible plans in respect to time. Annual crops are more flexible than perennial berries or fruit. On the side of production methods, a short-lived resource provides greater time flexibility than durable equipment. A pole barn may last only 10 years and represent a greater cost per annum than a tile cattle-feeding barn. Yet flexibility exists in the pole barn since the operator has a periodic opportunity to reappraise the future; if he ceases feeding to pursue a more profitable alternative which is in prospect, he does not sacrifice the greater investment in the more durable barn. Time flexibility is in conflict with long-term buying or selling contracts. It also places a premium on intermediate products of a unspecialized nature such as a young or "low grade" feeder animal. The steer can be "roughed" through the winter and, if prospects are not favorable in the spring, it can be sold elsewhere as a feeder; if prospects are favorable, it can be put on grass for the summer. In the fall, reappraisal can be made of the future outlook; if fat-cattle prices appear unfavorable, the animal can be sold as a feeder. In contrast, high-grade heavy steers started immediately on grain feed do not provide the same flexibility; the value of grain already fed can be recovered ordinarily only as the animal is carried to higher slaughter grades. Brood sows provide many points for redecision. Although the outlook for the future is entirely uncertain, gilts can be bred and carried on a non-fattening ration while they are held for reformation of expectations. If prospects for price declines develop before the animals appear "piggy," they can be sold as slaughter hogs; if prospects are favorable, they can be carried forward. Just before farrowing, the future can be reassessed and the gilts can be sold as brood sows or can be held for farrowing. The pigs, at the time of weaning, can be held for fattening, kept for further breeding, or sold as feeders. Time flexibility is important to many farmers; beginning operators are particularly interested in enterprises with "a quick turnover"; tenants with short-term leases definitely plan in the vein of time flexibility. If uncertainty has any one major effect on decisions, it is that of emphasizing short-run plans.

Cost and factor flexibility. The nature of flexible cost curves has already been discussed under factor-factor and scale relationships and requires only reference to uncertainty here. Previously, we assumed variability in factor-product price ratios and transformation rates but supposed that these were known with certainty for an individual with limited capital. If we now turn back to Figure 26 in Chapter 11, the role of cost flexibility under uncertainty becomes evident. First, cost flexibility is important where the possibility of time flexibility is limited. When production processes require durable equipment, costs must be committed in the form of a fixed plant which remains for some time into the future and reappraisal of investment alternatives cannot be made for the firm with limited funds.[16] Cost flexibility refers to variations in output within the structure of a long-lived plant. Cost flexibility, like time flexibility, may be selected to gain time and allow physical adaptations in output. It makes possible extension of output to take advantage of more favorable prices or yields at lower costs for a given plant. Similarly, it makes possible contraction of output with a smaller sacrifice in overhead costs in case prices slide downward. As already pointed out, farmers can and do invest in flexibility of the type suggested by the short-run cost curve AC_f in Figure 26 of Chapter 11. Rather than build permanent, heated farrowing houses which allow the saving of a maximum number of pigs per sow, they often choose

---

[16] Conceivably, 2 short-run plants, 1 flexible and 1 inflexible, might be set up with equal lives. Thus decision on investment in the plant would not allow time flexibility, but would allow cost and output flexibility in the sense that reappraisal could be made of production at different points in time (even if not in plant investment).

less durable farrowing sheds which result in fewer pigs per litter. The sheds may be more flexible, however, in extending farrowings over the year and also the fixed costs are not so great in years when farrowings are dropped back to low levels. Similarly, the beet or potato producer who expects his acreage to vary considerably between years may cling to hand rather than mechanical methods of production and harvesting. Rejection of equipment with high fixed costs, even though the latter gives the lowest cost per unit in years of a large acreage, makes possible a sharp curtailment in expenses during years of a small beet acreage.

Cost flexibility may also be selected to meet variations in factor prices. At 1 particular point in time the farmer may find that factor services from a combine of his own may result in lower costs than those provided by custom hire. Still he may provide for cost flexibility by continuing to hire his soybeans or small grain harvested by custom machines. Fixed costs which arise from interest and principle payments are important when land is owned. In contrast, costs are variable when land services are hired under share rental systems.

Weather is a variable with similar flexibility implications although it is of a different nature than price. While the time suited to planting or harvesting a crop may average 20 days over a period of years, the "exact average" comes about only in part of the years. (It is, of course, the most frequent outcome if weather phenomena is characterized by a normal frequency distribution.) Variations in the climate may allow as few as 8 or as many as 40 days for a particular operation in different years. If the farmer could always count on exactly 20 days (a weather population with a zero variance) his resource combination and cost structure could be adapted in an inflexible and minimum cost manner; he might employ a single power unit, a 6-foot combine, and similar medium-capacity machines. Given this machine combination, losses in yield may be great in years of very unfavorable weather. Two choices are open to the farmer: He can assemble an inflexible set of tools which is optimum for average weather. (The AC_i possibility in Figure 26 of Chapter 11.) He can adopt flexible machine services (AC_f in Figure 26) by investing in some surplus capacity while hiring custom machines or using hand methods.

Flexibility of the types outlined involves costs. The cost of producing a unit of product is greater than it would need to be: an optimum structure of costs could always be designed for a particular output if the conditions were known previously. Cost flexibility represents a "potential" form of inefficiency to the individual and society. The social product sacrificed in the form of flexibility to meet price and certain types of yield uncertainty might be lessened by the various programs outlined elsewhere in this chapter. However, the possibility of reducing machine investment designed to meet weather variability of the nature outlined above is not promising.

Product flexibility. The nature of product flexibility was outlined in detail in Chapter 9. Its purpose, like all other forms of flexibility, is to allow a producing structure which facilitates redirection of production as price change and expectations merit the move. The reasons why product flexibility is desirable when change is present and predictable has been explained. Somewhat similar logic applies to change which cannot be predicted with certainty at the time original plans are made. Even though price prospects may definitely favor selection of an inflexible plant such as C_2N_1 in Figure 13 of Chapter 9, the farmer with small capital may be very rational (aside from technical supplementary or complementary relationships) in selecting a flexible curve such as C_3N_3 in Figure 9. In addition to the building examples cited earlier, product flexibility is also possible in the selection of milk cows. If the beef or butterfat markets are uncertain, dual purpose cows can be selected over straight dairy or beef breeds: output can be switched between beef and butterfat as price ratios change. On the side of technical variability, forage crops are more flexible than small grains or vegetables; if weather is unfavorable during the harvesting season, grass may be cut for silage or left to be harvested for seed. Flexibility to meet technical uncertainty also can be introduced into beef ranching. Rather than keep 500 beef cows and market their offspring as calves, 250 cows can be kept while the calves are held over to be sold as yearlings when pasture is favorable; if a summer drought comes, the young stock can be sold while the cow herd is held intact. A carry-over of feed supplies also represents product flexibility in the sense that the feed resources can be marketed directly as a product or converted into a livestock product. All types of inventories can be looked upon as having this degree of product flexibility.[17] Flexible machines and buildings (such as a structure which can be used as a tobacco shed and a cow barn or a flexible barn for either dairying or cattle feeding) can be and are employed to meet price, yield, and technological change.

While product flexibility has its obvious costs (milk often or ordinarily could be produced cheaper with dairy than with dual purpose breeds, a shed costs less than a pen-type barn for cattle feeding) it again represents an outlay which the farmer as a resource administrator can select to be able to alter his course in a dynamic world where the exact one of alternative directions or extents of change cannot be foretold with certainty. As the reader will quickly grasp, product flexibility, time flexibility, and liquidity are partly different degrees of the same thing. Under product flexibility we have considered the form of physical resources (barns, machines, and so forth) which can be switched readily between products.

---

[17] See A. G. Hart, *Anticipations, Uncertainty and Dynamic Planning.* Chicago: University of Chicago Press, 1941, pp. 60-73. Hart emphasizes the role of inventories for the manufacturing firm.

In the next section we look upon cash or other intangible and tangible assets from the standpoint of "fluidity" and reversibility in decision-making.

Liquidity and asset structure. Liquidity, while it may also be considered a form of flexibility, represents a somewhat distinct method of preparing for unpredictable change. Like all other forms of flexibility, liquidity allows decisions to be made sequentially (an inflexible course of action need not be set up at an early point in time, but the opportunity to select new courses of action is retained). Liquidity also can be viewed as a method of preparing to withstand the ravages of economic setbacks. Liquidity refers to the structure or form of the firm's assets. It is characterized particularly by cash balances (cash, bank deposits) and unused borrowing power. Cash, like all "liquid bodies," can change its form freely: it can be freely transformed into other forms of assets.[18] A "liquid" asset also possesses "reversibility"; cash can be used to "reverse the field" of investment with an ease as great as or greater than for any other type of asset. Liquidity is, of course, a matter of degree. Assets can be arranged in terms of their ease of "fluidity" in being exchanged for goods, factors, or claims to other assets. At the top of the list are cash, bank deposits, government bonds, or other assets and "near moneys" which can be easily converted to cash and used to purchase commodities and resources, or to meet commitments of any sort. Slightly less liquid are products which can be sold and converted to cash. Ownership of resources such as farm land is somewhat less easily converted to other goods. A life estate or life lease, particularly when it is held jointly with other individuals as a partnership or similar legal arrangement, possesses minimum liquidity. If the title cannot be transferred to others, the lease will have little value as a claim to any other type of asset or in meeting commitments of any nature. Liquidity permits the firm to take advantage of favorable opportunities which call for purchase of additional resource services or investment in other assets. Prompt access to funds may allow taking advantage of a highly remunerative price rise. This aspect of liquidity is perhaps less important, however, than the ability it provides to weather unforeseen contingencies such as continued crop failure, economic depression, or mishaps to the entrepreneur himself. The farmer who has cash reserves may easily withstand a 2-year drought in the Great Plains, while his "less liquid" neighbor cannot; the Maine potato farmer with a 100 per cent equity may hold on to his assets through several years of low prices, while the operator with a 25 per cent equity cannot. Similarly, the rancher who carries a feed surplus from year to year may be in a better position to cope with drought than another rancher who immediately markets his feed or converts it to beef. The economic cost or sacrifice involved in liquidity

---

[18] See J. Marshak, "Role of Liquidity Under Complete and Incomplete Information," *Amer. Econ. Rev.*, Vol. 61.

is of this nature: The holding of reserves and the maintenance of liquidity implies that if the future could be foreseen more perfectly, the firm could increase its output and profit by reducing the proportion of assets held in the form of money or operator equity (since investment in physical assets such as capital, labor, and land could be greater).

Cash is held by farmers in order to carry on annual production and otherwise facilitate current business transactions. Perhaps very little cash is held merely in the speculative and flexibility sense (to prevent having "one's funds tied up if a high profit prospect" suddenly develops). In the immediate postwar period, farmers did hold record cash balances (including government bonds) as a liquidity measure to some extent. (However, while some were preparing for an "imminent depression," others were merely withholding investment because of the nature of the elasticity of their expectations (that future prices would decline by a larger amount than the small downward adjustment in postwar prices). Liquidity preference is undoubtedly high in farming, however, when account is taken of the "high value" which farmers attach to reducing debts before retirement.

Income Stability and the Capital Market

The attempt of farmers to ward off or eliminate income variability and uncertainty through the various precautions open to them is partly understandable in a purely utility context. Aside from discounts on future income growing both out of futurity and uncertainty, the distribution of income between 2 or more individual periods (years) which will maximize total utility over the entire period is that which equates the marginal utility of goods in the different time periods. Were the magnitude and sequence of income variation known with certainty even in an environment where prices and yields change, the farm family could hold back reserve funds from years of favorable incomes to be used in low-income years for meeting family-living expenditures, interest and principal payments and traditional operating expenses.

When production and income are variable, 2 alternatives are open for planning farm production and family expenditures: (1) A plan can be adopted which involves large variations from year to year but allows a greater income over time; the "surplus of lush years" can be carried forward to "lean years." (2) A course of action can be adopted which results both in (a) smaller variations between years and (b) a lower income over all years. While the optimum choice is unique to each individual, the first alternative can result in a greater welfare of the farm family over time. Stability *per se* is only an intermediate end; and it is a means to the more ultimate end of utility and welfare maximization. Where instability allows a greater economic product over time, both individual and governmental policies can be fashioned which are consistent with the optimum allocation of income between time periods and with maximum intertemporal utility. Generally policy of this nature involves the storage or carrying-forward of income of lush years to even out fluctuations. Many operators adopt systems of farming which, although subject to variation, result in greater incomes over time (as is evidenced by specialized wheat farming versus other more stable producing systems in the Great Plains). Why do not more do so? Many farmers are unable to practice this policy because of imperfections in the capital or credit market. Farmers with mortgages against their livestock, equipment, land, and other physical forms of capital frequently must make the full outlay for interest and principal in both good and bad years. Some are never able to build up a reserve to be carried into the more profitable years. Because of their high liquidity preference and risk aversion, others perhaps place a premium on using the surplus from favorable years to lessen indebtedness. Consequently the total quantity of physical capital employed does not increase as fast as their equity; funds for family living, debt servicing, and current operations become pinched in unfavorable years.

Uncertainty and Efficiency

Inefficiency growing out of uncertainty is of 2 sorts: (1) Precautions which are taken to meet uncertainty almost always necessitate a sacrifice; they either result in a less-than-maximum product from given resources or, conversely, do not allow a minimum cost for a given output. (2) Both the individual farmer and the consuming society sacrifice when production is geared to inaccurate expectations; if the farm operator expects hogs to be profitable and beef to be unprofitable, he sacrifices profit if the opposite relationship is realized. At the same time the consuming society sacrifices in the sense that, as is indicated in the prices which it eventually reflects to the farmer, it actually prefers that a greater amount of resources be devoted to beef and less to hogs. It is not sufficient that the expectations of farmers "average out" (which they hardly ever do). Even if one-half the farmers produce too much beef and the other one-half produce too little, inefficiency can arise because of the technical production relationships outlined in Chapter 4. (See discussion of allocation of resources between technical units and farms.) Uncertainty particularly discourages long-time capital investment and places a premium on the use of labor.

Means of lessening inefficiency. Numerous means exist whereby uncertainty might be reduced and the decision-making environment of farmers improved. While some of these have already been mentioned, they are outlined further in the following paragraphs.

Information to individuals. Education in agriculture, particularly through the Agricultural Extension Service, should have as one objective the improving of farmer's expectations and their managerial processes. It should attempt to supply estimates where information is now incomplete for planning. Educational services should not only provide expectations of price and yield quantities, but also be directed towards increasing the farmer's ability to observe, analyze and weigh data and formulate hypotheses. It should also be directed at increasing his ability to make decisions and plan courses of action. On the side of consumption planning, education directed at the farm family should explain the consequences of different courses of action. The family can then form its own set of values from the more complete information available to it and can better decide on the final course of action. Then if it still chooses to go on a "binge" in periods of favorable income while lowering consumption in low-income years, its actions must be considered irrational and inconsistent with maximum welfare. However, where individuals would select to but are unable to rearrange production or transfer income from one period to another (even out the flow of income over time) because of low income, debt commitments, and capital market imperfections, society possesses other means whereby income can be allocated optimally over time and the welfare of both the individual and the community can be extended.

Credit programs. Programs which allow general instability to remain but circumvent the consequences of income variability can be attempted by individuals and governments. Private credit firms or governmental credit policies can employ flexible payment provisions for this purpose; repayment schedules can be greater during high-income years and lowered (or dropped to zero) during low-income years. Procedures of this nature can lessen the impact of income variation on family living and cause the efficiency with which resources are employed to be increased (through lowering the probability of foreclosure in low income years). These points are discussed in greater detail in a later chapter. Extension of "disaster loans" in the nature of the crop and feed loans employed over the 1918-46 period and currently by the Farmers' Home Administration is another possibility. More widespread use should be made of this machinery in lessening inefficiency of production.

Tax measures. Progressive income taxes reduce income variability over time because the tax rate increases progressively with income. This tendency may itself cause farmers to adopt less efficient but more stable farming systems. Under the existing tax structure, an increasingly small portion of higher incomes in favorable years can be carried forward to emergency years. After the progressive tax is deducted, the marginal returns from resources invested in farming systems with fluctuating but high incomes tend to be driven towards (or perhaps even below) the level of those invested in more stable but less profitable farming systems. In this sense a progressive income tax has an unfavorable impact on efficiency. Limitations of this nature might be eliminated through arrangements which allow an averaging out of incomes over a period of years.

Removing instability. The 2 major sources of instability, national economic fluctuations and extreme weather fluctuations, can be partially removed by (a) a system of forward prices for agricultural products, (b) greater stability in the national economic organism through monetary and fiscal policy, or (c) storage programs which carry forward surplus crops to drought years and even out the flow of the agricultural product over time. Under these systems, national administrators would be charged with forming expectations of the future. The extent to which instability can be eliminated and efficiency can be improved through forward prices and storage programs depends on (1) the effectiveness of the means employed (whether political pressure would force forward prices to levels which have the main effect of redistributing income between agricultural and non-agricultural portions of the population at one point in time or whether these forces would be sufficiently absent to allow improving the efficiency of resource use on individual farms over time) and (2) the extent to which national administrators might form more accurate expectations of future quantities (structural changes in supply and demand) than several million individual farmers. To the extent that forward prices and storage programs allow attainment of the latter, instability might be reduced and efficiency in the use of agricultural resources might be increased. Farmers could then pattern resources into farming systems which result in the greatest income and economic product over time rather than into systems which, while returning a smaller total income flow, result in a more stable or more certain flow of income. The crux of the uncertainty problem falls in the direction of instability forces exogeneous to the agricultural industry.

All-purpose crop insurance. While insurance for particular contingencies such as hail damage has been available through commercial channels for a long period of time, all-purpose insurance with a coverage of all natural hazards has been available only since 1938. It covers only selected crops but has been tried on an experimental basis for other crops. The practical effectiveness of all-purpose crop insurance in stabilizing income depends upon the level of coverage offered and the extent to which premium indemnity schedules correctly anticipate the distribution of yields. Participation in the program has not been great, perhaps for 2 main reasons: (1) Premium and indemnity schedules have been applied to the average yields of broad and heterogeneous areas; farmers in hogomeneous regions of small losses have stayed out; farmers in homogeneous areas of large loss or high yield variability have taken out contracts. Consequently, an actuarial structure has never been built up under which premium receipts (and costs of administration) balance indemnity payments. (2) Insurance contracts are of a form which allows the farmer, especially in the Great Plains, to form expectations or predict yield outcomes. The winter wheat producer can predict to some extent, although the error is still great, his outcome in the year ahead. As indicated earlier in this study, the amount of fall moisture suggests the direction of yields for the next crop year. Because of this possibility a large number of contracts may be written in years for which the probability of loss is known to be great. These difficulties can be alleviated, however, if (a) insurance contracts can be extended over a period precluding the possibility of farmer-prediction of yields, and (b) an actuarial structure can be developed for each homogeneous farming region. Once technical uncertainty can be reduced in regions of highly unstable weather, more efficient use of resources is possible; fewer resources will be invested in enterprises *per se* which provide income in years of low rainfall but are least efficient over long periods. Much work needs to be done before crop insurance can serve effectively in reducing income variance and uncertainty to a point where it does not cause farmers to invest resources in "uncertainty precautions."

National welfare, stability and efficiency. From a national welfare standpoint, stabilizing policies should be directed specifically at redistributing the incomes of particular individuals over them (an optimum intertemporal distribution of income for farmer Jones in North Dakota) and in increasing efficiency through improving the decision-making environment in which farmers operate. Programs aimed at the general income distribution problem (transfers from persons with high incomes to persons with low incomes) can better be built around progressive income taxes and the public provision of needed health, nutritional, or other services. Stabilizing programs should not have the effect of holding factors in regions of production where they are inefficiently employed over time. The fact that previous citizens settle in highly unstable climatic regions does not establish an economic basis for income and cost subsidies which will hold human and capital resources in the area indefinitely into the future. But should not society provide income subsidies during the drought years, in order that resources will be on hand to harvest the bumper product of good yields in areas such as the Great Plains? While the productivity of resources in these areas may be high in individual years, it is low in others. Productivity concepts are meaningful only as they refer to extended time periods. Where the marginal productivity of resources is low as an average over time, means should be provided whereby human and other resources might be withdrawn and directed into other types of production or into other areas of agriculture. To the extent that bumper yields come in sequences and can be predicted, society might even keep a mobile task force of capital and labor resources on hand; it could be rushed into the area during favorable yield periods to reap the large product of resources; it could be withdrawn, except for that portion retained in extensive farming operations, in low-yield years, when productivity of resources is greater elsewhere. Machinery of this nature must await greater predictability of crop yield sequences. From a pure productivity or efficiency standpoint, however, the method has as much merit as income subsidies which imply knowledge of yield distributions and which stand to retain an excessive population in arid regions not only during drought years but also over extended time periods.

Selected References

Arrow, K. J., "Alternative Approaches to the Theory of Choice in Risk-Taking Situations," *Econometrica*, Vol. 19.

Boulding, K. E., *A Reconstruction of Economics*. New York: Wiley, 1950, Chs. 4, 5.

Friedman, M., and Savage, L., "The Utility Analysis of Choices Involving Risk," *Jour. Pol. Econ.*, Vol. LVI.

Hart, A. G., *Anticipations, Uncertainty and Dynamic Planning*. Chicago: University of Chicago Press, 1948.

Heady, Earl O., "Short-Run Resource Allocation," *Jour. Farm Econ.*, Vol. 32.

Hopkins, J. A., and Murray, W. G., *Elements of Farm Management*. New York: Prentice-Hall, Inc. (forthcoming), Chs. 4 and 11.

Hurwicz, L., "Theory of the Firm and of Investment," *Econometrica*, Vol. 14.

Johnson, D. G., *Forward Prices for Agriculture*. Chicago: University of Chicago Press, 1947, Ch. 4.

Jones, J. L., "Stabilizing Farming by Shifting Wheat Land to Grass in the Northern Great Plains," *Jour. Farm Econ.*, Vol. 32.

Katona, G., *Psychological Analysis of Economic Behavior*. New York: McGraw-Hill, 1951, Chs. 9, 10.

Marschak, J., "Money and the Theory of Assets," *Econometrica*, Vol. 6.

————, "Rational Behavior, Uncertain Prospects and Measurable Utility," *Econometrica*, Vol. 18.

Schickele, R., "Farmers Adaptations to Income Uncertainty," *Jour. Farm Econ.*, Vol. 32.

Stigler, G., "Production and Distribution in the Short-Run," *Jour. Pol. Econ.*, Vol. XLVII.

Von Newmann, J., and Morgenstern, O., *Theory of Games and Economic Behavior*. Princeton: Princeton University Press, 1947.

Williams, D. B., "Price Expectations and Reactions to Uncertainty by Illinois Farmers," *Jour. Farm Econ.*, Vol. 33.

18

Instability, Capital Use, and Farm Size

ALTHOUGH previous chapters dealt with the manner in which given resources can be managed to meet uncertainty, only passing consideration was given to the quantity of capital used. Problems of the quantity of capital used under uncertainty are also those of credit and farm size. Size of farm is as much a function of uncertainty and the capital market as of technical scale relationships. Accordingly, the focal questions of this chapter become these: How is the scale of the firm in agriculture affected by uncertainty and risk aversion? What are the interrelationships of size, capital, equity, and the credit market? The problems posed are indeed difficult ones.[1] Several precautions which farmers can take against uncertainty do affect the scale of output possible from given cost or resource outlays. This statement applies particularly to cost and product flexibility. The important uncertainty precautions which limit scale are in a somewhat different direction, however, and grow out of the interaction between uncertainty, management and capital.

Firm Size Under Perfect and Imperfect Knowledge

The effect of uncertainty on firm size *per se* may be understood best by contrasting a situation of economic uncertainty with a "purely static" environment wherein knowledge of the future might be perfect. Accepted theory suggests no size limit for the individual firm in a static or perfect knowledge situation; without uncertainty there would be no place for management in the coordinating sense, except, as outlined in Chapter 19, for establishing initial plans. Once the single set of expectations was established indicating the known changes to come about (the timing and extent of change), the perfect single plan could be laid out for all time; the consequences would be known and the routine duties of carrying through

---

[1] See F. H. Knight, Preface to London School of Economics edition of *Risk, Uncertainty and Profit*, 1933. He has stated that "The relation between efficiency and size of firms is one of the most serious problems of theory, being, in contrast with the relation for a plant, largely a matter of personality and historical accident rather than of intelligible principles."

could be left up to supervisory personnel. Without need for management beyond the initial plan, there would be, to the extent that a homogeneous supply of each factor is available, no fixed factor in production. (The supply would not have to be entirely homogeneous for each factor if the amount and characteristics of each unit were known.) Diminishing resource productivity comes about as firm size is increased only because some factor is limited in quantity. Ordinarily, management serves as a fixed and limiting factor in production. Under perfect knowledge, however, no single factor would be limited and fixed because management would not be needed. True, an optimum or limited size might exist for each plant; but limits would not exist for the firm. The firm could add any number of plants. If we go back to our original distinction between the firm and the plant we can see why this might be true. The firm is the choice or decision-making unit; the plant is the physical producing unit. The size of the firm can be increased by doubling the number of plants as well as by doubling the size of existing plants. Thus, rather than increase the size of the plant from SAC_2 to SAC_3 in Figure 9 of Chapter 12, 2 plants of the size SAC_2 might be employed. Without limitations in management or resources, the per-unit cost for 2 plants of the size SAC_2 are the same as for 1 plant of this size. While a limit might exist in the size of the industry (because of external market diseconomies and limitations in demand) no limit need exist in the size of the firm.[2] While it would appear that the addition of more plants and output would increase the number of decisions and the amount of management required, it must be remembered that, under perfect knowledge, all of these things would have been foreseen and courses of action prescribed for them. It is unpredictability of change rather than change itself which requires continuing decisions as to the course of action to be followed. If the nature of change could be predicted "once and for all," the best course of action for the future could be charted in advance, and the specified course could be followed in routine fashion.

Managerial limitations. Where knowledge of change and the future is uncertain, management must function continuously; therefore, it does become a limiting factor in the production for a single firm. The addition of more plants and a greater volume of output contribute uncertainty along with change and the imperfect knowledge of future prices and yields or production coefficients. As the uncertainty increases, the number of deci-

---

[2] It has been indicated in a previous chapter that the laws of gravity and other related physical factors limit the size to which 1 machine or plant might be extended: A plow "twice as large" may require either (a) more than twice as much power to double the acreage, or (b) fewer acres plowed with the same power. However, with no other limiting factors, 2 plows and 2 tractors should be able to plow twice as many acres as 1 plow of the same size. Thus an increase in the scale of the firm need not come about alone by enlarging one farm (a plant) in acreage but it can also come about by doubling the numbers of farms or plants.

sions which must be made by management also increases; the greater the number of decisions, the less perfect they become because the supporting knowledge upon which each is based becomes less perfect. Thus "diminishing returns for management" come about because of imperfect decisions and the corresponding misdirection of resources relative to price and production outcomes. In his original formulation of dynamic or uncertainty limits to firm size, N. Kaldor [3] has suggested that only entrepreneurship can be the limiting factor in production and, aside from differences in homogeneity or quality and changes in the proportionality of other factors, it cannot be increased in the same proportion as other factors. Even as an attempt is made to add management, all central policy decisions still must pass through the minds of one or a central group of persons. The more changes and the greater the extent of changes, the greater the amount of decision-making necessary for the central management. Similarly, the greater the amount of change and uncertainty, the greater are (1) the possible errors in prediction and choice and (2) the restrictions on the size of the firm. Conversely, the smaller is the change and uncertainty, the greater is the opportunity for expansion in firm size. While exceptions in respect to factor quality and divisibility can be made for the analysis above, the logic set forth appears important in explaining the optimum size of a farm (or other economic and decision-making units, including armies). Most individuals are aware that as the number of decisions which they make increases, less time can be given to obtaining information relevant to each and outcomes become less satisfactory. Perhaps management as the limiting force in firm size does not become effective until output has been pressed to considerable levels. There does, however, seem to be a greater tendency for farm size to increase in fairly stable and prosperous periods. This phenomena may result from a combination of forces which includes not only management considerations *per se* but also (a) greater certainty in the minds of farmers, (b) improved capital positions within agriculture, and (c) greater incomes outside of farming (for example, some operators give up their farms and hence allow consolidation by remaining farmers).

When uncertainty and the limitations of management are related to farm size, the early farm management hypothesis that an optimum size of farm exists for each individual merits important consideration. Persons with limited managerial ability may be efficient in handling small units with simple organizations which require few anticipations and decisions and no hired labor. Taylor's concept of "80-acre farmers" and "160-acre farmers" has foundation in uncertainty as well as in psychological and physical characteristics of individuals.[4] While the uncertainty-manage-

---

[3] Kaldor, N., "The Equilibrium of the Firm," *Econ. Jour.*, Vol. XLIV, pp. 60-76.
[4] H. C. Taylor, *Outlines of Agricultural Economics*. New York: Macmillan, 1925, pp. 177-183.

ment complex may introduce decreasing productivity and increasing costs to cause limitations in the size of firm, there are other elements of uncertainty which also relate to the profitability and psychology of capital use and hence farm size. These considerations merit major consideration.

Relation of uncertainty to farm size. Farm management economists have long suggested that uncertainty, apart from equity and credit considerations, is attached to farm size. Many studies have shown that profits and losses are relatively greater during prosperity and depression respectively for large farms as compared to small farms. Aside from imputational difficulties discussed elsewhere, there are reasons why the farmer might view uncertainty as a function of scale or farm size and distinct from the equity considerations. If dispersion or range of expected outcomes (or variance of actual outcomes) can be taken as a measure of uncertainty, uncertainty becomes a function of farm size in the following fashion. Firms of different sizes require varying amounts of capital. If investments are successful, the large farm adds more to the capital or equity than the small farm; if prices and yields are unfavorable, the large farm realizes greater losses and sees a greater part of the capital melt away. The relationship between farm size and uncertainty can be illustrated by comparisons with the theory of gambling or chance; farming or other business ventures fall in the realm of "games of chance" with the exception that the number of chances for any one farmer is not often great enough that the successful and unsuccessful outcomes can be averaged out. Suppose that an individual with $1,000 can gamble part or all of it at constant odds of 5 to 1; if successful he will win $5 for each dollar bet or invested. If he bets $100 dollars, he gains $500 if he wins and loses $100 if the outcome is unfavorable. The range of possible outcomes is $600. If he bets $200, the gain is $1,000 if he wins while the loss is $200 if he loses and the possible range becomes $1,200. The possible range of outcomes is $6,000 if he bets the full $1,000. While the rate earned or lost is constant (because the odds are constant) the absolute range of outcomes is a function of the amount bet. The same principle is involved in business ventures and while some entrepreneurs are concerned only with the rate earned on investment, others are concerned with the absolute magnitude of profit or loss. Knowledge that, for any given set of expectations, the range of possible outcomes will increase as the size of the investment increases causes them to view larger firms and greater capital outlays as involving "greater risk." [5] Of course it is fear of greater loss as firm size

[5] The point has been emphasized in J. R. Hicks, *Value and Capital.* London: Oxford University Press, 1948, p. 199:

"It seems first of all necessary to distinguish between the cases (1) where the entrepreneur, at the date in question, already has an established business, (2) where he is a potential entrepreneur considering whether to set up a business.... In the first case the entrepreneur already has ... the equipment of the firm. It is the firm's legacy of the past.... But what about the case of the new firm? Here there is no legacy of increases which causes farmers to restrict their operations; actual losses may never be realized if sufficient safeguards are taken to prevent them.

We can now define the "subjective opportunity or possibility curve" which faces the manager-investor when different quantities of capital are to be invested. It compares the combinations of (a) possible money income and (b) range of outcomes or uncertainty (risk of loss), as investment and scale are increased.[6] First let us consider the simple case where the entrepreneur thinks of "expected income" in terms of the modal or most probable outcome. He expects three outcomes are possible after costs have been met: (1) a return of $+15$ per cent with a subjective probability of .2 (he "expects" that there are 2 chances out of 10 that 15 per cent will be returned, (2) a return of $+5$ per cent with a subjective probability of .6 and (c) a return of -10 per cent with a subjective probability of .2. In other words, he expects (with a chance of 6 out of 10) that absolute earnings will be $500 on an investment of $10,000; $1,000 on an investment of $20,000; and $1,500 on an investment of $30,000. Yet, since other

---

the past to check expansion. Is there anything to stop firms from being planned on an indefinitely large scale—anything, that is, other than the imperfection of competition and the limitation of the market? Common sense replies that there must be something; even in industries which seem to approximate the perfectly competitive type, we do not observe new firms starting up at once on a mammoth scale, but rather the opposite. There must be some obstacles present, even obstacles which are particularly present in the case of new firms.... One of these obstacles is of course that which we have already mentioned when dealing with the static problem— the increasing difficulty of management and control as the firm gets larger. In a new firm, where everything has to be arranged from the start, and there is no possibility of proceeding by standing rules, this difficulty is particularly intense; so it does something to explain why firms usually start on a small scale.... Another obstacle, also present generally, but particularly present with new firms, is the element of risk. As the planned size of the firm increases, the possible losses become steadily greater; and people will usually become less and less willing to expose themselves to the chance of such losses. Now we have shown that this increasing risk-factor may be represented as a shift in expected prices to the disadvantage of the entrepreneur (as the actual rate at which we can borrow may shift to his disadvantage in fact); evidently it is quite capable of bringing expansion to a stop."

[6] Rather than use the term subjective opportunity curve, perhaps we should use the term subjective joint product scale line. We are not holding the quantity of capital constant while comparing the quantity of one product, probable money income, with a competing product, uncertainty. Rather we are increasing the input of capital and realizing the two as joint and inseparable products. (Joint products in fixed proportions.) The term subjective opportunity curve is justified, however, in the sense that if the entrepreneur has a given amount of capital, he can allocate it in one direction (which gives more of both joint products) or in a second direction (which gives less of both of these joint products of possible money income and investments) or, possible profits and uncertainty (range of outcome) can be considered complementary products with given resources: the entrepreneur can produce more of one and also more of the other or less of one and less of the other. In order to keep our analysis parallel with that of other treatments of the subject see K. E. Boulding, *Reconstruction of Economics*. New York: Wiley, 1950, pp. 117-125. We will continue to employ the term (subjective) opportunity curve. At a later point we show that the 2 products, expected money income and uncertainty, need not be forthcoming in fixed proportions when either increasing or decreasing returns prevail.

outcomes are also possible, the possible range of outcomes (if the differences between the maximum and minimum outcomes is compared) is
$2,500, $5,000 and $7,500 for investments of $10,000, $20,000 and $30,000
respectively. The range or dispersion of possible outcomes increases, indicating greater uncertainty as the scale of the investment and the size of
the business increases. The opportunity or possibility curve takes the form
of line *P* in Figure 1, where the magnitude of possible returns is measured
on the vertical axis, while the possible range of outcomes or uncertainty
(possible magnitude of loss) is measured on the horizontal axis.[7] If the
individual invests nothing, the prospective return is zero and the chance of
loss or the range of possible outcomes is zero (there is no uncertainty).
If he invests $30,000, the most probable expected return is $4,500, while
the range of possible outcomes is $7,500. We can also graph the indi-
vidual's preference curve in the manner of Chapter 14. Line *I* is such an
indifference curve and it slopes upward, indicating that the individual is
willing to assume a greater range of possible outcomes only if the income

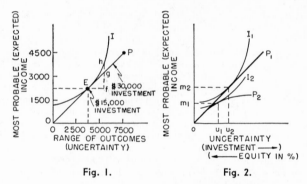

Fig. I.   Fig. 2.

Uncertainty and size of investment.

prospects become sufficiently great.[8] If his utility is to remain at the level
suggested by indifference curve *I*, the individual will accept great uncertainty only as long as it is associated with increasingly greater prospective
incomes. He must make a choice between larger or smaller investments
involving more or less uncertainty. Equilibrium is established, in a subjective sense, when the indifference curve becomes tangent to the oppor-

---

[7] The opportunity curve considers only returns from investment within the firm.
It does not consider the income which would be forthcoming were the quantity of
funds involved to be invested in some certain alternative such as government bonds.
If the latter possibility were taken into consideration, the curve *P* would originate
on the vertical axis at some point above zero (and would slope upward if the most
probable return were greater than the certain alternative and downward if the
opposite were true).

[8] Again, as indicated in the previous chapters, the willingness of individuals to
chance loss of a given amount of capital may well depend on the assets which they
own. A person with small capital may have an indifference curve with a greater
slope than a person possessing a large amount of capital.

tunity line indicating that maximum (expected) utility has been attained.[9]
Here the (1) marginal rate of substitution between (a) expected income
and (b) uncertainty as commodities (with positive or negative utility)
is equal to (2) the marginal rate of substitution between (a) income and
(b) uncertainty as products. The optimum choice is denoted by an investment of $15,000, a most probable expected income of $2,250, and a
possible range of outcomes of $3,750.[10] The equilibrium or stability con-
dition can also be interpreted this way: [11] The investor may refuse to go
beyond E because (1) increasingly greater amounts of prospective incomes are necessary (on the indifference curve) to make him willing to
undertake greater risk while (2) the most probable expected income (on
the opportunity curve) does not increase at a rate great enough to com-

---

[9] This chapter assumes quite largely, although not entirely, that the entrepreneur
is interested first in profit maximization. The utility in reference, therefore, is a
subjective preference on a scale of outcomes with increasing probability of failure.
This type of subjective discounting is somewhat apart from the type of Chapter 14
where ends other than profit maximization are involved. The family may "discount"
greater returns from a large farm because of the disutility of housing hired labor or
the dislike for greater entrepreneurial efforts, a different category of subjective
discount.

[10] Maximum utility is denoted since higher indifference curves could not be attained with the opportunities available while any combination on the opportunity
line above or below E would denote a lower indifference curve and hence a smaller
total utility. An increase in the most probable expected income for all levels of
investment would result in a steeper opportunity curve and hence in the possibilities
of a greater investment. (Higher indifference curves can be tangent to the opportunity curve at a point both above and to the right of the point E, indicating
willingness to take greater risks with improved money prospects.) Contrariwise, an
increase in the range (uncertainty) of outcomes (with most probable expected
returns remaining the same) lessens the slope of the opportunity curve and causes
the lower attainable indifference curve to become tangential below and to the left
of point E (a smaller investment).

If the most probable expected return is less than zero, the opportunity curve will
have a negative slope and no investment will be made if the entrepreneur is characterized by risk aversion in the sense that greater uncertainty must be accompanied
by higher prospective incomes (an indifference curve with a positive slope from the
outset).

We have said nothing about returns growing out of technical economies of scale.
If economies to scale exist, the opportunity curve will be convex from the horizontal
axis; if diseconomies exist, it may be concave; if there are both increasing and decreasing returns to scale, the opportunity curve will be convex-concave.

[11] The fact that E represents the maximum utility (anticipated satisfaction or
whatever subjective quantity the entrepreneur maximizes) can also be explained in
this manner. Suppose that we were to move up the indifference curve from point E
to point h. The same degree of satisfaction (amount of utility) would exist for the
entrepreneur only if the additional uncertainty involved (Ef) were accompanied by
a prospective increase in profits by fh. However, the subjective opportunity line
indicates that an increase in uncertainty by Ef is accompanied by only an fg increase
in probable returns. Since the prospective increase in profits (fg) falls short of that
amount (fh) necessary to compensate the individual for taking the added risk
(indicated by Ef), then point E denotes the optimum combination of probable
profits and uncertainty. Psychologically, he is willing to accept this combination as
the "most satisfying."

pensate for the greater uncertainty. He is, therefore, unwilling to select possibilities beyond E.

Not all farmers have to borrow capital to extend investment and farm size and many restrict size because of the uncertainty which arises apart from equity considerations. This condition may apply particularly to older operators who have full equities and are nearing retirement; they seek security or certainty of returns not only by refraining from extending the size of their business but also by investing in alternatives such as real estate mortgages and government bonds. The manner in which the probable outcomes and the magnitude of uncertainty are mentally visualized may be either "refined" or "rough." While one geometric model was cited for illustrative purposes, more complex methods might be employed by persons with the proper mental tools. The great magnitude of farmers do not possess these tools and simply reckon in rough fashion that although bigger farms are likely to bring in greater incomes the possible range of outcomes or chance of loss is greater than for small units. The size of farm which individual farmers view as subjectively optimum depends on their liking for risk or security. A sample of Central Iowa farmers indicated definite viewpoints in respect to the relationship between farm size and uncertainty. Their attitudes are expressed in Table 1.

Table I.
Central Iowa Farmer Estimates of Optimum Farm Size in Terms of Returns and Uncertainty
(Averages for all Farmers) *

Size of farm now operated	Size of farm which would give maximum net return aside from uncertainty[a]	Size of farm operator would select if he had 100 per cent equity[b]	Size of farm operator would select if he had 50 per cent equity and a cash lease[b]
Small	363	193	187
Medium	457	245	229
Large	664	432	402

* Source: Random sample of cash grain farmers under project 1135 of the Iowa Agricultural Experiment Station.

[a] Includes consideration of decreasing and increasing costs to farm size or returns to scale and an output which would equate marginal costs and marginal return of using more capital.

[b] Includes size farmers would select in terms of the degree of uncertainty surrounding farms of different sizes.

Even under full equity positions, farmers favor units somewhat smaller than the size considered as optimum in terms of cost economies.[12] Under

[12] The questions were asked during 1949 in terms of the price, cost, and yield expectations which farmers held over the 20 years ahead. The notions of optimum include farmers' subjective notion of future costs and returns. Differences in the optimum size (column 1) between groups of farmers may be explained partly in the fact that operators with large (small) capital were operating larger (smaller) farms and hence had better (poorer) knowledge of technical scale relationships and cost economies. Too, since each individual viewed the projected sizes in terms of his own ability, it is possible that the greater entrepreneurial ability of managers on large farms caused them to view somewhat larger farms as optimum.

low equities (the uncertainty facet discussed in the section below), the indicated size was even smaller.

Equity and the principle of increasing risk. While uncertainty may be related directly to size and capital investment, the scale of the firm may be "dampened" even more through considerations of borrowed capital and equity. This phenomenon has been termed by Kalecki as "the principle of increasing risk." [13] Business managers using equity as a barometer of the survival likelihood for their firm have this principle in mind. The so-called "principle of increasing risk" suggests that as a firm expands by use of borrowed capital, the chance of loss of its own capital increases. The arithmetic example of Table 2 may be used to illustrate the proposition: Suppose that a farmer starts out with $10,000 of his own and that, among other alternative outcomes, there is a chance of a loss amounting to 20 per cent on the investment. If the loss is realized under this situation

Table 2.
Effect of Equity on Range of Profit for an Entrepreneur Owning $10,000 in Capital
(Hypothetical Data)

Item	100 per cent equity	75 per cent equity	33 per cent equity	25 per cent equity
Total capital employed	$10,000	$20,000	$30,000	$40,000
Borrowed capital employed	0	10,000	20,000	30,000
1. Total profit with rate of earning at +20%	+2,000	+3,500	+5,000	+6,500
2. Total loss with rate of earning at −20%	−2,000	−4,500	−7,000	−9,500
3. Range (1 + 2 with sign disregarded)	4,000	8,000	12,000	16,000

of 100 per cent equity, the value of the operator's own assets drops to $8,000. Now if he borrows an additional $10,000 at 5 per cent interest, chances of loss include (a) 20 per cent on his own capital of $10,000 and (b) 25 per cent on the borrowed capital (the 20 per cent from the business outcome plus the 5 per cent interest charge). If the loss is realized and all expenses are paid, the value of his own assets now drops to $5,500. If he borrows $20,000 and the business venture results in a loss of 20 per cent, the value of his own assets and his net worth drops to $3,000. (The loss on his own and the borrowed capital amounts to $7,000.) Uncertainty can be expressed not only in terms of the effect of borrowing on the possible value of the entrepreneur's capital but also in terms of the possible range or dispersion (and also skewness) of possible outcomes. The table below illustrates how, in this sense, "increasing risk" accompanies decreases in equity. (Constant returns to scale is assumed for simplicity.) The possible range of outcomes is only $4,000 for an entrepreneur with a

[13] M. Kalecki, *Essays in the Theory of Economic Fluctuations.* London: Allen & Unwin, 1939, pp. 95-106.

$10,000 and a full equity. It is $16,000 for the same firm if $30,000 is borrowed and equity is pulled down to 25 per cent.

Since "bankruptcies are irretrievable," the specter of a vanishing equity always haunts farmers: once the firm is liquidated, the manager cannot simply "roll the wheel of chance" once again to "let the probabilities catch up," and borrowed capital itself imposes uncertainty on the firm. The entrepreneur who can borrow funds must arrive at some subjective equilibrium selecting an acceptable combination of prospective profits and uncertainty (or possible losses). This subjective equilibrium can be presented graphically if we again examine the nature of the individual's opportunity and indifference curves. When, as supposed above, the degree of uncertainty is increased as funds are borrowed to increase firm size because (a) the possible value of the entrepreneur's capital lessens as equity evaporates (possible losses become greater) and (b) the dispersion or skewness of possible outcomes increases as borrowing is extended, the opportunity line relating the most probable expected returns and the amount of uncertainty becomes concave in the manner of line P_2 in Figure 2. (It will also be concave if the interest rate increases with the amount of capital borrowed. The higher the interest, the lower are the profit prospects for a given set of product price and yield expectations.) This curve indicates that each extension in investment and possible profits is accompanied by a proportionately greater increase in the amount of "risk."

The illustration supposes that P_1 involves only equity capital, while P_2 involves both equity and borowed capital. Thus possibility line P_2 branches off from P_1 at the point where expansion takes place by means of borrowed capital. To attain a given level of expected income under borrowed capital (P_2) a greater amount of uncertainty is encountered than when expansion is with full-equity capital (P_1). Accordingly, investment and size of the firm will be restricted below the scale which would exist if the firm had access to unlimited quantities of full-equity capital. The difference can be illustrated by means of the subjective choice mechanism indicated earlier and the use of indifference curves I_1 and I_2. Indifference curve I_1 and opportunity curve P_1 define the subjective equilibrium when the size of the firm can be extended through equity capital. The optimum combination of possible income and uncertainty is m_2 and u_2. However, when expansion is through borrowed capital, the entrepreneur must drop to the lower indifference curve (I_2) and the possibility curve P_2. Subjective equilibrium is attained with prospects of a most probable income amounting to m_1 and uncertainty amounting to u_1.[14]

---

[14] We denote investment and equity with the arrows to illustrate that uncertainty (range of outcomes) increases with the amount of capital and the decline in equity and not as an indication that the axis is a cardinal measure of these things. While our geometry overly simplifies the phenomena, it has been employed to convey the notions in lieu of more complicated paraphernalia.

By returning the analysis to a firm-household curve interrelationship we are able to emphasize that questions of capital investment and size of the firm (use of capital) under uncertainty are subjective considerations which must be and are decided in the minds of managers. Other formulations of the problem can be made in a pure firm context. However, these also lead to the notion of "increasing risk" and hence a restriction on investment and farm size under borrowed capital.[15] Little is known about the

[15] The formulation can be in the early sense of M. Kalecki, *Essays on the theory of fluctuations*. London: Allen & Unwin, 1939. First we may suppose constant returns to scale or size as indicated by the "most probable expected" marginal rate of profit curve MVP_1 in Figure A. If interest is at the level r_1 and if, because of uncertainty, the firm adds a discount (at a constant rate) to the interest rate, the discounted marginal cost of capital becomes r_1'. However, in this case no equilibrium in the size

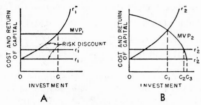

A   B

of the firm will exist since the marginal value productivity of capital will exceed the discounted marginal cost of capital throughout. However, if the firm views greater investment with increasing risk because of its lower equity, an increasing discount may be added to the constant rate of interest (r_1) and the discounted cost of capital becomes r_1''. Of course r_1'' is a subjective function in much the same manner as those discussed earlier in the text. Here an equilibrium in the use of capital is attained when the most probable expected rate of earning (MVP_1) is equal to the discounted cost of capital (r_1''). (An amount of capital equal to oC.) The amount of discount and the increasing rate of discount is denoted by the difference between curves r_1 and r_1''. It is interesting to note that this proposition supports the earlier one that under a static environment and no discount, no size equilibrium would be possible. Figure B illustrates the same proposition under decreasing returns to scale and an increasing rate of discount: the use of capital will be oC_1 under uncertainty whereas it would be oC_3 under certainty (and oC_2 with a constant rate of discount). These propositions are the counterpart of those proposed in J. M. Keynes, *General Theory of Employment, Interest and Money*. New York: Harcourt, Brace, 1936, p. 135 (in his marginal efficiency of capital).

A second formulation of the increasing risk proposition is that of J. Steindl, *On Risk*. Oxford Economic Papers No. 7, pp. 21-45, in the modified notations which follow:

I = total investment of firm
C = entrepreneur's capital
e = expected internal (firm) rate of return on capital
p = expected rate of profit on entrepreneur's capital
r = market rate of interest (cost of capital).

The total profit eI is equal to the entrepreneur's profit pC plus interest paid to lenders. Then

$$eI = pC + r(I - C) \tag{1}$$

or

$$p = \frac{I}{C}(e - r) \tag{2}$$

It can be seen that the rate earned (the most probable expected rate) on the entrepreneur's capital (assuming constant returns to scale), is a linear function of the amount invested: The rate of profit on equity C will be greater the higher is the extent to which farmers discount returns as equity declines and uncertainty prospects increase. It is known, however, that equity and increasing risk considerations are important in the agricultural credit market.[16]

Equity financing and size. In contrast to the corporate form of business organization in many other industries, a single proprietorship characterizes the agricultural firm. Consequently, since the capital of individual farmers is limited, expansion in the size of farms is brought about mainly by use of borrowed funds. The principle of increasing risk thus stands to place a heavy restriction on firm size in agriculture. It does not have the same implications under stock sales and the equity financing of corporate firms. The principle is a partial, although not complete, explanation of differences in firm size between agricultural and other industries. (Also, numerous other industries, like agriculture, are characterized by small units.) The corporate firm is faced with those uncertainties, discussed in the previous section, which attach directly to firm size and scale of capital and are distinct from equity considerations. However, the limited liability

---

amount of borrowed capital $(I - C)$ employed if the rate of profit (e) on investment (I) is greater than the rate of interest (r). The rate of profit (p) on equity capital is particularly high in case of success. If the rate of profit (e) on investment (I) falls short of the interest rate (r) the lower will the profit (the higher will the loss) be on entrepreneur capital (C). These relationships explain why a lessening of the equity ratio increases risk. The limit on investment thus arises from the uncertainty which surrounds the prospective rate of return e on total investment. The prospective rate of profit (e) must not only be larger than the interest rate r but it must include a premium for the uncertainty of returns. This excess of e over r can be called the uncertainty premium q. It is the relationship of q to the equity ratio which will now be investigated. The entrepreneur views the prospective return e in some fashion and ranks this enterprise, say S^*, in his uncertainty index. The entrepreneur, however, is primarily interested in the rate of profit on his own capital. From (1) then the uncertainty s^* associated with this rate of profit is related to S^* by

$$s^* = \frac{I}{C} S^* \tag{3}$$

Now q, the uncertainty premium, is related to s^*, since an increase in uncertainty will increase the premium required by the entrepreneur to induce investment. This may be written as

$$q = g(s^*) = g\left(\frac{I}{C} S^*\right) \tag{4}$$

It is evident that for a given S^* and for a given entrepreneur's capital C, an increase in borrowing will increase the uncertainty premium q. However, if q increases at a constant rate less than e (also increasing at a constant rate due to the assumption of constant return to scale) there would still be no limit to investment. Therefore q must not only increase with borrowing but it must increase at an increasing rate. The reason for this increasing rate of change in q is that errors in predicting e are magnified when stated in terms of errors in predicting the rate of return on the entrepreneur's own capital C. Therefore, at some point q becomes sufficiently large that the danger of impairment of the entrepreneur's capital deters further investment.

[16] An Iowa study suggests that farmers place the risk premium at a very high level as equity decreases. For a partial report of this study, see E. R. Swanson, *Resource Productivity and Attitudes Toward the Use of Credit in Southern Iowa.* Ph.D. Thesis, Iowa State College, 1951.

feature of the corporation does lessen the chance that the investor's complete financial foundation will decay if business outcomes are unfavorable.

Equilibrium in farm size and the use of capital in an uncertain market is not one which results in equation of the cost of credit and the marginal return of capital. Farm management studies have shown this to be true historically: As a group, large farms have greater profits than small farms. Still, the agricultural economist does not tread on solid ground when he advises the small farmer to "go thou and do likewise"; small farms can expand to the scale of larger units only if (a) they borrow more funds and (b) some of the present units are "squeezed out of existence." Because of uncertainty and the principle of increasing risk as the operator sees it, he may well continue to operate a unit of less than optimum scale and be entirely rational in his decision. Uncertainty (and the principle of increasing risk and "historic accident") helps explain the co-existence of farms of many sizes. Uncertainty is probably more important than scale relationships in explaining the varied pattern of farm sizes. It may offset entirely the large farm's cost advantage of a few dollars per acre. While constant physical returns to scale alone would lead to an indeterminant size, this scale relationship in combination with uncertainty would allow co-existence of farms of many sizes. "Historic accident" is important in this manner: The private capital of beginning farms differs greatly while the equity-risk principle applies similarly to all farmers. A beginner with $3,000 cannot, in the sense of increasing risk, expand to the capital base of the beginner with $12,000. The first man can borrow only $4,500 before he has driven his equity down to 40 per cent. The second operator can borrow $18,000 before his equity ratio is pushed to a similar level. In terms of equity ratios, both are faced with an equal degree of uncertainty and, aside from increasing returns to scale and incomes below subsistence levels, the small unit should be able to survive as well as the larger unit. Why, then, is there not a greater trend towards larger units in agriculture and other industries? Aside from scale considerations, one hypothesis is that the small-scale manager may be more nearly prone, because of a smaller stake in the outcome, to "gamble all" and drive his equity lower than the large operator. From this standpoint a steady stream of small-scale entrepreneurs might flow particularly into an industry such as agriculture. Starting with small capital, they may be "gamblers" who are willing to bet their small funds on the odds of making a success and becoming their own masters. In few other major industries can a firm with small stakes enter the game of chance. The presence of many small units making the first bet helps explain the low average farm size and the low capital intensity of agriculture. While many never make the grade some of these gamblers hang on persistently for several years. Others never give up, and under the expectations that the odds will eventually turn in their favor, make a career of farming although their returns are low.

While the continued life of the corporation allows it to accumulate capital and extend its borrowing base, the same opportunity is not open in agriculture. Since this vehicle whereby the equities of outsiders can be tapped does not exist to any important extent in agriculture, the responsibility for capital accumulation falls upon single households of single generations. While it is true that capital in the form of credit can be obtained from outside, the credit base is necessarily smaller than it would be if the major portion of farmer equity did not have to be furnished from within agriculture. One may point out the large number of rented farms and suggest that the opportunity for non-farmers to own real estate provides a substitute for the equity of corporations. However, this source is less important than at first it appears. Recent studies indicate that an important portion of tenant-operated farms is owned by retired farmers and farm widows. Families such as these also must be considered within the framework of the agricultural household. Absence of corporate stocks possibly deters the flow of capital into agriculture in still an additional manner. The purchaser of a share of stock in A.T and T., for example, need not, except in a very remote sense, provide any of the coordination or management input. If his entrepreneurial abilities are low, he can sell his labor to one coordinator and furnish his savings to another through purchase of stocks. These opportunities are in contrast to those of agriculture. Often the owner of farm real estate must himself be acquainted with the techniques of agriculture and furnish some input of coordination. While he has opportunity to invest in corporations and realize return from the outstanding coordinating ability of corporation executives wherever they may appear, returns to the owner of a tenant-operated farm depend more nearly on the productivity of the owner's individual coordinating ability; he may gain from the entrepreneurial efforts of an outstanding tenant but those tenants with greatest ability soon take the step to ownership whereby they can realize the full product of coordination efforts.

It is interesting to question why corporate firms have not emerged to greater extent in agriculture. The increasing risk principle suggests the hypothesis that under corporate organization farms would be larger than under single proprietorship. This hypothesis has been "accepted" by many people. Kansas even has a law prohibiting corporate farms. No suitable answer is at hand to explain the lack of corporate farming. Perhaps the very great uncertainty in agriculture discourages corporations. Lack of monopolistic markets may also discourage the giant business firm. Another explanation with some basis is this: Agriculture is a subsistence industry of low demand elasticities and a continuous flow of output-increasing innovations. Thus the declining-industry aspect and low resource returns of agriculture may themselves dampen the tendency for capital and large scale firms to be added.

Faced with the desirability of supplementing his own assets with outside capital, the farmer can hire resources through rental arrangements as well as through borrowed funds. From this standpoint then, the rental market in agriculture is a substitute for the corporate stocks of other industries. The tenant can increase the scale of his operations by renting more land or by renting a larger farm. Hiring of additional resource services through renting does not entail the same thinning of equity as does purchase of resource services through ownership. Accordingly, the uncertainty surrounding larger operations is less under renting than under owning. (A later discussion on leasing systems points out some important differences within rental arrangements.) Since the tenant must lay out greater expenses if he operates 320 acres rather than 160 acres, the principle of increasing risk also applies to his capital if it must be borrowed. However, the principle has little direct bearing on additional land which may be rented under a share lease (see Chapter 20 for cash rent exceptions). To the extent that there is, in the sense of unit costs, a general optimum size of farm, the rental market should facilitate adjustments in this direction.

The Iowa study of cash grain farmers indicated that farm managers believed this to be the case; after indicating the size of unit which would give minimum costs in an historic or *ex poste* sense, they suggested a somewhat smaller size as desirable under tenant operation with a large equity and a sharply smaller unit as most desirable under ownership with a low equity. The 2 sizes specified were in terms of the uncertainty which the farmers viewed as "being characteristic of the period ahead." Many studies show the average size of rented farms to be greater than that of owned farms. However, as is pointed out in a subsequent chapter, certain types of renting also pose problems in farm size.

Equity and variations in capital. While the principle of increasing risk stands to explain limits in the use of agricultural capital at 1 point in time, it also helps explain wide fluctuations in capital use throughout the phases of the business cycle. Equity is a function not only of the quantity of borrowed capital but also of the market value of the resources employed by the firm. A fall in the value of physical assets during a price decline is equivalent, in its effect on equity, to an increase in the amount of funds borrowed at a given price level. (A rise in commodity and resource prices has an opposite effect on equity.) Even aside from uncertainty associated with price level changes, the amount of borrowed capital which is optimal for a collection of physical assets at one price level is not optimal at another price level. The principle of increasing risks suggests that the firm should retrench in use of capital acquired through credit, during deflation and expand use of borrowed capital during prosperity, since, if equity is to be held constant at one level (say 40 per cent), one collection of physical assets provides a fluctuating monetary base.

The effect of equity upon the subjective uncertainty in the mind of the farm entrepreneur changes not only over different phases of the trade cycle but also through different stages of the individual's life cycle. While farmers are willing to press equity to the minimum limits in their early and middle age, one goal for most farmers is that of building up an equity of 100 per cent before retirement. A survey of 150 Iowa farmers indicated that the great majority looked upon a "full equity" as one end in farming When questioned further, they actually look upon a 100 per cent equity as a means to greater liquidity and income certainty in retirement or old age. Full equity in this context again is largely an uncertainty-bred consideration. Were this not true, each agricultural firm would, in the absence of major changes in the price level, continually expand capital over time as savings and a new credit base comes into being. A farmer with $10,000, setting his equity ratio at a lower limit of 50 per cent, would not repay any principal with savings of $2,000 in the first year. Instead, he would expand total capital to $24,000 and the process would be continued until death of the operator. Quantity of capital employed and farm size would become a direct function of savings and time.

Capital Rationing

The farmer may refuse to use borrowed capital in a quantity to approximate equation of its marginal cost and marginal return in an *ex poste* manner because of either of 2 reasons: One, *risk aversion* in the manner already outlined, represents the manager's psychological discount of returns due to uncertainty. The other, termed *capital rationing*, is the inability of the borrower to obtain all of the capital funds which he might desire at current or possible interest rates.[17] Capital rationing is largely the response of lending firms to uncertainty. Credit firms considering a farm loan must take into account the same technical, technological, and price uncertainties which face the manager. The lender's uncertainty surrounding the physical production on a single farm may be even greater than that of the farmer; the operator is better acquainted with the particular situation and may view technical yields, if not price prospects, with greater "knowledge" than the loaning firm. The individual farmer also knows more about himself as a manager than does the credit manager. In addition, the loan firm must form expectations in respect to the honesty and integrity of its client. Mainly because the uncertainty facing the

---

[17] A third obstacle to the use of borrowed capital is the farm family's tendency to view debt in a moral or ethical sense. Some social groups attach a stigma to debt, and use of borrowed capital is restricted as farmers abstain from debts or attempt to liquidate their mortgages as rapidly as possible. In the random survey of the 250 Iowa farmers mentioned earlier, the majority of operators felt that farmers should establish "being out of debt" as a life objective. When questioned further, the great majority do not think it bad that corporative firms never attain a full equity. To the extent that basic psychology can be distilled from the complex surrounding farm decisions, it appears that many of the farmers studied considered the building up of full equity mainly as an uncertainty precaution for old age.

lending firm is as great or greater than for the farm itself, loans are extended on an institutionalized basis revolving around value of security rather than around capital productivity. Often there is no appraisal of the productivity of the capital itself and banks are willing to make loans on crops or livestock if the family car or the refrigerator is used as security. While the farm firm directly faces the principle of increasing risk, the loan firm is faced with a parallel phenomenon: It stands the increasing chance that the borrower will abscond with the security as his equity thins out or that the household of the borrowing firm will appropriate the funds of the lending firm. For these reasons lending institutions have placed arbitrary limits on the basis and extent of loans. Rough rules of thumb are used which state that the farmer must have assets providing an equity of 40 to 50 per cent of his total capital.

While household relationships and the entrepreneur's risk preferences are always involved in determining how far investment will be extended, we illustrate the facets of capital rationing below in a pure firm context. Capital rationing and risk aversion (which might be termed internal capital rationing) provide several situations under which use of capital may be restricted to a point short of that which equates the marginal cost and marginal value product of credit.

Situation I: **Unlimited funds and capital limited by risk aversion on the part of the borrowing firm.** This situation has been spelled out in the technical detail of footnotes on previous pages. It is reviewed here to illustrate the nature of the supply function for capital funds which faces the agricultural firm. Curve VP_1 in Figure 3 can be taken to indicate the marginal value productivity of capital on a particular farm,[18] and while it can be viewed in an *ex poste* light, it more appropriately serves as the manager's expectation of the value productivity of capital. Curve VP'_1 is the discounted marginal value productivity curve. It represents the return under VP_1 discounted because of uncertainty; both uncertainty and the amount of the discount increases, because of the increasing risk or declining equity principle, as the quantity of borrowed capital increases. The latter curve thus serves as the borrower's effective demand curve since it indicates the amount of capital which would be used at any one interest rate were funds available at that price.[19] The curve S_1, representing the supply of capital

---

[18] VP_1 suggests diminishing productivity of resources from the outset but the reader easily can make adaptations to the case where increasing or constant returns might prevail. In contrast to the presentation of Kalecki (footnote 15 on page 545) we employ the "increasing discount" on the most probable expected marginal value productivity of capital. We follow this procedure since the cost of borrowed capital is known with greater certainty (with full certainty except in the case of dishonest lenders and similar situations) than the return on the investment. Our presentation is identical except for this point.

[19] Each entrepreneur has his own opinion of the degree of uncertainty involved and his willingness to bear risks. The slope and shape of VP'_1 will vary accordingly and may be considered to include the features of the preference curve illustrated in Figures 1 and 2.

facing the borrowing firm or farm, takes on roughly the form indicated for agriculture: Up to certain equity limits, capital can be borrowed on real estate at standard 4 to 5 per cent interest rates; interest rates are slightly higher for livestock, machinery, and working capital, where physical

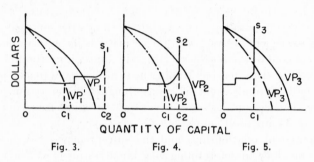

Fig. 3.   Fig. 4.   Fig. 5.

Risk aversion and capital rationing.

hazards are greater and the transformation period is shorter, than for land. Additional small amounts of capital can be obtained in the form of second mortgages, store credit, loans from finance agencies, and other high-interest sources. At some point, however, additional capital cannot be obtained at any price and the supply curve facing the borrowing firm becomes vertical or perfectly inelastic. Under this supply-demand situation, the firm will use oc_1 capital. This quantity is less than oc_2, the amount which is available through lending firms. Hence, the limiting factor in use of capital is risk aversion on the part of the borrowing firm rather than capital rationing on the part of credit firms; loan firms are willing to supply more capital than the borrowing firm could employ productively even if it did not discount returns due to uncertainty.

The mechanism of discount under uncertainty. A distinction should now be made between time and the interest rate as they affect the discount of future income and time and uncertainty as they affect the amount and rate of discount in a single time period. For the valuation procedures discussed in Chapter 13 one increment in income of any single time period was discounted at the same rate as any other income increment of the same time period. With interest at 5 per cent, an income of $110.25 at the end of 2 years was given a present value of $100, while an income of $220.50 of the same time was given a value of $200; both were discounted by the same relative amount. However, a $110.25 income forthcoming three years hence was given a present value of $95.24 and a $220.50 income was given a present value of $190.48. Here the amount of the discount is a function of time and is not related to the amount of income in any one time period. If we consider different amounts of income in one future time period under uncertainty, the amount of the discount becomes a function of uncertainty rather than time. Uncertainty increases with the amount of the most probable expected income and the size of the capital investment because of the forces outlined previously and discounting becomes a subjective procedure. Greater prospective incomes, when they arise from use of more capital and credit, have less "value" to the entrepreneur because they become less certain and pose increased probability of distasteful consequences (bankruptcy). Since each income increment involves greater uncertainty, each successive addition to prospective income is discounted by an increased amount. Different increments of income in a single time period of the future might be discounted by adding an allowance for safety to the market or internal interest rate. A different safety margin can be added for each increment of income. For example, the first $1,000 increment in prospective income may be discounted by 5 per cent, the third by 12 per cent, and the tenth by 40 per cent. The process of discounting also may be by simple rule-of-thumb procedures: income itself in the period might be estimated and then reduced by different rates in the sense of a safety margin. While we present a conceptual apparatus which can be used to illustrate increased rates of discount and choice as it relates to the income and use of capital in a single time period, the mechanics used by farmers may be of many different sorts. As Chapter 19 illustrates, both the period of time and the quantity of resources employed may result in increased uncertainty and hence discount rates arising under the two sources of uncertainty may be compounded. While Chapter 13 employed the market rate of interest as the basis for computing the present value of future income, this external rate is hardly appropriate for comparison of investment alternatives in an uncertain environment. Since few farmers have enough capital so that their opportunities include only (a) 1 investment opportunity or (b) loaning funds in the market, internal earning rates within the business become more nearly appropriate as the discounting base. It is to this rate that the entrepreneur may add subjective discounting rates in proportion to the increased risks which accompany larger investments. This problem of the discount rate is discussed further in the chapter which follows. The extent to which returns from additional resources should be discounted becomes an important subjective problem in marginality. The farmer should carry discounting to an extent that its marginal cost is equal to its marginal value to him. If he discounts added income too heavily, he rejects the opportunity to realize possible profit; if he discounts too lightly, he invites the possibility of loss.

Situation II. **Limited funds and capital limited by risk aversion by the borrowing firm.** This situation is illustrated in Figure 4. While the lending firms limit the supply of funds to oc_2, a point short of the most probable expected return of capital, they are willing to loan a greater quantity of capital than the borrowing firm will employ. The borrowing firm, because of its relatively great risk aversion, is willing to use only oc_1 of capital.

Situation III. **Risk aversion and capital limited by rationing through the lending firm.** This case is illustrated by Figure 5, where capital use is limited to oc_1.[20] The supply of capital to the borrowing firm is highly restricted by the lending firms and limitations in the use of funds come from the side of capital rationing rather than risk aversion. The borrowing firm cannot obtain enough credit to equate the cost of capital and the discounted value productivity of capital. The importance of capital rationing and risk aversion in restricting use of capital varies from locality to locality and from time to time. In low-income areas where the resources of the farm firm and the chattels of the household are small, the rationing of capital is widespread. Notable examples are those of share croppers and even beginning farmers of all regions. External capital rationing of the type outlined under III was important for the greatest number of farmers in the 1930's. War-bred prosperity and a continued full-employment economy eased this situation, however. Uncertainty of the magnitude viewed by bankers during the 1930's lessened with the return of prosperity and loans were again extended to the level of conventional equities. Immediately after the end of the war, large amounts of capital were added to agriculture and risk aversion rather than external capital rationing became the important force limiting use of credit in many prosperous farming regions. The absence of capital rationing as the predominant factor in one Iowa region is indicated by the data of Table 3. The second column provides farmer's estimates of the added quantities of capital which would "most likely be profitable" in the production period ahead. Risk aversion rather than capital rationing was the reason given by the majority of farmers for not expanding their operations to the limits indicated. It is also interesting to note that restriction in use of capital is greatest (the percentage difference between the current investment and that viewed as the margin to which capital could be extended profitably) in Table 3 for

---

[20] The effect of capital rationing and risk aversion can also be illustrated by means of the indifference curves in the figure below. Suppose that I_1 is an indifference curve of the nature outlined previously while P_1 is an opportunity line (relating the most probable expected profits and uncertainty) indicative of increasing risk under borrowed capital. (The line P_1 is concave both because of increasing risk as related to equity and because of lower profit prospects as borrowing is increased and higher interest rates must be paid. Here it will be rational for the firm to extend capital investment until equilibrium of probable profits and uncertainty are attained at point A. The limit on capital use here is risk aversion. Now suppose the lending firm will allow enough capital that only point R can be attained on the opportunity curve. (For capital beyond the rationed amount, the interest rate is again infinite and the opportunity curve turns straight downward.) The opportunity line now takes the form ORP_2 (has a corner at R) and is "tangent" to indifference curve I_2. Here investment is limited by capital rationing. Even if risk preferences change (the slope of the indifference curve changes) the equilibrium at R will be retained because it is a corner condition. The equilibrium is highly stable.

enterprises which farmers consider to be most "risky" (such as feeder cattle as compared to milk cows). This observation is consistent with an uncertainty environment: Because of the "increasing risk" feature of size and borrowed capital, the scale of the enterprise should be relatively

Table 3.

Quantity of Non-Real Estate Capital Which Would be Profitable Without Driving Most Probable Expected Returns Below Costs. Averages for a Sample of 110 Iowa Farmers *

Items of investment	Current investment per farm	Added investment which would be profitable	Per cent increase over current investment
Protein feed	$ 336	$ 246	73.2
Fertilizer, lime, crop improvement	304	145	71.1
Machinery, equipment	4058	1498	36.9
Feeder cattle	111	892	803.6
Beef herd	1808	2660	147.1
Sheep	357	312	87.4
Hogs	1012	410	40.5
Dairy cattle	1429	574	40.2
Poultry	125	46	36.8

* Source: E. O. Heady and E. R. Swanson, *Resource productivity in Iowa agriculture*. Iowa Agr. Exp. Sta. Bul. 386.

smaller for commodities characterized by great uncertainty. The entrepreneur is likely to discount the returns from an enterprise with a highly variable and unpredictable income by more than for one with a highly stable return.

Effect of interest rate. Interest rates stand to be less important than uncertainty in restricting use of capital in agriculture. Few firms characterized by single proprietorships press use of capital or credit to a point where its marginal cost is equal to its marginal return. Choice in the amount of capital used at best is in terms of a rough subjective equilibrium wherein profit expectations and uncertainty perform a more important role than changes in the interest rate. Studies have shown this situation to be true for corporate firms in non-agricultural industries.[21] It is probably even more important in agriculture. A drop in interest rates by 20 per cent (for example, from 5 to 4 per cent) provides less incentive for use of added capital than prospects for favorable prices and yields. Or, the expectation that product prices and land prices may increase by 25 per cent weighs much more heavily in the farmer's subjective profit calculus than an increase in interest rates from 4 to 5 per cent. The Iowa study indicated that few if any farmers in the sample considered changes in interest rates by 1 or 2 per cent to have any bearing on the amount of capital used.[22]

---

[21] See H. D. Henderson, "Significance of the Interest Rate," and J. E. Meade and W. H. Andrews, "Summaries of replies to questions on the effect of interest rates," *Oxford Economic Papers*, No. 1, pp. 1-32.

[22] E. O. Heady and E. R. Swanson, *op. cit.*

Form of capital and acquisition through renting. Because of the type of uncertainty involved, and since equity requirements are its main uncertainty precaution, the lending firm in agriculture makes greater amounts of capital available for some farm resources than for others. Feeder cattle represent a type of resource well adapted to equity loans. The resource appreciates until its sale and the production process is short; the value of the cattle often is only slightly more than the value of the feed which goes into them and hence the possibility of a sale value less than the amount of the mortgage is not great even when price declines are great. While cattle feeding is a "risky enterprise" from the farmer standpoint, it is a "fairly certain" enterprise as security for a chattel mortgage. Fertilizer does not lend itself so readily as security while tractors and machines are better adapted for bank loans than are new seed varieties or terraces. These differences in the security value of different resources have important impacts on the resources employed and the products produced in agriculture. The uncertainty capital market complex has many other effects, apart from the flexibility and purely precautionary measures mentioned in earlier chapters, on the form of capital employed in agriculture. Chapter 13 illustrated the manner in which discounting due to time alone may throw choice from one type of product (or one type of resource) involving extremely long investments to one with a shorter transformation period. When uncertainty is introduced, the rate of discount itself grows with time, due to the subjective component which increases with uncertainty as prediction extends further into the future and becomes subject to greater error. Uncertainty encourages short rather than long-lived investments. It causes returns from investments extending far into the future to be discounted to zero. Pasture improvement can be used as an example although the logic applies to barns, machines, or other resources. In many parts of the southern Cornbelt, semi-permanent types of pasture such as lespedeza can be established with investments of $50 per acre in seed, fertilizer, lime, and planting costs. The investment for a brome mixture may be as little as $20. If the lespedeza lasts 20 years and the brome lasts 5 years, the per year cost of the above items is $2.50 for the first and $4 for the latter. Part of the cost difference is erased when cost compounding is in the manner of Chapter 13. The gap narrows further as distant returns are discounted by increasing amounts to account for the greater uncertainty of the remote future. However, pasture and cattle are complementary resources; without animals the value product of pasture is zero. Suppose that the farmer with $3,000 in savings has 100 acres to improve and can extend his credit by no more than $2,000. If he invests in the 20-year pasture, he will have nothing for livestock. If he invests in the 5-year pasture he will have $3,000 for investment in livestock to consume the forage. Limited capital and the risks which attach to it place a premium on short-lived assets (1) to reduce uncertainty in the sense of shortening the planning period, and (2) to allow a given capital outlay to support a greater scale of operations since fewer funds are tied up in resource services which can be transformed only in remote production periods.

Credit Policy and Institutionalization of Interest Rates

Credit policy can be used either to (1) increase the efficiency with which resources are used in agriculture, or (2) to transfer income between different groups of farmers and between farm and non-farm segments of the population. The production economists' interest in credit policy relates to the first.[23] We briefly examine certain facets of existing credit programs as they relate to efficiency in production or resource use. In terms of the scale economies in credit services and the reduction of credit uncertainty, public credit programs have undoubtedly added to farming efficiency. The question can be raised, however, whether or not these same services should be provided to other small scale industries which are also faced with uncertainty. The provision of factors at a lower cost or the reduction of instability for one single industry need not increase the efficiency of resource allocation from a societal standpoint: too many resources may flow or be retained in agriculture if other occupations or industries are not treated similarly. Without attempting to fully analyze the income distribution aspects of credit programs and without further analysis of the efficiency considerations pointed out above, we raise some questions in respect to certain institutions which have grown up around agricultural credit and which may aid in the misdirection of agricultural capital. Not all of the considerations discussed below are direct outgrowths of public credit policies but are part and parcel of the credit market generally.

Basis of credit allocation. Credit is allocated to individual farmers, between farmers and between farming regions only indirectly on the basis of productivity or economic efficiency criteria but, in most cases, directly on the value of assets used as security. A minority of commercial banks employ a farm management expert to appraise the productivity of the

---

[23] National credit policies have been aimed as much or more at altering the distribution of income as in improving the efficiency with which agricultural resources are used. The attempt to obtain lower prices on factors employed by farmers (for example, lower interest rates on borrowed capital) have been as much an attempt to increase the income of particular groups of farmers as have parity prices, commodity loans above market levels, and other subsidies on the side of product prices. However, lower prices for capital have more nearly been directed toward low income farmers (those who must borrow capital). It is true that even for policies aimed at income redistribution, there are (1) economies inherent in public provision of credit services which cannot be attained by small firms and (2) certain phenomena which act as uncertainties to other lending firms, need not be so considered by society. Finally, public credit differs from commodity price subsidies in the sense that the former has been largely a self-financing venture.

capital to be purchased with credit. Farmers' Home Administration loans go as far in this direction as any type of credit. Under the equity basis of extending credit, capital need not be added to those farms and producing areas where it has the greatest value productivity. High income areas which already employ intensive capital inputs possess the equity base for obtaining additional credit. Capital can be obtained, as long as the qualifying equity is present, even though its productivity is low; or even when returns are zero. In contrast, farms and regions characterized by small quantities of owner capital and low incomes possess a small credit base and may not have access to additional capital even though it has high productivity; credit is not forthcoming on a low equity base even if productivity is as high as 300 or 400 per cent, a common situation for fertilizer, improved crop strains, and similar investments. If, in loan appraisals, the marginal value product of resources is capitalized to give an estimate of resource values, then should not credit extended on the basis of equity be consistent with productivity or efficiency criteria? The answer might be in the affirmative if all farms started from the same point in respect to capital use (equal marginal productivity of capital between farms) and if all borrowed to a similar extent. If any such "starting point" ever existed, however, it is now "far in the rear" and the contestants are staggered up the full length of the productivity course. Under this situation an equity-based system of credit allocation need not give a use of credit consistent with productivity criteria. A main reason is this: Types of capital needed on many low-income farms often are complementary with resources already on hand. Fertilizer, improved varieties, and other technical improvements may not only bring forth a product of their own but also add to the productivity of the land and other durable assets. Sections such as the Appalachian highlands, the southern Cornbelt or the Southeast are typical of these opportunities: if capital were available in the required forms, it would aid the accumulation of assets, result in higher land values and provide a greater credit base generally.

Improvements in the allocation of borrowed capital could be made through methods which recognize the criteria of production economics. More emphasis should be given to extension of credit where capital productivity is greatest.

Uniform and stable interest rates. Capital policies and private credit developments have resulted in a remarkably uniform pattern of interest rates between types of assets, between farmers, and between geographical farming regions. Differences do exist between first mortgages on real estate, loans on livestock, and other "working" capital, second mortgages on real estate, store credit, and other forms or sources of credit. Slight variations also exist on a regional basis. These differences are, however, tied mainly to the "thickness" of the equity and the risk involved.

One goal of public credit policy has been the equalization of interest rates. This effort was highly justifiable in terms of early credit market imperfections: Very great differences in interest rates existed between eastern and western farming areas. While part of this difference was based on risk, a more important element was the imperfect channeling of capital through the credit market. Accordingly, public credit programs were devised, among other things, to tap capital supplies in the metropolitan areas and increase the mobility of credit so that its marginal returns could be more nearly equalized in different parts of the nation. Abetting of credit mobility is a feature of the capital market which should be maintained and extended. Some of our present institutional arrangements tend to work in the opposite direction, however. With an important portion of the total credit supply furnished by Federal Land Banks, the Production Credit Associations, the Farmers Home Administration, and their allied agencies, interest rates have now become highly institutionalized. State legislation on maximum interest rates has also helped fashion uniform interest rates and the price of borrowed capital has become surrounded by custom and resistant to change. From a productivity standpoint, credit policy aimed at lower interest rates is justifiable when the price paid for borrowed credit in agriculture is, because of market imperfections, high relative to that of other industries and if an inefficient allocation of capital exists between industries. While uniformity of interest rates has positive features, it also has certain negative characteristics from the standpoint of productivity criteria.[24] Uniform interest rates give all firms and producing regions equal bidding power for a given stock of credit. With interest constant at 4½ or 5 per cent and with a marginal return on capital at 25¢ on an Alabama farm and at 7¢ on a Cornbelt farm, the latter has as much opportunity as the former to attract capital (and even greater opportunity if equities are geared accordingly). Highly productive investments were made in many pioneering farming areas because prospective (but uncertain) returns were high and the borrower and lender were able to pool uncertainties under interest rates which varied with the degree of risk involved. Much of this capital would not have been extended had the loaning firm been able to realize no more than a conventional interest rate. Uniform interest rates would equalize resource productivity between farms and areas only if all farmers used capital up to a point where its return was equal to its cost. This condition is not attained in fact and accordingly there is economic basis for variable interest rates in conformance with resource productivity.

Interest payments and variability in resource productivity. If borrowed capital is to be used in a manner paralleling productivity criteria, payment

---

[24] Uniform interest rates would prevail in the long run under a competitive credit market; also, rates between regions would be equal, except for lending firm cost differentials, if farm firms used capital in amounts to equate marginal costs and returns. However, even under competitive market conditions, short-run interest differentials could exist between areas; these would encourage credit mobility.

schedules for interest and principal should be tied to the value productiv· ity of the resource for which credit is employed. Under existing credit customs some variation in repayment schedules is made in line with the transformation period of the resource; loans on land are for long periods, while those on livestock and machinery are for shorter periods. Even then, interest and repayment schedules on machinery and livestock loans assume not only stable productivity but also that the resource returns 25 to 33 per cent. Insufficient recognition is given to the fact that the value product of farm resources is highly variable rather than a constant and unchanging amount. Credit geared to productivity principles should include interest and repayment schedules which recognize that the resource returns may fluctuate either because of unpredictable variations in prices or production coefficients. Involved here are those variable payment plans discussed in the previous chapter. Variable payment schedules based on productivity principles would not, of course, be tied to a single index such as prices or yields but to the total variance components of value productivity. Payment plans based on rental shares are of this nature. Further incorporation of these flexibility considerations into credit procedures would lessen the uncertainty surrounding use of borrowed capital (through decreasing the effects of fixed interest and principal payments) and could increase the efficiency with which capital in agriculture is used.

Equity loans. A possible means by which credit rationing growing out of uncertainty might be circumvented is present in the low equity loans of the Farmers' Home Administration. It is true that a loan near 100 per cent of the value of the assets poses extreme uncertainty to the owner's equity. The capital at stake is not great relative to the income possibilities, however, for F.H.A. clients, and the greater entrepreneurial inputs accompanying the F.H.A. farm management supervisor's efforts help lessen uncertainty. Finally, society assumes part of the risk which would otherwise fall on the lending firm and the borrowing farm.

Selected References

Black, J. D., *et al.*, *Farm Management*. New York: Macmillan, 1947, Ch. 32.

Boulding, K. E., *Reconstruction of Economics*. New York: Wiley & Sons, 1950, pp. 117-134.

Heady, Earl O., and Swanson, Earl R., *Resource Productivity with Special Reference to Uncertainty and Capital Use in Southern Iowa*. Iowa Agr. Exp. Sta. Bul. 388.

Hicks, J. R., *Value and Capital*. London: Oxford University Press, 1948, Ed. 9, 10, Vol. XLIV, pp. 243-257.

Kalecki, M., *Essays in the Theory of Economic Fluctuations*. London: Allen & Unwin, 1939, pp. 95-106.

Kaldor, N., "The Equilibrium of the Firm," *Econ. Jour.*, Vol. XLIV, pp. 60-76.

Johnson, D. G., *Forward Prices for Agriculture*. Chicago: University of Chicago Press, 1947, Ch. 5, pp. 261-288.

Lange, O., *Price Flexibility and Unemployment*. Bloomington: Principia Press, 1943, pp. 29-34, 67-70.

Makower, H., and Marshak, J., "Assets, Prices and Monetary Theory," *Economica*, Vol. 5, pp. 261-288.

Murray, W. G., *Agricultural Finance*. Ames: Iowa State College Press, 1939, Chs. 5, 6.

Robinson, A., "Problem of Management and Size of Firms," *Econ. Jour.*, pp. 1-3, 35-50.

Rudd, R. W., and MacFarlane, D. L., "The Scale of Operations in Agriculture," *Jour. Farm Econ.*, Vol. 24, pp. 420-433.

Steindl, J., *Economic Problems of Size of Firms*. Oxford: Blackwell, 1945.

19

Factor Pricing and Ownership Under Uncertainty

Numerous methods exist by which the farmer may obtain control of the productive services of resources. He can buy the resource outright and utilize the services of the resources as they are forthcoming over time. This is the main method by which the services of seeds, fertilizer, machinery, feed, livestock, and similar forms of capital in agriculture are obtained. Although a market exists whereby machines and livestock, chiefly breeding stock, can be hired without purchase of the resource itself, farmers generally purchase the entire stock of services embodied in these resources.[1] As owners, they then utilize the flow services as they are forthcoming over time and as their decisions dictate. At the opposite extreme, the services of labor are always hired; a market does not exist whereby a laborer and the stock of productive services which he embodies can be purchased outright. Between these 2 extremes fall the services of land, buildings, and other real estate. The entire stock and flow of productive services embodied in real estate can be purchased and the farmer becomes an "owner-operator."[2] However, the services forthcoming from land and buildings can also be purchased without resort to ownership of these factors. Services of real estate can be hired by tenant operators for a year or other period of time through various types of leasing arrangements.

---

[1] Artificial insemination is an excellent example wherein a bull as a factor of production is not owned but his services are purchased in much the same way as the services of an acre of land are purchased under a rental contract.

[2] Obviously, owner-operation is a thing of degree. A farmer who owns land and buildings but hires labor, breeding stock, or machine services is not a more complete owner-operator than the tenant farmer who owns all of his machines and livestock but hires the services of land. Because rigid demarcations have been arbitrarily established by agricultural economists between "owner-operators" and "tenant-operators" some of the more important facets of resource pricing and production efficiency have gone unanalyzed. This historic distinction has given rise to a highly unrealistic partial and incomplete equilibrium analysis centered on the land factor alone. There is nothing unique about the purchase of factor services through the owning as compared to renting of the land resource. The same considerations apply to all factors of production and complete analysis must be made in the production economics context wherein all resources are treated.

Questions of whether farm resources should be owned, hired, or rented are, from a production economics standpoint, problems of factor pricing and efficiency analysis. Ownership and renting simply represent different facets of the resource service market in agriculture and provide part of the production decision-resource use complex. On the one hand, the analysis of factor pricing and the comparison of ownership or renting and hiring of resources becomes an extension of the investment and uncertainty considerations outlined in the immediately preceding chapters; on the other, it represents an extension of those imputational and valuation problems considered in Chapter 13. These problems of choice are important in production economics for obvious reasons; they have effects on the efficiency with which the capital, labor, land, and management resources of agriculture are employed. The most difficult problems relating to factor ownership or hire are, of course, those which spring from long-term commitments where the future can only be anticipated. Because the problems posed often are not set out distinctly, this chapter is devoted to choice and efficiency considerations as they relate to the form and manner by which farmers may obtain control of resource services. Immediately preceding chapters have been concerned alone with problems in the dynamics of production. This chapter, as do those which follow, analyzes both the static and dynamic elements of particular problems in production. Our central interest is in these questions: (1) Under what conditions should individuals own or rent resources when profit maximization or family satisfaction is the end? (2) What are the possible effects of different methods of factor service control on the efficiency of agricultural production? An analysis of leasing systems *per se* is included in the next chapter. We are concerned with the production economics or economic efficiency aspects of factor pricing and hire and not with the purely legal, historic, and property rights aspects of resource tenure. While division of property rights and knowledge of evolution of different tenure arrangements are important, these considerations constitute the field of land tenure and land economics.[3]

Alternative Systems of Purchase

Farm entrepreneurs may obtain resource services in either 1 of 2 general methods: (1) They can become owners and buy the complete stock and flow of services embodied in the resource. The services then can be transformed into product over time at the discretion of the manager. (2) They can, through rental or hiring arrangements, buy (a) a specified number of units of service or (b) the number of service units given off in a specified time interval. The "a" alternative may involve hire of a machine to thresh a given number of bushels of wheat or a laborer to pick berries by the

---

[3] R. R. Renne, *Land Economics*. New York: Harper, 1947, p. 429. Renne outlines this area as the central concern of land economics and land tenure.

basket. The "b" alternative may involve renting of land for a year or a laborer for a day and the entrepreneur has the opportunity of using all of the services forthcoming from the resource during the period. In a pure firm framework and in the absence of time and uncertainty considerations, the farmer could view the alternative methods of obtaining factor services in the vein of any factor-factor decision: Services obtained from hired or rented resources are substitutes for services obtained from owned resources. Two possibilities exist in the manner in which services from hired and owned factors substitute. These are indicated in Figures 1 and 2. In Figure 1 the supposition is that services obtained from owned and hired or rented resources are perfect substitutes; the iso-product line I_1P_1 is linear and has a 45° slope. There is little reason to suppose that services from particular owned and rented resources substitute otherwise over the main range of agriculture. The services given off by a tractor or a farm which is owned should not differ from those given off by one which is hired if the tractors or farms, and the complementary resources used with them, are homogeneous. Under this situation the entrepreneur could be indifferent in a particular period as to whether he owns or hires resource services, if they were priced identically; the iso-cost line will, if no discounting element is present, have the same slope as the iso-product curve and the

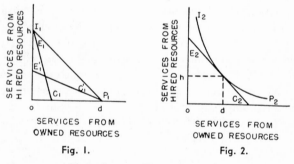

Fig. 1.   Fig. 2.

Choice between hire and ownership.

cost for any output will be identical whether produced with hired factors, owned factors, or any combination of the two.[4] If the services from hired and owned factors are perfect substitutes, while the cost of services differs under the two systems, resources employed in production should be entirely rented or entirely owned if profit is to be maximized. In Figure 1, for example, any time the price ratio for services from owned factors as com-

---

[4] If we consider that the firm aspect of the farm is related to a household and that the family attaches some direct utility to ownership, the situation is not indeterminate: total satisfaction is maximized with price and substitution ratios equal to 1.0, when resource services are owned alone since money return and the commodities which can be purchased with it will be as great as when the factors are hired, while direct utility also is forthcoming from ownership.

pared to rented or hired factors (P_o/P_h) is greater than 1.0 (the iso-cost curve has a slope greater than 45° as in the case of E_1C_1) then only hired resources should be employed; if the ratio P_o/P_h is less than 1.0 (the iso-cost curve has a slope less than that of I_1P_1, as is the case of $E'_1C'_1$), services from owned resources alone should be employed.[5]

If resource services substitute at diminishing rates, some combination of owned and hired factors may be optimal as is suggested in Figure 2. If services going into production are aggregated (instead of being viewed in the distinct form supposed above), it is likely that services from different classes of owned and hired resources do substitute at diminishing rates, particularly because of timeliness problems. In this case the farmer may wish to own some resources but purchase services of others through hiring or renting. He may elect to own his power unit, tillage machinery, and livestock and to hire or rent labor, harvesting machinery, and land. Services from a hired tractor may substitute at one rate for services from an owned tractor in one season of the year and at an entirely different rate in another season.[6]

Static time considerations. The preceding analysis supposed (a) a single production period and (b) perfect knowledge. As we progress to a situation of uncertainty, we now drop the first supposition and analyze resource ownership and hire when production considerations extend beyond a single period. Only occasionally does the farmer rent or hire mono-period resources. Infrequently he does "borrow" seed from his neighbor but ordinarily, if he is short on funds, the farmer borrows capital and purchases outright seed, feed, or fuel and their services. Questions of ownership or renting arise mainly in connection with poly-period resources such as machines which, although they represent a stock of services over the full life of the capital item, give off a sequence of services over a period of years, or land which embodies some stock services but also includes pure

---

[5] If services from rented and owned resources substitute at a constant marginal rate different from 1.0, the analysis above still holds true: if the rate at which hired services substitute for owned services, $\Delta S_o/\Delta S_h$, is less than the price ratio P_h/P_o, only services from owned resources should be employed; if $\Delta S_o/\Delta S_h$ is greater than P_h/P_o, services from rented factors alone should be employed. When $\Delta S_o/\Delta S_h = P_h/P_o$, the firm again can be indifferent as to which it employs. However, where the source of resource services relates to household utility, owned factors again may be selected over hired factors even where $\Delta S_o/\Delta S_h = P_h/P_o$.

[6] The iso-product curve for hired (rented) and owned factors may represent 2 or several segments, each one of which is linear indicating constant rates of substitution through a range. Here the optimum combination of owned and hired services may come at one of the "corners" (point joining 2 linear sections of the iso-product curve). If this is true, the combination will be highly stable; price ratios between owned and hired factor services can vary widely (as long as the iso-cost curve does not attain a slope equal to either linear sections of the iso-product curve) without causing the optimum combination of services from owned or hired services to change. If the price ratio swings far enough in either direction, however, it will cause either pure ownership or pure renting (hiring) to be most profitable in the period (particularly if the iso-product curve is composed of 2 linear sections).

flow services. If the farmer resorts to ownership of a combine or land, he purchases the services not for 1 or 2 periods ahead but for the entire life of the resource. While he can purchase the machine or land and resell it after a few years, he still must purchase not only the services given off during the few years of ownership but also all other service units embodied in the resource. In the absence of price change or uncertainty and household considerations, it can be said that services embodied in owned resources, which will be used at a future point in time, must always cost less at the present than will services given off by hired factors at the relevant point of time in the future. For example, suppose that a farmer, through ownership, purchases services in a machine today which will not be given off until after 5 years. He also has opportunity, through hire of a machine, to purchase only the services of the sixth year when the time arrives. The decision to be made in respect to machine services of the sixth year is this: Should he buy the machine today and store services until year 6 or should he wait until year 6 and buy machine services through the rental market? The answer depends on the relationship between the cost of owned machine services today and rented machine services in 6 years. If the farmer has unlimited capital, services purchased today have a compounded cost of $K_5 = c_o(1 + r)^5$ at the end of 5 years when K_5 refers to the compounded costs 5 years hence, c_o refers to the present cost and r refers to the interest rate (see equations I, II, and III in Chapter 13). Accordingly, if services from rented factors will be available at the end of the 5 years at a price or cost of c_5, services from factors purchased today and stored for 5 years have a maximum current value of $\dfrac{c_5}{(1 + r)^5}$; when services from owned and rented resources are perfect substitutes, the firm would be foolish to pay more than this amount for owned resource services, as can be illustrated by an arithmetic example: Suppose that the services from an acre of rented land will cost $10 at the end of 2 years (for example, a cash rental rate of $10) and that the interest rate is 5 per cent. The amount of money invested today which will grow into $10 at the end of 2 years is $10 \div (1 + .05)^2$ or $9.07. Without considering taxes and other later costs, the maximum value of services purchased in land today and stored for use in 2 years becomes $9.07. Thus if rented factor services can be purchased for less than $10 at the end of 2 years, this situation will cause ownership of resources to be less profitable than the renting of resources.

If a resource embodies services which are given off at equal rates annually and if rental rates in future years are constant, the maximum substitution or present value of the factor, if it is to be owned, is defined by the formula I below. Here V_s refers to the maximum substitution value of the owned resource at the present, the c's refer to the annual cost of the same amount of services from hired resources in each year ahead and n refers to the number of years which the resource in question gives off services. (Here we assume that costs are discounted for the particular year in which the services are used.) Or the costs of producing a given product with owned resource services or hired resource services can be made in the simple manner of Chapter 13: a new machine which will last for 5 years costs $100 now. The same services can be rented for $27 per year, a total of $135 in 5 years. The discounted present value of the 5 years of rented services is $27/(1.05) + 27/(1.05)^2 + 27/(1.05)^3 + 27/(1.05)^4 + 27/(1.05)^5$ or $116.84 when the discounting rate is 5 per cent and equal to the market interest rate; costs are lower under ownership than under hiring. If the farmer has limited capital and can earn 20 per cent on funds invested in hogs (see later discussion and also Chapter 13), the present value of rented services over 5 years becomes $27/(1.20) + 27/(1.20)^2 + 27/(1.20)^3 + 27/(1.20)^4 + 27/(1.20)^5$ or a total of $80.73, and renting is less costly than the owning of resource services. The same logic applies to bulls, land, plows, or any other resource used in production.

$$V_s = \frac{c_1}{(1 + r)} + \frac{c_2}{(1 + r)^2} \cdots \frac{c_n}{(1 + r)^n} \tag{I}$$

From the standpoint of time *per se* (in the absence of speculative changes in value) it is apparent that the farmer cannot afford to pay as much for services from owned resources purchased at the beginning of the first year for use in the second year, as the rented services will cost 2 years hence. If we aggregate all future years, the amount which can be paid for the owned resource cannot be as great, in a pure firm and a certainty context, as the total cost of services from rented services over the same time period. The analysis presented above also can be viewed from the standpoint of a resource owner (such as a landlord or custom-combine operator) who sells factor services through the renting of land or the hiring out of machines. He is a supplier of "resource services" and, in a perfect knowledge setting, cannot afford to sell services from resources (for example, rent out the resources) in future periods unless he can purchase the services, in the form of ownership, at a lower cost today. From the standpoint of the landlord, the services of rented land represent the product of the resource. His problem is one of maximizing returns in the sale of the services in the rental market as compared to investing in other alternatives. Under competitive conditions and in a perfect market, an environment which is never actually attained, prices of factors at one point in time and the value of services sold from them in later periods would differ by the discounted amounts suggested in equation I. On the one hand, the profit incentive for farmers to obtain resource services through owning rather than renting is much less in an uncertain market environment than in a certain one. However, it is lack of certainty (such as tenure uncertainty) which also causes one element of emphasis to be placed on farm ownership decisions.

Asset Values and Subjective Discounts

The preceding analysis is a useful step in our study of farm ownership and tenure. Its limitation lies in the fact that it does not fully recognize uncertainty and household considerations as they relate to resource ownership. Discounting or compounding must be in subjective terms and in terms of internal rather than market interest rates when uncertainty is introduced. While price uncertainty is present for both the owner and the renter, tenure uncertainty becomes an added variable which enters the discounting process for the tenant; price uncertainty becomes particularly important in ownership because of the time span involved and because of changes in asset values. While the problems of changing asset values were touched upon in sections dealing with valuation and uncertainty considerations, their importance in investment decisions and in choice between owning or renting resources has not been examined fully. Prospective changes in the value of the owned resource become important in determining whether resource services should be obtained through rental or ownership. If a farmer planned over a time span of only three years, the prospective value of owned resources at the end of the period might be more important than the relative cost of owned and rented resources in determining how factor services should be obtained. Similarly, farmers who are planning over a 20, 30, or 40 year period must consider the resource value at the end of the period. Real estate values 5 years hence become important to the farmer even if he expects to farm for 40 years. Should he buy now or should he wait for 5 years? Will the total value of his assets, including accumulations from annual earnings plus changes in the value of resources, be greater if he immediately becomes an owner or if he postpones this step? Since farm families must provide their own retirement income, the value of assets at the end of their operating career becomes an important concern. The decision of farmers to acquire factor services through ownership or renting stems, to an important extent, from the manner in which they expect asset values to change. Even the "direct utility" placed on farm ownership is explained in part by uncertainty of tenure. Hence it is important that we examine the process of resource valuation where future prices and values are not known with certainty but can only be anticipated.

Resource Valuation Under Uncertainty

Under uncertainty, the valuation equations outlined in Chapter 13 simply become expectation models for future values of assets purchased at the present time. The steps in resource valuation are the same under uncertainty as under the perfect knowledge conditions outlined previously and include (1) the anticipation or estimation of future sequences of income and (2) the discounting of future incomes back to the present. The estimates are purely subjective, however, and must be conditioned in the manner outlined below. The farmer or other investor, concerned with deriving income from the services of resources, is mainly interested in predicting future returns, and hence in placing a present value on these returns. However, parallel models might be used for predicting the future price of land itself. The investor who buys real estate in anticipation of changes in the value of money and the possibility of reaping profits through money-asset substitution is concerned with the future as compared to the present market value of the resource itself. The loan firm which uses farm resources as mortgage security likewise is concerned chiefly with predicting the future market value of the resources rather than in predicting future incomes and discounting them to the present, though obviously the 2 future quantities are highly related. Because of equity considerations, the farmer interested in the income sequences forthcoming from farm resources also is interested in future market values of real estate. The expectation models outlined below represent alternatives which might be used in estimating returns and hence in placing a present value on future income sequences. The accuracy of models such as these partly provides the answer to whether, in an environment of uncertainty, resources should be hired or rented.

Again, it should be emphasized that resource valuation differs not at all from other planning and decision-making processes in agriculture. Appraisal is not a unique branch of economics but is involved in the more general and basic field of production economics. The major portion of farm appraisals is made from the standpoint of investment and profit decisions. This statement applies not only for investment in agricultural resources by farm and non-farm persons but also to appraisals made from the standpoint of agricultural credit firms. The loan firm is interested mainly in the business of producing credit services and extending them to farm borrowers. Few are interested in a manipulation of appraisals and loans in a manner to attain title to the assets. In this sense appraisals made from the standpoint of farmer decision parallel those made for the purpose of loan decisions.[7] Alternative valuation models under uncertainty include these:

---

[7] Appraisals are made for other purposes. One is the settling of estates. An heir may wish to purchase a farm from his brothers and sisters who in turn are concerned with obtaining a market value for their interest. Here the "sale value" method of appraisal is obviously the appropriate system. Appraisals are also made for tax assessment purposes. The problem is mainly one of getting interfarm homogeneity in the value estimates, though, obviously, the outcome will depend on the productivity of the resources. The important task is that of using a comparable system on all properties regardless of whether it gives an estimate of the full value product or only a portion of it on all farms. As long as all units are treated in a comparable manner, tax assessment rates can be raised or lowered to produce the desired amount of revenue. Appraisal estimates for purposes of settling estates and tax assessment

1. **Income of the present year will extend infinitely into the future.** Equation X in Chapter 13 provides this expectation model, except that R in the equation becomes this year's income. As suggested later, however, the interest rate need not be the current market rate. When applied to product prices, this general type of expectation model was more accurate than most other mechanical models. It does not serve efficiently as a basis of valuation for durable resources, however. The difference lies in the time spans under consideration: The price expectation models of Chapter 16 extend only over 1 year. Expectation models which extend present quantities into the future become more accurate as the time period is shortened. Expectations relating to land and buildings must extend 5, 10, or 40 years into the future. Current incomes and values thus provide an inefficient basis for predicting resource values in the remote future. The mechanical model outlined here, or an adaptation of it, was used by many farmers during World War I and led to their financial downfall. It was an equally inefficient model during the 1930's, because it did not anticipate the windfall profits from increased land values during and after World War II.

2. **Income of a past "normal" period provides an estimate of future incomes.** It is this system, when employed in the manner of equation X in Chapter 13, that has been termed the "normal" system of farm valuation. Here the farmer or other person employs the income from a period such as (a) the 1910-14 average, (b) a moving average of the past 10 years, or (c) any other average of the past or present, and substitutes it in as the R of equation X. He is simply estimating that the future will prove to be similar to the period selected as normal. The formula again is only a mechanical expectation model. It may serve more or less accurately than other expectation models. Until the late 1930's, appraisal experts were still using 1910-14 as a normal period; since 1940, many have used a 10-year moving average (ordinarily the previous 10 years) as the normal or expectation period. The assumptions are the same in any case; prices and yields of the normal period are taken as expectations for the future and income is capitalized to give the so-called "normal value into perpetuity." Farmers can attest that this expectation model often is highly inefficient. The individual using this land-value expectation model in the period 1940-52 let some very great economic gains slip through his fingers; the system, especially if based on some period in the 1930's, predicted that "land values were out of line with normal values." Yet other farmers, basing their decisions on other expectation models, purchased farms and paid for them in 2 or 3 years. The "normal value" model of expectations, when based on a

are, however, quite apart from those for production or investment decisions by the firm. Here it is expectations of value productivity in the future which become the crucial issue. The practical problem at stake here is, of course, quite different from that of "equity in taxation." Economic considerations of taxation are problems of analysis in themselves and are somewhat, although not entirely, apart from problems in resource decisions.

period of low or conservative prices and yields, best serves those highly cautious investors who do not wish to take action endangering the survival of their firm. In this sense, the model is comparable to the crop yield expectation model outlined in Chapter 17 wherein typically low yields are taken as the basis of action to help (a) minimize the number of years in which loss may be realized, or (b) eliminate the danger of bankruptcy. The system, if adhered to rigidly and if the normal period is one of conservative prices or yields, guards against extreme losses growing out of deflation or long sequences of poor yields. On the other hand, it precludes the windfall profits associated with resource ownership in periods of increasing prices. Since the model, when employed in the form of equation X in Chapter 13, assumes a planning period with a nearly indeterminate horizon, it can lead to important decision errors.

3. **Income sequences include an expected and terminable increment.** Equation XV from Chapter 13 almost always provides a more efficient model for resource valuation than the single normal model. Here R and I represent expected rather than known incomes. In using this model in 1940, the following procedure would have been followed if the long-run "average expected" return for a farm was $800, and while incomes of $1,000, $1,200, $1,400, $1,200, and $1,000 were expected in the years 1941, 1942, 1943, 1944, and 1945 respectively. With an interest rate of 5 per cent used as the basis of capitalizing the $800 normal return, the normal method (equation X) would have given a value expectation of $16,000 for the farm. Use of equation XV as the expectation model would have given a value expectation of $17,557, however. (The surplus above $800 for each year would have had an expected value of $1,557.84 in 1940.) The model is a logical one if prices have been at some stable level over a period of time and the economy is being geared to war or other inflationary forces. Even in 1943 it had more basis than a normal model based on a moving average of the previous 10 years. There was little basis for supposing that the returns from farm real estate investment would drop back to the 1933-42 level as long as a full scale war was being waged. Still many appraisal experts stuck by the normal method in passing their expectations on to farmers.

4. **A constant and continuous trend in income and value.** This expectation model, represented by equation XIV in Chapter 13, partially describes the manner in which farm real estate values increased over much of the period prior to World War I. Farmers evidently took the spurt in incomes during the war (model 1 above) to suggest a new rate of permanent increase and capitalized it accordingly. The consequences are now history. Not only were farmers led astray by this expectation hypothesis, but lending firms, using it as a basis for extending loans, ended up during the 1930's owning nearly one-half the farms in many states. The model would have been highly efficient, as an average over time and without reference to single years, in predicting the future value of farm land over the last 200 years.

Because of world population growth, technological change, and the re-occurrence of war and monetary devaluation, the money value of products from land and other resources has increased continuously over 2 centuries. The limitation of the model for investment decision lies, of course, in the fact that no farmer lives for 200 years; the success of his investment decision hinges on price outcomes for products and factors within a period of 40 years or less.[8] While the subjective expectation figure employed in many estimates is the mean or mathematical expectation of past incomes, other "statistics" also might be employed, depending on the inclination of the entrepreneur to (a) accept chance and (b) trust the basis of his pre-dictions. Where commodity or resource prices are not normally distributed, the modal income over a 40-year period might be used in the place of the mean income over a 10-year period. The mean figure has one advantage over the modal figure, in that it considers positive and negative deviations away from the mean; it assumes, however, that years of high and low incomes are equally distant from the present.

5. **A parallel model.** This system would use some period from the past as parallel to that ahead. For groups of years, it would have served efficiently in the years 1914-18, 1919-23, 1924-29, 1930-34, 1935-41, and 1942-46 if a period of war, depression, and so forth from the past had been used. It would not have served well in 1946-51 since this period did not parallel the 1919-23 postwar period.

Many other expectation models might be employed as a basis for pre-dicting farm resource values in an uncertain environment. A few have been discussed to illustrate that the problem of use value (capital value) for factors is simply part and parcel of the general uncertainty and expecta-tion complex. Typically, income from resources fluctuates over time and the present or discounted value of 10 years each of high and of low in-comes differs depending on whether the 10 years of high income are ex-pected to come first or last in the sequence: In inflationary periods farmers discount the high expected incomes of the immediate future by only a small amount; during depression inflationary incomes of the remote future are discounted heavily. Finally, when the investor is characterized by high risk aversion or wishes above all else to guarantee survival of his business, he might employ an expectation model wherein the minimum income of the relevant past serves as the basis for capitalization. He would then be willing to own resources only when their market prices fell to this guarantee-of-survival level. Historically, this system would have justified

---

[8] The same can be said of the so-called "normal" model of valuation. Even if the R of equation X in Chapter 13 could be estimated for the future with zero error, it would suggest only the average income from land or other resources in an infinite period ahead. It says nothing about deviations away from this long-run mean expectation in individual years or in periods of a few years. Investment success is conditioned as much or more by these deviations as by the accuracy of income estimates used as an average over an infinitely long time period.

"becoming an owner" only once or twice in a farmer's lifetime. More complex systems would include a system of equations which include all of the relevant structural relationships relating to national income, product demand and supply functions, factor demand and supply functions, and a host of others. The difficulty is that the relevant quantities cannot be measured for the remote future when resource value is to be predicted.

Capital limitations and discount rates. The static models of Chapter 13 (and those employed in appraisal work) assume that the investor's capital is so great that his only alternative is to loan funds at the market rate of interest. While this system would be applicable in a "perfect knowledge" environment with profit as the single goal of farming, it fits few farmers; typically, the greatest number borrow rather than lend at the market rate. If an interest rate is to be employed as a basis for discounting future income and in making decisions between investment alternatives, an earning rate internal to the firm is more nearly appropriate than an external market rate when funds are limited because of either internal or external capital rationing. The static procedure of calculating the present value of future income states that income in a future year is worth no more than a current amount which, if invested at compound interest, will grow to a like level in the relevant year. Farmers in general do not use capital to a point where marginal costs and marginal returns are equated, and the net return on farm capital often is greater than the market interest rate. Hence, in placing a present value on future incomes from a resource such as land, the rate which can be earned currently from funds invested in hogs, poultry, fertilizer, or improved seed becomes more appropriate than the market rate of interest as a basis for discount and for comparing investment alternatives. Suppose that a dollar invested in mono-period resources will earn 20 per cent in this and succeeding years: it is then logical that when land is valued in the "opportunity cost" sense, future incomes should be discounted by this internal earnings rate of 20 per cent rather than by an external market interest rate of 5 per cent. Using the 20 per cent discount rate, the present value of a $10 forthcoming from an acre of land 4 years hence is only $4.82. The present value is $8.23 when discounting is based on a market interest rate of 5 per cent. Obviously, then, the beginning farmer who is extremely limited in capital may rationally put a lower "use value" on land than an established and wealthy operator; because of its lower "use value," the young farmer may refrain from investing in land and invest in livestock and machinery while purchasing the services of real estate in the rental market.

This same statement also applies to the use of competing resources even if both are owned. For the barn example of Chapter 13, the "cost" of the two thirty-year barns is only 5,063 + 289, or $5,352, when the interest rate is 10 per cent. While a farmer with unlimited capital might use the 60-year barn if it costs $6,100 (which is less than 5,063 + 1,151 or $6,214 for 2 30-year barns with discounting at 5 per cent), the beginning farmer who is short of capital and can earn 10 per cent on fertilizer may still prefer the 2 short-lived barns.

Subjective discounting. Subjective discounting of future incomes also becomes important for valuation under uncertainty.[9] Discounting procedures outlined in Chapter 13 and immediately above, as in the case of most agricultural economics literature on appraisal, were based on empirical interest rates or alternative earnings. Future incomes also may be "written down" in the purely subjective or psychological fashion of Chapter 18 and in a manner varying between individuals. Here the investor may discount future income (a) by an "actual" amount which he considers to be the appropriate alternative earning rate plus (b) a "subjective" amount to account for the fact that future income is uncertain. The less confident the entrepreneur is in his estimates of future incomes, the greater is the rate at which he will likely discount them. Under the discounting procedure used in Chapter 13, incomes further into the future had smaller present values because of discounting *per se*. Under imperfect knowledge, incomes of the more distant future are discounted at increasing subjective rates because prediction becomes less accurate and the greater dispersion of possible outcomes causes uncertainty to increase. In conducting an expectation study, the writer made queries on land valuation procedures employed by farmers. The subjective discount systems outlined above were employed along with others. A rule-of-thumb procedure of subjective discounting was in this fashion: When asked in 1948 what "use value" they placed on farm land, many Southern Iowa farmers answered, "Well, the present market price is $80. With things going down in price, chances are that land won't sell for more than $65 in 5 years. Just to be safe, I probably couldn't afford to pay more than $55-60 today." [10]

Perhaps it can even be questioned whether the farm firm does or should employ an interest rate in making investment decisions.[11] Hicks' statement is apropos at this point: [12]

---

[9] Subjective discounting can be put in 2 categories: (1) those discounts arising out of incomplete knowledge and uncertainty—where profit maximization is still the end, and (2) those discounts growing out of individual values or preferences which conflict with profit maximization as an end over a long period of time. The indifference curves of Chapter 14 explain the latter form of discounting, although the 2 systems are related.

[10] Most young operators indicated that land had very little "alternative value" to them because of the higher rate to be earned on short-term resources and also because they felt the earnings from hogs, chickens, and crop investment to be more certain than the future value of land.

[11] A. G. Hart, in *Anticipations, Uncertainty and Dynamic Planning*. Chicago: University of Chicago Press, 1940, p. 92, makes a similar point:

"To begin with, the optimum plan is necessarily the plan which offers maximum discounted value of net receipts by the criterion of the schedule of internal interest rates; this follows directly from the fact that under the optimum plan discounted

The length of time for which an entrepreneur will be prepared to plan ahead depends on technical conditions but it also depends, in a very important way, on risk. As we have often seen, the effective "expected price"... is not the most probable price, but the most probable price minus an allowance for risk.... After a certain point, therefore, the risk allowance will become so large as to wipe out any possible gains and the effective expected price will become nil.... Interest is too weak for it to have much influence on the near future; risk is too strong to enable it to have much influence on the far future; what place is there left for interest between these opposing perils?

In addition to the "productive" or "alternative return" aspects of real estate values, assets can be considered purely in terms of their speculative or security characteristics. The farmer may be concerned with the future rather than the present value of real estate in terms of (a) being able to sell the farm without loss in event of decline in land prices or (b) being able to maintain equity and solvency of the firm. Here interest rates, to the extent that they enter the valuation process, themselves serve in purely an expectation role; the farm investor's problem is one of estimating the rate at which prospective purchasers of the future will capitalize land values. While the farm firm is interested in both the security and the alternative return aspects of real estate values, its decision-making is also clouded by a short-term planning horizon and the high value placed on ownership as a means to retirement security. Returns beyond some short planning period often are discounted to zero and, as indicated in previous chapters, investment may be made in real estate at any time expectations suggest that an asset will return a high portion of its purchase price in a short time period. If prices have started upward and the farmer's elasticity of expectations are greater than unity, he may purchase irrespective of interest rates and the sequences of income to be expected over the next decade. Whatever the method employed, the subjective element of discount becomes a function of uncertainty. From an investment standpoint, the entrepreneur's economic horizon extends only so long as future net incomes have present values greater than zero. It is doubtful that many farmers place capital values on incomes forthcoming 75 or 100 years hence. However, the income of the 5 years immediately ahead is almost universally included in the economic horizon and the income expectations of such short period may be more important than other phenomena in explaining farmer

---

marginal revenue of input is equal to marginal cost of input. There is no doubt then that the optimum plan under capital rationing follows the maximum net receipts rule by the criterion of its own interest schedule.... If we discounted at the borrowing rate schedule, plainly, alternative plans under which net receipts would have a larger undiscounted aggregate but would flow in later might have larger present values.... One way out of this dilemma is simply to rule out all interest schedules as valuation criteria unless their application throughout the firm's calculations would give consistent results."
    [12] J. R. Hicks, *Value and Capital.* London: Clarendon Press, Oxford, 1939, pp. 225-226.

investment policies.[13] Subjective discounting of future returns is also involved in renting. Under leasing systems prevailing over much of the United States, tenure uncertainty may eventually weigh heavier in farmer-investment decisions than the uncertainty associated with ownership. Since the farm family must provide its own retirement income, it may wish to own a farm in order to invest in farm improvements and establish a flow of income consistent with household needs and values in later years.

Effect of Ownership and Renting on Efficiency

We are now ready to ask whether purchase of the full stock of services embodied in resources through ownership causes resource to be used differently or more efficiently than if a portion of the services is purchased through rental or hire of factors. (Different forms of resource rental and their effects on efficiency are discussed in the chapter which follows.) For analytical purposes, the problem can be viewed in the categories which follow:

1. **A single time period and perfect knowledge.** Under this situation there is no logic or basic relationship which would cause services from rented resources to be used differently than those from owned resources if (a) the rental or hiring system involves purchase of all services given off by the resource in the single time period, and (b) the production possibilities are the same for the 2 resources. The production opportunities can be considered in the vein of those in Figure 5 of Chapter 7. With no interperiod problems present the services available from the resource in the single time period should be allocated between the two products in a similar fashion if profits are to be maximized.

2. **Competing time periods, perfect knowledge, and stocks of resource services.** Purchase of the complete stock of services embodied in resources through ownership would lead to the same allocation of services between

---

[13] Subjective discounting also can differ between individuals depending on the degree of uncertainty and the manner with which they anticipate income flows of the future. As an elementary example, we might imagine that 2 individuals see the possible distribution of future income flows in the manner of A, B, and C in the figure below. Although the patterns visualized or anticipated are identical, the 2

individuals can differ widely in their subjective capital values for the farm in question; the degree of uncertainty, as it affects the rate at which future incomes are discounted, will be dependent on the nature of the "probability distribution" with which each visualizes income possibilities. If individual I places a "probability" value of .1 on A, .8 on B, and .1 on C, his subjective capital value, in terms of the degree of uncertainty and the subjective element of discount, may well be greater than for individual II, who attaches probabilities of .1, .5, and .4 to the 3 prospective flows; although both view the B stream to be "most likely" (the modal alternative), the dispersion and skewness of the anticipated outcomes differ greatly and may affect their discounting rates accordingly.

time periods as repeated purchase of limited stocks of services in each year through renting if the production possibility curves in time were not different in the 2 cases. However, either certainty of short tenure or uncertainty of long tenure warp the opportunity curve in the direction of the present on tenant-operated farms. Consequently, the complex of tenure uncertainty may bring about a resource use pattern over time which is both inconsistent with consumer tastes or values and long-term returns to both tenant and landlord. The details of this problem are left for discussion in the next chapter.

3. **Competing time periods, stocks of services and uncertainty.** While it can be outlined that certain rental systems may cause resources to be used less efficiently than resource ownership, it can be said that ownership does not alone guarantee the most efficient use of resources over time. While tenure uncertainty places a premium on current production at the expense of later output, market uncertainty can have equally great impacts when ownership is acquired with borrowed capital and survival of the agricultural firm is dependent on fluctuations in market prices. The last several decades of price change have illustrated how quickly the value of farm resources can tumble to a half or a quarter or mushroom into double or treble their previous value. The new owner knows that incomes from his farm in the future have zero present value to him until the survival of the firm is guaranteed. Consequently, he may follow cash-cropping or other production plans which give high present returns at the expense of those of the future.

4. **Equity considerations and tenure.** Market uncertainty and the subjective discounting of future incomes undoubtedly causes farmers to place a premium on obtaining services of real estate through renting rather than owning. The operator with limited capital often prefers to rent land with cost or rent outlays extending only over a year's time while funds are invested in livestock and machinery which gives off their stock of services in a shorter time period than does land. Not only does the longer time period involved in durable-resource investment cause future incomes to be discounted at subjectively greater rates, but the principle of increasing risk as related to equity ratios also causes income from owned resource services to be discounted by greater relative amounts than the services from rented resources. A crop share lease allows the tenant to obtain use of more capital without reducing his equity ratio to the levels dictated by ownership. The example below for a typical grain and livestock farm of

240 acres of land at $300 (including buildings)	$72,000
Machinery at 1946-1951 prices	9,500
Livestock equipment	2,500
Livestock	7,500
Seed, supplies and operating funds	4,200
Total	$95,700

the Cornbelt illustrates the arithmetic. A tenant with $11,850 operating under a share lease would have a 50 per cent equity in the non-real estate capital. Under ownership, the same fund would represent less than a 13 per cent equity. Not only may this farmer with $11,850 be restricted through credit institutions from owning a unit of this size but his own risk aversion also acts as a deterrent. Farmers with little capital who do place premiums on ownership because of uncertainty and life expectancy reasons and buy farms with low equities often find their debt position extended to a point where they are unable to obtain funds for economic levels of live-stock, soil improvement, and similar investments. In contrast, the tenant with limited funds may more nearly carry out an optimum degree of capital intensity in terms of factor/product price ratios. The English tenure system has an advantage over that of the United States in this respect: the tenant with tenure certainty can invest in mono-period semi-durable resources without exhausting his funds in land titles. The capital complex again comes into play on the side of rented farms, however. The number of widows and aged persons deriving their incomes solely from rented farms is large. Many have low incomes and short life expectancies. Rather than invest in soil improvements which will bring returns years later, they prefer higher current incomes. The problem here is not that the farm is rented but that the owner is a person who views the future with an extremely short horizon. The repeated family-firm life cycle (discussed in Chapter 14) also stands to twist resource use towards the present. First, the beginning operator who purchases a farm with borrowed capital may place a premium on farming systems with high present returns and continued ownership of a farm can be attained only if the life of the firm is secured. Second, when the last or retirement stage of the cycle is attained, uncertainty of life itself (or the certainty of a short life) causes the premium to be on near, rather than distant, production. In the first case, it is price uncertainty and the life of the firm which emphasizes short-term production; in the second case, it is life uncertainty and the span of the household which directs resources in the same direction.

5. **The price paid for real estate.** Once paid, the price for land and buildings becomes a "fixed" or "historic" cost on a farm of particular size. In this sense the price paid would not, under a static and perfect knowledge economic setting, affect the resource organization; the same organization (the intensity with which other factors are applied to land or the same allocation of land between competing enterprises) would be optimum whether the price paid for the land is $50 or $500 per acre. (However, the optimum farm size or short-run plant would vary depending on the price of the land resource.) When uncertainty and capital limitations are brought into the picture the level of the price has somewhat different implications for resource use. For greater purchase prices, a given down payment represents smaller equity ratios and the degree of uncertainty is accordingly

greater; because of this increasing risk element, a greater premium is placed on short-run production plans and cropping systems which exploit the soil at the expense of the future. Any drop in land prices while indebtedness remains fixed causes the owner's equity ratio to melt lower and lower and again the degree of uncertainty grows to cause even greater premiums to be placed on short-run plans.[14]

Credit Policies and Efficiency Under Ownership

Imperfections in leasing systems have their counterpart under ownership as credit imperfections. The difficulty arises not from credit arrangements *per se* but more exactly from price and yield uncertainty; mortgage and interest payments are highly stable while farm income is highly variable. Hence the great tendency is for indebted owners to maximize return in the near future in order that indebtedness can be decreased and equity ratios can be increased to a level guaranteeing firm-survival. Given this setting, credit programs can be developed, however, which facilitate rather than discourage efficient use of resources. Credit provisions which lessen the effect of uncertainty and indebtedness are outlined below.

1. **Repayment schedules and moratoria.** Variable interest and principal repayment plans may be used to lessen the pressure to "produce now." [15] These schemes allow the farmer to exceed scheduled payments in good years and to miss payments in poor years without being subjected to bankruptcy. Many lending firms have put these schemes into operation only since the depression of the 1930's. Variable payment plans are well adapted to sporadic yield failures. They are not all adapted for long periods of distressed income which grow out of a major depression. However, if they are in effect during a depression they stand to extend the indebted owner's planning horizon and hence to cause him to give greater weight to the future. Variable payment plans must, if they are to eliminate this main inefficiency which arises under ownership, give the farmer definite expectations of eventual solvency. The moratorium legislation of the 1930's provided a temporary halt in foreclosure proceedings. Lenders were given the right to act as receivers in collecting a rent from the farm and

---

[14] In a study of 150 Iowa owner-operators with indebtedness on their farms, the writer could find no relation between price paid for the land and the manner in which the resource was used. Differences were found, however, in the cropping and land use systems depending on farmers' equities. Low-equity farms on similar soil types tended to follow more intensive cropping practices and to apply fewer recommended conservation practices.

[15] Conventional appraisal techniques and loan repayment schedules view the future as pouring forth income continuously at the mean expectancy level. With repayment schedules based on these assumptions, the farmer still has to recognize that not the mean income over an infinite period but the deviations away from this "statistic" largely affect the firm's ability to survive.

using the proceeds to pay taxes and upkeep and to apply the remainder on the principal of the mortgage. Where the farm operator had little or no expectations of maintaining title to his farm, however, he tried to pull the greatest possible product from the soil in the three-year moratorium period; the time was extended for exploitation of the farm. In cases in which "real hope" existed in the owner's mind, however, he refused to exploit the farm for a single year. Many forms of variable payment plans can be devised and may allow flexibility in either interest or principal payments. These include (1) the customary landlord's share of the product, (2) the value of a fixed amount of product (so many bushels of wheat or pounds of beef), (3) an amount varied in line with the general index of prices or purchasing power of money, and (4) others. The first allows variations in interest and principal payments which parallel changes in both yields and prices. The second and third help lessen uncertainty and income variability due to price uncertainty but do not include allowances for yield variability, an important consideration in semi-arid farming areas.

2. **Period of loan and amortization.** While less important today than over the long history of United States farming, the length of time for which real-estate loans are extended also has important bearing on the degree of subjective uncertainty which attaches to farm ownership. While mortgages extending for only 5 years were typical in the early decades of the century, the majority of real-estate loans extended by the Federal Land Bank, insurance companies, and other important lenders now are for 20 to 35 years. A short-term mortgage emphasizes production within the period because of the uncertainty considerations mentioned earlier and because great importance attaches to the date at which the mortgage expires. While the short-term mortgage may be renewed, the life of the firm is endangered through the possibility of foreclosure each time the mortgage expires. Then, as has been mentioned previously, short-term mortgages are not consistent with the rate at which resource services are transformed into product. Land, like buildings and many other resources, embodies both stock and flow services. If the land values are based on the flow services as well as the stock services, a short loan period is inconsistent with the flow component. If the loan is to be repaid from the product of the resource it must conform to the factor/product transformation rates. This principle is basic for any credit program.

3. **The amount of the loan.** Aside from fluctuations in income, the rapidity with which loans can be repaid and full equity can be attained depends on the farmer's original equity (the amount of the loan as well as the productivity of the resources). This difference is not always recognized in farm loan procedures; loans often are extended over equal periods for operators with equities of 75 per cent or 40 per cent. Lending firms are not, of course,

primarily concerned with the productivity and efficiency aspects of resources but with selling credit on the basis of security; a loan over a long period to an operator with a high equity serves as efficiently for these purposes as one for the same period to an operator with a low equity. Some writers contend that in terms of "safety" the proportion of the appraised value loaned on poor land should be less than that for good land.[16] This logic misses the real crux of the problem, which is one of the degree of accuracy in predicting (a) the income from resources and (b) the variability of the income. In a pure firm context, the debt-paying ability of poor land is just as great as that for good land if the price of both represents the capitalized value of their productivity. With similar income variability the size of the loan relative to the value productivity (with proper recognition of taxes and other non-production costs) can be just as great on poor as on good land. The real consideration in loan ratios is one of income variability. If loan success is the criterion, the loan ratio should relate to the variability or uncertainty of returns. In other words, a 60 per cent loan, supposing the valuation expectations are comparable, might be granted on a low productivity soil as well as on a high productivity soil if income is equally stable or certain for both. Still, a loan of only 40 per cent might be granted on a medium productivity soil which includes a highly variable and uncertain income.

Loan experience during the 1930's was highly unfavorable on the less productive soils. While this historic outcome has led many persons to the conclusion that "the loan ratio should be lower for poor farms," the real problem again is one of product imputation and valuation accuracy. Loan firms and professional appraisers were in error in the income expectations which they used as a basis for capitalization and soils were over-valued relative to income realizations. (Evidently the "appraisal error" was greater for poor than for good soil.) If income expectations (for example, appraisal estimates) are equally accurate, there is no basis, except for family or household considerations, for varying the loan ratio between soils which have different productivity ratings but equal income variability. Historically, persons with small amounts of capital have tended to purchase farms on land with low physical and value productivity. In addition to the drive for ownership as a means to farming security, 3 forces seem important in explaining this tendency: One is the discontinuity in the supply of the land factor. Farms over much of the nation are sold traditionally in fractions or multiples of 160 acre units; small quantities

---

[16] This notion is put forth in R. R. Renne, *op. cit.* He states:

"In practice, of course, loans should not equal the full value of real estate on any grade of land, because there would be no margin of security to provide for contingencies. But, if 75 percent were the maximum lent on any grade, average loans on the poorer grades should be proportionately less."

of capital provide the equity for purchasing less productive units but not always for the more productive units of the same size. Uncertainty, the second consideration, also enters in since a small amount of funds allows a greater equity ratio on low as compared to high priced land. This tendency of persons with small capital to settle on less productive soils also helps explain the unfavorable loan experience on poor soils. Again, the nature of the problem is not one to suggest a smaller percentage loaned on poor soil (if methods of capitalization are comparable). Instead, it stems from the total capital of the farm family and the income withdrawals necessary for consumption or household purposes. For families requiring equal withdrawals, a farm on Shelby-Lindley soils in Missouri producing an annual net return of $5,000 should be able to support as great a loan as a farm producing the same return on the Tama-Muscatine soils of Iowa, or the Drummer-Flanagan soils of Illinois. The third consideration, one of farm size, comes in here to explain why individuals with little capital may better succeed on certain poor soils. On the basis of recent land values, $6,000 serving as 50 per cent equity would allow purchase of about 120 acres of Shelby soils but only 15 acres of Drummer soils. The "diseconomy of small scale" is undoubtedly less on Shelby than on Drummer soils. Drummer soils are highly adapted to mechanization and cash grain farming. To the extent that land values are based on returns for larger and more nearly "optimum sized" units, the 15-acre farm would have difficult sledding. In contrast, Shelby-Lindley soils are less adapted to mechanized, cash-grain farming and more nearly to livestock operations; topography dictates smaller fields and retention of a greater proportion of the land in forages. A small livestock farm may do relatively as well as a large farm on the same soil, since cost economies are less in animal than in crop production. In this sense, small investments on soils of low physical productivity have as great or a greater probability of providing the basis for successful loans as would the same investment and loan ratio on highly productive soils.[17]

---

[17] The fact that farms on the level, more productive soils are often larger than those on the less productive soils in the same general geographic and climatic area tends to support the hypothesis of greater cost economies under grain than under livestock or horticultural systems of farming. The tradition of the 160-acre unit (or its multiple) might well have broken down in a century had there been a market for small investment units in level soil areas. Had farmers been willing to bid more for units requiring a small capital outlay, it appears likely that a greater market would have developed wherein 160-, 240-, or 320-acre units would have been sold in quantities of 10, 20, or 40 acres. The fact that the trend has been as much in the opposite direction suggests that the cost economies associated with larger acreages and the land values based on large units have tended to prevent purchase of small farms by people with little capital. Yet operators with the same funds can purchase a "small" farm (a 160-acre unit on soils of the southern Cornbelt represents a small investment relative to a 40- or 80-acre unit in the central Cornbelt) on the less productive soils; because of the systems of farming adapted to the soils the disadvantage of a small unit is not so great as in other farming regions.

Selected References

Boulding, K. E., *Reconstruction of Economics*. New York: Wiley, 1950, Ch. 3.

Hicks, J. R., *Value and Capital*. Oxford: Clarendon Press, 1939, Ch. 13.

Makower, H., and Marshak, J., "Assets, Prices and Monetary Theory," *Economica*, Vol. 5, pp. 261-288.

Marshak, J., "Role of Liquidity Under Complete and Incomplete Information," *Amer. Econ. Rev.*, Vol. 39, pp. 182-195.

Murray, W. G., *Agricultural Finance*. Ames: Iowa State College Press, 1941, Chs. 10, 11, 12, 30.

Schultz, T. W., *Production and Welfare in Agriculture*. New York: McGraw-Hill, 1949, Ch. 12.

PART IV

Aggregate Aspects of Production

T HE CHAPTERS of this section focus on aggregate aspects
of agricultural production or resource use. Questions of
individual farm decisions and efficiency also are discussed in early chapters. The tools selected for presentation of logic and principle are those drawn from both
"statics" and "dynamics." The principles used, while
they are not the most complete, are those which serve
efficiently and simply in analysis of the subject matter
presented.

20

Leasing and Tenure Systems and Farming Efficiency

AN IMPORTANT part of the nation's agricultural resources is employed on farms operated under some form of leasing arrangement. Nearly one-half of our farms obtain control of part or all of their resources by this means. Because of the quantity of resources so controlled, the farm lease stands on a level with other important phenomena which condition the efficiency with which food and fiber are produced. It is a known fact that rental payments are determined by a maze of forces which, in addition to competition, include custom and elements of bilateral monopoly. Obviously, lease terms so determined may have varying effects upon the organization of resources on individual farms. Society and the individual resource owner or user (landlord or tenant) stand to sacrifice from resource inefficiencies stemming from imperfect leasing systems.

Leasing of farms is only 1 facet of the factor market. On the one hand, the tenant hires the services of land resource from the owner: he pays cash for these services under the cash lease and a payment in kind under the share lease. Conversely, the landlord hires the services of the tenant's labor and capital under crop or livestock share leases.[1] The factor service price is again a payment in kind (the tenant's share). The leasing of real estate (land and buildings) is not a unique market arrangement, by any means. Cash payment for factor services is the rule rather than the exception in the hiring of labor, custom machine operations, the borrowing of

---

[1] A "firm" attempting to maximize profits exists from the standpoint of either the tenant or the landlord as a resource owner. Commonly, the farm operated by the tenant is viewed as the business unit to which maximization of profits is related. In the case of complete business partnerships (and perhaps in the case of certain livestock share leases) the landlord and tenant may view the same resource collection as an entity from the standpoint of profit maximization and resource use. However, this situation does not hold true under many share and cash leases. The landlord represents "a distinct firm" from the standpoint of the use of and returns from such specialized factors and land and buildings. The tenant represents a "distinct firm" from the standpoint of use and allocation of specialized resources in the form of labor and particular forms of capital. Thus leases can be analyzed from the standpoint of the "distinct firm" representing either the tenant or landlord as a resource owner.

funds, and, of course, those resources such as fertilizer and feed which are entirely transformed into product in a relatively short production period. The cash lease falls in the same market framework. Payment in kind under share leases is also widespread in the use of other factor services. Many farms acquire the use of labor and machine services through factor rewards in kind; the outstanding example is the exchange of labor and machine use by neighboring farmers. The labor exchanged by one farmer is a product paid for the furnishing of factor services by the other. Labor-sharing arrangements between fathers and sons or non-related partners represents another expression of the price-in-kind market for resource services. While this chapter is devoted to the efficiency of leasing systems, it applies equally to those other facets of factor markets where prices are paid in kind.

Since each farm situation is unique, the specialist who expects to improve leasing arrangements through advice to tenants or landlords might well use the theoretically perfect lease as his point of departure. However, the economics of leasing systems and customs has never been fully developed, and it is possible that many leasing inefficiencies are perpetuated by experts in Land Grant Colleges. Quite commonly, the queries of tenants and landlords with respect to suitable leasing arrangements are answered by direct recommendation or the implication that the existing pattern serves as an "ideal model." The leasing customs which have grown up over time have become deeply ingrained in many communities. Landlords sometimes refuse to alter terms from the existing pattern because of the reluctance of tenants and people in the neighborhood to sanction deviations from the customs which have been perpetuated over time.

This chapter outlines the conditions of resource use which should exist for tenants and landlords if either is to maximize profits. It also points out means by which conflicts in the interests of the landlord and tenant can be resolved and a system of resource use, efficient from the standpoint of either, established. Leasing arrangements provide a small economic community (the landlord and the tenant) wherein the postulates of welfare economics can be applied to either (1) make both individuals better off at the same time or (2) make one better off and provide compensation so that the other is no worse off in terms of income and total utility. Finally, this chapter relates leasing systems to efficiency problems from the standpoint of the consuming economy. A major part of the analysis is in terms of firm and productivity analysis (farm management) since herein lie the most effective and appropriate tools for analyzing tenure and leasing arrangements. The question of "fair" rents is first subjected to the scrutiny of production economic logic but detailed examination of the effect of various leasing systems on the structure of decision-making relationships is given major emphasis. The method followed is that of setting forth the economic characteristics of perfect leasing systems, comparing known customs with these standards, and suggesting the means whereby the perfect lease would eliminate imperfections which now exist.

Perfect Leasing Systems

In setting forth the characteristics of perfect leasing systems or in analyzing existing customs, it is necessary to delineate the economic setting within which the evaluation is to take place. For the purpose of the analysis presented here, the following are taken as given: (1) competition (except for imperfections growing out of leasing systems) and the private ownership of resource prevail, and (2) the pricing system is looked upon as the appropriate means for expression of consumer preference and, hence, for allocation of resources in the most efficient manner.[2] A perfect leasing system must, therefore, result in (1) the most efficient organization of resources on the farm relative to consumer demand as expressed in market prices and (2) an equitable division of the product among the owners of the various resources employed in production. Under the conditions specified above, these are the appropriate criteria for evaluation of leasing systems. For the definitions of "efficient" and "equitable" which follow, attainment of one must result in the simultaneous attainment of the other. Distinction between the 2 is made only because this necessary condition need not hold true under the definitions of "equitable" used in certain instances.

Equitable division of product. Under the institutions of private resource ownership and market prices there can be, of course, only 1 definition of an "equitable" division of the product; the return to any one of the resource owners must be based on the marginal value productivity of the resources which the individual contributes. His share of the total product is then established by the quantities of the various types of resources which he contributes to the firm and the marginal productivity of specific resources. The reasons why "equitable" cannot be defined otherwise in a setting of market prices, competition and private ownership of resources are elementary: (1) Unless the marginal value product is imputed as a reward to each factor, the most efficient allocation of resources cannot be attained.[3] (2) The institution of private resource ownership honors no

---

[2] It is recognized, of course, that perfect competition does not hold in a large part of our economy, and also that the pricing system does not result in a most efficient allocation of resources even in agriculture. However, these assumptions are set forth in order to limit the scope of this study to leasing systems alone.

[3] Unless the firm pays a cost for the use of resources equal to their marginal productivity, the allocation of resources will not be in harmony with consumer preferences. Waste of resources will result, because inefficient firms may be able to exist, and especially because the wrong combination of products will be forthcoming. Even under public ownership of resources, maximization of the social product would require that each farm pay a cost for the use of resources equal to their marginal productivity. For a complete discussion along the lines of the latter, see O. Lange and F. M. Taylor, *Economic Theory of Socialism*. Minneapolis: Univ. of Minn. Press, 1939.

other definition.[4] Since, in the long-run, the most efficient allocation of resources cannot be attained without an "equitable" division of the product (as defined here) and vice versa, most of the analysis will be in terms of the former.

Efficient use of resources. A test of the perfect leasing system is in its effect on the total product available to consumers. Resource and commodity prices should, in a perfect market, indicate the pattern of production and combination of resources which is most nearly consistent with a maximization of consumer satisfaction. Leasing systems should facilitate an organization of resources within the individual farm which will bring about this pattern. Any characteristics of a lease which violates the pricing system in this respect is imperfect. If, at a given time, consumer satisfaction is to be maximized with a combination of products made up of x units of commodity Y_1 at price P_{y1} and z units of Y_2 at price P_{y2}, an imperfection of the leasing system occurs if the resulting output includes less than x units of Y_1 or more than z units of Y_2 at prices higher or lower respectively than the otherwise equilibrium prices. Finally, the leasing system is imperfect if it does not encourage adoption of the most productive combination of resources in the production of a unit of a given commodity. If the stock of resources in the economy is great enough to allow the output of q of all commodities under the most efficient technique, any characteristic of a leasing system which results in adoption of another technique and a total output of less than q is undesirable. Under competitive conditions, this maximum product can be forthcoming only if the firm has attained the necessary equilibrium conditions. Aside from other imperfections in the market these conditions are, in the long run, simply those which are necessary for the maximization of profits by the individual firm. The leasing system thus becomes imperfect if it hinders allocation of resources in any of these directions: (1) Factor-product relationships and cost structures for single products must be retained over time in a manner consistent with the technological conditions of the short-run plant which

---

[4] This statement refers only to the sale of productive services by the individual resource owner. Many policies of this nation's government have obviously resulted in personal incomes greater than would hold true if the marginal value productivity of resources were determined in the market alone. The consequent distortion of returns on resources relative to consumer preferences has resulted in an inefficient use of resources. However, these policies have not sanctioned a charge other than the marginal value productivity (as determined by market prices and governmental policy) for the use of productive services sold by the individual to the firm. Although there may be scattered instances in which legislation has resulted in a charge for resources (sold by the individual to the firm) out of line with their marginal value productivity (as expressed by market prices along, or by price and governmental policy), there is little evidence that this was the original intent. Labor union activity, for example, has undoubtedly resulted in wage payments out of line with the marginal value productivity of labor in numerous instances. Yet the objective of the original labor legislation perhaps was that of bringing wage payments into line with the productivity of labor.

relate to time. The scale of the firm must be one which defines a maximum return in a manner consistent with the market prices for factors and products and with the given technical conditions of production. (2) The marginal value productivity of substitute resources must be equated, and factor-factor relationships must not be distorted. (3) A combination of products must be attained which will equate marginal returns on the last unit of resources employed for each product at a given point in time and the leasing arrangement must facilitate retention of transformation functions as they would exist under other factor market and pricing systems. (4) The combination of products in time must be such that, with proper discounting of future returns, marginal value products are equated over time for all resource units. (5) The leasing arrangement must not bring about resource inefficiency through an increase of uncertainty above that which would normally exist in the market.

These conditions are not all attained on many owner-operator farms. However, the test of leasing systems is this: they should not cause further deviations from the conditions which define economic efficiency. Portions of agriculture do deviate from conditions of pure competition and a perfect market does not exist in the sense that it facilitates complete resource efficiency. However, these problems can best be analyzed in other studies and are somewhat distinct from leasing arrangement *per se*. In order that the scope of the analysis might be delimited to that of leasing efficiency alone they are not discussed below.

Intensity in the Short Run and Size of the Farm in the Long Run

Either share or cash rent may be paid on a single commodity. Under straight cash leasing arrangements, the rent paid is a flat or lump-sum amount per acre or for all acres in a farm of given size (a short-run plant). It thus enters into the tenant's total costs and affects the level of per unit costs of production from this standpoint. However, since it does not vary with yields, it is not a function of output and does not enter into marginal costs. Share rent is paid in kind and is, therefore, a function of yield and enters into marginal cost. How then may each of these forms of factor payment affect the intensity of resource use for a technical unit (acre or animal) or a farm?

Contribution of specialized resources and landlord costs. A fixed short-run supply of resources tends to be created under the leasing custom wherein the landlord and tenant each furnish specialized resources, while the product is divided along parallel and equally rigid lines. Under the typical crop-share (or cash) lease the landlord furnishes the fixed assets in the form of land and buildings while the tenant furnishes all or a major part of the labor and working capital. Often, the kind and quantity of buildings found on a rented farm are those which existed when the landlord obtained title, and hence are the result of the price-cost relationships of the past or the financial situation of previous owners. Input of these resources may not be extended, even though the potential marginal return is greater than for other types of resources; since the landlord does not receive a direct share of the product, he may be unwilling to add investment in buildings. Often he has no strong inducement for furnishing buildings beyond a minimum necessary to attract competent tenants under a crop-share lease, since his share of the product comes not from the livestock but from the land.

Numerous divisions of annual factor costs are made under crop-share or cash leasing arrangements. Under the cash lease, annual expenses of the landlord tend to be those which take the form of fixed costs (taxes, insurance, and depreciation, or other costs of factor services which flow forth over the production period in a manner not entirely correlated with the level of output). Great variations exist for share leases. In areas such as the Great Plains, the landlord pays only costs associated with the real estate which he furnishes. These costs include taxes, insurance, and depreciation, and again take the form of fixed costs. In the Cornbelt, landlords frequently pay one-half the seed and fertilizer costs and sometimes a share of weed spraying, threshing, and similar outlays. Analysis of the effect of cash or crop-share leasing systems must then consider the costs and profit maximization from the standpoint of either (1) a tenant, where (a) the cash rent is a fixed cost and the full marginal product is realized for each input of resource or (b) the share-rent is considered as a variable cost or as a reduction from the marginal product of resource inputs; or (2) a landlord, where (a) cash rent represents a fixed return and outlays are in the form of fixed costs (taxes and so forth), (b) share-rent is a variable return and outlays for factors are in the form of fixed costs, and (c) share-rent represents a variable return and outlays are for both variable and fixed costs. In the immediately following analysis we consider pure cases where the landlord furnishes land as a fixed cost while the tenant furnishes labor and capital and bears variable costs.

Decision-making and the production function. Either the landlord or the tenant can look upon the stock of resources which he possesses as the fixed factor (the plant or technical unit). The resources furnished by the other party thus become, in his eyes, the variable factor. In the terms of leasing there are 2 relevant periods of production, which again can be specified as the long run and short run. (These terms are used here to refer to leasing situations specifically and do not necessarily coincide with the definitions given earlier.) The important long run in leasing does include a fixed set of factors on the part of each resource owner. It refers, however, to the period in which the tenant is free to select between land or farms (select a landlord) and the landlord is free to select capital and labor (select a tenant). The tenant has a fixed stock of labor, machinery, and other forms of capital. In looking for his first farm or for a new farm, he can envision land as a variable factor and, within the institutional limitations which exist, can consider which amount of land (which farm) is optimum when combined with his own constant set of resources. Once he has selected a farm (if indeed he has more than 1 farm to select from), his decisions are then short run in the sense that production now must be carried on with acreage and buildings fixed.[5] Before the landlord has entered into a leasing agreement, he can consider tenant resources as entirely variable, and hence has the opportunity to decide on the number of units of tenant resources which can be most profitably combined with his own fixed stock of land and buildings. Given the opportunity to select tenants of different managerial ability, he too should select the one who will cause the marginal value productivity of his own resources to be greatest. Once he has selected a tenant with given resources and a given stock of managerial ability, decisions turn to the short run which constitutes the leasing period or year.[6]

A share lease and short-run landlord decisions. The production function which serves for decision-making under owner operation (or the cash lease) is altered for either the share landlord or tenant in the manner illustrated by Figure 1. The curve Y is the production function showing the total product forthcoming for each level of input of tenant resources; it refers to a fixed input of landlord resources. The full curve Y is relevant for decision-making by the owner-operator or the cash tenant where both can market the full product. However, under share rents which include two-thirds of the product to the tenant and one-third to the landlord, the input-output curve relevant for short-run decision-making by the tenant becomes $2/3Y$. Similarly, the landlord's short-run, decision-making production function (for a single-product and single-period type of production) is the curve indicated as $1/3Y$. The marginal productivity of tenant resources can be derived from these production functions and are indicated in Figure 2. Here the curve MP represents the total marginal product of resources (of the type furnished by tenants on rented farms) and is the relevant decision-making marginal quantity for an owner-operator or cash tenant. Since the share tenant receives only two-thirds of the total yield, his decision-making marginal curve becomes $2/3MP$ while that for the landlord becomes $1/3MP$. Here we suppose that the marginal productiv-

---

[5] Given the opportunity to choose from farms of the same number of acres but of different soil types, he should select the one for which the marginal value productivity of his own resources is greatest. In case part of the product is represented in settlement near the home community, the analysis falls in the vein of that included under firm-household relationships.

[6] Once the tenant "selects" a farm, the quantity of land available for the production period is generally fixed. However, once the landlord has "selected a tenant," the outlay of labor is not always fixed in an absolute sense, and he may "exhort" the tenant to apply more of these resources to the technical unit represented by the given acreage and building establishment which constitute the farm plant.

ity of tenant resources becomes zero with an application of ox_3 units of "tenant resources" to the fixed input of landlord resources. (The total product is a maximum at oy_4 units of output when input is ox_3 in Figure 1.)

Given the fixed costs for both landlord and tenant and the prices for factors, these physical relationships can now be translated into cost situations. First, for the landlord who pays out fixed costs on land and buildings only, the average cost curve is of the nature indicated by AC_1 in Figure 3.

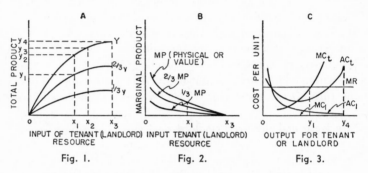

Share leases and decision-making factor-product relationships.

It is a rectangular hyperbola, indicating that although cost per unit varies with output, total cost remains constant at the given level. Thus the marginal cost per unit of product (MC_1) to the landlord is zero. Second, the tenant's average cost curve (cost per unit of product for the tenant's share) is of the nature indicated as AC_t and will be of the conventional U-shape to the extent that fixed costs are great enough to cause it to decline in small ranges of output, while diminishing productivity of variable factors causes it to rise in large ranges of output. It includes not only the variable costs for producing the tenant's two-thirds share but also a one-third greater outlay representing the cost of producing the landlord's share (plus the per unit fixed cost associated with the tenant's resources). Paralleling the tenant's decision-making average cost curve is his decision-making marginal cost curve MC_t. It is derived from the total variable costs attributable to the total production function Y and includes a one-third cost above the tenant's share (that associated with the portion of product going to the landlord).

Given this set of decision-making costs the conditions can be outlined under which landlord and tenant profits are maximized in the short-run. A possible source of tenant-landlord conflict can also be pointed out. The share tenant, if he has ample capital and wishes to maximize profits, will want to produce oy_1 units (Figures 1 or 3) of product for himself (a total of oy_2 in Figure 1 for the farm of given size including the landlord share) where marginal cost is equal to marginal revenue, MR. However, since the marginal cost is zero throughout all ranges of output for the landlord, he will wish to have output pushed to the physical limit indicated as oy_4. If he possesses full short-run, decision-making powers, this factor combination (ox_3 of tenant resources applied to the fixed input of landlord resources in Figures 1 or 2) will maximize his total profit. On this basis the landlord would prefer that the tenant apply resources to maximize the physical product for each acre and for the farm as a whole. The share tenant would prefer a much lower level of intensity and, as is pointed out later, would be willing to go an even smaller distance than the cash tenant or the owner-operator.

Share rent and long-run landlord decisions. We may now view long-run situations where the landlord attempts to select the optimum tenant and the tenant attempts to select the optimum landlord. Each is interested in the quantity of resources furnished by the other. If the landlord views the rental arrangement in the vein of a situation where he is paying rent to the tenant for the use of tenant resources, the following productivity conditions become relevant. Using the curves in Figure 2 to represent value productivity of different quantities of tenant resources used with a fixed quantity of landlord resources, the landlord can consider MP as the full marginal value product forthcoming from "hiring" tenant resources. If profits are to be maximized, he should employ tenant resources up to the point where the marginal value product of tenant resources is equal to the marginal cost of tenant resources. The tenant's two-thirds share (of the total marginal value product) becomes, for the landlord, the marginal cost of using tenant resources. Since the marginal cost of a unit of tenant resource (the tenant's share) declines with the total marginal value productivity of tenant resources, landlord profit is at a maximum (marginal value productivity of tenant resources "hired" by the landlord is equal to the marginal cost of tenant resources to the landlord) when the marginal productivity of tenant resources is zero (when ox_3 units of tenant resources are used in Figure 2).

Cash rent and landlord long-run decisions. Under a cash lease, the landlord could be indifferent as to the quantity of tenant resources employed with his own fixed input of specialized resources. Since both cost and return are constant, his return is the same in any case and decisions can be left entirely to the tenant.

Share-leases and tenant long-run decisions. A similar long-run situation arises when the tenant views his own resources as fixed while the land input of the landlord is considered to be variable. This condition can again be illustrated with Figures 1 and 2. Figure 1 now illustrates the total product forthcoming as land is varied in amount relative to the fixed stock of tenant labor and capital; the curves in Figure 2 indicate the marginal productivity of land with tenant resources held constant. The tenant must decide on how many acres of landlord resource to "hire" (how large a farm to rent). He can maximize profit when the marginal value productivity of an acre of land is equal to the marginal cost of an acre. Curve *MP* again is the relevant total marginal value productivity curve. The marginal cost of an acre of land to the tenant is the one-third share of the total product which goes to the landlord. Thus curve $1/3MP$ in Figure 2 is the marginal cost of land to the tenant. Since it too declines with the total marginal value product, the marginal value productivity and the marginal cost of land are equal for the tenant only when the marginal value productivity of land is driven to zero. In other words, rented farms would be expanded under share leasing to a size indicated by ox_3 acres of land in Figure 2 if tenants were free and able to maximize profits.

Thus the shoe fits the tenant and landlord equally well under share renting. If either is to maximize his own returns with resources fixed in quantity, he must seek out resources of the other until the marginal value productivity of the latter resources become zero.[7] Many conflicts arise in practice over these points. Landlords tend to search out the tenant who has the greatest quantity of resources (including managerial ability), and, other things being equal, continually push him to employ added techniques and greater factor inputs. Tenants "brace themselves" and refuse to do so unless the landlords make proportional contributions. Conversely, tenants search out larger farms or field rent on the outside. The landlord complains about (or refuses to allow the possibility of) "outside farming" by his tenant for fear that yields and returns will decline on his own land.[8]

Cash leases and tenant long-run decisions. In order to compare the optimum farm size for the tenant under share and cash leasing, we now turn to Figure 4 (which is similar to Figure 2, except for the enlarged scale). Again the tenant looks upon his resources as fixed while land (or all landlord resources) is considered to be variable. Curve $MP_{1.0}$ illustrates the (gross or total) marginal value product of land when it is used in varying

---

[7] Because leasing represents, in a sense, a case of bilateral monopoly, this condition is perhaps never fully attained. Furthermore, general leasing considerations and respect for the other party undoubtedly keep these conditions from being completely fulfilled. The direction to which leasing arrangements tend and the power in selection and decision-making which rests in the tenant or landlord also varies with the supply of tenants or farms for rent and hence the competitive position of tenants and landlords.

[8] The discussion above has been in terms of "distinct categories" of tenant and landlord resources, where each considers his resource stock as fixed while that of the other is variable. We can remove these assumptions. Even where either party is able to consider long-run decisions in use of the other's resources, the one may furnish factors which are technical complements with resources contributed by the other. Under this situation, tenant profit will be at a maximum when the marginal value product of the resources which he furnishes is equal to their marginal cost. Thus, since he will never extend use of his own resource (tractor fuel) to a point where its marginal value productivity is zero, he will never extend land (as a complementary factor) to a zero productivity level. When the landlord furnishes a share of some resources which are pure complements with tenant resources, the situation is similar.

quantities with the fixed labor and capital of the renter. The marginal cost of land to a tenant operating under a one-third share lease is $MP_{.33}$; it is equal to one-third of the full marginal product, $MP_{1.0}$. Under a one-third share rent, the tenant can again maximize his own profits when the marginal value product of land has been driven to zero; the marginal value productivity of land and its marginal cost to the share tenant are then equal for a farm of this size (ox_3 acres in Figure 4). Under the same long-run production function, a cash tenant is faced with a somewhat different situation. Equation of the marginal value product and the marginal cost of the land factor also defines maximum profits for him. However, the cash rent per acre now represents the marginal cost of land. Suppose cash rent amounts to oc per acre in Figure 4. The cash tenant can maximize profits if he rents ox_2 acres of land. The marginal productivity of land is not driven to zero. Thus if tenants were free to make long-run decisions, farm size would differ under cash and share renting. In Figure 4 for example, a farm of ox_3 acres would maximize profits to a share tenant, while a farm of only ox_2 acres would maximize profits to a cash tenant.

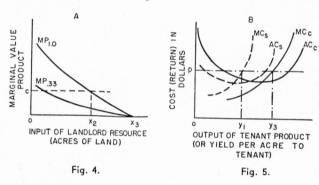

Fig. 4.   Fig. 5.

Leases and short-run intensity.

In practice, it is true that tenants must rent farms of the sizes which are available. There are also other forces (see later sections of this chapter) which may cause cash and share-rented farms to differ in size. However, in most farming regions where both types of lease prevail, cash farms tend to be smaller than share farms. Cash-rented farms in Iowa averaged 137 acres in 1950 while all share and cash-share farms averaged 196 acres. Corresponding figures for Illinois were 102 and 200 acres respectively. These data include small tracts rented on a cash basis and somewhat over-estimate the actual farm difference.

Differences in costs and short-run intensity under cash and share leases. We have illustrated how the optimum farm size (the best scale of long-run factor-product application) may differ between a cash and crop-share tenant. We now return to the short-run situation (the factor-product relationship when a farm of a given size has been rented) and compare the cost structure and the optimum degree of intensity (yield per acre or for a farm of fixed size) under cash and share-renting. (The production function is now of short-run nature and the farm acreage is fixed while fertilizer, labor, and other tenant resources can be applied at different rates.) The degree of intensity which is optimum under share and cash leases, if tenants are to maximize profits, is illustrated in Figure 5. The curves AC_c and MC_c are the average and marginal costs respectively under a cash lease and relate to the full product of the farm (for example, the total product curve in Figure 1 or the marginal product curve $MP_{1.0}$ in Figure 4). Given the same production function, the share tenant's average and marginal cost curves are AC_s and MC_s respectively in Figure 5. They include all his costs but refer only to the tenant's share of the total farm production (curve $2/3Y$ in Figure 1).[9] The cash tenant's per-unit cost will be greater for small outputs because cash rent represents a fixed cost and is not a function of output. The share tenant's average cost will be greater for large yields per acre or large outputs for the farm because he receives only two-thirds of the total product.[10] The marginal cost (of his share) for the share tenant will be greater for any output (to the tenant) than for the cash tenant; while the two lay out the same amount of variable resource or cost for a specified level of total output, the cash tenant receives the full product, while the share tenant receives only two-thirds but pays all variable costs. (Although the marginal cost curve for the total product on a share rented farm also might be MC_c, only the curve MC_s is relevant for decision-making by the tenant). With a price of op for the product, the share tenant can maximize profit per acre or for a farm of a fixed size by producing oy_1 units as his own share (a total output of oy_2 in Figure 1 with ox_1 inputs of factor). The cash tenant can maximize short-run profits by producing oy_3 units (which corresponds to the total product of oy_3 in 1 and is forthcoming with ox_2 inputs). If share and cash tenants are to maximize profits, different quantities of tenant resources (fertilizer, seed, labor, spray, tractor fuel, and so forth) should be applied to a given land area under the two systems.

As is brought out in later sections, the landlord may include specifications in the lease which cause the share tenant to apply more resources and to obtain a higher yield per acre. Also, some inputs are discontinuous and their nature causes the same level of intensity to be profitable to share

---

[9] The share tenant's average and marginal costs will include the costs of producing the total farm product, but since he receives only a two-thirds share, the per-unit costs relate only to his share (average costs are computed by dividing total costs to the tenant by two-thirds of the total output; marginal costs are computed by providing the full cost of any resource increment by two-thirds of the increment in product).

[10] Other situations may also exist depending on the level of fixed costs or cash rents relative to share rents. The curve AC_s in 5 may cross AC_c at any particular point (or in exceptional cases remain below it) depending on levels of rents. Only the most likely possibilities have been outlined.

and cash tenants. However, there are many differences under the 2 systems. An Iowa study indicated that tenants generally consider the cost structure of a cash lease to be more conducive to efficient farming. In support of the logic outlined above, the Iowa study showed the differences in intensity illustrated in Table 1, where different arrangements existed on share-rented farms.

Table I.

Effect of Share and Cash Leasing on Intensity of Fertilizer Application Per Acre *

Item	Farms where landlord shared costs	Farms where landlord does not share costs
Per cent fertilizing corn	60.0	6.9
Per cent fertilizing oats	42.2	3.4
Pounds fertilizer applied on corn per farm	5104	795
Pounds fertilizer applied on oats per farm	4227	466

* Source: E. O. Heady and E. W. Kehrberg, *Effect of Share and Cash Renting on Farming Efficiency.* Iowa Agr. Exp. Sta. Bull. 386.

The same logic also applies to owner operation as compared to share renting. If land costs are fixed in nature, the owner is faced with the same marginal cost curve (curve MC_c in Figure 5) as the cash tenant. While the average cost curve may differ (since fixed costs under ownership may differ from the rent as a fixed cost under a cash lease), the curve of marginal costs will be identical; both the owner and cash tenant receive the full product forthcoming from any unit of factor input. Given a price of op in Figure 5, an owner would extend output to oy_3, while the share tenant would go no further than oy_1. These 2 outputs correspond to factor inputs of ox_2 and ox_1 respectively in Figure 1.[11]

Elimination of share lease imperfections. The discussion above has assumed a "pure form" of share lease, wherein the tenant and landlord both furnish distinct categories of resources. In practice there are many cash-share combinations. Wide variations also exist in sharing of costs for variable resources on share-rented farms. In some instances fertilizer, seeds, and similar supplies are paid by the landlord or tenant alone; in other cases the costs are shared. Either the landlord or the tenant may find the application of lime or fertilizer unprofitable when he must bear the full cost; or the same obstacle may be encountered for investments which the landlord alone is customarily expected to make. If the tiling of land results in a

---

[11] Both the owner and cash tenant could maintain production under price relationships causing the share tenant to cease production. Even though price is below average cost, all can minimize loss by equating it with marginal cost, as long as price is above variable cost per unit. (Variable cost curves are not shown in Figure 5.) However, under the situation being discussed, wherein the share landlord pays only fixed costs attached to real estate, the variable cost per unit of the product to the share tenant (the marginal cost of the tenant's share alone) is always greater than for the owner or cash tenant.

product worth $1.90 for each $1 input, the landlord will be unwilling to make the investment if the return must be split with the tenant under a one-half share lease. Yet the imperfection is not inherent in the share characteristics of the lease. Instead, it grows out of established customs in sharing costs. A perfect share lease would provide the profit incentive for the most efficient combination of resources in the same manner as a cash lease or owner operation. Only 1 condition, a complex provision, is necessary for a perfect lease in this respect. The cost of variable factors (where land is fixed) must be divided between the landlord and tenant in proportions paralleling the division of the product. Theoretically, a share lease in which landlord and tenant separately furnish single categories of resources and in turn realize a fixed share of product would approximate perfection in only 1 case. It is the appropriate arrangement only if the resources must be combined in fixed proportions (pairs of technical complementary resources with the landlord and tenant each furnishing 1 resource). Whenever a resource can be combined with others in varying proportions, the cost of the variable factor should, under the perfect lease, be borne by landlord and tenant in proportion to the share of the product which each receives. In a practical sense, costs for inputs which are near the periphery of profitability for either tenant or landlord should always be divided in the same proportion as the product.

Some landlords furnish all of the fertilizer, lime, and similar materials. Obviously, they are willing to do this only in instances where their share of the expected returns is greater than the full cost. More landlords as well as tenants might be willing to invest in these improvements if costs were shared in a rational manner. Even though the landlord's (or tenant's) share of the product is greater than the full cost, the return on the resources concerned will be distorted relative to the return on still other resources. The shares of inputs and products, where some are variable and some are fixed and furnished by 1 party, must be in line with the productivity of the specialized resource. A share-rent contract which conforms with the principles of marginal productivity when the landlord furnishes only the fixed land resource and the product is divided 50-50, cannot likewise conform to productivity principles were the landlord to furnish one-half the distinctly variable resources.[12]

Under conditions approximating those outlined above, the quantity of variable factor applied to maximize profits for either a tenant or landlord would be, under short-run leasing conditions, the same as for an owner or a cash tenant. If both parties to the lease pay one-half of the variable

_____

[12] Under a switch of this nature (for example, from a customary lease to one under which the landlord pays one-half the variable cost) the landlord should receive either a greater share of the product (and pay similar shares of the variable cost) or receive some lump-sum cash rent as a contribution to the marginal productivity of his specialized factors

cost and receives one-half the product, the marginal cost per unit of product (or the marginal value product per unit of variable factor) is the same for landlord and tenant as for owner or cash renter. Similar alterations must also be made if long-run decisions by the share tenant and landlord are to be compatible with the conditions of resource use which define economic efficiency (and which would be found on owner or cash lease farms). Perfection of arrangements for long-run leasing conditions (where the resources of both the landlord and tenant are variable) are somewhat more complex. Any desire of the tenant to acquire landlord resources until the marginal product of land is driven to zero (or conversely for the landlord to acquire tenant resources until the marginal return of labor and capital is driven to zero) cannot be eliminated by changes in rental rates; the share provision causes the marginal product of the factor and the marginal cost of the factor always to be equal when marginal productivity is zero. Perfection in this respect (with cash rental or owner operation as the benchmark of comparison) can be brought about only if both parties own some of each category of resource, the proportion depending on the share of product to be received by either. Thus perfect share leases would almost always require complete partnership arrangements. Tenants and landlords can get together in a practical manner, however, and arrive at mutually satisfactory arrangements for investing in new techniques and added resource inputs even if value productivity of specific resources is only roughly approximated. For example, if the tenant wants a new milk house for producing grade A milk, or if the landlord wishes the tenant to spray for cornborers, the two can, through simple budgeting procedures, estimate the total added cost and the total added return from the practice or investment. Then costs and returns can be divided in a manner which is agreeable and favorable to both. Similar arrangements can be made where only one of the resource owners provides the investment. If the lease is 50-50, cornborer control will benefit the two by equal amounts, and a simple solution is for the added costs of insect control to be divided equally. As in the case of tiling, the landlord may be unwilling to invest in buildings under a share lease unless he can realize some return on his investment.

The buildings on most share-rent farms are mainly historical phenomena having resulted from the plans of some previous owner. Many landlords keep the buildings in good repair or provide new facilities in order to obtain tenants who are good crop farmers; the marginal product of buildings thus shows up in the crop product for the landlord. Even more landlords handle building, fence, and improvement funds in a "niggardly but rational fashion" because they do not see and never realize any return on building investment. The building resource (even in tenant houses) should return its value productivity to the landlord as a resource owner. Lump-sum or standing rents, while creating some added risk, are entirely justi-fied, under the haphazard customs of share rentals, as a basis for encouraging building investment where its marginal productivity is sufficiently great.[13] While added shares of crops or added cash rent on pasture and hay can be charged to compensate for building investment, this practice represents an intra-firm cost transfer of the nature outlined later.

While share leases are found in "pure form" in small grain and cotton producing areas, share rent on grain crops is combined with cash rent on hay and pasture in most of the Cornbelt. Combination of the 2 leasing provisions can have the positive or negative effects outlined elsewhere. The pure cash lease provides a cost and returns environment which facilitates economic efficiency in the use of resources within the farm. One weakness of the cash lease, however, is the tendency for rental rates to lag behind changes in prices and hence the value productivity of resources. Also, it is extremely doubtful that the adjustments in the share-lease market parallel the changes in techniques of production, consumer demand, and other forces which condition the marginal value productivity of agricultural resources. A system which has some merits and which would substitute for the inertia of present customs (rents at given levels over a long period of years) is this: Each time a new occupant is required the landlord might advertise his farm for bids by tenants. Tenants could bid in either share or cash terms and in a manner to conform with the standards set out above.[14] The landlord could then consider tenant managerial ability and trustworthiness in combination with the rentals offered; he would select the particular combination which promised greatest returns.[15]

Allocation of Given Resources Between Competing Enterprises

In the previous section we examined the effect of share and cash leases on decisions which fall in the factor-product category. The problem for analysis, a product-product decision, now is that of allocating a given

---

[13] Tenure experts often frown upon building rents, particularly for the tenant house. A tenant house should not be treated differently from city apartments and rental property. Investors invest in apartments, where the demand is sufficiently great, rather than more stock in automobile firms in a manner consistent with the values of consuming households. The same should hold true on rented farms. If leasing terms were arranged to provide for returns on these investments, better living facilities might be found on rented farms.

[14] This system is approximated under British leasing customs, wherein the "incoming" tenant buys the lease from the "outgoing" tenant.

[15] Both crop-share and cash leases have characteristics other than those set out above, some of which offset the negative effects outlined in this section. The research worker might expect to find marked differences in resource use between farms operated under share leases, owner operation, and cash leases. However, distinct characteristics of each system may cancel out other effects of the same system. The equity and uncertainty aspects of ownership and cash leasing may restrict intensity of resource use to the level of share leases. The short lease may be productive as a landlord threat which brings about more efficient husbandry by the tenant. Thus the fact that differences are not found on farms using different systems does not indicate that each system of factor hire is without defects.

amount of resources between competing products within a specialized plant. The flexible resources are represented by the labor and capital of the tenant. The specialized resources are represented by the land and buildings of the landlord. For analytic purposes we suppose that the 2 distinct categories of resources are furnished separately. How might the allocation of resources between different products (the combination of enterprises) differ under share and cash leases or owner operation? From a production economic standpoint, it includes land use considerations.

To simplify the discussion, we first suppose a farm of fixed size (say 200 acres) upon which 2 independent and competitive enterprises Y_1 and Y_2 can be produced. The production functions for each enterprise are of the nature illustrated in Figures 6 and 7. Maximum output of Y_1 possible

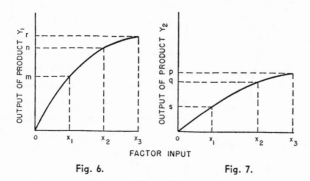

FACTOR INPUT

Fig. 6.   Fig. 7.

Production functions as basis of inter-product allocation.

from the given acreage is r and is forthcoming with an application of ox_3 of capital and labor; the maximum output of Y_2, p, is also forthcoming with ox_3 of resources; yields for Y_2 are only two-thirds those for Y_1. The allocative possibilities (possible choices of the 2 crops from the given stock of land, capital, and labor) are given in Figure 8. Curves rp, nq, and ms are transformation functions or iso-resource (production possibility) curves.[16] Curve rp shows the production possibilities when the stock of capital and labor is constant at ox_3 (in Figures 6 and 7) and the quantity of land is fixed at 200 acres. If the available quantity of capital and labor (to be applied to the given acreage of land) is ox_2 (Figures 6 and 7), the production possibility curve becomes nq. A stock of capital and labor equal to ox_1 (Figures 6 and 7) gives the iso-resource curve ms in Figure 8.

Ownership of resources and tenant selection. In order to simplify the analysis which follows, we will henceforth denote landlord-furnished resource services with the term "land" or factor Z and tenant-furnished resources services as "labor" or factor X. (The outcome would be similar

[16] The production possibility curves are of a short-run nature. (See Chapter 9.) The same analysis can, however, be applied to long-run allocative opportunities.

if any number of resource categories were considered.) We further suppose a firm where the landlord owns and furnishes the services of factor Z and the tenant furnishes all of the services of factor X.

The first problem in leasing is again selection of a tenant: Either the landlord must find a tenant or the tenant must find a farm. Under a cash lease (and in the absence of long-run effects of the tenant's activities on productivity of the landlord resources), the landlord can be indifferent about the quantity of resources owned by the tenant. He can select any one of three different tenants with varying amounts of labor (such as ox_1, ox_2, and ox_3 in Figures 6 or 7) without affecting returns from his own resources. This statement applies, of course, to a competitive market where the landlord is able to exact the same cash rent from the several competing tenants. The situation is entirely different under a share-lease where the landlord receives a portion (one-half, two-fifths, one-third) of the output from each increment of tenant resources. For a share lease the landlord's returns will be maximized if he is able to obtain a tenant with

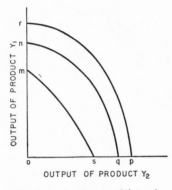

Fig. 8. Production possibilities for tenants with different capital.

a stock of resources great enough to maximize the physical product on the fixed land area (for example, ox_3 or more units of tenant resources, as illustrated in Figures 6 and 7). However, since this extreme is generally impossible, the landlord is faced with selecting from the tenants who bid for the farm, the one with the greatest resources (including managerial ability). Suppose a tenant with ox_2 resources (Figures 6 or 7) is obtained. The central problem now remains. How should the ox_2 of tenant resources be allocated between products Y_1 and Y_2 if either the landlord or the tenant is to maximize returns?

Under owner-operation of all resources (a farm operator owning the 200 units of factor Z and the ox_2 quantity of factor X), returns to the farm firm and hence to the single resource owner can be maximized by allocating resources to products Y_1 and Y_2 in the conventional manner. Profit maximization is illustrated in Figure 9 by tangency of the "total" production possibility curve nq and the iso-revenue curve E_1R_1. Maximum profits are forthcoming when the given resources (ox_2 of X and 200 units of Z) are allocated between the enterprises in a manner to give the oc output of Y_1 and the og output of Y_2. Given the setting of perfect competition and the absence of market imperfections (for both commodities and factors and, hence, assuming that price ratios accurately reflect the relative choice or values of consumers), this combination of Y_1 and Y_2 is most efficient from the standpoint of the individual firm (profit maximization) and society (a pattern of resource allocation consistent with consumer choice).[17]

Cash lease and tenant decision. A tenant who owns ox_2 of factor X and who rents the 200 acres of land for cash also can make decisions on the basis of the total transformation function nq in Figure 9. His profit will be at a maximum with production of oc of Y_1 and og of Y_2. This use of resources need not conflict with the interests of the landlord. Since the

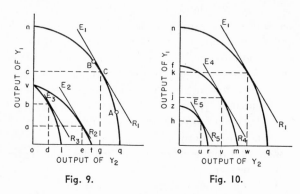

Fig. 9.   Fig. 10.

Inter-farm allocative patterns under different leasing systems.

cash price paid by the tenant for use of the land is the same regardless of the manner in which resources are allocated between competing enterprises, the return to the landlord is the same in any case. The allocation of resources which will maximize revenue to the cash tenant thus can be consistent with the choice of the consumer, the allocation of resources on an owner-operated farm, and the interests of the landlord.

The outcome may differ greatly, however, under a share contract, and depends on the manner in which rentals are determined. Long-standing customs have grown up in the rental market, with different shares paid by the tenant for different crops. Customary share rents over a large area of the Cornbelt include one-half of the corn and soybeans and two-fifths of the small grains (with cash rent paid for forage crops or a share given of the hay). Even within homogeneous soils areas of the Cornbelt, some landlords charge one-half while others charge two-fifths of the soybean production. (The lower rate is often offset by a higher share on other crops or a greater cash charge for forage crops). Shares vary over parts of the Great Plains between two-fifths and one-third or one-third and

---

[17] We recognize again that markets are imperfect and do not always accurately reflect consumers' values, and that distribution of income (the allocation of Y_1 and Y_2 between different consumers) is a variable along with production in determining the conditions under which welfare can be maximized. However, these are problems apart from the phenomenon being analyzed here and space limitations do not allow their treatment.

one-fourth for corn and small grains respectively. Similar variations in share rentals can be found in other regions of the United States. These variations in share rents between crops are historical or of long standing and their bases are hard to determine. A possible hypothesis is that variations between crops are designed to give the tenant somewhat equal returns from resources devoted to different crops. For example, if costs are $15 per acre for corn and $10 per acre for flax while gross returns are $40 and $25 respectively, the shares of one-half for corn and two-fifths for flax would accomplish this equalization for the tenant. Other hypotheses suppose that share rents are established between crops to give (1) equal returns for the landlord and (2) equal value productivity of resources employed for different products. We seriously doubt that the latter is approximated to any fine degree. Customs, regardless of their original foundation, are evidently of great importance in freezing share rentals in fixed proportions between crops. In the following sections we examine the possible consequences of differential share rents.

Differential share rent and equal returns to and decisions by the tenant. On many farms the exact acreage of crops to be grown is not specified in the lease, but is a decision to be made by the tenant. How will the allocation of resources be affected (differ from the cash-rented or the owner-operator farm) under this arrangement? Possible outcomes can be illustrated by the simple model in Figure 9. We first suppose that differential share rents have been established (in this case) to give equal physical quantities of the 2 products to the tenant.[18] If the share rent is one-half for Y_1, shares can be equalized (to the tenant on "the average") if the share rent for Y_2 is one-third of the total product.[19] The production possibilities important to the tenant in decision-making are now no longer represented by the "total" curve nq in Figure 9, the relevant possibility curve for decision-making by the owner-operator or cash tenant. Instead, the "post-share" possibility curve vt is relevant for his decision-making. It represents the quantity of the total product remaining after share rent has been paid and

---

[18] Similar assumptions to those outlined here will be followed in other situations discussed below. Equal value return is more relevant than equal physical return. In order to simplify our analysis and include value aspects we further assume that the price per unit of the 2 commodities is the same (the slopes of all revenue curves are of 45°). It is also true that one level of differential shares alone would equate returns between crops only if (a) the transformation function is linear or (b) the transformation function is concave and returns comparisons are made between crops when all of the resources are devoted entirely to Y_1 or entirely to Y_2. We suppose that the transformation function is concave (as is generally the case in agriculture because of the biological and seasonal nature in production) and that the differential in rents is given in constant proportions for a single farm (does not vary with the quantity of either product being produced on the particular farm).

[19] For example, if the yields are 36 and 27 for Y_1 and Y_2 respectively, a one-half share rent will leave the tenant 18 units of Y_1, and a one-third share rent will leave him 18 units of Y_2. If costs bear the same proportional relationships, his profits will also be equal.

Total returns, economic welfare, and interproduct efficiency under shares.
Another observation of the cases presented above is this: While each case
illustrates maximum returns to the landlord or tenant (depending on where
the nature of the decision-making or post-share possibility curves and
where the decision-making power rests), the total return to the tenant and
landlord in combination is not as great in any case as for a cash tenant
or an owner-operator possessing the same aggregate of resources. This is
obviously true because maximum returns from the aggregate of resources
are forthcoming only if curves E_1R_1 and nq in Figure 9 are tangent.
Neither point A nor point B, the equilibrium points for the tenant or landlord taken under differential shares, represents this necessary condition.
Accordingly, we have one of those rare cases in welfare economics where
all individuals concerned (the tenant, the landlord and the consumer)
might be made better off through a reorganization of resources: Movement
along the total possibility curve from point A or B to that indicated by
tangency of nq and E_1R_1 would allow a greater product to consumers (an
output more nearly consistent with consumer choice) and a greater total
return to be divided between landlord and tenant.

Again, the leasing imperfections and the interproduct inefficiencies mentioned above are not inherent in share leasing *per se*, but instead grow out
of the manner in which differentials and customs have been established
over time. Conceptually, share rents can be established whereby the use
of resources will conform to the efficiency conditions outlined above. These
conditions are attained when shares are identical for all competing crops,
even though the production coefficients (yield, cost, resource requirements,
and so forth) differ between products. They are illustrated in Figure 10,
where the total possibility curve is again nq. The decision-making (or
"post-share") possibility curve facing the tenant is fm and represents a
two-thirds share of both Y_1 and Y_2; the landlord's post-share (or decision-
making) possibility curve is zr and represents a one-third share of

---

of constant returns to scale for factor X when factor Z is fixed in quantity, and (2)
with the production coefficient for A 2.5 times that of B (2.5 units of A can be produced for each unit of B) and (c) with the price of B 2.0 times greater than that of
A (B sells for twice as much per unit as A). Under the situation (an A/B substitution
ratio of 2.5/1.0 and a B/A price ratio of 2.0/1.0) a cash tenant could maximize
profits by specialization in A alone (producing none of B). However, under a share
arrangement to equalize the product (per unit of resource) to the tenant, the post-
share substitution ratio becomes 1.0/1.0. Thus under a price ratio of 2.0/1.0, the
share tenant would specialize entirely in B (the opposite from the cash tenant). A
1.0/1.0 share ratio to the tenant would leave a 4.0/10 share ratio (A/B substitution
ratio) for the landlord when the tenant receives one-half of B and one-fifth of A.
Thus he would wish to use all resources for production of A under a B/A price
ratio of 2.0/10.

Although share rents are not necessarily arranged to equalize physical shares
(to the tenant or landlord), the logic developed in this study applies as long as
differential share rents exist between competitive crops regardless of the particular
basis.

both total products. Since shares are the same for both Y_1 and Y_2, the slope of both post-share possibility curves (fm and zr) is the same as the slope of the total possibility curve (nq). Given the previously indicated price ratio denoted by the slope of E_1R_1, the allocation of resources which will maximize returns to a share tenant is identical with the pattern of resource use which will maximize returns to the landlord. This same combination of products will (1) maximize returns to a cash tenant or an owner-operator with the same resources and (2) maximize consumer utility from the aggregate of resources employed. Since tangency of curves E_5R_5 with zr and E_4R_4 with fm denote the same total outputs (ok of Y_1 and ow of Y_2) as tangency of E_1R_1 and nq, the same proportions of product can be attained regardless of whether decision rests with the landlord or the crop-share tenant.[24]

Shares and part ownership. An interproduct problem somewhat parallel to those outlined above is found on farms where the operator owns part of the land and rents the remainder. It can be considered in the short-run leasing context where the stocks of both tenant and landlord resources are given. (While long-run leasing decisions pose still other problems in analysis, these are only variations of the logic outlined below.) The question to be solved by the part-owner farmer is this: How should his limited stock of labor and capital be allocated between products from his own land and products from rented land? The decision can be considered as one of product-product relationships (product from the operator's own land against product from rented land) in the manner suggested by Figure 11. Here the product forthcoming from use of the operator's capital and labor on his own land is indicated on the vertical axis. The product forthcoming from use of the same capital and labor on rented land is illustrated on the horizontal axis.

Under a system of cash rent for the rented land the decision-making production opportunity curve is f_3r_4. This same curve would face a complete owner operator (if he had title to both tracts of land). Given the price relationship indicated by iso-revenue line ER (it has a 45° slope because a unit of product from the rented land sells for the same price as a unit of product from the owned land), the allocation of resources which will maximize the cash tenant's profit is indicated by an output of of_1 product from the owner's land and or_3 from rented land.

Under share renting of the leased land where one-half of the product is paid to the landlord, the relevant opportunity curve becomes f_3r_2. The operator realizes the full product from his own land but only one-half the product from the rented land (or_2 is equal to one-half of or_4). The opportunity curve f_3r_2 has a greater slope than f_3r_4, denoting a lower rate of

---

[24] The Y_1/Y_2 ratios of (a) oh/ou for the landlord (b) oj/ov for the tenant and (c) ok/ow for the total are equal and define the optimum post-share product for both the landlord and share tenant, as well as for a cash tenant or owner-operator.

substitution of "rented product" as compared to "owned product." Given the same iso-revenue curve as previously (equal prices for the product from the owner and rented land as indicated by the slope of ER and $E'R'$), the part-owner's profit will be at a maximum when he realizes a product amounting to of_2 from his own land and or_1 from rented land. Since he receives only one-half the total product from rented land, the total product combination actually includes of_2 of product from his own land and or_2 from rented land. The part owner will, when compared to a cash renter with the same capital and labor, produce a relatively greater product from his own land and a smaller product from rented land. Production economists have long proposed this hypothesis, particularly for Cornbelt farms. The part owner often feeds the hay and grain from the rented acreage and spreads the ma-

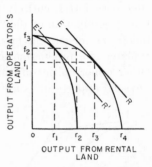

Fig. II. Part-owner farms.

nure on his own land, or he first plants and cultivates the crops on his own tract. He gets the greatest reward for a day's labor or a tank of tractor fuel spent here where he does not share the product. If the operator has funds for only a very limited amount of fertilizer, its use will obviously return most when applied to his own land.

Only one share arrangement is possible which will not distort the opportunity curve from the standpoint of operator decision-making: The resource inputs applied to the rented land must be shared between tenant and landlord in exactly the same proportions as the product. Aside from any other technical differences, return per dollar of resources furnished by the tenant will then have the same value productivity as a dollar of resources applied to his own land. Restrictions can be and are placed in leases which clearly define the manner in which rented land is farmed. However, it is entirely possible that part-owner arrangements lead to great inefficiencies in some agricultural areas and on particular farms.

Time Relationships in Leasing

A final product relationship similar to those outlined above, but peculiar to both share and cash leasing arrangements, involves the allocation of tenant resources over time.[25] If he is to maximize returns over the total time span (t_1 plus t_2), how should a tenant allocate a given outlay of funds or physical resources between the product of one time period (t_1)

[25] The analysis of this section (as in the case of part-owner operation) applies to short-run leasing situations (where the quantity of resources provided by either landlord or tenant is given or fixed in amount).

and the product of a later time period (t_2)? How may leasing arrangements temper the intertemporal use of resources?

Figure 12 illustrates decision-making opportunities under this situation. The tenant operator has 2 competing uses for his resources in respect to time: He can allocate them entirely to production of product in the current time period (t_1), entirely to production in a later time period (t_2), or to some combination of the 2. If he uses all resources (a constant or limited quantity) for current production, physical output can be oc_6. Use of all resources for production in the later time period allows an output of op_8. Other opportunities are indicated by the opportunity curve c_6p_8. These physical opportunities are expressive of the technological transformation conditions which exist over time. They are relevant for decisions by the owner who will be on the farm for the full time span under consideration (t_1 plus t_2). Given the discounted price relationships suggested by the iso-revenue line E_1R_1, profits (or profit expectations) can be maximized, with the proper discount of returns in t_2, by the production pattern which includes oc_5 in period t_1 and op_7 in period t_2.[26] The physical opportunity curve c_6p_8 is irrelevant for decision making on the part of a cash tenant who will not realize the full product in the future. The time span t_1 may refer to corn which can be attained in the next two years (through planting all acres to the crop and a heavy application of nitrate fertilizer). Time span t_2 may refer to corn output which can be attained in the third and fourth years (through planting land to legumes in the first and second year to make nitrogen and crop residues available to corn in the third and fourth years). Hence, when the tenant will not be on the farm in the fourth year, his opportunities over the full physical transformation period (the 4-year period) do not include the product from the fourth year. This knowledge may be held with certainty and the following resource use patterns then develop.

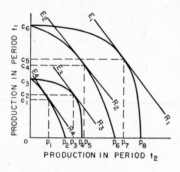

Fig. 12. Profit maximization over time.

Cash and share leases and tenant decision. The decision-making opportunity curve for a cash tenant who will be on the farm only 3 years takes the form of c_6p_6 in Figure 12. Given the same price relationships (or the same price expectations) as the owner (indicated by the fact that the slope of E_2R_2 is the same as that of E_1R_1), the optimum combination of prod-

[26] The slope of the iso-revenue line, E_1R_1, accounts for discounting of returns in t_2. If prices for the 2 periods are expected to be the same, E_1R_1 will have a slope greater than 45° because of futurity discounts. Price uncertainty can cause it to have an even greater slope.

ucts over time is oc_4 in the earlier and op_5 in the later period. While the tenant may produce less in both periods, emphasis is on output in early as compared to later periods.

Under a share lease in which the tenant gives one-half the product as rent, the decision-making opportunity curve becomes c_3p_4 if the tenant will be on the farm over the 4-year time span. (See earlier discussion of share rentals.) Under this situation tenant profit will be at a maximum when the share realized by him is oc_2 in t_1 and op_3 in t_2. This combination of tenant product over time corresponds to that of the total farm (oc_5 in t_1 and op_7 in t_2) under owner operation. Again, however, the share tenant's decision-making opportunity curve undergoes a change if he will not be on the farm over the entire production period. If he will be on a farm in only 3 out of 4 years, it takes the form c_3p_2. Thus, given the same price relationship suggested earlier (an equal-revenue line indicated by E_4R_4), tenant profits will be at a maximum with his share of output amounting to oc_1 in t_1 and op_1 in t_2. Again the tenant will emphasize production of the present relative to that of the future.[27]

A wide variety of intertemporal opportunity curves exists on tenant farms depending on the particular form of resources to which investment alternatives relate. Alternatives in investment may be between brood sows and movable hog equipment which allow a complete product throw-off in a short period as against investment in a dairy barn or conservation installations which will be completely transformed only over a long period. Comparisons also may be between investment of $100 in baby chicks which will give full returns within the year and investment in drainage tile or other conservation practices which give a complete return only over several years. The decision-making transformation curve (from the tenant standpoint) will vary for any one of these pairs of investment opportunities, depending on the time span to which opportunities apply (or to which the expectations apply). Not only must the tenant discount the future in terms of time and the uncertainties which face the owner, but he must also discount future production possibilities of the future because of tenure uncertainty. Rather than view the future in terms of curve c_3p_2 as his decision-making opportunities, he may think in terms of one which curves even more sharply towards the t_2 axis, and which represents his subjective appraisal of remaining on the farm under tenure uncertainty. With this discounting of opportunities because of tenure uncertainty, resources will be directed even more toward products of the present.

Other time problems also arise in the use of rented resources: Landlords may press for production in early rather than deferred time periods. This tendency is particularly true for the large number of farm widows who

---

[27] In the case of share renting the ratio of "present product to future product" is oc_1/op_1. For cash renting it is oc_4/op_5. The ratio in both cases is greater than the ratio oc_5/op_7 under owner-operation.

own land and depend on it for a livelihood. The complementary relationship which is expressed between forage and other crops can be realized by the tenant only if his tenure is long enough so that the product, such as nitrogen from legume crops, becomes available as inputs for grain crops. This phenomena has been discussed in detail in Chapter 8 on product-product relationships. Again it is worth emphasizing that rental arrangements can be devised which allow tenants to realize the benefits of complementarity. Landlords often charge such high cash rents for forage that the tenant cannot profitably produce forage through the complementary range. Rather than follow this practice, the landlord should charge no rent for complementary forages. He might even have greater returns if he paid the tenant for producing hay within this range. When forage or other crops are competitive, however, he has a basis for charging a cash rent for hay which will return as much as the most profitable alternative crops, a point often overlooked in standard lease recommendations.

Compensation for unexploited resources. What means exist for eliminating leasing imperfections which grow out of time considerations and the length of the lease contract? A partial solution is to be found in compensation for unexhausted resources (resource inputs which have not been transformed into products at the time of moving by the tenant). This system is widespread in Europe and the United Kingdom, where resources are sometimes divided into 3 categories. The first includes resources such as seed and fertilizer, which are transformed into crops in 1 or a few production periods. The tenant is free to apply these materials without landlord consent and cannot claim compensation for unexhausted portions. A second category includes durable resources such as ditches, certain types of tile drains, and other materials which have an intermediate life. Generally the tenant is allowed to invest, up to a specified limit, in these techniques without the consent of the landlord and to claim compensation for unexhausted portions. Finally, durable or long-lived resources such as buildings, irrigation systems, and major drainage outlays may be provided by the tenant alone with the privilege of compensation only if approval is made by the landlord. The exact combination of these several arrangements varies between areas. While laws have been passed in some instances to guarantee arrangements such as those outlined above, they are voluntary in other cases.

Compensation for unexhausted resource services has never found widespread application in the United States. Where practiced, it is mainly on a voluntary basis. An increasing number of landlords are applying the procedure to terracing, lime, and fertilizers. A few go so far as to allow tenant construction of buildings (with purchase by the landlord from the outgoing tenant or resale to the incoming tenant). The role of compensation as a means of promoting resource efficiency is obvious. It is a step toward maintaining the tenant's decision-making opportunities in the manner which would exist if he were able to remain on one farm over a long time span. Where the system is used, the landlord pays the tenant a sum equal to the value of the unused portion of factors. Suppose that the tenant applies a ton of fertilizer and 45 per cent of its services is transformed in the first year while 35 and 20 per cent is transformed in the second and thirds years respectively. With the cost amounting to $10 per ton, the landlord pays $2 per ton to the tenant if the latter moves at the end of the second year (or $1 if the landlord originally paid one-half the cost of application). This system of compensation has merits; it guarantees that the future product from a current input does not become zero. It does not, however, maintain production opportunities in a manner which would exist apart from the leasing contract. In order that decision-making opportunities are not distorted, the compensation system must provide that a transformation curve such as c_3p_4 in Figure 12 for the share lease (or c_6p_8 for the cash lease) is retained from the standpoint of tenant decision. In other words, compensation for a tenant with unlimited capital must in effect amount to the difference between opportunity curves c_3p_2 and c_3p_4 in Figure 12 (or between c_6p_8 and c_6p_6 for a cash tenant). The perfect leasing system would call for compensation greater than the cost of the resources; compensation would equal the value productivity of the unexhausted portion discounted back to the present. Otherwise, investment will still be in favor of resources transformed within a season. The tenant with limited capital is not likely to invest in lime, for which he will realize the original cost 2 years hence when he can invest in hogs, which will return the original outlay plus the normal profit within the year. For the tenant with limited capital, if profit maximization serves as a criterion, the compensation rate for long-lived resources such as terraces should be as great as the return on hogs or other resources which give full income within the year. As was indicated in Chapter 19, the proper compounding or discounting rate for the firm with limited capital is not the market interest rate. In a practical sense, compensation should cover not only the original outlay but also some return on the unexhausted portion of semi-durable resources. Compensation for unexhausted improvements should not be looked upon as a perfect substitute for the provisions outlined in the other sections of this study (such as direct rents representing the marginal value product of buildings to encourage landlord investment). Compensation best applies to lime and fertilizer or other semi-durable resources. Other arrangements are appropriate for buildings and permanent improvements which require a large capital outlay and can be transformed into product only over a very long period. The most profitable organization on a given farm may call for a dairy enterprise and erection of a new barn. Even though he will receive compensation upon termination of the lease, the tenant who has limited capital is unlikely to invest funds in a barn which will stand empty because he cannot then buy cows.

The length of the lease. A second alternative by which the true techno-logically-based opportunity curve can be maintained as a basis for tenant decisions is through the span of the lease. Long leases can provide a time period which allows tenant decisions to conform with those of an owner-operator. Tenure environments such as these are found in Great Britain, where several generations of the same family have operated a single tract of rented land. One of the greatest shortcomings of the leasing systems in the United States is the "1-year" aspect. Some states have enacted laws which provide that the landlord must notify the tenant of lease termina-tion at least 6 months or 1 year in advance. The lease laws of other states do not provide even this much certainty. Perhaps it is true that efficient farm planning cannot be accomplished for less than 15 years in livestock producing economies. The other extreme in tenure spans is to be found in the leasing of state school lands in some states or the life estates provided in the wills of some farm owners. Both of these provide a longer planning period than the year-to-year leasing contracts. However, they too may encourage exploitation of resources in late years of the contract. Whereas the tenant is willing to repair buildings and install fences or soil improve-ments at the beginning of the lease, he may let them depreciate without repair at the end of the leasing period.

Given other imperfections which exist in leasing systems, the short span of the lease may also make positive contributions to resource efficiency. The landlord often holds lease termination as a threat over the tenant's head. In addition to many other discrete practices which may be encour-aged in this manner, farming intensity may be extended to a level parallel-ing that of owner-operation. Commercial farm managers have coined a phrase "short leases but long tenure" to describe the possible contribution of short leases to good husbandry. However, the perfect lease is far from being attained when the imperfections inherent in short-term leases are used as a positive mechanism for offsetting more serious leasing limita-tions.

Intra-Firm Cost Transfers

The typical lease of the Midwest and other parts of the nation is one which combines the cash and share characteristics. Under the typical arrangement, share rents are paid for grain crops, while cash rents are paid for hay and pasture. Cash rent also is sometimes charged as a distinct rent on buildings. Since share rents are deeply imbedded in custom (shares tend to remain as a fixed percentage over long periods of time even though price/cost ratios or the techniques of production fluctuate widely), some landlords feel that cash rent provides a mechanism whereby "rents can be made equitable." If it appears that a higher share rent on grain crops may be in order, the cash rent for hay or pasture or buildings can be increased instead. While this situation is partly inherent in other cases discussed, it represents an intra-farm "bookkeeping" cost transfer which merits detailed and individual discussion. We employ the simple models below for this purpose.

While the cost structure within the firm is distorted by transfers which shift rents from one enterprise to another, the tenant often is free to allocate resources in a manner to maximize his own profits within the stipulation of the lease. With sufficient capital, and under a short-run leasing situation, he can maximize profits by equating marginal costs and marginal revenue for each individual enterprise. However, as long as he must adhere to the "bookkeeping" rather than the true cost structure, the resulting allocation of resources will again differ from that which would hold under an unrestricted system of prices. This outcome is illustrated diagrammatically in Figure 13. The "true" marginal costs (where rents approximate market conditions and the marginal productivity of resources in each enterprise) for 2 commodities A and B are represented by mca_1

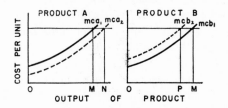

Fig. 13. Inter-enterprise cost transfers.

and mcb_1 respectively. On the basis of the true costs, resources will be used for the two commodities to give the output OM of both A and B. However, if a bookkeeping transfer of costs is effected from A to B as indicated by the marginal costs mca_2 and mcb_2, the use of resources (on the basis of the bookkeeping costs) will be such as to give outputs of ON and OP respectively.

There are many examples of cost transfers under farm leases. One of these is the tendency toward uniform rental shares over wide areas.[28] Some persons contend that uniform rentals over areas of varying productivity have no important effect on the equitableness of the lease or the efficiency with which resources are used, since (1) if the share rents for the better land underestimate the true economic rent, the difference can be and is made up by higher cash rent and on hay and pasture, or (2) higher share

---

[28] It is common knowledge, of course, that share rents vary between certain wide areas. Even then, the discrete breaks in share rentals between broad regions cannot conform accurately to the gradual decline in economic rent resulting from increased transportation costs or less favorable weather. However, numerous studies have indicated that uniform rental shares tend to exist within areas which are fairly homogeneous in respect to prices and weather but widely heterogeneous in respect to soil resources.

rents on less productive land include not only a payment for use of productive resources but also a payment for rent on consumer's goods in the form of a house and other living facilities. In an Iowa study cited previously, a significant cash premium on hay and pasture was found to exist. This arrangement effects a bookkeeping transfer of costs from grain to hay and pasture crops. Accordingly, more grain (and grain-produced livestock products) and less forage (and forage-produced livestock products) will be forthcoming at a given time than would be if resources were allocated strictly in accordance with market prices and resource productivity. A similar premium is sometimes charged for special housing facilities or outstanding improvements. The premium here may take the form of higher than normal cash rent on hay or pasture, while share rent is held constant at the customary rate. This again represents a bookkeeping transfer of costs from "household products" to "firm products"; less hay and pasture may be expected as a result.

The imperfections outlined above are not inherent in the crop-share lease but grow out of special customs which have developed around the lease. Under the perfect lease, special premiums for use of buildings, if they are to be charged, should take the form of a flat payment *per annum* rather than a rent on crops. As a fixed cost the premium does not alter the structure of marginal cost within the firm and, consequently, encourages the most efficient resource allocation.

Distortions in cost and transformation relationships do not arise directly under owner operation of farms. However, it is not "given" that this system of obtaining use of factor services must result in more efficient resource use than leasing systems. While owner operation has certain positive features not associated with leasing, it also can have negative characteristics which equally impinge on efficiency. Perhaps an owner-farm operating under a full (or near-full) equity and long-term expectancy on the farm most nearly provides the ideal tenure environment from the standpoint of entrepreneurial decisions. However, farms operated under low equities cause the entrepreneur to plan over short periods alone; survival of the firm in the few years ahead becomes the basis for farm operation.

Straight Cash Lease and Degree of Uncertainty

The rent paid under a straight cash lease is a fixed cost and, since it is not a function of output, the payment has no bearing on the firm's marginal cost for any unit of product. Aside from uncertainty, the straight cash lease makes profitable the most efficient combination of fixed and variable resources. Since the firm pays the full marginal cost and receives the full marginal return, it can apply inputs of variable factors (lime, fertilizer, number of cultivations, improved seed rotation, and so forth) to the fixed factor (land) in such a manner as to equate marginal revenue and marginal cost at an output which reflects market prices for resources and commodities. Aside from time considerations, the cash lease also encourages the most efficient allocation of resources between alternative commodities within the firm. As a cost of using resources, the rent payment is not explicitly tied to any single enterprise, and the original transformation function is retained for decision-making.

Allocation of resources between different enterprises may be imperfect, however, because of uncertainty and the degree of returns-discounting growing out of the fixed payment. The fixed rent obligation has an effect akin to that of reducing the tenant's equity in his capital. (See Chapter 18.) The tenant operating under a cash lease stands a greater chance that his equity will be erased and bankruptcy will result if the price level drops by more than a given amount than does the tenant operating under a share lease. The firm can partially hedge against this eventuality through its selection of products. Since the probability of differences between expected and realized prices is less for the near future than for later dates, the operator may select products (even if the span of the lease creates no uncertainties) which will result in the transformation of resources in the shortest possible period of time. By selecting commodities such as grain crops and hogs for which the production period is less than a year, the hedge against insolvency is greater than if resources are invested in hay crops and roughage consuming livestock for which transformation extends over a longer time-period. This fixed rent payment may also have the effect of curtailing the over-all scale of operations: Since the probability becomes greater that a price decline or other unfavorable event will result in bankruptcy as the firm takes on additional liabilities, it will tend to borrow fewer funds and employ fewer resources than it would if the rent were not a fixed payment to be made at a later date. This element of cash rents should also cause farms rented under this system to be smaller than those operated under share contracts. In a study of Iowa farms the writer found that tenants believed, when the "risk" or uncertainty of cash rents was considered, a cash-rent farm of 110 acres or a share-rent farm of 260 acres to be optimum.[29] Improvement, if not perfection, of the cash lease may be brought about through the modification suggested in the next paragraph.

Flexible cash lease. Under flexible cash leasing arrangement, the amount of cash rent varies with the price level. The estimated rent (R_0) is established for the price level of a given year or base period (P_0). The rent actually paid in a given year (R_1) bears the same ratio to the base period rent as the price level of a given year (P_1) bears to that of the base period

---

[29] See E. O. Heady and E. W. Kehrberg, *Effects of Cash and Share Leases on Farming Efficiency.* Iowa Agr. Exp. Sta. Bul. 386.

$[R_1 = R_0(P_1/P_0)]$.[30] The flexible rent (price or yield) does not have the same effect as the straight-cash lease in lowering the tenant's equity in the case of crop failure or price decline. Therefore, it should not place the same premium on selection of commodities for which the production period is short and for which prices can be predicted with a greater degree of accuracy. It should also be more favorable to a scale of operations consistent with the product and resource prices of the market.

Livestock Share Leases

Although there are numerous variations, the most common arrangements under livestock share leases include the following provisions: The landlord furnishes the real estate; the tenant the labor, power, and machinery; and each bears the expenses directly related to his resources; each furnishes one-half the investment in productive livestock and feeds and assumes the same relative share of the operating costs. The receipts are divided on a 50-50 basis (or other fixed proportion) for the business as a unit and ordinarily without regard to individual enterprise (except perhaps for poultry). This system has certain advantages over others in respect to efficient use of resources. The very nature of the lease tends to eliminate some of the imperfections which have been discussed: (1) The tenure is ordinarily for a longer period. Discounts due to tenure uncertainty thus tend to be less. (2) The division of marginal costs and returns for such semi-durable resources as fertilizer and lime is of a nature to make the optimum combination of resources profitable for a given crop; landlord and tenant each receive one-half the return and costs are split in the same manner. (3) There is less tendency for rationing of durable resources: The landlord receives the marginal return on buildings directly in the form of a share of the livestock. In addition, the role of the landlord in the contract makes available a still greater quantity of capital because (a) his funds are used and (b) credit institutions may loan more to the tenant because of the presence of the landlord in the operations.

This lease is sometimes looked upon more nearly as a business partnership than are other leases. However, the return imputed to either the tenant's or landlord's resources can properly be looked upon as the cost of these resources to the firm when considered from the standpoint of either party separately. Although this system of leasing has characteristics which facilitate efficient use of resources, an "equitable" division of the product or the best use of resources is not always inherent in typical arrangements. In reality, this is an over-all lease which results as a livestock lease is

---

[30] Although it is somewhat uncommon, the cash rent also can be varied on the basis of deviations of crop yields away from the average (deviations for a given geographic area rather than for an individual farm since in the latter case the lease becomes a simple crop-share lease).

superimposed on a modified crop-share lease. The over-all lease is inequitable in any instance when the crop-share component is out of line.

There are reasons why a livestock-share lease might not result in a perfect allocation of resources within the firm. Ordinarily, the receipts are divided in fixed proportions for the business as a whole without regard to individual enterprises. When there is more than 1 enterprise and the combination of inputs differs between enterprises, this arrangement may again have the effect of distorting the structure of costs within the firm. These points are discussed in detail elsewhere and need no further elaboration here.[31] Since the tenant furnishes all labor, he is reluctant to employ these services beyond those represented in himself. The analysis pointed out previously for crop share leases also applies, with slight modifications, to the tenant's labor; if he hires labor, he pays the full cost but gets only a share of its product. The same short-run and long-run considerations also apply to the landlord, since he furnishes all of the real estate.

Selected References

Black, J. D., *et al., Farm Management*. New York: Macmillan, 1947, Chs. 30, 34.

Case, H. C. M., and Ackerman, J., *Leasing Systems in Illinois*. Ill. Circ. 503.

Forster, G. W., *Cropper Farming in the Coastal Plains*. North Car. Agr. Exp. Bul. 72.

Heady, Earl O., "Economics of Farm Leasing Systems," *Jour. Farm Econ.*, Vol. 29.

———, "Flexibility of Agricultural Rents," *Jour. Land Econ.*, Vol. 27.

———, "Effect of Leasing Systems on Inter-Product Allocation of Resources," *Southern Econ. Jour.*, Nov., 1951.

———, and Kehrberg, Earl W., *Effects of Cash and Share Leases on Farming Efficiency*. Iowa Agr. Exp. Sta. Bul. 385.

Hill, E. B., *Father and Son Partnerships*. Mich. Spec. Bul. 330.

Johnson, D. G., "Efficiency of Share Leasing Contracts," *Jour. Pol. Econ.*, Vol. 58

Langsford, E. L., and Thibodeaux, B. K., *Plantation Organization in the Yazoo-Mississippi Delta*. U.S.D.A. Tech. Bul. 682.

Miller, C. E., and Brown, W. O., *Farm Tenancy and Rental Contracts in North Dakota*. N. Dak. Agr. Exp. Sta. Bul. 239.

Ratchford, B. C., *Farm Tenure in a Dynamic Economy*. N. Car. Agr. Exp. Sta. Bul. 299.

Schickele, R., "Leases and Farming Efficiency," *Jour. Farm Econ.*, Vol. 24.

---

[31] See Earl O. Heady, "Economics of Farm Leasing Systems," *Jour. Farm Econ.*, Vol. 29.

21

Levels and Flexibility of Rent and Tenure Systems

FREQUENTLY in the United States and commonly in other nations, the level of agricultural rents is questioned from the standpoint of "fair treatment" of the tenant. At one extreme, systems of so-called "land reform" have evolved in European and Asiatic nations.[1] Some of these reforms involve the transfer of wealth (ownership of land) from landlords to tenants. Others simply involve the transfer of income (and not the title to resources) to the tenant. The latter is accomplished by changes in levels of rents in directions which favor the tenant. These flat or low-rent "reforms" are aimed especially at large land owners and peasant-type tenants. Clearly, the objective is one of redistributing the total income forthcoming from the aggregate of resources owned by the landlord and tenant in a manner to return more to the tenant and less to the landlord.

Some individuals in the United States suggest that rent payments be varied from those established in the market. While less extreme than other "land reforms," the objective of these proposals is the same. Under lower rents the tenant would receive a larger portion of the total product. A parallel proposal is that redistributions of tenant and landlord shares be made in areas of variable returns in order to lessen the income hardships which fall on the tenant-operator. While suggestions for alterations in rents along these lines most often relate to agricultural areas where incomes are low, or highly variable, resistances and objections to the level of rents are often expressed in other farming areas. Frequently any attempt

---

[1] We place the term "reform" in quotation marks for this reason: the dictionary definition and popular use of the term "reform" refers to "improvement, making better or returning to a previous good state." In an economic context, alterations made in rental terms or resource ownership may represent "improvement" in respect to certain income distribution problems (although there are particular instances here where the readjustments are not "reforms" in the sense of improving the total position of 2 persons). On the other hand the so-called "reforms" may represent a "worsening" of the situation in terms of other economic criteria (particularly the long-run efficiency in resource allocation). Thus the word "reform" can be greatly misleading. We raise some of these points in respect to rent "reforms." We are not concerned with ownership "reforms."

of the landlord to "break away from custom" and increase rents is frowned upon by economists as well as tenants.

Literature on the subject of rental "reforms" has not recognized all of the economic facets of the problem. What is generally overlooked is the dual role of agricultural rents. As a price for the services of land, rent performs 2 functions in a price economy: (1) It acts as an allocator of resources between different alternatives in production. (2) It acts as an allocator of income between different individuals. While these 2 goals, efficient allocation of resources and an "equitable" distribution of income, need not be conflicting in terms of the total of means available in the economy (the sacrifice in "equity" of income distribution can be offset by progressive taxation or other means as rents are used for allocative purposes), they are often in conflict when the price for either a factor or a commodity is manipulated in a manner which favors one as compared to the other function. The purpose of this section is to examine some of the proposals in respect to rent "reforms." We are concerned not only with those which involve outright income transfers but also with those less extreme redistribution proposals concerning variability of landlord and tenant returns; changes in the distribution of the total product over time to either a tenant or landlord is simply 1 facet of the distribution problem.

Role of factor returns. In a perfect market the price for any factor of production (wage to labor, rent to land, interest on capital) would approximate the marginal value productivity of the particular resource. To the extent that prices for products and prices for factors accurately reflect consumer values and factor productivity respectively, competitive market rents then provide (with the distribution of income given) a basis for the most efficient allocation of resources. Given the appropriate choice indicator, a total product (whether in physical terms or monetary or other units expressive of consumer values or social welfare) can always be maximized when resources are arranged in a manner consistent with their marginal products. Thus any attempt to lower rents below their competitive market rate can increase efficiency only if rents have, for some reason, been greater than a level expressive of the marginal value productivity of the land, buildings, and other real estate. Attempts to lower rents below the marginal value product of the resources in question may bring about inefficiency in this manner: if the marginal productivity of resources furnished by tenants is low compared to alternative uses, income to tenants as factor owners will also be low relative to alternative employment or use of tenant resources. If tenants were to transfer elsewhere and sell the services of their labor or capital to producers of other industries (or employ them in production of alternative or non-farm products) the total value of product available to society might be increased. Eventually, the pull of income forces may draw these individuals from agriculture to other lines of activity where factor productivity, and hence family incomes, are greater. A sufficient reduction in rents (rent "reforms") will, however, divert part of the marginal product of land (or other landlord resources) away from the landlord to the tenant. Thus the tenant's total income (marginal value product of his own resources plus the share of marginal value product of land diverted from the landlord) may be raised to a level where his "reservation price" (level of income which he is willing to accept) for staying in agriculture is met and he will be unwilling to move his resources into alternative employments.

Rent flexibility. The same logic applies to flexibility in rents. The English tenure system, wherein cash rents have been maintained at low levels over several decades without variation, is often cited as a "renting ideal." [2] Not only may this system result in a redistribution of income, but also the inflexibility feature *per se* can serve as a negative rather than a positive attribute. To the extent that the marginal value product of land rises over time, flexible rents would maintain factor returns in line with productivity of either tenant or landlord resources. Inflexible rents would result in returns to tenants beyond the productivity of their resources as the marginal product of land increases. Thus the "surplus in tenant returns" may result in the use of too many tenant resources in agriculture. A decline in land productivity accompanied by inflexible rents would have the opposite effect.

Similarly, the inflexibility of share rents in the United States may be accompanied by inefficiency. While the product and income forthcoming under share leases change with price levels and techniques of production, the relative shares to the various factors of production remain constant over long time periods. Share rents in some sections of Iowa have included two-fifths of the small grain and one-half the corn over a period as long as 30 years. Under the tremendous strides in techniques it is hardly likely that these same shares can express the marginal product of landlord resources equally as well in 1955 as in 1920. Rent inflexibility may have certain positive attributes (such as reducing uncertainty) but it cannot be looked upon as a "leasing ideal."

Other means of income transfer. Incomes of many tenants may be so low as to be inconsistent with a maximization of national welfare. Yet, if they are acceptable in the value framework of society, other means exist for remedying the income problem and for increasing total welfare. Mere lowering of rents does not remove the basic cause (low resource productivity and insufficient quantities of resources) of low incomes. A positive approach might well include programs which (a) increase the mobility of tenant resources and (b) aid in shifting labor and capital to more productive employments. Included here should be measures which (1) provide better information on employment and living conditions elsewhere, (2)

---

[2] Under the British custom wherein the "incoming" tenant pays a competitive cash sum to the "outgoing" tenant, rents are actually made flexible.

subsidize transfer of resources, and (3) invest in the human factor to the extent of providing training for other employment in lines of production. Direct income transfers allow additional alternatives which can be made in other manners: One possibility is progressive income taxes to all members of society and the provision of direct services and subsidies to all low-income families, including tenants.

Landlord and Tenant Uncertainty

Crop failure and uncertainty is another reason sometimes given for a lowering of rents below the competitive level of the market. These proposals refer particularly to arid farming regions. A tenant on a Great Plains wheat farm may have an outlay of $2,000 to $4,000 for capital and labor services which he alone provides: His landlord may have an annual outlay of only $200 to $400 for taxes and upkeep of buildings. Under frequent crop failures associated with this type of farming, cash outlays and reductions in income for the tenant are sometimes much greater than for the landlord.

Even in the face of greater annual outlays by the tenant, it cannot be said that crop failure places a greater burden on every individual tenant than on every individual landlord. The same variation in income may impinge heavily on the landlord who depends on the farm for a livelihood and does not have outside sources of income. Finally, the same form and degree of uncertainty faces the owner-operator; he must stand the costs associated with land and real estate as well as the annual outlay for services of labor and capital in other forms. While lower share rental rates would lessen the squeeze on tenant farmers in areas of high yield risks, there appears to be little reason why this group of operators should be singled out for particular treatment of a phenomenon which touches all farm operators alike. The renting system *per se* is not the basic problem. Adjustment in rental rates alone is not the appropriate solution to income and efficiency questions which stem from weather and price variability. Storage programs, crop insurance, sufficient cash reserves, or appropriate credit facilities, and perhaps commodity pricing policies, are means by which owners and tenants alike can be given greater income stability.

Sharing alternatives. In the absence of general programs and policies to treat income and resource problems growing out of weather variability, arrangements can be made within the framework of share-leasing systems, the predominant form of rental contract in high-risk areas. One sometimes suggested is that the tenant product be established at some minimum level below which it would not fall, if the total product is great enough, even in years of low crop yields. For example, this minimum might include 1,500 bushels of wheat on a farm which would average a production of 2,815 bushels over time.

Again it is true, however, that if the one-third and two-third shares (or one-fourth and three-fourths, as the case may be) approximates the average marginal product of land and other resources over time, then a minimum tenant product which raises the operator's share above two-thirds and lowers the landlord's share below one-third as an average over time results in factor returns out of line with the productivity of specific resources. Table 1 has been prepared to show the possibilities here. The data are for 200 acres based on the experimental fields at Akron, Colorado. A 20-year period, 1909-1938, has been used, since even this span of ownership is greater than for many landlords and a period of tenant operation of this length is the exception rather than the rule. Thus, while 20 years may not be long enough to establish actuarial yield expectations, it is long in terms of tenant or landlord planning. Line 1 shows the tenant and landlord products under a conventional one-third and two-third lease arrangement. Line 2 shows the annual product to either resource owner when a minimum tenant product of 1,500 bushels is in effect. The tenant receives a two-thirds share when total production is sufficiently in excess of 1,500 bushels. In case production is greater than 1,500 but less than 2,250 bushels, the tenant receives 1,500 bushels while the landlord receives the residual (which is less than a one-third share if total production is less than 2,250 bushels). The tenant share averages somewhat above two-thirds of the total product over the twenty years. Variability of the tenant product has been decreased, while variability of the landlord product has been increased. For an arrangement in which a minimum product to the tenant

Table I.

Landlord and Tenant Products from 200 Acres of Land Under Various Sharing Arrangements *

Lease Arrangement	Share of product		Coefficient of variation	
	tenant	landlord	tenant	landlord
1. Conventional one-third share to landlord	1877	938	65	65
2. 1,500 bushel tenant minimum; no adjustment	1976	839	57	85
3. 1,500 bushel tenant minimum; 38.8 per cent to landlord	1877	938	55	86
4. 1,500 bushel tenant minimum; absolute equalization	1877	938	57	89

* Source: based on Akron, Colorado, yield data from U.S.D.A. Cir. 700.

results in a return to tenant resources above their marginal productivity, the logic of economics would lead to the hypothesis that an over-investment of tenant labor and capital might come about in wheat production. The increment in return to tenant resources forthcoming as a portion of the marginal product from the land diverted to them should hold more people in this field of production relative to other opportunities. Any reduction in risk or uncertainty by other means would have a similar tendency but would be economically beneficial to the extent that under-investment of resource had existed previously because of the discount in prospective returns. Thus the minimum should not represent a net addition to the tenant's product over time (if the existing share rates actually allow an approximation of the marginal productivity of tenant and landlord resources). Either 1 of 2 adjustments should be made in the leasing contract if factor returns are not to deviate from resources productivity over time:

1. **With the minimum in effect for poor years the landlord share might be increased in order that the reduction in his product during lean years can be recaptured in years of favorable yields.** If a one-third, two-thirds arrangement allows rents and labor and capital returns which approximate resource productivity in the absence of a minimum tenant product, then under this tenant "risk reduction" scheme, the landlord share might be boosted to (say) two-fifths of the total product in good years. An arrangement of this nature is illustrated in line 3 of Table 1. Here the tenant receives (a) a minimum product of 1,500 bushels in years when total output is greater than 1,500 bushels but less than 2,250 and (b) all of the product when output is less than 1,500 bushels. In other years, however, the landlord receives 38.8 per cent and the tenant receives 61.2 per cent of the product. Over the entire 20 years, the shares average one-third and two-thirds. If these shares approximate the productivity of tenant and landlord resources, consistency of factor return and factor productivity has been maintained over time even though it is violated within individual years. Variability of the landlord product is slightly greater under this system than under the previous system of a tenant minimum. However, the landlord would never be "worse off" over time (as compared to the first tenant minimum system) in the criteria of welfare economics. The greater variability comes about only through addition to his share in favorable years. He never receives less in any individual year than under the previous minimum system. The slight reduction in relative variability of the tenant's product (as compared to the first system of a tenant minimum) comes about, however, always through a reduction in product in some years, and never through an addition to product. Of the 2 minimum systems, tenant welfare would be less under the second than under the first.

2. **Absolute adjustments might be made in years when the product is sufficiently above the tenant minimum.** Here an absolute amount would be added to the landlord product in favorable years to offset the reduction in an unfavorable year. This possibility is illustrated in line 4: The tenant again receives two-thirds of the product in years when yield is above 2,250 bushels. He receives 1,500 bushels when total yield is greater than 1,500 bushels but less than 2,250 bushels and the landlord receives the remainder. In years when production is less than 1,500 bushels the tenant receives

the entire product and the landlord receives none. However, as the land-lord product drops below a one-third share in one year, it is replaced by an equal amount from the tenant's share of the following year (or as soon as yields will allow if a run of unfavorable years occur together). With a total production of 1,800 bushels in the first year, the tenant would receive 1,500 bushels while the landlord would receive 300 bushels (in contrast to 1,200 and 600 bushel shares under an unadjusted one-third and two-thirds lease). With production of 2,700 bushels in the second year, the landlord would receive 1,200 bushels (the one-third share of 900 plus 300 to cover the deficit of the previous year), while the tenant would receive 1,500 bushels (the two-thirds share of 1,800 minus the 300 bushel transfer from the landlord in the previous year). For the data of Table 1, transfers to the tenant were made consecutively in the fourth, fifth, sixth, and eighth years. The entire accumulated "landlord deficit" was replaced from the tenant's share in the tenth year. The average products for the 20-year period are two-thirds to the tenant and one-third to the landlord. This system results in greater variability of the landlord product than either the first and second systems of a tenant minimum. As compared to the first system (line 2), this greater variability need never lessen the land-lord's welfare.

Three systems have been outlined for reducing variability in tenant returns. One of these lifts the share of output to the tenant above the marginal productivity of his resources. Two systems maintain shares in line with factor productivity. Thus they need not distort resource efficiency in the sense of consistency between factor productivity and resource re-wards over time. However, these 2 also reduce variability in the tenant product at the expense of stability in the landlord product. The end effect on resource efficiency need not be entirely positive. Part of the risk and uncertainty surrounding tenant resources has been transferred to landlord resources, and this "adjustment" may itself breed inefficient resource use. Some persons claim that all facets of risk and uncertainty in variable yield areas should be tied to the land, because land is inseparable from climate of an area, while labor and capital are mobile and have alternative uses in other areas. However, landlord investment is also mobile and has alter-natives in other industries and other geographic areas. A Great Plains landlord also might invest in a livestock production system in the Corn-belt or in the stocks of General Motors. The materials put into tenant houses and other buildings has alternative uses or the land of high risk area can be left to lie idle while funds are invested in other alternatives.

Tenant investment and landlord investment should bear directly the uncertainties which impinge on or are peculiar to each. Certain factors of production furnished by the tenant are pure technical complements to factors furnished by the landlord. It is doubtful that any satisfactory method exists for separating the uncertainty that attaches to each category of factors in cases where resources are technical complements. An undue shifting of uncertainty from tenant to landlord resources might well have the effect of forcing a curtailment in landlord investment. Agriculture has been pointed out as an industry notably low on capital investment. Part of the difficulty here is alleviated through the willingness of landlords to make investment in land, buildings, and other resources which give off productive services for a long period of time. The tenant then is able to use his limited funds for extending input of machinery, improved seed, and other capital forms which have a shorter life span and are transformed to product in a relatively short time period. Accordingly, there is little logic in shifting the uncertainty of tenant resources to the landlord where it might curtail investment.

Non-transfer adjustments. Rather than attempt to (a) stabilize income and (b) transfer uncertainty which surrounds tenant resources to landlord resources, other leasing "revolutions" are perhaps needed. One possibility is a general scrapping of the customs which permeate share-leasing arrangements. Changes can be made even within the framework of share leases found in the Great Plains region. In order to lessen the "squeeze" on the tenant who has cash outlays in years of crop failures, the landlord might pay a share of seed, hired labor, tractor fuel, and other major production costs which represent annual out-of-pocket expense. The "squeeze" (associated with variable costs) would then fall equally on tenant and landlord. The tenant would not have such great outlays in years of crop failure and he would not realize as great a share of the product in years of favorable crops. (Although his share in these years would be consistent with productivity of his resources, he would furnish fewer resources.) The landlord would bear a greater share of the variability burden not because of a transfer of uncertainty from tenant to landlord resources but because he would furnish a share of the "conventional tenant resources." He would assume uncertainty which attaches to both real estate and operating capital or labor.

Where conventional lease shares (such as one-third and two-thirds or one-fourth and three-fourths) allow returns to tenant and landlord in line with the productivity of real estate furnished by the former and the labor and capital furnished by the latter, adjustments in shares would need to be made under this alternative arrangement. The objective under the new arrangement would again be one of establishing factor returns in a manner consistent with their marginal value productivity. Its advantage is that while it lessens the burden on the tenant in poor crop years (his cash outlay is not so great) it does not transfer uncertainty from distinct tenant-furnished to distinct landlord-furnished resources.

Welfare criteria. It should be emphasized that the criteria of welfare economics provides no basis for singling out landlords as a group from which income should be transferred over time (a return to tenants above the marginal product of their resources) or between time periods (a shift of returns variability from tenant to landlord with shares equal to productivity as an average over time) in order that tenants have greater incomes or more stable incomes. While landlords in the aggregate may have greater income and wealth than tenants in the aggregate, many individual renters have high incomes while many individual owners fall at the low end of the income scale. Many widows, disabled operators, and retired farmers depend entirely upon rental incomes for a livelihood; income of many people in this particular group is low, and if a general income redistribution were to be made, these individuals would be recipients rather than donors. Even in a pure variability context economic logic cannot say that the welfare of (a) a tenant and (b) a widow as a landlord, can be increased in total by transferring income to the former in poor crop years and to the latter in good crop years. The utility sacrificed by the low-income landlord in years of poor crops and transfers to the tenant may be less than the utility gained by the tenant. Conversely, the gain in utility to the landlord in years when the transfer is "repaid" need not (and would not be expected in terms of accepted notions of the utility function) be as great as the sacrifice in utility to this same landlord during years when the "transfer" is made to the tenant.

While economists have been somewhat prone to think in these terms, landlords and tenants cannot be looked upon as 2 separate but homogeneous groups in terms of wealth and income. Means more appropriate and fundamental than leasing distortions are available for effecting income transfer between individuals of society. In areas where agricultural populations are dense and incomes are low, these transfers might best be made through investment in individuals to fit them for work in non-agricultural pursuits (or for opportunities elsewhere in agriculture). The revenue for these income transfers and investments in the human factor might best come from progressive income taxes on all strata of society (or other sources consistent with the criteria of welfare economics). Transfers and investments of this nature would increase the efficiency with which human and capital resources are organized. In contrast, income transfers through rental manipulations (in low-income or unproductive agricultural areas) makes the transfer of income from the landlord as one member of society to the tenant as another member of society contingent upon the tenant's remaining on the farm and in the area.

Resource Productivity and Rents

Agricultural production economists have made only slight progress in relating rent levels to resource productivity. The problem involves, as do all problems in production economics, imputation of rewards to all factors of production including land. Important gaps do exist in factor productivity. Uncertainty, institutional barriers, general lack of knowledge, and time itself cause rent for land as well as returns to other resources to deviate from the resource's value product. In an initial study the writer and others have compared rental returns with factor productivity. Using a Cobb-Douglas function, where Y refers to the value of product, X_1 refers to real estate, X_2 refers to labor, X_3 refers to machine and power services, and X_4 refers to general crop services, the following production function was derived for a sample of eastern Iowa farms:

$$Y = .91X_1^{.80}X_2^{.13}X_3^{.09}X_4^{.01}.$$

The following data were then derived: *

Item	Value (dollars)
Average landlord rental return per acre on share-rent farms	$18.90
Average landlord return per acre on cash-rent farms	10.29
Mean marginal value productivity per acre	31.42
Marginal productivity at upper fiducial limit [a]	37.39
Marginal productivity at lower fiducial limit [a]	25.45

* Source: E. O. Heady and E. W. Kehrberg, *Effects of Cash and Share Leases on Farming Efficiency*. Iowa Agr. Exp. Sta. Bul. 385.

[a] Range is based on fiducial limits at the 5 per cent level of probability.

One would not, of course, expect marginal value products and rental rates for landlord resources to be equal in an uncertain world. Given imperfect knowledge and expectations, rental rates will fall below the marginal value product of land because of discounts due to uncertainty. In the eastern Iowa case, however, it was fairly certain that existing lease customs gave a rental rate far below discounted marginal value products for the year 1950.

Fundamentals of Resource Ownership Policy

Many farm families place farm ownership high in their means-end scale. While not all attempt to purchase a farm, the majority of operators in the United States start with ownership of land as well as other resources in mind. It is true, of course, that there are few operators who are never owners in the sense of having title to some machinery, livestock, and mono-period resources. But most beginning farmers extend their vision to ownership of buildings and land resources as well. National and state production policies long have been directed at farm ownership. The marketing system employed for publicly owned land was in this direction (although it also was directed towards goals other than ownership). The homestead act wherein farmers were given title for living on and operating a specified acreage was another step in this direction. The preemption act and the low price at which other segments of the total stock of land represented similar steps. Other state and federal policies have been in the same direction down through time. Low interest rates under the Federal Land

Bank system have been partly for this purpose. The attempt to allow low-capital tenants to become owners under the tenant purchase program of the Farmers Home Administration has been another step in this direction. In some states, real estate taxes are scaled to favor owner operation of farms. Attempts to establish a large number of small ownership units have been more extreme in other parts of the world. In postwar years, "land reforms" in eastern European nations, Japan, South Korea, and Italy have resulted in the confiscation of large landed estates and the redistribution of these among the peasants. "Land reform" in Italy has also included use of a graduated land tax to discourage large farms. The Liberal Government of New Zealand employed a similar tax as early as 1893 to bring about "closer settlement."

Some agricultural economists have taken farm ownership as an end *per se*, and have directed their efforts largely towards retaining or increasing the number of people on farms and the number of owner-operated farms. Any increase in the number of rented farms or the acreage of rented land is taken to be "bad." Sometimes the precedents of history are set forth, and "agrarian principles" are cited as the basis and as the justification for pursuing the end of owner-operation to its extreme limits. Farm economists have been known to "raise their eyebrows" at purchase of farms by city people, since this development excludes the possibility of ownership by the man who operates the farm. Church bodies, farm organizations, and other rural-oriented groups also support farm ownership in the vein of an ultimate end. We thus need to inquire whether farm ownership is a means or an end and the conditions under which it becomes either. Obviously, ownership ranks high in the minds of a large number of people. Yet why do not industrial workers and society in general insist that the "non-farm worker must own his own tools"? If the ownership principle is carried to the extreme, there is no reason why the product of non-agricultural industries could not be produced under a handicraft system in the homes of the workers. Is there any basis to cause ownership of the factors of production to differ between agriculture and non-agricultural industries? Do the ends of production or resource use differ so drastically that a unique line must be drawn between agriculture and non-agricultural industries?

Ownership as a means. In the great majority of cases, farm ownership is or can be a means to the attainment of "higher" ends (which, in turn, become means directed toward even more remote ends). First, with the historic and individualistic system of capital accumulation in United States agriculture, the ownership of a farm has become a means of providing an income flow in the retirement period of farm families. The farm is "the annuity of agriculture" and, while income is highly uncertain and variable when viewed *ex ante* in years remote from retirement, it is the system of investment which farmers best understand. They reinvest their savings in farms rather than in the securities of other industries. Perhaps it is the paucity of knowledge of returns from non-farm investments which causes them to view "outside investments" with a high degree of uncertainty. Second, farm ownership can be a means to farming efficiency, even when efficiency is measured in operator profits. This statement applies to the leasing systems typically found over a wide range of American agriculture. The owner-operator often realizes greater returns than a tenant from a given collection of resources because of the distortion which the lease causes in production possibilities at a given point in time and over time. (See Chapter 20.) Under these conditions, ownership becomes a means to a greater money income and a higher level of living. Arthur Young's adage "the magic of property turns sand into gold" is partly a reflection of these imperfections in the resource service market. Farm ownership also provides a means whereby the individual family can adjust the use of resources over time to conform with its own time preference. The short stay or the leasing regulations on rented farms may require that the tenant extract only a limited amount of productive services from the soil. The owner who is not inhibited by the stipulations, interests, and decisions of a landlord can farm his land as severely as he pleases if he or his family places a high value on early as compared to later incomes.

Farm ownership is also a means to security in modes of family living. Since the farm home is physically joined to the producing unit in American agriculture, farm ownership allows the farm family to build and develop its home in the manner of any other home owner. Direct utility is attached by most families to the home which they own. Through home ownership they are able to decorate the house, landscape the grounds, and add the modern conveniences which today are characterized as necessities. Where the farm family must move every few years, or is faced with the uncertain prospects of moving, it has little opportunity to expend time or money in developing the items of consumption such as running water, electricity, and other goods which attach to the home and give off a flow of utility or satisfactions. These problems are less acute in some European regions because farmers live in village communities and travel each day to their farms or farming plots. Under this system it is possible for the family to enjoy the satisfactions which attach to home ownership without resort to ownership of the land resource as a part of the business firm. (In many of these cases, however, the majority of the farm families do own the farm land which they operate.) Farm ownership as a means to home satisfactions has not been so important in England, where an important percentage of farms has been in the estates of wealthy families. The major portion of these has been rented to the same tenant family for one or several generations; the tenant is able to develop conveniences and household amenities as if he owned the farm. In contrast, the United States tenure system, with its great degree of uncertainty, has caused farm families to place high values on farm ownership as a means to the ends of home security and greater family welfare. (The industrial worker can own his home without owning the resources with which he produces.) The "consumption items" which are important include not only home beautification and the opportunity to install electricity, running water, and other conveniences, but also the ability of the family to be secure in the community which it selects for a home. Frequent farm moves require that the family uproot itself from the church, the community, the school, and other organizations which provide direct satisfaction to the household. In this sense, farm ownership or tenure security may also become a means to community stability and the democratic participation of farm families in public affairs.

Ownership also may be looked upon as a means to freedom (with its various connotations). This aspect of ownership weighed heavily in the minds of original settlers in the United States. They were only shortly removed from repressive feudal estates wherein their position was one of subjugation; the tenant was both politically and socially subservient to persons between him and the king in the feudal landholding hierarchy. Personal freedom was also lacking for workers and tenants on estates such as those of William Penn and the large 19th century estates of the southern gentry. The political environment has changed so greatly, however, that this facet of resource control has little direct importance in the United States. From this standpoint, the political environment is more important than ownership considerations. Ownership of small plots in dictatorial nations does not give rise to freedom and democracy.

Farm ownership as an end. Consideration of farm ownership as an end in and of itself is pronounced among such religious groups as the Amish farmers of Lancaster County, Pennsylvania. These farmers look upon themselves as stewards of the soil, and ownership is given a high value for this reason. At some level, however, farm ownership is competitive with other consumption goods for most farm families. In many instances the farm family must decide between the alternatives of (a) hiring the resources from which it obtains services and having a greater money income, or (b) owning the resources and, while enjoying the direct utility of factor ownership, having a smaller money income. As competing goods it is unlikely that ownership and goods purchased with money income substitute at constant rates. Let us suppose that in Figure 1 resource ownership as a consumption good can be measured on the horizontal axis, while the goods which can be purchased with farm profits can be measured on the vertical axis. The individual or family has a given amount of funds which can be used for purchase or hire of resources or resource services and a production possibility curve of the nature of RL exists. It compares the opportunities of using the given fund in obtaining resource services (the vertical axis) to produce products and money income with ownership of resources *per se* (the horizontal axis). Within a range resource ownership is complementary (the portion of *RL* with a positive slope) with profits and goods which can be purchased with profits. In another range ownership becomes competitive with profits. Two sets of forces cause ownership and income to be complementary: (1) the forces mentioned above which can lead to more efficient operations under ownership, and (2) prices for owned resources which are sufficiently lower than the price of the same resource services in the rental market. (If factor prices are sufficiently low in the ownership market, the relationship will be complementary throughout and ownership should be extended indefinitely.) The individual's indifference curve is *MB* and indicates the rate at which money income (the goods which can be purchased with money income) substitute for the direct utility of ownership. In the case illustrated, utility or living level is at a maximum when farm profits (goods purchased with profits) are *op*, and ownership (or the direct utility derived from it) is extended to *ow*. Ownership is not extended to the limits

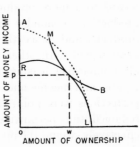

Fig. I. Optimum investment in ownership.

possible and the operator may maximize his utility by owning machinery, livestock, and other working capital, while owning part and renting part of the real estate resources. The indifference curve will vary between individuals, of course, and for some ownership as a good may substitute for other goods at a rate high enough so that investment in property will be pushed to the limit. Other operators may attach lesser values to ownership and consequently push it only to the apex of the opportunity curve (where complementarity is exhausted and beyond which ownership and profits become competitive).

Figure 1 provides the relevant framework for analyzing ownership as an end standing at a level with other goods and services. The problem of choice is one of getting the optimum amount of ownership and other goods which give rise to satisfaction. (Ownership is a non-competing means to other ends within the complementary range.) Ownership is not similarly an end for all people. Many choose the acquiring of resource services through renting and the consequent higher money incomes to the operation of small under-sized owned units and the consequent low standard of living. Some "well meaning" persons suggest farm ownership as a paramount end of individuals, and, therefore, that society should go to unlimited extremes in settling more and more people on smaller and smaller units. Ownership above all else is advocated by many tenure enthusiasts because they view ownership as an end which has priority over all other goods, rather than relating it to the more general means-end framework. Some cite historic precedents to illustrate that individuals (or society) have (has) favored farm ownership in the past. It is not necessarily true that even past generations of our society viewed ownership as an end that should be selected over all others. Land was abundant and "free"; the situation is now changed and the values of current generations are more nearly relevant.

Alternative means. With the increased price of the resources employed in agriculture, we need to examine the mechanisms which serve as substitutes for ownership as a means to more ultimate ends. Where ownership is a means to a more productive use of resources we are interested (from a production economics or efficiency standpoint) in whether the total of products, and hence the level of living, can be increased by substitute arrangements. In other words, as we examine Figure 1, is it possible to alter imperfect leasing arrangements so that production possibilities are greater and income and satisfactions can be increased? Many leasing imperfections were pointed out in Chapter 20. If these imperfections were removed, thus permitting resources on rented farms to be organized more effectively, would the opportunity curve be altered from RL to AL? Where these changes can be made in leasing arrangements, ownership becomes less a complement to production and profit, or it may substitute at a lower rate for money profit and other goods in the range of competition. Wherever changes of this nature can be made, a smaller amount of ownership is necessary for a maximization of individual and society welfare.

Intra-agriculture investment. A second proposal ordinarily accompanies the suggestion that all families should own the farm which they operate. It is the notion that all children born to farm families should be given the opportunity to become farmers (and to become farm owners).[3] The proponents of this policy point with alarm to investment in farms by city dwellers. Also, they are highly concerned that a large number of farm boys cannot find units to rent except at high prices.

The notion that all boys born in agriculture should remain in the industry is, of course, quite absurd. As the important industry where births exceed deaths, all boys born in agriculture could become farmers and owners only as the number of farms grew indefinitely larger and the size

---

[3] Representative of this notion is the statement by H. Belshaw, in J. Ackerman and M. Harris, *Family Farm Policy,* Chicago: University of Chicago Press, 1946, p. 196, that the land tenure system should enable one with the necessary training and ability to engage in farming whether he has capital or not. The expression is also reflected in the great concern of agricultural economists and others that farm boys either (a) are unable to find a farm to rent, (b) must pay high rents and land values or (c) must have a sizeable amount of capital to start farming. Land tenure economists even propose that land prices be controlled or stabilized (see Harris and Ackerman, *Family Farm Policy,* p. 52), to facilitate farm ownership. The crux of the problem, of course, is making product and factor prices more effective in guiding resources into and out of agriculture as well as within agriculture. Even larger amounts of capital are required to become an entrepreneur in other industries. Stabilization of land prices would not eliminate the uncertainty problem of agriculture; instability must be attacked at its source, which is variability of product prices.

of farms grew indefinitely smaller. Had this process taken place continually since the birth of the United States, farm units would now average small parcels. If this vein of thinking were applied to all industries, it, would mean, on the one hand, that only the sons of dentists could enjoy the "right" to become dentists; only salesmen's sons could become salesmen, and only professors' sons could become professors. On the other hand, it would mean that capital invested in the automobile industry could come only from persons currently owning automobile stock or from their sons; the "right" of investment in city rental property would be restricted to persons now engaged in this undertaking or to their children. In other words, each industry would be set aside in a tight compartment. While industries would be allowed to trade products, they would not be allowed to transfer investment and resources across the "industrial borders." The final result would be a segmented producing organism wherein returns on resources would be extremely great in some sectors and extremely low in other sectors.

The basic need from the standpoint of fundamental problems in agriculture is of an opposite nature. Rather than holding increasing amounts of labor in agriculture where it must drudge out a meager living, we need to help farm children move out of distressed areas of agriculture into other areas and other industries where returns are greater and the level of living can be higher. At the very least, farm children should be acquainted with outside opportunities and provided with the education and skills which fit them for non-farm occupations. Labor and human resources represent the most important products produced by agriculture. The gain to be had from these resources, in excess of replacements needed in agriculture, is in producing the commodities and services of non-farm industries in order that the general standard of welfare can be raised even higher. With full knowledge of alternative employments, farm children could then better apply their own choice indicators (preference functions) in selecting agricultural as compared to other forms of production. To the extent that farming is preferred solely because of its security from major business cycles, the important task before society is one of eliminating this major economic imperfection rather than one of designing, as an imperfect substitute, a policy of "more and smaller farms." Rather than view the basic problem in the very narrow setting of "providing every boy born on a farm with a place in agriculture," we must view it from the broader angle as one of providing every person in agriculture (and other industries) with an opportunity to acquire education and skilled training in line with his inherent abilities, find employment where the productivity of these very basic human resource services are greatest, and allow the individual choice of occupation and a suitable level of living. Finally, it should be remembered that non-operating farm owners provide an important part of the real estate investment in agriculture, just as many persons outside of the telephone industry provide capital for the American Telephone and Telegraph Corporation. To eliminate this source of capital (that furnished by city persons who own farms) would cause agriculture to suffer further hardships and would have the productivity consequences outlined elsewhere.

Selected References

Ackerman, J., and Harris, M., *Family Farm Policy*. Chicago: University of Chicago Press, 1946.

Clark, C., "Weak Points in Land Reform," *Jour. Farm Econ.*, Vol. 34.

Heady, Earl O., *Levels and Flexibility of Agricultural Rent and Farming Efficiency*, Land Econ. Vol. 17.

Heady, Earl O., and Kehrberg, Earl, *Cash and Share Leases in Relation to Farming Efficiency*, Iowa Agr. Exp. Sta. Bul. 386.

Heady, Earl O., Norton, L. W., and Renne, R. R., *Tenure Discussions*. Proceedings, Fifth International Conference of Agricultural Economists.

McPherson, W. K., "A Critical Appraisal of Family Farms," *Jour. Farm Econ.*, Vol. 34.

Mynt, H., *Theories of Welfare Economics*. Cambridge: Harvard University Press, 1948, Ch. 7 and 9.

Reder, M., *Studies in Theory of Welfare Economics*. New York: Columbia University Press, 1947, Ch. 8.

Schickele, R., "Tenure Systems and Agricultural Efficiency," *Jour. Farm Econ.*, Vol. 24.

22

Location of Production: Interregional Resource and Product Specialization

THE FORCES which determine or condition the pattern of production and resource allocation in different geographic areas are of interest not only to the production economist in his analysis of efficiency at the farm or national level; they are of direct concern to the individual farmer as he tries to ascertain the extent and nature of forces which determine the most profitable combination of factors and products. At the other extreme legislators and other public managers of resources also are concerned with the efficiency aspects of regional resource specialization. A maximum national product is forthcoming from given resources only as mobile resources (capital and labor) are applied to immobile resources (land) in a geographic pattern which allows the greatest economic product to each unit of mobile resource. The problems of production location and factor specialization come into sharpest focus at the level of international trade. Here the citizenry of nations seems to be least informed, and passes tariff laws, quota systems, and other legislation (indirectly through their power as voters to sanction or reject the direct expressions of their elected representatives) which alter regional or national production patterns.

General Equilibrium of Production

Analysis of interregional specialization patterns represents 1 facet of general equilibrium production economics. A general equilibrium study in agricultural production economics is concerned with the allocation of resources within individual farms, between farms, between producing areas, and between industries in a manner to maximize the national economic product. General equilibrium analysis is concerned particularly with resources which are mobile or transferable. The current chapter on production location thus should be looked upon as 1 step in the general equilibrium analysis which follows in subsequent chapters. We touch only

639

briefly upon the problems of interrelated supply and demand curves because these are treated in detail elsewhere.[1]

Relationships in Regional Specialization

The degree and nature of specialization found in different geographic areas are dependent on 2 sets of relationships. One is the regional production possibility relationship (the regional transformation curve or iso-resource curve). It establishes the physical opportunities which are open to the particular region. The nature of the production possibilities for a region depends, obviously, on the production function for each individual commodity and for each farm. The analysis which follows refers to long-run opportunities unless exceptions are noted. The second important relationship is that of price ratios for commodities and factors when possibilities of resource transfers are concerned. These relationships have been encountered previously in analysis of the individual farm as a producing unit. The kinds of relationships which help define (a) the degree of resource specialization and the geographic location of production which is optimum and (b) the gains forthcoming through these opportunities are largely the same on an individual farm (or firm of any industry) as on a national or international basis. A farm operator may be more proficient than his hired hand at milking cows, but may still gain by hiring laborers to specialize in manual tasks while he devotes his own efforts entirely to the managerial functions: if hired labor requires an outlay of $1 per hour while the return on management amounts to $4 per hour, the gains in terms of returns to the farm as an economic unit are obvious. Study of inter-regional specialization thus requires no knowledge beyond these basic concepts. These relationships explain the patterns of production which define the use of labor, capital, and land resources over the United States as is illustrated in Figure 1.

Soils, climate, and physical production possibilities. The physical or technological phenomena which define the production possibilities open to particular producing regions are as follows:

1. Climate. Climatic factors include rainfall, surface evaporation, temperature, length of the growing season, amount of sunshine, intensity and direction of prevailing winds, and any other factors associated with these. The growing season places sharp lines on production possibilities for cotton in Virginia and Tennessee. The marginal rate of substitution of cotton for corn falls sharply within this location. Temperature and length of the growing season place limits on corn production in Northern Wisconsin and Minnesota. While the growing season is also important, rainfall causes

---

[1] For a treatment of regional supply and demand functions, see R. L. Mighell and J. D. Black, *Interregional Competition in Agriculture.* Cambridge: Harvard University Press, 1951, Chs. 2, 3, 4.

corn to substitute for wheat at low rates in the dry-land farming areas of Montana. Oats, peas, and potatoes have the greatest advantage in cool climates with short growing seasons. Climate often varies greatly over short distances. Differences here help explain why peaches are grown commercially on the east side but not on the west side of Lake Michigan.

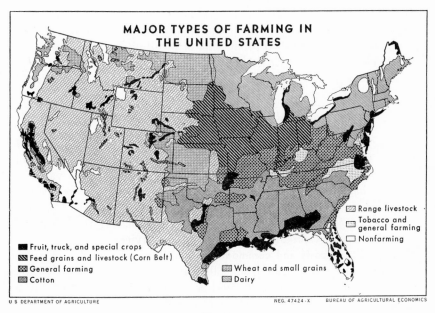

MAJOR TYPES OF FARMING IN THE UNITED STATES

Range livestock

Tobacco and general farming

Nonfarming

■ Fruit, truck, and special crops

▨ Feed grains and livestock (Corn Belt)

▩ General farming

▨ Cotton

Wheat and small grains

Dairy

U S DEPARTMENT OF AGRICULTURE   NEG. 47424-X   BUREAU OF AGRICULTURAL ECONOMICS

Fig. I.

2. Soil. Soils differ greatly between different geographic regions. Part of the variations in soil is associated with regional variations in climate. There are, however, much greater local variations in soil than in climate. Every state in the nation includes a wide range of soil types. Commonly, as many as 3 or 4 types can be found on one farm. Soil scientists have grouped soils into soil types that represent an important degree of homogeneity in this basic resource. The chief characteristics of soils which condition the production function for individual crops, and hence the production possibilities of a geographical area, are topography, texture, structure, and fertility (the presence of chemical elements including phosphorus, nitrogen, potassium, and trace elements, as well as the acidity or alkalinity). Watermelons grow well on sandy soils, while substitution ratios are in favor of potatoes over alfalfa on many soils of high acidity. Production possibilities favor beef cattle as a final product as compared to wheat on the sandhills of Nebraska, while the limestone area of Kentucky causes transformation rates to favor bluegrass and livestock over corn.

3. Biological. While subject to change over time, biological factors are also important in tempering the production possibilities which are unique to each geographic area. Emergence of the boll weevil has lowered the physical rates at which cotton competes with alternative products in much of the southeastern United States. Absence of this pest plus certain price advantages has increased the relative productivity of resources employed in cotton production in the western Cornbelt. Climatic, soil, and biological factors together help specify the production functions for individual products and hence the physical production or possibility relationships which exist in each producing area. Directly, these physical forces are reflected in the yield of product per unit of resources employed in production.

Transportation and Regional Price Variations

Production and resource use patterns are affected by price ratios and differ as (1) the ratio of the price of product relative to that of the mobile factor varies between regions, (2) the ratio of product prices varies between regions, and (3) the ratio of mobile factor prices varies between regions. Numerous forces cause geographic differentials in prices for either products or factors, chief of which is the cost of transportation (and other forms of secondary production or processing) services.

Transportation costs and commodity prices. The price at any particular producing point tends, aside from collusion or special agreements between rival producers of transportation and processing services, to vary directly with distance from the central market or consuming center. Under competitive conditions, the price to the producer would be the central market price less the cost of transportation services between the production location and the consuming center. Under this situation and in the absence of variations in costs of other processing or in-transit services, the geographic pattern of prices would tend to be of the nature outlined in Figures 2 and 3. The upper portion of Figure 2 assumes that (a) each producer has equal access to the consuming center indicated as C, and (b) transportation mediums (railroads, navigable streams, truck lines) are not more favorably situated for one producer than for others (or, if some producers are located along streams or rail lines, other producers have access to trucks which will take products to the market at the same cost per ton-mile). Accordingly, an iso-price boundary (circles such as P_1, P_2, P_3, and P_4, indicating equal prices to producers) exists for each point equally distant from the market. The price is the same for all producers on a given price line and is equal to the central market price less the cost of transportation services from the producing point. (The concentric circles can also be looked upon as iso-cost lines for transportation services. They are sometimes called isotims.) On boundary line P_1, the producer price of $1.80 represents the central market price of $2.00, less 20¢ for transport costs.

The lower portion of Figure 2 illustrates the nature of the decline in producer price as the point of production becomes more distant from the market. The price gradient (relationship between price and distance) is easily detected in data which relate prices received by farmers and mar-

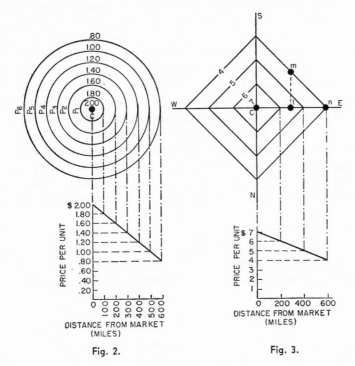

Fig. 2.   Fig. 3.

Distance and product prices.

kets. In 1950, Chicago butter prices averaged 0.4 of a cent per pound lower than in New York; San Francisco prices averaged 2.6 cents higher than Chicago prices. In the so-called "base" period of 1910-14, wheat prices received by farmers along the eastern seaboard averaged about $1.10. Producers in the soft winter wheat belt (Ohio and so forth) averaged about 95¢, while those in the eastern part of the hard winter area (Kansas, Nebraska, Iowa, and so forth) averaged about 85¢. Producers in the northern spring wheat areas realized from 65 to 75¢ per bushel. In recent decades prices have been more nearly "administered" through government programs than "determined" by market forces. Since the distance from market is directly proportional to the producer price in the case presented (Figure 2), the per-ton-mile cost of transportation does not vary with distance. In practice, however, railroads may lower the rate per ton-mile for greater distances. This is possible because of the relatively lower overhead for long as compared to short hauls. Conversely, the rate for short hauls is sometimes less per ton-mile than for long hauls; the latter comes about particularly where railroads compete directly with truck, water, or other types of transportation which provides low cost services in the vicinity of markets.[2]

The upper portion of Figure 3 illustrates a second extreme possibility in the geographic pattern of commodity prices. Here all products travel from primary producer to the consuming center via the main transportation routes indicated by lines SN and WE (which may represent railroads or waterways). The product is hauled in a lateral fashion to the main transportation artery where it is relayed to the final consuming center. Figure 3 assumes that the cost of lateral transportation is the same per ton-mile as that over the direct transport routes. Thus the price to a producer at the point m is the same as the price to a producer at point n because the distances ml and nl are equal. Point m is, however, nearer the consuming center C than is point n. All producers on the $4 quadrangle realize the same price, as is the case for the other iso-price lines indicated. The iso-price lines thus have an apex which centers on the main transportation route.[3]

Seldom do iso-price lines display as much uniformity about a market as is indicated in Figure 2 or 3. Due to (a) topography, (b) differences in access to main transportation arteries, (c) rates which vary with distance, and (d) other physical and economic forces, the price contours around a single market tend to take on a pattern such as that illustrated in Figure 4; the line defining an iso-price boundary tends to vary irregularly from the consuming center or central market.

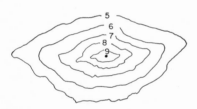

Fig. 4. Location and price boundaries.

Where 2 or more markets compete for products, price patterns are modifications of those outlined above. The New York milk shed overlaps those of Boston, Pittsburgh, and Philadelphia; Pittsburgh in turn overlaps the one for Detroit. Similarly, Chicago competes with South St. Paul for slaughter of hogs and other meat animals shipped from the Cornbelt. Omaha and Sioux City compete with each other and also with Chicago for hogs and feeder cattle. While potatoes from the Red River Valley of North Dakota and Minnesota do not move to the New York market, they com-

---

[2] An iso-price map representing lower rates as distance increases will cause the space between equal price lines to increase (the space betwen the 1.60 and 1.80 price lines will be greater than the space between the 1.80 and 2.00 lines) as distance increases. When per-ton-mile rates increase as distance from market increases the iso-price lines become closer together as distance increases.

[3] If the internal or lateral costs of transportation are greater than transportation on the main line, the apex will extend farther out on the main transportation artery. Lower lateral costs will result in the opposite.

pete with Maine potatoes which do; potatoes from Minnesota compete with Maine potatoes because those produced in Wisconsin or Michigan may move either to Chicago or to eastern markets. Interrelationships such as these tend to give a producer price pattern such as that illustrated in Figure 5a. (The modifications due to major transportation lines have not been included.) With milk prices at $2.20 in each of 2 consuming centers, the iso-price boundaries begin to overlap and both markets are tied together to give "binocular-shaped" iso-price lines. Aside from differences in the production function, similar production and resource use patterns should be found along the entire "binocular-shaped" iso-price boundary of $2.20. While points d and a are equidistant from the right-hand consuming center R, producers at d will receive a higher price for their product since they are nearer market L. If a producer at point a were to receive a lower price for his product in 1 of the 2 markets, he would ship to the other. Thus a line such as DN can be drawn

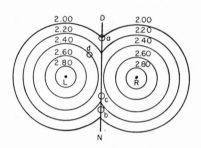

Fig. 5a. Interrelated markets.

which defines the intersection of the iso-price lines for the 2 markets and indicates where each has an equal advantage in bidding for product of a single producer. The product supply curve for 1 market is interrelated with that for the other markets. At points a or b competitive forces should cause the same price to be realized whether the product is shipped to 1 market or the other.

Transportation rates and regional price ratios. In addition to causing price differentials for a single commodity between geographic points, the costs of transportation services or other processing and in-transit costs also may cause price relationships between products to vary at locations differing in distance from the central market or consuming center. Price ratios are important in determining regional production patterns when (a) the commodities under consideration are "end products" such as pork and grain-fed beef or beef and milk (and hence are competing enterprises in the sense that the farmer must choose which to produce) (b) one is a product such as corn which can serve as a factor of production while the other such as pork is clearly a product (and hence give rise to factor-product transformation decisions such as whether the farmer should sell corn or feed hogs). If the ton-mile cost of transportation represented an equal percentage value of the product and were constant with distance for all products, price ratios would be the same for all producing localities irrespective of their distance from market. Where the relative costs of transportation vary differently between products, price ratios change between producing regions with the effects on production to be outlined later. Numerous forces cause the per-ton transportation costs to differ between products. Some of the more important are as follows:

1. Perishability and fragility of the product. Prevention of rapid loss in quality necessitates more costly transportation services in the case of fresh fruits, vegetables, and milk or eggs than in the case of corn or cotton.

2. Relative costs of transportation before and after processing. Transportation costs differ between some raw materials and finished products even though both are equal in respect to perishability. Freight rates on clothing are higher than on raw wool because the former is generally packaged in a form to require more space per unit weight of fiber. The same is true of raw and refined or packaged sugar.

3. Handling charges in route. Livestock require feeding and watering when shipped long distances. These special services do not have to be furnished for grain fiber crops which can move continuously once they have been loaded.

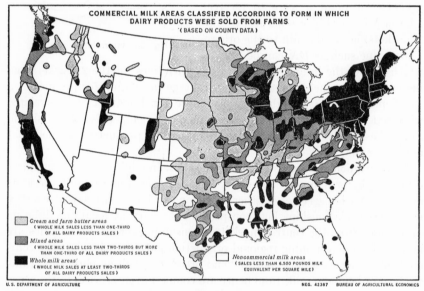

Fig. 5b.

4. Specific value of product. Products with a high value relative to their volume and weight can be transported at a lower relative rate (cost of transportation relative to value of the product) than products with a low specific value. The cost of transporting a bushel of corn is lower than the cost of transporting a bushel of tomatoes because of differences in weight per bushel, perishability, and nature of packaging and containers. Accordingly, the cost of transporting corn is generally much lower relative to its value than for tomatoes. Corn/tomato price ratios thus widen as the distance from central market or consuming center increases. Livestock ordinarily has a lower transportation rate relative to its price than do feed grains. Feed grains, while less favorable than food grains, are more favorable than hay in this respect. Transport costs are low relative to the value of the product price for grains as compared to most fruits and vegetables. Fiber crops generally have the lowest transport costs of all products relative to their specific value.

5. *Length of haul and nature of transport facilities.* Costs per pound of product transported increase with distance from market. Yet the costs are not ordinarily in proportion to distance because, as was mentioned earlier, of lower costs associated with savings of loading and general overhead or fixed costs.

Lower rates are sometimes given the same product for directions in which traffic is light; costs are little greater for a run with a load than for empty cars. Some farming areas are located on these "haul-back" routes while others are not.

6. *Political and indirect economic considerations.* Costs of transportation services relative to the value of the product also vary for other reasons. Some regions are able to focus pressure on legislators to an extent that favorable transport rates are obtained.

While each of the items listed above explain the cost of transportation for single commodities, they are more important in explaining why the ratio of product prices or factor and product prices vary with geographic regions in the manner illustrated in Figures 6 and 7. Figure 6 illustrates the uncommon case where the costs of transportation are the same relative to the value of product for all commodities. Starting with the iso-price line of $2 for product Y_1, the cost of transportation to the next boundary is 20¢, or 10 per cent of the value of the product. At the price boundary P_1, the price of Y_2 is $10. The cost of transporting it to P_2 is $1, or 10 per cent of the value of Y_2. While the cost of transportation as a percentage of the value of the product varies between price lines, it is always the same for both products. Thus the Y_1/Y_2 price ratio is identical at all distances from the market. Here transportation costs (as related to price of the product) may affect farming intensity but they will not, aside from the exceptions to be explained later, affect the allocation of resources between products.

The more realistic effect of transportation costs on commodity price ratios is illustrated in Figure 7. Here the cost of transportation relative to the value of the product differs at each location. The cost of transporting Y_3 from P_1 to P_2 is equal to 10 per cent of the value of the commodity at the first boundary, while transport cost is only 5 per cent of the value of Y_4. Whereas both prices fall with distance from the market, the price of Y_3 falls at a faster rate than the price of Y_4. Thus the ratio of price changes at each contour line or distance from the market. (P_1 can be taken to represent a distance of 100 miles from the market while P_2, P_3, P_4, and P_5 represent 200, 300, 400, and 500 miles respectively.) The Y_3/Y_4 price ratio is 1:10 at P_1 but changes to 1:11.3 at 300 miles (P_3) and 1:13.3 at 500 miles (P_5). The effect of these geographic variations in price ratios in explaining regional patterns of production and resource use or type-of-farming influences is outlined in detail later.

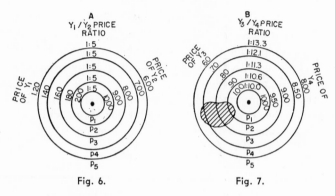

Fig. 6.   **Fig. 7.**

Differences in price and production ratios.

Transportation and mobile factor prices. Figure 7 also illustrates the effect of transport cost on factor/product ratios. Y_3 may be taken to represent corn (or hay, oats, or other feeds) while Y_4 is a product such as pork (or beef, mutton, dairy, or other animal product). If the region bounded by P_5 is a surplus corn producing area, and if grain values are either directly or indirectly based on prices in a central market or consuming center, the pattern will again take the form illustrated in Figure 7 and the factor/product (corn/hog) price ratio also will decrease with distance to market: it varies from 1:10.0 at P_1 to 1:13.3 at P_5.[4]

Feed crops represent farm-produced factors of production and their geographic prices tend to be tied to central markets and livestock population centers. Other forms of capital have an entirely different location network. Rather than originating in "surplus" producing areas, as in the case of feeds as factors of production, with movement to population or "feed deficit" centers, many forms of capital originate in population centers and move outward to farms in more distant areas. Manufacture of machines and tools and their repairs is centered somewhat (although not entirely) in the central market areas of the Cornbelt. Nearness to the factors of production (labor and steel) partly leads to this location pattern. The cost of these farm-used resources tends to increase with westward

---

[4] If Y_1 in Figure 6 is taken as a factor such as corn while Y_2 is considered a product such as pork, prices are equally favorable to transformation of grain into pork at any geographic point.

distance from Chicago while the price of farm products decreases with distance westward (until the dividing line, such as DL in Figure 5a, is reached which separates the more heavily populated Pacific coast consuming centers from those of central and eastern markets). Here the factor/product price ratio becomes less and less favorable with distance from market as is illustrated in Figure 8; the factor/product price ratio increases from 1.5:1 at P_1 to 5.8:1 at P_5.

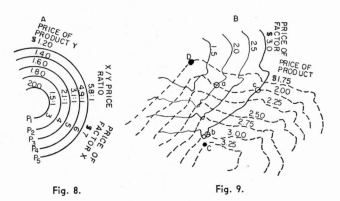

Fig. 8.   Fig. 9.

Regional differences in product and factor prices.

Factors of production such as fertilizer, irrigation water, tractor fuel, and other capital forms generally are distributed from their points of extraction as natural resources. As material-oriented industries, they furnish a different pattern of regional price variation relative to commodity prices. An example of this nature is provided in Figure 9. A factor such as fertilizer may be distributed from a point of origin such as D. Due to transportation costs, the price of the factor increases with distance from manufacture in the manner illustrated by the solid iso-price lines. The product price is based on a consuming market C, and prices decline in the manner illustrated by the dotted iso-price lines. The factor/product ratio is not uniformly consistent with distance from either the distributing and consuming centers alone but depends on both. At point a (near to the factor distribution center and distant from the consuming center) the ratio is 1:1 (2.00:2.00). Similarly, at point b (distant from the distributing center and near to the consuming center) the ratio is 1:1 (3.00:3.00). In contrast, point c (which is nearer the consuming center than a and nearer the distributing center than b) has a factor/product price ratio of 1.5:1.00 (3.00:2.00). Producers at point c are not as well situated as those at either a or b in respect to factor-product transformation. A final possibility is that 2 or more factors decline in price at different rates with distance from market. This situation can be illustrated geometrically by means of Figure 7 (where Y_3 and Y_4 are now considered as factors rather than products). The fact that the costs of transportation represent a percentage of the value for one resource causes the factor price ratio to fall in a direction favoring use of Y_4 near the market and Y_3 distant from the market. Hay and grain present such a situation.

While the same forces play on the prices of factors used in agriculture and the prices of products produced in the industry, the geographic uniformity (or tendency) is nowhere near so evident for the former as for the latter. Prices for factors such as machinery and other tools of production often display a wide similarity over broad regions; "fair trade" and related practices lead manufacturers to set retail prices on a uniform basis irrespective of distance. The heterogeneous sources of such production elements as fertilizer, tractor fuel, and building materials cause no distinct factor price gradient from one section of the nation to another. Labor also presents a heterogeneous price pattern because dense populations and low wage rates are found together (as in the case of the southeast).

Patterns of Production and Resource Use

The interplay of the forces discussed above provides a complex framework in which the regional pattern of production and resource use is determined. The effect of any one force may be augmented or offset by other forces. Thus the exact pattern of any single price or production phenomenon may not be easily isolated when regional data are examined. For this reason some "pure cases" are outlined below in order that the student of production economics can better understand the effect of each individual force on the pattern of production. When it is remembered that (a) a myriad of individual markets in the forms of cities and scattered towns exist in homogeneous production areas and (b) yields or production functions differ due to differences in soils even within small areas near single markets, each of these individual "models" has application in itself. The forces mentioned above may cause regional production patterns to differ in terms of either (1) the intensity of production, (2) the combination of different crop or livestock products, or (3) the combination or substitution of factors. These situations are discussed separately below.

Intensity of production and single product patterns. Regional differences in the intensity of production may be brought about by geographic differentials in factor productivity, product prices or factor prices. In this section we study these three variables as they relate to a single product. The characteristics outlined would exist if there were only a single agricultural product. However, they are partly obscured in the world of multiple products because of the switch from product to product as a means of increasing intensity between areas.

Situation I: **Regional differentials in commodity prices but homogeneity in factor prices and the production function.** If only a single agricultural product were grown, regional differentials in commodity prices would result in the production pattern illustrated in Figure 10. Here the production function (oY in Figure 10a) is identical for each producer of the 3 regions which might lie 200, 400, and 600 miles from the central market or consuming center. Since factor prices are the same, producers in each of the 3 regions will have identical marginal costs, as illustrated by Figures 10b, 10c, and 10d.[5] Yet because of the price gradient producers in each region will be faced with prices of different levels. Producers in the region 200 miles from market can profitably produce oy_3 units of product per acre. Production of only oy_2 and oy_1 units is profitable for farms in regions of 400 and 600 miles respectively from the market. The intensity with which resources are applied per acre of land or other technical unit will be greater near than distant from the market; producers at 200 miles will employ ox_3 units of factor (see Figure 10a), while those at 600 miles will employ only ox_1 units. The level of grain feeding of cows as well as the level of fertilizer application per acre may well increase with nearness to the central market.

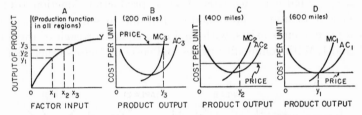

Fig. 10. Regional differentials in price and in production intensity.

While the marginal physical productivity curve of resources is the same in all of the producing areas, the value productivity of parallel resource units differs with each change in commodity price. While the first, second, and third resource inputs may give marginal outputs of 20, 15, and 10 units of product respectively in all regions, the third unit (the "parallel" unit) of factor applied per technical unit will produce a marginal value product, with prices of $1.60, $1.20, and $.80, as indicated in Figure 2, of $16 at 200 miles, $12 at 400 miles, and $8 at 600 miles. However, if all producers equate marginal cost and marginal revenue, the marginal value productivity of the last unit of resource employed in one region will be equal to the marginal value productivity of the last unit of resource employed in any other region.

The costs in Figure 10 include outlays for mobile factors only. Thus land rent is not included as a cost. Regional productivity and resource use

---

[5] It is obviously true that the techniques employed do not give the same input-output ratios for all producers even within a single area. Our interest is in areas, however, which have similar production functions, and not in differences between farmer operation in a single area.

is of greatest concern as it relates to those resources which can be transferred into alternative opportunities in other locations (or different industries in the same locations). While rent is a cost to each individual enterprise or firm (it must pay as much rent as competing units if it is to have use of the land), rent is not a cost in the sense that a specified return must be realized or the land will be withdrawn from production. (Any resource, in fact, realizes a rent in the sense that its economic reward is above that necessary to keep it employed in production.) Where regional product price differentials follow a price gradient due to transportation costs, a parallel rent gradient also exists. In Figure 2, for example, the sloping line in the bottom part of each graph could be taken, with proper adjustments of the vertical scale, to indicate the level of rent for land of the same quality situated at different distances from the market. Without the introduction of other variables, the commodity price gradient and the rent gradient would be parallel.

Situation II: **Regional differences in the production function but homogeneity in commodity and factor prices.** This situation is illustrated geometrically in Figure 11, where a different production function (different yield per acre or unit of labor and capital due to soil, climatic, or other physical phenomena) exists, with land area equal, for each of three areas —3, 2, and 1. With commodity prices and costs of factors other than land

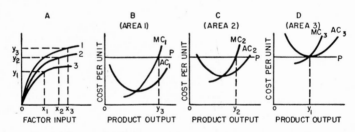

Fig. 11. Regional differences in factor productivity and intensity.

the same in the 3 areas, per-unit costs will differ because of variability in physical productivity.[6] Farms in area 3, if they are to maximize profits, will produce only oy_1 per acre, while those in areas 2 and 1 will produce oy_2 and oy_3 respectively. Different intensities are represented (Figure 11a), since ox_1, ox_2, and ox_3 units would be employed in areas 3, 2, and 1 respectively. In contrast to the previous case, greater intensity is brought about through regional variability in resource productivity than through regional differentials in prices.

[6] The price of land will not be homogeneous since the differential rent growing out of differences in productivity will be capitalized into the land value. However, in this case as in the previous one, the AC curve is taken to represent all costs excluding land costs.

Parallel resource units (the second unit of resource applied per technical unit in either region) have neither equal physical productivity nor equal value productivity. Again, however, if marginal costs and marginal revenue are to be equated for each technical unit in all regions, the value productivity of the last unit of resource employed must be the same in all regions; the value productivity of the x_1 resource unit in region 3 must be equal to the value productivity of the x_2 and the x_3 resource units in regions 2 and 1 respectively.

Situation III: **Regional differences in factor prices but homogeneity in the production function and product prices.** This situation is a modification of the 2 already presented. Here a homogeneous production function such as curve 3 in Figure 11a exists for all producing regions. However, if the price of the factor is greater with distance from market, cost will differ in the same manner as illustrated in Figures 11b, 11c, and 11d and greater intensity will be found near the market.

Situation IV: **Homogeneity of the production function but regional variations in product and factor prices.** If both factor and product prices declined with distance from the market, and if the decline were always by the same percentage of value for both (see Figure 6), the factor-product price ratio would not differ between regions, and equal degrees of intensity would be found in all producing areas irrespective of their distance from central markets. If both commodity and factor price gradients fall with distance from market but at rates representing different percentage values (see Figure 7), then greater intensity is likely to be found in areas distant from the central market. Corn as a factor and hogs as a product provide a good example here since both can originate in the same soil and climatic area. The corn/hog ratio falls in a fashion favoring conversion of corn into pork in regions distant from the market and the sale of cash grain near the market. The existence of cash grain farming in the Drummer-Flanagan soil area near Chicago while corn is converted into pork on the higher yielding Tama-Muscatine soils of Iowa is partly an expression of this set of forces. (The relative advantage of Drummer soils in producing corn also is important in explaining why this area produces cash grain while the Chicago milkshed extends far beyond into Wisconsin.) [7] The same is true of milk in its relationship to butter or cheese. Products which lose weight in the transformation process tend to be more concentrated as commodities. As products with a higher specific value, transportation rates are lower relative to their prices than for very bulky products. Packing houses tend to

---

/   [7] If the price gradient for the commodity falls while the gradient for the factor rises with distance from consuming market then the product/factor price ratio must fall with distance from market. Prices of fertilizer rise while corn price falls with westward distance in the Cornbelt. Historically, a greater use of rock phosphate in Illinois than in Iowa may be partly a reflection of gradient in fertilizer prices (as well as the nature of the soil and recommendations of agronomists).

be located in or near the hog-producing areas. Whole milk is often processed on the farm and cream, rather than whole milk, is transported to the creamery. Similarly, milk is converted into cheese in distant milk producing areas and the cheese as a product with a greater specific value is shipped to central markets. Cotton and wool weigh about as much in the raw state as when processed into yarn. Accordingly, there is a greater tendency to locate the processing of these farm commodities near centers of skilled labor and power. W. J. Spillman, one of the pioneer farm management experts in the United States, was able to show as early as the 1920's that the average marketing weight of hogs was 260 lbs. in Omaha and 200 lbs. in Chicago.[8] This early finding was, of course, consistent with the principles defining regional production and resource use patterns, since the price of corn is lower relative to the price of hogs in Omaha than in Chicago.

In very rough form, regional differentials in both factor productivity and price ratios favor a less intensive farming in the mountain and Great Plains states and a more intensive pattern with movement through the Cornbelt into eastern and southeastern producing and market areas. These "twin forces" cause an "intensity gradient" which slopes from east to west and result (1) because the product price gradient is so oriented from eastern consuming markets and (2) because rainfall and length of the growing season generally increase with movement southward and eastward over the United States. While the "productivity gradient" is roughly of this direction, there are, of course, many geographic differences at any given latitudinal location.

Combinations of products and types of farming. It is often pointed out that dairying and vegetable production are carried on near central markets because the enterprises are of the intensive type. We have seen, however, that intensity would be greater near consuming centers if only one product could be produced. It is not necessary that intensity be attained by shifts from one to another product between regions. Neither are regional differences in enterprise combinations or farming types solely an expression of intensity. In order to study the effect of various forces acting on regional patterns of product specialization, the following situations are again set out as "pure cases." They are in terms of regional patterns of *resource use* rather than in simple terms of *land use* patterns. The pattern of production in any particular area is as much or more a function of the use of labor and capital as of land use. Products can never be produced with land alone. The analysis which follows assumes enough homogeneity within individual producing regions so that the marginal rates of product substitution, at any particular ratio of products, is the same for all farms in the area, and, therefore, that substitution rates are the same for a farm

---

[8] W. J. Spillman, *The Law of Diminishing Returns.* Chicago: World, 1924, p. 52.

and the region as a whole. While this assumption passes over scale considerations and represents a sacrifice in detail, it allows a gain in simplicity of presentation.

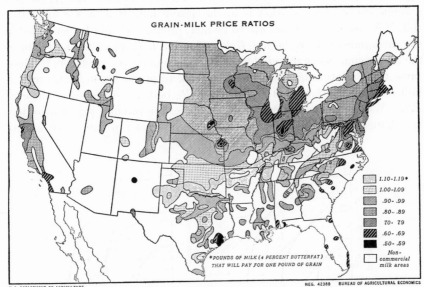

GRAIN-MILK PRICE RATIOS

▨	1.10-1.19*
▦	1.00-1.09
▨	.90- .99
▨	.80- .89
▨	70- 79
▨	.60- .69
■	.50- .59
□	Non-commercial milk areas

*POUNDS OF MILK (4 PERCENT BUTTERFAT)
THAT WILL PAY FOR ONE POUND OF GRAIN

U. S. DEPARTMENT OF AGRICULTURE   NEG. 42388   BUREAU OF AGRICULTURAL ECONOMICS

Fig. 12.

Situation V: **Homogeneity in production opportunities and regional variations in product prices.** Homogeneity in production opportunities specifies that, although the size of the different producing areas may vary, the marginal rate of substitution is the same for competing products.[9] In other words, soil, climatic, and other physical conditions must be homogeneous between areas in terms of the production function or yield possibilities for single crops or livestock enterprises. Regional variation in prices can again take the 2 forms where (a) the ratio of prices does not vary with distance from market and (b) the ratio does change with distance.

Figure 13 can be used to illustrate the case where regional price variations exist but the ratio between prices does not differ between producing areas (the price pattern of Figure 6). Here the production possibility curve P_1 exists for an area close to the market such as that along price contour P_1 in Figure 6; the expanse of the area is small. The production possibility curve P_5 is for a larger area distant from the market, such as that along price contour P_5 in Figure 6. The marginal rates of substitution of Y_2 and Y_1 are the same for both areas. (Curves P_1 and P_5 in Figure 13

---

[9] Resource or product discontinuities are unimportant in aggregate analyses. The indivisibility of a tractor in the total of Cornbelt production is no more important than the indivisibility of fertilizer units on a single farm.

have identical slopes and the latter represents greater resources than the former.) The total production possibilities available to the consuming economy is thus illustrated by curve T which is a summation of P_1 and P_5 in Figure 13. Given the preferences of the consuming economy, the iso-revenue curve of the market is of the nature indicated by CI indicating that if choice of consumers are to be met, products should be combined in the ratio indicated by the line E_0R_0. The line E_0R_0 can then be taken as the iso-revenue curve reflected to individual competitive producers.[10] These same price relationships are reflected back to producers in both areas as indicated by the fact that E_1R_1 and E_5R_5 both have the same slope as E_0R_0. While prices are lower with distance, the product price ratio does not change. Under this price ratio pattern, types of farming or patterns of

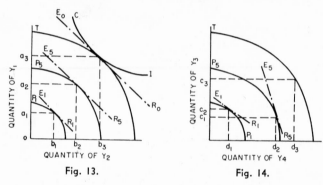

Fig. 13.   Fig. 14.

Regional price patterns and inter-product allocation of resources.

production will not differ between producing regions. Region P_1 will produce oa_1 of Y_1 and ob_1 of Y_2. (This combination of products will maximize returns to each individual farmer if the slope of his opportunity curve is the same as the slope of P_1.) While this is less total commodity than is produced in area P_5, products are forthcoming in the same proportions as in P_5 where combinations include oa_2 of Y_1 and ob_2 of Y_2. The capital-labor intensity of farming should, assuming diminishing returns and because of greater distance from the market, be less in the area represented by P_5 than in that represented by P_1. The allocation of resources between

---

[10] We might suppose, for purposes of simplicity that areas P_1 and P_5 are the only producing regions, or we might suppose that, considering all other producing regions, the relative consumer values at the market for the product from all regions including P_1 and P_5 can be represented by CI. The slope of the industry iso-revenue curve is thus related equally to the product of regions P_1 and P_2 as to the product of other producing regions. While we have shown a convex iso-revenue curve for the market, it may also be concave for products with inelastic demand curves. The linear revenue lines in Figures 13, 14, 15, and 16 are used to reflect the price ratios which might exist at equilibrium while iso-lines of similar shape and slope face all individual producers. The revenue curve of any one region will be non-linear if the producing area is large enough to affect market prices.

competing products will not differ, however. Small grains such as oats and barley partially represent an example of this type. They maintain a near-constant price ratio with distance from market. Hence soils, climate, and other physical factors which affect the slope of the opportunity curve are more important than price ratios in determining the degree of specialization in crops such as these.

Figure 14 illustrates differences in patterns of production when price ratios do change with distance from market (as shown in Figure 7). Here again, P_1 and P_5 represent production possibilities for regions near and distant from the market. The consuming economy prefers a total product including oc_3 of Y_3 and od_3 of Y_4. Because of differences in relative transportation costs for products Y_3 and Y_4, these preferences are reflected to individual producers in region P_1 through a price ratio represented by the slope of revenue line E_1R_1. The price ratio to each producer in region P_5 is represented by an iso-revenue curve with the slope of E_5R_5. Given identical production possibilities for individual farmers as well as for areas, different patterns of farming will exist in areas P_1 and P_5 because of differences in price ratios. Area P_1 will tend to specialize in Y_3 (e.g., will produce oc_2 of Y_3 and only od_1 of Y_4), while area P_5 will tend to specialize in Y_4 (will produce od_2 of Y_4 and only oc_1 of Y_3).

This situation typifies a great amount of agricultural production. Product Y_3 may represent corn while Y_4 represents pork. Price pressure is thus on cash grain sales near the market and on conversion of corn into pork in more distant areas. Similarly, Y_3 may represent milk, vegetables, or other bulky commodities with high transportation costs relative to their value while Y_4 represents meat animals, cotton, or tobacco. Because of differences in price ratios, specialization will be in the bulky products near the market and in the more concentrated products in distant areas. Even though soils are the same, gradients in price ratios may cause the optimum rotation to differ with distance from markets. Pricewise, the more distant areas are best adapted to grain production while areas near markets are better adapted to hay production for cash sale. Very remote regions are adapted to pasture production and livestock sales. Cotton, which has been an intensive labor crop, would undoubtedly have been found largely in distant areas had the important variable been space and price differentials rather than differences in soil, climate, and labor costs.

Situation VI: **Homogeneous commodity price ratios but variability in production possibilities.** Soils and climate may vary between areas which are equi-distant from the market and thus give rise to different types of farming even though the areas are on the same price contours. This situation can again be illustrated by reference to Figure 7. The shaded portion at the lower left-hand corner can be taken to represent one soil type or climatic area; the unshaded portion to represent a soil or climatic region where land, labor, and capital have an entirely different productivity. Thus the region along the price contour P_3 and within the shaded area of Figure 7 has a production possibility curve of the nature indicated as P_{3a} in Figure 15. The region represented along contour P_3 but outside the shaded area in Figure 7 has the production possibility curve represented as P_{3b} in Figure 15. The soil and climate cause the marginal rate of substitution of Y_3 for Y_4 to be higher in region P_{3b} than in region P_{3a}. Thus, with consumer preference reflecting a total product choice of *oa* of Y_3 and *ob* of Y_4 (as represented by the aggregate production possibility curve T), price ratios are the same for farmers in regions P_{3a} and P_{3b}. (Both are on the same price contour in Figure 7 and have the same slope as indicated by iso-revenue lines $E'_3R'_3$ and $E''_3R''_3$.) However, area P_{3a} will produce only Y_3 (the iso-revenue line intersects the Y_3 axis before it becomes tangent with the opportunity curve), while area P_{3b} will produce only Y_4. Differences in resource productivity and production possibilities in the 2 regions cause different production patterns or farming types.

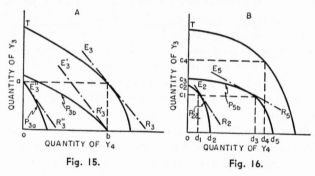

Fig. 15. Fig. 16.

Regional differentials in production possibilities and product specialization.

Types of farming will differ even within the soil or climatic portion represented by the shaded portion of Figure 7. The pattern of resource allocation will change between price contours P_2 and P_4 in the manner set out under Situation I and similar differences also will exist in the unshaded area. If Figure 7 were to be presented as a geographic picture showing different farming types by use of different colors, it would appear as a brightly colored map with different hues in both the shaded and unshaded regions.

Individuals sometimes question why milk, a bulky and labor-intensive product, is shipped from Wisconsin to Chicago and Tennessee when nearby regions in Illinois produce cash corn as an "extensive crop" and Tennessee produces cotton, a crop with lower transportation costs relative to its specific value. The answer is to be found largely in the nature of physical production possibilities and can be illustrated in Figure 16. Opportunity curve P_{2a} may be taken to represent production possibilities in the Drummer-Flanagan soil area of Illinois. Product Y_3 represents corn and Y_4 represents milk. (P_{2a} can be looked upon as falling on price contour P_2 inside the shaded area of Figure 7.) Opportunity curve P_{5b} may be taken to represent a milk producing area in Wisconsin and other Lake states (and falls outside the shaded area on price contour P_5 in Figure 7). The price of Y_4 (milk) is higher relative to the price of Y_3 (corn) for region P_{2a}, which is near the market, than for region P_{5b}, which is far from the market. Yet area P_{2a} will produce mainly Y_3 (corn) while area P_{5b} will produce mainly Y_4 (milk). This pattern of production comes about because the marginal rate of substitution of Y_3 and Y_4 is high in much of area P_{2a} as compared to area P_{5b}. These differences fairly well typify production patterns found in much of Illinois as compared to Wisconsin.

Many other production opportunity-price relationship situations are possible. An added possibility of interest is this: a region outside the shaded area on price line P_1 may possess a production opportunity curve with high rates of substitution of Y_4 for Y_3. A region inside the shaded area on price line P_4 may possess an opportunity curve where the rate of substitution of Y_4 for Y_3 is low. Both regions may produce similar patterns of commodities, however, because the price and substitution relationships offset each other. The relationships outlined above also explain why the factor combinations used in producing given amounts of particular products may vary between regions. Land prices in regions near consuming markets are of a nature to bring about a substitution of labor and capital for land in its spatial aspect. Even where homogeneity exists in soils and in the price for factors other than land, the commodity price gradient causes more intensive production per acre to be profitable near the market. Thus a given product (100 bushels of grain or 100 pounds of livestock product) embodies relatively more capital and labor services and relatively fewer services of land in regions near the market than in regions distant from the market. If acres per farm can be varied, then the price of land as a factor may also cause smaller producing units, in terms of acreage, to exist near the market.[11]

Comparative Advantage

No discussion of production location would be complete without some reference to comparative advantage. Use of this term is made with reser-

---

[11] While the higher prices for land as a factor of production should lead to fewer acres per farm near the market, the greater price for the product should lead to more acres per farm in the same proximity. The final effect will depend on whether the product price, the factor price, or the production function effect is greatest. (Conceivably, 2 forces might cancel each other and cause farms to include the same number of acres in regions of varying distance from the market.) Black has assembled data which show a high correlation of density of population and acres per farm. See J. D. Black, *et al., Farm Management.* New York: Macmillan, 1947, Ch. 19.

vation, however. Many elementary discussions of comparative advantage provide mistaken inferences about production possibilities. Treatment of comparative advantage at the elementary level often is in such terms as follows: *First, each of 2 regions may have an absolute advantage in production of a single commodity.* Region P can produce 100 bushels of corn or 80 bushels of wheat with a composite unit of resources (made up of capital, labor, and land), while region R can produce 80 bushels of corn or 100 bushels of wheat with the same resources. If 2 resource units are available in each region and 1 of each is used for corn and wheat, the total product forthcoming from the 2 regions will include 180 bushels of wheat and 180 bushels of corn. If the 2 regions specialize, with region P producing wheat and region R producing corn, the total product forthcoming will include 200 bushels of wheat and 200 bushels of corn, and a greater product is available for distribution. *Second, both regions may have a comparative advantage in 1 of 2 products, while one region has an absolute advantage in both.* Region M can produce 100 units of pork or 80 units of milk with a composite unit of resource. Region N can produce 50 units of pork or 72 units of milk. Thus, while region N has an absolute *disadvantage* in both products, it has a *comparative advantage* in the production of milk. Its ratio of disadvantage is least here; N can produce only .5 as much pork as M but can produce .9 as much milk with 1 unit of resource. While M has an absolute advantage in both products, it has a comparative advantage in pork because it is here that resource productivity is greatest. The gains in physical product forthcoming under specialization can be illustrated when 3 resource units are available in each region. If 1½ resource units are used for both milk and pork in the 2 regions, the total product forthcoming will include 225 units of pork and 228 units of milk. However, if the 2 regions specialize, with M producing pork where it has a comparative advantage and N producing milk where it has a comparative advantage (still with 3 resource units available in each region), the total product from the 2 regions will include 300 units of pork and 216 units of milk.

The limitations of the comparative advantage principle so defined are these: (1) The principle stated in this manner supposes that resources cannot be transferred. While this is largely true between nations, it is by nowhere near the situation within a nation. Extreme emphasis on the principle of comparative advantage in the classical sense tends to obscure the possibility of resource mobility and hence the gain in product forthcoming as factors are rearranged between regions. (2) The statement of the principle of comparative advantage in the manner outlined above supposes that the marginal rate of substitution between products within a region is constant. The notion of absolute advantage as stated above assumes linear production opportunity curves of the nature indicated in Figure 17A. Here, the marginal rate of substitution of wheat for corn is greater throughout for region P than for region R. Conversely, the marginal rate of substitution of corn for wheat is greatest in region R. The comparative advantage notion supposes regional production possibility curves of the nature outlined in Figure 17B. While region M can produce more of either product with a given outlay of resources (both production possibility curves M and N assume the same quantity of resources), the marginal rate of substitution of milk for pork is greater in region M than in region N. (The slope of the production possibility curve towards the milk axis is greater for region M than for region N.) Pork substitutes for milk at a greater rate throughout in region N.

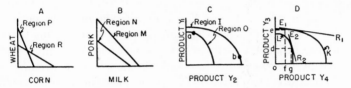

Fig. 17. Assumptions of classical comparative advantage principle.

The implications of the assumption of linear production possibility curves are obvious. First, it supposes that each region should produce a single product. Second, it is unrealistic, because most areas, however small, have increasing rates of product substitution (production possibility curves concave to the origin). Furthermore, the principle so stated completely overlooks the possibility of complementary and supplementary enterprises in agriculture. The statement that "Iowa has a comparative advantage in corn production" is somewhat elliptical. The statement implies that the state should produce a single product. Although a greater portion of the capital, labor, and land is devoted to corn production than any other single product, Iowa also has, over a specified range, a comparative advantage in hay and other crops. Hay has an "unqualified advantage" over the range where it serves in a complementary role to grain. Although the Cornbelt proper produces more pork than eggs or butterfat, it also has a "comparative advantage" in the latter products within the range where they serve as supplementary enterprises in the use of resources.[12]

The term "comparative advantage" has meaning only as it is related to a choice indicator and the marginal rate of product substitution. Rates of substitution are crucial even when consideration of the so-called "comparative advantage" relationships is in physical terms. Figure 17C can be

---

[12] Examples of complementary and supplementary enterprises were not included in figures such as 13 and 14 for reasons of simplicity. The reader may readily integrate models including complementarity or supplementarity relationships from Chapter 7 with those of this Chapter. Obviously, an area should produce no less of a complementary enterprise than that which allows a maximization output of the auxiliary product. This statement applies irrespective of price relationships.

used as an illustration. Classical examples would cite region I as having a comparative advantage in product Y_2 while region O has a comparative advantage in Y_1; the *average* rate of substitution of Y_2 for Y_1 over all resource units is greatest for region I. Yet, when reference is to marginal substitution rates at particular points on the possibility curve, it is obvious that region O, like region I, has a "comparative advantage" in product Y_2; the absolute gain in Y_2 for each unit of Y_1 sacrificed is greater at point a in region O than at point b in region I.

If price and substitution relationships are compared together, a region may specialize in 1 product, even though its "comparative advantage," in the classical sense, is low. This point can be illustrated with Figure 17D. The substitution rate of Y_3 for Y_4, as an average over the entire possibility curve, is higher for region K than for region L, indicating that region K can produce product Y_4 with relative advantage. Yet region K should, as indicated by tangency of the iso-revenue lines and the production possibility curves, produce mostly Y_3, while region L should produce mostly Y_4. This pattern of specialization is specified because price ratios more than offset substitution ratios.[13] Product Y_3 may be milk while Y_4 is beef, and region K is near to consuming centers while region L is distant. Both regions have a range of economic advantage in either product and if resource units are allocated properly, resources have equal marginal value productivity in both regions.

Other forces affecting regional production patterns. Other forces are sometimes cited as affecting regional production patterns. One of these is nationality. A common suggestion is that, since Scandinavians settled in northeastern Iowa and Minnesota, dairy production should be concentrated in these areas where the dairying skills of the people were developed in their homelands. This notion of nationality, as a direct cause-effect

---

[13] The "law of first choice" is equally nebulous. This term, like that of "comparative advantage," has been used with numerous meanings. One notion of the "law" is this: an area will give first choice to the product for which it has the greatest "comparative advantage." Since "comparative advantage" has economic content only in terms of substitution rates and choice indicators, the same must hold true for "first choice." Renne, borrowing from Black, suggests that "The principle of first choice states that any occupation for which only a limited number of persons are qualified, in proportion to the need for it, will be first choice of these persons. The same principle can be stated in terms of regions and locations." Again, however, this notion has meaning only as it relates to substitution rates and price ratios. A "limited area" may be able to produce 2 commodities, W and V, but the substitution ratio $\Delta W/\Delta V$ may be low over all resource units. If many other areas can produce W while the area adaptable to V is limited, in the sense of substitution ratios, our given area may produce the latter if the V/W price ratio is high. On the other hand if the marginal rate of substitution of V for W is sufficiently low, the "limited area" may still produce commodity W. The degree to which an area is "limited" for a single product can be indicated only in terms of price ratios and substitution ratios.

See R. R. Renne, *Land Economics*. New York: Harper, 1947, p. 169; J. D. Black, *Production Economics*. New York: Holt, 1926, p. 147.

association, may or may not have basis. The initial skills of Scandinavians as dairymen (or their lack of skills as hog or beef producers) perhaps caused the marginal rate of substitution of milk for other products to be higher for them than for settlers of other nationalities. More directly, it is likely that peoples who place a high value on one particular type of production, or have particular skills for a product, may migrate to areas where that particular commodity has a high rate of substitution for other products. It is also sometimes suggested that patterns of production are affected by the presence of processing facilities. Dairy products again are cited in showing that milk production is concentrated in areas where cheese factories and creameries are located. Mainly, however, the processing facilities are on hand in a particular dairy region because the advantage of milk production is great relative to other products in the area. Once creameries and cheese factories have been established, however, fixed costs are associated with their operation and an advantage exists until the plants become depreciated to allow long-run decisions of replacement.

Short- and Long-Run Regional Opportunities

Discussion to this point has been in terms of long-run regional production possibilities. The nature of adjustments in farming systems now needs to be examined when short-run production possibilities are considered. Once a pattern of commodity specialization has been established in a particular region, the short-run adjustment to changes in price relationships is likely to be much less extreme than adjustments which come about in the long run. This statement can be illustrated by means of Figure 18. The production possibility curve LM represents the long-run opportunities which face a particular producing region. The curve SN denotes the short-run production possibility curve consistent with point P on the long-run curve. Given an initial Y_1/Y_2 price relationship for individual producers indicated by revenue line E_1R_1, the corresponding production pattern will include oa_1 of commodity Y_1 and ob_4 of Y_2 if producers in the region maxi-

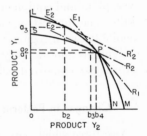

Fig. 18. Short- and long-run regional adjustments.

mize returns in terms of either long-run or short-run production opportunities. If market forces cause the price of Y_1 to rise relative to the price of Y_2 (or conversely, the price of Y_2 to fall relative to Y_1) as indicated by the individual firm's iso-revenue line E_2R_2, the immediate effect will be an adjustment of the pattern of resource allocation (with resources still constant) to include only ob_3 of Y_2 but oa_2 of Y_1. This small adjustment takes place because it is the short-run production possibilities that are of immediate relevance (adjustment from point P along curve SN). In the long run, however, output of Y_1 may increase still further to oa_3 while production of Y_2 should drop to ob_2. The greater adjustment would be expected as buildings and machines adapted particularly to Y_2 are worn out and opportunity exists for investment of the same funds in resources adapted to Y_1. It is also possible that the skills of labor used in producing Y_1 increase to a greater extent in the long run. Short-run adjustments will scarcely ever be as great as long-run changes in regional specialization growing out of price or other changes. The ability to change is greatest for crops which employ the same or similar equipment (such as soybeans and corn or the several small grains). Greater differences exist in livestock, orchards, or specialized crop production where resources employed are highly adapted to the product and are transformed only over long periods of time.

Short-run resource supply and factor mobility. The pattern of regional production at any one point in time is a function not of long-run production possibilities and current prices, but is largely determined by short-run production possibilities based on farmer decisions of the past and current prices or expectations of price relationships. Hence regional adaptation in resource use is not made simultaneously as techniques, competing regions, or product demand changes come about. In most instances, the pattern of production and resource use in a particular area is a function of the short-run supply function of resources. As brought out in a later chapter, the short-run supply function for agricultural resources is highly inelastic. Accordingly, the allocation of resources and the intensity of production changes only gradually over time. In several decades, however, plant and equipment wears out and new generations can acquire new skills. The interest of society is that labor, capital, and management be mobile between regions; one goal in production is, if work preferences of individuals and mobility costs are considered, that resources migrate until returns are equalized between regions.

Changes in Patterns of Production and Interregional Competition

Any force which causes changes in the price relationships reflected to a region or the nature of production possibilities in a region can change the pattern of production. Changes in price relationships in any one producing area are brought about by forces affecting the demand for and the supply of particular commodities including (a) changes in relative consumer demand for 2 or more commodities, (b) changes in processing costs or transportation rates with a relatively greater impact on 1 product, (c) the opening up of new competing producing regions, (d) changes in techniques at a greater rate in one area than in another, and (e) monopolistic manipulation of the market supply or demand forces. Wheat retreated from the New England States and partly from the Cornbelt as Great Plains producing areas opened up and new techniques were developed, and as consumer demand for cereal crops fell relative to other food products. In addition, improved techniques in Cornbelt corn and oats producing methods have outpaced improvements in wheat with the effect that the marginal rate of substitution of wheat for corn and oats has fallen. Barley has largely disappeared from the Cornbelt because of rapid strides in the technology of oat growing. Historically, the competitive advantage of corn has undoubtedly increased in the Cornbelt as compared to hay as Land Grant Colleges concentrated greater resources on improving the techniques of corn growing. Absence of the boll weevil and the development of varieties adapted to Texas and similar regions has caused the boundaries of cotton production to shift from the Old South to the western Cottonbelt. Mechanization of cotton production may bring about far-reaching changes in cotton specialization. Current developments in winter legumes and possibilities of harnessing the sunshine, year-around warm temperature, and rain of the southeastern states may increase the advantage of beef and dairy production in these areas relative to the Cornbelt. Farmers of the Cornbelt have been keeping a weather eye on this development as well as on the possibilities of greater grain-fed beef and pork production from grain sorgums in the Great Plains and greater quantities of grass-fat beef from the range areas. Conversely, many fringe areas of the Great Plains have dropped corn production because of summer fallow wheat techniques; ranchers of nearby areas fear competition in beef growing in the Cornbelt should conservation programs be extended sufficiently. In any case the pattern of production in one area is linked to that of other areas through the structure of market prices.

Interregional resource adaptations. From the standpoint of overall efficiency in use of resources, adaptations between regions should be made as rapidly as possible when changes in the productivity, supply, or demand cause the value return on labor and capital to be altered. Since labor and capital are the resources which possess mobility characteristics, flexibility and mobility should be built into the structure of production if the nation is to realize the most efficient use of resources employed in agriculture. Resources should not only be transferred between products at one particular point but, also, adaptations should be made between regions in a manner to increase or decrease the amount of labor and capital employed in particular regions. These problems are given detailed attention in later chapters on aggregate efficiency. An important problem worthy of attention by agricultural production economists is to be found in the apparent geographic and regional pattern of low farm incomes and underemployment of resources.[14]

---

[14] For a framing of this problem, see T. W. Schultz, "Reflection of Poverty Within Agriculture," *Jour. Pol. Econ.*, Vol. 58.

Effect of Government Programs on Regional Specialization and Production Possibilities

Tariff and related legislation heads the list of governmental programs and policies which affect regional patterns of production and resource use. As mentioned previously, existing tariff duties have perhaps had greatest effect in changing price relationships to favor beet and wool production in many localized areas of United States agriculture. Removal of these duties would bring about important patterns of resource allocation in the favored regions. Recent developments in the mechanization of beet growing, however, may have altered the production possibility curve in a manner to allow retention of some beet acreage in many areas where it would not exist without tariff protection. Sanitary milk regulations which are designed as "protective devices" for restricted market areas have similar effects as they are put into effect or removed. Other more recent forms of governmental programs have similar effects in altering regional production patterns. Included are such programs as production control, soil conservation, and storage and loan programs.

Acreage allotments and production control. Numerous forms of production control programs have been tried in the United States and other nations. The chief method in the United States was that tried for a large range of crops in the 1930's and put into effect again for the production year 1950. Control on acreage has been in effect continuously for tobacco. Acreage allotments have been tied in with marketing quotas for some crops: the farmer is required to reduce acreage of the crop and is given a marketing quota which establishes an upper limit on the amount which he can market in any one year. Of more widespread use has been the acreage allotment or quota system where farmers are required to reduce acreage of the particular crop but are free to market any quantity of product which is yielded from the reduced acreage. In the case of either market quotas or acreage allotments, the land withdrawn from the controlled crop can be used for crops which are not under control. Under the agricultural program of 1950, Cornbelt farmers were asked to reduce corn acreage. The land so released could in turn be planted to hay crops or oats and soybeans. Farmers in cotton producing areas were requested to reduce cotton acreage but were allowed to divert the released land to corn as a noncontrol crop. Similar "offsetting" control programs were put into effect in other areas.

As a result of control programs, tobacco acreage and production generally has moved into those fringe areas where the soil and climate is less advantageous to tobacco as compared to other crops. Under the controls of the 1930's, some wheat acreage was squeezed out of the soft red winter and hard spring and winter wheat areas to fringe wheat producing areas. Controls such as those included in the 1950 Act use a historic base in establishing acreage allotments and change production opportunities in a manner which can be illustrated with Figure 19. As in the case of corn and hay (corn was a control crop in the Cornbelt but a replacement crop in the Cottonbelt) each of 2 regions (I and II) can produce commodities Y_1 and Y_2. In area I production opportunities are greatest in the direction of Y_1; substitution rates of Y_2 for Y_1 are, on the whole, greatest in region II. Now with control of Y_1 acreage and production in area I and Y_2 acreage and production in area II, changes in regional production opportunities are brought about when the original opportunity curve is I_1C_1 in region I and I_2C_2 in region II. While these curves may be considered short-run opportunities, they indicate production possibilities when all existing forms of resources can be shifted back and forth between Y_1 and Y_2; land as well as labor and capital in its many specialized forms can be shifted. Previous

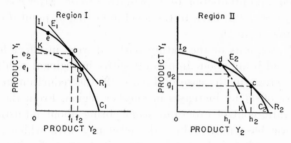

Fig. 19. Control programs and regional production adjustments.

to acreage control area I produced oe_2 of Y_1 and of_1 of Y_2 (point a), while region II produced og_1 of Y_1 and oh_2 of Y_2 (point c). Under the acreage control program region I is requested to reduce the land which is planted to crop Y_1; crop Y_2 can be planted on the released land. Since marketing quotas are not in effect, more labor and capital, but less land, can be allocated to Y_1. Thus the opportunity curve now becomes KC_1. Up to point b the opportunity curve is the same as before acreage control. While point b marks the maximum land acreage that can now be planted to Y_1, output of Y_1 can be extended beyond that indicated at b by shifting more labor and fertilizer or other capital to Y_2. Thus the new opportunity curve KC_1 suggests a lower rate of substitution of Y_2 for Y_1 above the point indicated as b. Under the modified production possibility curve in region I, output of Y_1 may drop only to oe_1 of Y_1 while output of Y_2 increases to of_2. Output of Y_1 need not drop to the extent suggested by point b since the region can shift labor and capital to this product even if acreage is limited. The price relationship reflected to each producer in the region is indicated by iso-revenue line E_1R_1 for area I and E_2R_2 for area II and we suppose similar substitution rates for each farm in the area. The original outputs oe_2 of Y_1 and of_1 of Y_2 are defined by tangency of the original production possibility curve and revenue line E_1R_1 for each farm, and hence for the region as a whole. While the tangency condition has not been shown for the modified possibility curve, it would occur at oe_1 of Y_1 and of_2 of Y_2. If the "control" program increases the Y_1/Y_2 price ratio, the new product combination will include more than oe_1 of Y_1 in region I. (Point b illustrates the output combination which might be attained by rigid and effective marketing quotas.)

The situation is similar in region II. Here Y_1 and Y_2 are originally produced in the quantities suggested by point c. As acreage restriction is put into effect, the transformation curve is altered from I_2C_2 to KI_2: down to point d, land, labor, and capital can be shifted freely between Y_1 and Y_2. After the control program, only labor and capital can be shifted to increase output of Y_2 beyond that indicated by d. Whereas og_1 of Y_1 and oh_2 of Y_2 would be produced before control, output of Y_1 will increase to og_2 and production of Y_2 will drop to oh_1 after control. (Again output of Y_2 would fall back to the level indicated at point d under effective marketing quotas.)

If control programs of the nature outlined were in effect long enough they might well bring about important shifts in regional production patterns. However, as in the case of Figure 19, the reduction in one region can be partly offset by increases in another region. From the standpoint of total welfare, control programs which bring about adjustments on a purely historic base may reduce the efficiency with which agricultural resources are employed. In the example cited, resources in area I were used most effectively when Y_1 was produced in amounts consistent with the appropriate choice indicator and the original production possibilities.

Adjustment programs can be devised which do increase efficiency. Rather than adjust acreage along a historic base, programs of this nature would be made to fit the conditions of particular soils and climatic conditions. For example, if farmers in region I have been producing at point e (Figure 19), a product combination which is not consistent with consumer choices and price relationships, incentives might be put into effect which would result in a shift to point a. Here output of Y_2 would be increased rather than decreased and if efficiency is measured in criteria which reflect the wants and values of the consuming economy, this change represents an improvement in use of resources. Of course it runs counter to the main objectives of production control programs: the historical control objective has been to reduce output in order that, on a basis of inelastic demand functions, monopoly production policy might increase farm income.

Means other than production control are available for transferring income from non-agricultural segments of society to farmers if the nation deems this redistribution desirable. Furthermore, many of these methods are more nearly consistent with the criteria of welfare economics: it is unlikely that each dollar transferred to a single farmer through production control adds more to his utility than is sacrificed in welfare by the particular consumer who pays the dollar in the form of higher food prices.

Commodity loans and price controls. Commodity loans of the nature in effect since production controls were initiated in the United States may also alter regional production patterns. Initially, corn loan rates were made uniform over wide regions. The expected outcome for a loan structure of this nature is obvious. Suppose that the original regional price pattern for two products is of the nature indicated in Figure 7. Because of differences in relative transportation rates and hence in price ratios, emphasis is on conversion of corn (Y_3) into pork (Y_4) at distant points and on cash grain sales at points near the market. Now if a loan rate of $1 is put into effect over all entire regions, this rate becomes the market price for corn (Y_3). With the price of pork (Y_4) remaining as indicated at the various regional points, the product/factor price gradient is now reversed: instead of a ratio which widens with distance, the ratio will now more nearly favor conversion of corn into pork in regions near the market and sale of cash grain in distant regions.

In more recent years, loan rate differentials have been established to more nearly conform with regional price differentials. However, retention of loan rates above market prices for feed grains has, over various periods of the 1930's and 1940's, had differential effects on farm income in different areas. On the one hand, the direct effect has been that of increasing the income of farmers in cash grain or surplus feed producing areas such as central Illinois and Iowa; on the other, the higher feed costs have the indirect effect of lowering the relative income of dairy farmers or other livestock producers in regions where grain is imported as feed. Finally, the high loan rates tend to retain surplus resources in the grain producing areas and dampen the use of more resources in livestock areas.

Ceiling and floor prices in effect on agricultural commodities during periods of national emergency similarly may affect patterns of production. If these mechanisms are to be used to guide the production of each region, they should be consistent with the production possibilities of each region as well as with transportation costs and the need of the nation for particular products.

Interregional Transfer of Soil Fertility

Many agriculturists put forth the notion that each producing region should be an importer rather than an exporter (or "self sufficient" in use) of soil fertility elements. Some scientists have gone so far as to compute "soil balance sheets" wherein the amount of each element removed by a crop is compared with the inputs from fertilizer, manure, hay, and other sources. Others frown upon farming systems which allow grain exports from an area. If these "suggestions" were carried out in the extreme, production patterns in different producing regions would be altered materially. Dairy and poultry regions such as those of the New England or Lake states would necessarily reduce output, and milk sheds would be extended over more distant areas where price and production relationships are not now so favorable. While "self contained" adjustments of this nature may be desirable for attainment of economic levels of conservation, much of the nation's cash grain sales comes from the level soils of the central Cornbelt or the Great Plains, where permanent deterioration of the soil is not threatened. Corn or other grain represents joint products: as a feed it can be transformed into milk or eggs; in the form of manure it provides nitrogen, phosphate, and potash which can be transformed into primary crops. As long as production opportunities in 2 regions cause the productivity of labor and capital to be greatest when devoted to cash grain in one area and when devoted to milk and manure-produced crops in another, the welfare of society will be increased as interregional transfer of soil elements takes place. Historically, gains in levels of living for the world community have occurred as the productivity of soils in nations such as Denmark have been maintained and even increased through grain importations.

Factor Mobility

This chapter has been concerned with regional patterns of production and resource use. One of the great problems in the structure of American agriculture is the allocation of resources between regions. While some factors are highly mobile, others fail to flow to geographic locations where their returns are greatest. Each major change in factor or product price ratios or in the production possibilities of particular regions should call for a redistribution of resources between locations. While the reader may feel that the current chapter has treated location in the vein of "isolated states," we save the problems of interregional resource allocation for Chapters 24 and 25.

Selected References

Baker, O. E., and Genung, A. B., *A Graphic Survey of Farm Crops.* U.S.D.A. Misc. Publ. 267.

Black, J. D., *et al., Farm Management.* New York: Macmillan, 1947, Ch. 16.

Elliot, F. F., *Types of Farming in the United States.* 1930 Census Monograph.

Haberler, G., *The Theory of International Trade.* New York: Macmillan, 1936, Chs. 1-7.

Heady, Earl O., "Resource and Revenue Relationships in Agricultural Production Control Programs," *Rev. Econ. and Stat.,* Aug., 1951.

Holmes, C. E., *Types of Farming in Iowa.* Iowa Agr. Exp. Sta. Bul. 256.

Hoover, E. M., *Location of Economic Activity.* New York: McGraw-Hill, 1948.

Johnson, S. E., "Interregional Competition and Comparative Advantage, *Jour. Farm. Econ.,* Vol. 19.

Kellogg, C. E., *The Soils That Support Us*. New York: Macmillan, 1941. Chs. 6, 7, 8, 9, 10.

Mighell, R. L., and Black, J. D., *Interregional Competition in Agriculture*. Cambridge: Harvard University Press, 1951.

Mosak, J., *International Trade and General Equilibrium*. Bloomington: Principia Press, 1944, Chs. 4, 5.

23

Aggregate Production and Product
Supply Functions

Questions of the aggregate production and supply functions in agriculture are of concern to all individuals, whether or not they are directly engaged in agriculture. Supply functions, of course, are of particular concern to persons engaged in agriculture either as operating farmers or as persons relaying advice to serve as the basis for decisions by farmers, to production economists who are engaged in analysis of production phenomena and to national administrators of farm programs. They are also important from the standpoint of efficiency analysis. The nature of the supply and mass production function in agriculture does not represent a unique set of phenomena but simply an extension of those relationships discussed previously under the heading of technical units and farms. The person who has specialized knowledge of the production function for producing units and the reactions of farms as business firms also is equipped to handle questions of aggregate food supplies in agriculture. The explanation of the national food and fiber supply is to be found in the technical production function of agriculture, the structure of factor and product prices, and the price response of individual farmers.

Static Supply Concepts

In a producing environment of perfect knowledge, the supply curve of the farm which serves as a pure firm would be identical with its marginal cost curve. The industry supply curve would then be the sum or aggregate of the marginal cost curves for all individual farms. In practice the farm's marginal cost does not represent its "exact supply curve" because of the uncertainty and household considerations outlined earlier. The output which farmers produce at a particular time is not a function of the price at this moment but of an amount which was determined in an earlier decision-making process when an attempt was made to predict future prices. The output of any 1 period in agriculture results as some farmers decrease output and as others increase output. Finally, the production of crops in a single year is highly dependent on the vagaries of the weather.

Notwithstanding all of these complexities, the industry supply function is necessarily the sum of the supplies of the many individual firms in agriculture. Our use of supply concepts below will suppose that the reader can readily incorporate any qualifications which need to be made because the historic output curve in agriculture is not identical with the farmer's "expectation-to-produce curve."

Short- and long-run supply functions for individual products. Distinction between short-run and long-run cost curves was made in an earlier chapter. Although time was involved, the distinction was based upon the fixity of resources rather than on time *per se*. Although there is a very great number of "lengths of run" (time periods) for which costs can be considered, some interesting distinctions can be made from the standpoint of supply. The hog farmer has a short-run marginal cost and supply curve or function once pigs have been farrowed and weaned. If he has 120 pigs from 20 sows, he can produce varying amounts of pork simply by varying the amount of feed fed and the marketing weight of the 120 pigs. The same is true for the hog industry; after the spring litters have been farrowed, total pork output can be varied as farmers carry a given number of pigs to different weights. The short-run marginal cost or supply function for the spring pig crop on an individual farm will then have the general appearance of the curve *s* in Figure 1. Because of the nature of physical returns under the short-run feed-pork production function, the curve of marginal costs for pork forthcoming from a fixed number of pigs on a single farm will have an "upward curvature" of the nature indicated. Over a longer "time" period the farmer can vary the number of sows farrowed, and additional pork can be produced at lower costs because it comes from additional pigs rather than from carrying a given number of pigs to heavier weights. If pig numbers are varied while hog equipment is held constant, diminishing productivity of feed and labor may still be encountered and the farm's

Fig. I. Short- and long-run cost and supply functions.

marginal cost or supply curve may be of an intermediate nature such as curve *m* in Figure 1. Over a longer "time" period, hog equipment as well as hog numbers may be varied and the farm's marginal cost and supply function, with modifications for uncertainty, takes the form of the long-run curve *l*. With constant returns to scale, *l* would become horizontal. However, alternative use of resources for feed and labor would always cause the long-run supply curve for a single product in agriculture to have a slope greater than zero.

Similarly, short-run and long-run supply curves will exist for the total hog industry. The slope of the supply curve will be relatively great within a year; additional pork output must be forthcoming from a given number of pigs farrowed in the spring and fall. Between 2 years, however, the curve will have less slope, because added pork output can be brought forth through greater hog numbers. Over an even longer period, the aggregate supply function may become even "flatter" as more farmers add hog equipment. The same basic relationships apply to any single product within agriculture. The supply curve has a lower elasticity within a year or short period than between years or over a long period.[1]

Production and supply periods in agriculture. We can distinguish further between short-run and long-run supply functions, but it must be remembered that there are many degrees between the extremes of short run and long run. For purpose of analyzing agricultural production and resource use, supply periods in agriculture might be broken down into these categories:

(1) *The intra-year or postplanting supply period.* While shorter periods could be considered important, production and resource-use patterns do revolve around adjustments which can be made after annual crops are planted and after animals have been bred and their offspring have been born. The number of technical units in the form of acres and animal units then becomes fixed and adjustments in output can be made mainly as a given number of animals are fed and/or marketed at heavier weights and as more or less fertilizer, labor, and other resources are applied to a given acreage of each individual crop.

(2) *The interyear supply period when changes occur in the ratio of farm product prices but the general level of prices or food needs remain constant.* Between 2 successive years it is possible for farmers to make important adjustments in the acreage of specific annual crops or in the numbers of the various types of animals. The ease with which these types of adjustments can be made and the time required for them vary, of course, with the period of production for the particular enterprise.

(3) *The interyear or multi-year supply period when the general level of farm product prices or food needs change.* This period deals with adjustments in farm supply and output when the general level of prices swings through the various phases of the business cycle or when war or other needs place emphasis on increased production. Several years may

---

[1] The elasticity of supply E_s can be measured as the percentage change in quantity or output divided by the percentage change in price or

$$E_s = \frac{\Delta q}{q} \bigg/ \frac{\Delta p}{p} = \frac{\Delta q}{\Delta p} \cdot \frac{p}{q}$$

The elasticity of the supply curve would normally differ at each point on the curve. Of course, when we speak of the "elasticity of the supply curve," we are roughly considering arc (or average elasticity over the range of the supply curve) rather than point elasticity. Elasticity of supply, like other uses of the term elasticity, can refer to either point or arc elasticity.

be allowed for adjustment in either case. The problem to be analyzed is mainly one of the elasticity of production and supply functions as they relate to the aggregate quantity of resources used and the output of agricultural products over a period of years.

Assumption of Production and Supply Functions in Agriculture

Historically, many persons, viewing the tendency of agricultural output to remain constant, have put forth the hypothesis that either (a) farmers are not price responsive and lack profit motivation or (b) the agricultural supply function has an elasticity near zero. Year-to-year changes in farm production are viewed or agricultural and industrial outputs over the various phases of the business cycle are compared to illustrate that agriculture holds its output constant and "thus has an inelastic supply function." [2] Sweeping generalizations such as these can have little meaning, however, until the total supply phenomenon has been broken down into its several elements in the manner of the following pages.

The historic explanations given to account for agriculture's failure to contract output during depression or its "assumed" inability to expand output in high price or food emergency periods are these:

1. Agricultural costs are composed largely of fixed costs. Losses can be minimized by maintaining production as long as the price is above out-of-pocket or variable costs. It is also sometimes suggested that if farms were organized on a corporate basis and labor were represented mainly by hired rather than family workers, agricultural output might display an instability paralleling that of industry.

2. The agricultural production function has elasticity characteristics causing maintenance of output over wide price ranges.[3]

3. Farmers are mechanistically rather than economically motivated.[4] One or 2 writers propose that the ultimate end of farmers is that of driving

---

[2] Some outstanding examples of this hypothesis can be found in J. Brewster and H. Parsons, "Can Prices Allocate Resources in Agriculture," *Jour. Farm Econ.*, Vol. 28; and W. W. Wilcox, "Effects of Farm Price Change on Efficiency in Farming," *Jour. Farm Econ.*, Vol. 33. While Wilcox does consider interproduct change, in the pattern of resource use (although lacking a complete analysis of the aggregate supply function), Brewster and Parsons have simply eliminated the possibility of adjustment of output to price by assuming that farmers are "mechanistically" rather than "economically" motivated.

[3] This is the hypothesis put forth in Wilcox, *op. cit.*

[4] See Brewster and Parsons, *op. cit.*, pp. 939 and 958 for the foremost presentation of this hypothesis of the motivating force behind farmer action. Obviously, though, a farmer who "produces in the direction of 'a maximum physical product per technical unit' because he enjoys the direct utility from fat animals and record crop yields" may still act in a purely economic manner under price

the output per technical unit and the total product for the farm to maximum physical limits. Under this motivating force, price change would bear little relevance to the manner in which resources are used.

4. Farmers attempt to maintain income at constant levels. Under this reaction to price decline, farmers supposedly work harder and longer hours and otherwise increase resource inputs in an attempt to offset price reductions through the greater product.[5]

5. Agriculture is a subsistence industry. Under a pure subsistence industry, individual producers would not be concerned with prices and price relationships, since the total product would be consumed in the household.

6. Agriculture is a competitive industry. This argument gained greatest popularity in the 1930's as an explanation of high-level agricultural production during a depression. It supposes that flexible farm product prices allow the "same product" to move into the market during depression as during prosperity; rigid prices of monopoly industry should necessitate a sharp cut-back in output.

7. The period of production in agriculture is long. Several months are required for annual crop plans to be terminated, while several years are required for livestock and perennial crops.

Although each of the points outlined above plays some part in explaining the nature of the agricultural supply function, individual aspects can be overemphasized. Accordingly, several of the elements of supply functions are given detailed consideration in the section which follows. Supply considerations are of interest and importance, not only in explaining mass behavior of farm firms, but also in providing knowledge on expansion of food production during war and other emergency periods. Data which are available indicate that, when supply phenomena are broken down into their various components, farmers definitely are responsive to price.

---

change. He would simply compare (a) the utility from "watching fat animals and record yields" with (b) the utility to be derived from goods purchased with money income. The task then is one of getting the optimum combination of the 2 goods. If "fat animals" and "record yields" as consumption goods come at the expense of income (and market goods which it will buy) then any change in price of products would change the optimum combination of "fat animals" goods and goods purchased with money income. These conditions are implied and discussed in the simple models of Chapter 14. Since only a minor or irrelevant fraction of farmers attempt to or do press output per technical unit or farm to the physical maximum, this "explanation" of the farm product supply function will not be incorporated into later discussion which evaluates and further develops agricultural supply characteristics.

[5] This reaction is logical on the individual farm only if (a) underemployed resources are present or (b) marginal costs have been much lower than marginal returns and the operator has additional funds or is able to obtain credit. Because of their micro environment many farm operators may view increased production from a given collection of resources as one means of offsetting income losses through price declines. While a single farmer might offset the decline through this type of adjustment, farmers in the aggregate can only push profit to lower levels because of the highly inelastic demand for agricultural products.

Foundation of the Supply Function

The nature of the supply function in any one period for a single agricultural product or the aggregate product of agriculture depends on (1) the nature of the physical production functions in the relevant supply period, (2) the nature of the market for factors used in production including (a) the supply function for agricultural resources and (b) the flexibility of factor prices, (3) the structure of firm costs as related to fixed and variable outlays, (4) the nature of firm household interrelationships including the motivating forces behind the production response of farmers, and (5) the expectations of farmers. In order that the reader may better visualize the effect of these several forces on the supply response of individual firms and the agricultural industry, this section is devoted to examination of the nature of the production function, the effect of price flexibility, and the impact of fixed costs on the agricultural supply function. The problems of motivation and expectations will be discussed later. Following sections will also examine empirical data which are available. Distinction between time periods as they relate to the elements of supply will be discussed in a later section.

The nature of the production function. Many persons have raised questions as to the nature of the aggregate production function in agriculture. Some have extended the hypothesis that it is highly elastic over one range

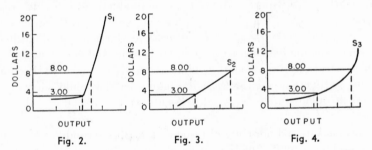

Fig. 2.   Fig. 3.   Fig. 4.

Elasticity of marginal cost or supply functions.

but highly inelastic over another range.[6] Other concepts of the production function and elasticity of production were outlined in Chapters 2 and 3. We saw that it was possible for elasticity to be constant at either a high or low level or for elasticity to change but to do so either rapidly or gradually. Finally, we saw that the production function may be linear over all technical units for a farm of given size; addition of variable factors to units of the fixed factor, starting from zero, until all technical

---

[6] W. W. Wilcox, "Effects of Farm Price Change on Efficiency in Farming," *Jour. Farm Econ.*, Vol. 30. Wilcox based the conclusions of his study largely on this hypothesis.

units are employed, presents this possibility for a single farm. The elasticity of the farm's marginal cost curve is affected accordingly. Figure 2 illustrates a marginal cost curve where the elasticity of production is very high over one discrete range of inputs but "breaks" to a low level at another range. In Figure 3 the production function underlying the marginal cost curve has a constant elasticity of .5. The elasticity of production for Figure 4 starts at .9 but declines throughout all ranges of input. The first cost curve has a range of extremely low elasticity. The second cost or supply function increases at a near constant rate, while the third slopes upward at a sharply increasing rate.

In terms of price response and use of resources for price increases or decreases which fall in the segment of low elasticity for the first marginal cost curve, adjustments will be very small. Ordinarily resources would be used up to the "sharp kink" in the production function. However, if prices were only slightly above the "kink" in the supply curve, slight price declines would cause great decreases in output and the amount of resources employed in production. Because of the more gradual decline in resource productivity, an absolute fall in price will cause relatively large adjustments in output under the second and third production functions. Which of these production situations best describes agriculture either within a year or over a period of years? If agriculture were represented by the first, price increases during inflation or business recovery would cause farmers to use only slightly more resources and to increase production by relatively small amounts when output already falls within the range of low elasticity. Conversely, resource use and agricultural production would decline by only small amounts during depression. If the price fell very low (below $3 in the illustration) adjustments would, of course, be very great. Production and supply functions such as those in Figures 3 and 4 would allow or cause farmers to make fairly large adjustments in resource use and product output.

Factor markets and flexibility of resource prices. A second "pure element" of the product supply function in agriculture is that of the elasticity of supply for resources used in farming and hence in the flexibility of factor prices. Earlier chapters explained the importance of the factor/product price ratio in determining the level of output and resource use which is profitable for the individual entrepreneur. If the price of a factor is $2 and the price of its product is $1 (a ratio of 2/1 or 2.0), profits are maximized when the marginal product of the resource is 2.0. If the price of the product falls to 50¢ and the price of the factor falls to $1 (a factor/product price ratio of 2.0), the previous level of output and resource use is still profitable. Here both factor and product prices are flexible. If factor prices are inflexible, a small change in product prices may cause wide swings in the levels of agricultural output and resource use. Flexible prices will tend to have an opposite effect. We can illustrate the effect of flexible and inflexible factor prices on farm output and resource employment by use of Figures 5 and 6. In order to analyze this single aspect of product supply (namely, flexibility of factor prices) we assume a single production function such as P in Figure 5. The initial supply and demand curves for the agricultural industry are D_1 and S_1 respectively in Figure 6. Assuming for convenience that a previous market equilibrium has existed with (1) a

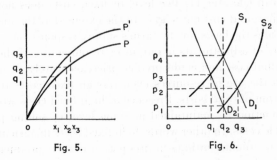

Fig. 5. Fig. 6.

Factor price flexibility and levels of resource use.

price of P_4, (2) an output of oq_2 (Figure 6), and (3) resource use at a level of ox_2 (Figure 5), the demand function drops to D_2 when depression comes about.[7] If the price of factors is entirely inflexible, the supply function (marginal cost to each individual farmer) will remain at the previous level, S_1. Under this situation, the new equilibrium will be defined by a price of op_3 and output will fall back to oq_1. Consequently, the quantity of resources employed may, if all farmers maximize profits, drop back to ox_1 on production function P in Figure 5. Suppose, however, that factor prices are as responsive to changes in the structure of the economic system as are product prices. If the drop in product demand is paralleled by a sufficiently great drop in factor prices, then, with the production function remaining unchanged, the supply curve for products will drop to S_2. With a simultaneous change in supply and demand functions to S_2 and D_2 respectively, commodity price will decline to op_1, output will remain at oq_2, and resources employed will remain at ox_2. Output and resource intensity do not decline with lower prices or increase with higher prices.

If this situation characterizes agriculture and agricultural firms, can it be said that farmers are not price responsive? [8] Constancy of agricultural output cannot be taken as a pure and simple sign that farmers are not price responsive or that the agricultural supply function is vertical. Suffi-

---

[7] As mentioned earlier, the more appropriate cobweb supply mechanism has not been employed in order to conserve space.

[8] If the 2 historic levels of output oq_1 and oq_2 are related to the prices op_4 and op_1, and a production response curve is drawn into the graph, it becomes perfectly inelastic in the manner of q_2i. This line is not, of course, representative of a supply function.

cient flexibility in the price of factors can cause output to vary only slightly with product price change. Farmers cannot be characterized as lacking profit motivation and price responsiveness when maximum profits or minimum losses are denoted by constancy of output. We will examine the factor price flexibility for agriculture at a later point.

Fixed costs. The relationships of fixed and variable costs to price response were discussed in Chapter 11. The level of fixed costs does not affect the nature of the marginal cost curve and, to the extent that the marginal cost of output provides the basis for the farm's supply response, need not determine the nature of adjustments in output or resource use. If the farm firm knew its marginal cost and could predict price accurately, it might make wide swings in the use of resources even though fixed costs represent an important portion of total costs. Presence of high fixed costs would specify only that production be maintained at some level of selling price above average variable costs. In other words, high fixed costs in agriculture would mean that farms might continue in production even if product prices declined by relatively large amounts; the farm firm would not cease production during depression as in the case of non-agricultural firms. Yet as long as the marginal cost and hence supply curve in agriculture had an elasticity greater than zero, adjustments in quantities of resources employed would still be made as long as price was above unit variable costs; even greater adjustments would be made if price fell below variable costs.

If family labor and land are taken to fall in the category of fixed costs along with interest, taxes, and depreciation on buildings and machinery due to weather rather than use, it can be said that fixed costs represent the major portion of agricultural costs. Presence of fixed costs in agriculture obviously does contribute to maintenance of production during major price recessions. Fixed cost considerations should not, where the 2 are distinct, be confused with fixity in factor supplies or flexibility in factor prices, however. It is not necessarily true that land and labor charges represent fixed costs to each individual farmer. Instead, the price or opportunity return for these resources may drop in proportion to product prices during depression; maintenance of output may then still be profitable. Even with an important portion of costs falling in the fixed category, the quantity of other resources employed would still depend on the nature of the production and supply functions. Fixed costs are more important in some lines of agricultural production than others. Farm management studies have shown the major costs in livestock production to be variable costs. Feed alone constitutes from 60 to 85 per cent of all costs in livestock production. Similarly, certain types of vegetable production require a large outlay of variable costs in the form of labor. Thus, while presence of fixed costs, or the consideration of many costs as fixed by the farm family, may explain why farm firms do not cease production altogether, it does not explain maintenance of livestock and vegetable output during depression where costs are mainly of a variable nature. Then, too, the level of variable costs is not the same for all farms in a nation. If it were possible to compute the point of minimum average variable costs for each farm in the nation and if these were plotted on a single graph, they undoubtedly would trace out a curve increasing gradually from left to right. This curve of minimum per unit variable costs differs from farm to farm, depending on soil productivity and other forces. Under a situation of this type, each lower level of price attained during a depression would cause some farmers to withdraw from production while others maintained some level of output. Even if farm firms had only variable costs, output maintenance during wide swings in product prices would be possible. The only necessary condition for this supply reaction is that the prices for resource services be sufficiently flexible.

The Intra-Year Production and Supply Function

The intra-year or post-planting production function has implications both in explaining the very short term response of farmers to price and in providing one basis for planning food expansion during emergencies of short duration. In this section we are interested in adjustments which can be made in the quantity of resources employed and the output of products after annual crops have been planted and animals have been bred and their offspring have arrived. The period under consideration is so short as to exclude all possibilities of shifting crop acreages and may allow only slight changes in the number of livestock units.

Post-planting crop production functions. After farmer plans have been put into effect through planting of annual crops, the opportunities for aggregate expansion or for major changes in output of any single crop are small. Once a given acreage of corn, wheat, tobacco, or other crop has been planted (a fixed number of technical units) only slight increases can be made in resource application. Fertilizer can be applied through side dressing, more cultivations can be made, and, in some instances, the amount of irrigation water can be varied. Yet, if the possibilities of output above the "normal" level are considered, the opportunity of increased output is very small. The post-planting portion of the intra-year crop production function has a very low elasticity; the exact level of output is more nearly dependent on such exogenous forces as weather than upon changes which can be made in the quantity of resources employed.

On the side of contraction below "normal" levels of resource application, however, it is possible that the relevant range of the production function is quite elastic. Once the ground has been prepared and crops have been planted, opportunities are open for decisions on whether or not the crop should be cultivated and harvested. This is a decision to be made by the farmer when depression breaks between planting and harvesting dates.

The range of the production function over which the farmer normally extends resources is the more elastic portion. The strong tendency for farmers to go ahead and cultivate and harvest annual or perennial crops once they have been planted is largely because: (1) The greatest portion of costs are "historic" or "fixed" once the crop is started underway. (2) The elasticity of production is great, from zero to full employment of acres, for that portion of the post-planting production function over which farmers must make decisions. It is known, of course, that under highly unfavorable price relationships farmers sometimes do not harvest vegetables, fruits, or other crops because the return is less than the cash costs involved. Finally, farmers may play "long odds" with hope or expectations that prices will reverse their trend before harvest.

The intra-year livestock production function. Data are not available to allow estimates of farmers' supply responses and the nature of the intra-year and post-planting production function for crops. Figures are more abundant for post-breeding adjustments in livestock; the livestock product production function is less dependent on exogenous variables. Data on hog marketing weights and dairy feeding rates indicate that farmers definitely do make very short-run or intra-year adjustments in output and resource use. Not only is the post-farrowing production function much less subject to weather variations than the post-planting crop production function, but, also, less uncertainty is involved in use of added resources. When a pig reaches 200 lbs. the hog/corn ratio can be viewed at the moment or anticipated for the next few days and marketing weights can be adjusted accordingly. Similar "instantaneous" adjustment can be made in milk production and feeding rates. The period of decision-making in dairy feeding is shorter and probably involves less expectation error than predicting whether nitrogen should be side dressed on corn in July when the crop will not be harvested until December.

Most intra-year and intra-animal production function studies show a gradual decline in elasticity of production as animals are fed to heavier levels. These functions for technical units do not give a sharp break in marginal costs such as illustrated in Figure 2. Instead they give cost functions of the nature indicated in Figures 3 and 4. Atkinson and Klein, in analyzing input-output ratios for hogs, found no "sharp break" in the production function.[9] Neither were they found in the recent Iowa study cited in Chapter 3 where elasticities per hog were about .84 for 2 feeds.

The elasticity of the feed-milk production function employed by Jensen approximates .7 throughout six ranges of feeding.[10] An Iowa study derived

[9] L. J. Atkinson and J. W. Klein, *Feed Consumption and Marketing Weight of Hogs.* U.S.D.A. Tech. Bul. 894. See Figures 2 and 3 and Table 11. Also see the footnote to Table 11, indicating the function employed.

[10] E. Jensen, *et al., Input-Output Relations in Milk Production.* U.S.D.A. Tech. Bul. 815, 1942. Since the coefficients for the equation were not listed by Jensen, the

an elasticity per animal of .73 for 3 feeds to feeder cattle and of .87 for dairy cows. These per animal elasticities more nearly parallel Figures 3 and 4 than Figure 1. It appears fairly definite that the elasticity of production with the animal constant does not give a production function with a "kink" such as illustrated in Figure 2. While data which have been derived refer to livestock product/feed transformation rates alone, the elasticity of production for labor and other factors which serve as pure complements to feed will have similar elasticity coefficients. Table 1 gives

Table I.

Rates of Livestock Feeding per Head for Specified Types of Livestock, 1929-1947 *

Year	Milk cows	Grain-fattened cattle	Hens and pullets	Hogs per 100 lbs. produced	All live-stock per animal unit
1929	4813	3375	67	506	5233
1930	4580	3259	63	485	4900
1931	4796	3139	69	498	5143
1932	4600	3607	68	515	5135
1933	4013	3855	60	486	4442
1934	4347	2789	60	489	4594
1935	4568	3539	70	501	5027
1936	4435	2756	59	479	4700
1937	5058	2960	73	506	5495
1938	5056	3718	68	482	5305
1939	5224	3568	66	476	5393
1940	5464	3789	72	494	5714
1941	5542	3970	75	487	5784
1942	5498	4204	78	509	5835
1943	5472	4085	77	503	5732
1944	5662	4077	82	504	5847
1945	5560	4712	80	537	5921
1946	5708	3766	84	506	5927
1947	5672	4110	83	483	5760

* Source: *Consumption of Feed by Livestock.* U.S.D.A. Circular 836.

a rough notion of the manner in which farmers do adjust feeding and production rates within the year for livestock. Year-to-year changes in planned production by farmers exceeds by far the adjustments made between years for firms of most industries if depression is excepted. (The degree of adjustment by individual farmers is partly obscured by these aggregate data which also include trends in practices as well as adjustment to other forces.) The magnitude of feed supplies within a year does not, except for extreme droughts, limit feeding rates by individual farmers in the same period; they cause feeding rates to change directly because feed prices rise or decline relative to livestock product prices. While some writers have suggested that variations in feeding rates between years is an indica-

elasticities have been computed in an "average" or "arc" fashion from Table 10 in U.S.D.A. Tech. Bul. 815. These provide "averages" between the 6 levels of feeding of the magnitudes.

tion of fluctuations in the physical efficiency with which livestock is produced, these changes are mainly intra-year adjustments to feed supplies and hence livestock/feed price ratios.

Obviously the intra-year aggregate or "all-farm" production function for livestock has a lower elasticity than the interyear production function. Increased feed and labor must be applied mainly to a given number of animal units in the first case; additional resources can be applied to a greater number of animal units between years. Within a single year the livestock production function is of the nature $P = f(L,F,S/B,E,A)$ where the resources refer to labor, feed, medicines (supplies), buildings, equipment, and animals. Buildings, equipment, and animal units are fixed for the period. Between years the production function moves in the direction of $P = f(L,F,S,A/B,E)$ or $P = f(L,F,S,A,B,E)$ where animal numbers can be changed or buildings and equipment also can all be varied. Using simple procedures for estimating the elasticity of production within the year with animal units approximately constant, Breimyer arrived at an intra-year production elasticity figure of .4; [11] a 1 per cent increase in feed fed resulted in an increase in aggregate output by .4 per cent. Lorie's estimates based on a production function with constant elasticity (but diminishing productivity) gave the following intra-year figures: [12] with animal units fixed at an index of 80 (1910-14 = 100) a 1 per cent increase in feed fed resulted in a .36 increase in aggregate output; with animal units increased to an index level of 120, the elasticity was .44. Hildreth and Jarrett, using alternative estimating procedures, arrived at an intra-year feed elasticity of .57 with least squares regression techniques and .46 with simultaneous equations.[13]

Interyear Production and Supply Functions

The supply function for individual crops and livestock has a high elasticity between years. Some notion of the extent to which interyear responses in resource use and supply take place for individual agricultural products is given in Table 2. While the short-term change in the aggregate output of agriculture is smaller, quite wide swings do take place in use of resources and the number of acres or animals produced in a single year. (Changes in the number of crop acres is a better indication of farmer decision in respect to use of resources than changes in crop production; the

---

[11] H. F. Breimyer, "Efficiency of Feeding Livestock," *Jour. Farm Econ.*, Vol. 25.

[12] J. H. Lorie, *Causes of Annual Fluctuations in the Production of Livestock and Livestock Products.* Chicago: University of Chicago Press, 1947.

[13] C. Hildreth and F. Jarrett, *Some Estimates of a Livestock Production Function*, University of Chicago (Mimeo), 1951. The regression coefficients for a function linear in logarithms were .57 for feed, .17 for livestock on farms (lagged on year), and .004 for time under least squares. The simultaneous equation (limited information) procedure gave elasticity coefficients of .46, .28, and .004 respectively.

former are not affected by weather variations. Animal numbers and crop acres are indicative of farmer planning units between years.) Farmers as a group make important adjustments between years since their given quantities of capital, labor, land, and management resources are reallocated between enterprises. Supplementary and complementary relationships as well as other short-run opportunity curves with "corners" do provide the basis for stability in resource use as product price ratios change. For example, in Figure 9 of Chapter 8 or Figure 18 of Chapter 9 (curve $n'i'$), the iso-revenue line can pivot over a wide range without causing the optimum combination of enterprises to differ from that indicated at the "corner" position of the production possibility curve. The majority of resources in agriculture at any one point in time is not characterized by these unique transformation conditions. However, farmers who maintain poultry production at supplementary limits cannot be termed "non-responsive to price" and "mechanistically motivated."

Table 2.

Inter-Year Production Adjustments for Selected Agricultural Products, 1920-1949
(Thousand Units)

Resource or product	Average year-to-year change	Average year-to-year change as per cent of mean quantity	Coefficient of variation
Feed fed to hogs	3877 tons	9.4	18.7
Feed fed to beef cattle	3116 tons	6.7	24.0
Feed fed to poultry	1764 tons	7.2	27.0
Feed fed to dairy cattle	3110 tons	4.1	15.8
Feed fed to sheep	1807 units	9.0	16.0
Pigs saved	9007 units	11.0	7.5
Hens on farms	6618 units	4.4	8.8
Feeder cattle fed	358 units	10.0	18.9
Cattle other than milk cattle on farms	1960 units	4.2	14.8
Sheep and lambs fed	497 units	8.4	13.3
Sheep on farms	1969 units	4.0	13.8
Chickens raised	82379 units	11.2	10.4
Turkeys raised	3273 units	10.9	26.0
Cotton in cultivation	2888 acres	10.2	28.8
Wheat seeded	4386 acres	6.4	11.7
Corn planted	3200 acres	3.3	27.0
Oats planted	1672 acres	3.9	17.3
Soybeans planted	1037 acres	11.0	44.1
Flax planted	993 acres	30.2	41.2
Tobacco harvested	226 acres	13.6	15.7

The interyear crop supply function. In this section we are interested in the nature of interyear production and supply functions for *individual* crops. First, it can be said that within the acreage limitations existing, the interyear supply function for any single crop can have a high elasticity on the individual farm. It is obvious that, between years, an increase in oats and wheat and a decrease in barley acreage on a Great Plains farm or a similar shift between corn and soybeans on a Cornbelt farm can cause output to change by an amount paralleling the quantity of resources shifted back and forth between the crops. The elasticity of the production function and the marginal cost function is very high. The marginal cost curve for a single crop on an individual farm may approach infinite elasticity over an acreage range which starts at zero and finally includes all acres in the farm. The cost and supply functions for a single crop in the agricultural industry need not, or does not, have an elasticity nearly as great, however. This difference is due to the fact that a wide range of variation exists over the nation in soil productivity, rainfall and climate. The adaptability of crops varies likewise; whereas one level of prices or price relationships will cause a shift of resources from one crop to another in one producing area, higher and lower prices will be required in areas less or better adapted to the same crop. Because of the manner in which soil productivity, rainfall, and other yield-affecting forces differ by gradual degrees between different geographic locations, the aggregate supply curve (in contrast to the marginal cost curve on an individual farm) for a single crop most likely has a gradual positive slope in the manner of the "classroom model."

While hypotheses have been extended that the soil production function has elasticity characteristics of the nature suggested by C and D in Figure 4 of Chapter 3, early and recent agronomic investigations suggest that the "fertilizer input—crop output" relationship is as well described by curves A and B in the same figure.[14] Even if the production function which relates input of fertilizer, irrigation water, or seed to crop output with land area devoted to a single crop constant were of the nature indicated under C and D of Figure 3 in Chapter 3, the industry supply function would still have a gradual positive slope because of gradations in soil productivity between farms and regions.[15]

The interyear livestock production function. The interyear livestock production function displays much greater elasticity than the intra-year

---

[14] The elasticity of production (for fertilizer and complementary labor and capital) will again approach 1.0 if we view fertilizer application in the vein of 20 lbs. on 1 acre, 40 lbs. on 2 acres, and so forth, until 4,000 lbs. have been applied on 200 acres. While this form of the fertilizer production function for the individual farm (land as well as fertilizer variable and the 2 factors combined in constant portions up to 4,000 lbs. of fertilizer) has a high and nearly constant elasticity, the supply function for the industry will have a gradually declining elasticity because of gradual changes in soil fertility, rainfall, and so forth, between farms and geographic areas.

[15] See W. J. Spillman, *The Law of Diminishing Returns.* New York: World, 1924; and U.S.D.A. Tech. Bul. 348 for exhaustive empirical treatment of the fertilizer production function with land constant. While techniques change over time, it is highly likely (and has empirical basis) that the similarities and differences between soils which he uncovered exist under present farming techniques. Spillman's findings (see especially page 59) illustrate many different magnitudes of production elasticities.

input-output relationship partly for the same reasons cited for crops. (Elasticities vary of course between livestock types and between farms for the same type of livestock.) Whereas the elasticity of pork production over a range in hog weights extending upward from 250 lbs. may be considerably less than 1.0 when feed input is increased on a farm with hog numbers fixed, the elasticity may be as great as 1.0 if both hog numbers and feed are increased within limits and facilities are available on individual farms. Our concern here, however, is with the aggregate production and supply functions rather than those of the individual farm. The few rough empirical estimates available do suggest wide differences between intra-year and interyear production elasticities. Whereas Lorie's figures show an aggregate intra-year elasticity for feed of .36 with livestock numbers constant at an index of 80, and .44 with numbers at an index of 120, they show a total interyear output elasticity of .85 when both feed inputs and aggregate livestock output is varied (starting from an index of 100 for both). In other words, an increase in both feed inputs and livestock numbers by 1 per cent were associated with an .85 per cent increase in livestock output. Hildreth's total elasticity for feed and livestock was similarly greater between years, as compared with the intra-year figure.

Although the data employ no powerful estimating techniques, the figures of Table 3 also suggest that the aggregate livestock production function displays a relatively high elasticity between years. On the basis of 2 contrasting periods in which quite rapid increases were made in feed

Table 3.
Changes in Quantities of Feed Used and Livestock Output in Selected Periods
for the United States

Period	Total feed units fed (1,000 tons)	Total units of livestock produced	Percentage increase in livestock units divided by percentage increase in feed fed
1. 1910-14	51,035	123.9	—
2. 1915-19	56,584	134.8	—
Per cent increase period 2 over 1	10.9	8.8	.81
3. 1936-40	239,411	149.0	—
4. 1941-45	301,397	185.8	—
Per cent increase period 4 over 3	25.9	28.0	1.08

consumption and livestock numbers, the percentage increase in output was high relative to the increase in quantity of feed used. A very large national expansion in feed inputs was impossible in 1941-45 as compared to 1936-40 because of the stocks of grain on hand at the beginning of the former period and because of the record output of feeds during the period. The increase in livestock units in 1941-45 as compared to 1936-40 was 1.08 times the increase in feed consumption. Of course several phenomena are confounded in data of this nature: the makeup of the aggregate output does not remain constant and changes in techniques occur between periods even as short as these.[16] However, it is unlikely that any more than a fifth of the increase in production during 1941-45 can be attributed to technical revolution. The increase in 1915-19 is, according to animal scientists, mainly a result of increased feed inputs with some small gain attributable to innovations and greater adoption of known practices. The interyear aggregate livestock production function undoubtedly has high elasticity and is of a nature to encourage changes in the quantity of resources employed in livestock production as factor/product price ratios change. Evidently, there is no unique characteristic of the production function which would cause individual farmers or the agricultural industry to attempt to maintain aggregate livestock output at one particular level. This statement has even greater application, except for supplementary relationships and corner positions on short-run opportunity curves, for single types of products than for the aggregate of livestock production. Given its competitive setting and the nature of its aggregate production function alone as the conditioning forces, agriculture should be able to make fairly wide adjustments in output as price relationships change over time.[17]

Emergency food planning. Since we have drawn contrasts between intra-year and interyear production and supply functions, this setting also becomes appropriate for examining certain food production and expansion problems which arise under national emergencies. Our concern here is mainly with characteristics of the production function and transformation function rather than with the supply function. Changes in national outlook (war emergency, world food famine, and so forth) sometimes cause food needs to rise sharply in a very short time interval. The elasticity with which production can respond in a single year is, of course, quite low. If the emergency arises after crops are sown, very little can be done to increase output of primary products. Immediate (within year) increases in the utilization of grains, hays and fibers must come largely from a reduction in stocks and carry-overs unless weather, which can neither be predicted nor controlled, is favorable. Greater flexibility for intra-year increases in output exists in livestock production. Even with the number

---

[16] In our earlier discussion of productivity, we saw that measurement of scale relationships was possible only when products and factors were held in constant proportion. Neither of these conditions is attained in the aggregate response data presented in Table 3.

[17] See D. G. Johnson, "Allocation of Agricultural Income," *Jour. Farm Econ.*, Nov., 1948. Johnson fitted a logarithmic function to the aggregate observations of resource input and product output over the period 1910-43 and arrived at an elasticity figure of .44 for labor, .17 for capital, .12 for current expenses, and .27 for land. The total elasticity of 1.0, to the extent that it serves as a rough estimate given the nature of the data and the estimating technique, indicates that the physical production function would provide a basis for wide changes in output with small changes in factor/product price ratios. Even if the derived coefficients overestimate elasticity by as much as 40 per cent, expansion and contraction possibilities are still great.

of technical units fixed, increases in livestock production can be made, if feed is available, through heavier levels of feeding. Feed and labor are ordinarily the resources of crucial scarcity in periods of emergency. With animal units highly fixed, the increment in livestock output forthcoming for increased feed inputs must be small when compared to interyear possibilities where animal units also become variable. A question is that of how a given stock of feed grain, for example, should be used over a period of 1, 2, or more years. Suppose that a food emergency arises after the spring pig crop has been farrowed. Should the national carry-over of feed grains plus the year's production be used entirely to produce a greater amount of pork within the year? The answer depends partly on the timing of food needs. If they are very great within the year but will return to "normal" thereafter, greater production from more intensive feeding rates may be highly desirable. However, if food needs will be equally great in the following or later years, part of the stock and/or annual production of feed may be carried into the second year if total livestock production is to be maximized from the aggregate quantity of grain available over the 2 years. The nature of relationships involved here can be illustrated by means of Figure 7. Without considering rates of feeding so low that complementary

ranges of production exist, the interyear production possibility or opportunity curve for a single type of livestock or an aggregate of livestock products is of the nature of IG. The curve IG might be termed an iso-feed or an iso-grain curve since it illustrates the quantities of livestock which can be produced in the first and second year (a) from the stock of feed on hand at the beginning of the first year, (b) the production in the first year, and (c) the production in the

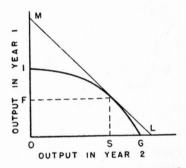

Fig. 7. Inter-year allocation of feed.

second year. The interyear opportunity line "curves sharply" towards the vertical axis. This situation indicates (1) each increase in output in the first year necessitates much greater sacrifices in output in the second year, because (a) the increase in the first year must come mainly from a fixed number of animal or technical units with a low feed-product elasticity and (b) any increase in the second year can come as the number of technical units is also increased; and (2) the feed produced in the second year cannot be used in increasing livestock output during the first year. The maximum amount of livestock product possible in the first year, OI, is much less than the maximum possible in the second year, OG. If interest is in maximizing the product over the 2 years, the "choice indicator" becomes of the nature of ML (which indicates the maximum output which can be produced in the two years): ML will be linear and have a 45° (1:1) slope since a pound of product in the second year has as much "weight" as a pound of product in the first year. This end can be accomplished by concentrating the greatest feed input in the second year since the marginal rate of substitution of output in the first year for output in the second year is low because of the conditions already outlined. (The rates of substitution indicated on the feed-livestock possibility curve will depend, of course, on the amount of labor and capital of various forms which is available to complement the increased numbers of livestock in the second year.) The output in each year consistent with a maximum output in the 2 years includes OF in the first year and OS in the second year.

The gain in total product forthcoming over time through price and output stabilization policies is also apparent from the differences in the intra-year and interyear elasticities cited earlier and illustrated in Figure 7. Stabilization policies (commodity storage and perhaps forward prices) designed and perfected for the purpose would have the effect of evening out livestock-feed price ratios between years. Consequently, the "profit emphasis" for heavy rates of feeding in individual years would be lessened and a carry-over of feed into later years would allow a greater livestock output over time. Short-run and interyear elasticities also have important implications in international trade policies. Schemes which allow an importation of feedstuffs and animals will permit a greater increase in livestock output from given labor and non-feed capital than will policies which prohibit imports of both resources. An individual nation might keep resource productivity at a maximum by importing (a) feed during years of deficits and (b) animals during years of feed surpluses.

While the post-planting elasticity of production is low for crops, the elasticity is much greater for shifts in grain and feed output which can be made between years. Through shifts in acreage, for example, from hay to grain crops, an increase in total feed can be attained in a single year at the expense of output in later years on many soils. The procedure may in fact be kept up for several years as the store of soil fertility is drawn upon heavily. If, however, the emergency is to last over an extended number of years, food output over the total time span cannot be maximized by treating each year in isolation. If the nation were to attempt crop maximization in 1955 without thought of output in 1956, a cropping and production pattern could be followed which would result in a shift from forages to grain in the Cornbelt and a diversion of land from fallow to second or third-year wheat in the Great Plains. The same procedure could be used in 1956 alone, in 1957 alone, and so forth for the following 15 years. Yet, while output in each single year taken by itself would be at a maximum (with the cropping pattern of previous years given and without consideration of future years) the total output over the period 1955-70 would not be maximized by this "single year" planning.

The Aggregate Production Function and Depression Stability of Farm Output

In the 2 previous sections we examined intra-year production and supply functions for the aggregate agricultural product and the interyear production and supply functions for individual farm products. This section deals almost entirely with mass production adjustment in agriculture. We are concerned with the problem especially as it relates to production response and resource adjustment during depression and inflation periods in the national economy. Later we will examine the secular nature of production and supply functions in agriculture. It is because resource employment and product output in agriculture do not display the very great instability found in selected non-farm industries that historic inferences have been in the direction of inelastic supply functions for the agricultural industry.[18]

Statistics on aggregate production response. The popular presentation of the farm versus industrial contrast in production response is partly correct and partly incorrect. Table 4 offers some comparisons between agriculture and other selected industries during periods of extreme deflation and inflation. The greatest contrast is between agriculture and construction. Not only does construction output fall to a much lower level during depression but it also increases to greater heights in inflation periods.[19] While less marked, similar contrasts exist between agriculture and other industries presented. The smallest difference is between agriculture and mining and non-durable manufacturing.[20] While the increase in agricultural output over the period 1940-45 is sometimes cited as phenomenal, it hardly compares with increase in non-agricultural product during the same period. A difference does exist in the fact that agriculture started with a near "full-employment" plant while the other industries still had an unemployed plant at the beginning of the recovery period.

---

[18] For indications or analyses of arguments along these lines refer to the following: Wilcox, *op. cit.*; Brewster and Parsons, *op. cit.*; J. K. Galbraith and J. D. Black, "Maintenance of Agricultural Production During Depression: The Explanations Reviewed," *Jour. Pol. Econ.*, Vol. 46; W. Cochrane, "Farm Price Gyrations," *Jour. Farm Econ.*, Vol. 29; and D. G. Johnson, "The Supply Function for Agricultural Products," *Amer. Econ. Rev.*, Vol. 40. The articles by Johnson and by Galbraith and Black are not based on suppositions of inelastic supply functions but are more detailed examinations of the bases of the agricultural supply function.

[19] Qualifications have to be made in comparison of 2 industries, 1 of which went ahead full blast during the war and 1 of which was nearly closed down with a great backlog of demands in the postwar period. However, the same general contrasts exist for earlier fluctuations in national employment and the price level.

[20] It must be remembered that the dip in agricultural production in the period 1934-37 was more nearly due to drought than to price response. The lower level of production in 1933 was even partly due to low moisture conditions over the preceding year or 2.

Table 4.

Indexes of Production for Agriculture and Selected Industries, 1929-48 (1929 = 100)

Year	Agriculture	All manufacturing	Durable manufacturing	Construction contracts	Non-durable manufacturing	Iron and steel	Fuels
1929	100	100	100	100	100	100	100
1930	98	82	74	79	90	73	88
1931	107	68	51	54	85	46	80
1932	104	52	31	24	75	24	70
1933	96	62	41	21	85	41	78
1934	81	67	49	27	87	46	80
1935	99	79	63	32	97	61	86
1936	88	94	82	47	108	86	96
1937	111	103	92	50	114	92	106
1938	108	79	59	68	102	51	96
1939	109	99	82	69	117	86	102
1940	112	114	105	76	124	110	111
1941	118	153	152	127	153	140	118
1942	132	193	211	201	170	150	121
1943	129	234	273	79	189	156	128
1944	134	229	267	52	184	155	141
1945	133	194	208	81	178	138	139
1946	137	161	145	138	177	113	138
1947	137	176	167	144	185	147	150
1948	139	180	170	162	190	156	156

The data of Table 5 are also of interest: the products presented are quite similar to agriculture in respect to output maintenance during the last major depression. The industries presented are mainly those which process agricultural commodities. Thus it may seem "self-evident" that as long as agricultural output is maintained, food processing industries should also maintain employment and production during depression. The important consideration, however, is this: are the economic forces which cause agriculture to maintain output in depression the same as those which cause food processing industries to maintain their output? If it is true that fixed costs, subsistence production, the period of production, mechanistic motivation and the other supply characteristics mentioned above explain the response of agriculture to major price variation, do not these same characteristics explain the tendency of still other industries to maintain output? These questions are to be examined in a later section. However, we can also "reverse the hypothesis" and ask whether or not the forces that explain depression-maintained output in the industries cited also help explain the same general phenomena in agriculture. The forces explaining output maintenance seem highly parallel in the 2 cases, particularly when factor costs are included in the analysis. Monopoly per se cannot be used as the sole explanation of differences between agriculture and other industries. While organization of industry into monopoly firms may be important in certain cases, it apparently is not a full explanation. Many of the industries listed in Table 5 include monopoly or oligopoly characteristics on the buying side. We see then that as compared to some industries the output of agricultural products is highly stable; as compared to still other industries, agriculture appears little if any more stable.

Table 5.

Indexes of Production in Selected Industries, 1933 *

Industry	Index of output in 1933 (1929 = 100)
Agriculture	96
Beet sugar	151
Butter	110
Knit goods	100
Shortening	98
Canned milk	98
Soap	98
Cheese	95
Meat packing	95
Canned fruits and vegetables	88
Cotton goods	87
Woolen and worsted goods	87
Petroleum	80

* Source: S. Fabricant, *The Output of Manufacturing Industries, 1899-1937.* New York: National Bureau of Economic Research, 1940.

While the discussion on stability has been in terms of output it also applies to employment of resources. Total employment in agriculture declined only by two per cent from 1929 to 1933 or from 11,289,000 to 11,023,000 workers. Family workers increased from 8,230,000 to 8,590,000 while hired workers declined from 2,984,000 to 2,433,000 persons. Employment in manufacturing as a whole declined by roughly 35 per cent, while total hours worked declined even more. Total employment in private construction declined by over 75 per cent, while the decrease was as much as 40 per cent in automobile manufacture. In contrast, employment in food industries declined by only 15 per cent from 1929 to 1932 and increased somewhat by 1933. It cannot be said that agriculture maintains a given level of resource use throughout all phases of price cycles, however. The data of Table 6 illustrate that adjustments are made in the quantity of resources employed. While change was small in the quantities of land and labor employed in 1933 as compared to 1929, fertilizer and lime consumption dropped by nearly one-half.

The agricultural production function in recapitulation. Although a small amount of non-farm land exists in the nation, the quantity of land incorporated into farms over the last several decades has been unimportant. Thus, the aggregate production function of agriculture, starting from a position of full employment of land, is of a "short-run nature" only; added capital and labor must be employed on a given land acreage. This situation is somewhat in contrast to that of other single industries where the total plant can be increased by expansion in both the number and size of firms as all classes of resources can be diverted from still other industries. While agriculture has the opportunity to bid labor and capital away from other industries, it has little opportunity to secure added land as a means of expanding its basic plant. Hence, in the analysis which follows, we make little distinction between short-run and long-run supply functions. The

Table 6.

Use of Selected Resources in Agriculture, 1929-48 *

Year	Crops planted (mil. acres)	Fertilizer (mil. ton)	Lime (mil. ton)	Labor employed Total (mil.)	Hired	Power and machinery (mil. dollars)
1929	363	8.2	3.7	11.3	2.98	466
1930	370	8.4	3.5	11.2	2.85	471
1931	371	6.5	2.5	11.2	2.69	468
1932	375	4.5	1.8	11.1	2.50	452
1933	373	5.1	1.6	11.0	2.43	416
1934	339	5.8	2.4	10.9	2.33	391
1935	362	6.5	3.3	11.1	2.43	389
1936	360	7.2	6.3	11.0	2.56	391
1937	363	8.4	7.1	10.9	2.63	403
1938	354	7.8	7.9	10.8	2.62	419
1939	343	8.0	9.0	10.7	2.60	428
1940	348	8.7	14.4	10.6	2.57	434
1941	348	9.4	15.9	10.4	2.53	445
1942	351	10.1	19.8	10.4	2.54	466
1943	361	11.8	18.9	10.3	2.41	487
1944	365	13.3	19.6	10.0	2.23	494
1945	357	14.0	18.0	9.8	2.12	517
1946	355	16.1	23.4	10.7	2.17	542
1947	359	17.4	23.2	10.8	2.25	549
1948	362	18.3	24.1	10.7	2.31	567

* Sources: *Agricultural Statistics. B.A.E.* Farm wage rates, farm employment and related data. 1943 and *Agricultural Statistics.* From U.S.D.A. Misc. Publication 630 and derived from *Agricultural Statistics* for 1947 and 1948. Based on 1935-39 value of the dollar to suggest the physical quantity of machinery capital. Includes value of horses and mules. These data represent the value of machinery and power existing on farms and not the annual purchase of new machines which did show extreme variation.

supply relationships discussed are short-run in the sense that they refer to a fixed land acreage; they are long-run in the sense that they refer not to post-planting or post-breeding production function but to a period in which resources aside from land can be added or rearranged. On the contraction side, it can be said that the total farm producing plant is of a long-run nature; starting from a full employment of land, this resource as well as labor and capital can be withdrawn from use.

Flexibility in factor prices. The aggregate agricultural production function has been examined to an extent (given the few empirical observations available) to indicate that it has no unique characteristic which would cause farm production to center around one particular level of resource use irrespective of factor/product price ratios or farmer capital positions. The interyear or long-run production function for livestock possesses an elasticity great enough so that, if farmers were to maximize profits, important adjustments would be made in conformance with anticipated changes in price ratios. From the standpoint of the crop production function the wide and gradual variation in soil productivity over the nation most likely causes a gradual decline in the productivity of labor and capital applied to an agricultural plant of a given expanse. Thus while individual farms may have production and supply functions with "inflection points" dividing segments of high and low elasticity (and thus causing stability in output), it does not explain why farmers at extreme ranges of soil productivity maintain their acreage in production during depression; while some land abandonment may occur, historic data show that the tendency is small during major depressions. Accordingly, we are now ready to examine other characteristics of the agricultural supply function which tend to encourage output maintenance in depression and perhaps to dampen expansion in inflation. The role of fixed costs and firm-household interrelationships have been treated in this and earlier chapters. Thus we turn to flexibility in factor pricing in explaining this phenomenon. Even for production functions with elasticities as low as zero or as high as 1.0, no resources would be used unless the factor/product price ratio were sufficiently favorable (or unless expectations were in this direction).

Flexibility of factor prices appears to play an important part in explaining why agricultural production remains highly stable even during depression and partly why expansion is limited in prosperity. That an important number of resources employed in agriculture have a price flexibility paralleling that of agricultural products is obvious. *First,* an important portion of the output is not only a primary product in agriculture but also becomes a resource used in the industry. Feed crops are the outstanding example and represent a major portion of the total value product in the industry. When the prices of corn, oats, or hay (as products) decline for the selling farmer, they also drop for the farmer who employs them as a resource in livestock production. Similarly, the same logic applies to feeder cattle and sheep which are viewed as a product by the rancher but as a factor by the feeder. This situation also exists for the operator who feeds his crops and considers feed crop prices only in an "opportunity cost" sense. Studies in the economics of farm production indicate that feed represents the major cost in livestock production and, "normally" represents from 60 to 70 per cent of the cost of dairy and poultry production and 75 to 85 per cent of the total cost of pork and beef fattening. Prices of feed crops fall as much or even more than livestock prices and thus support stability in livestock production. *Second,* the costs of land services are, in the main, fully as flexible as prices for primary crops. This statement applies directly to rented farms. The very great majority of farms are rented either on a crop-share or a livestock-share basis. The rental payment on these farms necessarily falls in proportion to the decline in prices of products. (Past experience has shown a lag in cash rental rates, but only a minor portion of all farms obtain use of land services in this manner.) Farmers on rented farms evidently considered rental rates to be low enough relative to product prices to justify continued operation during depression. Alternatively, the price of land services for farm owners is highly flexible; the price of services from owned land and buildings is the rent which could be obtained by hiring the resources to other farmers. Few, if any, owners lacked the opportunity to rent out their farms even in the depression of the 1930's. Considering this as the "opportunity price" of land services, owners also viewed the price of the land factor as sufficiently low to merit continued production. *Third,* other groups of factors are represented by inelastic supply curves in the short-run and hence also have flexible prices. The buildings, machinery, and equipment on farms largely represent a fixed and inelastic supply during major depression. Opportunities do not always exist for selling them as salvage. While the price of newly manufactured machinery is somewhat "sticky" during price deflation, a large market exists in used machinery. The few observations available suggest that because of the fixed or inelastic supply of machine services on farms, prices for second-hand equipment fluctuate equally as far and almost as rapidly as the product prices received by farmers. *Fourth,* the price of agricultural labor is sufficiently flexible during major depression to cause declines in wage rates to parallel roughly declines in farm product prices.

Farm produced services and inelastic factor supplies. An important portion of the resource services employed in agriculture possesses short-run flexible prices and thus either (a) encourage maintenance of production during depression or (b) retard expansion in inflation periods. If we examine this set of services and inquire into the cause of their flexibility, two characteristics stand out. (1) The group of resource services with highly flexible prices has its origin largely in the agricultural industry. The crops or livestock which serve as a factor to some farmers originated as a product from other farms. The total land supply comes from within agriculture. The labor force in agriculture is mainly furnished by the households within the industry. Finally, the services forthcoming from buildings and machinery at the beginning of a depression are furnished, in the main, from the stock of these resources which exists on farms at the time. (2) The supply of these farm-furnished resources is highly inelastic during depression. During depression the supply curve for agricultural labor is inelastic because laborers do not have the opportunity of employment elsewhere. Since his alternative return in industry may be zero, the farm worker is willing to accept a wage rate even as low as "board and keep" for himself or his family. Similarly, the reservation price for land is nearly zero during depresson. It has no alternative employment opportunities outside of agriculture. The supply function for agricultural products is then partly explained through the nature of the supply function for agricultural resources. Where the supplies of resources have a low or zero elasticity, the prices of services decline along with farm product prices and encourage maintenance of agricultural production during an extended depression. The timing of price declines for resources with inelastic supply functions does not coincide exactly with declines in product prices. Changes in farm

Table 7.

Indexes of Prices Received by Farmers and Prices for Selected Factor Inputs, 1929-48 (1929 = 100)

Year	Index of prices received by farmers	Index of farm wage rates	Index of feed grain prices and hay prices received	Index of feeder cattle prices
1929	100	100	100	100
1930	84	94	90	89
1931	59	71	63	65
1932	44	53	41	61
1933	47	48	48	48
1934	61	53	80	46
1935	74	59	91	89
1936	77	63	87	79
1937	82	71	107	97
1938	66	69	60	104
1939	64	69	58	111
1940	68	70	69	118
1941	83	86	75	135
1942	107	111	93	161
1943	130	146	124	155
1944	132	175	141	156
1945	139	196	136	174
1946	158	213	166	221
1947	186	227	211	262
1948	192	238	212	317

wage rates lag behind changes in farm product prices and consequently small declines in use of hired labor might be expected during depression. This was the case during the early 1930's. While hired labor in agriculture decreased by around 15.4 per cent from 1929 to 1933, part of this decline merely represented a shift of paid workers to the unpaid family category.

Fixed coefficients and inflexible factor prices. A large number of miscellaneous resources employed in agriculture do not display price flexibility during depression. Included in this category are new machinery, building materials, repairs, twine, and farm supplies in general. Of the total product produced in agriculture only a small fraction represents the share attributable to these factors. The major portion is attributable to labor, land and forms of capital falling in the short-run inelastic supply category.[21] Thus

---

[21] See Earl O. Heady, "Changes in Income Distribution in Agriculture with Special Reference to Technological Change," *Jour. Farm Econ.*, Vol. 26; and D. Gale Johnson, "Allocation of Agricultural Income," *Jour. Farm Econ.*, Vol. 30.

inflexible prices for resources such as twine would not be expected to have any great effect on agricultural output over several years of the business cycle. From 1929 through the depths of the 1930's depression, fertilizer prices fell by only 35 per cent (as compared to a 55 per cent decline in all farm product prices) and use of fertilizer and lime fell by about 50 per cent. Prices of building materials fell by 20 per cent while new purchases declined by 80 per cent; farm machinery prices declined by less than 10 per cent while purchases declined by nearly 75 per cent. Prices for minor materials such as twine, seeds, and fuels declined relatively little in price but the total quantities used did not lessen greatly. The reason is obvious. Over an important range these resources fall in the category of limitational or pure complementary factors. Thus, as long as their cost represents a minor portion of total farm costs, inflexible prices need not greatly retard their use or materially affect agricultural output.

Parallel industry adjustments. The fact that certain of the agricultural processing industries cited maintain output at high levels during depression also has important explanation in factor price flexibility. An important resource employed in food processing industries is the farm product. Thus, since the price of the farm product as a factor is highly flexible, the processing firm is partly in the position of agriculture during depression. The factor/product price ratio remains at a level encouraging output maintenance. In contrast, industries which operate in a pure monopoly setting wherein all factors and factor services must be purchased under monopolistic and inflexible prices find depression price ratios to be unfavorable for production.

Other Elements of Supply Behavior

Although empirical data are not available for their quantitive expression, other forces also play some part in explaining the farm firm's supply behavior. One is that of farmers' expectations. Farmer expectations during depression are "favorable" in the sense that business recovery is "expected eventually." As long as alternative employment opportunities are not present and the farm can be operated to cover variable expenses, anticipation that prices may recover and that asset values may return to former levels can cause farmers to keep their producing plant in operation. Many plant crops or breed animals with the hope and expectation that price declines will be arrested or upturns will come about before the production period is terminated.

While expectations may be of a nature postulating eventual business recovery, the farm firm can take precautions to meet contractual costs and guarantee survival of the firm during depression. These precautions also add to output maintenance during depression. Production and income at the present can be substituted for that of the future by various forms of

disinvestment in the farm. One open avenue is the production of annual
row crops at the expense of legumes and grasses. Action based on expectations that prices must eventually recover would lead, if capital limitations
did not prevent, to the building up of inventories of resource services and
products during depression. Soil investment in the form of legumes and
fertilizers with long transformation periods, while causing sacrifices in
current income, would allow an increased income over a long planning
period; a product will return a greater revenue if it is placed on the market
in the future when prices have recovered rather than during a price reces-
sion. Incomes over the total planning period also might be increased if
inventories of durable products such as grains were carried into the future.
Perhaps the majority of American farmers have been able to foresee these
possibilities during depression. Few believed that the dismal prices of 1932
and 1933 were to permanently characterize the future. Why, then, did they
refuse to build up and carry forward large inventories of soil fertility and
feed grains? The answer is to be found mainly in their precarious capital
position and the driving urge to guarantee the firm's survival in order that
income of whatever level might be realized in the future. The data of Table
8 are suggestive of the adjustments which farmers made in inventories of
soil elements and durable products during the depression. Farmers in aggregate moved in the direction of a more exploitative cropping pattern. While
carry-over of corn and wheat increased somewhat during the extremes of
the depression, the increases representd a relatively small portion of total

Table 8.

Acreage and Farm Stocks of Selected Crops, 1927-32 (Million Acres and Bu.)

Year	Acres corn	Acres all feed grains	Acres wheat	Acres all feed grains	Stocks corn Oct. 1	Stocks wheat July 1
1927	98.4	155.1	59.6	64.9	192.4	27.6
1928	100.3	159.8	59.2	64.2	85.3	19.6
1929	97.8	155.9	63.3	67.9	143.9	45.1
1930	101.5	160.5	62.6	67.8	131.5	60.2
1931	106.9	165.8	57.7	62.3	162.2	37.9
1932	110.6	173.4	57.8	62.5	251.6	93.8

crop production and suggest that only a small portion of farmers were in a
position to carry forward inventories in anticipation of business recovery.
    Other forces entering into an explanation of the agricultural supply
function are less important than those discussed in detail on previous
pages. The case in which the farm will furnish more labor resources from
the household and hence provide a "backward sloping" supply function
has its basis in the firm-household relationships discussed in Chapter 14.
The major part of output maintenance during depression is not explained
by this force, however. Neither does the subsistence characteristic of agriculture provide the basis for a large output during depression. While

nearly all farms produce some subsistence products and 20 per cent derive their income mainly from subsistence production, little more than 15 per cent of the total agricultural product moves into direct use by the household. Finally while the 4 to 9 months involved in crop production and the 2 to 4 years involved in certain types of livestock production represent longer production periods than are found in many non-farm industries, the period of production does not provide the basis for output maintenance over several years of depression.

Production Expansion and the Secular Movement of the Supply Function

This movement whereby agricultural output expands during periods of full employment but fails to contract as much during periods of general unemployment has led to the observation that the agricultural supply function "is elastic in the direction of expansion" but "inelastic in the direction of contraction." If Figure 8 is examined, it is obvious that, aside from nation-wide drought and minor retraction during depressions, the

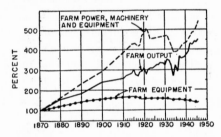

Fig. 8. Total volume of farm power and machinery and equipment. Farm output and total farm employment, United States, 1870-1946 (volume in terms of 1935-1939 dollars; index numbers, 1870 = 100).

annual output of agricultural products has maintained a steady climb over the past several decades. While the fixed costs and flexibility of factor prices in agriculture provide an important basis for output maintenance over a 5- to 10-year depression period, it does not entirely explain the tenacity with which output is maintained over much longer periods when farm stocks of resources such as buildings and machines have had time to be fully depreciated and labor has had opportunity during full employment periods to move to non-farm alternatives. Is it possible for a long-run supply function to be "elastic on the upward side" but "inelastic on the downward side"?

Under secular expansion, agricultural output slides up a long-run supply curve but during depression contraction it falls down a short-run supply function; the fixed cost-flexible factor price complex is an expression of short-run supply functions.[22] Over extended periods different long-run supply functions also come into being and cause expansion to trace out a different path from contraction. The long-run supply function may move continuously to the right either because the price of resource services declines or because the production function changes in a direction to increase the productivity of resources. The effect of either force on long-run output maintenance can be illustrated in Figures 5 and 6. Starting with the demand function given as indicated by D_1 and the underlying production function and supply curves as expressed by P and S_1, a sufficient decrease in factor prices, with the production function remaining constant, will result in the new supply function, indicated as S_2. Whereas the previous equilibrium output would have been oq_1, the new equilibrium quantity, with demand remaining unchanged, will be oq_3. (Even with a decline in demand, output will be maintained in the factor flexibility sense at oq_2.) Similarly, a change in techniques as denoted by a production function P', with factor costs unchanged, will move the supply function from S_1 to S_2. If farms acted purely as firms and if knowledge or expectations were sufficiently accurate, output would again move to oq_3 when demand remains at D_1. It would continue at oq_2 with a drop in the demand function to D_2 during depression. Innovations, and hence change, in the aggregate production function have provided a long-term base whereby the agricultural supply curve has been lowered continuously. Technological change would not, of course, cause farm output to be maintained over a long period if technical change, demand, and resource productivity in nonfarm industries were to outpace that of agriculture. The approximate data which are available suggest that the technical revolution in agriculture, at least in the 1930's and 1940's, nearly paralleled that of other industries.

Form of resources. The secular tendency for agricultural output to increase in the face of declining factor/product price ratios has partial explanation in the use of added resources as well as increased resource productivity. True, the greatest change in farm capital over the last 4 decades has been in form rather than in quantity. The shift from horses and horse-drawn machinery with larger and fewer farming units has allowed, if automobiles are excluded, an equal or only a slightly larger total capital investment to replace older forms of power and equipment. While major changes have taken place in the form of capital, agriculture

---

[22] The expansion is of a long-run nature in the sense that it allows addition of semi-durable resources in the form of buildings and machines. It is still short-run in the sense that the basic plant or land area is largely given, however. In the remainder of this chapter the terms long-run and short-run will be employed to refer respectively to production when (a) major adjustments can be made in buildings, machinery and the general structure of agriculture on a given land area and (b) short-term adjustments when the supply of other resources as well as land is highly inelastic.

has at the same time used greater quantities of capital over time. Starting with 1900, the amount of farm power and machinery increased by slightly over 60 per cent by 1920. In this same period capital in livestock increased by at least 12 per cent, current operating expense by as much as 100 per cent and the aggregate of capital by 30 per cent. In this early period total cropland increased from 319 to 402 million acres or by 25 per cent while labor employment in agriculture remained approximately constant. Thus during the 20-year period 1900-20 the additional input of resources was perhaps sufficient to account for the major addition to output over the same period. In the period 1920-29 employment of labor declined by less than 1 per cent, cropland increased by around 1 per cent, some increase was made in the quantity of capital in the form of livestock and fertilizer and current expenses increased slightly. Changes in power and machinery capital were almost entirely in form rather than quantity. Estimates suggest that about one-half the increase in agricultural output during the 1920-24 period can be attributed to increased resource inputs with the remainder attributable to technological change and exogenous forces.[23] The 1930's have already been discussed. Employment of major resources declined only slightly with purchase and use of fertilizer, new machines, and building materials, and selected other capital declined abruptly. Although the decrease in output from forces aside from weather was slight in the period 1930-34, output increased very rapidly in the period 1935-39. An important part of this increase must be attributed to innovations and changed forms of capital as farmers shifted from horses to tractors and from open pollinated to hybrid seed corn and also incorporated other biological changes into their farming operations. During the period 1940-49, farm output increased somewhat over 25 per cent. Harvested cropland increased by about 3 per cent, while labor employment decreased by around 4 per cent. Current operating expenses increased by 60 per cent, while power and machinery on farms increased by around 35 per cent. If the services of all resources are aggregated, it appears that physical input of services increased by not more than 10 to 12 per cent while physical output increased by twice this amount. Over time then it appears that the short-run supply curve (the one down which agricultural production first recedes as depression comes about or as farm prices and returns decline relative to non-farm prices and returns) has shifted continuously to the right as greater capital has been added to agriculture. At the same time, the long-run supply function has also moved to the right because of technological advance.

Technical advance in itself, however, does not guarantee that farmers must produce a greater quantity over time at the same or lower prices. Other conditions are necessary if agricultural output maintains a con-

---

[23] Johnson, *op. cit.*, p. 560.

tinuous and extended climb. If the demand for agricultural products were sufficiently inelastic while highly elastic demands, along with even greater technical revolutions, characterized other industries, the relative value productivity of resources employed in the farming might decline to a point where the shift of resources would result in a diminished agricultural output.

Selected References

Boulding, K. E., *Economic Analysis*. New York: Harper, 1948, Ch. 23.

Breimyer, H. F., "Efficiency of Feeding Livestock," *Jour. Farm Econ.*, Vol. 25.

Cochrane, W., "Farm Price Gyrations: An Aggregative Hypothesis," *Jour. Farm Econ.*, Vol. 29.

Galbraith, J. K., and Black, J. D., "The Maintenance of Agricultural Output During Depression," *Jour. Pol. Econ.*, Vol. XLVI.

Gislason, C., "Nature of the Aggregate Supply Function for Agricultural Products," *Jour. Farm Econ.*, Vol. 34.

Johnson, D. G., "The Supply Function in Agriculture," *Amer. Econ. Rev.*, Vol. 40.

Schultz, T. W., *Agriculture in an Unstable Economy*. New York: McGraw-Hill, 1945, Ch. 3.

———, "Farm Price Gyrations by Cochrane," *Jour. Farm Econ.*, Vol. 33.

Shepherd, G. S., *Agricultural Price Analysis*. Ames: Iowa State College Press, 1941.

Stigler, G., *Theory of Competitive Price*. New York: Macmillan, 1947, pp. 147-171, 186-191.

Waite, W. C., and Trelogen, H. C., *Agricultural Market Prices*. New York: Wiley, 1951, Chs. 3, 4, 5.

Wilcox, W. W., "Effects of Farm Price Change on Farming Efficiency," *Jour. Farm Econ.*, Vol. 33.

24

Economic Efficiency in the Agricultural Industry

Pʀᴏᴅᴜᴄᴛɪᴏɴ efficiency is a complex field of analysis even when it is studied from the standpoint of an individual farm. Difficulties are encountered, not only in making empirical estimates of the relevant physical, cost, and revenue relationships, but also in delineating the relevant ends to be maximized and the proper choice indicators to serve as a basis for resource administration by farmers. In addition to these several considerations, imperfect knowledge and uncertainty add both to the complexity of the farmer's decision-making process and the process of empirical measurement. These difficulties do not, however, cause farmers to cease production. Neither do they cause economists to withdraw all attempts to describe the production process and the behavior of producers or to make recommendations on resource use.

We now encounter a second problem of analysis which is equally or more complex even though it is simply an extension of the production relationships and maximization conditions outlined earlier. This chapter deals with aggregate or over-all efficiency in the use of agricultural resources. Not only are we concerned with defining the conditions under which resources are used most efficiently, but also in describing or explaining why differences in resource productivity arise. These points have been touched on in earlier chapters; we now deal more specifically with them.

Efficiency Criteria

Production efficiency might be analyzed from several different standpoints. First, we might take the distribution of personal incomes and the organization of industries as given and analyze the extent to which agricultural efficiency is attained within this setting. Here we would not concern ourselves with the fact that, while agriculture is competitive, other industries are organized on a monopoly basis and thus restrict production and condition the aggregate efficiency of resource allocation. Second, we might leave the organization of industry as given and consider that both the organization of production in agriculture and the distribution of incomes are subject to variation. The pattern of production and resource use which is most efficient in this setting may differ widely from that outlined in the first case. If the pattern of income distribution which maximizes national welfare resulted in a more nearly equal income to each family or individual, less of some products and more of other products would be produced than under the existing pattern of income distributions. Third, we might consider both the distribution of incomes and the organization of industry as variables. With an opportunity to convert some industries from a monopoly to a competitive basis, one barrier to the inter-industry flow of resources would be removed. Under this situation agriculture might employ fewer total resources, while industries which are currently organized on a monopoly basis would employ more, and the marginal productivity of resources in the several industries would be brought closer together.

A full examination of resource productivity and efficiency in these several settings would require a major effort. For this reason the analysis which follows focuses on agricultural productivity within the first framework; production and resource efficiency is analyzed under an environment wherein the distribution of income and the basic organization of industry are given. We will have occasion at various points, however, to examine the effect of monopoly and competitive organization on agricultural production efficiency. It should be remembered that the pattern of income distribution does not at all negate the efficiency criteria to be outlined. While the exact patterns of production and resource allocation would differ, depending on the distribution of incomes, the basic principles or conditions defining aggregate efficiency would remain unchanged. If the production economist understands how these apply under one pattern of income distribution, he also has knowledge of their application under other patterns.

Criteria of efficiency. When a farm is analyzed as a pure firm, profit maximization becomes the sole end of production organization and, conceptually, the optimum use of resources is denoted by relating the choice indicator to the production possibilities of the farm. Choice indicators are given in the form of price relationships. Delineation of the choice-making process and choice indicators is more complex when the farm family is considered as the relevant economic unit. The value productivity of resources and net profit can no longer be used as a gauge of whether resources are used efficiently; the direct utility which farm persons derive from resources must also be considered. These difficulties are multiplied when aggregate efficiency is under consideration. They represent, however, the same phenomena expressed in different magnitudes. While we were able to provide few empirical data indicating the quantitative importance of these "intangible" products on the individual farm, we were able to outline basic principle and relationship with some degree of satisfaction. The same procedure must be followed in analysis of aggregate production efficiency.

The conditions of maximum efficiency. The conditions which define maximum economic efficiency when the agricultural industry is considered differ. not at all from the basic principles outlined for individual farms. Since the conditions and principles of economic efficiency were considered in detail in earlier chapters, they need only be reviewed in this one. A multitude of production or technical units, in the form of different acres and animals, exist on the individual farm. Whether or not the economic quantity to be maximized is profit, resources must be distributed between all of these units in a manner such that their marginal productivity is equal in all cases. With resources given and limited, maximum efficiency is attained only as it becomes impossible to reshuffle resources without decreasing the total value of the product. If the marginal value productivity of resources applied to one technical unit within the farm is greater than that for a second technical unit, an optimum pattern of resource allocation has not been attained. These same basic principles also apply when the end of the farm production is that of maximizing family satisfaction rather than profit alone. Only the unit of measurement differs.

Questions of the appropriate index for measuring efficiency revolve especially around the individual farm; profit and direct utility from resources become rivals as the family attempts to maximize its satisfactions. The remote, off-farm consumer is not, however, so closely connected to the direct satisfaction arising from farm production. Therefore, to the extent that the pricing system accurately reflects the value system and choices of the consumer, the value productivity of resources can serve as an index of production efficiency. If the consumer desires more beef and less pork, he can attach a relatively higher price to the former commodity and thus cause the value of the product for a unit of resource to be higher if used for beef rather than for pork. A perfect meshing of resource allocation and consumer desire or choice is then reflected if the marginal value productivity of the last unit of each resource is the same in each line of production. It is known, of course, that the market mechanism is far from perfect and perhaps can never allow perfect attainment of the necessary conditions outlined above. For one thing the variability of the production process excludes the possibility of instantaneous equilibrium. Even if the pricing mechanism did not itself cause errors to arise in resource administration, physical variability would. Recognizing these limitations of value measurements, we will, however, employ value productivity as a very rough tool in analyzing aggregate resource efficiency in agriculture. When we use value productivity as a measure or criterion of how efficiently agricultural resources are used, we suppose the consumer to be the sovereign or focal unit of an economic system wherein democracy prevails. We simply want to outline the conditions under which resources are used in conformance with consumer preference, and examine the extent to which resource use deviates from this norm. It is obvious that in a democracy the goal of production organization is use of resources in a manner consistent with the desires of the society as a unit. Thus, while we employ the concept of value productivity as one criterion of production or resource efficiency, the basic principles to be outlined are exactly the same as they would be if some other unit of measurement were to be employed. For example, a nation at war or faced with a population pressing food consumption to the subsistence level might be concerned mainly with the quantity of food nutrients forthcoming from given and limited agricultural resources. The relevant index might then be one of "calory productivity" and the most efficient use of resources would be attained from the consumer and society standpoint if units of resources were always used where their "marginal calory productivity" were greatest; maximum efficiency would be attained when the "marginal calory productivity" of the last unit of each resource was equal in all lines of production. The principles remain unchanged. Accordingly, we employ value productivity for our first steps in analyzing efficiency in the agricultural industry.[1]

The conditions of efficiency. Without stopping to concern ourselves with problems in income distribution, the conditions which define over-all efficiency in resource use can be outlined simply. First, we can return to Figures 11 and 15 in Chapter 4. When these figures were examined previously, we were concerned with the manner in which a given amount of a resource would be arranged between technical units to maximize the total product and the profit of a farmer. Now, rather than view the production functions in a purely physical sense, we can suppose that they relate physical input (or the value of input) to the value of product and thus allow comparisons of marginal value productivity. If prices can be taken to reflect consumer choice, the marginal conditions outlined for maximizing the physical product of the farm, with resources limited in quantity, also become the marginal conditions necessary for attaining maximum efficiency from the standpoint of society. We are again concerned with allocating resources between different producing segments. These producing segments

---

[1] Value productivity does have other limitations. When the level of living index or the value of money differs sufficiently between industries and regions, unadjusted monetary returns to resources do not equally reflect their true productivity. Some resources may rationally be retained in agricultural production if living costs on the farm are sufficiently lower than those encountered by households in other industries; money values do not fully measure the "real" product or income of specific resources. Similarly, the costs of transferring resources between areas leads to qualifications in the conditions of maximum efficiency. Our procedure is to outline the conditions of maximum efficiency when these 2 considerations are not included, and then to make exceptions to them later. We do this only to simplify the procedure. The conditions outlined hold without reservation between farms and between agriculture and industry (where the location is common or the value of a dollar does not differ importantly within households).

now include different technical units within a farm, different farms, different producing regions, and, finally, even different industries. Within this
framework, resources are allocated most efficiently when these conditions
hold true: (1) Resources must be allocated within each farm in a manner
so that the marginal value productivities of the resource services are
equal; a unit of labor or capital should not be used for corn if it can
produce a greater value product in wheat. (2) Resources must be distributed between farms so that marginal value productivities are equal.
(3) Resources must be distributed between producing and farming areas
to allow attainment of equal value productivity. (4) The various factors
must be allocated between industries to bring about attainment of these
identical conditions. (5) Resources must be allocated over time such that
their discounted value products are equal.

Labor and capital are focal. Analysis of agricultural efficiency from the
aggregate or national standpoint centers on labor and capital, of course,
since these are the resources which can be readapted and moved between
parcels of land, between farms, and between farming regions. Land simply
provides a physical base over which other resources can be deployed. While
an acre of Webster soil in Central Iowa cannot result in an economic product unless this resource is combined with labor and capital, in combination
with these resources it can produce corn, oats, or other climatically suited
crops. Labor and capital, however, need not be restricted to the production
of corn and oats at a single location in Iowa but have alternatives in
producing tobacco in the Connecticut Valley, citrus fruit in Florida, cotton
in Alabama, olives in California, or automobiles in Detroit.

Technical Conditions

If we wish to include the direct utility derived from resources by farm
operators along with the market values which consumers place on commodities, the technical conditions defining the most efficient use or allocation of resources become those outlined below. The conditions set out as
necessary for maximum production or allocative efficiency apply equally
between technical units within farms and between different producing
areas (if transport services are included in resource outlays). While they
are "spelled out" only as they relate to the allocation of resources between
farms, they relate in similar fashion to producing units of all magnitudes.
The conditions outlined are postulated on the basis of a fixed stock of
resource services. They represent a refinement of the efficiency conditions
set out above.

*1. The marginal rate at which factor is transformed into product must
be the same for any pair of farms using the same factors and producing
the same product.* In simple form, this statement says that if society wants
another 5 bales of cotton it should obtain them from a farm which will

require only 300 hours of labor rather than one which will require 600 hours, or if another 100 lbs. of pork is to be obtained, it should come from a farm where the job can be done with 350 lbs. of grain rather than on one where 450 lbs. are required. The details of this condition have already been explained in Figure 11 of Chapter 4 in terms of maximizing the physical product from a given quantity of variable resources for a farm as the relevant accounting unit.

2. The marginal rate of substitution between any pair of factors must be the same for any 2 firms using both to produce the same product. In a very practical sense, this statement says that if one tractor and four men are required to produce 5,000 bushels of corn on one farm, fewer total resources will be required if the tractor is transferred to a farm which can produce the 5,000 bushels with 1 tractor and 1 man. Likewise, if 100 lbs. of beef can be produced with 100 lbs. of oilmeal and 12 bushels of corn on one farm and 100 lbs. of meal and 10 bushels of corn on a second, use of the meal on the latter farm will allow the same beef output with less corn or more beef with the same corn. Again, the geometry and logic of this statement have been illustrated in Chapter 6.

3. The marginal rate of substitution between 2 factors must be the same for every product in which they are used. Given a limited stock of resources, this condition applies to different farms producing different products in the same manner that Chapter 8 illustrated resource allocation between 2 products on the same farm. The same condition must hold true between farms. Some farms have relatively large amounts of labor; other farms have relatively large amounts of capital. Recombining the resources, including management, between farms could allow a much greater product from the resources now in agriculture.

4. The marginal rate of substitution between any 2 products must be the same for any 2 farms producing both. This condition states that the total amount of product forthcoming from a given stock of resources will always be greatest if product substitution ratios are equal between farms. In simple form, it means that if society wants another 1,000 bushels of wheat it should obtain them from a farm which must sacrifice only 1,500 bushels of corn rather than one which must sacrifice 2,500 bushels of corn to produce the 1,000 bushels of wheat. The logic also has been illustrated in Chapter 8.

5. The marginal rate at which 2 crops substitute as products on one farm must be equal to the marginal rate at which they substitute as factors on another (or the same) farm. This statement defines the organization of labor, capital, and land resources in primary crop production which will allow a maximum output of secondary livestock product from a given collection of resources. Details of the condition were outlined previously.

6. Marginal rates of substitution must be equal between (a) the income and direct utility (leisure) of a resource in production and (b) the income and direct utility of a resource in consumption for any single resource owner and between resource owners. These are the conditions outlined under firm-household relationships with the exception that they can also be extended between individuals. In other words, the individual cannot increase his utility by investing more labor in production if the utility given up by working on the farm another 3 months of the year is greater than the utility gained from the $500 forthcoming as money income.

7. *Marginal rates of substitution of products in time or resources in time must be equal for all farms which produce or use both.* This statement is simply an adaptation of those outlined previously. If we consider a commodity produced at 2 different points in time as 2 different products and apply proper discounting procedures, our solution becomes that outlined under 5 above. Similarly, considering use of a single factor at two different points in time as 2 distinct resources, we get the solution under 2 above. These relationships entail no new logic, but are outlined in detail in a later chapter under the heading of conservation. It should be remembered, however, that soil conservation is only 1 problem in the broader field of production economics and the principles outlined apply equally to the use of feed or machine services over time.

The 7 propositions outlined above indicate the technical or physical conditions which are necessary for (a) maximization of output from given resources or (b) minimization of resource input for a given output. If the problem of resource allocation falls in a war setting they are applicable without modification. Similarly, they are applicable in terms of the real product or total of goods and services available to society. When consumer expression is through the pricing system, equal value products are attained for all units of resources when the eighth condition outlined below is attained.

8. *Price ratios must equal substitution and transformation rates in all cases such that (a) the factor-product price ratio equals the marginal rate at which factor is transformed into product, (b) the product-product price ratio is equal to the marginal rate of substitution of any 2 commodities, (c) the factor-factor price ratio is equal to the marginal rate of substitution between any pair of factors, (d) the discounted price ratio is equal to the substitution ratio for 1 product produced at 2 points in time, and (e) the compounded price ratio is equal to the substitution ratio for two resources extending into time.* Or we can say simply that the marginal cost of a unit of resource for each farm and farming region must be equal to its marginal value product. This condition, if adopted in an interfarm and interarea manner, is the one stated by equation IV and its corollary, V, in Chapter 6. This condition supposes that the work preference of individuals should be considered; the marginal cost for a unit of labor in one use will depend partly on the value attached by the individual to leisure or work in other occupations or locations. It also considers consumer preference for

products. Attainment of this omnibus condition (in conjunction with the technical conditions outlined above) guarantees that no unit of resource can be transferred to increase the value of the product produced. Inasmuch as prices reflect consumer choice in use of resources, and given the pattern of income distribution, consumer satisfaction or welfare is then at a maximum.

Necessary and sufficient conditions. Attainment of maximum economic efficiency is possible only if the 8 conditions outlined above are satisfied simultaneously. Simultaneous attainment of these physical conditions allows a maximum of product from a given stock of resources, or, conversely, a minimum input of resources for a given output of product. Under the price conditions mentioned, the marginal value productivity is equal for each use in which a unit of resource is employed. Again it may be said that the conditions of efficiency outlined above not only apply between producing firms in an industry but have similar application between technical units within a single farm and between farming regions. From a standpoint of basic principle, the maximum or minimum conditions defining the fullest attainment of the farm families' ends or objectives are the same as those defining maximum consumer welfare for the nation, regardless of the magnitude or composition of producing units. Thus the economy of factor use can be studied not only for a single farm but the same farm management framework can be extended to a study of resource efficiency at the level of the agricultural industry or the national economy. Agriculture itself is a highly composite industry which includes many contrasting types of products; the processing of tobacco on the farm, for example, more nearly resembles certain non-farm industries than it does cattle feeding or wheat cultivation. In the final analysis, the efficiency with which agricultural resources are employed can be determined only as a criterion is employed which compares farm with non-farm industries and allows comparisons between firms of the different industries.

While the conditions outlined in the previous section are *necessary conditions* if efficiency in the use of resources is to be attained, they are not *sufficient conditions*. They alone do not guarantee that a maximum product is forthcoming from a given stock of resources (or contrariwise, that a given output is being produced with a minimum of factor services).[2] In this context, maximum efficiency is guaranteed only if single products are produced under conditions of decreasing returns (increasing costs) and if commodities produced in combination are never produced within ranges of complementary and supplementary relationships. In other words, the

---

[2] The term *maximum value product* could be substituted for the term *maximum product* to indicate that the choice of consumers is reflected in the final combination of factors and products. Although it is not spelled out in detail at each point where the term is used, our use of the concept efficiency relates either directly or indirectly to a maximum in terms of goods and services which consumers choose.

factor-product and the production possibility curves must be concave to the origin in the relevant area of equilibrium for each producing unit. If some farms are producing under conditions of increasing returns while others are operating under decreasing returns, a greater total product would be forthcoming in agriculture if the total of resources employed by the 2 were rearranged to give 1 more and the other fewer resources. A farm of less than optimum size in terms of costs can never allow maximum economic efficiency if the value of the product produced is used as the criterion. Then, of course, maximum efficiency is never attained on a single farm if the proportions of 2 crops such as grain and forage are not combined over time to allow a maximum output of grain for any quantity of hay. These particular conditions are those outlined in detail in early chapters and are very important in agriculture.

Unless the *necessary* and *sufficient* conditions are all attained simultaneously, resources are not used efficiently; they can always be rearranged to allow, with resources given and limited, a greater total output of the products "desired" by the consuming society. We are able to make this statement for any given pattern of income distribution. For any other pattern of income distribution, efficiency is attained under exactly the same set of *necessary* and *sufficient* conditions. Since the steps above define the optimum pattern of production for any given pattern of income distribution, we could soon outline the conditions of consumption which define maximum economic welfare when the pattern of income distribution also is considered variable.[3]

Details of resource use. Attainment of maximum economic efficiency thus becomes an intricate and detailed problem. It is not sufficient that capital in broad aggregate and labor in broad aggregate be allocated between farms in a manner that substitution rates are equal. These same conditions must be attained for each particular form of capital such as tractor fuel, fertilizer, repairs, and other specific resource items. In the same manner, particular price and physical ratios must be equated. The feed/milk price

---

[3] These are simple and can be stated as follows:

a. The marginal rate of substitution between 2 products, including time considerations, in consumption must be the same for every pair of individuals consuming both. This condition defines the manner in which products (income) should be distributed among individuals.

b. The marginal rate of substitution of any 2 goods in consumption must be the same, for any person consuming both, as for the marginal rate of substitution of the 2 goods in production. This condition employs the consumer's preference function as the final choice indicator in defining the optimum pattern of production. These conditions define how the total product or income should be distributed and then related to the production conditions already outlined, and define the optimum pattern of production when the allocation of income is not fixed. They are outlined in greater detail by M. R. Reder, *Studies in the Theory of Welfare Economics.* New York: Columbia University Press, 1947; H. Mynt, *The Theory of Welfare Economics.* Cambridge: Harvard University Press, 1948; and I. M. D. Little, *Welfare Economics.* Oxford: Clarendon Press, 1950.

ratio must equal the milk/feed transformation ratio. The corn/protein substitution ratio must not only be equal between farms but must also equal the protein/corn price ratio. The machinery/labor substitution ratio must be equal between farms producing wheat only and also between one farm producing wheat and another producing flax. Indeed the conditions of maximum efficiency cannot be attained by any broad, sweeping concept of labor-capital equilibrium, as much recent agricultural economics literature might lead one to believe. They have their roots as much in the ration fed on a particular farm as in the relative quantities of labor used in the Appalachian Highlands and the Cornbelt.

As in the case of the farm as a firm, the conditions of maximum efficiency at the aggregate level can never be attained in fine detail because plans for production and resource use must be based on expectations and imperfect knowledge. While we can measure efficiency in the historic or *ex poste* sense, we can never define the pattern of resource use which will be optimum in a period ahead for which information is incomplete. However, society, like the individual farmer must, by employing systematic expectations and planning, attempt to attain conditions of efficiency. The complete lack of planning is not a rational adjustment to uncertainty. Society has an advantage over the individual in this respect; it has the power to eliminate or at least reduce imperfect knowledge. Hence *ex poste* measurements of the gaps in efficiency are of importance. They suggest the extent to which society has been able to provide an expectational and planning framework which is consistent with the actual or realized production possibilities.

Measurement of efficiency. The problem of empirical measurement is difficult when the entire agricultural industry is to be viewed from the standpoint of economic efficiency. The very greatest difficulty arises because not all products are traded in the market but some are derived directly from resources. The enjoyment which the farmer realizes from "living in the country" or being "his own boss" falls in this category, as do the virtues of "sunshine and hard work." While these facets of production were included under the necessary conditions outlined above, it is measurement of their quantities that is difficult. However, the production economist is faced with the same problem, whether he is analyzing efficiency from the standpoint of a single farm or from the standpoint of the industry. At the farm level it is an obvious fact that farmers do not attempt to maximize dollar profit; if they were to maximize money income alone they would work on Sundays as well as engaging the labor of the family for 16 hours per day over the entire year. In spite of the fact that few, if any, operators actually do attempt profit maximization alone, thousands of empirical studies have used dollar returns as an efficiency criterion for the individual farm. In the same vein it may be possible to use the value productivity or return on resources as the criterion of aggregate farming efficiency. Failure to include subjective income (the enjoyment of farming) as part of the total agricultural output is no more serious in the one case than in the other. Because it is the only tangible or measurable criterion which can be obtained, money income or value productivity will undoubtedly continue to be a commonly used index of economic efficiency for either individual farms or the agricultural industry. The value of product per unit resource is thus employed in the following section to provide some notion of agricultural efficiency.

Resource Efficiency in the Agricultural Industry

To obtain some notion of whether production and resource use are organized efficiently, we must examine the possibilities of reshuffling resources (1) within single farms, (2) between farms of the same producing regions, (3) between producing regions, and (4) between agriculture and other industries. The possibilities of rearranging resources to increase the total economic product to the consuming society must be examined both within single time periods and between time periods. The applied science of agricultural economics was founded largely upon resource efficiency studies. Farm management and production economics studies have been and are being employed to indicate whether resources in farming have equal or differing returns or value productivities. These economic efficiency studies originally were and still are designed to suggest to farmers as administrators of resources and to public administrators whether farming resources are being used in a manner to maximize value products or returns. The method most widely applied was developed by Warren and has been extended by others.[4] Other attempts in production economics and farm management to employ modified systems of these procedures include those of Schultz, Clark, Barton, and Ducoff.[5] The system of these studies has been to estimate the return to a single factor as labor or capital in the residual method outlined in Chapter 13. This return or value of product per unit of resource is computed for farms producing different products, for farms using different factor combinations, and for farms of different scales. The same procedure has been employed by farm management

---

[4] See G. F. Warren, *Farming in Tompkins County, New York.* N. Y. Agr. Exp. Sta. Bul. 295, 1910.

[5] See C. Clark, *Conditions of Economic Progress.* London: Macmillan, 1940, Chs. 3-11; T. W. Schultz, *Production and Welfare of Agriculture.* New York: McGraw-Hill, 1949, Ch. 7; L. J. Ducoff, and M. J. Hagood, *Differentials in Productivity and Farm Income of Agricultural Workers by Size of Enterprise and by Regions.* Bureau of Agricultural Economics, Mimeo, 1944; and T. G. Barton, and M. R. Cooper, *Farm Production in War and Peace.* U.S.D.A. Bureau of Agricultural Economics, Mimeo, 1945, FM53. Clark makes an international productivity comparison of labor productivity, while Schultz compares productivity of agricultural labor with industry and between regions. The other studies are mainly concerned with regional or size differentials within agriculture.

workers to examine differences in resource returns and productivity between farming regions. Less exact tests of interregional productivity differentials have been made by imputing the entire product to labor.[6] More complex attempts to derive marginal productivities for different classes of resources have also been employed.[7] While the procedures themselves are open to question, they do suggest possible differences in resource returns. Most of them estimate average productivities: the residual imputed to labor or capital is divided by the number of workers or the amount of capital to suggest labor income per person or return per dollar of capital.

Intra-area and interregional productivity comparisons. If we examine input-output or transformation rates in agriculture, we find that most of the conditions outlined above are violated. An Iowa study found neighboring farms on which grain requirements for hogs produced to the same weight ranged from 300 to 800 lbs., while other resource inputs were similar.[8] Similar ranges exist between other farms and regions. Since the initial empirical studies in agricultural economics, research workers have illustrated very great gaps in the value productivity of all agricultural resources. Conventional farm management surveys and studies have served as indicators of these differences. As early as 1916, Warren illustrated that wide differences existed in returns to labor (on the basis of the residual imputation process) between farms in the same area, between farming areas, and between farm and non-farm industries. Reporting a Tompkins County, New York, study made in 1907, he indicated that approximately one-third of the sample fell in each of the following labor income intervals: $0-200, $200-400, and $400 and over. Similar differences in labor income existed for a Livingston County study, where the average labor return of the entire sample was $666. The labor return for a sample of farms in southern New Hampshire was $337 for 1916. A large portion of the farms in these early studies was shown to have labor incomes lower than for farm laborers and non-farm workers. Warren also was able to illustrate very great differences over other regions of the United States. Farm management studies have continued down through time to serve as a basis indicating wide differences in labor productivity and returns between farms and between farming regions. Very great differences are found even among the selected groups of farms which keep records in cooperation with Land Grant Colleges. Even though the imputational process em-

---

[6] The limitations in imputing the full return to labor when making comparisons between farm and non-farm labor productivity is outlined in G. F. Warren, *op. cit.*, p. 16; and E. O. Heady, "Production Functions from a Random Sample of Farms," *Jour. Farm Econ.*, Vol. 28.

[7] See the following studies for indication of marginal productivities derived from production function estimates: Earl O. Heady, *Ibid.*; and G. Tintner, "A Note on the Derivation of Production Functions from Farm Records," *Econometrica,* Vol. 12.

[8] Based on data obtained for Iowa Agricultural Experiment Station Bulletin 381.

ployed in these studies allows very rough approximations of resource productivity, it does indicate that farms of different size, farms producing different products, and farms in different regions do have widely differing value products per unit of resources. Contrasts between regions can be seen in the labor data of Table 1. While these are averages and our interest is chiefly in marginal quantities, few if any production economists would not argue that marginal productivity of labor also differs between regions.

Table I.

Average Crop and Livestock Production Per Man Hour, Regions of the United States, 1943-45 (U. S. Average = 100) *

Region	Crop production per man hour	Livestock production per man hour
West North Central	165	128
New England	154	133
East North Central	149	120
Mountain	141	124
Pacific	130	130
Middle Atlantic	118	113
South Atlantic	63	74
West South Central	62	72
East South Central	56	63
United States	100	100

* Source: R. W. Hecht, and G. T. Barton, *Gains in Farm Labor Productivity.* U.S.D.A. Tech. Bul. No. 1020.

While the magnitudes are quite different, more refined statistical studies suggest similar differences in resource productivity between farming regions. An Iowa study covering 1939, for example, indicated widely-differing returns on capital in the 5 major farming areas. Marginal productivities of livestock capital was much greater in southern Iowa, where investment and income per farm were low as compared to other areas of the state.[9] Contrariwise, the marginal value productivity of labor in this geographical area with a relatively high labor concentration was much lower than for other areas of the state.[10] More recent productivity esti-

[9] The marginal value product per dollar invested in livestock was 3.81 in southern Iowa as compared to 1.07 in northeastern and central Iowa. Similarly, the marginal value product of equipment and machinery was twice as great in the southern part of the state as in northeastern Iowa and 50 per cent greater than in central Iowa. In contrast, labor productivity was only half as great in southern Iowa as in the other 2 areas. For further details on this study see E. O. Heady, *op. cit.*

[10] The same geographical pattern exists for Iowa when labor returns are computed by residual methods from census data. See E. O. Heady and E. R. Swanson, *Resource Productivity in Iowa Farming.* Iowa Agr. Sta. Bul. 388. The labor returns per worker for 1939 and 1944 are as follows:

Area	1939	1944
Northern cash grain	$1421	$3854
Western livestock	1295	3817
North central cash grain	1335	3550
Eastern livestock	1046	2941

mates in southern Iowa also indicate wide differences in the value productivity of resources.[11] Except for labor, the returns on resources were clearly greater than interest costs. While the empirical methods employed (least squares regression analysis) are open to scientific scrutiny, even more complex systems (simultaneous equations) indicate similar relative differences.[12] While similar data do not exist on a national basis, the widely held observation of agricultural economists is that marginal value productivities differ as much between farming regions as do labor income or other average resource returns based on residual imputation methods.

Farm management surveys and general equilibrium analysis. There are very few major farming regions in which farm management studies have not been made over the past 4 decades. Using the average productivity estimates explained above, one finding from these stands out: the return per unit of resource differs greatly between farms within the same region and between farming regions. If these cross-sectional studies (observations drawn from different farms rather than from within one farm) can be used as an indication, very great differences also exist within farms. It is true, of course, that many but not all such studies are made to determine whether, in an *ex poste* sense, resources are allocated in a manner to maximize the value product or profits of the farm. Where farms are on widely differing soils these studies are better indicators of interfarm differences than of intra-farm differences; one farm, even if it had the same amounts of labor and capital combined in the same fashion, could never attain the same productivity of resources as another farm on a different soil type. While the historic farm management survey has certain limitations for

Northeast dairy	886	2650
South central pasture	847	2251
Southern pasture	589	1679
State	1079	3061

While these figures would differ if the return imputed to non-labor resources were their marginal value productivity rather than market rates, the differences between areas probably would be increased because of limited capital and high returns to this factor in southern Iowa.

[11] See E. O. Heady and E. R. Swanson, *op. cit.*, for derivation of marginal value productivities in 1950. These estimates showed a much lower return on a dollar invested in labor than any other of the resource groups studied. The figures were .08, .05, .18, .33, and 2.51 for real estate, labor, machinery, livestock, and feed and crop services respectively.

[12] See C. Hildreth, *Problems in the Estimation of Agricultural Production Functions.* Iowa State College, Mimeo. In deriving production functions for the same southern Iowa area in 1949, he obtained the following marginal return rates by means of simultaneous equations (all inputs in dollars):

Resource	*Marginal return in dollars*
Labor	.019
Livestock land (mainly pasture)	.326
Crop land	.949
Crop machinery and crop services	.515
Livestock and equipment	5.620

use in guidance of the individual farm it provides, more than anything else, outstanding data as a study in general equilibrium economics. If doubts exist that average and residual resource returns differ greatly between farms within a farming region, between farms in selected populations and between farms in different farming regions, one need only consult a few of these farm management summaries.[13] While they do not explain the forces which keep farmers from attaining optimum resource combinations, these several decades of empirical analysis can be taken to indicate that the organization of resources in United States agriculture does not result in equal average value products and returns to labor or other resources.

Other aggregate comparisons. While the general equilibrium-type of farm management study provides an important set of aggregative data for making interfarm and interarea productivity comparisons, production economists have employed secondary data and mass estimates in examining the degree of inefficiency which exists in the use of agricultural resources.[14] Because of their very composite nature, these data are in some respects less valuable than data of the type outlined above. They obscure the fact that resource returns may differ as greatly between farms within a region as between the average of all farms in different regions. With these limitations in mind we may examine the estimates provided below. It should be remembered that productivity differences, to the extent that they are accurately reflected in the data presented, do not represent any unique set of phenomena or relationships but are simply indicative of a particular disequilibrium of the nature outlined previously.

Table 2 combines data from several sources to suggest differences in gross average productivity per worker in agriculture. They are gross in the sense that they are computed from data in which the total value of agricultural product or the value of product added in agriculture has been divided by the estimated number of workers; the value figures do not show the value productivity of labor but only the value product of agriculture relative to the number of workers. They are average productivity figures in the sense that the figures are on a per-head basis and give estimates of marginal productivity only under the conditions to be outlined later. These data suggest that the average gross product per worker has differed consistently and by large amounts over time. Interregional differences in the average gross product per worker cannot be designated as a depression or drought period phenomenon. While the total value product per worker was low in the years 1937, 1940, and 1939 in the west north central states because of low rainfall and was high in the 1942-44 period

---

[13] A few selected bulletins might include New York Agr. Exp. Sta. Bul. 295; U.S.D.A. Circ. 132; Illinois Agr. Exp. Sta. Bul. 491; Maine Agr. Exp. Sta. Bul. 378; Indiana Agr. Exp. Sta. Bul. 452.

[14] While census data include the entire population of farms, the various categories of resources are not broken down sufficiently to allow use of any refined imputational processes in arriving at the returns to any single category of resources.

Table 2.

Regional Differentials in Average Value of Output per Worker Within United States Agriculture (Pacific Region = 100) *

Region	1929	1937-40	1939	1942-44	1945
Pacific	100	100	100	100	100
West North Central	99	87	81	111	80
Mountain	99	84	85	95	71
East North Central	70	83	79	89	66
Middle Atlantic	63	73	68	71	50
New England	57	60	67	64	49
West South Central	50	43	51	45	35
South Atlantic	44	37	41	39	32
East South Central	36	31	35	34	25

* Source: Based on calculations from the following: column 1 from Colin Clark, *The Economics of 1960*. New York: Macmillan, 1943; column 2 calculated from unpublished data by Barton and Cooper of the Division of Farm Management and Costs of the Bureau of Agricultural Economics; column 3 from L. J. Ducoff and M. J. Hagood, *op. cit.*; and column 4 from Barton and Cooper, *op. cit.* The 1945 data are from D. Gale Johnson, "Functioning of the Labor Market," *Jour. Farm Econ.*, Vol. 33.

when wheat yields were extremely favorable, differences for all regions were roughly of the same magnitude and order in several years. The striking feature of this table is that the first 3 regions have a gross value product per worker roughly half again greater than for the second 3 regions and 2½ times as great as for the last three. Gross value product per worker in the east south central region has hung at a level only one-third as great as that of the Pacific region. Differences in gross, average productivity may actually be more important than these data indicate, since one-half of the units defined as farms by the census fall in the latter 3 regions; less than one-third fall in the first 3 regions. It is true, of course, that these data are based on census classifications of farmers and under-estimate gross value productivity per worker in agriculture. Many census-defined farms are really not firms or producing units in the economic sense but are more nearly household or consuming units in the form of semi-retirement units, country estates, and subsistence farms of city workers. However, estimates which exclude units such as these show that, while the absolute differences are lessened between regions, the rank of regions remains roughly the same while the gaps between regions and between economic classes of farms are still very great.[15] Also, it should be pointed

[15] A farm management study based on 1945 census data (K. L. Bachman and R. W. Jones, *Sizes of Farms in the United States*. U.S.D.A. Tech. Bul. 1019, 1950) allows estimates of the average gross value product per worker in the United States as follows:

Class of farm	No. farms (000)	Gross value product per man equivalent
Large scale	102.1	$4447
Large commercial	408.9	4218
Medium commercial	1173.0	2832
Small commercial	1661.9	1432
Small scale	923.5	748

In addition 1,590.5 part-time and nominal farm units existed in 1945.

out that the regions, grouped on the basis of census classifications, are themselves highly composite and result from aggregating quite different farming regions within the states selected. For example, the most and least productive farming areas of Iowa are thrown in with numerous contrasting areas of the Great Plains. Tentative estimates by the writer indicate that Cornbelt areas with highly productive soils have a gross value product per worker greater than indicated above for the aggregate Pacific region while the southern portion of the Cornbelt ranks somewhat lower than the dairy areas of the New England states.

Interindustry comparisons. The results of both simple and complex research procedures can be taken to suggest that differences in the value productivities of resources do exist within farms and between farms spread over fairly wide areas.[16] While few persons would question that the marginal value productivities for specific factors such as labor or capital, like the average gross figures, differ greatly by regions, the exact magnitude of the differences and the method of measuring the differences have yet to be established.

Table 3.

Gross Average Value Product per Worker in Agriculture and Manufacturing, 1939 *

Region	Value added by agriculture per man equivalent	Value added by manufacturer per employee	Ratio of value added by manufacturer to value added by agriculture
Pacific	$1409	$3222	2.3
Mountain	1204	3372	2.8
West North Central	1135	3084	2.7
East North Central	1112	3094	2.8
Middle Atlantic	952	2862	3.0
New England	950	2261	2.4
West South Central	716	2754	3.8
South Atlantic	583	2092	3.6
East South Central	493	2122	4.3
United States	867	2762	3.2

* Source: T. W. Schultz, *Production and Welfare in Agriculture.* New York: Macmillan, 1949, Ch. 7.

We are now ready to examine descriptive data for agriculture as compared to other industries. If very rough data such as those in Table 3 are

The geographic distribution of farms by economic class is of a pattern which necessarily results in regional differentials in productivity: One-half the farms in the Appalachian region are classed either as small commercial farms or small-scale farms while nearly 60 per cent of those in the Southeast and Delta regions fall in these groups. Less than 3 per cent of all farms in the Southeast are large commercial farms or large scale farms, while nearly 14 per cent of those in the Cornbelt fall in these 2 groups.

[16] We retain the term average gross value productivity to refer to data such as those in Table 1, since they represent the gross value product divided by the number of workers and do not impute any marginal product to other factors employed in production.

employed, equally great differences in the average gross value productivity are seen to exist between agriculture and manufacturing industries of the several composite regions. The procedure of estimating in itself magnifies differences because the computational procedure "imputes the entire product to labor." Therefore, in industries where a large amount of capital is used relative to labor, labor productivity appears to be higher than in those industries where small amounts of capital are used per worker. Approximations such as those in Table 3 thus may provide erroneous inferences when industries which employ entirely different combinations of resources are compared. The same statement applies to comparisons between gross average productivity within agriculture. The great difference in amount of capital employed per worker is not as great between agriculture and manufacturing as between agriculture and other industries, however.[17]

In making estimates of the labor return in agriculture as compared to other industries, Wilcox used a residual imputational process as a basis for calculating the return per worker in agriculture. The remainder of the

Table 4.

Average Earnings per Full Time Man Equivalent, United States Industries, 1946 *

Industry	Earning
Transportation	$2,937
Mining	2 677
Contract construction	2,581
Finance, insurance, real estate	2,567
Communications and public utilities	2,560
Manufacturing	2,512
Wholesale and retail trade	2,392
Government and government enterprises	2,346
Agricultural labor, imputed residual a	2,300
Services	1,842
Hired agricultural workers	1,181

* Source: Taken from W. W. Wilcox, *op. cit.*, and "Survey of Current Business," Supplement in *National Income*, July 1947, Tables 24 and 26.
a Residual net value product after imputing a return to capital at 4 per cent.

total value of product added in the agricultural production process after a share was imputed to capital on the basis of a 5 per cent interest rate was attributed to labor. These data are given in Table 4, along with other data on earnings of workers in selected industries. If wages of hired em-

[17] Estimates of the National Resources Committee (p. 63) give the following estimates of capital used per laborer in 1935:

Public utilities	$11,900	Manufacturing	$3,700
Mining	8,700	Consumer ser.	3,700
Agriculture	3,900	Trade	2,000

Other rough estimates suggest that these same relative differences still exist between industries, although W. W. Wilcox, in "Efficiency and Stability and American Agriculture," *Jour. Farm Econ.*, Vol. 30, estimates that capital values per worker in agriculture exceeded those of manufacturing in postwar years.

ployees and the average residual return per worker in agriculture are used as an estimate of the value productivity, then agriculture compares favorably with numerous other industries. Of course, it is again true that the variations within these groups are perhaps more important than differences between groups. It is probably true that the marginal value productivity of labor in agriculture is lower than the $2,300 computed under the residual technique. The actual value productivity of capital in agriculture was far above 4 per cent in 1946, and hence the imputational process probably overestimates agricultural labor returns in this year. Breakdown of data such as these again displays striking regional differences in productivity data.

Productivity of particular resources. Disagreement over value productivity of agriculture resources is mainly one of the location and extent of the differences. One can find few persons who cannot turn to data indicating wide differences in the efficiency with which agricultural resources are used. Greatest agreement is on differences between farms producing similar products in individual farming areas. Further, differences in average productivity are so great and so obvious between areas such as the Pacific states and the southern Atlantic states or north central states and east south central states that there can be little doubt that wide differences also exist in marginal productivities. Less can be said about differences between other regions for reasons to be pointed out later. Also, while it is generally accepted that the average product averages less in many sectors of agriculture than in numerous non-farm industries, the exact location and extent of these differences has not been fully established. Farms producing a high value of product per unit of resources exist within even the very low income regions; farms low in productivity exist even in regions which, on the average, have a high return per unit of resource. Selected, highly productive farms in all areas compare favorably with firms in certain non-farm industries if gross average labor productivity is used as the criterion. Using 1945 as the year of comparison and relating firms of approximately the same scale (in terms of value of product added), the average residual product of labor for Iowa farms compared favorably with that of other firms. While the value of product added per worker was very low for small units, farms producing a product of $2,500 had a residual labor return as great as manufacturing firms adding up to $50,000 per worker in the production process. The figure for farms producing a product of $10,000 or over was as great as for manufacturing firms producing an output of $500,000. Comparisons between firms of comparable scales within other states also show gross average productivity to be equal between farms and manufacturing industries both in 1939 and 1949.

Industry location, part-time farming, and productivity. Data presented previously on productivity are highly aggregative in the sense that they throw together commercial, part-time, and subsistence farms. Only the farm product is shown for part-time farms. However, if off-farm returns are added to the value of farm products produced, part-time farmers in many low-income areas have returns as great or greater than their commercial-farm neighbors. This statement applies to much of the old cotton and mountain areas of the Southeast. Many families prefer to live on a small acreage while one or more member does off-farm work. This combination is a system of diversification in the use of labor and helps the family guard against the uncertainty of employment in textiles, furniture, or other industries. The situation suggests that an important opportunity is that of drawing diversified industry into low-income areas where feasible. Existence of industry allows persons with values tied to that of the community or who view long moves with great uncertainty to take advantage of off-farm employment opportunities. It may particularly allow harnessing the labor resources from subsistence farms and increasing the welfare of the individuals concerned. Once subsistence and part-time farms are improved or taken from the accounting sheet, labor productivity on commercial farms falls in that category of analysis traditionally included in farm management; namely, the direction of capital, labor, and land resources into uses within farms, between farms and between industries in a manner to allow greater attainment of the ends of farmers and the consuming society. Subsistence and part-time farming represent a simple extension of this analysis and as a problem in production economics can be treated similarly.

Stratification of farms. In preliminary data not yet published, the writer found that differentials in productivity in 1950, as aggregates based on census data, followed the same order as those presented previously. However, when regions are broken down into more homogeneous farming areas, and farms are compared by economic classes within these areas, labor and capital productivity generally are parallel for farms of the same economic class (farms producing a comparable total value product).[18] It is true, of course, that regions such as the southeastern United States, the southern Cornbelt, and other scattered areas have more farms in the economic classes defined by small value products. In the Southeast, these low productivity farms are largely those of share-croppers, small mountain farms, and scattered units; farms of the same economic class in the Cornbelt also have low incomes and a low labor product but they do not make up such a great proportion of the total. In this sense, problems of labor productivity are present in all farming areas but they differ in extent.

A further indication of regional differentials in resource productivity is given in the figures of Table 5. These estimates are derived from a production function of the Cobb-Douglas type and are from farm samples in

---

[18] Data showing this same general relationship can be found in C. E. Bishop, *Underemployment of Labor in Agriculture, Southeastern United States*, Ph.D. thesis, University of Chicago, 1952.

the Alabama Piedmont, a dry-land wheat area of Montana, north central Iowa and southern Iowa. The "mean" marginal productivity follows an expected pattern with high labor productivity in this favorable year for

Table 5.

Marginal Product of Labor on Crops with Inputs of Labor and Other Resources at Mean of Sample, 1950. (Dollars per Month.)

Item	Mont.	N. Iowa	S. Iowa	Ala.
Marginal labor product	95	85	58	36
Labor per farm (mo.) [a]	11.2	8.9	8.0	8.8
Machine expenses per farm ($) [a]	3328	1471	873	213
Crop expenses per farm ($) [a]	913	452	246	206
Acres per farm [a]	1089	174	148	37

[a] Refers to inputs and output of crops only.

Montana and very low returns in Alabama. The two Iowa areas show a differential which is known to exist over the central and southern Cornbelt. Among other things, these differences are to be explained particularly by capital inputs. Smaller labor inputs on the same farm give, of course, larger marginal products.

Form and amount of capital. Obviously, it is the productivity of particular resources in particular farming areas and industries which is of focal concern in analysis of general economic efficiency. We wish to know whether particular forms of capital have greater productivity than other particular forms within an individual farm; the form of capital is more important than the quantity of capital on many farms and in many farming regions. The concepts and problems are the same whether a farm or industry is being considered.[19] The only difference is one of magnitude.

When viewed from the standpoint of individual resources, all factors which can be classed as capital are not equally productive or unproductive. The marginal return on particular forms of agricultural capital is very great: agronomists and animal scientists provide empirical data to indicate that the return on added fertilizer, improved breeding stock, and even added protein feeds may range from 100 to 300 per cent on farms over much of the Cornbelt, a region which is near the top of the list in terms

---

[19] See T. W. Schultz, *Production and Welfare in Agriculture*. New York: Macmillan, 1949, p. 52. Schultz draws a mistaken contrast in his emphasis on techniques between inefficiency within a farm and between farms. Obviously, different techniques represent different combinations and different productivities for factors whether the problem is viewed through scrutiny of all farms which could profitably substitute machinery for labor or from the standpoint of one such farm. The basic relationships within a farm are the factor-product, the factor-factor, and the product-product relationships. Efficiency of a single farm is gauged by relating these relationships to the ends, and hence the appropriate choice indicator of the producing unit. The same relationships and framework of efficiency exist for central Iowa as a producing region, the east south central states as a producing unit, or the whole of agriculture as a producing unit. Only the choice indicators and never the relationships are different.

of aggregate productivity comparisons. The returns on machinery, new crop techniques, livestock, and complementary capital are equally as great in many regions of the nation but particularly so in the regions of low productivity indicated in Tables 1 and 2. Productivity of capital in most forms is evidently great on small units in many farming areas, as indicated by budget studies, refined analyses and conventional farm survey estimates.[20] Capital invested in soil conservation adjustments on productive Marshall soils of Iowa or in crops and livestock on the erosive brown loam soils of Mississippi can well return 50 to 100 per cent on investment.[21] In all producing regions it is possible to find farms side by side where some have pushed investment in particular forms of capital to a point where returns approach costs while others have not even begun to exploit the capital productivity opportunities.

When possibilities for farm consolidation and farm size expansion are considered along with the possibility of substituting machinery for labor, the marginal value product of labor on many farms and in many areas must indeed be as low or lower than the estimates of previous tables suggest. It is obviously true that if the agriculture of a particular region or of the nation were to be considered as a single unit in the vein of the factor relationships outlined in previous chapters, important quantities of capital and labor resources would be complementary. If farms were consolidated less of both capital and labor could be employed to produce the same product. (See discussion of Figures 11 and 12 in Chapter 5; also the discussion of complementary interfarm adjustments in Chapter 6.)

Implications of Productivity Measurement and Comparisons

While value productivity of resources was examined in previous sections, it should again be recognized that agricultural production does provide some direct utility for farm families. When we consider low income groups along with their cultural environments, many things become elements of non-money income. These groups have their own social classes and their own culture. They are conscious of where they fall in this system with the limitations they possess. Recognition for families and individuals is greater in this group than it would be outside and direct utility is so derived from the low income status. Given the abilities and training, opportunities do not always exist for people from this group which will allow them to increase their money returns. Yet even though

---

[20] Direct productivity estimates include those such as Tintner, *op. cit.*, Heady, *op. cit.*, and Heady and Swanson, *op. cit.* Studies such as Heady and Allen, *Iowa Agr. Exp. Bul. 281*, Hampson and Christopherson, *S. Dak. Circ. 21*, Pubols, Orr, and Heisig, *Wash. Agr. Exp. Sta. Bul. 228*, Conner *et al.*, *Ga. Agr. Exp. Sta. Bul. 221*, Christopher and Roy, *Ala. Circ. 91*, and O'Leary, *Miss. Agr. Exp. Sta. Bul. 384* also provide various types of estimates.

[21] Refer to Heady and Allen, *op. cit.*, or O'Leary, *op. cit.*

part of the product of agriculture is not reflected in dollar returns, it is highly unlikely that the greatest number of farm families attach enough weight to "coon hunting" and the "virtues of sunshine and hard work" to be willing to remain in agriculture at a return only half as great as might be earned elsewhere. Value productivities provide one of the more useful tests of allocative efficiency in an economy where consumer sovereignty is paramount and where prices are used as the vehicle by which preferences are reflected to producers. We cannot say, however, that the gain to the consumer from shifting one laborer from agriculture to soda jerking is greater than the sacrifice to the individual who must make the move. Certain other problems also arise in the measurement and application of productivity estimates. We can raise the question of whether, if accurate marginal value productivity estimates were available for a single year or for a period of a few years, these data could or should be used as the exact criterion for organizing resources between farms, areas, and industries. It is our purpose in this section to investigate estimation and use of average productivity figures. This step is important: since opportunities are not great for deriving marginal productivities on widespread basis, census or other data are likely to continue to be used in deriving average productivities and making resource recommendations.

Average productivity. The productivity estimates provided in several of the tables of this chapter are residual averages. As residuals they embrace the empirical limitations outlined in Chapter 13 for guidance of individual farms and for resource valuation. The residual averages especially cause errors in estimating labor productivity for regions such as the mountain states; the amount of capital used per worker is great in ranching. Average productivity data are used not alone in tables such as those set out above but also in their counterpart, the farm business or account summary made annually at many Land Grant Colleges. As averages, the estimates do not always serve as the appropriate basis for resource and production organization.[22] The extent to which average resource productivities can be used as a basis for guiding resource use, either by an individual within his farm or by a public administrator, depends on the nature of the production function. Averages alone can serve without qualification to suggest marginal productivities and to provide the allocative basis when the production function for each resource is homogeneous of the first degree (i.e., constant returns exist for each factor); here marginal productivity is constant and equal to average productivity.

---

[22] For limitations of productivity measurements other than those mentioned here, see the following: T. Barna, "Productivity of Labor: Its Concept and Measurement." *Bulletin of Oxford Univ. Inst. of Stat.*, Vol. 8, 1946; P. O. Steiner, "The Productivity Ratio: Some Analytical Limitations in Its Use," *Rev. Econ. and Stat.*, Vol. 32; S. Fabricant, "Of Productivity Statistics, an Admonition," *Rev. Econ. and Stat.*, Vol. 31.

If the production function for individual farms or agricultural regions is identical and includes ranges of both increasing and decreasing marginal returns then use of average productivity figures necessitates qualifications of the nature illustrated in Figure 1. The logic is simplified in terms of a single product and a single resource, but applies equally to all factors. Three regions (or farms) to be compared are represented as I, II, and III. Region I employs ox_1 resources, while regions II and III employ ox_2 or ox_3 respectively. If we compute the average resource productivity for each of these regions (or farms since productivity analysis is identical for all producing units and all resources) we find that the average value product for region I is oa_1 while it is oa_2 for both regions II and III. What can we conclude from these figures? Is resource use equally efficient in the latter 2 regions? Should an equal quantity of resources be diverted from II and III to region I if a maximum value product is to be forthcoming from all areas?

Obviously, the average comparisons are misleading. Although the average value product is equal in the regions II and III, marginal productivities differ by m_1m_3; the resources of the 2 regions could be recombined to give a greater product in spite of the fact that the average productivity figures are equal. If average productivities are compared for regions I and III, our inference might turn in either one of two different directions:

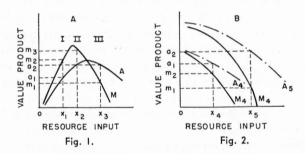

Fig. 1.   Fig. 2.

Analysis of value productivity in average and marginal terms.

since the average value product is oa_2 in region III but only oa_1 in region I, we might conclude that marginal productivity is also greater in region III. On this basis we would recommend that resources be transferred from I to III if the value of the product is to be maximized. Yet a transfer of this type would obviously decrease the total value product since marginal value productivity is greater in the former than in the latter region. Resources actually should be transferred from III to I until the marginal product in region I has risen "over the hump" and fallen to the level of region II; equal amounts of resources should then be transferred from III to I and II until equal value productivities have been attained between all regions.

While some farmers in all regions and perhaps the majority in particular regions operate under conditions of increasing returns to capital, a more common case is that of decreasing marginal productivity for a region and entirely different crop production functions. Figure 2 illustrates the implications of average productivity figures under the situation where one region (IV) has a less productive land base than another region (V). The average productivity of resources in region V is oa_2, while it is only oa_1 in region IV. Yet, because region IV uses so few resources relative to their productivity, marginal returns are greater than in region V. Since marginal and average productivities differ in the opposite direction, the magnitude of the averages cannot be used as an accurate index of how resources should be rearranged. This condition may be approached in data of the nature presented in previous tables. While average and marginal productivity may be great for a limited quantity of resources in dry-land wheat regions, use of additional resources might well drive returns on capital much lower than in more humid regions such as the Delta, Cornbelt, or other farming regions where elasticity of the production function stands to be greater.

Other assumptions in productivity analysis. Average value productivity figures also can be used to estimate marginal productivities if certain conditions hold true in respect to the nature of the production function and sufficient information is available. This possibility exists even where the marginal and average productivity decline as greater quantities of resources are used. The system of estimation can be applied in simple fashion when the average and marginal productivity curves are of a straight-line nature; the decline in average or marginal productivity is by equal absolute amounts. A situation of this nature is illustrated in Figures 3 and 4 where both the average (A) and marginal (M) product curves are linear. The marginal product declines at twice the absolute rate of decline in the average product when the latter curve is linear.[23] A corollary condition is this: Inputs defining equal magnitudes of average and marginal products are twice as great for the former as for the latter. In Figure 3, for example, an average product of 14 is forthcoming with six units of resources; a marginal product of 14 is forthcoming with 3 units of input. This geo-

---

[23] This point can be illustrated also by means of the arithmetic example below where the average product of each input unit is *one* less than for the previous input while the marginal product declines by two units.

Input	Total output	Average product	Decline in average product	Marginal product	Decline in marginal product
1	20	20	—	20	—
2	38	19	1	18	2
3	54	18	1	16	2
4	68	17	1	14	2
5	80	16	1	12	2

metrical relationship is illustrated further in Figure 4, where the length of *KR* is one-half of *KS;* *KR* also is equal to *RS*. This same relationship exists for every point on the average curve.[24]

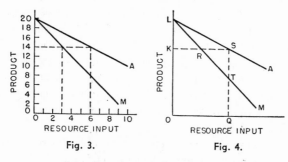

Fig. 3.   Fig. 4.

Estimation of marginal productivity.

Now suppose that we make, through use of census or other mass data, measurements of average resource productivity. We know only that the total value product of the region is *KSQO* and the quantity of resources employed is *OQ*. The average product can be computed by simple arithmetic and is *QS*. Can we say anything about the marginal product? Assuming a linear average product curve, we can say only that the same marginal product is forthcoming when the region employs an amount of resources equal to one-half of *OQ*. We can say no more because we do not know the slope of the average product curve or where it intersects the vertical axis. However, if we can obtain estimates of two points on the average product curve we can, since the functions are linear, estimate the marginal product curve. If we could be certain that the productivity curves are linear and if the region can be broken down into 2 subareas using different quantities of resources, estimates of marginal productivity can then be derived. Use of a system such as this, even where the average curve is not linear, would give better estimates of marginal productivity than does the system which assumes that differences in marginal products are of the same order as differences in average products (the assumptions of Tables 1 and 2).

Rates of resource transformation, time, and productivity comparisons. When the period over which resources are transformed into product differs, regional and industry productivity comparisons also encounter exactly

---

[24] The geometrical proof of this proposition is given in Robinson, *Economics of Imperfect Competition*. London: Macmillan, 1950, p. 30. Where we wish to prove that *KR* equals *RS:*

The area *KSQO* is equal to the area *LTQO* since both quantities define the total product when *OQ* units of resources are employed.

Hence area *LKR* = area *RST*

Both angles *LKR* and *RST* are right angles and the 2 angles *LRK* and *SRT* are equal. Therefore, *KR* = *RS* since triangles *LKR* and *RST* are equal in all respects.

the same difficulties outlined in Chapter 13 for intra-farm inferences. For meaningful productivity comparisons, the value of the product must be related to the flow of resource services rather than the stock of services which gives rise to the services. Otherwise, the product/capital ratio for farming types involving long-lived resources such as dairy barns and equipment will be low relative to farming systems such as cotton or vegetables which involve mainly labor and short-lived capital.[25] As mentioned at an earlier point, capital productivity comparisons or even residual labor comparisons may well differ, depending on whether the residual ratios have been computed on a basis of capital services given off in the particular time period for which product is measured or on the basis of total capital investment.

Time considerations become even more complex in relation to productivity analysis and comparisons when aspects of cost compounding and returns discounting are considered. Since production decisions must be made in advance for dairying and other types of livestock production involving barns and other long-lived capital, the farmer is not likely to invest in a barn in 1953 which will give off services in the year 1997 unless the revenue, when discounted, appears sufficiently great to merit investment over this time period. In contrast, investment in vegetable, cotton, or broiler production may be made in 1987 and extended to 1997 even if returns are not nearly so great in the last year (1997). A $100 return in 1997 has a discounted value, on the basis of a 5 per cent interest rate, of $61.39 in 1987; it has a value of only $11.69 in 1953.

If a study of resource productivity is made in regions of "dairy" and "poultry" production for the year 1997, computed returns are likely to be greater for the long-lived assets than for the short-lived assets. Investment at a previous point in time would never have been made unless returns in "dairying" in 1997 were sufficiently greater than returns in "poultry"; the longer period of discount gives rise to this situation. The differences, except for mistaken expectations, cannot be taken to define disequilibrium. Differences in 1 year can actually be taken to indicate that resource allocation and investment conform with the necessary marginal conditions which relate to time. This consideration also is of great import in inter-industry comparisons such as railroads and agriculture. Even as a rough

---

[25] When we speak of resource life we should also remember the distinction between short-run and long-run opportunities in Chapter 9. A resource productivity analysis based on sample or secondary data, since it more nearly provides estimates of the long-run opportunity curve, may infer that the farmer and society both would benefit from a shift in use of resources. However, if farmers are operating short-run inflexible plants, both the individual operator and society may gain from continuance of the established pattern of resource allocation, until long-run opportunities emerge. This point was discussed in Chapter 9 and, while the analysis was applied to an individual farm, it applies similarly to producing units of other magnitudes.

approximation, productivity comparisons need to make some allowance for the period of investment and the discounting of returns. Of course, uncertainty unique to the producing firm may cause excessive discount rates and hence define a use of resources which is inefficient and inconsistent with consumer preferences over time.

Monopoly and productivity. Interindustry efficiency comparisons, even if in terms of marginal rather than average quantities, must also recognize differences in the competitive structure of firms within individual industries. When a monopoly industry is compared with one of pure competition, differences in the value of productivity of resources may arise not only because the latter is inefficient but also because the former restricts employment of resources and output of product. In an environment of perfect knowledge the monopoly would exercise both a pricing and a production policy wherein marginal cost equaled marginal revenue. Competitive firms, if they maximized profits, would be able to exercise a production policy only and in final equilibrium average costs for the industry would equal average revenue. Under these conditions both the marginal and average productivity of resources would be greater in the monopoly than in the competitive industry. Differences in value productivity could then be taken to indicate the inefficiency of monopoly organization rather than of the agricultural industry. The lower productivity of resources in the competitive industries would be indicative of efficiency in this sense; the competitive industry employs the resources "rejected" by monopoly industry and society is provided with a greater product than it otherwise would have.

While non-farm industries are far from being organized on a complete monopoly basis, this aspect of industry structure must be considered when resource efficiency is to be gauged. Some of the gap in resource productivity between agriculture is undoubtedly explained by this phenomenon. However, not all aspects of low productivity of agricultural production can be so attributed; differences within agriculture are too great as also are differences between agriculture and selected non-farm industries which are competitive. The important question is one of whether commercial agriculture is any more inefficient from a resource efficiency standpoint than are monopoly industries.

A final note on the implications of productivity measurement and interpretation is also in order. The year or period of comparison must be one which provides employment opportunities. The year 1939 was not such a year. Because of the large force of unemployed persons in 1939 there was little opportunity for workers to shift between industries. While non-farm productivity may have appeared to be high, the marginal product of a person who transferred from agriculture was zero if he could not find employment in manufacturing industries.

Levels of Living

Agricultural production economists then have a gigantic task ahead of them in refining efficiency criteria, in delineating the location and extent of existing inefficiency, in devising methods of measuring resource productivity, and in devising policies and methods by which it can be overcome. The goal towards which analysis in economic efficiency is directed is the welfare of individuals and groups of individuals. The statement applies equally to investigations aimed at the individual farm and the farm family, the farm population, or society in general. That much is still to be done in increasing the productivity, income, and welfare of farm people is indicated by the approximations in Table 6. Not only are there important differences between major agricultural regions, but the level of living of farm peoples differs greatly both within states and within counties. The living level indices of Table 6 are expressive of both the

Table 6.

Farm Operator Level of Living Index, Selected Counties, 1940 and 1945
(U. S. ave. = 100) *

County and state	Level of living index		1945 as per cent of 1940
	1940	1945	
Elliott, Ky.	5	9	180
Choctaw, Ala.	8	19	238
Pickett, Tenn.	8	17	212
Wayne, Miss.	12	18	150
Chicot, Ark.	12	18	150
Pope, Ill.	45	54	120
Iron, Wisc.	47	69	147
Carson, S. Dak.	53	74	140
Harrison, Miss.	57	69	121
Orange, Ind.	59	74	125
Morton, Kan.	67	136	203
Washington, Maine	68	98	144
Lake, Tenn.	72	95	132
Appanoose, Iowa	90	100	122
Washington, Colo.	97	120	124
Aroostook, Maine	110	153	139
Minnehaha, S. Dak.	127	162	128
Brown, Kan.	132	164	124
Hendry, Fla.	136	231	170
Rush, Ind.	146	177	121
Waukesha, Wisc.	148	168	114
Dekalb, Ill.	161	201	125
Monterey, Cal.	168	228	136
Grundy, Iowa	169	196	116

* Source: *Low Income Families and Economic Stability*. U. S. Senate Document No. 231.

income and productivity of farm families. Even though the level of living index doubled in some low income areas between 1940 and 1945, the standard of consumption was still extremely low in these counties as compared to the national average. Also, while increased incomes have resulted in some savings during prosperity periods, not a large amount of physical capital has been added to production in the extremely low income areas.[26] The addition has been much greater in high income areas where capital productivity is perhaps less.

While it is true that the income of the farm family depends (a) on the quantity of resources at its command and (b) the manner in which these resources are combined, the quantity of resources owned by many farm families is simply so small that the supply of labor from the family household produces a very small product and a low income. The agricultural production economist has an important role to play in increasing the welfare of these persons and of society generally through aiding the reorganization of resources between farms and farming regions and even in helping to transfer resources now in agriculture to other occupations where productivity of labor and family income and welfare can be increased. The goal and principle in transferring a unit of labor between cotton in Alabama to corn in Iowa or industrial products in Tennessee is the same as transferring an acre of land and a day's labor between oats and corn at a particular spot in the southwest corner of Rush county, Indiana.

---

[26] Two production functions derived from southern Iowa (an area of low labor productivity as compared to the Cornbelt proper but high as compared to the standards of the Mississippi Delta, the Piedmont of Alabama, the mountains of eastern Tennessee, or the scattered cut-over sections of the nation) suggested that addition of resources since 1940 has lowered the elasticity of particular categories of resources. The 2 production functions, while perhaps obsolete in terms of empirical methods, but still suggestive of magnitudes and directions, were as follows:

$$1939: \ P = 1067R^{.020}L^{.11}M^{.31}S^{2.64}E^{.40}$$
$$1950: \ P = .2016R^{.23}L^{.13}M^{.10}S^{.50}E^{.25}$$

Where P refers to the value of product produced, R refers to real estate, L refers to labor, M refers to machinery and equipment, S refers to livestock, and E refers to operating expense for crops and livestock. As these data suggest, the elasticity coefficient for machinery decreased from .31 to .10. Decreases also took place for other capital in line with an addition of capital in general between 1939 and 1940. The marginal productivity figures for 1950 still indicated high returns on capital.

Selected References

Black, J. D., et al., *Farm Management*. New York: Macmillan, 1947, pp. 793-1052.

Clark, Colin, *The Condition of Economic Progress*. London: Macmillan, 1940.

Cooper, M. L., et al., *Progress of Farm Mechanization*, U.S.D.A., Misc. Bul. 630.

Fisher, A. G. B., *Economic Progress and Social Security*. London: Macmillan, 1945.

Heady, Earl O., "Production Functions from a Random Sample," *Jour. Farm Econ.*, Vol. 28.

Hecht, R. W., and Barton, G. T., *Gains in Farm Labor Productivity*. U.S.D.A. Tech. Bul. 1020.

Little, I. M. D., *A Critique of Welfare Economics*. Oxford: Clarendon Press, 1950, pp. 121-159.

Reder, M. R., *Readings in the Theory of Welfare Economics*. New York: Columbia University Press, 1947, pp. 13-46.

Rostas, L., *Productivity of Labor in British, German and American Agriculture*. Royal Econ. Soc. Memorandum No. 107.

Schultz, T. W., "How Efficient is American Agriculture?" *Journ. Farm Econ.*, Vol. 29.

Warren, G. F., *Farm Management*. New York: Macmillan, 1916, Ch. 8.

Wilcox, W. W., "Efficiency and Stability of American Agriculture," *Jour. Farm Econ.*, Vol. 30.

25

Causes of Inefficiency with Special Reference to Labor and Capital

WHILE PRODUCTION economists are not in full accord as to the magnitude of inefficiency in agriculture, they are in general agreement that inefficiency does exist. The existing stocks of resources in agriculture obviously could be organized to give a greater product with the same inputs or the same product with fewer resources. Perhaps more is known about the existence of inefficiency than about its exact causes. The purpose of this section is to examine possible causes of over-all inefficiency in production. Those causes inherent in the analyses of previous chapters are treated only briefly in this chapter.

The Goals of Efficiency

The causes of inefficiency in the use of agricultural resources are to be found in an intertwined set of forces. Little is known about the relative importance of each particular conditioning force. To the extent that these forces are important, they serve as the obstacles to be overcome in increasing efficiency in production. Not only is it necessary that the production economist isolate and measure the extent and causes of inefficiency but also he should devise effective means of overcoming these imperfections. At this level the goal becomes one of not only increasing the welfare of farm families, through facilitation of greater returns from the resources which they administrate, but also in providing society in general with a greater economic product from the limited capital, labor, land and management resources at its command. Economic changes which cause resource productivities to diverge between areas or industries can be thrown into a few general categories. These include: (1) relative changes in the demand for and price of products which cause the value of output produced from given resources to rise or fall, (2) changes in the production function which increase the physical productivity of factors, and with price and quantity of resources remaining constant, cause value productivity to be altered depending on price elasticities of demand, (3) the nature of the supply function for resources, which causes resources to back up in a region and their value productivity to decline, and (4) the structure of competitive and monopoly prices. The forces discussed on the following pages fall directly and indirectly in these categories. Mainly, they explain why the quantity of capital used on some farms and regions is so low as to cause its marginal productivity to be high or why the quantity of labor is so great as to cause its productivity to be low.

Resource reorganization and agricultural revenue. While the efficiency gap in use of agricultural resources is great and a reorganization of production in the direction of the maximum conditions set out in the previous chapter would result in a greater total product, it need not result in an increased total or net revenue to agriculture in aggregate. The very low price elasticity of demand for farm products actually points in the opposite direction; a full-dress reorganization of agricultural resources would result in a smaller rather than a larger revenue to the industry were the present stock of resources to be retained in the industry. A likelihood of a smaller total revenue from a greater product at any one level of demand signifies that, if agriculture is to be made more productive, maximum efficiency may be attained only as the flow of certain resources from agriculture to other industries is increased. It is at this point that agricultural efficiency can be gauged only as it is tied to the use of resources in other industries. The average incomes of families remaining in agriculture can best be increased as persons are moved from small undersized farms and the scale of remaining units increases to a level consistent with modern farming methods and acceptable levels of living.

The over-all or societal aspect of efficiency is necessarily the goal toward which efforts of all agricultural production economists are directed. Even those who work with, and direct the results of their findings, to individual farmers must justify their efforts largely on this basis. The reason is this: were a large portion of all farmers to adopt the resource reorganizations suggested to them, the greater aggregate product forthcoming would, for most products, bring a smaller total revenue and a lower revenue per farm for any given demand situation. Consequently, because of an inelastic demand for farm products, society and individual farmers would gain while farmers in mass would sacrifice income. (Some individual farmers would gain at the expense of still others.) It is for these reasons that efficiency analysis in agriculture must ultimately focus on the consuming society of which farmers represent one segment. The goal is (a) to increase the physical productivity of agricultural resources through resource reorganizations within the industry; and (b) to increase the value productivity of these same resources by transferring them either within the industry, including intra-farm and interfarm changes, or to other industries. These reorganizations are most easily designated and implemented during war emergency or similar periods when choice indicators are given largely in physical terms and the methods and procedures for bringing about resource transfers are direct and effective. They become less apparent and more complex in an environment of depression, when employment opportunities are limited, and in the so-called "normal periods" of a price economy where monopoly and competition exist side by side. Increased efficiency in the latter environment necessitates reorganizations at the national level as much or more than at the farm industry level and necessarily calls for policies and programs which will lessen general economic instability, reduce the extent and consequences of monopoly organization and fully facilitate resource mobility.

Causes of Inefficiency

With the above qualifications in mind, we can turn again to the forces which condition agricultural efficiency. These appear to fall in the major categories outlined below. As the reader will become aware when he examines each of the considerations outlined, the value productivity of resources on a particular farm, of a particular region, or in agriculture as an industry is a reflection especially of the demand function for agricultural products and the supply function for agricultural resources. Forces conditioning the productivity of agricultural resources are both endogenous and exogenous to the industry. Lack of knowledge on the part of farmers, leasing arrangements, farm birth rates, technical uncertainty, and similar considerations fall in the endogenous category and are determined within the industry. General economic instability, changes in consumer demand and the uncertainty to which they give rise are representative of the exogenous category. More than anything else, however, regional productivity differentials result from the nature of the resource supply function within agriculture. While no attempt has been made to segregate them, the forces fall into categories explaining why (1) the resources of an individual farm are not organized to maximize the value of the product, (2) the return on resources differs between agricultural areas, and (3) the value product of agricultural resources is (a) low relative to that of certain other occupations and (b) less than maximum for the resources employed in the industry.

Costs and returns to society and the firm. While a competitive industry such as agriculture does provide an important setting wherein use of resources to maximize the ends of the individual farmer also results in a maximum economic product to society, the statement cannot be applied to agriculture in its entirety. It is true that, in many and perhaps most respects, an increase in returns to the individual farmer also results in a greater economic product for society. A shift of resources from pork to beef production in a manner to increase profits is generally consistent with consumer desires as expressed through relative prices; yet there are many areas of agricultural production where the costs and returns to the firm are not the same as the costs and returns to society. An example here can be found in erosion control and soil conservation. Control of water run-off on a single farm may increase the product not only on that farm but also on other farms; yet the individual farmer may not find erosion control to be profitable because he must pay all of the cost but realizes only part of the return. In contrast, a firm which owned all of the farms, or a society (all individuals taken together), can realize the full return and the expenditures involved are thus economic. Another major area wherein returns to the firm are not the same as returns to society is that of leasing arrangements. Even if we consider only the tenant and the landlord as the "relevant society," many existing leasing arrangements cause the pattern of production which is most efficient from the tenant's standpoint to conflict with the pattern which will give the greatest returns to the farm as a unit, including the resources of both the landlord and the tenant. While many of the resource combinations employed by tenant farmers would be irrational to an owner-operator, they become entirely rational and economic within the decision-making framework of the individual tenant or landlord. The contrasts drawn between rented and owned farms in a previous chapter effectively points out this possibility. Other cases in which costs and returns to the agricultural firm deviate from those of society could also be listed. However, the 2 mentioned are important in explaining 1 facet of inefficient resource use in agriculture. They are mainly important in helping to explain why resource productivity is low on some farms and in agriculture generally. They are not important, except indirectly, in explaining regional differences in productivity of agricultural resources.

Certainly, an important extent of resource inefficiency exists in agriculture because of gaps in costs and returns to the individual as compared to society. The most important cause here is that of leasing and tenure imperfections.

Lack of farmer knowledge. Lack of knowledge of alternative techniques and resource organizations is also important in explaining why farmers individually do not maximize the value of product from given resources and why the mass physical product from given quantities of agricultural resources is not as great as it might be. The purely irrational resource and production organizations cited in early chapters can be attributed mainly to lack of knowledge. The services of extension specialists in Land Grant Colleges are provided by society under the assumption that existing knowledge is not fully extended. While specialists in the various technical fields devote a portion of their time to extending information on new techniques, most of these individuals assert that knowledge is still not fully disseminated even for production methods which have long been known at Land Grant Colleges. This statement applies particularly to practices in animal nutrition, soil conservation, cropping varieties, and fertilizer application. Similarly, farm economists speculate that knowledge by farmers on how resources can be organized most effectively has not reached the majority of operators. Again, these facets of inefficiency explain why profits are not at a maximum on an individual farm or why the aggregate physical product from given resources is not at a maximum in the agricultural industry, but they do not explain regional differentials in productivity or low value productivity on an industry-wide basis. It is true, of course, that knowledge of farmers is generally less in low-income areas than in the highly efficient farming localities. Yet part of this lack of knowledge stems from low income and the fact that the farm operators concerned do not have the education to fully interpret research findings or the funds to attend all field days and educational demonstrations which provide greater technical knowledge. It is probably true that failure of farmers to apply recommended practices is often erroneously attributed to lack of knowledge. In many instances the failure of farmers to adopt "proven techniques" is to be found in their income and capital position, their inability to withstand risks, and their personal preferences. Knowledge *per se* explains only why agriculture in total might be less efficient than possible. It does not explain regional differentials in resource productivity except as knowledge becomes a function of income or other considerations outlined below.

Uncertainty and capital limitations. The complex of uncertainty and capital limitations was explained in detail in earlier chapters. These imperfections of the capital market along with the firm-household complex are important in explaining why capital in its many particular forms is not employed more intensively in agriculture as a whole and particularly in individual farming regions. Some very great increases in agricultural output could be attained either through the reorganization of present capital between neighboring farms or by a net addition of capital to the existing farms of individual producing regions. While a reorganization of existing capital, labor, and management between farms (such as a different distribution of these resources over the existing land area) would without question increase the physical product of the industry, the value product of agriculture would increase only where the aggregate price elasticity of demand is greater than 1.0. Since empirical information suggests an aggregate elasticity of less than 1.0, this mass reorganization of agriculture alone would be expected to cause the value product of the industry to decrease. Similarly, predictions of the value productivity of added capital in agriculture may be overestimated if they are based entirely on the existing structure of the industry (such as productivity coefficients based on observations of capital employed from farm samples or mass data). The logic here is again apparent in Figure 2 of Chapter 24: If the current input of capital is ox_4 and its marginal productivity is om_2, the marginal productivity of added capital would not remain at this level but would drop below om_2.

Early chapters on uncertainty provide hypotheses and facts to suggest (a) why farmers do not use as much capital as might be economic, and (b) why the capital they do employ is not organized optimally within the farm, in terms of *ex poste* efficiency criteria. Uncertainty also becomes important in explaining why so much labor is embodied in agricultural products. The distraught conditions of industrial workers during depression has been seared into the minds of many farm people. While the extent to which they fear transferring from operation of a small low-productivity farm to a laboring position in non-farm occupations is not known, the observation is commonly held that many farmers stick to agriculture because they fear the possibility of industrial unemployment. Perhaps they are also uncertain in the sense that they have little knowledge about life in a town or city and thus fear the consequences of shifting to an entirely different life. While farming as an industry involves much uncertainty, the uncertainty attached to non-farm alternatives evidently helps prevent the adaptation of labor between agriculture and other industries. The true subsistence farmer need fear only technical uncertainty; he is little affected by price variation and looks upon farming as relatively safe because "one can always raise what he eats." Although the extent of this force has never been measured quantitatively, it is likely that inefficiency growing out of economic uncertainty is more important than any other single source of inefficiency. Economic instability and uncertainty do not explain why very great regional differences in resource productivity and income exist over long periods. They do explain, however, why efficiency is less than maximum in the economy generally as well as in agriculture as an industry and in individual firms of agriculture. They cause farmers to place premiums on short-term production plans and to select resource and product combinations which do not allow a maximum of product from given resources.

Net labor product in relation to capital. Another measure of both cause and extent of low labor productivity is portrayed in Figure 1. These average data, prepared by Bishop of North Carolina, relate net income per worker to capital per worker for economic classes of farms in 2 broad areas, the Southeast and the Cornbelt; the points represent the average situation for different economic classes of farms reported by the census of 1945, while the dotted lines suggest what the relationship would be if the in-between segments were linear (an unlikely situation). Net income per worker is a function of the amount of capital employed per worker (land is classed as capital); movement to the right on the horizontal axis represents an increase in C/L, the capital-labor ratio and, in the manner of Chapters 2 and 3, is equivalent to increasing the quantity of capital with labor held constant. (Slopes of the lines may be slightly overestimated.)

These figures from Bishop bring out important comparisons obscured in the more aggregative averages presented previously. With the same amount of capital per worker, labor has a greater net product in the Southeast than in the Cornbelt. The former region is not inefficient in total relative to the latter. The more aggregative figures of previous sections give this "apparent conclusion" because all farmers in each region are thrown together, while the Southeast includes more subsistence, small-scale, and share-cropper units than the Cornbelt. The 3 solid dots in Figure 1 show

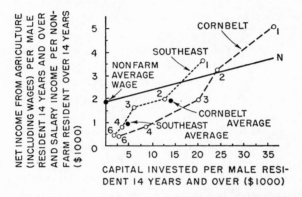

Fig. I. Relation of capital per worker to income, 1945 (Source: C. E. Bishop, *Underemployment of Labor in Agriculture*. Unpublished Ph.D. thesis. Chicago, 1952).

the average incomes of non-farm workers, Southeast agriculture, and Cornbelt agriculture respectively. If we examine only these averages, the apparent conclusion is that net labor productivity is highest, during full employment, in the non-farm sector of the economy, although the Cornbelt is a close second, while net income per male over 14 years in the Southeast is only about one-half as great. The economic class comparison shows, however, that with sufficient capital per worker, the net return in the Southeast can be as high or higher than that of the Cornbelt or in non-farm employment. The solid line N indicates what the net income for non-farm workers might have been with different amounts of capital or savings earning 5 per cent. For situations in which each individual has less than $17,000 in the Southeast and $24,000 in the Cornbelt, returns would have been greater in non-farm employment with the funds invested at 5 per cent; for greater amounts of capital returns would have been greater in farming. These figures suggest that, because of favorable climatic conditions and markets, farmers of the Cornbelt might even increase the productivity of their labor and machine capital by moving to the Southeast and applying an equal level of managerial ability. It is not true, as some writings suggest, that the problem in over-all agricultural efficiency is mainly one of moving resources out of the Southeast or similar regions to other agricultural areas. The low-income and low-labor productivity segments of Southeastern agriculture are particularly those of share-cropping units and subsistence farms where the amount of capital per worker is extremely low. (Share croppers should, in fact, be classed as agricultural laborers rather than managers of farm firms; they generally furnish labor to a decision-making concern which pays them in kind.) The task in the Southeast is as much one of reorganizing farms to increase size, add better enterprise combinations, substitute machinery for labor, and to move many share-cropper and subsistence families into higher income alternatives of industry or part-time farming. Similar logic also applies to mountain, cut-over, southern Cornbelt, and other agricultural areas where low-income and low-productivity farms are found. Labor productivity can be high or low in any region depending on the quantity and form of capital employed per worker and the technique of production. The problem is one of spreading labor between its farm and non-farm opportunities in a manner that equal marginal productivity is attained with proper recognition given to the likes and values of people.

While the discussion above (and that of Chapter 18) helps explain why farm firms with little capital and low labor productivity can't or don't borrow additional capital, the data of Table 5 in Chapter 24 also are useful in explaining how the quantity of capital affects marginal returns to the human resource. In the table below we have used the same functions and data to illustrate (a) what farms in low-income areas can do if more capital were made available or (b) what holds true on farms in these areas when they have greater capital per worker. While techniques of production may not allow exactly this adjustment, we simply hold labor per farm constant and increase the capital to equal that of the Montana average. While the labor techniques prohibit the full adjustment, labor productivity in Alabama jumps beyond that of Montana when capital services applied to crops are equalized. Even a tripling of capital inputs, a more nearly feasible adjustment considering the techniques in use, push the product in Alabama up to that of Montana and Iowa. Total capital per farm would still be less than $20,000 on Alabama farms while it would be over $40,000 in Montana.

Table I.

Marginal Product of Labor on Crops with Capital Set at Different Levels for 4 Farming Regions. Labor Held Constant at Level of Table 5, Chapter 24.

Level of Capital	Montana	N. Iowa	S. Iowa	Alabama
Equal to Montana	95	87	68	247
Doubled in each region	181	150	75	65
Tripled in Alabama				91
Quadrupled in Alabama				115

Primary production. Some persons have extended the hypothesis (and some quantitative suggestions) that resource returns in primary or extractive industries continually press below those of secondary industries. Some, such as agriculture, not only produce primary materials which are later fashioned into consumer goods but also carry forward certain of the processing steps: livestock production, for example. However, agriculture is generally classed as a primary industry. If there are common elements in returns of primary industries, it is possible that one explanation of low resource returns in agriculture falls in this category. (Previous comparisons between agriculture and service industries indicate that qualifications need to be made here.) On the one hand, primary products or raw materials are highly homogeneous and do not lend themselves to product differentiation and monopolistic profits as in the case of manufactured goods or final consumer services. Perhaps equally or more important in a progressive society is the nature of the preference system of consumers. While the value attached to food, clothing, and shelter relative to other products is great when consumption of the former is at low levels, these products soon fall in the category of near-subsistence goods once incomes are at a level allowing "full stomachs." In other words, the preference systems of wealthy societies may not be in the direction of more raw materials but in the direction of more complex forms for given quantities of raw materials; the consumer evidently prefers the same quantity of automobile steel "wound into more complex and intricate designs" to "more steel made up in the automobiles of the past." Emphasis falls not so much on the quantity of raw materials but more on the varied services injected into the raw material. Opportunities for embodying greater services into raw materials is not great at the farm level because of the small scale of the producing unit. The turning and twisting of the raw materials or primary products into more varied forms is associated more nearly with the larger scale manufacturing or agricultural processing firm. The processing of breakfast cereals is an example. As will be brought out subsequently, however, the importance of this phenomenon turns largely on the wealth of the society and the rate of technical progress in agriculture and non-farm industries, as well as on the rate of population growth. The primary industry hypothesis mainly explains why the value product of agriculture is low relative to other industries. It is less important in explaining why such mammoth differences exist within agriculture.

Population growth and technical advance. The interrelationship of population growth and technical advance, like the primary industry consideration, stands to be of importance in explaining why resource returns in agriculture as an industry might continue at low levels relative to other industries. Since the impact of technological change on resource productivity and returns is discussed in a later chapter we can devote our major attention here to population growth. The rate of population growth in either agriculture or the nation may affect the value productivity of agricultural resources. First, population growth for a nation as a whole may interact with technical advance to cause resource returns to increase or decrease. A rate of expansion in population, and hence in the demand or "need" for food, which is greater than the rate of technical progress in agriculture may well cause the value productivity of agricultural resources to be maintained or increased relative to returns in other industries. Indications are that this relationship was important in the early history of the nation. (See Chapter 27.) While agricultural output increased from the addition of more farms, the settlement of more land, and some improvement in techniques, population grew more rapidly through high immigration and birth rates. In recent decades, however, the process has been reversed and food perhaps increasingly takes on the subsistence characteristics outlined later.

Population growth within agriculture and specific segments of agriculture also has a bearing on resource productivity. Sociological studies indicate that the number of births in agriculture not only exceed those of all other segments of the population, and particularly of certain segments, but also that birth rates are generally greater in the low income areas of agriculture than in those areas of relatively high resource productivity. In other words, the nature of the labor supply is such as to continually press returns of the resource to low levels. Individuals, ordinarily, first turn to endeavors or occupations close at hand or of which they have greatest knowledge as a means of livelihood. Thus the number of persons seeking employment in agriculture is great relative to the economic importance of the industry. In a price economy consumers can indicate their preferences for different uses of particular resources only by directly attaching a low price to the product of the resource and indirectly attaching a low price to the services of the resource. If market returns are to be used as the means whereby resources are channeled to uses consistent with consumer preferences, labor income in agriculture must necessarily fall to low levels if the supply of the resource growing out of the industry is great relative to the derived demand. In this sense, low labor returns need not give rise to undue concern; they simply indicate that the consuming society desires a transfer of the resource to other industries and locations. They are cause for concern, however, in the sense that a low value productivity means low incomes and low living standards for individual farm families and a less-than-maximum product for society as a whole. They are also cause for concern in the sense that policies might be devised to speed up and facilitate these transfers between industries and to reduce labor immobility between farming regions.

Institutions serving as adjustment base. Initial institutions are partially important in explaining why some regional differentials in income and productivity arose. The (1) initiation of a slave economy in the Southeast with a sudden conversion to small-scale firms and (2) creation of homesteads and preemption units in the southern Cornbelt, small relative to an acreage of the same size in the central Cornbelt, gave rise to undersized units from which adjustments were necessary. These adjustments were retarded by the capital, uncertainty, firm-household and mobility forces outlined elsewhere. In both regions the nature of scale returns allowed existence of small and labor-type farming to exist more nearly than would have been true in mechanized or grain farming.

Income and firm-household complex. The low level of income on many small scale farms prevents families from accumulating any sizeable amount of capital and thus also restricts their credit base. It is a force explaining why differentials in resource returns and farm income may persist over long time periods. Not only does low income prevent the acquisition of added capital which would have a high productivity on existing small units, but it also restricts the training, education, health, and skills which can be afforded children on low income farms. Resource adaptations brought about through new farming practices and innovations are not only dependent on availability of capital but also may have high entrepreneurial requirements. While some innovations require only the ability to recognize a new variety of machine, others require greater management ability. Attainment of these abilities is often as difficult or more difficult than the obtaining of added capital. Conversion from cotton or single crop farming to dairying or other forms of livestock production is an example. In many cases managerial abilities can be obtained only through education, whether it is manifested in the ability to read and study or the opportunity to travel. Lack of funds for transportation to job opportunities and for tiding the individual or family over a short period of job seeking or through an extended period of unemployment has probably kept many workers from transferring to other locations and industries. Perhaps the sentiment of direct utility attached to the operation of an inadequate but certain (in the sense of subsistence income) producing unit also keeps some persons from moving to other locations or from becoming hired workers on other farms. This consideration is highly important for older persons on small farms in mountain and cutover regions and inhibits their movement to other industries. It is less important for able-bodied workers and young children for whom the opportunity of incorporating new values into their preference systems is still appealing. Flexibility in training and movement of labor is greatest for young people and declines with age. An important number of the census-defined farms are operated by older persons who are in a state of semi-retirement or voluntarily idle and would not otherwise add greatly to the national product were they to move to other occupations and locations. Perhaps this group should be excluded in agricultural resource productivity estimations.

The household complex and cultural considerations are known to be important in restricting the mobility of capital within agriculture. Not a great amount of inter-area movement of farmers can be evidenced even between such short distances as the northern and southern Cornbelt. It is even less common for movement of farmers from the Cornbelt or Great Plains to the South. An occasional farmer with ample capital does move from Iowa or Illinois to Alabama and Georgia, for example. While many farmers could make these transfers and realize a high return on their capital and management, not many do so because of family ties and because of cultural considerations. Where 1 isolated Iowa farmer will not move to the Alabama Piedmont, he might do so if residents of an entire county would make the move, thereby subjecting his cultural environment to less extreme alterations.

The household aspect of the farm labor supply and market is both complex and challenging to production economists or rural social scientists generally. Farm people not only lack knowledge (in the sense of ignorance of economic opportunities elsewhere) and have insufficient capital to effect movement but also place a high subjective discount on alternative returns off the farm because of limited experiences "away from home": the fear of the transition from farm to non-farm living or even rejection of non-farm modes of living may mitigate the strong family and community ties which hold people to farms and farming communities. The cultures of farm families bring about immobility of the type discussed in Chapter 24. Scattered data indicate that migration of farm labor takes place mainly over short distances. Census figures show that in the period 1935-40, 84 per cent of the white and 94 per cent of the non-white males moving from farm residences in the South remained in the region.[1] For the nation as a whole, 80 per cent of the moves from farms were within the state and 20 per cent were to contiguous states.

Productivity data also must be adjusted in terms of the real return to the individual or household. In fact, the criterion of efficiency must necessarily become one of real income to resources rather than market or money return if great differences in living costs exist between areas and industries. It is an acceptable fact that a dollar in money income, even aside from any direct utility farm families might derive from the production process, represents a greater real income on the farm than in the city. Some estimates indicate that the difference is as much as 25 per cent.[2] When these allowances are made, part of the difference between the real product to labor in farm and non-farm industries disappears. If conservative estimates of the farm labor force are employed the residual gross product per worker in agriculture can be estimated at $410 in 1940 and $1,770 in

---

[1] U. S. Census: Population, Internal Migration, 1935 to 1940, Economic Migrants, Tables 10 and 3.

[2] See D. G. Johnson, "Functioning of the Labor Market," *Jour. Farm Econ.*, Vol. 33, and Nathan Koffsky, *Studies in Income and Wealth*, Vol. XI. New York: National Bureau of Economic Research, 1949.

1948.[3] When these are adjusted for cost of living differences they become $560 and $2,210. If farms are broken down by region and size of product, the adjusted real income on large scale and large commercial farms indicates a gross residual labor return exceeding the average of wages in manufacturing industries and far above the return to workers in service industries.

The firm-household complex helps explain why low-capital and low-income farms are perpetuated in some areas relative to other areas. We need only return to Chapter 14 to understand why families with little capital have low incomes and hence because of the "propensity to consume" pressure, can accumulate but little capital. This phenomena, although it does not explain the original cause, does explain why interfarm and interregional differences continue to be perpetuated.

Labor supply function. The nature of the supply function in agriculture also relates to the farm household and undoubtedly is important in explaining the low value product of an important segment of farm labor. The major portion of the labor used in agriculture is supplied by the farm operator and members of his family. The housewife and children of the family have restricted opportunities for year-round and off-season work; the location problem in itself prevents these family members from walking a few blocks or driving a few miles to employment outside the farm sector. The supply price of this segment of the working force is low. Labor thus might be expected to be used in less remunerative employments on the farm than in the city. Whereas a housewife with extra time may invest her labor in a gardening or poultry enterprise with a low output of product per unit of labor invested, the city housewife may easily find more remunerative employment during periods of full employment. Equal value productivity of labor in farm and non-farm industries actually might be taken as an indication of disequilibrium as long as family labor constitutes an important part of the total labor force in agriculture and enters into the production process at a lower supply price than non-farm labor. The seasonal nature of farm production causes operator labor to have a lower physical productivity than would hold true were the production process continuous.[4] While physical productivity may be low for this reason, the same need not hold for value productivity. In the absence of other forces limiting resource mobility, agricultural labor probably would not remain employed in a production process with low physical productivity due to

---

[3] Figures based on Johnson, *ibid.* The aggregate data available for estimating resource productivity are themselves open to error and misinference. One extreme difficulty is in accurate measurement of the farm labor force.

[4] For an excellent discussion of the relationship between seasonality, productivity, and income in agriculture and other professions, see A. W. Ashby, "General Causes of Poverty," *Farm Econ.*, Vol. 7, 1946.

weather-born fluctuations in output if the value of the smaller output were not as great as the value of a larger output in alternative opportunities.

Monopoly structure. The possible role of monopoly markets in explaining differences in farm and non-farm productivity was outlined at an earlier point. An added monopoly consideration is that relating to the (non-farm) labor market in itself. To the extent that closed shops, seniority, initiation fees, and apprentice rules serve as effective devices in restricting entry of workers into specific occupations, the opportunity for farm migration might be lessened and labor productivity returns would thus be lower in agriculture and other competitive industries. However, these differences should be equally as great and as important between highly-unionized and non-unionized industries outside of agriculture. The final answers to this problem are still to be given, although there are many hypotheses and scattered observations to suggest that the monopoly policy of unions has pushed wage rates to excessive levels: industrial firms may, because of union wage levels, restrict output to a level where the marginal value product of labor is still great. Not all studies provide this conclusion, however. Differential changes in wage rates between industries over time apparently can be attributed as much to changes in labor productivity as to union wage structure.[5] In addition to variations in wage rates due to differences in output per man-hour, wage rates also relate to race, scale of plant, regional concentration of manufacturing, and population, as well as the scale of producing firm. Studies of the labor market over the period 1943-46 indicate that wage rates were as high or higher in non-union plants than in union plants in about one-third of the cases.[6] While data indicating the effect of monopoly policy by unions are not conclusive in either direction, seniority and other regulations may add uncertainty to the transfer of labor resources; as long as unemployment is a possibility and cannot be predicted with certainty, a farm person moving to the city may fear that he will be among the first laid off during unemployment and one of the last rehired. While the degree to which non-farm industries are monopolized or otherwise represent imperfect competition is much less than commonly supposed, this force explains only differences in farm and non-farm resource productivity. It does not explain why individual farmers are inefficient or why regional differences exist in productivity.

Investment in the human agent. Another important obstacle which gives rise to deviations between returns to the individual firm-family and society is the lack of a vehicle whereby capital can be invested in the individual

[5] Refer to Colin Clark, *The Economics of 1960*. London: Macmillan, 1942; Johnson, *op. cit.*, and Paul Douglas, *Real Wages in the United States, 1890-1926*. New York: Houghton-Mifflin, 1930; J. W. Garbino, "A Theory of Inter-Industry Wage Structure," *Quar. Jour. Econ.*, Vol. LXIV; and R. A. Lester, "Some Reflections on the Labor Monopoly Issue," *Reading in Economics*. New York: Blakiston, 1948.

[6] R. A. Lester, *ibid.*

(the human agent of production) except by the public or the person's immediate family. This economic problem area in itself is one of challenge to economists. Education is one of the main methods of investing capital in the individual. From an economic standpoint, education and educational policies can be viewed as they relate to (a) income distribution, (b) resource productivity, (c) consumption *per se*, or (d) ethical considerations.[7] Without opportunity to acquire skills and scientific ability in fields which require long educational periods, persons with low incomes must remain in fields where the labor supply is great and the supply price is low. Policies and programs which increase the opportunity of low income persons to acquire advanced skills and education can in the long run bring about greater equality in economic opportunities and income. Historically, agricultural economists should have placed greater emphasis on this possibility rather than on the concentrated attempt to maintain the numbers of opportunities in agriculture for farm children and guard against the intrusion of outsiders in farm ownership and operation.

Our interest here is mainly in the productivity aspect of training and education. Education is a productivity consideration in the sense that the product available to society is a function of the skills and abilities embodied in individuals as laborers, specialists, or resource administrators. While the inherent abilities of many children from low income farms is very great, these latent resources are never tapped because the family lacks funds to provide education beyond the elementary levels subsidized by the public.[8] The returns on capital invested in the human agent can be very great, yet, since no person can "mortgage his body," the opportunities for obtaining borrowed capital for educational and training purposes is very limited. Consequently, capital investment in the human agent, aside from that which can be made by the immediate family and isolated informal arrangements, must depend on public action. Investment in the individual involves more than formal education. It can include investment in employment outlook services, in subsidies for the travel of migrants to other industries and locations, and in developing skills for new employments. Without question, the incomes of some farm families are so low that they cannot finance extended excursions into other locations or living costs in order that job opportunities can be examined. During periods of

---

[7] From an ethical standpoint, society can attempt to "indoctrinate" the individual in order that his value system will conform with that of the community. From the standpoint of consumption *per se*, education becomes a good in the sense that being an "educated person" and having ability to appreciate art, literature, and other "higher goods of consumption" provides utility to the individual or his family.

[8] While public subsidy exists through college education, only persons from families with income sufficiently great can avail themselves of the subsidy at this level. The veterans' educational program has been a commendable exception and should be extended to peacetime for competent individuals in line with the recommendation of the President's report on education.

full employment, farm persons apparently can find employment in industry at salary levels approximating, or only slightly less than, those of persons already employed in these particular lines of work. In postwar years, migrants from farm areas received employment at wage rates roughly 90 per cent as great as the median received by the non-farm population of comparable sex and age.[9] At this level of skill and training it would appear that capital investment in the individual is important mainly as it allows the individual to tear away from his present location and move to other employment. In the absence of formal or systematic programs for capital investment in the individual, constant prosperity evidently is necessary to allow people to accumulate funds for transfer and to reduce the uncertainty of employment to a point where farm people are willing to "pull up stakes."

Race barriers. Another institutional barrier to efficient resource adaptation between industries and locations is that of racial discrimination. The great amount of labor used grows partly out of the low price for this factor as compared to capital. Labor is low in price in these areas because its supply is great relative to production opportunities. Negro families cannot migrate with such great facility as workers of other races in other regions, and, because of the lower wage rates, use of labor on farms can be pushed to an extent that its physical and value product is low. Also, within the area, opportunities in part-time work or farming often are restricted because positions in the plant are restricted to janitorial or other menial tasks while white workers have priority on skilled jobs. Since a large portion of the agricultural labor force lives in the areas affected, these phenomena may explain why resources employed in agriculture may have lower returns than resources of other selected industries, and why important regional differentials may exist.

Regional Variations in Resource Productivity and Income

Since productivity of resources and incomes of farm families differ so greatly between regions, the observation is sometimes put forth that resource returns is largely a function of location *per se*. Thus we examine this consideration alone and in detail. To what extent might those 2 main facets of location, price and soil productivity, give rise to differences in resource productivity? We saw in Chapter 22 that, although other considerations have some importance, these 2 were the central relationship in determining patterns of production and systems of farming on a regional basis. In the immediately preceding sections, we examined forces which affect the supply of labor and capital in particular locations and in agriculture. These forces, in causing the quantity of capital or labor to be large or small relative to the total plant or land base, cause factor prices

---

[9] Johnson, *op. cit.*

to favor large or small uses of capital in different regions. Accordingly, the marginal value productivity of resources can vary between regions even with similar production functions and equal product prices.

The data of the preceding chapter indicated that resource productivity varies greatly between regions. While it is true that the data are only rough approximations and do not include any refined imputational methods or allowances for differences in real income, few people would question that differences in resource productivity do not exist between the Pacific Mountain and Cornbelt regions as compared to the South in general and the Alabama Piedmont or the Mississippi Delta in particular. Neither would they question that important differences exist between central Iowa and southern Illinois or the Appalachian Mountain region. Now we wish to determine whether differences in (a) product prices growing out of location and transportation costs and (b) soil productivity at different locations can cause the value productivity of resources to vary so greatly by regions.

Soil productivity. The hypothesis has been put forth many times that low resource productivity and low income are the result of "poor" land.[10] Hence, in this section, we examine the possible effects of differences in soil productivity of labor and capital. We did see in the logic of Chapter 22 that, while physical productivity of soil may vary between regions, this criterion is not, in an economic context, a sufficient index of productivity; value productivity may be high on a soil of low physical productivity and low on a soil of high physical productivity. Price differentials can themselves offset differences in physical productivity. After this passing reminder that physical productivity is not a sufficient index of value productivity, we turn to basic principles which relate to regional productivity. There are ample facts to show that returns to labor and capital are not always low in areas with "poor" soil nor always high in areas with "good" soil; the sandhill ranching area of Nebraska and the grazing land of the intermountain area are, because of very limited rainfall or lack of fertility deposits, underlain with soil which produces a very low output per acre. Yet the product produced per unit of labor and capital in these areas is, in the aggregate, greater than that produced on the "more productive" soils of the southern Cornbelt and most of the South. Soils of the Mississippi Valley are capable of producing a greater physical product per acre than the soils of the midwestern dairy areas or the central Cornbelt, yet the product per laborer is much less. Hence we can hardly formulate an empirical law which relates productivity of capital and labor resources to soil productivity.[11]

---

[10] For indications of this notion, see excerpts from state reports in *Low Income Families and Economic Stability*. U. S. Senate Document No. 231.

[11] At another point we did indicate that pricing of the land factor may cause persons with small capital to settle in regions of low soil productivity where the economics of farm scale are not so great. See Chapter 19.

Land as a passive factor. In a settled nation where the supply of land has largely been incorporated into farming, land becomes a passive factor, and the important consideration from the standpoint of aggregate economic efficiency is the adaptation of labor and capital between alternative uses. Labor and capital, like land, can be shifted back and forth between alternative uses at one particular geographic spot. However, these resources can also be transferred between regions. Thus the important problem of aggregate efficiency is not that of equating marginal productivities for land between regions but of organizing capital and labor over the many farming regions or fixed land areas in a manner to equate value productivities of the latter resources. Since the land is immobile and cannot be transferred, the social product is at a maximum when the marginal product (measured in value or other relevant index) of the last unit of labor or capital is, with proper consideration of transfer costs, the same for each region. With the problem of maximum efficiency largely one of capital-labor productivity, we may then ask why any production analysis should ever be concerned with the return to land. The productivity of land is important to the individual farmer from the standpoint of valuation and farm size, but, since the task of maximizing the social product is one of optimally allocating labor and capital resources between particular regions (which include fixed and immobile quantities of land, as well as rainfall, sunshine, and other factors of production), need the production or resource efficiency expert have any concern over land returns and productivity? Can he not impute the full product to labor and capital and carry forth his analysis in this fashion? While it is true that aggregate efficiency is directly concerned only with labor and capital productivity and only indirectly to land productivity, determination of the return of land becomes of interest in productivity analysis in the manner outlined below. It is of interest not because we are concerned with land or the returns to land for any particular reason but because the imputational process requires that all factors be considered together. Economic analysis cannot be made of isolated factors.

Regional differences in the production function. We may now come to grips with analysis of regional resource productivity as it relates to land quality. Suppose that we have 2 agricultural areas of different land quality but with identical prices for factors and products. (One region may fall within, while the other falls outside, the shaded area of Figure 7 in Chapter 22. Both fall along the iso-price line P_3.) Thus we get 2 different aggregate production functions for areas I and II as illustrated in Figure 2. Supposing further that the 2 land areas are of equal extent or acreage; then, the physical product of a given number of units of a factor such as labor used in region I, the area of "high quality" soil, is much greater than for the same amount of labor used in region II. We may now compare the value productivity of labor employed in the two regions. In Figures 3 and 4 curves denoted as A refer to the average value product of labor, while those denoted as M refer to marginal value products. The marginal and average value productivity is much higher for any given quantity of labor in region I than in region II. However, it need not be true that the value productivity of labor is greatest in region I simply because it has the "more productive soil." If ox units of labor are employed in this region, while ow

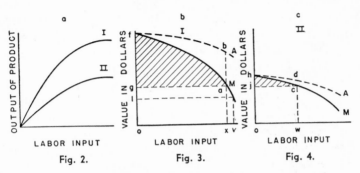

Fig. 2.   Fig. 3.   Fig. 4.

Regional productivity analysis.

units are employed in region II, the marginal value productivity of labor is equal between regions: og, the marginal value product of a unit of labor in region I, is equal to oj, the marginal value product of a unit of labor in region II and the total value product could not be increased by shifting a unit of labor between regions. It is true, of course, that the *average* value product of labor is much greater in region I than in region II; it is equal to xb in the first region and wd in the second region. Similarly, the total value product of $ofax$ in region I is greater than the total value product of $ohcw$ in region II. Yet, as long as the marginal returns are equal, resources are allocated optimally and, in terms of efficiency criteria, productivity of resources in the two areas is equal even though land differs greatly in its physical yielding ability.

It is possible, in fact, for the marginal value productivity of labor to be lower in the region of "good" soil than in the region of "poor" soil. For example, suppose the supply of labor in region I is ov, while it is ow in region II: the marginal productivity of labor in region I then is only ol, while it is oj in region II. The situation illustrated here is of the nature of that existing in such regions as the sandhill ranching area of Nebraska where soil productivity is low as compared to the delta of the Mississippi, where soil productivity is high but the productivity of the labor force employed is low. The many forces mentioned previously rather than soil productivity cause the supply function of labor and capital to differ by region and hence cause differentials in labor and capital productivity.

A corollary problem is that of farm income. Must farm incomes be lower in regions of low soil productivity than in regions of high soil productivity? Again, examples from the real world provide a negative answer to this question. The income per farm in many semi-arid ranching areas, regions with low-yielding soils, is in many instances greater than that of the more humid regions of the nation, where soils yield a greater physical product per acre. Economic logic also suggests that low soil productivity need not cause low incomes. Figures 3 and 4 illustrated that, if labor is allocated optimally between regions, returns to this resource can be the same in the two producing areas. This condition should hold true in perfect markets where the wage or return to labor approximates its marginal productivity. But, since farm income includes the return to land and capital as well as the return to labor, will not the greater total value product in regions with good soils cause income per farm to be greater than in regions with poor soils? The total value product *oxaf* in region I of Figure 3 should include not only a total product of *oxag* attributable to labor, but also *gaf* attributable to land. The product attributable to land for region II is only *jch*. Thus, while returns per unit of labor can be the same in the 2 regions, is it not necessary that the greater total product in region I must also result in a greater income per farm? If the market for resources and the imputational process result in a price for land which is in line with its marginal value productivity and farming systems and the population are appropriately adapted in both areas, then again it is possible for farmers with the same amount of funds in regions I and II to have equal incomes. Income per farm may actually differ between regions either because farmers have different quantities of resources or the market and imputational processes do not result in factor prices which conform with resource productivity. These differences arise, however, not because of differences in soil productivity *per se* but because of the many forces mentioned previously which affect the quantity of resources per farm and the concentration of labor and capital on a given land area.

Price differentials and regional variations in productivity. Location as it relates to price differentials need not cause the value productivity of mobile resources to differ between regions. This statement can also be illustrated by means of Figures 3 and 4.[12] We simply assume that both regions have a production function such as I in Figure 2. However, since prices differ between the 2 regions, we again get differences in the value productivity of labor, as are indicated in Figures 3 and 4 for the areas near and distant respectively from the central market. Again it is true that labor resources may have equal value returns in the 2 regions: if *ox* labor is employed in region I and *ow* is employed in region II, the marginal value products are equal at *og* and *oj* respectively.

Factor prices and the transfer of resources within agriculture. In the earlier chapter on production location we discussed regional differences in factor

---

[12] Turning back to Figure 7 in Chapter 22, we can now suppose that 2 regions of equal soil productivity exist and that these fall in the unshaded area. However, one falls on iso-price line P_1 while the other falls on P_3.

prices. However, we must now recognize that costs are involved in the transfer of resources between producing regions within agriculture. Transportation costs cause the price of farm-produced resources such as feeds or feeder stock, and non-farm resources, such as fertilizer, tractor fuel, and new machines to differ between regions. These factors of production move between regions, however, and perhaps the pattern of use is roughly in accord with their prices. Some transfer of machinery does take place within given farming regions as second-hand machinery or custom equipment move between farms.[13] A small interregional movement of machinery (and also labor) takes place in the wheat regions as custom combines move from south to north, but does not approach the interregional movement of feeds and feeder livestock. Costs of transferring resources are more important in limiting mobility of durable capital forms such as buildings. Buildings represent a case which is even more extreme because, although a few are moved between farms in a given locality, they seldom are moved between major producing regions. Costs of transfer are prohibitive.

Transfer costs must be considered for labor as well as for capital in its many forms. An important difference exists between these resources, however. While the costs of transfer are prohibitive in the case of farm buildings and even partly so for second-hand farm machinery, marketing firms exist which realize profits in transporting certain forms of farm-produced capital between areas. The interregional and interfarm movement of feeder stock and feed is again an example. Investment is not made similarly in the labor resource. While some few large firms do go into regions of large labor supplies and pay transportation costs to the location of their plants, the practice is not widespread; ordinarily, the worker must pay the costs of transferring to a new job in another location. The practice is even less prevalent in agriculture. In few cases do farm entrepreneurs make excursions into distant regions to hire labor, and the worker in a low-income and surplus labor region often does not have the funds to make long transfers. This lack of knowledge about the location of openings, the conditions of work, and similar considerations provide uncertainty, which in turn causes the agricultural laborer to discount heavily the returns in other regions and industries. Without a market mechanism whereby marketing firms can specialize in financing the transfer of labor between regions, this cost may well have to be paid by society if resource efficiency is ever to approach the degree desirable in a full-employment economy.

Other location considerations. Differences in land productivity and product and factor prices need not cause value productivity of resources to differ between regions. Differences exist between locations mainly because

---

[13] Here we have in mind capital of farm origin which includes buildings and machinery used on farms as well as feed and feeder stock. The lumber purchased to produce buildings or new machinery cannot be classed as "farm supplied."

of the nature of resource supply functions and because imperfections exist in factor markets. Location is involved, however, in the sense that some forces which tend to raise or lower the value product of farm resources hit entire producing regions in a similar manner. These forces, exogenous to individual farms and agricultural regions, include any force affecting the demand for products or the productivity of resources in a particular area. These are the forces which explain why one area may either decay or bloom. Often these changes in the competitive position of one area are not sudden and abrupt but slow and gradual in their effect. The adjustment and adaptation to these changing conditions is even more gradual. Labor resources are slowly being transferred out of the southern part of the Cornbelt, where incomes are low relative to neighboring farming areas and as compared to local industries. While size of farms is being increased and added capital is being brought into the area, the progress is very gradual and may not be completed for several decades. Adjustments have taken place more rapidly in abandoned farming localities of New England; they have taken place more slowly in the South, where the need for the adjustment was brought about partly by changes in the relative demand for products in the area, but also because of the change in social institutions which converted laborers into small scale entrepreneurs with little or no capital, decimated large capital holdings, and otherwise altered the structure of the producing plant.

Once an economic force brings about a change in the demand for products of an area, adaptations of 2 sorts can be made in resource use: (1) Resources already in the region can be shifted from one agricultural product to another and retained in the area. (2) Resources can be shifted from the particular area to other farming regions or to other industries. Close alternatives must exist if the first type of adjustment is to result in factor rewards as great as previously. In case this opportunity exists, few adaptations are required in the amount of resources employed by the regions. However, most major changes in the structure of the agricultural economy do require the withdrawal of resources from individual producing regions. Immediate response to a decline in resource returns may include a lessening of the rate at which short-lived capital (in the form of fertilizer, feed, seed, and tractor fuel) is used. But as was indicated in the chapter on product supply, the supply function for farm resources such as buildings and machines is highly inelastic. These resources may continue to be employed in production until they have been fully depreciated or transformed into product. In the same vein, established farm operators with deep cultural and family ties are not quick to pick up and move their labor and capital to other regions or industries when the value productivity of their resources declines. A middle-aged farmer may be willing to remain in one location and on the farm which he has developed, even though his income is only half of what it might be from the same resources in a distant region. Major resource adjustments between regions must come largely over a generation, as young persons, attempting to benefit from higher paying alternatives, transfer to other regions and industries. Because the birth rate in agriculture generally is greater than the death rate, labor transferred out of a region of declining incomes must move mainly to non-farm opportunities; developing agricultural communities can largely fill their labor needs from workers coming from households of the region.

Unequal changes in supply and demand. Aside from fluctuations due to drought or unfavorable climate in particular years, regions such as the South, the southern Cornbelt, and other isolated areas have been faced for decades with incomes which are low relative to neighboring and distant producing regions within agriculture. Since supply characteristics for factors have been outlined previously, we may now turn briefly to other forces which appear to explain the continued depressed state of factor rewards and income in particular areas. Schultz has classified these non-supply forces as those of economic development.[14] Perhaps they are more nearly demand considerations which relate first to the products of particular regions. Increases in the value products of isolated regions have not kept pace with the returns of other locations in agriculture and the American economy generally. The values placed on products of these regions have not retained their relative position but have fallen behind. In other regions technical advance has not been a rapid as for more favorably situated areas. Concentration of public funds in experimentation and farmer education was, for many years, on those areas with the most productive farm resources and the greatest return per farm. The first several decades of crops and soils research in the Cornbelt were carried out on such soils as Webster-Clarion, Canfield-Wooster, and Drummer silt loam. Early development of new corn and oat varieties (and even improved hog rations) increased the physical and value products of labor, capital, and land on these soils by more than on the rough, claypan, and shallow soils of the southern Cornbelt (where a great amount of land is in pasture). The same comparison can be made between such broad aggregate regions as the Middle West and the South: the wealth of the region (plus the system by which federal research funds are apportioned between states) allowed a greater investment in technical innovation in the Middle West than in the South, a region where investment in research and education falls at a low level relative to the quantity of human and land resources in the area.

Since it is true that particular regions are technically favored for production of a specific group of products, development of substitute supplies

---

[14] T. W. Schultz, "Reflections on Poverty Within Agriculture," *Jour. Pol. Econ.*, Vol. LVIII

and sources affect different regions differently. Perfection of synthetic fibers has provided a substitute for the fiber crops of agriculture, and thus has not favored the demand for products of the South. A shift in the preference system of the American consumer, as national income has increased, has not placed the same premium on resources devoted to wheat and potatoes as those devoted to meat. Somewhat by rough coincidence, relative changes in demand and price have favored products in regions where the value product of agricultural resources was already at the fore. Bulky products of farming regions near the dense centers of population have continued to realize a demand increase somewhat paralleling the increase in population. In a developing and expanding economy such as that of the United States, consumer expenditures for agricultural products cannot be expected to parallel increases in the national income; the income elasticity of demand for farm commodities in aggregate and for most individual items is less than unity, indicating that each 1 per cent increase in national income is accompanied by an increase in expenditures for farm products of less than 1.0. per cent. Since, however, the elasticity coefficient differs between commodities, future increases in national income must place a differential premium or penalty on the income and use of more or less resources in different farming regions. This is the force which has been tremendously important in the past. Income elasticity of demand is greatest for products such as certain vegetable, fruit, and livestock products; it is lowest for cotton and most food grains. (See Chapter 27.) In the future, then, we can expect premiums on production from major livestock areas and penalties on that of cotton and perhaps wheat areas except as these regions can adapt resource use.

The structure of an efficient agriculture. Were the conditions of maximum resource efficiency to be attained in agriculture to a degree only roughly approximating our basic criteria, changes of many sorts and magnitudes would be necessitated. Perhaps the more important adjustments should be made outside of agriculture in eliminating monopoly policy and general economic instability. The rough empirical approximations which are available suggest that adaptation of labor, capital, land, and management resources are the watchword of individual producing areas and the agricultural industry. Production economists do not know the exact extent and direction of the needed adjustment, however. It is possible, and even a likely hypothesis, that attainment of the basic efficiency conditions would require not only less labor but also a smaller total capital in agriculture. A reconstruction of the total farm plant to eliminate undersized farm units would mean that not only could the labor from these units leave agriculture, but much of its cooperating capital also could make a similar exit. Consolidation of a small farm with a large farm would, in most cases, allow operation of the combined unit with the machines and buildings of the latter.

Steps in Reducing Inefficiency

To the extent that the forces outlined above are important in conditioning the economic efficiency of agriculture, then the necessary steps in production policy become quite obvious and include the following:

1. Reduction of uncertainty. Paramount among measures to bring about more efficient production is elimination of depression and general economic instability. The consequent reduction in uncertainty would increase efficiency in non-farm production no less than in agriculture. Fiscal policy and other means whereby general economic instability might be lessened are the storage programs, crop insurance, disaster credit, and other particular production policy elements outlined in Chapter 18.

2. Education directed at increasing productivity on small low-income farms. More intensive education is needed for all farm family members, but it is needed particularly for those persons on farms possessing highly underemployed resources. The educational services of Land Grant Colleges can be looked upon largely as management services which provide yield expectations and short-run price expectations for farm commodities and resources. This assistance has been concentrated more nearly on farms of high productivity than on farms of low income.[15] Television programs, meetings at state colleges, and similar educational media are out of reach of farmers extremely short on funds who cannot avail themselves of these opportunities for additional information. Even the publicly financed technical bulletins are of little use to the farmer who has limited schooling. Most experts in agricultural education will quickly admit that the information extended to low-income farms and units with meager returns to resources falls far short of that desirable.[16] Because of their income level and limited education, persons on farms of extremely low returns cannot be reached by the usual educational media. Perhaps information needs to be in the form of broad *scientific* principle to the better-educated, high-income farmer; he can adapt the principle to his situation and coverage can be larger than if "specific answers are given for specific farms." (No state has enough resources in extension work to answer all specific questions for all farmers.) For low-income farms with little education, the education procedure may more nearly parallel *art* rather than *science* in the sense that practices, resource combinations, and courses of action are "prescribed exactly." In other words, broad principle may best relate to one group while detailed farm management and farm-home planning is called for in the other case. Additional educational resources are needed to provide

---

[15] See N. Okanay, *Economic Analysis of Extension Education.* M.S. Thesis, Iowa State College, Ames, 1949.

[16] See Joint Committee Report, *Underemployment of Rural Families.* 82nd Congress, 1st Session, Washington, 1951, pp. 64-65. One of the great difficulties in improving use of underemployed resources is lack of educational manpower.

specialists who can make individual farm visits and aid in decision-making both in production and family living. Public educational funds should not be restricted to increasing the income of persons if they remain on farms.

3. **Credit for acquisition of capital and expansion of farm size.** As has been mentioned in other chapters, the effect of the uncertainty-equity complex on limiting capital and bringing about inefficient resource use can be eliminated perhaps only through low equity loans of the FHA type. Private credit agencies can provide funds to low-income farms under these conditions but the risk and uncertainty to the loaning firm is beyond that which the public should expect it to carry. The public itself should carry these risks in the form of low equity loans. A loan program of this nature need not entail great credit risks if integrated with extended education and the provision of management assistance to aid in the selection of crops, livestock, and technical production methods. The need for a farm enlargement program is so great that material progress can be made only if the efforts of educational institutions and private and public credit agencies are integrated and intensified. It has been estimated that productivity per worker can be increased more on small farms by improving the organization of resources than by extending the scale of the unit.[17] However, it is an obvious fact that if output were pushed to the limit on small units, the productivity per worker and the income per family member would still be low; the opportunities for productive year-round work simply are not available on a small acreage. In many instances 2 or more small unproductive units can be combined to result in an efficient unit. In other cases small farms can be consolidated with larger neighboring units where the operator does not need outside capital. Widespread accomplishment in expansion of farm size would necessitate the transfer of many individuals from agriculture. For this reason auxiliary steps of the nature listed below are important.

4. **Provision of employment outlook services.** Families which desire farm or non-farm employment outside their home communities should be aided by a national employment outlook service. In reiteration, it can be said that assistance in the transfer of labor between 2 types of production in 2 different localities or industries is equally or more important than the transfer of an acre of land between beans and potatoes at 1 location. Extension education and outlook are focused almost entirely on the latter. At the present time there are no government agencies which have programs designed to help families in areas of low productivity find the best opportunities open to them. The United States Employment Service has only a few offices and no special informational programs for these families. Means should be provided whereby farm persons can be encouraged and assisted in their search for outside opportunities. Greatly expanded informational

---

[17] Joint Committee Report, *ibid.*

service is needed not only for purposes of indicating outside opportunities but also in lessening uncertainty about non-farm living conditions.

5. Job training and transfer assistance. Empirical data do suggest that immobility of labor arises as much because of the lack of knowledge or uncertainty of outside opportunities, fear of non-farm living conditions, and because of the cost of moving from one locality to another as from lack of skill in new jobs. However, aid in acquiring new skills would facilitate movement of labor from farms of low resource productivity, particularly if it were integrated with a national employment outlook service. The individual could then be given greater certainty about non-farm employment and the ability to succeed in another occupation as well as the prospects of higher returns at the outset.

6. Steps to eliminate differences in costs and returns for the individual and the community. Since one of the major areas of conflict between the farm firm and the society of consumers is that of production economics aspects (cost structure, resource use) of leasing and tenure arrangements, urgent action should be taken on leasing arrangements. A necessary step should be education wherein tenants and landlord can better be made to understand where their interests are mutual. Other needed action, outlined in an earlier chapter, includes especially state legislation on compensation and on arbitration of tenant-landlord conflicts and provisions for extending the effective span of planning for tenant farmers. While a minor portion of the nation's land acreage is involved, state and national legislation is also needed for (1) acquisition of farms in small scattered parcels such as those found in cut-over and similar regions (and which do not have a sufficient economic basis for providing adequate family living and health, educational, and recreational facilities without outside subsidy), (2) ownership of forest or other land where use of the resource can be best made to conform with national interests through public ownership, (3) zoning the use of land, labor, and capital (land is never used alone in production) where this procedure alone can cause individual and community interests to correspond, and (4) effecting other programs where firm, family, and society interests can be reconciled only through legislation. In addition public subsidy is needed, and has a basis in welfare economics, for compensating the farmer for production practices and resource use systems where returns to society are greater than the returns to the individual.[18]

---

[18] In a strictly welfare economic context, society has no basis for employing police and taxing powers alone in establishing and enforcing zoning regulations which cause the individual to sacrifice income and utility in order that other persons of the same or another generation can gain. Inability to make interpersonal comparisons prohibits any statement that the gain to others is greater than the loss to the individual. Hence a subsidy justified by society or the community and which causes the individual to adopt the desired use of resources is acceptable in the welfare context if it causes him to be as well off as or better off than before its introduction without causing others to be worse off. Conversely, zoning rules and regulations which force

This statement applies particularly to noxious weeds, water runoff, and conservation practices generally.

Industrialization and part-time farming. One of the most promising alternatives in areas of population concentration and low labor productivity, such as the share-cropping and other regions of the Southeast, is industrialization. The presence of employment opportunities in the neighborhood is more conducive to off-farm work than the opportunity of movement to new locations. Younger family members can take off-farm work while older members apply their labor on the farm; the operator or his wife may even become employed in industrial or processing firms, although he would never break community ties and move to a distant city. The fear of depression and the consequences under city living is lessened also under part-time farming operations; variability of income can be considered in the manner of Chapter 17. Therefore, it appears that industrialization in areas of surplus labor and underemployment, where it is in line with locational principles, has great promise for concentrated areas of subsistence units, under-sized farms, and underemployment of labor on farms.

Other measures directed toward production adjustments and improved resource use in agriculture are also necessary if rapid and complete adaptations are to be made. Some of the greater adjustments in location and use of agricultural resources can be made only as racial barriers and similar institutional obstacles are removed. These are, however, problems unique to the society rather than the agricultural industry.

---

change in the use of capital, labor, and land (land is never the only factor used in production) can guarantee that welfare has been increased only if the individual farmer is compensated to the extent of his loss in income and if the rest of society is not at the same time made worse off.

Selected References

Ashby, A. W., "General Causes of Agricultural Poverty," *Farm Econ.*, Vol. 5.

Bishop, C. E., *Underemployment of Labor in Agriculture, Southeastern United States*. Unpublished Ph.D. thesis.

Clark, Colin, *The Economics of 1960*. London: Macmillan, 1942.

Dixey, R. N., "Note on International Comparisons of Agricultural Efficiency," *Farm Econ.*, Vol. 4.

Fisher, A. G. B., *The Clash of Progress and Social Security*. London: Macmillan, 1935.

Johnson, D. G., *Forward Prices for Agriculture*. Chicago: University of Chicago Press, 1948, pp. 38-71.

Schultz, T. W., "Some Reflections on Poverty in Agriculture," *Jour. Pol. Econ.*, Vol. LVII.

Underemployment of Rural Families. U. S. Senate Document 231. Washington, Feb., 1951.

26

Fundamentals of Conservation
and Land Use

LAND, as a factor of production, has no unique characteristics which should cause it to be set aside by itself in economic analysis. The principles defining the optimum use of land are those drawn from the more general production economics principles. From the standpoint of contemporary production economics or economic efficiency, land differs from other factors only in the sense that its opportunities are more restricted. Land can be shifted back and forth only between alternatives at 1 geographic location; capital, labor, and management can be transferred between production opportunities in different locations as well as at 1 particular point. Land differs from certain other factors in respect to legalistic and institutional characteristics. It can be purchased and sold in the United States and, in the form of "property," persons or groups have protected rights in the factor. In the case of labor and management resources, however, this private privilege is not permitted. The individual cannot be sold into bondage and firms cannot obtain the right to lease labor in perpetuity or the right to sell the human factor of production. The reader is aware, of course, that the institution of private property is permitted in the case of capital, and, in the not distant past, was widespread for labor in the form of slavery. Analysis which relates to institutions *per se* has come to be known as land economics. Most institutions do, however, have impacts which lend themselves to analysis via economic tools drawn from the basic principles of production, distribution, pricing, and consumption. No new principles unique for land can or need be formulated. The principles which are applicable have been set forth in previous chapters and have been applied to labor, management, and capital in its many forms, as well as to land.

Land perhaps takes on unique importance only in respect to its use and allocation over time. Even here the tools of analysis and basic economic principles are identical with those which apply to any other production or resource use problems over time. Production always involves time as was emphasized in chapters dealing with uncertainty. Problems of production in time are only matters of degree when they relate to specific resources. In terms of our previous discussions of flow and stock resources, we know that services are given off from pasture forages for only a limited period of time; the alternatives over time are few. Grain, while subject to deterioration over a period of a few years, allows more choice over time than hay or pasture forage. Services from a tractor can be extended further into the future than can those for grain. All resources, except those which provide evanescent services, involve questions of investment and disinvestment, and the principles which guide choice for one resource are identical with those which provide the decision-making framework for other resources.

If land must be singled out for special treatment in production economics, the differentiation might best be based on time, however. While the principles of using land over time differ not at all from those principles guiding the use of other resources over time, certain of the resources embodied in land have a life extending beyond that of labor and the common forms of capital. Accordingly, we turn to problems of conservation in this chapter, with emphasis on particular problems in land use. The general principles of land use have been given adequate treatment in previous chapters devoted to more general aspects of resource efficiency. The analysis of this chapter also applies to resources such as grains in storage, sunshine, rainfall, labor, or any other specific category of capital or labor. The chapter has been given the title of *conservation,* but we refer more nearly to the optimum rate of using resource services over time; efficiency is denoted as much by using as by the storing of resources and resource services. Our prime purpose in this chapter, however, is one of setting down some fundamental concepts in conservation.

Contemporary and Individual Land Use Problems

Before we proceed into the heart of the society conservation problem we will review the application of production principles to (a) conservation within the individual farm and (b) contemporary or "current period" public land use problems. We use the term "contemporary" simply to indicate that our concern in the section immediately following is not with long range problems of conservation or production in time but with questions of resource use at particular points in time (though obviously the two are not distinct). If any contemporary society, or even an intertemporal society, could have one single objective for the land factor, it would be the driving of agricultural rents or returns of land to zero. Returns of zero would indicate a stock of land services so abundant, relative to techniques, that a minimum of labor and capital need be used in agriculture. Greater amounts of these factors could be diverted to non-farm industries for the production of secondary and tertiary products, commodities that characterize wealthy societies. It is known, of course, that crop production involves the use of labor, capital in many forms, management, rainfall, sunshine, and other resources, in addition to the many indestructible characteristics of the soil. When we shift an acre of land from cotton to grass we change *labor use, capital use,* and *management use,* as well as *land use.* Conversely, if we shift labor and management from wheat to flax, we cause a shift in capital use and land use. Any attempt to single land out as a separate resource and to define optimum land use apart from other resources stands to lead to grave errors. The soil specialist can carry forward researches in the structure of soils without reference to the labor or capital which might be employed on a particular tract. Yet economic efficiency in the use of land can be defined only within the framework of production economics principles wherein the alternatives of using labor and capital at other locations as well as at a particular geographic point are considered.[1]

Product relationships at 1 point in time. From the public or welfare standpoint the relationships and principles outlined in previous chapters apply to, and were applied to, land as to other resources. Where enterprises are complementary for all resources taken together, we can always say that the product to society will be increased if individual crops are extended as long as they are complementary. A greater economic product can always be produced with given resources or the same product can always be produced with fewer resources, even if the consuming public places no value on one crop. One of the greatest problems in public crop and soil programs is that of bringing about a production organization wherein a full range of complementary forages is grown. Beyond the range of complementarity, crops should be grown only as the consumer attaches sufficient value to them. The principles of optimum resource use then, as in all cases where crops are competitive, are attained within the conditions of aggregate efficiency set forth in Chapter 24. If there is any one rule of thumb for contemporary public soil use programs, it should be one of providing legislation and funds for technical education and assistance (such as that provided by the Soil Conservation Service) which facilitate production of grasses and forages to an extent that their complementary attributes are expressed. Beyond this point the public of consumers should become the relevant body, whether their choices are indicated through the pricing or the voting

---

[1] Aside from those important studies which deal solely with the institutional aspects of the land resource, historic attempts to study land in isolation have perhaps arisen because of the ease by which "land use" can be counted and geographic maps can be drawn. It is possible, for example, to count exactly the number of acres of land used for different purposes in a township, county, state, or nation. A precise map can be drawn. In contrast, it is much more difficult to determine exactly how much labor or capital of any one farm is devoted to a single crop or all crops at one particular location. The difficulty is increased by the fact that labor and capital resources are also used on livestock.

mechanism, for determining how land along with capital and labor should be used. Public questions of supplementary land use (see Chapters 7 and 8) revolve particularly around recreational versus other aspects of production. Hunting, fishing, boating, camping, and similar activities engaged in by humans for the direct utilities can be viewed as products as much as can beef, potatoes, or wheat. Over a large part of the nation's land area, recreation products are supplementary to food and fiber products. This is particularly true over much of the remaining public domain which also is used for grazing purposes. Within the range of supplementarity, recreation products do not compete with other products and society can consider the former independently from the latter. *Questions of public investment in recreational products then hinge around labor and capital rather than land.* The question becomes one of whether the labor and capital going into recreational facilities in the Rocky Mountains would add greater consumer utility and welfare if they were to be used for public schools in Chattanooga, health services in Mobile, or automobiles in Detroit. Recreational products may also become competitive with other products produced "on the spot." Hunters may become so numerous as to interfere with beef or sheep production; campers may be responsible for forest fires to an extent that this product becomes competitive with lumber production and we are returned again to our general efficiency criteria wherein production possibilities for the competing products must be related to the relevant choice indicator. Here again the relevant indicator of choice is the public preference function as expressed either through market prices or legislation.

If we now turn to conservation from the standpoint of the individual farm, we find that the greatest number of farm practices and resource combinations which, in every day terminology, are called conservation investments are simply part of the general farm management problem and may or may not have important implications in use of soil resources over long periods of time. Rotations, liming and phosphate, or potash fertilizers fall in this category, as may contours or terraces employed for the purpose of capturing rainfall in moisture-deficit areas. The relationships and principles discussed previously with respect to crop combinations, livestock practices, and similar resource and product problems then serve as sufficient principles in outlining efficiency within this framework (see Chapters 2 through 10).

If the farm as a pure firm were to view soil conservation practices in the light of time alone, the principles of selecting the production plan with the greatest discounted or capital value would then come into play. In the absence of uncertainty and capital rationing, investment would be made in true conservation resources (those denoted at a later point) as long as the discounted marginal returns of the investment are greater than the external or market interest rate. In this setting, conservation practices would not compete with alternative investments such as a hog enterprise which give immediate returns. With unlimited capital the farmer could consider investment independently. (This consideration need not be pursued further, since it has been fully discussed under a more general heading in Chapter 13.) In the presence of uncertainty and capital rationing a farm-firm would invest limited resources in conservation practices only if expectations of returns from this investment were greater than expectations of returns from alternative investments. Stating the problem in another manner, investment in conservation practices would be discounted by means of an internal interest rate comparing returns from the best alternative short-run enterprise plus some discount premium to allow for the degree of uncertainty involved. With capital limited by different amounts, the optimum level of investment in conservation practices will differ between the farmer who is short on funds and the one who has access to ample capital.

Finally, farm conservation practices can be related to the firm-household combine in the manner of Chapter 14. Some nationality groups look upon soil conservation as an end in itself. Conversely, persons with very low incomes, families pressed for funds because of sickness and individuals possessing great risk aversion characteristics, may place a very low value on distant returns. They tend to select production plans which are the antithesis of soil conservation. (See the discussion of Figure 4 in Chapter 14.) These considerations, like those previously mentioned, are all included under the relationships and principles discussed in earlier chapters. The terms *conservation* and *"good" land use* have become so imbedded in *movements* and *promotions* of one sort or another that the uninitiated believe some entirely different and mystic set of scientific principles to be involved. Obviously, this is not true. Accordingly, we turn our attention to the central assignment of this chapter. That conservation is one part of the more general production problem has been stated aptly by Black and Kiefer: [2]

> For the most part, however, erosion enters into the modern food problem of the world and its separate parts, not as a hunger threat because of vanishing topsoil, but as one of the factors to be considered within agriculture, like soil depletion, uncertain rainfall, early frosts, weeds, diseases and pests. Like these, it needs to be managed in such a way to keep the costs of contending with it at as low a figure as possible.... Presenting the conservation problem in this more accurate way does not make it less important, however.

Since the individual farm and household aspects of conservation have been discussed with sufficient detail in earlier chapters, the remainder of this chapter is concerned with certain fundamental questions of conservation, particularly as they relate to a maximum welfare of society over time

[2] J. D. Black and M. E. Kiefer, *Future Food and Agricultural Policy*. New York: McGraw-Hill, 1948, p. 102.

and to public programs which deal with conservation. Except where indicated otherwise, the analysis is presented mainly in the framework of "perfect knowledge." Rather than repeat the uncertainty analysis presented previously, we assume that the reader can draw on the content of earlier chapters when the need arises.

Intertemporal Production Relationships in Conservations

Conservation is not a unique problem in economics. As in other areas of production economics, the problem is one of allocating scarce resources between competing alternatives. Competition, however, with respect to the conservation problem is between products of different time periods. With this exception, the optimum level of conservation might be defined within the usual framework of production economics principles. Competition is, of course, between "many periods" on into eternity. In order to present the basic logic and principles in simple form and to minimize the analytical paraphernalia in the analysis which follows, the problem has been restricted to competition between 2 time periods, t_1 (the present) and t_2 (the future). The basic relationships in time and the conditions of maximum utility or welfare remain the same regardless of the number of periods involved.[3]

Intertemporal joint products. Resources can be divided into 2 "pure" categories, depending upon the nature of relationships between the resource *services* that become available in different time periods.[4] In the first category are those resource services which are available in fixed proportions over time; they can be called intertemporal joint products and are sometimes termed *"flow" resources*. Well-known examples include rainfall, sunshine, scenery, power from streams, and wind. These resource services are "joint" in the strictest sense; the possibility does not exist for substi-

---

[3] Additional periods could be incorporated into the analysis by resorting to higher mathematics. However, this step has not been taken in order that simplicity be retained. The basic principles and conclusions are similar in any case. The length of the time period (t_1 or t_2) is also irrelevant. It may be a time span of any number of years. The simple geometrics employed understate the complexity of the problem and its solution, but use of other mathematics would increase the complexity of analysis. It must be recognized that the mode of analysis employed here is inadequate for analysis of sufficient time periods; obviously, consideration of more than 2 time periods can hardly be handled by means of production or utility surfaces. In this sense our presentation is overly elementary (the problem involves infinite numbers of periods and individuals), and while it is possible to imagine the utility relationships present here for 1 individual for a total time span T (made up, for example, of 2 time periods, t_1 and t_2 of 1 or a few days each) it is less easy to visualize these relationships as they relate to a time span (T) of several hundred years. However, within the framework of these limitations, the analysis provides some elementary but basic logic which is helpful to the non-mathematician.

[4] For more detailed notions on these points see Earl O. Heady, "Some Fundamentals of Conservation Economics and Policy," *Jour. Pol. Econ.,* Vol. 59.

tution of the "flow" from one time period for that of another period.[5] The case is illustrated in Figure 1 by letting the axes measure the quantity of the *service* itself that becomes available in t_1 and t_2. The service itself cannot be withdrawn from t_2 to be used at an earlier date, t_1. These joint services might also be termed supplementary since the flow of one period does not compete with the flow of another period.

Flow resources can be divided further into two classes: (1) those which produce non-storable services, such as wind, sunlight, or scenery, and (2) those which yield services which can be stored, such as water for power or irrigation. For the non-storable services, the intertemporal relationship is again that of Figure 1. The services are produced in fixed proportions of OU in t_1 and OV in t_2. This is the only possible combination in which they can be used, because utilization cannot be postponed from one period until the next. The situation for storable flow services is

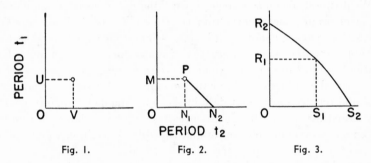

Fig. I.   Fig. 2.   Fig. 3.

Basic nature of resource relationships over time.

illustrated in Figure 2 by the intertemporal opportunity curve MPN_2. Since the resource services are produced in fixed proportions between time periods, utilization of the services at the time they become available in periods t_1 and t_2 would allow utilization of OM in the former and ON_1 in the latter period. However, since all of the service produced in the earlier period (t_1) can be stored until the later period (t_2), the maximum quantity available in t_2 is equal to that produced in this period plus N_1N_2 stored from the earlier period (N_1N_2 is equal to OM if the resource service does not deteriorate in storage).[6] Thus the possible intertemporal combinations of resource services include OM in t_1 and ON_1 in t_2, none in t_1 and ON_2 in t_2, or anything between these two extremes.

The second pure category includes those resources which yield services permitting a latitude of substitution between time periods. They arise

---

[5] Aside from short-run fluctuations in climate, the quantities of the important flow services available in different time periods are equal.

[6] Certain qualifying statements can be made for many of the propositions presented on these pages. While they have not been included because of space limitations, they can be found in the footnotes of Iowa Agr. Exp. Sta. Bul. 382.

from stock or exhaustible resources such as coal, petroleum, and certain soil mineral deposits. Here sacrificing the use of the service in one period increases the quantity available in another period. The case is illustrated in Figure 3, where the axes indicate the quantities of resource service available in different time periods. The line R_2S_2 is the intertemporal opportunity or iso-resource curve. It indicates the various possible intertemporal combinations of services possible from given stock resources. A greater use in one period always necessitates a sacrifice of services in another period. The points along the line R_2S_2 in Figure 3 indicate all possible combinations of resource services in t_1 and t_2 which will completely use up the services from the resource.

A third category of resources could be added to our list. This is the *replaceable resource*. A forest, for example, can be used up and replaced. However, our interest is in more basic resource relationships in this chapter. We do not dwell on aspects of replaceable resources since these have no unique characteristics apart from the common problems of production discussed in earlier chapters. The off-spring from a beef herd is a "replaceable resource" paralleling trees from a farm woodlot or a forest. Another crop of calves comes along in the same manner that another crop of trees can be brought forth, or the breeding herd can be partially liquidated and replaced at a later date in the same manner that forests can be rejuvenated. Even a barn as a resource is one with replaceable characteristics; as the shingles deteriorate and the sills decay, the resource can be restored to its original form.

Commodities. The relationships presented above have been in terms of the productive services derived from basic resources. They also can be applied to consumption commodities which, although derived directly from the resource services, are derived indirectly from the basic resources. The analysis remains the same, except that the relevant relationship is now directly between the basic resource and the commodity (product). In Figures 1, 2, and 3 the axes now indicate the combinations of intertemporal products available for consumption in the different time periods. For nonstorable commodities produced in fixed proportions over time (atmosphere, scenery, and so forth), the intertemporal relationship is again that of Figure 1: direct consumption of the services cannot be postponed from one period until the next. Services and products of this kind are represented by many resources which go into agriculture production. In Great Plains farming areas, the limitations of moisture cause a supplementary relationship to exist between soil nitrogen available in different years. The rate at which nitrogen from the atmosphere can be transformed into compounds of the soil is greater than the amount necessary to combine with the limited rainfall. Nitrates removed from the soil in any one year tend to be supplementary with those of later years; removal in one year does not limit production in a later year.

For commodities which can be stored from one period to another (derived either from storable or nonstorable flow resources), the situation is illustrated by the intertemporal opportunity curve MPN_2 in Figure 2. For commodities produced from stock resources, the intertemporal relationship between products is similar to that for stock resource services illustrated in Figure 3, with 1 exception: the marginal rate of substitution between time periods may not be the same for the commodity as for the resource service. This situation is illustrated by Figure 4, where AC represents a given stock resource available in 2 time periods and AB represents the quantity of a consumption commodity which can be produced and made available in the 2 time periods. The stock resources might be phosphate for example, and the commodity, wheat. If all the phosphate is used in t_1 to produce wheat and some wheat is stored until t_2, part of the wheat can be expected to deteriorate. (Opportunity curve AB is then relevant.) The product available in t_2 will then be less than if the resource had been stored for later production (opportunity curve AC is relevant when the resource itself is stored). With other resources and products, the reverse might be true. The trees blown down by the New England hurricane of 1938 represented a stock

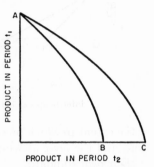

Fig. 4. Effect of resource use on production opportunities in 2 time periods.

resource which deteriorated rapidly unless converted into a product lumber. A similar situation exists for some soils in the southeastern United States. That portion of soil elements which is subject to leaching (and is not available for use in later years) can be viewed as supplementary in early years; if it is not used it will not be available for production henceforth.

Intertemporal consumption relationships. Up to this point the discussion has considered intertemporal production alone. Attention is now turned to intertemporal consumption relationships. These are expressed by means of the conventional indifference curves and indicate the various intertemporal combinations of products which make possible a given (equal) total consumer utility. An acceptable hypothesis is that future and present goods substitute at diminishing marginal rates. This situation is expressed in the convexity and slope of indifference curve GH in Figure 6: the smaller the quantity of t_1 goods used in consumption the greater is the quantity of t_2 goods necessary for their replacement and vice versa. A convex curve is more realistic than suppositions in many expositions on interest and conservation (that the total of goods in a future period is discounted by a given amount such as 5 per cent). At some level of consumption the consumer or society places an increasingly lower value on present (t_1)

than future (t_2) goods and vice versa.[7] The slope of an intertemporal indifference curve will then depend on 2 major factors: (1) the relative values which present individuals attach to their own consumption in different periods and (2) the values which present individuals attach to consumption by individuals of future generations. The latter is a question

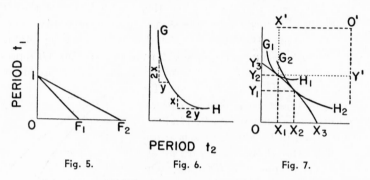

Fig. 5. Fig. 6. Fig. 7.

Inter-temporal indifference curves and resource use over time.

of the extent to which present generations value survival of future generations and the level at which they wish future generations to live relative to their own standard.

Intertemporal Welfare

Given the production and consumption relationships outlined previously, the rate of resource use which maximizes intertemporal welfare can be defined. First, the three production opportunities set out above are examined separately as pure cases. Later, these unique cases are related to each other.

Stock-derived products. For a society in which stock resources alone are available, the conditions which define a maximum intertemporal welfare are illustrated in Figure 7, where opportunity curve Y_3X_3 provides the intertemporal substitution rates for goods in production, while indifference

---

[7] It is obviously true that the intertemporal utility surfaces are not identical for all individuals. However, the notion of a community indifference curve is useful at this point and leads through the same logic whether one supposes that it (a) can be derived from heterogeneous individual curves, (b) is for a community of individuals with identical utility surfaces, or (c) represents a community of 1 individual. It is also likely that the individual's *ex ante* notion of his intertemporal indifference curve differs from his *ex post* notion of this same relationship. Thus if economic action is based on the *ex ante* indifference curve, total intertemporal utility is never maximized. This is a problem in consumer dynamics for which current economic theory provides few solutions. Without "solutions" here it is impossible to formulate a simple optimum time-use of resources in the vein presented. We do not have space for the details here, but if we allow compensation, a community indifference curve can be constructed in the manner of L. Baumol, *Rev. of Econ. Studies*, Vol. 17.

curves G_1H_1 and G_2H_2 represent provide the intertemporal substitution rates for goods in consumption. (Disregard the ordinates $O'Y'$ and $O'X'$ at this point.) G_1H_1 represents a high value attached to present relative to future goods, while G_2H_2 represents a relatively greater value attached to future goods. Intertemporal welfare can be maximized when the marginal rate of substitution of goods in consumption (indifference curve G_1H_1 or G_2H_2) equals the marginal substitution rates of goods in production (transformation curve Y_3X_3). Geometrically, this is denoted by the tangency of the production opportunity curve and the indifference curve. In respect to the intertemporal indifference curve G_1H_1, welfare is maximized over time by production of OY_2 and OX_1 in the time periods t_1 and t_2 respectively. The quantity Y_2Y_3 (which equals OX_1 if resources do not appreciate or depreciate over time) should be conserved. This is the economic level of conservation. It can be defined in no other sense if the criterion is one of intertemporal welfare.[8] For indifference curve G_2H_2 (a higher value on future consumption) OY_1 should be consumed and Y_1Y_3 (equals OX_2) should be conserved in period t_1 if welfare is to be maximized over time.

Flow-derived products in direct consumption. Only 1 possibility exists in maximizing intertemporal welfare over time if non-storable flow resources and products alone are available. The flow-derived products must be consumed in exactly the proportion in which they are forthcoming. The slope of the intertemporal indifference curve has no relevance: an indifference curve with the slope of either G_1H_1 or G_2H_2 (Figure 7) would denote the same intertemporal rate of use (OU in t_1 and OV in t_2 for Figure 1). The only economic question here is one of equating marginal cost (in terms of working capital and labor) with marginal return of utilizing the service in any one period.

Flow-derived products with storage alternatives. A society falling within this pure case and attempting to maximize intertemporal welfare should always consume products during the period in which they are produced if the future is discounted by any amount whatsoever. Any indifference curve with a slope of less than 45° (denoting a greater value on present than future consumption) would be tangent to the intertemporal opportunity curve MPN_2 in Figure 2 at the point P (denoting consumption at the rate of OM in t_1 and ON_1 in t_2). In order for future consumption to be increased at the expense of present consumption in this pure case, the indifference curve must, at some point, have a slope of more than 45°, denoting a premium on future over present consumption. If the discrete periods are long enough, commodities produced from flow services cannot

---

[8] One additional point is of interest previous to our subsequent analysis. In terms of production relationships, the output of one period is not always competitive with that of another period but may be complementary, even though the supply of resource services is of fund or stock nature.

be stored into the next period. This is true for agricultural commodities: meat and other perishables can be withheld from consumption only for short periods and length of storage for grains and other staples is also limited. If the relevant time periods (t_1 or t_2) are long enough, the category of flow-derived products which are storable becomes synonymous with flow-derived products which are not storable.

Two categories of changes affect the level of resource use (conservation) which will maximize intertemporal welfare. These changes affect the intertemporal rates of substitution of goods in production and of goods in consumption. Major forces altering the consumption substitution rates are changes in population and changes in tastes of given populations. Changes in the intertemporal rate at which goods in production substitute for each other are brought about mainly by improved techniques (including discoveries of new, or loss of existing resource deposits). Changes in techniques may conceivably increase, leave unchanged, or decrease the rates at which resources should be conserved (consumed) between time periods. In agriculture, such innovations as hybrid corn change the transformation ratio toward the present and encourage increased yields, and hence a greater soil exploitation relative to the future. Innovations such as improved terracing and forages tend to throw an advantage in the opposite direction because the rates at which future goods substitute for those of the present are increased. In extractive industries, innovations which have greater application to easily accessible deposits have the effect of speeding up early as compared to later consumption. Since the effects of changes in techniques, consumer tastes, and population are analyzed in detail elsewhere, we do not treat them further.[9]

One of the greatest problems in conservation or resource use over time is that of expectation of technical change. Technical change has the effect of causing increased quantities of resource services to be available from given resource stocks or flows. The future can thus be compared with the present in terms of expectation of the intertemporal production possibilities. Several expectation models might be employed. One evidently followed by societies of the past is that technical advance (or even discovery of resources) in the future will proceed at the rate of the present. The rate at which individuals and societies select to use resources over time undoubtedly depends on their expectations of the intertemporal opportunities. Thus the nature or slope of the intertemporal curve is dependent partly on the expectations of production possibilities. The assumption or expectations of unlimited resource services would cause individual members of society to place a lower value on conservation than would knowledge that stocks of resources will become extremely limited in the near future. This

[9] See E. O. Heady, "Fundamentals of Soil Conservation Economics," *Jour. Farm Econ.*, Vol. 32, pp. 1182-1196; also E. O. Heady and O. J. Scoville, *Fundamentals of Conservation Economics and Policy.* Iowa Agr. Exp. Sta. Bul. 382.

environment has been reflected in the use of soil resources in the United States. The framework of free and unlimited land caused the nation as well as individual farmers to place a premium on exploitive farming methods in early years.

Composite supply and substitution of stock and flow resources. Two pure cases of intertemporal production [joint products (1) in fixed proportion and (2) competitive products with a latitude of substitution] have been examined previously. Both categories of resource services exist side by side. An important practical economic problem is the extent to which flow resource services (flow-derived products) should be substituted for stock resource services (stock-derived products) in current periods in order that the latter may be conserved. This is partly the problem in the irrigation and reclamation projects of agriculture where there are alternatives of (1) exploiting the soil in developed farming regions now and initiating irrigation in undeveloped regions at a time when depletion and perhaps erosion has diminished the product from the former region or (2) developing irrigation projects at the present and saving the chemical elements of developed regions for the future.

The analysis which follows treats equilibrium of production and consumption under the conditions of a supply of flow and stock resources in combination. It is retained as a pure case, and hence is simply a variant of the situations already discussed. Presentation is abbreviated by means

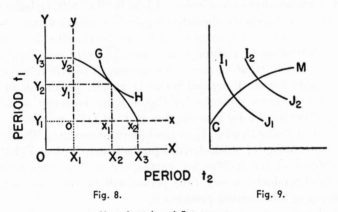

Fig. 8.　　　　　　　　　　　Fig. 9.

Use of stock and flow resources.

of the simple geometrics of Figure 8. First, refer to the oy and ox axes (independent of the OY and OX axes) which indicate the situation for stock resources alone. The transformation curve y_2x_2 indicates the intertemporal production opportunities. Production can be, for example, at the rate of oy_2 in t_1 and zero in t_2, ox_2 in t_2 and zero in t_1, or any combination (consistent with the opportunity line y_2x_2) between these 2 extremes. Given the intertemporal indifference curve GH, the optimum rate (as denoted by tangency of GH and y_2x_2) at which the product derived from the stock resource should be consumed in t_1 is oy_1 if intertemporal welfare is to be maximized. The product conserved in t_1 and consumed in t_2 is y_1y_2.

Second, consider the situation of flow resources alone and refer to the OY and OX axes (disregard the oy and ox axes and any of the geometric figures which fall within these). The point o represents the available flow-derived products (joint products in fixed proportions) in the period t_1 and t_2. Only 1 intertemporal combination of products, OY_1 in t_1 and OX_1 in t_2, is possible. Irrespective of the slope of the indifference curve (the marginal rates at which consumption goods substitute for each other between the 2 time periods), consumption must be at these rates for the reasons previously outlined.

Finally, the products derived from stock resources can be added to those derived from flow resources. In reference to the OY and OX axes, the maximum supply of products available in periods t_1 is then OY_1 flow-derived product plus Y_1Y_3 (equals oy_2) stock-derived product, a combined total of OY_3. Similarly, the maximum supply possible in t_2 is OX_1 flow-derived product plus X_1X_3 (equals ox_2) stock-derived product a total of OX_3. The composite intertemporal transformation curve is now $Y_3y_2x_2X_3$. It has 2 supplementary ranges, Y_3y_2 and X_3x_2.

What rate of consumption [of (1) total product and (2) stock-derived product] in each time period will maximize intertemporal welfare when flow and stock resources are considered jointly? Let GH (relative to the OY and OX axes) indicate the intertemporal substitution rates for consumption goods. Thus we assume no change in the marginal intertemporal rates of substitution of consumption goods, but GH now represents a greater total utility (than in previous employment of GH relative to the ox and oy axes for stock-derived products alone). Maximum intertemporal welfare is again indicated in Figure 8 by tangency of GH and $Y_3y_2x_2X_3$, denoting a total consumption in t_1 of OY_2, composed of OY_1 of flow-derived product and Y_1Y_2 of stock-derived products. The optimum level of conservation of stock-derived product in t_1 is thus Y_2Y_3. Given identical slopes of the indifference curves, the level of consumption of stock-derived products in any time period will be the same regardless of the supply of flow-derived products.[10]

Substitution of services and anticipations. Previous discussion has assumed the basic stock of resources to be the limiting factor in production. The quantity of capital and labor available for transforming basic stock and flow resource services was considered great enough to allow an output of flow-derived plus stock-derived products in t_1 or t_2 indicated by the

---

[10] An added alternative is that the slope of the intertemporal indifference curve does change (changes in tastes or utility surfaces still absent) and the total of goods available or utility possible is greater (and hence the indifference contour that can be attained on the total utility surface is higher).

transformation curve $Y_3 y_2 x_2 X_3$. Suppose that the quantity of working capital and labor is limited to the extent that attainment of the maximum output in 1 period, indicated by $Y_3 y_2 x_2 X_3$, is impossible. Suppose, for example that if the output of flow-derived product is OY_1 in t_1, the limited supply of working capital and labor restricts output of stock-derived products to less than $Y_1 Y_3$. The supply of basic resources or raw materials is not then the limiting factor in maximizing welfare over the total time span, T (t_1 plus t_2). Instead, the limiting factor is the supply of working labor and capital. Timing of production is not then a central problem in maximizing welfare in the total time span, T. The crucial problem is the extent to which the given stock of labor and capital should be allocated to production of stock-derived as compared to flow-derived products in any single period, t_1 or t_2. The solution lies, of course, in equating the marginal productivities of labor and capital when allocated between the 2 alternatives of flow-derived and stock-derived products.

An important substitution problem arises out of dynamics and anticipation. The possibility always exists that a society will be called upon to draw heavily and rapidly upon its resources in case of future emergency. Availability of resource services which can be converted to product in a short-time span is thus important. Conversion of the given stream of flow services cannot be speeded rapidly. A premium may be placed on retaining (building up) a store of stock resources (services) which can be converted to product on short notice. This may be accomplished by substituting flow for stock resource services in early production periods. A sacrifice or a cost occurs in early periods if the working capital and labor employed in converting raw materials into product has a lower productivity when the source of raw materials is flow rather than stock resources. The loss in welfare is also for all time should the eventuality (war, emergency, and so forth) fail to be realized. However, the cost is one of flexibility and is not only consistent with an *ex post* maximization of welfare if the eventuality occurs but also with an *ex ante* anticipation of welfare maximization even if the eventuality does not occur.

Intergeneration Welfare

Although interpersonal utility comparisons are impossible at a given point in time (within a generation), an optimum allocation of production and consumption over time can be formulated if objective means exist whereby each individual can express his relative values. In a democracy the mode of expression is provided in voting through either the price mechanism or the ballot system. In this sense, reflection of a community indifference curve of the nature suggested by GH in Figure 8 is possible for a single generation. Expression is in the structure of market prices and in the legislation of the society. This utility expression or comparison is impossible, however, between distinct generations. An individual of a generation 200 years hence has no method of expressing his intertemporal indifference curves; he can vote neither through the market mechanism nor through the ballot system. The welfare of a future generation (g_n) would stand to be greater, had not an increment of stock resources been consumed by an earlier generation (g_{n-100}). The marginal utility derived from consuming the increment of product might well be greater for generation g_n than for generation g_{n-100}, and vice versa. The impossibility of interpersonal and intergeneration utility comparisons excludes proof that either holds true.

Modern welfare economics handles the problem of (inability to make) interpersonal utility comparisons at a given point in time by the principle of compensation. Two general types of economic reorganization are recognized: (1) those which increase the total utility of some individuals without decreasing the total satisfactions of other individuals and (2) those which increase the total utility of some individuals but at the same time decrease the satisfactions of the other individuals. Social welfare increases under the second type of reorganization only if the increment in utility to the recipient group is greater than the decrement in utility to the sacrificing group. Because of lack of interpersonal utility comparisons, however, increased welfare can be guaranteed only through the principle of compensation: those who originally sacrificed as a result of the reorganization must be provided with compensation to completely redress their loss while the welfare of recipient groups must increase. The problem of intergeneration conservation is identical with the elements outlined above: (1) Conservation relates to a reorganization which improves the utility position of some persons (generations) but lessens the utility position of other persons (generations). (2) Intergeneration (and hence interpersonal) utility comparisons are impossible.

Cannot the principle of compensation be applied to guarantee that while some generations will be made better off, no generation will be worse off and, accordingly, an increase in intergeneration welfare be guaranteed? The answer is negative under specified full-employment conditions. Compensation to a present generation for a greater level of conservation can be made only through use of the very resources which otherwise are to be conserved. An increment in conservation by X quantity of resources (beyond that which defined the optimum for the current generation) would require use of the same X quantity of resources for compensation if the present generation were to be left as well off as previously. In this vein conservation compensation is impossible for an intergeneration society. What, then, is the optimum level of conservation for an intergeneration society? Existing scientific logic can only state this: The optimum level of conservation is what each succeeding generation thinks it to be (including the relative value placed by the current generation on consumption for future generations). The values of discrete generations cannot be linked together *ex ante* into a single index for all time to give one optimum level of conservation into eternity. In this vein, the level of conservation which is ideal or optimum changes with the values of each succeeding generation. If today's generation chooses to be spendthrift and squander resources at the expense of consumption by future generations, the level of conservation expressed is the optimum at the time and through eternity as far as can be determined by existing tools of science. If tomorrow's generation chooses to be miserly, merely subsist, and hoard resources which are then used for luxury consumption by a succeeding generation, existing economic tools would specify that the level of conservation is optimum and that welfare has been maximized between generations.

Intrageneration relationships and compensation. We have referred above to a community indifference curve. Use of this aggregative relationship, even for a single generation, must recognize that the community indifference curve is a composite expression of the intertemporal substitution rates for many individuals. Accordingly, we outline below the particular conditions of equilibrium which must exist in order that intertemporal equilibrium be attained. Reference is to a single generation.

At least 2 important conditions must be attained between particular producing and consuming units before aggregate intertemporal and intrageneration welfare can be maximized: (1) The intertemporal substitution rates for consumption goods must be equal for every pair of consumers. (2) The marginal rate of intertemporal substitution of goods in production must be equal between every pair of specific resources. Since consumption problems are discussed in detail elsewhere, we examine in detail only the necessary production relationships.[11] The (product from) various classes of resources within the overall category of fund or exhaustible resources must be related in establishing the optimum level at which each particular class should be conserved. It is not a sufficient condition that coal be used up in one period and petroleum be largely conserved until a later period or that one soil type be exploited in one period while a substitute soil type be reserved as a later replacement. The ratios at which products from each particular resource substitute over time must be equated.[12]

---

[11] See E. O. Heady, *ibid.*

[12] If (a) use of (the product from) one unit in t_1 requires sacrifice of 2 units of resource K (growing timber) in period t_2 while (b) use of (product from) 1 unit in t_1 requires sacrifice of only 1 unit of resource L (building stone) in period t_2, the nature of intertemporal substitution is clear. (The examples assume certain conditions in respect to quantity of both specific resources and working capital but which are not enumerated for lack of space.) Resource L should be used in t_1 (in a magnitude to replace the quantity of K which might otherwise be used) while K is conserved until period t_2. Conversely, if (a) conservation of 1 unit until t_2 requires sacrifice of 2 units of resource K in period t_1 and (b) conservation of 1 unit until t_2 requires sacrifice of only 1 unit of resource L in period t_1, then K should be used in t_1 and L should be conserved until t_2. (K may be a soil for which erosion or

Two possibilities exist in attaining these conditions: (1) Certain reorganizations of production and resource use increase the product for all time periods and all individuals (especially in some parts of agriculture where readaptation of the management program increases both present and future output and income. Here an improved utility position of each of two individuals A and B within a generation and between generations (individual C of another generation as well as A and B) can be guaranteed. Two types of social action are justified here since an improved position of all individuals and hence a greater total welfare is given. These include education to stimulate conservation and direct legislation to effectuate readaptations in the use of resources. (2) Reorganization may lessen the welfare of some individuals (A) while increasing the welfare of others (B or C). Since interpersonal utility comparisons are impossible a greater total welfare cannot be guaranteed by simply transferring resources to an intertemporal use which will conform with the preferences of individual B as compared to another individual A. The transfer must guarantee that no one is left worse off. This can be accomplished, in the lack of interpersonal utility comparisons, only through compensation from individual B who prefers more product in the future to the individual A who prefers less conservation. Increased welfare cannot generally be guaranteed by police power alone which forces readaptation in intertemporal resource use in the absence of compensation; it considers neither interpersonal utility nor compensation.

Many discussions of conservation imply a highly divergent interest between society and individuals. From the consumption standpoint this distinction is highly misleading for a democracy; the society is nothing but the sum total of individuals. No body, political or otherwise, sits in the capital of a democratic nation representing a society distinct and separate from sovereign individuals. What actually should be stated is that the individual acts differently when he acts singularly, and believes all others to be acting singularly, than when he acts as part of a group. He may vote for soil conservation subsidies and legislation but at the same time express his desire for exploitative crops by paying high prices for corn-fed beef. Using the 2 methods of choice indication, the voting and price mechanisms, his expressions seem to be in contradiction. This is not necessarily true, however, except as the conflicting expressions grow out of lack of knowl-

---

leaching is extremely rapid while L is a stable soil, or K may be natural gas that might otherwise escape while L is coal.)

These equilibrium conditions can also be illustrated in Figure 7 by letting Y_3X_3 represent the intertemporal transformation curve for (the product from) K type resource and G_1H_1 suggest the (obverse) opportunity curve for the product from L type resource. Marginal rates of intertemporal substitution are equated and maximum welfare is possible with consumption of OY_2 of K and $O'Y'$ of L in period t_1 with conservation of OX_1 of K—derived product and $O'X'$ of L—derived product until period t_2.

edge. His preference system or indifference curve simply has different values attached to it when he acts as an individual or as part of a group.

Efficiency in Soil Conservation

After having examined the fundamental relationships involved in resource conservation, we now turn to some applied aspects of soil investment. Our analysis again revolves around the production economics aspects of public soil conservation programs. We do not go into the fine details of time and discounting in this section, because they have been covered sufficiently in earlier chapters. We simply start our analysis with the proposition that the amount of product needed after the proper comparisons have been made between all alternatives and the length of the time in each future period has been ascertained. The analysis can be viewed as one illustrating efficiency in the sense of maximizing a product in the relevant time period from a given input of current conservation resources (or conversely, of minimizing the input for a given product of the future). The means by which planning can be adapted to imperfect knowledge or uncertainty are touched upon only briefly since these simply represent, from either an individual or public standpoint, adaptations of those outlined earlier.

Public subsidy of soil conservation has been carried out for the 1930's and 1940's. Subsidies are in the form of monetary assistance provided by the Production and Marketing Administration and technical assistance provided by the Soil Conservation Service. If efficiency is to be the criterion, the very first action of a public agency charged with soil conservation should certainly be the establishment of a basic definition of conservation. Otherwise, there can be no systematic manner in which public funds and resources are used. The distinction between soil conservation and other general production problems cannot be made on the basis of "production from the soil" *per se;* seed corn, tobacco plants, and insect spray would qualify equally with terraces, lime, and other resource inputs eligible for public assistance. The distinction cannot be on the basis of time. Soil conservation is simply 1 element of the larger problem of the timing of production and investment; farm buildings, machinery, and livestock in general would receive "conservation" subsidies if use of public funds were based on the time variable alone. In the true sense, conservation does refer to the allocation of production and consumption over time. The economic decision is as much one of the quantity of resources to be used in the present as the quantity to be conserved for the future. However, for purposes of the analysis which follows, we will refer to soil conservation in a somewhat different and restricted sense. A meaningful definition of soil conservation over time is this: it refers to prevention of diminution in future production on a given area of soil and from a given input of labor and capital with the technique of production otherwise constant. Thus conservation refers only to the retention of a given production function over time. It does not refer to an increase or decrease in product as resource inputs are varied for a given production function.

This definition and its implication is illustrated in Figure 10. Soil "conservation" is not involved if we travel only along production function A in varying resource inputs. For example, if the original input of resources (labor and capital in the form of tractor fuel, seed, fertilizer, and so forth)

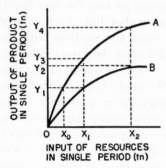

is OX_1 with a resulting output of OY_3, we are not concerned with "conservation" as the level of input is raised to OX_2 and the product to OY_4. We have simply moved along a single production function (in respect to our X resources). Neither need we be concerned over time as price relationships change and input falls back to OX_1 and output OY_3 if the process can be reversed again. The concern of soil conservation should instead be that of "preventing

Fig. 10. Nature of soil conservation.

a "fall" from production function A to production function B. If this permanent break (from one productivity curve to another) does come about, our previous condition is no longer fulfilled. An equal application of resources in the future will not result in an output of the original magnitude. For example, if the input of labor and capital is increased from OX_1 to OX_2 (after the fall to B) it results in an output not of OY_4 (production function A) but only OY_2 (production function B).

Intertemporal complementarity. In the terms of production economics, conservation practices are thus denoted by resource inputs (labor and capital) which are technical complements between time periods with resources which are transformed into product within single time periods. Non-conservation resources are characterized as competitive (technical substitutes) with other resources within a single time period. The distinction can perhaps best be explained with an example: suppose that an initial input of a resource combination (say, 7 hours of labor, 50 lbs. of fertilizer, and a given physical quantity of other factors) is equal to X_1 and results in an output of 50 bushels of corn per acre in the early period (t_1). If input of an additional resource input equal to Z_1, along with the original input X_1, results in an output of 60 bushels in a later period (t_2), the additional resource (practice) is a substitute; some smaller input of fertilizer, labor, or other resources in the original combination of X_1 can be used along with the Z_1 resource input to attain an output equal to the original 50 bushels. However, if in the later period (t_2) the original X_1 input of resources results in an output of (a) only 40 bushels without the Z_1 resource input but (b) 50 bushels with the Z_1 resource input, the latter is a conservation resource (practice); unless Z_1 resources are employed the original output cannot be attained over time from the original X_1 combination. Prevention of gullying is thus a conservation measure because future production will be diminished as the original inputs of capital and labor are applied to the remaining (non-gullied) land area in the absence of "conservation" practices or resources. Sheet erosion is not yet directly related to future production if its rate is at a fraction of an inch per year on a deep top soil wherein the same application of non-conservation inputs results in an equally great output in successive production periods. Sheet erosion causes a break between production functions, however, if the remaining subsoil results in a smaller output (as compared to the original top soil) from equal applications of labor and capital. Applications of nitrate fertilizer on level land which simply increases production when applied with previous resource combinations does not meet our test as a conservation measure.

It is true that some types of farm practices or resource inputs act immediately as substitutes but serve as technical complements to other resources over long time periods. Addition of legumes in a rotation may simply add to given yields during a rotation cycle; the same product could then be produced with smaller inputs of land, labor, and capital in other forms. If society were interested in the 4 or 5 years of the rotation cycle alone, the rotation resources would not be considered as essential in conservation. However, in a 20- or 40-year period, the existing level of output (with input of land, labor, and capital constant in each year) may not be maintained without the addition of resources in the form of rotation forages. In the longer period the forages can then be considered as complementary to other resources and hence as conservation inputs.

Without some such criterion as the one outlined above, there is no limit to the short-run production practices in which public funds might be invested. Funds might equally well be invested in improved livestock techniques as in agronomic and soil engineering practices which have a primary effect of increasing production. In the discussion which follows we refer to conservation practices (resources) only as those which prevent diminution in output of the future from given resource inputs (retention of a given production function over time).

Necessary conditions for maximum conservation. A necessary condition for attainment of maximum conservation is that funds be used in fact for conservation practices. An important part of public monetary assistance has not met this elementary test over time. Irrigation, drainage, and weed control are not practices which are generally necessary to prevent a diminution in future production: the practices are substitutes over time for other types of resources except as they prevent permanent deterioration of the soil. If irrigation is not developed or improved on a tract of land now there is nothing to preclude its initiation at a future date with the result of an increase in production. The same can be said for mechanical drainage practices and weed control. Although the line cannot be drawn so clearly, certain other practices subsidized historically by PMA can also be questioned. Green manure and cover crops often fall in this category. A legume or grass crop used to prevent erosion or permanent deterioration in soil structure is related to production of the future. However, where these crops are used simply to boost short-run production of subsequent grain crops on level soil types, they hardly qualify for public subsidy if emphasis is on maintenance of future productivity. Payments for liming materials and inorganic fertilizers for grasses and legumes on level land with a main effect of increasing short-run grain yields fall in a similar category. Subsidization of practices with no effect in preventing diminution of future production represents an inefficient use of public resources when processes which do lessen future production are taking place.

A similar analysis might be applied to technical assistance. Soil conservation districts were generally formed first in those areas with the greatest erosion hazard and hence where a true conservation problem existed. As the number of districts expanded, however, these have generally been in the direction of soil associations with less critical erosion hazards. A portion of technical assistance has been devoted to developing irrigation systems, drainage, and similar practices. Certainly, the technical assistance used for irrigation, improved rotations on level land, or drainage developments (where these are of a non-conservation nature) could better be employed where permanent deterioration of the soil is taking place. Given the objective of maximum conservation attainment, the efforts of a farm planner in York County, Nebraska, for example, should be allocated to erosion control on the rough land rather than to irrigation development on level lands. Similarly, 1 farm planner each in Champaign County, Illinois, and Switzerland County, Indiana, woud not represent the best use of resources (in terms of our criterion of conservation maximization) if effort were directed to drainage in the former and to erosion control in the latter county.

Sufficient conditions and allocations between soils. Allocation of public funds to practices or soils where potential diminution in future production is prevented is a *necessary* condition for maximum attainment of conservation from given funds. It is not, however, a *sufficient* condition. On the basis of this criterion alone, public funds would be allocated to the various soil areas on the basis of the number of acres of soil subject to erosion or other permanent deterioration. An acre of one soil subject to erosion would have as much claim on public assistance as an acre of any other soil subject to erosion, but this would not guarantee the greatest degree of conservation (the smallest diminution in future production from given resource inputs).

Present funds should be given allocative priority between soil associations in terms of their marginal productivity in the relevant future time period. Each increment of investment in monetary or technical assistance should be spent in a manner which minimizes the diminution of future production (due to erosion or other processes which permanently lower productivity). For example, if a given current investment averts future loss of 100 bushels of corn (or equivalent units of other crops) on soil A but only 60 bushels on soil B, then public assistance which is limited should be devoted to the former soil. Limited conservation resources should have priority in preventing loss of an acre of the Tama-Muscatine soils of eastern Iowa over an acre of Shelby-Sharpsburg in southern Iowa or northern Missouri. Similarly, investment of limited public funds would call for preventing loss of an acre of Decatur-Dewey-Cumberland soils of Madison County, Alabama over the Guin-Atwood-Savannah soils of Franklin County, Alabama.

The analysis outlined above is given greater refinement in Figures 11, 12, and 13. The goal should be one of equating the (future) marginal productivity from current investment between soils. Figure 11 suggests the future productivity of various quantities of current conservation investment on soil A. Figure 12 represents the situation for soil B.[13] Figure 13 combines Figures 11 and 12.[14] With a total possible current investment of OZ_1 in Figure 11 (which equals $O'Z'_1$ in Figure 12) the entire investment should be made on soil A. The marginal productivity of all investments up to this point on soil A is greater than any investment, however small, on soil B. Given a total possible current conservation investment of OZ_2 (equals $O'Z'_2$) for the 2 soil types as indicated in Figure 13, OZ_1 should be invested in soil A and Z_1Z_2 (equals $O'Z'_1$) should be invested in soil B. Under this combination, the marginal productivity of investment is equated between the 2 soil types in the single period of the future.

Where allocation of conservation funds is to be based on the criteria of

---

[13] The situation for the 2 soil types might be represented by 2 production functions such as $Y_n = f(X_n, Z_o)$ and $Y'_n = f'(X'_n, Z'_o)$ where the first refers to the output from the resources applied to soil type A while the second refers to the same product and resources for soil type B. Y_n and Y'_n represent the product of the future (t_n) time period, X_n and X'_n represent the input of non-conservation resources of the same period (t_n) and Z_o and Z'_o represent the input of conservation resources from an earlier period (t_o) for the A and B soils respectively. In Figures 11, 12, and 13 we are holding the input of X resources constant to examine the productivity of Z resources. This is consistent with our presentation in Figure 10 where we are in effect, holding Z resources constant to examine the productivity of X resources. Figures 11 and 12 thus also represent the future product sacrificed from given applications of non-conservation resources (X) if the relevant quantities of conservation resources (Z) are not applied earlier. For example, if the input of the conservation resource is OZ_1 in t_o on soil A the given application (say OX_1 of Figure 10) of X will result in output of only OY_1 rather than OY_2 in t_n.

[14] Figure 13 represents Figure 12 inverted and transposed over Figure 11.

maximum attainment from given or limited conservation funds, annual investment in either direct subsidies or technical assistance in one soil area might well amount to several times that of another soil with an equal

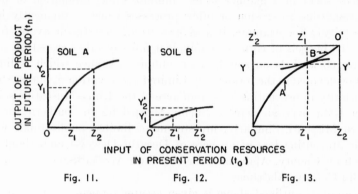

INPUT OF CONSERVATION RESOURCES
IN PRESENT PERIOD (t_0)

Fig. 11.   Fig. 12.   Fig. 13.

Optimum allocation of conservation resources.

acreage subject to erosion. These possibilities are suggested in the experimental data of Table 1. If annual conservation appropriations are limited and if diminution of future production is to be minimized, it is more important to save 2 acres of Marshall silt loam while 2 acres of Shelby silt loam erode away than to save 1 acre each of Marshall and Shelby while 1 acre of each also erodes away. Certainly, within the framework of annual appropriations short of those necessary for complete safeguarding of future production, some soil areas should go entirely without subsidies while payments are concentrated on productive soils which are most important over the long run. There is little evidence that major allocations of public assistance between soil areas have been based on the principles outlined here. There is little relationship between the marginal productivity of resources and their use.

Between practices on given soils. Current allocation of public funds between conservation practices also suggests some lack of economic system. Evidently one PMA criterion has been the selection of qualifying practices which enables all farmers to collect some amount of payment. This system has no basis (except in terms of income distribution) within the framework of our efficiency criteria. Another basis for allocation of funds between practices and one which evidently has been used to some extent is the cost of the installation or practice. For example, with cost of terrace construction at 15¢ per cubic yard of earth moved and waterways at 12¢, 70 per cent of the cost of each might be subsidized. Absolute cost is not, however, a sufficient basis for allocating funds between practices. Greater conservation might result from given annual appropriations were 80 per cent or all of one practice subsidized while 40 per cent or more of still a

Table I.

Experimental Yields for 2 Different Soil Types Under Similar Management Practices, 1932-42 [*]

Rotation	On Shelby silt loam, Bethany, Mo., 9 per cent and 72.8 ft. slope [a]	On Marshall silt loam, Clarinda, Ia., 9 per cent and 72.6 ft. slope [b]
Continuous corn	19.7 bu.	28.5 bu.
Corn-small grain-meadow	26.1 bu.	42.9 bu.

[*] The small grain was oats for the Marshall experiment and wheat for the Shelby experiment. Meadow included red clover for the former and red clover and timothy for the latter soil.

[a] From *Investigations in Erosion Control and Reclamation of Eroded Shelby and Related Soils at the Conservation Experiment Station, Bethany, Missouri, 1930-42.* U.S.D.A. Technical Bulletin No. 883, April, 1945.

[b] From *Investigations in Erosion Control and the Reclamation of Eroded Land at the Missouri Valley Loess Conservation Experiment Station, Clarinda, Iowa, 1931-42.* U.S.D.A. Technical Bulletin No. 959, October, 1948.

different practice were subsidized.[15] In practical application of efficiency principles, public agencies providing monetary assistance should discriminate carefully between the rates of payments for different practices even within a given soil area or farm. Where conservation problems do exist, funds should be spent on those practices which result in the greatest degree of conservation per dollar invested. The economic incentive should be greater (on a given soil type) for establishing a rotation with at least 1 year of meadow on a farm which has previously had no meadow than for establishing a rotation with 3 years of meadow on a farm which previously has had 2 years of meadow. It is more important to encourage terracing on a farm with continuous corn than on a farm with a meadow rotation. Possibilities do exist for differentiating between practices, as suggested in Table 2.

Technical assistance. Technical assistance should also be allocated between practices on the basis of productivity principles. Widespread application of those practices which have greatest effect in erosion control, and hence in preventing diminution of future production, should be attained before resources are devoted to simple practices which have less relation-

---

[15] The economic logic underlying the optimum allocation of conservation funds between practices and within soil types can again be illustrated by Figures 11 and 12. Given the goal of maximum conservation from given funds, allocation of assistance should be in terms of maximizing (future) marginal productivity of each increment of investment. Suppose that Figure 11 represents practice A, such as terracing which can be applied in different degrees over the soil area through terrace spacing, number of acres terraced, and so forth. Figure 12 might represent practice B such as lime, inorganic fertilizer, forage, or cover crops which can also be applied to the land in varying degrees. Diminishing productivity would be expected. Given a total quantity of funds OZ_1 (equals $O'Z'_1$) to allocate between practices A and B, the "cost of installation" criterion would result in investment of one-half on practice A and one-half on practice B. However, on the basis of the productivity criterion, the entire fund OZ_1 would be invested on practice A. Future production from current investment would thus be maximized.

Table 2.

Effect of Crop Rotations, Terracing, and Direction of Slope on Soil Loss per Acre
from Small Watersheds, 1934-41 *

Practice	Computed reduction in soil loss per acre
Terraced over unterraced with:	
(a) Continuous corn	4.80
(b) C-C-O-M	1.38
C-C-O-M over continuous corn with:	
(a) Unterraced	4.03
(b) Terraced	.61

* Source: U.S.D.A. Technical Bulletin 959, p. 69, Table 24, column 1. The data on the unterraced results are for a southeast slope, while those for terraces are for a northeast slope.

ship to potential future output. Yet farm planners have devised complete plans for some farms while waiting lists of other farms existed to be planned even on the same soil association. Optimum allocation of limited technical assistance would require application of "fewer but critical erosion control practices on greater number of farms" rather than application of "the greatest number of practices on fewer farms."

The logic of this statement also is illustrated by Figure 11. Suppose that 2 farms of the same soil makeup exist. Both have identical intertemporal production functions of the nature suggested by the relationship between present erosion control input and future output in Figure 11. The available amount of present input (technical assistance in this case) is OZ_2. In the vein of "complete farm planning," a limited input OZ_2 of technical assistance would be applied on one farm while none was being applied to the other. However, in terms of the optimum allocative principle, OZ_1 (equals one-half OZ_2) would be applied to both farms. Future production would be augmented since the combined product then equals $2OY_1$ on the 2 farms as compared to only OY_2 under "complete farm planning." The output gained (OY_1) on the second farm is greater than the output sacrificed (Y_1Y_2) on the first farm. Application of the entire input of technical assistance on one farm with none on the second could be justified only in the case of a linear production function.

Returns to the individual. Returns to the individual should be a basic consideration in any governmental conservation program which involves subsidy payments. Given a goal of maximum conservation from limited appropriations, distinction should be drawn between these practices which (1) are not profitable to the individual farmer and would not be carried out in the absence of subsidy and (2) those which are profitable and would be adopted even in the absence of public subsidy. There is foundation for public subsidy of enterprises, resource combination, or practices which are economic to society but which are unprofitable to the individual. Economic criteria, however, do not justify subsidization of private production where returns to the individual and society do not diverge. This distinction has not been made in monetary payments. Farm practices which are clearly profitable have not only been subsidized, but also payments have been made widely for practices which farmers would have adopted even in the absence of subsidies. One outstanding historical example here is the payment for plowing under second-year red clover in the Cornbelt; red clover is a biennial and the only alternative is to plow it under. A portion of the liming, fertilizer, and seeding practices also falls in this category.

There are numerous reasons why certain erosion control practices are economic to society but are unprofitable to the individual. These divergences arise mainly in case of (1) leasing arrangements whereby either tenant or landlord does not realize the full marginal product from his investment because of (a) sharing systems and (b) the length of tenure, (2) capital situations whereby the operator with limited funds realizes either (a) greater returns from investment in other alternatives or (b) greater family welfare by consuming now rather than in investing for future returns, (3) general economic instability wherein uncertainty of future returns discourages conservation development (along with other long-lived investments), (4) flood control or other conservation measures where the necessary investment is large and clearly unprofitable to the individual, and (5) differences in the rate at which the future is discounted.

Should public subsidy be used as a permanent offset to these forces which tend to prevent conservation? Public subsidy, while the answer in the case of the last 2, is clearly not the basic economic remedy for the first 3. It is a poor substitute for their elimination. Unless emphasis is placed upon elimination of these obstacles society must stand ready to subsidize conservation for score upon score of years. Positive steps would include action along the following lines:

(1) *Tenure arrangements.* (a) Developing leasing arrangements which resolve economic conflict between landlord and tenant,[16] (b) extending education which facilitates adoption of improved leasing systems and (c) developing legislation (where this is the only alternative) to guarantee compensation for conservation and related investment.

(2) *Lack of capital.* Designing credit systems to conform to the discounting and the timing of returns from conservation farming.

(3) *Economic instability.* Designing fiscal policy and other means to eliminate the uncertainty and the wide fluctuations in returns which accompany inflation and depression.

Obviously, these forces cannot be treated adequately in a period of 1 or 2 years. Conservation subsidy may be necessary as an offset in the interim of their solution. A more effective long-run use of public resources might

---

[16] For more details, see E. O. Heady, "Economics of Leasing Systems," *Jour. Farm Econ.*, Aug., 1947.

well be diversion to research and education in the areas concerned that portion of funds currently used for practices which either (a) have little relation to preventing long-run diminution in production or (b) are profitable to the farmer and would be adopted anyway. The press of income on low-income farms also prevents them from saving and making long-term investments in conservation as well as in other long-lived assets. Public subsidy can, of course, lessen the pressure of income and cause them to install conservation practices. However, the main consideration for farms of meager incomes should be the salvaging of the labor force and the extension of family living rather than in tying these persons to inadequate farming units for the purpose of earning paltry conservation payments. The form of payment is also of economic interest when the subsidy is for practices which are unprofitable to the individual.[17]

Up to this point the analysis has focused on the efficiency of using given funds once these have been appropriated. Attention is now turned to the total quantity of society's resources which should be allocated to conservation. The quantity of resources to be invested in direct conservation activities cannot be separated from alternative employment of the same resources. Potential conservation funds can be used in intensifying and increasing production on soils which are not subject to permanent deterioration. They can also be used in developing new techniques which increase the product from given resources. Society's demand for food is not apart from its demand for non-food products. As food production is expanded, it takes on lower and lower consumer values relative to other products. Obviously, conservation should be extended only as long as the marginal productivity of resources so invested is not less than for the many competitive uses of these same resources. The primary purpose of the analysis which follows is to relate soil conservation (as defined earlier) to soil development opportunities.

In the isolated industry case discussed in this section, soil conservation does not have all the connotations of resource conservation (competition in production between time periods whereby a greater product in one necessitates a lower product in another). The same level of output may be attained in various time periods even if conservation of the soil (erosion control by means of terraces, dams, contouring, etc.) does not take place. For example, the initial output on a soil area may be OY_3 from an input of OX_2 in Figure 14 (production function OA, including the virgin fund of fertility plus purchased inputs). Input may then drop back to OX_1 with a corresponding fall in product to OY_2 (production function OA), and eventually to OY_1 (production function OB) as erosion takes place. However, in a later period, output may again be pushed to the original OY_3 level

---

[17] For additional details on this point, see E. O. Heady, "Efficiency in Public Conservation Programs," *Jour. Pol. Econ.*, Vol. LIX.

by a greater application of input to the eroded soil (OX_3 units of resources on OB). In fact, the output can be boosted even beyond the level of the earlier period by employing an input of even greater magnitude than OX_3.

Even if it were true that erosion took place to the extent of removing one-fourth the United States land areas, output of various levels (including that of the present, or greater) could be attained on the remaining area through application of sufficient labor, fertilizer, irrigation water, and other resources. Production of one time period does not preclude production of the same or greater level in a later time period.

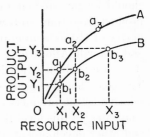

Fig. 14. Production under conservation.

Actually, the economic problem here is one of capital and labor substitution. The given output (OY_3) can be attained in various time periods by either 1 or 2 methods: (1) by a smaller application of specific capital in the form of fertilizer, irrigation water, and so forth, and a larger capital investment in terraces, dams, and other erosion control measures or (2) by larger outlays for specific capital and smaller investments in erosion-control capital. Obviously, the optimum combination (either for an individual or society) of the 2 types of production factors depends on their relative costs; the marginal productivity of capital in the form of fertilizer and related resources should be equal, with proper adjustments for time differentials, to the marginal productivity of capital in the form of terraces and related erosion control investments.[18]

Conservation should especially be related to irrigation and other national soil development programs. Actually, conservation and development can be used as substitutes in providing future food and fiber needs in the

---

[18] Given the cost of the various classes of resources, equal marginal productivity would be defined at the point of tangency of an outlay contour and the product contour, denoting a ratio of prices equal to the marginal rate of substitution. Obviously, the marginal rate of substitution between the 2 major classes of resources (erosion control versus fertilizer, labor, water, and associated inputs) will depend on the total (given) output to be attained and the portion of the total lands of various classes already under cultivation. Rather than represent the case of "conservation" in terms of different production functions, we might have presented it as a production surface or single production function as $Y = f\ (L_d,\ L_b,\ C_e,\ C_n)$ where Y is the total product, L_d is the land input, L_b is the labor input, C_e is the capital invested in erosion control input, and C_n is the non-erosion control capital input. Then the OA curve (output OY_3 in Figure 14) represents, for the same output, the given production function with some magnitude of C_e and smaller magnitudes of C_n and L_b than OB, which represents a zero C_e input and a greater L_b and C_n input. However, there is some doubt about this concept since once OB has been attained, an increase in the L_e input (after erosion has taken place) will not always result in the same output as if the L_e input had been made before occurrence of erosion.

relevant time period.[19] The two should be developed congruously in the sense of equating marginal productivity of investment in each. The important economic consideration is the extent to which limited public funds should be invested in (a) controlling erosion in order that agricultural product from some soils will not be sacrificed in the future or in the alternative of (b) extending future production on other soils through irrigation and so forth. Allocations of this nature would require that a goal or objective be established relative to the future need for agricultural products. The goal should suggest (1) the quantity of agricultural products needed relative to the products of other industries and (2) the minimum cost of guaranteeing this level through (a) conservation of soil and (b) irrigation and other development. Obviously, establishment of goals of future production is not easy. The needed extent of future production and hence erosion control (or its substitute, irrigation or other development) depends on (a) growth of population and aggregative demand, (b) changes in general techniques and the efficiency with which soil resources are transformed into product, (c) tastes of consumers for agricultural relative to other particular products, (d) war needs and international trade, and (e) other variables. Prediction of these variables and hence the need for future agricultural production (relative to non-agricultural products) is obviously subject to error. This complexity does not, however, justify unlimited and unregulated public investment in soil conservation or development. Even though they be subject to error of prediction, careful inventories should be made (1) of the expected trends in techniques and demand, and (2) of the quantities of the various soil types, both (a) subject to erosion and (b) capable of development through irrigation and otherwise. The total level of required conservation-development might then be estimated. After estimation of the aggregative portion of future product which depends on either increasing output through irrigation or preventing diminution of production through erosion control, the exact components of this development-conservation quantity should be derived. Here we are concerned with attaining the quantity of product in question with a minimum cost, with due consideration to time.

Uncertainty and flexibility. Given certainty (or expectations otherwise single valued) in prediction of future events, the entire portion of soil for which conservation is uneconomic (for example, where the product lost through erosion can be offset at a lower cost by irrigation and other development) might be allowed to erode away over time. However, error of prediction is a reality which must be faced. Unexpected events (those not inherent in empirical trends: wars, changes in population growth, lags in techniques, or other contingencies) may actually come to exist. There can be no turning back if soil needs have been underestimated and an impor-

---

[19] Perhaps we should say that development or conservation resources provided to give a product in the future should be selected in terms of the plan which gives the greatest discounted return or capital value at the present for a given outlay.

tant quantity has been allowed to erode away. For this reason, provision for intertemporal flexibility in the use of soil resources is doubly important; society must place itself in a position whereby standby production capacity is available if the low-probability and hence unfavorable expectation does come about, but need not be carried at an extreme cost sacrifice if the contingency fails to materialize. Should the contingency never materialize then society has sacrificed in the sense that it has invested resources in an alternative of low productivity.

Flexibility would not be achieved were only a minimum soil area (that consistent with the expectation to which the greatest subjective probability is attached) retained for future production. The possibility for turning back does not exist if the single expected outcome fails to materialize. However, if some range of surplus soil is carried into the future, it (1) can be used if the need arises or (2) can be left out of production if the need never arises. The important question is one of how the range of flexibility can be carried at the lowest possible cost. Should the land which is needed only to meet future contingencies (and not for current production) be maintained in annual use through annual subsidies paid for the contouring, terrace upkeep, and the seeds and fertilizers necessary for erosion control? This is not a necessary procedure. The margin of land carried for flexibility purposes might be better retired from production and returned only if the need arises. The alternative to be selected (withdraw from production or maintain in production with continuous annual subsidy of erosion control practices) should obviously depend on costs. In many cases the first alternative will require a smaller outlay over time (once the land has been seeded down or otherwise prepared to prevent deterioration). There are possibilities that the soil area retained for purposes of flexibility might also be employed for grazing or other extensive operations.

Selected References

Bunce, A. C., *The Economics of Soil Conservation*. Ames: Iowa State College Press, 1941.

Ciriacy, S., "Economic Aspects of Conservation," *Jour. Farm Econ.*, Vol. 20.

Ely, R. T., *et al.*, *The Foundation of National Prosperity*. New York: Macmillan, 1913, pp. 370-390.

Gray, L. C., "Economic Possibilities of Conservation," *Quar. Jour. Econ.*, Vol. 27.

Heady, Earl O., and Scoville, O. J., *Principles of Conservation Economics and Policy*. Iowa Agr. Exp. Sta. Bul. 382.

Hotelling, H., "Economics of Exhaustible Resources," *Jour. Pol. Econ.*, Vol. 39.

Reder, M. W., *Studies in the Theory of Welfare Economics*. New York: Columbia University Press, 1947, Ch. 2.

Wilcox, W. W., "Economic Aspects of Soil Conservation," *Jour. Pol. Econ.*, Vol. 39.

Zimmerman, E. W., *World Resources and Industries*. New York: Harper, 1951.

27

Technological Change and Economic Progress

Technological change is one of the more important forces which alters the structure of the agricultural production process. The physical and value productivity of farm resources has changed continuously under the constant flow of innovations in agriculture over the past half century. It is one of the forces which may cause economic decay in one region while other regions bloom and prosper. Each specific innovation calls for readjustments of resources within the farm while technical change in the aggregate calls for changes in the total amount of resources employed in agriculture relative to other industries. The nature and consequences of technical improvement is an important area of analysis in production economics.

Role of Farm Technological Advance in Economic Progress

Economic progress is denoted by an increase in ends relative to means.[1] Progress is attained when the goods and services in whatever form desired by society can be increased to effectively result in greater welfare. The means, and hence the ends, of a nation can, of course, be increased not only through technical progress, but also through acquisition of added resources both by conquests of other nations and by discovery and development of new resource areas and deposits. While the ends of one particular nation can be extended through conquest, the welfare of the world's community cannot be increased in this manner. Discovery, innovation, and capital accumulation remain as the main foundation of progress for democratic and peace-loving communities. While early societies particularly were able to extend their resource base and production potential through

[1] Problems in economic progress are only special cases of economic efficiency analysis. Each new technique for the use of known resources (or each discovery of new resources) causes previous equilibrium or optimum allocations of resources to become obsolete and calls for readaptation of resources in line with their changed opportunities. In this sense economic progress, from whichever source it stems, is simply a continuum of production economics or resource efficiency analysis.

discovery, this avenue promises little prospect in a world where most habitable and accessible regions are already settled. There do exist many arid, temperate, and semi-arctic regions from which little or no production is forthcoming. However, these areas are uncultivated or their resources go unextracted not alone because techniques are lacking but also because the productivity is low for labor and capital which might be so engaged. Basic resources of these areas may need to be utilized at future times because of either 1 or both of 2 reasons: 1. *The population of the nation or the world may increase to a point where labor and capital must be moved into areas with currently unemployed natural resources.* This use of capital and labor becomes economic, however, only when their marginal productivity, when applied to currently undeveloped resources, is greater than when applied to currently developed farming areas. Irrigation practices and techniques which might be applied in arid farming regions are already known. They are not employed in many regions because the return on resources is too low. Extension of the nation's or world's production plant to the hinterlands does not denote economic progress if the development results alone from population growth. Instead, the movement of labor and capital into regions where productivity is low can denote economic retrogression in the sense that expanding populations cause the average output per person to decline. 2. *Techniques may be developed which cause capital and labor to become more productive when applied to arid, temperate, or semi-arctic regions.* Application of capital and labor to otherwise unemployed land and natural resources does denote economic progress when it is brought about through innovations rather than population pressure. Since the existence and extent of all major land bodies and their resource deposits apparently are already known and their mineral content has been estimated (although it is not known with certainty) economic progress in advanced and densely populated nations must result mainly from technical innovations. Technical advance can apply equally or more to those natural resources now employed in the production process as to undeveloped resources.

The interest of highly populated and impoverished nations in technical advance is not always one of economic progress and a greater output of goods and services per capita but instead one of "holding the line." Approximately one-half the world's population lives under the Malthusian specter. Asiatic countries as well as certain nations in eastern Europe must concern themselves with populations which promise to press to the limits dictated by food supplies. Many ardent proponents of "conservation and land use" also paint this grim picture as the prospect for highly advanced nations such as the United States. As most students of economics are well aware, technical advance has been one facet of the complex which has allowed the food production potential in the Western World to outpace population growth. Along with "voluntary abstinence," technical advance has allowed diversion of relatively greater quantities of resources to non-subsistence industries and hence has meant an ever-increasing total welfare potential. In the early history of the United States, the rapid rate of population growth, rooted both in a high birth rate and a large immigration of persons from Europe, caused some concern over the food potential of the nation. While land was still available to be settled, the rate of increase in farm production was far outpaced by population growth (in the last half of the 19th century. See Table 1). The young nation did have basis for directly encouraging the development of new techniques both as a food precaution and as an important element of foreign trade. In years prior to World War I, however, the role of farm exports as a basis of

Table I.

Changes in Agricultural Production and Total Population. United States, 1870-1950
(1870 = 100) *

	Agricultural production		Total population		
Year	Index	Per cent change	Number (million)	Index	Per cent change
1870	100	—	33.6	100	—
1880	152	52	50.2	130	30
1890	190	25	62.9	163	26
1900	242	27	76.0	197	21
1910	276	15	92.0	239	21
1920	304	10	105.7	274	15
1930	338	11	122.8	318	16
1940	378	12	131.7	341	7
1950	482	28	150.7	449	14
1975[a]	—	35-45	190.0	566	25

* Source: Based on U. S. Bureau of Census Decentennial Censuses of the United States; and J. M. Brewster, "Farm Technological Growth," *Jour. Farm Econ.*, Vol. 27 and Agricultural Statistics 1951.

[a] Prospective; Based on productive capacity reports of the U.S.D.A. and Land Grant College and the President's Material Policies Commission.

securing foreign exchange for debt repayment and purchase of non-farm products had declined greatly. At this point in history, the population increase was overtaken by the growth in the total farm product. Based on expectations of population growth and future technical change, it appears that innovation will allow the growth in farm output to continue to outrun population until the latter reaches its maximum in 50 or more years.[2] Hence the overall role of public-financed innovation in agriculture must now be viewed either as one rooted in general economic progress or in feeding the democratic world and in stabilizing its political organization. If the problem of agriculture were only one of production, output could be increased tremendously by pulling enough resources into agriculture

[2] See W. S. Thompson, and D. K. Whelpton, *Estimates of Population of the U. S., 1940 to 2000*. National Resources Planning Board, August, 1943; and *The Agricultural Production Potential*. President's Committee on Agricultural Resources, Mimeo, 1951.

even without changes in techniques; output might be tripled or quadrupled by drawing labor and capital out of other industries to a sufficient extent. This step is not in prospect for the United States, however. Through technological advance and the use of slightly more capital but somewhat less labor it has been estimated that agricultural production can be increased in the neighborhood of 40 per cent by 1975. While population may increase by only 25 per cent, prospective increases in the national income may cause expenditures on agricultural products to increase to 40 per cent of 1950; while the income elasticity of demand for farm products is low, increases in the national income plus prospective exports will probably cause the value productivity of agricultural resources to hold its own in the aggregate while it may decline for products such as cotton, wheat, and others.

Ability to produce. The question of whether American agriculture can maintain production at a level to provide food for a growing population has been used partly as a "scare phenomenon." Any agriculturist who wishes to obtain a "band wagon" following is likely to point out that we

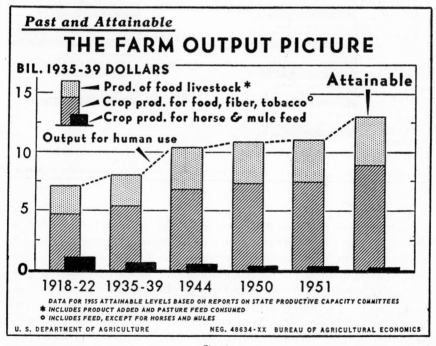

Fig. 1.

have several thousand more mouths to feed each morning and, over a quarter of a century, our population can increase by one-fourth; the implication often is that "adoption of this practice," "conservation of this soil particle," or "initiative of this legislation" is, therefore, a necessity if the nation is not to go hungry. While we have indicated above that, with techniques given, resources could always be drawn into agriculture and food producing ability is not a "discrete if-or" question, there are indications that threat of food shortage is not serious for the nation. The United States Department of Agriculture and the Land Grant Colleges conducted a study to examine the possibility of stepping up food production should the need arise. The bench-mark year used was 1955, not

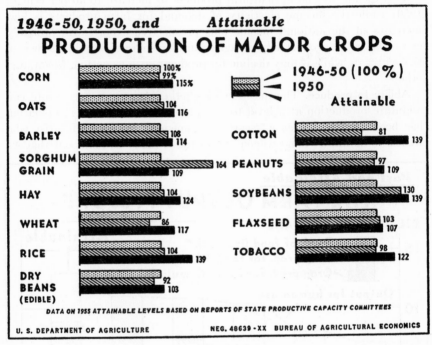

Fig. 2.

so much as a specific point in time but as an indication of production potential over a short period of time under favorable price ratios. (The expected output likely would not be realized in the absence of a favorable economic framework. The study and its assumptions are reported in *Agriculture's Capacity to Produce*, U.S.D.A. Agr. Info. Bul. No. 88.) This summary predicts that farm output can increase as much as 20 per cent in a 5-year period, if necessary, from known techniques. Grassland and conservation farming would be encouraged while a higher-level diet would be provided through more emphasis on livestock and livestock products (Figure 1). Greatest increases would be in the South where, with capital made available, large increases would be possible from fertilizer, pasture improvement, and livestock production. Output in this region could exceed that of 1951 by 25 per cent; the figures are 16, 13, and 9 per cent for the

North Central, Mountain and Pacific, and Northeast regions (Figures 2 and 3). These increases in output would require several changes in inputs. The main resource to be added would be livestock, a factor coming from within agriculture but requiring added capital on the part of farmers. Slightly less total labor would be needed while fertilizer input for the nation would be stepped up by 70 per cent over 1950. A 8-12 per cent increase in machine and building services also would be necessary.

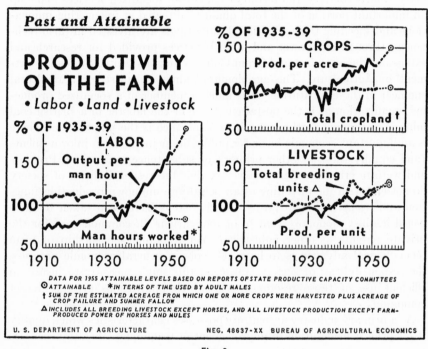

Fig. 3.

Accordingly, we believe that the ability of agriculture to produce food is not currently a fundamental question in the United States; the basis for forging ahead on the technological front is not one of hunger and starvation. It is more nearly one of fitting agricultural resources and production into the national economy and into the world framework, a setting wherein agriculture has basic importance in maintaining freedom. With this slight summary of prospects we now turn to the fundamental problems of technical change. These are the questions of allocation of research and extension resources. Administrators and specialists in these fields have the power to make persons rich or poor, or to augment the income of one group at the expense of another. What are the fundamental relationships involved? Even the changes outlined above would require major adaptations in resource use. Given prospective increases in our population and national income over a 25-year period, expenditures on livestock, tobacco and fruit products may increase by as much as 43 per cent while additional consumer outlays, including population increases, may go up by less than 20 per cent for food crops, cotton, and wool. What are the implications of these differences for investment in research and education?

Public investment in techniques. Society has assumed a major role in furthering technological advance in agriculture. In contrast to other primary (and secondary and tertiary) industries, socialized services make up an important portion of the total quantity directed at uncovering innovations and speeding their adoption. Public funds are invested in farm technology through manpower and other resources provided for research and extension education in Land Grant Colleges and the United States Department of Agriculture. The agronomist, animal scientist, or agricultural engineer in these institutions is as much a member of a socialized producing organization as is the postal employee or the laborer in a British coal mine. The product forthcoming in this instance is the innovation.[3] There is an important economic basis for public financing of farm improvements (and equally those of other primary or subsistence industries). Progress and welfare criteria suggest, however, that the responsibilities of society do not end with the unveiling of an heretofore unknown production function and its extension to farms. Positive steps have been taken to safeguard against monopoly control of innovations (a common case for the private patents of other industries). Yet if public sponsorship of farm technological advance is to have its roots in general economic progress, the responsibilities of society transcend this single measure to insure an efficient use of those resources over which innovations give a greater command.

As a primary industry agriculture possesses characteristics which qualify it for prior consideration in improvement of techniques. Wealthy societies are characterized not by how many but by how few resources are invested in primary industries (the basic materials from which consumer goods are ultimately fashioned). The fewer resources necessary here the more are available for secondary (fashioning raw materials into consumption goods—especially in extending the degree of quality and luxury embodied) and tertiary industries (personal services and other activities which produce a non-material output). Progress is represented not by an economy with 95 per cent of its resources tied up in primary production but rather by the opposite. Not only is the logic apparent, but empirical studies

---

[3] Since an economic problem is created for each technological improvement which is uncovered and put into practice society, without reservation, should extend its investment in production economists or economic efficiency experts as a means of speeding and guiding the resource adaptations which are called for with each innovation.

provide quantitative verification of the relationship. The data of Table 2 while of an approximate nature suggest the nature of real productivity per head as related to the number of persons engaged in primary industries, the chief of which is agriculture.

Table 2.

Per Cent of Working Population Engaged in Primary, Secondary, and Tertiary Industries and Average Productivity Per Person. Selected Countries, 1924-35 *

Country	Per cent of working force in: [a] Tertiary industry	Secondary industry	Primary industry	Average real production per head all industries [b]
England	53.1	42.0	6.4	1069
New Zealand	48.7	24.2	27.1	1435
United States	45.8	30.2	24.0	1368
Canada	45.1	23.2	31.7	1337
Australia	44.4	33.4	21.2	980
Germany	37.2	38.5	24.3	649
Denmark	44.4	33.4	21.2	980
France	33.5	40.0	24.5	684
Ireland	33.9	14.6	51.5	627
Argentina	34.4	43.0	22.6	1000
Japan	30.2	19.5	50.3	408
Czechoslovakia	29.1	43.6	27.3	455
Esthonia	24.1	24.3	51.6	341
Hungary	21.8	24.8	54.1	359
India	20.8	13.5	65.7	198
Roumania	15.0	17.0	68.0	243
U.S.S.R.	10.5	15.4	74.1	285

* Source: Colin Clark, *Economics of 1960*. London: Macmillan, 1942, pp. 24-28; and *Conditions of Economic Progress*. London: Macmillan, 1939, p. 179.
[a] Primary refers to agricultural, pastoral, forest, fishing, and hunting industries. Secondary industry includes manufacture, electric power, mining, building, and construction. Tertiary industry includes all other economic activities.
[b] International value units.

In the same vein, agriculture as a source of subsistence goods qualifies for public investment in technology prior to luxury goods industries. Only after the basic requirements of subsistence goods have been met is the vista of the consumer opened for full exploitation of the utilities to be derived from non-subsistence or luxury goods which in modern times indicate a wealthy society. Again, economic progress is marked by a paucity of resources invested in subsistence goods production. The fewer resources required here, the more are available for production of various ranges of luxury or non-subsistence goods.[4]

The small scale of the firm in agriculture perhaps provides an additional

---

[4] Obviously, the difference between subsistence and luxury goods is one of degree, see K. E. Boulding, "Wealth and Income," *Canadian Jour. Econ. and Pol. Science*, Feb., 1939; and "Economic Analysis and Agricultural Policy," *Canadian Jour. Econ. and Pol. Science*, Aug., 1947.

basis for public sponsorship of farm technological advance.[5] Individual farmers do not have funds for organizing research on a scale which will insure a high probability of discovery. However, society presumably has some goal such as higher farm income or general progress as a basis for its prior investments in technological advance in agriculture (as compared to other small-scale industries which are numerous).

The Firm and Nature of Advance

Technical advance is manifested in the new crop varieties and fertilizer combinations developed by agronomists, by the improved rations and breeds uncovered by animal scientists and the mechanical practices developed by engineers. Technological improvement has 2 general properties. The first, development of a new production function such that a greater

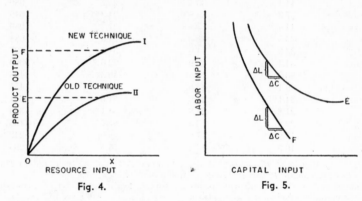

Fig. 4.   Fig. 5.

Nature of innovation.

output of product is forthcoming from a given total input of resources, is illustrated in Figure 4.[6] A corollary of this universal proposition is that technological improvement must momentarily increase the discounted profits (or decrease the losses) of the firm.[7] The firm would never adopt an innovation if output were not increased from given resources or conversely, input decreased for a given output. (In other words, the firm's

---

[5] Had not research and education in agriculture been partly socialized, private research and extension work (salesmanship) would undoubtedly have developed to a greater extent. There are many obvious examples in hybrid seed corn, machinery, and elsewhere. However, the spread of findings is undoubtedly greater than it would have been without public investment (and under the patent system).

[6] Production function I represents technological advance as compared to II since with an input of resources of (say) OX, output is OF and OE respectively.

[7] This does not mean that individual firms are always in an improved economic position after all or a large number have adopted the improvement. All can be worse off yet failure to adopt the technique by an individual would diminish his profits even more.

cost curve must be lowered.) The only exception would be the case in which the innovation increased *ex ante* profit expectations (discounted profits) through uncertainty or risk reduction. Even here the long-run and aggregate effect is likely of an output-increasing nature.[8]

Factor and product effects. In a purely physical and firm sense it is possible for an innovation to be either factor-saving, factor-using or output-increasing. The change also may combine the factor-using or factor-saving features with the output-increasing features. Hybrid corn approaches the output-increasing category because, although seed costs more, the main immediate and physical change at the farm level has been one of using the same quantity of seed but increasing the output. Development of improved tractors and machines have, at the immediate level of individual farms, been in the direction of factor-saving (with output constant) because a smaller cash outlay or even a smaller quantity of steel can now produce the same product. Improved fertilizer formulas have been both output-increasing and factor-using. Not only do improved formulas result in a greater output of product from a given mass of raw resources, but the lower costs may cause greater use of fertilizer by farm firms. It is only those practices or resources representing "discrete breaks" in factor units (discontinuous or limitational inputs) which continue to be singularly factor-saving, factor-using, or output-increasing. Artificial insemination was perhaps only factor-saving on many farms. On other farms, however, it was both output-increasing and factor-saving because the semen from high quality bulls resulted in an upgrading of the cow herd compared to that of the common-type bulls previously employed. One would expect that, in the long-run, cost reductions resulting from innovations would always result in the increase in output of farms as individual firms. However, as pointed out below, this statement need not apply similarly to an industry: the nature of demand elasticity and the role of the industry in the total economy may cause the aggregate effect to be one of the ejection rather than the attraction of resources.

While the notion of innovations which are singularly factor-using may seem a bit far-fetched, there is no reason why this should be so. We know of many farmers who employ brome-alfalfa rather than lespedeza pasture mixtures even though the former, because of the short life of the mixture, requires greater capital (seed) inputs over a 20-year period. They do so perhaps for 2 reasons (both based on *ex ante* planning and discounted profits). First, the lesser uncertainty of the short-term production plan for brome may itself cause *ex ante* discounted profits to be greater, al-

---

[8] Development of production function II after I is already known could not be considered technological advance where the transformation coefficients (rate at which resources are transformed into product) are known with (or near) certainty. However, it would qualify as an improvement under the situation where uncertainty is reduced and hence the value of anticipated returns is increased.

though *ex poste* or realized profits are greater from lespedeza. Second, the shorter span of the investment alone may cause discounted returns to be greater for brome. This possibility is obvious from the dairy barn example in Chapter 13. The flexible or pen-type barn can be considered in the factor-using category where it does not save resources over the total time period.

Distinction between technological improvements which are output-increasing and those which are factor-saving may apply to an individual industry or firm but do not exist similarly on an economy-wide basis. The basic nature of technological improvement is always the same in the economy as a whole. Aside from the uncertainty exception noted elsewhere, all technological improvements are output-increasing for given resources, or conversely, input-decreasing for a given output. An innovation is always output-increasing in the aggregate since although it may result in the same output from a smaller resource input by a given firm or industry, it frees resources for output expansion in other industries. In this sense all innovations are likely to extend economic progress regardless of the industry to which they apply.[9]

The greatest portion of technical innovations in agriculture have been of an output-increasing nature to the extent that they have lowered the average per unit cost of producing farm products and of a factor-using nature in the sense that the lower marginal costs have caused farm firms to employ more resources (and also to increase output for the latter reason). While, as was pointed out earlier, the agricultural industry has tended to employ less labor, slightly fewer acres and about the same total physical quantity of capital over the last several decades, the total of resource services employed per farm has increased because of the accompanying decrease in the number of farms. (Here we are discussing cost structure and resource employment from the standpoint of the farm as a firm. The answer can be entirely different when the industry is considered.) Changes in money costs per unit of resources employed by individual farms is difficult to compute because of abrupt and almost continuous changes in the value of money over the past century. Data which are available allow inferences that real unit costs in agriculture have declined if the measure is a ratio of output to input of labor, capital, and land. The output of agriculture has not only increased upwards of 40 per cent over the past half-century but aggregate input of all factor services has increased only slightly if at all. While the data of Table 3 perhaps do not

---

[9] Progress can be defined as an increase in attainment of ends relative to means. See K. E. Boulding, *Economic Analysis*. New York: Harper, 1948, p. 647. This paper is concerned with a particular aspect of progress—minimizing the quantity of resources necessary for the "required" output of subsistence goods or minimizing the input of resources for the flow of primary materials from the given stock of basic resources.

remove all price level changes, they are expressive of reductions in the real cost per unit of farm output. These data are for the aggregate of United States agricultural production; smaller and larger changes have taken place for individual products. These relative changes are important in providing background for the productivity and welfare analysis to be made later. They also apply to the discussion of Chapter 24 relative

Table 3.

Index Numbers of Production Per Man Hour and Labor, Power, Machinery, and Equipment Costs Per Unit of Production. United States 1935-39 = 100 (costs are in 1935-39 average dollars to suggest physical input per unit of output) *

| Average of years (inclusive) | Total farm production | Output per unit of labor | | | All farm, labor power, and machinery costs per unit of farm output |
		Meat animals and animal products	All crops	
1910-1914	74	95	76	126
1915-1919	76	97	80	128
1920-1924	81	99	85	124
1925-1929	86	102	87	113
1930-1934	88	99	87	109
1935-1939	100	100	100	100
1940-1945	124	119	123	90

* Source: Labor data from Hecht and Barton, *Gains in Farm Labor Productivity*. U.S.D.A. Tech. Bul. 1020. Cost data from Cooper, Barton, and Brodell, *Progress on Farm Mechanization*. U.S.D.A. Misc. Publ. No. 630.

to regional differences in resource productivity. Changes in resource productivity correspond somewhat generally with regions where resource productivity and farm income have increased by large relative amounts. They have been greatest in the order of food grains, feed grains, oil crops, vegetables, cotton, hay, and tobacco. Labor productivity increased from 88 to 198 for food grains and from 82 to 188 for feed grains over the period 1910-48. The increase was only from 70 to 124 for cotton and from 103 to 113 for tobacco.

Nature of Advance and Factor Substitution and Rewards

We have discussed the nature of technological change as it affects the firm's output and use of resources. We now turn to the effect of innovation on resource substitution and factor rewards. The second universal property of innovations in agriculture is this: the marginal physical rates of substitution (the elasticity of substitution) are always altered in favor of one factor by specific innovations. In other words, the entire production surface is altered. (The production coefficients are increased more for some factors than for other factors.) This property is illustrated geometrically by the iso-product contour of Figure 5. For a given output of product (say 100 bushels of wheat or 100 lbs. of pork) the iso-product line representative of a new technique, F, will always have a greater slope in the direction of one factor than under the old technique, E. The position of new contour must be partially or entirely lower (to the left) than the old. (One which falls entirely to the right would indicate a greater input of all factors for a given output and thus would not coincide with our first general property of innovation.) Thus a smaller quantity of one factor such as "capital" will be necessary to replace a given quantity of another factor such as "labor" after the innovation (in terms of a given product) has been introduced. This concept is obvious in the figure, where an equal change in capital (ΔC) in both cases offsets a greater amount of labor under the new technique than under the old one. In the example illustrated, substitution rates have been increased in favor of "capital" as is indicated by the greater slope of contour F. The marginal physical and value productivity of "capital" has been increased relative to that of "labor." This characteristic is obvious for engineering innovations in which machines substitute for labor. It is not so apparent for biological improvements such as hybrid corn. Yet the basic relationship is the same. Prior to the advent of hybrid corn, for example, a given quantity (or increment in output) of corn might have been forthcoming by cultivating fewer acres with more intensive applications of labor and capital on the remaining area (substitution of labor and capital for land). The hybrid seed itself and the greater input of "non-land" resources used in harvesting the greater yield represented added resources for a given acreage. However, the same product could now be produced with hybrid seed and less land (and perhaps even less labor).

The innovations which might possibly fall outside of this classification are unimportant in number and effect. Although specific techniques may appear to so qualify, closer scrutiny places them within the proposition. For example, it may appear that an exception holds for a crop which is planted at a more favorable time with the consequence that a greater product is forthcoming from the same input of labor, capital, and land (planting potatoes in "the light of the moon"). While the increased output will be from the same land resources, additional capital will be required, however, for harvesting and processing the greater product. Accordingly, the previous output can now be produced from relatively less land and relatively more labor and capital and the innovation again alters the marginal physical rates of factor substitution. Marginal physical productivities may be changed in "favor" of any one factor or any pair of factors such as labor, land, capital, or management. For purposes of later analysis we will classify innovations here in terms of the manner in which they change the technical rates of substitution. If the marginal rate of substitution of labor for land ($\Delta \text{land}/\Delta \text{labor}$) is increased for a given output, we will term the innovation as labor-land substituting. If it increases the technical rates at which land substitutes for labor and capital, we will call it land-labor and land-capital substituting. Characteristically, innovations have been capital-labor and land-labor substituting. This technical consideration is apparent in the fact that a greater product is now forthcoming from agriculture with less labor and relatively more capital and land. There are many instances, however, where the rates of substitution of labor and capital for land have been increased. In the aggregate the relationship between capital and land has been of a capital-land substituting nature. Although only slightly less land and only slightly more physical capital is employed in United States agriculture, the greater product denotes that a given output can now be produced with less land than in previous decades. This phenomenon in itself has made for economic progress since it has allowed an absolute and relative decline in labor inputs in agriculture and thus has provided the basis for a greater flow of labor to production of non-subsistence goods and services. It has not been necessary in the United States, as envisioned by Malthus and maintained by the "conservation and land use devout," to push increased labor and capital resources into the hinterland with a consequent reduction in average productivity of labor and output per capita.

The farm and adoption of techniques. Extension specialists in the technical fields of agriculture often view the apparent tardy rate at which farmers adopt new technologies with despondency. Why do not all farmers adopt innovations as readily as others? The answer is partly given in lack of knowledge. Yet little of the technological tardiness can be so described. Failure of many farmers to adopt new techniques has deeply rooted economic causes. We have defined innovations in agriculture as generally being output-increasing, cost-decreasing, or both. Then why do not all farmers who know of the technique immediately seize upon this opportunity to increase profits? The answer is given partly in the fact that innovations typically result in a new form of capital and quite frequently in additional capital requirements. While the innovation might well be profitable for farmers who have the necessary capital, not all farmers are similarly situated. Then too, it is discounted profits which are important in investment and production planning. The uncertainty surrounding technical change may alone cause extreme discounting of returns from innovations and thus deter adoption.

There is great variance in the rate at which specific innovations are adopted. Cornbelt agriculturists point with pride to the rate at which innovations of recent vintage were adopted. Clinton oats and other recently-improved varieties swept the central Cornbelt in a span of 2 or 3 years. Use of hybrid corn was widespread in 10 years. But, in contrast, use of fertilizer and lime increased at a slow but steady pace in prewar years as did adoption of improved livestock sanitation and feeding methods. The rate of adoption of hybrid corn has been much slower in the South, while adjustment to mechanized farming has lagged far behind that of other major agricultural regions. Equally slow has been the shift from single-crop to diversified livestock production. Why does this great difference exist in the rate at which innovations are adopted? Obviously, information about new techniques does not cause farmers to adopt them outright. It is our purpose in this section to examine some of the forces which cause adoption to be slow or rapid or to spread out unevenly over time. Some suggest that innovations come in swarms and that their application follows a similar pattern. This interrelated set of happenings was in fact the basis of the Schumpeterian theory of the business cycle.[10] The rapid rate at which output increased in the 1940's is also sometimes taken to indicate that technical advance comes about by leaps and bounds. There is little previous data to indicate whether or not this is true in agriculture, however. It is also difficult to say whether or not the sudden upswing in the 1940's should be looked upon as a period of sudden innovation or as one merely representing the addition of capital to agriculture; many farmers knew in the 1930's about the techniques which they adopted in the 1940's, but were able to apply them in the latter period only as their income positions increased and credit tension decreased. In any case there is basis for examining the possible forces which lie behind technological tardiness. Each postponement in adoption of techniques, where they are clearly profitable to the individual or society, spells economic sacrifice or efficiency foregone. By the term "economic" we imply that, while the first-adopting farmers may increase returns temporarily and some farmers may increase returns permanently, all farmers may "end up" with smaller returns (depending on demand elasticities). Yet those whose returns are lessened can still "minimize profit reduction" by adopting the new technique (if they are to remain in the industry). Then why are farmers evidently so hesitant in changing the form of capital and/or quantity of capital in relation to new techniques?

Uncertainty of transformation coefficients. Another factor in explaining the tardy rate at which the form of capital is changed is that of *uncertainty*. While farmers may obtain early and scattered information on the productivity of new techniques, the new "data" must be viewed in the vein of an expectation and with a high degree of subjective uncertainty attached. The information provides only a rough basis for formulating anticipations in yield changes on the many individual farms. This is especially true (the experience of farmers) because experiments ordinarily

---

[10] See J. A. Schumpeter, *Business Cycles*. New York: McGraw-Hill, 1939, Vol. I; and *The Theory of Economic Development*. Cambridge: Harvard University Press, 1934. Schumpeter's innovators were those daring entrepreneurs who set the stage for turning depression into recovery by adopting new techniques. Swarms of imitators then "fed the fire" until overinvestment occurred and prosperity turned again to depression with the process to be repeated over again.

refer to highly selected and "unrepresentative" plots of land or groups of animals. Inferences from these extremely small and "unrepresentative" samples to an entire species of animals or all soil areas are subject to wide error. (Ordinarily the fiducial limits within which the probability statement applies are wide even for the particular animals or plots in the experiment.) Thus, many farmers may discount the physical scientists' predictions because of the uncertainty attached; they simply wait for more observations. As other farmers adopt the technique, enough observations can be obtained to establish the "mathematical expectations" of yields under the new technique. Yield estimates then more nearly pass from the realm of uncertainty to that of risk.

Uncertainty and limits of coordinating ability. Uncertainty generated by technical change may itself result in adoption of innovations (change in capital form) in clusters or at a tardy pace. This possibility takes on importance once we consider the role of management or coordination in decision-making. Innovations may be adopted at a normal and continuous rate during the "placidity" of a fully employed economy such as 1900-1915 or 1922-1929 without placing extreme pressure on the stock of coordinating ability in agriculture. However, emergence of wide price swings, expectations of further changes, and general turbulence and confusion under developing unemployment such as in 1929-33 may require that limited entrepreneurial services be focused on obtaining information about the insights into the latter phenomenon. Because innovations may be characterized by uncertainty of their own (see above) and because the equity position of farm firms is pushed to lower levels during depression, there may be less interest in change of any sort if it stands to increase income variance. Expected returns from new capital forms and investments are discounted very heavily during depression. Closely related to this complex is the general uncertainty in venturing far afield from routine production methods and procedures.

Period of transformation and amount of capital. Once capital is committed in specialized form to the production process, it does not become profitable immediately to switch from an old technique to a new one. This situation is especially true where the specialized resource, denoting the old technique, is transformed into product only over a number of production periods. For example, it becomes fairly simple for a farmer to shift to a new variety of an annual crop or a nitrate fertilizer since, as the capital of a particular form is transformed into income in one year, it can be invested in a different form for the next year. This characteristic (plus the considerations pointed out above) perhaps explains why Clinton oats received almost full adoption over the Cornbelt in the span of 3 years. The principle is the same when we consider buildings and machinery and other forms of specialized capital with longer transformation periods. However, more production seasons are necessary before the physical resource can be transformed into product and income to an extent which makes profitable the shift to the new technique. This is an important consideration in the comparison of long-lived capital such as conventional as compared to pen-type dairy farms. Added to this is the fact that the supply of a specialized form of capital is highly inelastic, and hence its price drops to a level such that returns on the "written down" investment still may be as great as capital of the new form; a horse barn may be used for a tractor shed even though the physical productivity of a new horse barn may well be below that of a new tractor shed. The time consideration is important in application to changes in techniques for a given type of fruit or between fruits. While a new technique in peaches may cause this fruit to be more profitable than apples in the long run, few apple producers will uproot their orchards immediately.

Since technical innovations in general represent a change in form of resources and an entirely new production function, adjustment from old to new forms and organizations of production cannot often be made in the sense of small increments in the quantity of resources used. Instead they necessitate a "jump" between forms of resources with particular reference to capital. Innovations fall in 3 categories in respect to capital requirements (including quantity as well as form of assets): (1) innovations that require less capital, as is the case of artificial insemination for farms with small dairy herds; (2) innovations which require about the same or a very small additional capital outlay, as is the case of many new seed varieties and fertilizers and insecticides; (3) innovations which require large capital investments. The last type of innovation is involved in the substitution of a tractor for mules on a cotton farm with 30 acres of cropland, the use of cotton pickers on larger farms, or a shift in any region from row-cropping and grain farming to a grassland operation with a large outlay for livestock. Capital is not a limiting factor for the first 2 changes outlined above. From the standpoint of the individual farmer, continuance of the "old practice" may be entirely economic even though it is highly "inefficient" in terms of input-output ratios.

Managerial requirements. Many changes which appear simple are actually complex in terms of their capital and managerial requirements. An increase in yields of from 12 to 15 bushels through use of hybrid corn in Georgia or Alabama represents a large percentage increase. However, the absolute increases in yields and returns over costs are unimportant and the innovation becomes highly productive only if adjustments are made in rate of fertilization application and number of plants. Management then becomes important and is required not only as a basis for formulating plans under the change but also in comprehending the manner in which resources must be combined and altered if new techniques are to be effective. Managerial ability, the power to predict and foresee outcomes and plan accordingly, must be present before innovations can be put into effective operation. Inability of many farmers, particularly those on units in the poverty belts of American agriculture, to read and understand widely causes new ideas to fall sterile except as they are demonstrated in simple form. Innovations differ widely in their entrepreneurial requirements. Some require only the sight of the innovation in the form of new capital. Others are more complex and require education above the fourth- or even eighth-grade level. For this reason, the rate of technical and economic progress may always be more rapid in those farming areas where incomes are high, education is obtainable and farm families have the money and time for travel, study, and association with fellow managers of outstanding ability. Conversion from outmoded crops and production processes may lag continuously in such low income areas as the Delta of Mississippi, the Piedmont of Alabama, the mountain region of Tennessee, Kentucky, and Virginia and even the poverty belt of the Cornbelt unless greater educational assistance is provided.

Technical improvements and price ratios under economic instability. While some innovations may be technical improvements, they need not be economic improvements considering the relative prices attached to different resources and to products. A changed form of capital, representing a new technique, is not profitable if the ratio of its price to that of the old form (the old technique) is greater than the ratio of their productivities. For example, even though oat yields were increased by as much as 6 bushels per acre on some farms by the use of Clinton oats, many farmers could not profitably use the seed when it was priced at $10 per bushel in the first year of distribution. The same economic consideration undoubtedly applies to use of fertilizer and other improved technology during depression. However, as product prices rise relative to factor costs (fertilizer in the new form) during prosperity, it becomes profitable for the farmer not only to "apply fertilizer" (more capital) but also to apply it in the new form.

The same type of adjustment may take place in the case of techniques which require the substitution of entirely different categories of resources (and even if the output remains unchanged and the period of transformation is not an important consideration). A new machine such as milking machine, hay baler, combine, or cotton picker may be developed during a period of generally unfavorable income and while its existence is known by farmers, few may adopt it. Then, given a change in the ratios of factor costs during recovery in the price level, farmers may swarm to its adoption. This outcome applies particularly to engineering innovations since (1) the unique characteristics of many of these is the technical substitution of capital for labor and (2) the price of labor increases at a faster rate under economic recovery than the price of new farm machinery. The logic here is illustrated in Figure 6 by a special type of innovation where iso-product contour OO represents the old, while NN represents the new technique. Both contours represent equal outputs. The ratio of capital labor prices is given at the outset by iso-line I_oC_o. Even though the technical rate of substitution under the new technique is changed in favor of capital it is still profitable for the firm to retain the old technique and employ more labor: the given product can be produced at a lower cost outlay under the old technique with the prevailing prices for labor and capital. (The iso-

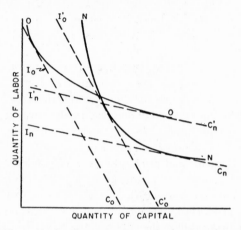

Fig. 6. Change in factor price ratios and adoption of innovations.

cost line I_oC_o is of the same slope as $I'_oC'_o$, representing the same ratio of factor costs, but lies lower in the plane thus representing a smaller total outlay.) However, once the ratio of labor/capital prices rises (a shift to iso-cost lines I_nC_n and $I'_nC'_n$), it pays not only to substitute capital for labor but also to shift to the new (but known) technique.

Nature of Advance and Resource Returns

Although innovations always increase the technical rate of substitution of one resource for another, they may have varied effects on the value productivity and returns to particular resources. The absolute return to a single resource such as labor, capital, or land may be increased, decreased, or left unchanged. Similarly, the relative share of the total product imputable to a single resource may be increased, decreased or left unchanged. A technological change can affect the income imputed to a given factor of production in these ways: (1) Both the absolute and relative shares of the product imputed to a given factor may be decreased. (2) Both absolute and relative shares may be increased. (3) The absolute share may increase while the relative share is decreased.[11] The final outcome depends on how

---

[11] These distinctions between innovations depending on their relative shares has been employed in J. R. Hicks, *Theory of Wages*. London: Clarendon Press, 1932, pp. 121-122; A. Pigou, *Economics of Welfare*. London: Macmillan, 1938, p. 674; and J. Robinson. "Classification of Inventions," *Rev. Econ. Studies*, 1938, pp. 139-40.

the marginal productivity of the given factor is affected. The discussion of general principles may be simplified by assuming that only 2 factors, land and capital, for example, are used in producing a given commodity. Accordingly, improved techniques which affect both absolute and relative shares of the total product imputed to the 2 factors may be classified as land-decreasing, capital-increasing, neutral, and so forth. Labor-decreasing (capital-increasing) devices are those which increase the marginal product of capital by more than they increase the marginal product of labor. Similarly, capital-decreasing inventions increase the marginal product of capital by less than that of land. A neutral invention means that the marginal products of the 2 factors are increased in the same ratio.

A land-decreasing invention can mean (1) that the marginal value product of both capital and land is increased but that the marginal value product of capital is increased by more than the marginal value product of land, or (2) that the marginal value productivity of capital is increased while that of land is decreased. In both cases the relative share imputed to the land factor is changed in the same direction but the absolute share moves in opposite directions. In the first case the absolute share of the total product going to both capital and land will increase but the relative share going to land will be less (whereas the relative share imputed to capital will be greater than before the adoption of the improved technique). If the improvement falls in the second category, absolute and relative shares imputed to capital still increase but both the absolute and relative shares going to land decrease. If the improvement is of a capital-decreasing nature, relative to land, the above analysis still holds except that the positions of land and capital are reversed. If the improvement is neutral the relative shares imputed to the 2 factors will remain the same and it can be expected that the absolute share of both will be increased. Otherwise there would be no incentive for adopting the new techniques. The same principles apply when more than 2 factors are concerned. However, there are many more possibilities as to the outcome. We illustrate 2 possible outcomes below.

For the purpose of considering the effects of technological improvements on the shares and importance of the various factors in agriculture we might well follow the customary demarcation of land, labor, capital, and management. This classification is useful because numerous problems in the industry follow along these very lines. Using some primitive examples, we can illustrate types of technological innovation which cause the absolute or relative shares of factors to change or stay the same. For these purposes we assume 2 factors, land and capital, constant returns to scale, a fixed amount of land, and diminishing productivity of capital.

Illustration I: **Neutral effects.** Figure 7 illustrates the case in which the technical change increases the absolute shares to both capital and land but leaves their relative shares unchanged. The average and marginal productivity of capital is indicated by curves A_o and M_o respectively for the old technique and by A_n and M_n for the new technique. (The curves can be taken to indicate either physical or value productivity under competitive conditions.) Under the old technique the marginal product of capital is BC for OB inputs, and the proportion of the total product going to this factor is $OBCH/OBDI$, while a proportional share $HCDI/OBDI$ goes to land. The ratio of the relative shares of capital to land in the total product is BC/CD. Now a new technique employing a different form of capital is developed with the consequent average and marginal productivity curves A_n and M_n. If the cost of capital is again OH and if OE units of capital are employed, the marginal product of capital becomes EF and the share of the total product imputable to this factor is $OEFH/OEGI$. By the same token, the proportional share of the total product going to land is $HFGI/OEGI$ and the relative share of capital to land in the total product is EF/FG. The ratio of the relative share of capital and land in the total product is the same under the new as under the old techniques; BC is equal to EF while CD is equal to FG, and, therefore, BC/CD equals FE/FG.

The specific conditions under which the relative shares will remain unchanged are these: the elasticity of the average productivity curve (elasticity of capital in respect to product) must be the same under both techniques at the point of equilibrium (or the specific amounts of capital employed).[12] In other words, the returns ratio cannot change as it moves from BC/CD to EF/FG. This raising of the average productivity curve iso-elastically is highly unlikely for the very great number of innovations in agriculture. Therefore, to the extent factor rewards are imputed in a competitive manner it is unlikely, under rapid or continuous technological

---

[12] Robinson (*ibid.*) illustrates this point: the elasticity of curve A_o at D is equal to BD/CD and the elasticity of curve A_n at G is equal to EG/FG. Thus the share of capital is increased, decreased, or left unchanged depending on whether the elasticity at G is greater, less than, or equal to the elasticity at point D. This concept of elasticity used by Robinson is one of capital in respect to product and differs from the more conventional concept of capital in respect to average product wherein we define the marginal product as $MP = A(1-\frac{1}{A})$, where A refers to the average product, MP refers to the marginal product, and E refers to the elasticity. From this equation we can derive these:

$$MP = A(1 - \frac{1}{E}) \tag{1}$$

$$\frac{MP}{A} = 1 - \frac{1}{E} \tag{2}$$

$$\frac{1}{E} = 1 - \frac{MP}{A} \tag{3}$$

$$E = \frac{A}{A - MP} \tag{4}$$

If equation (4) is applied to Figure 7 of the text, we have $E = \frac{BD}{CD}$.

change, that the absolute or relative rewards to factors should remain unchanged in agriculture. The consequences then are those outlined later.

Illustration II: **Increasing absolute but decreasing relative returns to capital.** Figure 8 illustrates the case when the post-innovation return to both fac-

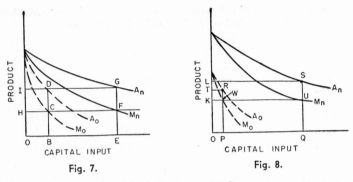

Fig. 7.

Fig. 8.

Change in factor rewards.

tors increases but the relative share and ratio of shares turns in the favor of land. The geometry is again obvious since $OQUK/OQSL$, the share to capital after the innovation, is less than $OPWK/OPRT$, the share to capital before the innovation. Similarly, the decrease in the ratio of returns to capital as compared to land is expressed by the fact that $\frac{SQ}{UQ}$ is less than $\frac{RP}{WP}$. In this case the elasticity of curve A_n at point S has been decreased relative to the elasticity of curve A_o at point R: the total product of capital, while it has been increased, has not been raised in proportion to the increase in the total product and the marginal productivity of land.

We could also illustrate other changes in factor rewards, but will not do so because of space limitations. Some innovations in agriculture undoubtedly decrease both the absolute and relative shares of land. This type of innovation is one which results in a low marginal productivity for small amounts of capital but causes the marginal productivity of capital to be maintained at a high level as its use is extended by larger amounts over limited ranges. Summer fallow of wheat is an example: the product is small where the capital and labor input is small (the land is not kept clean) but results in a greater product than previously when capital and labor inputs are extended somewhat above conventional dry-land farming methods.

Changes in relative importance of factors. Technical change has brought about important change in the relative importance of the various resources in agriculture. The structure of the industry has changed so that the total output and the output per worker has doubled in a half-century. Capital has been substituted for labor and land in the sense that a given amount of product now embodies more of the former services and less of the latter factors. Even then, the increase in capital has not been nearly proportional to the increase in total output. In this sense it has been the change in form

Table 4.

Index Numbers of Farm Power and Machinery on Farms, Farm Employment, Output Per Worker, and Real Income Per Worker (1935-39 = 100) *

Year	Farm power and machinery	Farm employment	Farm output per worker
1900	80	105	70
1910	105	111	71
1920	126	104	88
1930	118	102	93
1940	106	97	113
1950	165	90	153

* Source: Adapted from S. Johnson, "Technological Change and Rural Life," *Jour. Farm Econ.*, Vol. 32.

of capital which has been important.[13] With present forms of capital, one worker can now produce the agricultural products for 15 other persons. In 1920 he could produce only enough for himself and 9 other persons. In 1820 he could clothe and feed only 3 persons besides himself. Technical advance, which has transformed capital from horses to tractors, has freed 60 million acres of cropland from production of horse feed to production of food and fiber products. Changes in the relative physical importance of the various factors are thus obvious. It seems only logical that technological improvement might be one of the more influential forces in altering the share of income attributed to land, labor, capital, and management.

Table 5.

Capital in Agriculture, 1910, 1920, 1930, 1940, 1945, and 1950

Year	Average farm employment [a] (millions)	Total capital in agriculture [b] (millions)	Capital per worker in agriculture (dollars)	Tractors on farms Jan. 1 [a] (thousands)	Work animals on farms Jan. 1 [a] (thousands)
1910	12.1	7042	582	1	24,211
1920	11.4	7459	654	246	25,742
1930	11.2	7440	664	920	19,124
1940	11.7	6277	536	1545	14,481
1945	10.8	9315	862	2422	8,246
1950	10.8	10,413	966	3825	7,463

[a] *Agricultural Statistics.*
[b] BAE, "Net farm income and parity report, 1943," and "The Farm Income Situation, June-July 1947." Data adjusted to a 1910-14 price level or value of dollar base to suggest the physical volume.

---

[13] For a preliminary but still inclusive indication of greater returns to capital over time see E. O. Heady, "Changes in Income Distribution in Agriculture With Special Reference to Technological Progress," *Jour. Farm Econ.*, Vol. 28. Many time studies such as those carried on from farm accounts in Land Grant Colleges also indicate, on the basis of the residual imputational procedures used, an increasing portion of the total product imputable to capital and a smaller amount imputable to labor.

The technological advancements which have the most direct effect on rents are those which increase the total output per acre of land. Higher yielding strains, improved production practices, and control of insects and pests as applied to either crops or livestock fall in this category. Improvements of this type may conceivably either increase or decrease absolute rents depending upon whether the demand for the product is elastic or inelastic. An increased output of a commodity for which the demand is inelastic should result in lower absolute money rents unless the land has a very close alternative use. Even then, the money rents will be less if the demand for the alternative is inelastic. In case the demand is elastic, this type of improvement should normally result in greater absolute rents but may or may not result in larger relative shares imputed to land. Although the relative share would probably increase, the final outcome depends on whether or not the marginal product of land is increased by more than that of other agents used in conjunction with it. The fact that attempts to measure demand elasticities point to a predominance of inelastic demands in agriculture suggests that the effect *per se* of greater production per acre is to lower absolute money rents and consequently land's relative share of income. Apart from improvements which increase the physical productivity of land are those which result mainly in a substitution of capital for labor but which may also affect rents. Part of any increased net returns for this type of substitution probably tends to be capitalized into the land. An exception to this statement may hold true in the shift away from work animals to power-driven machines. A quantity of grain formerly required as feed for horses and mules is now freed for other uses. Here again absolute rents may rise or fall depending upon whether the elasticity of demand is greater or less than unity. The short and long run outcomes will certainly differ: the profits of innovation forthcoming to a few operators before general adoption of a method which substitutes machines for labor are not likely to be capitalized into the land.

Shares to factors and personal incomes. Because it may cause the absolute or relative returns to the different factors to turn in different directions, technological improvement in agriculture need not have the same impact in increasing (or decreasing) the incomes of all farm persons or families. The existence of a large number of rented farms denotes the fact that some persons, namely landlords, own mostly land while tenants own mostly labor and capital. Low-income farm families such as those in the Appalachian highlands, the Ozark and Ouachita Mountains, the eastern part of the Cottonbelt and the cutover areas of the Lake states, own mostly labor and little capital or land. Innovations which increase the value productivity of land relative to capital favor the landlord portion of the economy more than the tenant. Capital-increasing innovations have the opposite effect. The main gains from technical advance in agriculture have largely by-passed those small-scale, low-income farmers who own little land or capital. Even if capital-labor substituting innovations were uncovered for these farms, the gains would be small since the labor comes mainly from family labor without outside alternatives, and the units are too small to merit mechanization. Finally, the hired man who is displaced by capital in the form of machinery sacrifices directly as an owner of labor resources. Numbers of hired workers in agriculture dropped by over 50 per cent the period from 1925 to 1950. At the minimum, the hired laborer is interested in whether a capital-labor substituting innovation is made when other employment is available for displaced labor or whether it comes in a period of unemployment.

Agricultural science indeed need not serve all farm people equally, because of the differences in patterns of resource ownership and because innovation may change the relative returns to specific resources even in a given producing region. Later we can illustrate that this statement also applies to producers in different regions.

Industry and Regional Aspects of Technical Advance

We have examined the relationship of innovations to (a) the output of the firm and the rate of technical innovation, (b) the return to specific factors of production. We now turn our attention to the relationship between technological change and the income of the agriculture industry or subindustries such as wheat or cotton. We also examine the possible differential impact of technical improvement on income in competing farm areas. Is it true that technological improvement is of a nature to increase the aggregate net return to the agricultural industry? Which specific types of innovations may add to the net income of the industry? In order to throw light on these questions, we need to turn to further classifications of innovations.

Over the last 100 years, technical innovation has allowed an increase in the food and fiber available to a growing national population. This increase in output to meet the needs of a growing national economy has come even with a decline in labor employment in agriculture. Viewed from an historical standpoint, the release of farm workers from agriculture has provided a labor force for developing urban industries and for increasing the output of secondary and tertiary products. This net benefit is obvious when the level of living in the United States is compared with that of other nations where about 50 per cent of the working population must be employed in agriculture.

Biological and mechanical innovations. From a purely physical standpoint, farm innovations can be classified as biological or mechanical. By the term "biological," we will refer to those which have a physiological effect in increasing the total output (per acre, animal, unit of feed) from a given land base. The term "mechanical" refers to innovations as a machine which substitutes capital for labor but does not change the physiological outcome of the plants or animals to which it may apply. Many mechanical innovations also have a physiological effect in increasing timeliness of operations or on soil structure or may otherwise directly affect the plants or animals. For the sake of simplicity, techniques which have both effects are termed "biological-mechanical."

The immediate effect of biological innovations (as classified here) is one of increasing both total output and total costs (per acre or per farm or per aggregate of farms which retain production). Hybrid corn, fertilizer, improved rations, and similar techniques result in a greater total output. However, they also increase total costs (even though costs per unit ordinarily decrease) because not only are the original costs of rearing, cultivating, and harvesting incurred, but also the added costs of seed, supplies, and harvesting and handling the greater output are included.

Those biological innovations which relate to livestock such as improved breeding, sanitation, and nutrition may at first appear to lower costs alone because they allow a greater output with less feed and other resources. This may be true in the short run. However, in the long run, the saving in feed allows and leads to a greater number of animals and output of livestock products. As the slack is taken up in feed and other resources saved, added resources in housing and labor are also necessary to handle the greater number of animals and amount of products. Otherwise, this effect is of the mechanical nature outlined here. It should be remembered that this analysis is in terms of the industry. Although some farms may produce the same livestock with less feed, as feed "saved" is used on increasing output on other farms, total industry costs may increase as total costs decline on some farms. The first effect of mechanical innovations is that of reducing total costs. A biological-mechanical innovation may increase or decrease total costs of agriculture, depending upon whether the added expense associated with the harvesting and handling of the greater output is less than the reduction due to the engineering recombination of resources.

Revenue and cost. Public sponsorship of technical advance was perhaps originally drafted as a specific policy to increase farm income. Many still view public research and extension education in this light. The manner in which net returns are affected by specific technological improvements depends, however, upon the price elasticity of demand for the specific product and the effect of the innovation on (1) the total output and (2) the total costs of production and (3) the nature of the short-run supply function for individual factors of production. Our interest here is in the short-run effect of innovation on industry returns (before long-run equilibrium in resource transfer can be approached). Under continuous change, however, the so-called short-run effect becomes a permanent or continuous effect.

Models of possible outcomes are illustrated by Figures 9 and 10. The curves labeled R indicate total revenues from sale of various outputs. The inclining portion indicates a price elasticity of demand greater than unity (a greater output sells at a lower price per unit but brings a greater total revenue). The declining portion represents an elasticity of less than one (a larger output sells at a lower price and brings a smaller total revenue). The curves labeled C_1 and C_2 represent the total cost curves for the indus-

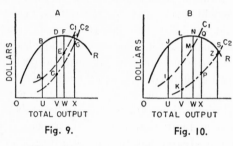

Effect of innovation on industry returns.

try. For our purposes, however, we refer only to out-of-pocket costs and do not include implicit costs such as wage to operator labor or interest on the farmer's capital investment. We use this procedure because we are concerned with the net disposable return to the farm industry.[14]

I. **Demand elastic: total output and total cost-increasing innovation.** An innovation which increases both total output and total costs to the industry is illustrated in Figure 9. Distinction between innovations with respect to their effects on the cost in a single industry must be in terms of total costs. All innovations lower the per-unit costs of production. Otherwise they would not be adopted (with the uncertainty exception already noted).

Net returns must increase if the increase in total revenue is greater than the increase in the total costs. This is illustrated by curve C_1 in Figure 9, which represents the schedule of total costs for the old technique and by C_2 representing the same thing for the new technique. Total output, total cost, and total revenue for the old technique (cost curve C_1) are OU, UA, and UB respectively. Under the innovation (cost curve C_2) output increases to OV, costs to VC, and revenue to VD. Net returns, AB, for the old technique are less than those, CD, for the new technique (since net returns = total revenue minus total cost).

---

[14] Under competitive conditions costs will equal revenue for the industry. However, this is true only for the sum of explicit and implicit costs. The diagrams indicate only explicit or out-of-pocket costs. The net incomes AB and CD represent returns to unpaid operator and family labor, and capital and any "pure" profits. For a single firm maximum net profit is represented by that point which defines the greatest difference between the total revenue and cost curves. However, this need not be the point of equilibrium for cost and revenue curves representative of a competitive industry where only out-of-pocket or cash costs are considered.

Presence of an elastic demand does not, however, guarantee an increase in net income. Net income will be decreased by an innovation which increases gross revenue but by a smaller absolute amount than the increase in total costs. Suppose that the pre-innovation output, costs, and revenue are OU, UA, and UB respectively (Figure 9). A biological-type innovation which increases the corresponding items to OW, WE, and WF will decrease net income from AB to EF.

II. **Demand inelastic: total output and total cost-increasing innovation.** Under this combination, net revenue of the industry must always decrease. Diminution of gross revenue always accompanies an increase in output where demand is inelastic. The greater costs reduce net return even further. This is illustrated in Figure 9, where EF, the net income before the improved technique (C_1) is greater than GH, the net return under the new technique (C_2) after the increase in total output and cost. Only biological-type innovations fall within the situations outlined under I and II.

III. **Demand elastic: total output constant and total cost-decreasing innovation.** Net revenue must always increase since gross revenue remains unchanged while total costs decrease.

IV. **Demand inelastic: total output constant and total cost-decreasing.** Net revenue must always increase for the exact reasons outlined under III. Innovations of the pure mechanical type fall under the number III and IV categories.

V. **Demand elastic: total output-increasing and total cost-decreasing.** This combination must always result in a greater net income to the industry because total revenue increases while total costs decrease. This situation is illustrated in Figure 10 where the net return (KL) under the new technique (C_2) is greater than the net return (IJ) under the old technique (C_1) for total outputs OV and OU respectively.

VI. **Demand inelastic: total output-increasing and total cost-decreasing innovation.** Two outcomes are possible here. Total revenue must be less. If the decrease in total revenue is greater than the decrease in total cost, net revenue will also decrease as is illustrated by Figure 10: the net return MN under an old technique (C_1) is greater than that ZS under a new technique (C_2). However, if the reduction in total revenue is less than the decrement in total costs net revenue must increase. This possibility is also illustrated in Figure 10, where net income increases from MN under an old technique (C_1) to PQ under a new technique (C_2) since the reduction in total revenue (from WN to XQ) is less than the decrease in costs (from WM to XP). Biological-mechanical innovations result in the outcomes outlined under V and VI.

All innovations extend progress. However, specific innovation may or may not increase the income of the agricultural industry. The final outcome depends on the combination of forces outlined. In final equilibrium all individual firms may have smaller net incomes than in a pre-innovation period, but failure to adopt the technique would result in an even greater diminution in returns. Individual firms remaining in a segment of the industry (for example, cotton producers) may have as great or a greater income, but the industry may have a smaller net return because of fewer firms. Finally, it should be recognized that even though the long-run and aggregate effect of an innovation may be to reduce net income to all farmers, the few farmers who first adopt the technique will have greater income (until the number adopting becomes great enough to lower prices sufficiently to decrease incomes). As is brought out later, some farmers

Table 6.

Production Costs and Index of Farm Output for Specified Periods *

	Annual production costs (*1910-14 dollars*) *	
	Million	Index
Period	dollars	1935-39 = 100
1910-1914	2,360	80.1
1915-1919	2,272	77.1
1920-1924	2,830	96.0
1925-1929	3,208	108.8
1930-1934	2,957	100.3
1935-1939	2,949	100.0
1940-1944	3,762	127.6
1945-1949	4,720	159.2

* Source: Based on data from Agricultural Statistics and BAE Processed Report, "Net Farm Income and Parity Report, 1943." Includes all production expenses of farm operators and landlords except taxes and mortgage interest payments. Does not include charge against land, capital, or operator or family labor. Also feed and livestock have not been included since these represent purchases within agriculture. This system perhaps excludes 5-10 per cent of total production costs to farm operators and landlords. Farm wage payments are included. Absolute quantities have been adjusted to a 1910-14 whole-sale price base (in an attempt to correct for value of the dollar). Unadjusted figures indicate, of course, an even greater increase in costs.

may "end up" with a larger income although net returns to the industry decrease. What actually happens over time, of course, is that we have somewhat fewer but larger farms in total, making as much or more income as previously. In addition, increases in population and national income cause demand to increase. However, it still holds true that, even if the demand curve does shift to the right, income from commodities with inelastic demands, under the new demand curve, would always be greater in the absence of increase in output.

Innovations of the various types have taken place side by side. However, available evidence indicates that aggregate farm technological advance has been of an output-increasing and probably of a total cost-increasing nature (the number II model outlined above). At the minimum, costs have not decreased. Demand analysis suggests an aggregate elasticity of demand for farm products far less than 1.0 (under a given demand situation the greater the total production the smaller the total revenue).[15] Although other economic forces bring about increases in demand and income, aggregate technological advance *per se,* if it falls under model II, results in a revenue lower than would otherwise hold.

Income transfers. New techniques may transfer income and wealth between individuals regardless of whether total net farm income is increased or decreased (and in addition to the interfactor productivity effects mentioned earlier). The transfer may be of an intra-industry nature in the sense that it increases the income of some people in agriculture at the expense of other people within the industry. Income will be transferred when the techniques for one commodity or geographic region are improved at a faster rate or beyond that which applies for a competing commodity or region. This situation can hold regardless of the elasticity of demand, as is illustrated by Table 7. In the period 1937-46, for example, corn yields

Table 7.

Yield Per Acre of Corn in Two Periods for Specified Geographic Regions *

Region	1920-29 average	1937-46 average	Per cent change
Wayne County, Iowa	34.0	36.3	+ 6.8
Switzerland County, Indiana	31.6	34.2	+ 8.2
Tipton County, Indiana	42.8	56.3	+31.5
Grundy County, Iowa	43.0	63.1	+45.8
State of Georgia	10.3	11.4	+10.7
State of Kansas	21.8	21.6	− .9
State of Pennsylvania	42.1	42.3	+ .5
State of Missouri	29.0	30.6	+ 5.5
State of Iowa	40.5	52.1	+29.0
State of Illinois	35.9	49.1	+36.8

* Source: Agricultural statistics and crop reporting statistics for the specified states.

in Iowa were greater by 45.8 per cent in Grundy County but by only 6.8 per cent in Wayne County, as compared to the pre-hybrid era, 1920-29. A decline in price by 25 per cent (because of the innovation and greater total output or for any other reason) would result in a greater total revenue per given acreage in the former and a smaller total revenue in the latter county.[16] Sometimes all farms in a large area are affected adversely

---

[15] Cochrane has arrived at an aggregate price elasticity of −.41 for food products. W. Cochrane, "Farm Price Gyrations—An Aggregate Hypothesis," *Jour. Farm Econ.,* May, 1947. G. S. Shepherd of Iowa State College (unpublished data) has arrived at a similar figure. For any elasticity of less than −1.0, an increase in output must be accompanied by a decrease in revenue since an increase of (say) 1.0 per cent in output will result in a price decline by more than 1.0 per cent. Data indicating an elasticity of around −.5 are also found in D. G. Johnson, "Econometric Models and Agricultural Policy," *Jour. Farm Econ.,* Feb., 1948; and T. Haavelmo, "Quantitative Research in Agricultural Economics," *Jour. Farm Econ.,* Nov., 1947.

[16] The varying responses indicated in Table 7 are not necessarily due to hybrids alone, but the result is the same as long as innovations do not apply equally to areas or are not adopted at equal rates.

by technical advance. Extension of cotton production to the high plains of Texas and Oklahoma and to the irrigated areas of the Western States had a great impact on a large portion of the Cottonbelt. A similar type of transfer may also take place in the sense that the first few "innovator" farmers who adopt an output-increasing technique realize higher incomes even if the demand is inelastic because, in a competitive marĸet, small changes in supply have small effect on price. However, as the majority adopt the innovation, the total income is reduced and all operators may have smaller incomes (even though net income would be even less for the "followers" were they not to adopt the new technique).

Alternative Goals

Great strides are being made in the contribution of farm technological advance to national well-being. The direction given farm technological advance might well differ, depending upon the specific ends to be attained. Among others, alternative goals toward which publicly sponsored technological improvement might be directed include (1) increasing the total net income of the agricultural industry, (2) increasing the total utility or welfare of individuals now in the agricultural industry, and (3) maximizing aggregate economic progress.[17] These alternative goals are not identical and without conflict. Attainment of a greater net farm income does not guarantee a greater total welfare of people now in agriculture. Total utility or welfare of a community of individuals is a function not only of the magnitude of the income but also of the distribution of this income. To the extent that increases in income are accompanied by a transfer of income, total utility will increase or decrease, depending on whether the gain in utility to individuals with augmented income is greater or smaller than the loss in utility to those whose income is lessened. Similarly, improvements which lessen the gap in incomes in the face of a smaller total income may or may not increase total farm welfare depending on the nature of the inter-personal transfer of income. Attainment of economic progress (in the sense of minimizing resource inputs for the "necessary" output of subsistence food products) would generally exclude attainment of the other 2 objectives. Under the pricing system, a continuous depressing of net income and welfare to people in agriculture would be necessary to drive innovation-freed resources to other industries.

---

[17] Other goals might include (a) the greatest net income per farm and (b) increasing the income of farmers who first adopt new techniques. Obviously, these are partially compatible and partially conflicting with each other and with other goals outlined. Total economic welfare might represent still another goal and while partly allied with the total farm welfare or economic progress goals as defined here, it is not identical. Consideration of total economic welfare as it related to the economic progress goal is made at a later point.

The outcome of resources invested in research on a specific commodity or innovation cannot be predicted with certainty. However, the probability of success along the line of any specific innovation (say, improvement in wheat as compared to soybeans) is dependent to a fairly large extent on the quantity of research resources marshalled in the specific area of investigation. Given this degree of control over discovery and adoption (through allocation of funds between and within agricultural experiment stations and extension services) society has the power to exert an important influence over farm technological advance. What type of technical innovations might be extended were any single one of the above objectives to serve as the criterion in guiding technological improvement in agriculture?

1. **Increasing the total net income of the agricultural industry.** If this were the goal of farm technological advance, price elasticity would serve as an important gauge in directing development and adoption of innovations. Total output and total cost-increasing (biological) innovations would be withheld where demands are inelastic and extended only for commodities with elastic demands (and then only as long as the increase in total revenue is greater than the increase in total cost). Output-constant and total cost-decreasing (mechanical) innovations would be extended for all commodities irrespective of demand elasticities). Total output-increasing and total cost-decreasing techniques (biological-mechanical) would be developed for all commodities with elastic demands but for those with inelastic demands only if the decrease in costs were greater than the decrease in revenue. Finally, if the goal of public investment in techniques were only one of increasing or maximizing agricultural income, a large portion of effort would be focused not on discovering new production functions in agriculture but on increasing the (price) elasticity of demands for farm products. This would especially mean development of new industrial uses for farm products.

2. **Maximizing or increasing the total welfare of individuals now in the agricultural industry.** If increasing net farm income were the single objective of public-financed technological improvement, no regard would need to be given the nature of the total utility function or the distribution of income. However, distribution of income is as important as magnitude of the income if maximizing the total welfare of people in agriculture is to be taken as the goal. If all innovations resulted in an increase in the magnitude of net farm income and none resulted in a transfer, the innovations outlined under 1 would also be applicable under 2. However, on the basis of the total farm welfare criterion, these improvements would not qualify if the increase in total income associated with an income redistribution were such that the increment in utility to the "receiving" group would be less than the decrement in utility to the "losing" group.

Progress towards the total farm welfare goal might be attained (at the expense of the total net farm income goal) by output and total cost-increasing innovations, even where demand elasticity is less than unity provided these conditions hold: (1) the percentage increase in output is greater on low-income farms than (a) the percentage decrease in price and (b) the percentage increase in output on high-income farms; (2) the increment in utility associated with greater revenue on low-income farms is greater than the decrement in utility associated with the decrease in revenue on the high-income farms. Special emphasis would be given to extending output-increasing techniques in low-income areas relative to other geographic areas (the innovation would be equally applicable to high-income farms in the area, of course). For example, a greater quantity of society's funds might be spent on output-increasing techniques in southern Iowa than in central Illinois or in Alabama than in Indiana. If the producers of one commodity (A) were predominantly poor while the producers of a closely competing commodity (B) were predominantly wealthy, resources might be concentrated on innovations which improved the former relative to the latter product. Total farm welfare might thus be increased to the extent that the increment in utility to A producers were greater than the decrement in utility to B producers. The simple transfer would, however, represent a crude system of transferring income where some producers of A have high incomes and some producers of B have low incomes. Other techniques which would especially qualify under the "total farm welfare" criteria might be "engineering" or cost-reducing techniques which are adapted to farms with small quantities of resources.

3. **Maximum economic progress.** Given this goal of farm technological advance, a somewhat different set of innovations would be emphasized. Continuous progress toward this end would require both lower total farm returns and total welfare of people on farms in order that the pricing system might effect a transfer of resources to nonsubsistence industries. In order that resources be driven out of agriculture, any increments in income from some innovations would have to be more than offset by decrements in income by other innovations. Output-increasing techniques would never be extended (except one category of biological-mechanical innovations) for commodities with inelastic demands under the total farm returns goal. Yet these are the very commodities which would be given heavy emphasis for the progress goal. The greater the price elasticity of demand the higher the commodity ordinarily (but not always) stands in the scale of luxuries. For the progress goal, luxury farm commodities with an elastic demand would have no greater priority on public-financed technological improvements than non-farm luxuries.

Instability

Technological improvements which are founded on economic progress must result in continuous instability of subsistence or primary product industries. Resources must be in a constant flow out of these industries. Measured by the same criterion, the value productivity or returns on resources must be constantly lower than in other industries. Measured by the same criterion, the value productivity or returns on resources must be constantly lower than in other industries to which surplus resources are being transferred. Progress becomes characterized by low returns on resources in agriculture (and other subsistence goods and primary product industries). Higher resource returns in subsistence than in luxury goods industries represents retrogression rather than progress. A progress goal of publicly financed farm technological advance must necessarily be one of increasing the physical product while decreasing the value of product per unit of resources in agriculture. This tendency has undoubtedly been manifested in agriculture, where the supply of farm products has increased relative to the demand.

Welfare Criteria and Compensation

Economic reorganizations can be segregated into the 2 categories, depending on their effect upon the welfare of individuals, which either (1) increase the welfare of one person or group without diminishing the welfare of others or (2) increase the welfare of some individuals at the expense of others. Total economic welfare is always increased under the first. It increases under the second only if the increment in utility or satisfactions to the recipient group is greater than the decrement in utility to the sacrificing group. Since interpersonal utility comparisons are impossible, objective measurement of outcome under a transfer (the second category) is impossible. However, the impossibility of interpersonal utility comparisons does not exclude society's ability or responsibility to fashion policies which it deems consistent with a greater total welfare.

Although interpersonal utility comparisons are impossible, society has based policies on obvious differences in individual welfare. The poor are not taxed at a heavier rate than the rich, for example, in order that elementary education be furnished the latter. There are many other areas in which the order and direction of needed reorganization are clear. However, the nature of transfers in income which grow out of farm technological advance are not of an orderly fashion: consumers who realize gains in the form of more food for less money are not generally poor and farmers whose income may diminish are not universally wealthy. Similarly, producers of one commodity or region who gain from a specific improvement are not universally of the lower-income strata while others within agriculture who sacrifice as producers in a competing region or of a competing commodity are not universally of the high-income strata. Perhaps, at the outset, social investment in farm technological advance was thought to fall under the category of leaving some individuals better off without leaving any others worse off. Present knowledge of demand elasticities questions any such unwitting assumption for agriculture as a whole and for a very great number of single products. The principles developed in modern welfare economics provide the basis for guaranteeing that total welfare can be increased even though the reorganization is in the form of transfers. The difficulty of interpersonal comparisons can be removed by compensation to redress impaired income positions and guarantee that no person is "worse off."

A bulk of the agricultural policy legislation of the past several decades can be interpreted literally as society's belief that (1) farm income is less than it would have been had the capacity of agricultural resources not been increased so greatly by technological improvements and (2) compensation is in order to redress general impairment of the farm economic position which has grown out of increased output and technological advance. The provision for production control is prime evidence of the first (a smaller output to attain a greater revenue) while the cordon of subsidies designed to restore farm earnings at historical levels is material evidence of the second. Society has simply recognized that the greater flow of production growing out of its designed policy of improved farm technology has increased total welfare at the expense of returns to the farm population. Although the action conforms with principles of modern welfare economics, a conflict must be recognized. If farmers are made as well off relatively in post-innovation as pre-innovation periods, forces will not be generated to drive the surplus resources to other industries. The apparent dilemma is not insoluble. Means exist both for redressing impaired farm returns and speeding the flow of resources to non-subsistence industries. Society has an *ipso facto* policy designed to bring about surplus resources in the farming industry. It should have an equally positive policy directed at speeding the movement of resources out of agriculture.

There are few precedents whereby society has provided full compensation to guarantee that all individuals are "as well off after as before" economic reorganizations. (There is a question of whether the status of the past provides better criteria than the "possibilities of the future" as a benchmark from which reorganizations might be fashioned.) Accordingly, it is debatable whether society should attempt a full scale, innovation-inspired program of compensation or whether such a program is feasible. Yet a minimum program of compensation is certainly in order. Society should provide the mechanism whereby those resources whose returns have been lowered can be moved into alternative opportunities where returns on resources are higher.

Application in Allocation of Educational Resources

The principles outlined above apply not only to the allocation and administration of research resources and funds; they have equal or greater application in extension education. The question of goals has implications for the subject matter carried out to farm people: given the basic objective of total welfare, information should be carried out on all commodities, irrespective of demand elasticities. With the objective one alone of increasing farm income, information extended would refer to biological innovations only if the elasticity of demand is greater than 1.0; it would apply to all mechanical innovations but the exceptions mentioned earlier. With the farm welfare objective as the paramount one, emphasis would be focused on information for low income farms.

The methods of education also can be related to the principles mentioned. If the goal of extension education were one of increasing farm income, television might be an appropriate medium. Information on biological innovations could be extended in this manner in the hopes that enough farmers (and there would be no concern over any particular group of farmers) would adopt the technique so that demand elasticity would be pushed down to 1.0. Or the same logic would apply to holding single meetings in counties or one field day at the college. However, if the relevant goal is the farm welfare consideration mentioned previously, the same techniques of education are no longer most appropriate. Low income persons do not have television sets; some cannot read and the majority cannot travel to the state college. Hence detailed farm planning and home visits would be more efficient. In any case, the information to be carried out and the methods of putting it across must relate to the basic objective. The principles of production or resource allocation can be applied even further in extension education. They provide the basis for determining how funds should be allocated between different subject matter fields, between regions of the nation and between counties of a state and between problems at one point in time. The conditions are simply those illustrated in the early chapters of this book. They cannot be applied, of course, until a sufficient objective or end for extension education is set forth so that choice indicators can be devised.

Selected References

Agriculture's Capacity to Produce, U. S. D. A., Agr. Info. Bul. No. 88. Wash. 1952.

Ayres, C. E., *Theory of Economic Progress*. Chapel Hill: University of North Carolina Press, 1946.

Brewster, J., "Farm Technological Advance and Population Growth," *Jour. Farm Econ.*, Vol. 27.

Cooper, M. L., *et al.*, *Progress of Farm Mechanization*. U. S. D. A. Misc. Publ. 630.

Fisher, A. G. B., *Clash of Progress and Security*. London: Macmillan, 1936.

Heady, Earl O., "Changes in Income Distribution with Reference to Technical Change," *Jour. Farm Econ.*, Vol. 26.

————, "Basic Economic and Welfare Considerations of Farm Technological Advance," *Jour. Farm Econ.*, Vol. 31.

Hecht, R. W., and Barton, G. L., *Gains in Farm Labor Productivity*. U. S. D. A. Tech. Bul. 1020.

Hicks, J. R., "Distribution and Economic Progress," *Rev. Econ. Studies*, Vol. 4.

Johnson, Sherman, *Changes in Farming in War and Peace*. U. S. D. A., B. A. E., mimeo, F. M. 58.

Lange, O., "A Note on Innovations," *Rev. Econ. Studies*, Vol. 25.

Pigou, A., *Economics of Welfare*. London: Macmillan, 1932, Ch. 4 and pp. 185-190.

Robinson, Joan, "Classification of Inventions," in W. Fellner and B. Haley, editors, *Readings in theory of income distribution*. New York: Blakiston, 1946, pp. 175-180.

Technology on the Farm, U. S. D. A. Interdepartmental Report, Washington, 1941.

Index

A

Ability to produce, 797-800
Accumulation of capital, 423-426
Ackerman, J., 380, 636
Acquisition through renting, 556-557
Acreage:
  allotment and production control, 666-669
  control, 293-294
Adaptations of interregional resource, 665
Adjustment:
  of factor relationships, 133-134
  institutions serving as base for, 744-745
  of production to uncertainty, 500 ff.
  of resource use to uncertainty, 500 ff.
Administration of resources, 465 ff.
Advance, nature of, and firm, 802-805
Advantage, comparative, 659-662
Aggregate production, 672 ff.
Aggregation, 299 ff.
  of resource substitutes, 306-308
Agricultural cost situation, 369-370
Agricultural production, 693-694
  indexes of, 692-693
Agricultural production economics:
  basic problems of, 6-7
  development and history, 17
  fundamental principle in, 14-16
  goals of, 3
  maximizing and minimizing, 5-6
  meaning of, 3-5
  means and ends in, 3-4
  nature of, 8-18
  objectives of, 12
  relationship to other sciences, 12-13
Agricultural revenue, 736-737
Agriculture, nature, 17-18
Allocation:
  of credit, 557-560
  of educational resources:
    technological, 829
  farmer, 186

Allocation—(*Cont.*)
  of fertilizer, 125-126
  of given resources, 602-611
  interfarm, 186-188
    agricultural productivity, 122-124
    of resources, 272-273
  inter-technical unit, 183-184
  intra-farm, 183-184
  of resources, 413-414
    chart, 183
    defined, 116
    human, 241-242
  between soils, 784-786
  in uncertainty, 292-298
Allocative patterns, interfarm, under different leasing systems, 605
Allocative principles, 129
Allocative problems:
  in planned economies, 128-129
Alternate purchases, 563-568
Alternative criteria:
  and derived demand, 113
Alternative goals, 824-826
Alternative long-run costs situation, *chart,* 368
Alternative products:
  in time, 390
Alternative resources:
  in time, 390-394
Alternative storage:
  flaw-derived products in, 773-775
Alternative systems of expectation, 478-479
Amalgam resource input, 53
Amortization, 580
Antagonistic competitive enterprises in agriculture, 221
Anticipation, substitution of service and, 776-777
Appraisal, farm, and costs and revenue, 401-402
Arrow, K. J., 12, 422
Ashby, A. W., 747
Asset:
  structure, 528-529

831